# Trinity Hymnal

*... Holy, holy, holy, is the Lord of hosts: the whole earth is full of his glory.*
Isaiah 6:3

PUBLISHED BY THE ORTHODOX PRESBYTERIAN CHURCH • PHILADELPHIA 1961

©
The Committee on Christian Education, Inc.
The Orthodox Presbyterian Church
1961

## ACKNOWLEDGMENTS

Thanks are rendered to the United Presbyterian Church of North America for permission to use those numbers which are drawn from *The Psalter,* 1912. Copyright owners who have given similar permission are acknowledged in footnotes. To all who granted free use of copyrighted words or music gratitude is due, especially to the Christian Reformed Church for many numbers drawn from the *Psalter Hymnal* of 1934, and to the Wm. B. Eerdmans Publishing Co. for hymns from *The New Christian Hymnal.* Care has been taken to trace the owners of hymns; if however in any case proper credit has not been given, this will be corrected in future editions.

*Tenth Printing, 1973*

The Orthodox Presbyterian Church • 7401 Old York Road, Philadelphia, Pa.

*Printed in the United States of America by Rayner Division -*
*Walter M. Carqueville Co., Elk Grove Village, Illinois*

# P R E F A C E

TRINITY HYMNAL is presented with the prayer that it may supply a recognized need for a truly ecumenical hymnal, theocentric in orientation, biblical in content, and containing suitable hymns for every proper occasion of public and private worship of God. It has been compiled with the full consciousness that "the acceptable way of worshipping the true God is instituted by Himself, and so limited by His own revealed will, that He may not be worshipped according to the imaginations and devices of men . . . or any . . . way not prescribed in the holy Scripture" (Westminster Confession of Faith, XXI:I).

TRINITY HYMNAL is published by a Presbyterian church. Yet its ecumenical character is evident, for it contains hymns from hundreds of original sources representing many communions and every era in the history of the church. Its theocentric orientation is apparent not only from the theological arrangement of its hymns but from its emphasis upon the function of worship in bringing glory to the Triune God. As for the biblical character of its content, hymns based upon nearly a thousand portions of the Word of God, including a large part of the Book of Psalms, will be found among the 730 selections. These hymns were chosen to meet the various needs of the people of God, from the simplest informal services in the home among the smallest children to the most solemn occasions in the life of the church.

TRINITY HYMNAL is published during the twenty-fifth anniversary year of a church which, from its inception, has been deeply conscious of the need for a hymnal in which each selection conforms to the requirements for the acceptable worship of God set forth in the Bible and in the subordinate standards of the church. As early as 1943 a committee was elected to give preliminary consideration to the matter and for several years thereafter the subject of song in the public worship of God was under discussion. The committee which prepared this hymnal was erected in 1949 and its membership has included, in addition to those named below, the Rev. Messrs. R. B. Kuiper, Edward L. Kellogg, and the late James W. Price, and Mr. Wilfred G. Clelland. Grateful acknowledgment must be made of the services of all who worked on the hymnal and especially of the devoted labors of the Rev. Robert S. Marsden who served as chairman from the very beginning until his death in October 1960.

The publication of a complete hymnal by a small and young denomination is most unusual, yet it was undertaken because of the realization of the importance of song in the worship of God. It is well known that the character of its song, almost equal with the character of its preaching, controls the theology of a church. In more than one communion where the preaching has departed from biblical truth the remnant of sound theology contained in favorite hymns has prevented the spiritual life of the church from becoming entirely blighted. However, as the older hymnals have become unavailable, newer editions have introduced ideas foreign to the Word of God. And, as the more formal hymnals often fail to provide hymns for informal occasions, many evangelical congregations have turned to smaller hymnals and song books. These, at best, have presented a truncated view of the place of song in divine worship, and, at worst, they have turned worship into something unworthy of a holy God and his people. Thus there is need for the resurgence of reverent worship of the Lord in song. It is essential that he be worshipped in accordance with his own infallible Word, and that that worship seek to reflect the whole counsel of his will. It is our earnest hope that *Trinity Hymnal* will be found to satisfy this manifest need.

If, in some small measure, our sovereign God will graciously use *Trinity Hymnal* to restore to his church the joy and blessing of worship in song, the committee will be well repaid for the work of love which has filled many days of rewarding labor.

> Robley J. Johnston
> Arthur W. Kuschke, Jr.
> LeRoy B. Oliver
> Edward J. Young
> *Robert S. Marsden, Chairman*

# TABLE OF CONTENTS

| | PAGE |
|---|---|
| Preface | v |
| The Ten Commandments and their Summary | ix |
| Opening Sentences | x |
| The Lord's Prayer and The Apostles' Creed | xii |
| Musical Responses | xiv |
| Gloria Patri | xv |
| Doxologies | xvi |
| Amens | xvii |

## THE HYMNS

| | HYMN |
|---|---|
| **GOD: HIS BEING, WORKS, AND WORD** | |
| The Glory of God | 1-86 |
|   The Divine Perfections | 1-20 |
|   God: Infinite | 21-23 |
|   God: Eternal | 24-26 |
|   God: Unchangeable | 27-30 |
|   God: His Being | 31-32 |
|   God: His Wisdom | 33-35 |
|   God: His Power | 36-41 |
|   God: His Holiness | 42-43 |
|   God: His Justice | 44-48 |
|   God: His Goodness | 49-53 |
|   God: His Truth | 54-56 |
|   God: His Sovereignty | 57-68 |
|   God: His Love and Grace | 69-73 |
|   God: His Faithfulness | 74-86 |
| The Holy Trinity | 87-92 |
| The Decrees of God | 93-94 |
| Election | 95-96 |
| The Covenant of Grace | 97-101 |
| The Work of Creation | 102-109 |
| God's Works of Providence | 110-114 |

| | HYMN |
|---|---|
| The Lord Jesus Christ | 115-243 |
|   The Only Mediator and Redeemer | 115-121 |
|   His Deity | 122-125 |
|   His Praise | 126-136 |
|   His Love and Grace | 137-144 |
|   His Advent | 145-149 |
|   His Birth | 150-168 |
|   His Life, Ministry and Obedience | 169-173 |
|   His Atoning Work | 174-176 |
|   His Suffering | 177-183 |
|   His Death | 184-196 |
|   His Resurrection | 197-209 |
|   His Ascension | 210-214 |
|   His Exaltation | 215-219 |
|   His Prophetic Office | 220-221 |
|   His Priestly Intercession | 222-223 |
|   His Kingly Office | 224-230 |
|   His Second Coming and Judgment | 231-243 |
| The Holy Spirit | 244-255 |
| The Holy Scriptures | 256-267 |

## THE HYMNS CONT.

### THE CHURCH

| | HYMN |
|---|---|
| The Church of Christ | 268-280 |
| The Communion of Saints | 281-285 |
| The Covenant People | 286-293 |
| The Kingdom of God | 294-301 |
| The Lord's House | 302-310 |
|     The Opening of Worship | 311-315 |
|     The Close of Worship | 316-319 |
|     The Lord's Day | 320-327 |
|         Morning | 328-334 |
|         Evening | 335-349 |
| Baptism | 350-355 |
| The Lord's Supper | 356-365 |
| Stewardship | 366-368 |
| Missions | 369-386 |
| The Free Offer of the Gospel | 387-395 |

### THE CHRISTIAN LIFE

| | |
|---|---|
| Salvation by Grace | 396-403 |
| Calling | 404-406 |
| Repentance | 407-418 |
| Faith in Christ | 419-432 |
| Union with Christ | 433-438 |
| Justification | 439-441 |
| Adoption | 442-443 |
| Obedience | 444-447 |
| The Law of God | 448-451 |
| Sanctification | 452-460 |
| The Forgiveness of Sins | 461-467 |
| Conflict with Sin | 468-476 |

### THE CHRISTIAN LIFE (cont.)

| | HYMN |
|---|---|
| The Christian Warfare | 477-490 |
| Christian Service | 491-496 |
| Pilgrimage and Guidance | 497-505 |
| Tribulation and Suffering | 506-511 |
| Deliverance | 512-515 |
| Consolation | 516-518 |
| God's Refreshing Grace | 519-527 |
| Prayer | 528-534 |
| Thankfulness | 535-538 |
| Hope | 539-541 |
| Love for Christ | 542-549 |
| Communion with Christ | 550-553 |
| Love for God | 554-557 |
| Trust in God | 558-571 |
| Submission | 572-579 |
| Assurance | 580-586 |
| Peace and Joy | 587-592 |
| Perseverance | 593-596 |
| The Resurrection and the Life Everlasting | 597-609 |

### OCCASIONAL HYMNS

| | |
|---|---|
| The Opening and Closing of the Year | 610-613 |
| Harvest and Thanksgiving | 614-615 |
| National | 616-623 |
| Marriage and the Home | 624-628 |
| Hymns for Special Purposes | 629-632 |
| Children's Hymns | 633-662 |
| Hymns for Informal Occasions | 663-730 |

---

| | PAGE |
|---|---|
| PSALTER SELECTIONS | 607-665 |
| FORMS FOR PUBLIC PROFESSION OF FAITH, BAPTISM, THE LORD'S SUPPER, AND SERVICES OF ORDINATION AND INSTALLATION OF CHURCH OFFICERS | 666-671 |
| THE WESTMINSTER CONFESSION OF FAITH | 673-689 |

| | PAGE |
|---|---|
| INDEXES | 691-744 |
|   Authors, Translators, Arrangers and Sources | 691 |
|   Composers, Arrangers and Sources | 695 |
|   Alphabetical Index of Tunes | 700 |
|   Metrical Index of Tunes | 702 |
|   Index of Scripture References in Hymns | 706 |
|   Index of Subjects and Occasions | 709 |
|   Index of Hymns | 739 |

# THE TEN COMMANDMENTS

GOD spake all these words, saying, I am the Lord thy God, which have brought thee out of the land of Egypt, out of the house of bondage.

I. Thou shalt have no other gods before me.

II. Thou shalt not make unto thee any graven image, or any likeness of any thing that is in heaven above, or that is in the earth beneath, or that is in the water under the earth: thou shalt not bow down thyself to them, nor serve them: for I the Lord thy God am a jealous God, visiting the iniquity of the fathers upon the children unto the third and fourth generation of them that hate me; and showing mercy unto thousands of them that love me, and keep my commandments.

III. Thou shalt not take the Name of the Lord thy God in vain; for the Lord will not hold him guiltless that taketh his Name in vain.

IV. Remember the Sabbath day, to keep it holy. Six days shalt thou labor, and do all thy work: but the seventh day is the Sabbath of the Lord thy God; in it thou shalt not do any work, thou, nor thy son, nor thy daughter, thy man-servant, nor thy maid-servant, nor thy cattle, nor thy stranger that is within thy gates; for in six days the Lord made heaven and earth, the sea, and all that in them is, and rested the seventh day: wherefore the Lord blessed the Sabbath day, and hallowed it.

V. Honor thy father and thy mother: that thy days may be long upon the land which the Lord thy God giveth thee.

VI. Thou shalt not kill.

VII. Thou shalt not commit adultery.

VIII. Thou shalt not steal.

IX. Thou shalt not bear false witness against thy neighbor.

X. Thou shalt not covet thy neighbor's house, thou shalt not covet thy neighbor's wife, nor his man-servant, nor his maid-servant, nor his ox, nor his ass, nor any thing that is thy neighbor's.

HEAR also the words of our Lord Jesus, how he saith: Thou shalt love the Lord thy God with all thy heart, and with all thy soul, and with all thy mind. This is the first and great commandment. And the second is like unto it: Thou shalt love thy neighbor as thyself. On these two commandments hang all the law and the prophets.

# OPENING SENTENCES

O COME, let us worship and bow down: let us kneel before the Lord our maker. For he is our God; and we are the people of his pasture, and the sheep of his hand.

---

O COME, let us worship and bow down: let us kneel before the Lord our maker. Know ye that the Lord he is God: it is he that hath made us, and not we ourselves; we are his people, and the sheep of his pasture.

---

THE LORD is in his holy temple: let all the earth keep silence before him. Exalt the Lord our God, and worship at his holy hill; for the Lord our God is holy.

---

PRAISE ye the Lord. Praise God in his sanctuary: praise him for his mighty acts: praise him according to his excellent greatness. Let every thing that hath breath praise the Lord. Praise ye the Lord.

---

GRACE be to you and peace from God the Father, and from our Lord Jesus Christ, who gave himself for our sins, that he might deliver us from this present evil world, according to the will of God and our Father: to whom be glory for ever and ever. Amen.

---

WE have not an high priest which cannot be touched with the feeling of our infirmities; but was in all points tempted like as we are, yet without sin. Let us therefore come boldly unto the throne of grace, that we may obtain mercy, and find grace to help in time of need.

---

THERE is therefore now no condemnation to them which are in Christ Jesus. For as many as are led by the Spirit of God, they are the sons of God. For ye have not received the spirit of bondage again to fear; but ye have received the Spirit of adoption, whereby we cry, Abba, Father.

---

LORD, I have loved the habitation of thy house, and the place where thine honour dwelleth. I was glad when they said unto me, let us go into the house of the Lord.

---

PRAISE ye the Lord. Sing unto the Lord a new song, and his praise in the congregation of saints. For the Lord taketh pleasure in his people: he will beautify the meek with salvation.

---

PRAISE waiteth for thee, O God, in Sion: and unto thee shall the vow be performed.

---

O GIVE thanks unto the Lord; call upon his name: make known his deeds among the people. Sing unto him, sing psalms unto him: talk ye of all his wondrous works. Glory ye in his holy name: let the heart of them rejoice that seek the Lord.

---

NOT unto us, O Lord, not unto us, but unto thy name give glory, for thy mercy, and for thy truth's sake. Help us, O God of our salvation, for the glory of thy name; and deliver us, and purge away our sins, for thy name's sake.

---

OUR help is in the name of the Lord, who made heaven and earth. It is better to trust in the Lord than to put confidence in man. O taste and see that the Lord is good: blessed is the man that trusteth in him.

---

BEHOLD, bless ye the Lord, all ye servants of the Lord, which by night stand in the house of the Lord. Lift up your hands in the sanctuary, and bless the Lord. The Lord that made heaven and earth bless thee out of Zion.

---

I WILL come into thy house in the multitude of thy mercy: and in thy fear will I worship toward thy holy temple. Let the words of my mouth, and the meditation of my heart, be acceptable in thy sight, O Lord, my strength, and my redeemer.

# OPENING SENTENCES

WHO shall ascend into the hill of the Lord? or who shall stand in his holy place? He that hath clean hands, and a pure heart; who hath not lifted up his soul unto vanity, nor sworn deceitfully. He shall receive the blessing from the Lord, and righteousness from the God of his salvation.

---

O LORD, open thou my lips; and my mouth shall shew forth thy praise. For thou desirest not sacrifice; else would I give it: thou delightest not in burnt offering. The sacrifices of God are a broken spirit: a broken and a contrite heart, O God, thou wilt not despise.

---

SEEK ye the Lord while he may be found, call ye upon him while he is near: let the wicked forsake his way, and the unrighteous man his thoughts; and let him return unto the Lord, and he will have mercy upon him; and to our God, for he will abundantly pardon.

---

ONE thing have I desired of the Lord, that will I seek after; that I may dwell in the house of the Lord all the days of my life, to behold the beauty of the Lord, and to enquire in his temple. Wait on the Lord: be of good courage, and he shall strengthen thine heart: wait, I say, on the Lord.

---

THE LORD is nigh unto all them that call upon him, to all that call upon him in truth. He will fulfill the desire of them that fear him: he also will hear their cry, and will save them. O thou that hearest prayer, unto thee shall all flesh come.

---

HOW amiable are thy tabernacles, O Lord of hosts! A day in thy courts is better than a thousand. For the Lord God is a sun and shield: the Lord will give grace and glory: no good thing will he withhold from them that walk uprightly. O Lord of hosts, blessed is the man that trusteth in thee.

---

GIVE unto the Lord, O ye kindreds of the people, give unto the Lord glory and strength. Give unto the Lord the glory due unto his name: bring an offering, and come into his courts. O worship the Lord in the beauty of holiness: fear before him, all the earth.

---

IT is a good thing to give thanks unto the Lord, and to sing praises unto thy name, O most High: to shew forth thy lovingkindness in the morning, and thy faithfulness every night.

---

THE HOUR cometh, and now is, when the true worshippers shall worship the Father in spirit and in truth: for the Father seeketh such to worship him. God is a Spirit: and they that worship him must worship him in spirit and in truth.

---

BUT now is Christ risen from the dead, and become the firstfruits of them that slept. If ye then be risen with Christ, seek those things which are above, where Christ sitteth on the right hand of God.

---

PUT on the whole armour of God, that ye may be able to stand against the wiles of the devil. For we wrestle not against flesh and blood, but against principalities, against powers, against the rulers of the darkness of this world, against spiritual wickedness in high places. Wherefore, take unto you the whole armour of God, that ye may be able to withstand in the evil day, and having done all, to stand.

---

BLESSED is the man whom thou choosest, and causest to approach unto thee, that he may dwell in thy courts: we shall be satisfied with the goodness of thy house, even of thy holy temple.

---

O COME, let us sing unto the Lord: let us make a joyful noise to the rock of our salvation. Let us come before his presence with thanksgiving, and make a joyful noise unto him with psalms.

## THE LORD'S PRAYER

OUR FATHER which art in heaven, hallowed be thy name. Thy kingdom come. Thy will be done in earth, as it is in heaven. Give us this day our daily bread. And forgive us our debts, as we forgive our debtors. And lead us not into temptation, but deliver us from evil: For thine is the kingdom, and the power, and the glory, for ever. Amen.

## THE APOSTLES' CREED

I BELIEVE in God the Father Almighty, Maker of heaven and earth:
And in Jesus Christ his only Son, our Lord; who was conceived by the Holy Ghost, born of the Virgin Mary, suffered under Pontius Pilate, was crucified, dead, and buried; he descended into hell; the third day he rose again from the dead; he ascended into heaven, and sitteth on the right hand of God the Father Almighty; from thence he shall come to judge the quick and the dead.

I believe in the Holy Ghost; the holy Catholic Church; the communion of saints; the forgiveness of sins; the resurrection of the body; and the life everlasting. Amen.

MUSICAL RESPONSES

GLORIA PATRI

DOXOLOGY

# Musical Responses

## Response To the Ten Commandments

*I will put my law in their inward parts, and write it in their hearts.* Jer. 31:33

Anon. / Anon.

Lord, have mer-cy up-on us, and write all these thy laws in our hearts, we be-seech thee.

## Offertory Response

*The silver is mine, and the gold is mine, saith the Lord of hosts.* Hag. 2:8

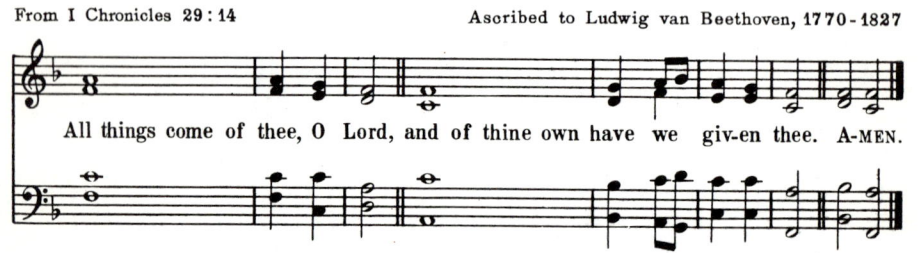

From I Chronicles 29:14 — Ascribed to Ludwig van Beethoven, 1770-1827

All things come of thee, O Lord, and of thine own have we giv-en thee. A-MEN.

Hymn No. 367 may also be used as an Offertory Response.

## Prayer Response

*My peace I give unto you.* John 14:27

WHELPTON 5. 5. 6. 5.
Anon. / George Whelpton, 1897

Hear our prayer, O Lord, Hear our prayer, O Lord,
In-cline thine ear to us, And grant us thy peace. A - MEN.

# Gloria Patri

*Give unto the Lord the glory due unto his name.* I Chron. 16:29

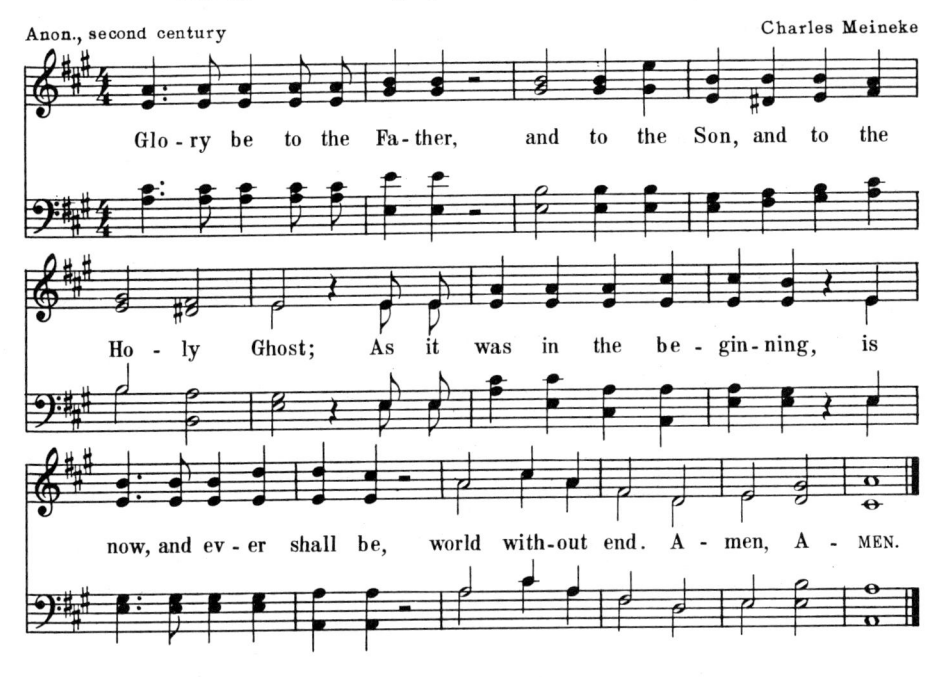

Anon., second century — Charles Meineke

Glo - ry be to the Fa - ther, and to the Son, and to the Ho - ly Ghost; As it was in the be - gin - ning, is now, and ev - er shall be, world with - out end. A - men, A - MEN.

Anon., second century — Henry W. Greatorex, 1851

Glo - ry be to the Fa - ther, and to the Son, and to the Ho - ly Ghost; As it was in the be - gin - ning, is now, and ev - er shall be, world with - out end. A - men, A - MEN.

# Doxology

*Let every thing that hath breath praise the Lord.* Psalm 150:6

Thomas Ken, 1709

THE OLD HUNDREDTH L. M.
Louis Bourgeois, 1551

Praise God from whom all bless-ings flow; Praise him, all crea-tures here be-low; Praise him a-bove, ye heav'n-ly host: Praise Fa-ther, Son, and Ho-ly Ghost. A-MEN.

Thomas Ken, 1709

THE OLD HUNDREDTH L. M.
Louis Bourgeois, 1551

Praise God from whom all bless-ings flow; Praise him, all crea-tures here be-low; Praise him a-bove, ye heav'n-ly host: Praise Fa-ther, Son, and Ho-ly Ghost. A-MEN.

# Amens

Twofold Amen — DRESDEN

Threefold Amen — DANISH

Sevenfold Amen — Peter C. Lutkin

Sevenfold Amen by Peter C. Lutkin. Copyright 1959 Theodore Presser Company. Used by Permission.

THE HYMNS

# THE GLORY OF GOD

## THE DIVINE PERFECTIONS

1

*Make a joyful noise unto the Lord, all ye lands.* Psalm 100:1

PSALM 100  
William Kethe, 1561

THE OLD HUNDREDTH L. M.  
Louis Bourgeois, 1551

1. All people that on earth do dwell,
   Sing to the Lord with cheerful voice;
   Him serve with fear, his praise forth-tell,
   Come ye before him and rejoice.

2. The Lord ye know is God indeed;
   Without our aid he did us make;
   We are his folk, he doth us feed,
   And for his sheep he doth us take.

3. O enter then his gates with praise,
   Approach with joy his courts unto;
   Praise, laud, and bless his Name always,
   For it is seemly so to do.

4. For why? the Lord our God is good,
   His mercy is for ever sure;
   His truth at all times firmly stood,
   And shall from age to age endure. A-MEN.

# 2                                           THE GLORY OF GOD

*I will extol thee, my God, O king... Psalm 145:1*

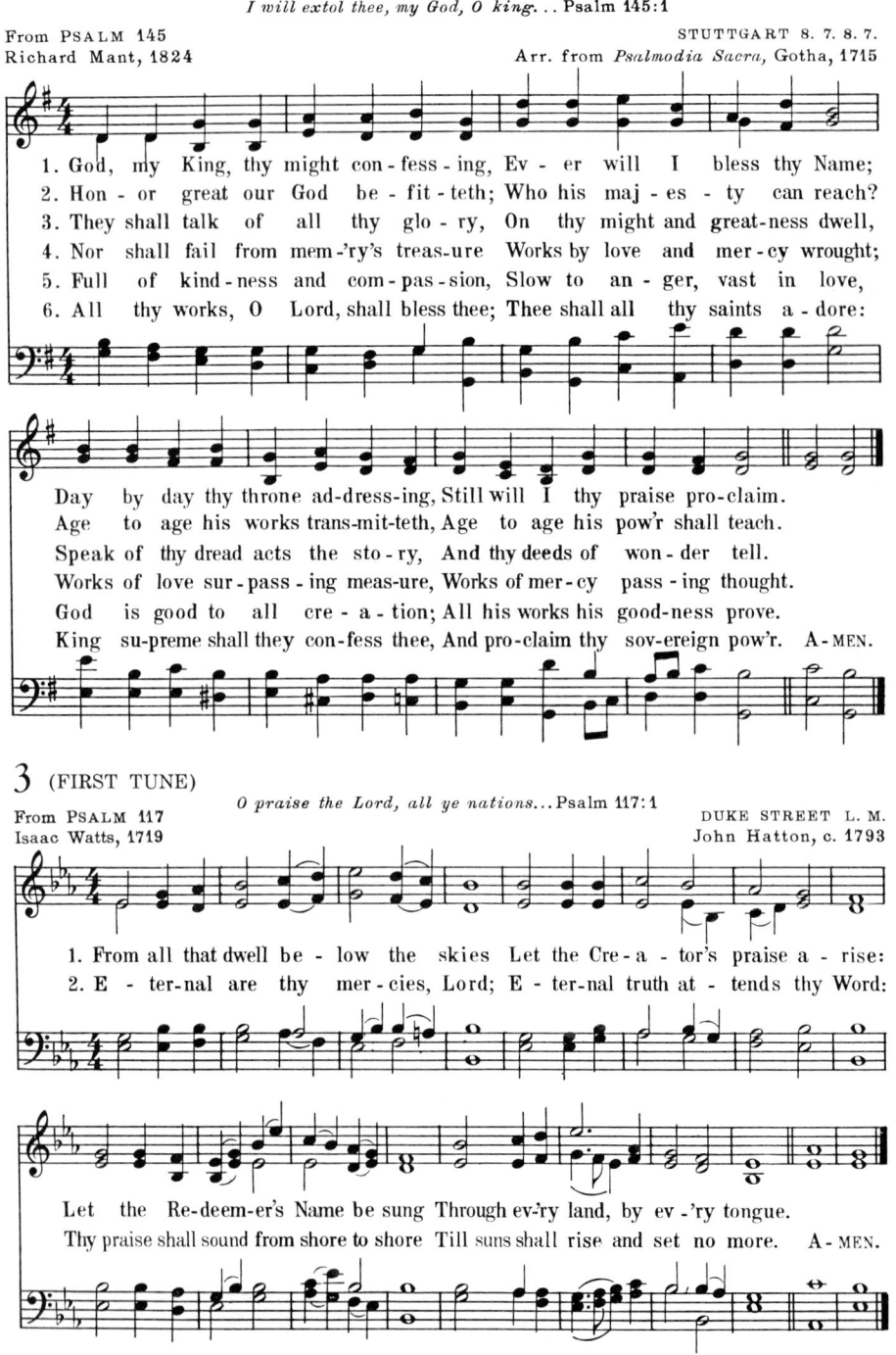

From PSALM 145                                       STUTTGART 8. 7. 8. 7.
Richard Mant, 1824                      Arr. from *Psalmodia Sacra*, Gotha, 1715

1. God, my King, thy might confessing, Ever will I bless thy Name;
   Day by day thy throne addressing, Still will I thy praise proclaim.
2. Honor great our God befitteth; Who his majesty can reach?
   Age to age his works transmitteth, Age to age his pow'r shall teach.
3. They shall talk of all thy glory, On thy might and greatness dwell,
   Speak of thy dread acts the story, And thy deeds of wonder tell.
4. Nor shall fail from mem'ry's treasure Works by love and mercy wrought;
   Works of love surpassing measure, Works of mercy passing thought.
5. Full of kindness and compassion, Slow to anger, vast in love,
   God is good to all creation; All his works his goodness prove.
6. All thy works, O Lord, shall bless thee; Thee shall all thy saints adore:
   King supreme shall they confess thee, And proclaim thy sov'reign pow'r. A-MEN.

# 3 (FIRST TUNE)

*O praise the Lord, all ye nations... Psalm 117:1*

From PSALM 117                                       DUKE STREET L. M.
Isaac Watts, 1719                                      John Hatton, c. 1793

1. From all that dwell below the skies Let the Creator's praise arise:
   Let the Redeemer's Name be sung Through ev'ry land, by ev-'ry tongue.
2. Eternal are thy mercies, Lord; Eternal truth attends thy Word:
   Thy praise shall sound from shore to shore Till suns shall rise and set no more. A-MEN.

# THE DIVINE PERFECTIONS (SECOND TUNE) 3

*O praise the Lord, all ye nations...Psalm 117:1*

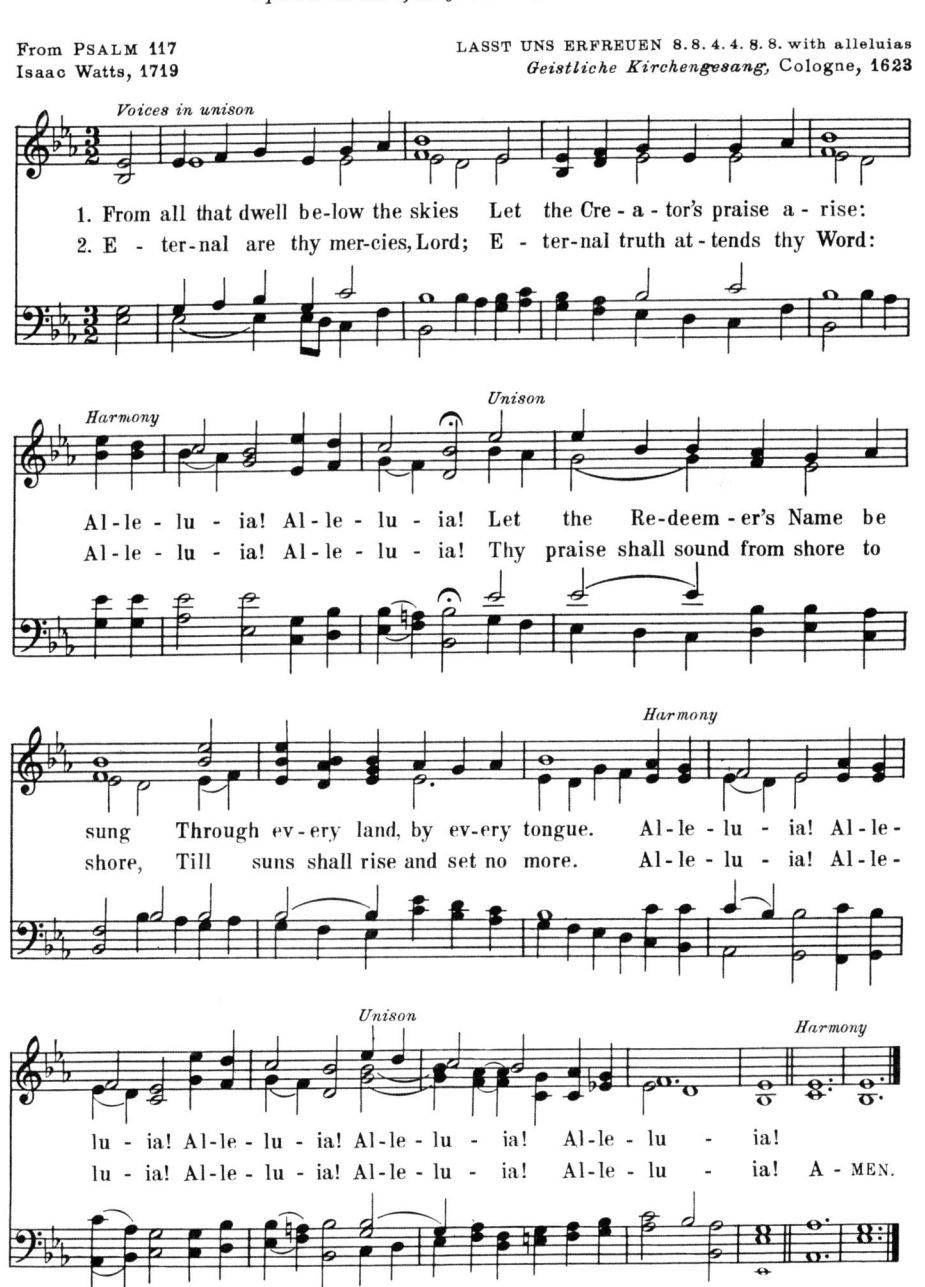

From PSALM 117
Isaac Watts, 1719

LASST UNS ERFREUEN 8.8.4.4.8.8. with alleluias
*Geistliche Kirchengesang,* Cologne, 1623

1. From all that dwell below the skies Let the Creator's praise arise:
Alleluia! Alleluia! Let the Redeemer's Name be sung
Through every land, by every tongue.
Alleluia! Alleluia! Alleluia! Alleluia! Alleluia! Alleluia!

2. Eternal are thy mercies, Lord; Eternal truth attends thy Word:
Alleluia! Alleluia! Thy praise shall sound from shore to shore,
Till suns shall rise and set no more.
Alleluia! Alleluia! Alleluia! Alleluia! Alleluia! Alleluia! A-MEN.

Harmony from *Songs of Praise* by permission of the Oxford University Press, London

# 4                                                        THE GLORY OF GOD

*Oh that men would praise the Lord for his goodness, and for his wonderful works to the children of men!* Psalm 107:15

Johann J. Schütz, 1675, cento  
LOBET DEN HERRN, IHR 8. 7. 8. 7. 8. 8. 7.  
Melchior Vulpius, 1609

1. All praise to God, who reigns a-bove, The God of all cre-a-tion, The God of won-ders, pow'r, and love, The God of our sal-va-tion! With heal-ing balm my soul he fills, The God who ev-'ry sor-row stills, To God all praise and glo-ry!

2. What God's al-might-y pow'r hath made His gra-cious mer-cy keep-eth; By morn-ing dawn or eve-ning shade His watch-ful eye ne'er sleep-eth; With-in the king-dom of his might, Lo, all is just and all is right, To God all praise and glo-ry!

3. I cried to him in time of need: Lord God, O, hear my call-ing! For death he gave me life in-deed And kept my feet from fall-ing. For this my thanks shall end-less be; O, thank him, thank our God, with me, To God all praise and glo-ry!

4. The Lord for-sak-eth not his flock, His cho-sen gen-er-a-tion; He is their Ref-uge and their Rock, Their Peace and their Sal-va-tion. As with a moth-er's ten-der hand He leads his own, his cho-sen band, To God all praise and glo-ry!

5. Ye who con-fess Christ's ho-ly Name, To God give praise and glo-ry! Ye who the Fa-ther's pow'r pro-claim, To God give praise and glo-ry! All i-dols un-der foot be trod, The Lord is God! The Lord is God! To God all praise and glo-ry!

6. Then come be-fore his pres-ence now And ban-ish fear and sad-ness; To your Re-deem-er pay your vow And sing with joy and glad-ness: Though great dis-tress my soul be-fell, The Lord, my God, did all things well, To God all praise and glo-ry! A-MEN.

# THE DIVINE PERFECTIONS  5

*I heard the voice of many angels round about the throne... and the elders...*
*saying with a loud voice, Worthy is the Lamb that was slain... Rev. 5: 11, 12*

Robert Robinson, 1774  
St. 1, line 2, alt.

ALLELUIA (LOWE) 8. 7. 8. 7. with alleluias  
Albert Lowe, 1868

*Voices in unison*

1. Might-y God, while an-gels bless thee, May a mor-tal sing thy Name?
2. Lord of ev-'ry land and na-tion, An-cient of e-ter-nal days,
3. For the grand-eur of thy na-ture, Grand be-yond a ser-aph's thought;
4. But thy rich, thy free re-demp-tion, Dark through bright-ness all a-long,
5. Bright-ness of the Fa-ther's glo-ry, Shall thy praise un-ut-tered lie?
6. From the high-est throne in glo-ry, To the cross of deep-est woe,

*Organ*

Lord of men as well as an-gels, Thou art ev-'ry crea-ture's theme.
Sound-ed through the wide cre-a-tion Be thy just and law-ful praise.
For cre-at-ed works of pow-er, Works with skill and kind-ness wrought.
Thought is poor, and poor ex-pres-sion, Who dare sing that aw-ful song?
Fly, my tongue, such guilt-y si-lence, Sing the Lord who came to die:
All to ran-som guilt-y cap-tives, Flow my praise, for ev-er flow.

*Voices and Organ*

Al-le-lu-ia! Al-le-lu-ia! Al-le-lu-ia! A-men. A-MEN.

# 6                                                     THE GLORY OF GOD

*Ye that fear the Lord, praise him ... Psalm 22:23*

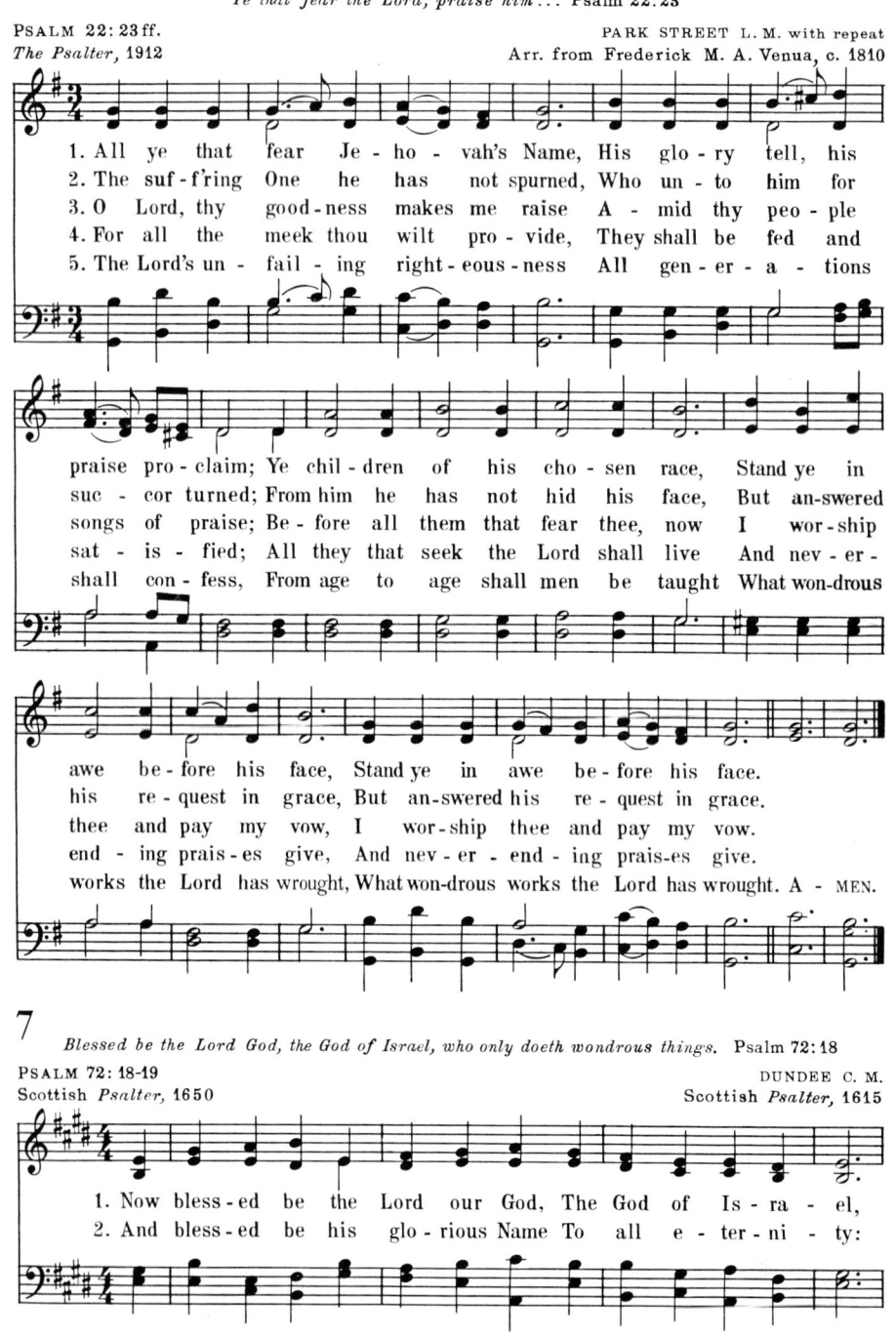

PSALM 22:23 ff.                                           PARK STREET L. M. with repeat
*The Psalter*, 1912                                    Arr. from Frederick M. A. Venua, c. 1810

1. All ye that fear Jehovah's Name, His glory tell, his praise proclaim; Ye children of his chosen race, Stand ye in awe before his face, Stand ye in awe before his face.
2. The suff'ring One he has not spurned, Who unto him for succor turned; From him he has not hid his face, But answered his request in grace, But answered his request in grace.
3. O Lord, thy goodness makes me raise Amid thy people songs of praise; Before all them that fear thee, now I worship thee and pay my vow, I worship thee and pay my vow.
4. For all the meek thou wilt provide, They shall be fed and satisfied; All they that seek the Lord shall live And never-ending praises give, And never-ending praises give.
5. The Lord's unfailing righteousness All generations shall confess, From age to age shall men be taught What wondrous works the Lord has wrought, What wondrous works the Lord has wrought. A-MEN.

# 7

*Blessed be the Lord God, the God of Israel, who only doeth wondrous things. Psalm 72:18*

PSALM 72:18-19                                                   DUNDEE C. M.
Scottish *Psalter*, 1650                                          Scottish *Psalter*, 1615

1. Now blessed be the Lord our God, The God of Israel,
2. And blessed be his glorious Name To all eternity:

# THE DIVINE PERFECTIONS

For he a-lone doth won-drous works In glo-ry that ex-cel.
The whole earth let his glo-ry fill. A-men, so let it be. A-MEN.

*Bless ye the Lord, ye his angels... Bless the Lord, all his works in all places of his dominion... Psalm 103: 20, 22*

**8**

ANGEL VOICES 8.5.8.5.8.4.3.
Sir Arthur S. Sullivan, 1872

Francis Pott, 1861

1. An-gel voic-es, ev-er sing-ing Round thy throne of light,
2. Thou who art be-yond the far-thest Mor-tal eye can scan,
3. Yea, we know thy love re-joic-es O'er each work of thine;
4. Here, great God, to-day we of-fer Of thine own to thee;
5. Hon-or, glo-ry, might, and mer-it, Thine shall ev-er be,

An-gel harps, for ev-er ring-ing, Rest not day nor night;
Can it be that thou re-gard-est Songs of sin-ful man?
Thou didst ears and hands and voic-es For thy praise com-bine;
And for thine ac-cept-ance prof-fer, All un-worth-i-ly,
Fa-ther, Son, and Ho-ly Spir-it, Bless-ed Trin-i-ty:

Thou-sands on-ly live to bless thee, And con-fess thee Lord of might.
Can we feel that thou art near us, And wilt hear us? Yea, we can.
Crafts-man's art and mu-sic's meas-ure For thy pleas-ure Didst de-sign.
Hearts and minds, and hands and voic-es, In our choic-est Mel-o-dy.
Of the best that thou hast giv-en Earth and heav-en Ren-der thee. A-MEN.

# 9            THE GLORY OF GOD

*Praise ye the Lord. Praise God in his sanctuary... Psalm 150:1*

From PSALM 150  
*The Psalter,* 1912

ALLELUIA (LOWE) 8. 7. 8. 7. with alleluias  
Albert Lowe, 1868

1. Hal-le-lu-jah! Hal-le-lu-jah! In his tem-ple God be praised;  
In the high and heav'n-ly plac-es Be the sound-ing an-them raised.
2. Hal-le-lu-jah! Praise Je-ho-vah For his might-y acts of fame;  
Ex-cel-lent his might and great-ness; Fit-ting prais-es then pro-claim.
3. Hal-le-lu-jah! Praise Je-ho-vah With the trum-pet's joy-ful sound;  
Praise with harp and praise with or-gan, Let his glo-rious praise a-bound.
4. Hal-le-lu-jah! Hal-le-lu-jah! All that breathe, Je-ho-vah praise;  
Let the voi-ces God has giv-en Joy-ful an-thems to him raise.

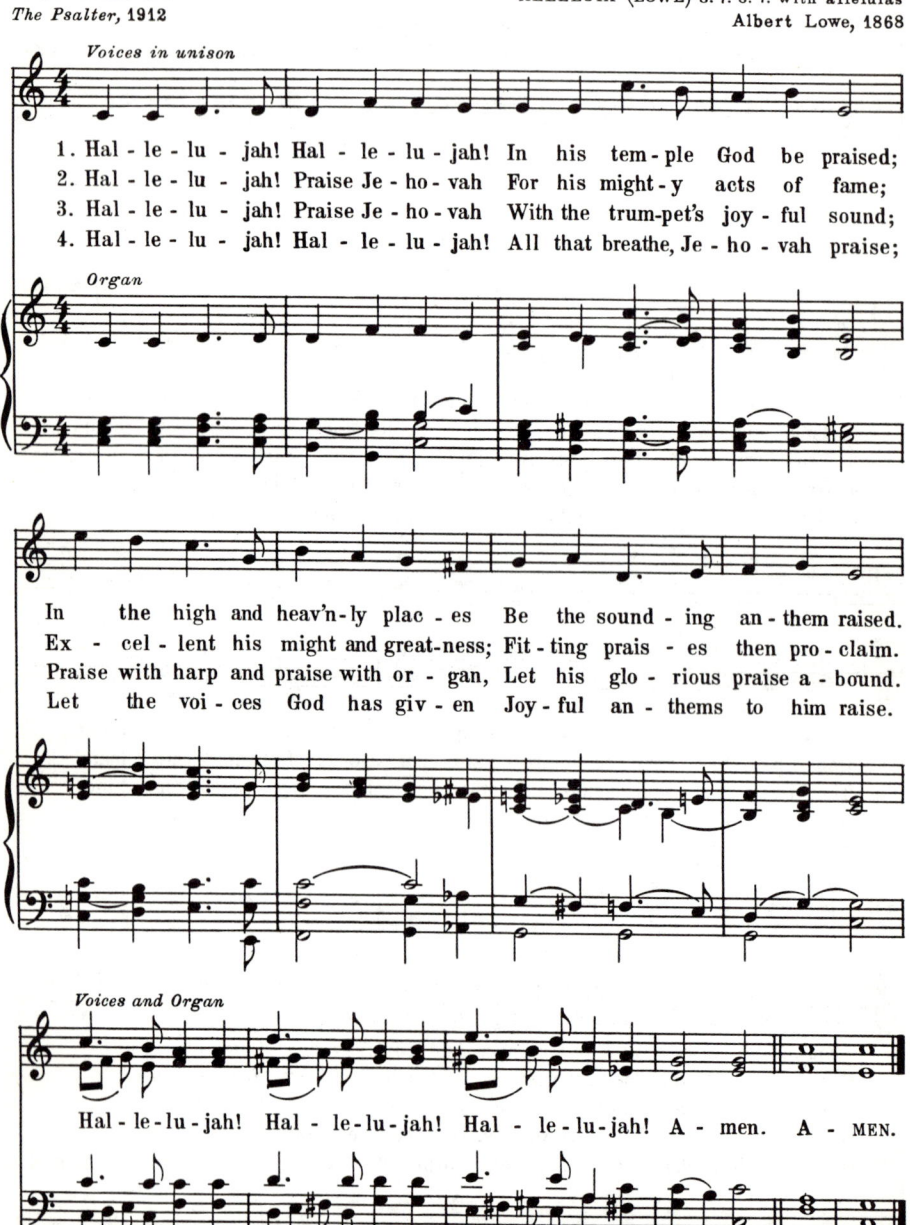

Hal-le-lu-jah! Hal-le-lu-jah! Hal-le-lu-jah! A-men. A-MEN.

# THE DIVINE PERFECTIONS  10

*Bless the Lord, O my soul: and all that is within me, bless his holy name.* Psalm 103: 1

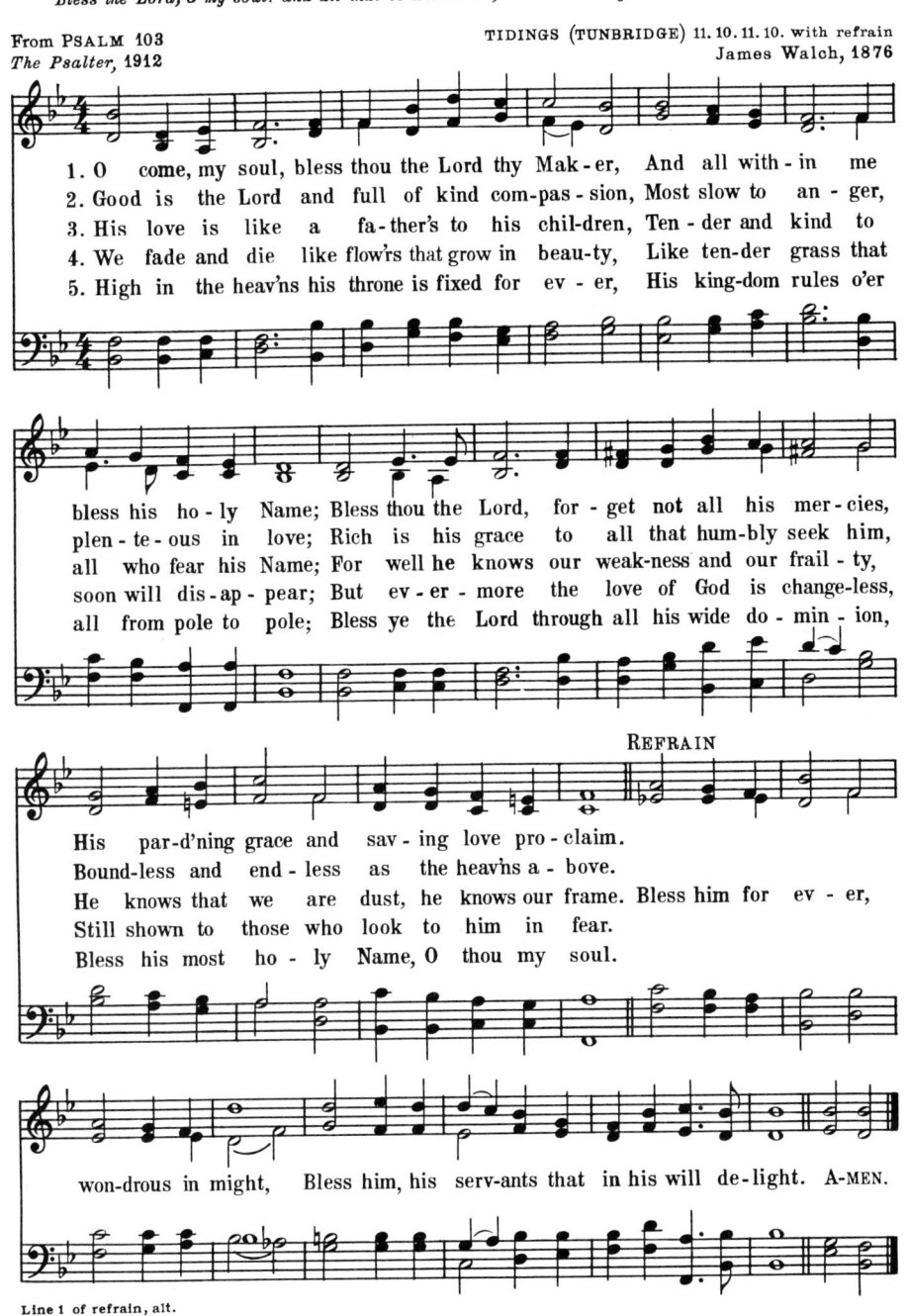

From PSALM 103  
The Psalter, 1912

TIDINGS (TUNBRIDGE) 11.10.11.10. with refrain  
James Walch, 1876

1. O come, my soul, bless thou the Lord thy Mak-er, And all with-in me bless his ho-ly Name; Bless thou the Lord, for-get not all his mer-cies, His par-d'ning grace and sav-ing love pro-claim.
2. Good is the Lord and full of kind com-pas-sion, Most slow to an-ger, plen-te-ous in love; Rich is his grace to all that hum-bly seek him, Bound-less and end-less as the heav'ns a-bove.
3. His love is like a fa-ther's to his chil-dren, Ten-der and kind to all who fear his Name; For well he knows our weak-ness and our frail-ty, He knows that we are dust, he knows our frame. Bless him for ev-er,
4. We fade and die like flow'rs that grow in beau-ty, Like ten-der grass that soon will dis-ap-pear; But ev-er-more the love of God is change-less, Still shown to those who look to him in fear.
5. High in the heav'ns his throne is fixed for ev-er, His king-dom rules o'er all from pole to pole; Bless ye the Lord through all his wide do-min-ion, Bless his most ho-ly Name, O thou my soul.

REFRAIN

won-drous in might, Bless him, his serv-ants that in his will de-light. A-MEN.

Line 1 of refrain, alt.

# 11                                           THE GLORY OF GOD

*The Lord hath done great things for us; whereof we are glad.* Psalm 126:3

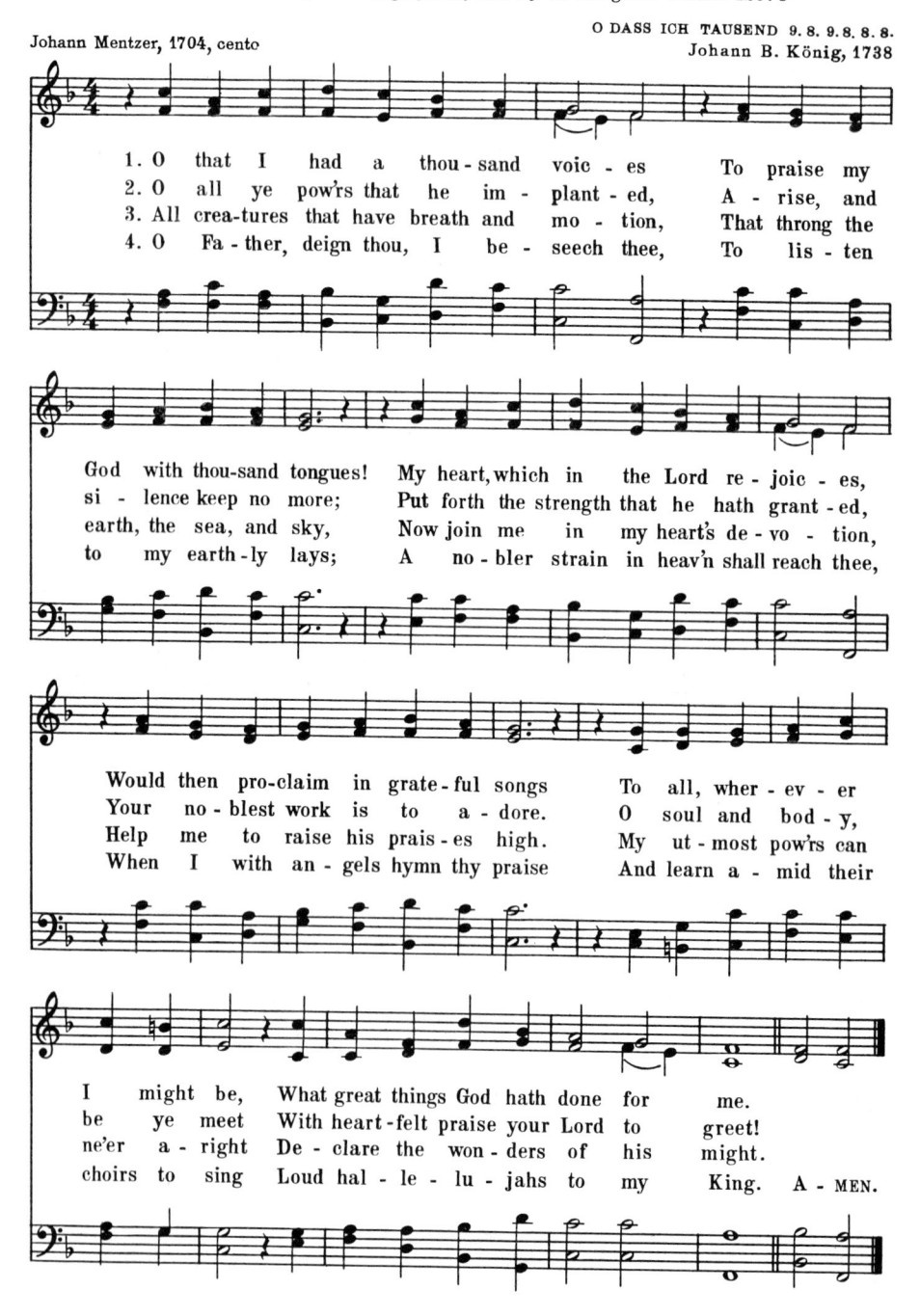

Johann Mentzer, 1704, cento

O DASS ICH TAUSEND 9.8.9.8.8.8.
Johann B. König, 1738

1. O that I had a thousand voices To praise my God with thousand tongues! My heart, which in the Lord rejoices, Would then proclaim in grateful songs To all, wherever I might be, What great things God hath done for me.

2. O all ye pow'rs that he implanted, Arise, and silence keep no more; Put forth the strength that he hath granted, Your noblest work is to adore. O soul and body, be ye meet With heart-felt praise your Lord to greet!

3. All creatures that have breath and motion, That throng the earth, the sea, and sky, Now join me in my heart's devotion, Help me to raise his praises high. My utmost pow'rs can ne'er aright Declare the wonders of his might.

4. O Father, deign thou, I beseech thee, To listen to my earthly lays; A nobler strain in heav'n shall reach thee, When I with angels hymn thy praise, And learn amid their choirs to sing Loud hallelujahs to my King. A-MEN.

# THE DIVINE PERFECTIONS 12

*Praise ye the Lord...O ye servants of the Lord.* Psalm 135:1

PSALM 135:1-7, 21
*The Psalter,* 1912

CREATION L.M.D.
Arr. from Franz Josef Haydn, 1798

1. Ex-alt the Lord, his praise pro-claim; All ye his serv-ants, praise his Name, Who in the Lord's house ev-er stand And hum-bly serve at his com-mand. The Lord is good, his praise pro-claim; Since it is pleas-ant, praise his Name; His peo-ple for his own he takes And his pe-cu-liar treas-ure makes.

2. I know the Lord is high in state, A-bove all gods our Lord is great; The Lord per-forms what he de-crees, In heaven and earth, in depths and seas. He makes the va-pors to as-cend In clouds from earth's re-mot-est end; The light-nings flash at his com-mand, He holds the tem-pest in his hand.

3. Ex-alt the Lord, his praise pro-claim; All ye his serv-ants, praise his Name, Who in the Lord's house ev-er stand And hum-bly serve at his com-mand. For-ev-er praise and bless his Name, And in the church his praise pro-claim; In Zi-on is his dwell-ing place; Praise ye the Lord, show forth his grace. A-MEN.

## 13 THE GLORY OF GOD

*All thy works shall praise thee, O Lord... Psalm 145:10*

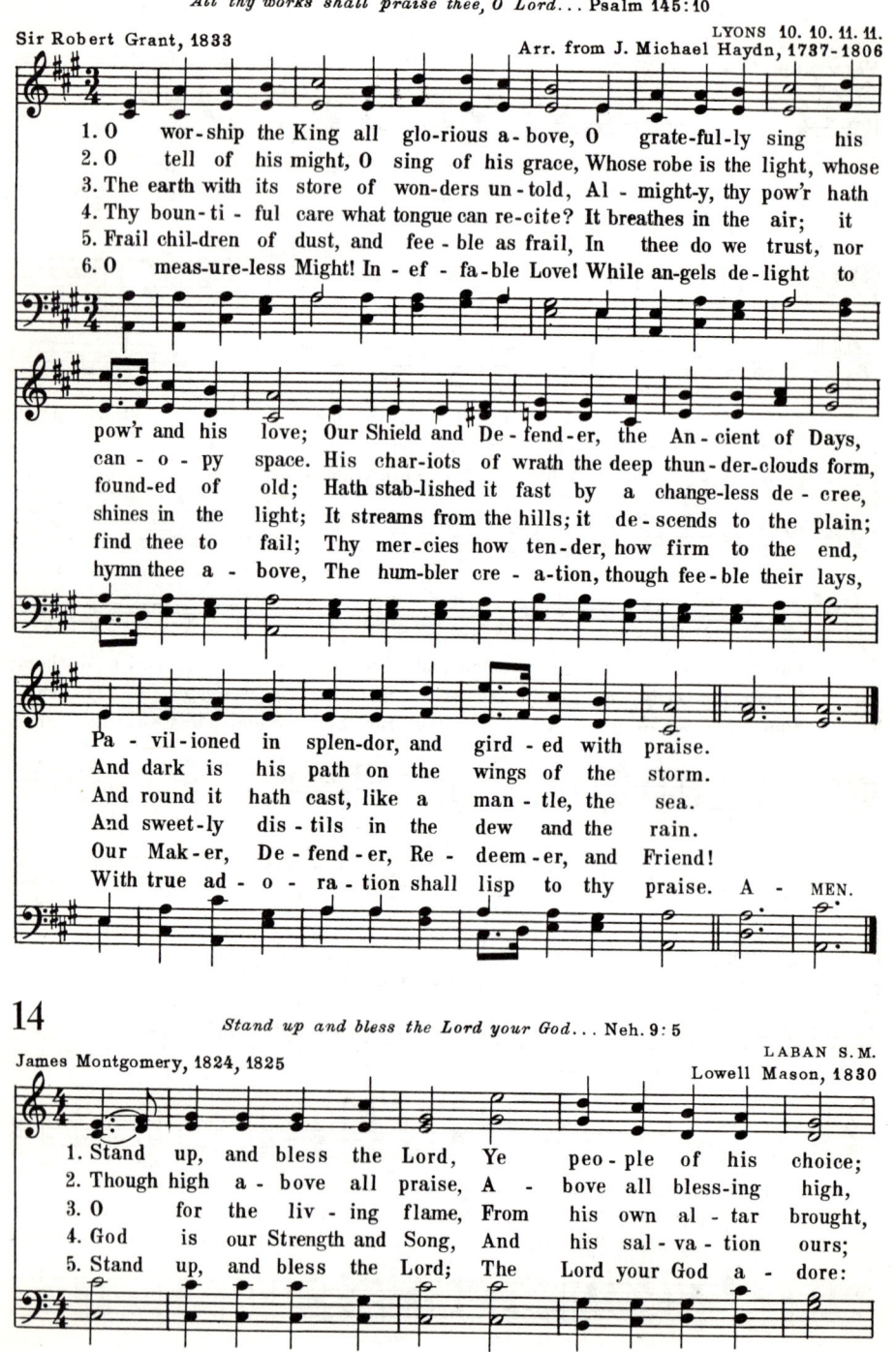

Sir Robert Grant, 1833
LYONS 10. 10. 11. 11.
Arr. from J. Michael Haydn, 1737-1806

1. O worship the King all glorious above, O gratefully sing his pow'r and his love; Our Shield and Defender, the Ancient of Days, Pavilioned in splendor, and girded with praise.
2. O tell of his might, O sing of his grace, Whose robe is the light, whose canopy space. His chariots of wrath the deep thunder-clouds form, And dark is his path on the wings of the storm.
3. The earth with its store of wonders untold, Almighty, thy pow'r hath founded of old; Hath stablished it fast by a changeless decree, And round it hath cast, like a mantle, the sea.
4. Thy bountiful care what tongue can recite? It breathes in the air; it shines in the light; It streams from the hills; it descends to the plain; And sweetly distils in the dew and the rain.
5. Frail children of dust, and feeble as frail, In thee do we trust, nor find thee to fail; Thy mercies how tender, how firm to the end, Our Maker, Defender, Redeemer, and Friend!
6. O measureless Might! Ineffable Love! While angels delight to hymn thee above, The humbler creation, though feeble their lays, With true adoration shall lisp to thy praise. A-MEN.

## 14

*Stand up and bless the Lord your God... Neh. 9:5*

James Montgomery, 1824, 1825
LABAN S.M.
Lowell Mason, 1830

1. Stand up, and bless the Lord, Ye people of his choice;
2. Though high above all praise, Above all blessing high,
3. O for the living flame, From his own altar brought,
4. God is our Strength and Song, And his salvation ours;
5. Stand up, and bless the Lord; The Lord your God adore:

# THE DIVINE PERFECTIONS

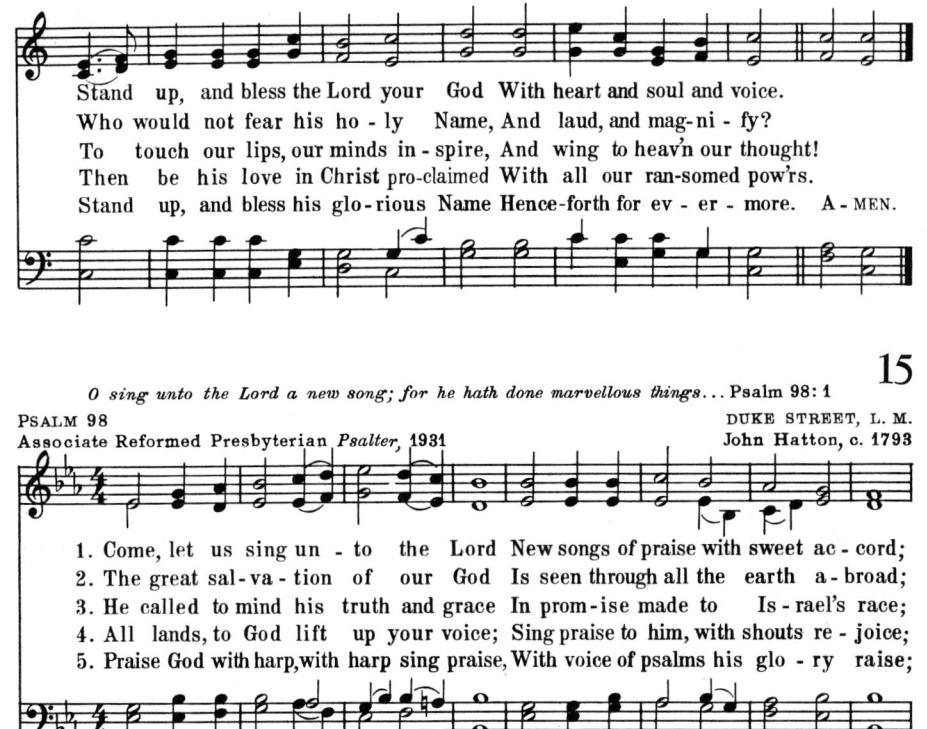

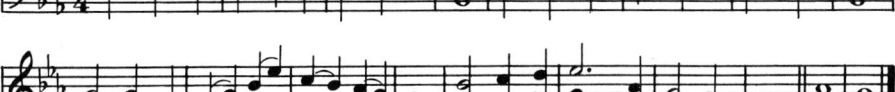

Stand up, and bless the Lord your God With heart and soul and voice.
Who would not fear his ho-ly Name, And laud, and mag-ni-fy?
To touch our lips, our minds in-spire, And wing to heav'n our thought!
Then be his love in Christ pro-claimed With all our ran-somed pow'rs.
Stand up, and bless his glo-rious Name Hence-forth for ev-er-more. A-MEN.

## 15

*O sing unto the Lord a new song; for he hath done marvellous things...* Psalm 98:1

PSALM 98  
Associate Reformed Presbyterian *Psalter*, 1931

DUKE STREET, L. M.  
John Hatton, c. 1793

1. Come, let us sing un-to the Lord New songs of praise with sweet ac-cord;
2. The great sal-va-tion of our God Is seen through all the earth a-broad;
3. He called to mind his truth and grace In prom-ise made to Is-rael's race;
4. All lands, to God lift up your voice; Sing praise to him, with shouts re-joice;
5. Praise God with harp, with harp sing praise, With voice of psalms his glo-ry raise;

For won-ders great by him are done, His hand and arm have vic-t'ry won.
Be-fore the hea-then's won-d'ring sight He hath re-vealed his truth and right.
And un-to earth's re-mot-est bound Glad ti-dings of sal-va-tion sound.
With voice of joy and loud ac-claim Let all u-nite and praise his Name.
With trum-pets, cor-nets, glad-ly sing And shout be-fore the Lord, the King. A-MEN.

6. Let earth be glad, let billows roar
   And all that dwell from shore to shore;
   Let floods clap hands with one accord,
   Let hills rejoice before the Lord.

7. For lo, he comes; at his command
   All nations shall in judgment stand;
   In justice robed and throned in light,
   The Lord shall judge, dispensing right.

## 16     THE GLORY OF GOD

*All thy works shall praise thee, O Lord; and thy saints shall bless thee.*    Psalm 145:10

Stanzas 1-2, Anon, c. 1801                                       FABEN 8. 7. 8. 7. D.
Stanza 3, Edward Osler, 1836                                    John H. Willcox, 1849

1. Praise the Lord: ye heav'ns a-dore him; Praise him, an-gels, in the height;
2. Praise the Lord, for he is glo-rious; Nev-er shall his prom-ise fail:
3. Wor-ship, hon-or, glo-ry, bless-ing, Lord, we of-fer un-to thee;

Sun and moon, re-joice be-fore him; Praise him, all ye stars and light.
God hath made his saints vic-to-rious; Sin and death shall not pre-vail.
Young and old, thy praise ex-press-ing, In glad hom-age bend the knee.

Praise the Lord, for he hath spo-ken; Worlds his might-y voice o-beyed:
Praise the God of our sal-va-tion; Hosts on high, his pow'r pro-claim;
All the saints in heav'n a-dore thee; We would bow be-fore thy throne:

Laws which nev-er shall be bro-ken For their guid-ance hath he made.
Heav'n and earth and all cre-a-tion, Laud and mag-ni-fy his Name.
As thine an-gels serve be-fore thee, So on earth thy will be done. A-MEN.

# THE DIVINE PERFECTIONS 17

*Praise ye the Lord from the heavens... Praise the Lord from the earth...* Psalm 148:1,7

Richard Baxter, 1672, alt.

DARWALL'S 148th 6. 6. 6. 6. 8. 8.
John Darwall, 1770

1. Ye ho-ly an-gels bright, Who wait at God's right hand, Or through the realms of light Fly at your Lord's com-mand, As-sist our song, For else the theme Too high doth seem For mor-tal tongue.
2. Ye bless-ed souls at rest, Who ran this earth-ly race, And now, from sin re-leased, Be-hold the Sav-iour's face, God's prais-es sound, As in his sight With sweet de-light Ye do a-bound.
3. All na-tions of the earth, Ex-tol the world's great King; With mel-o-dy and mirth His glo-rious prais-es sing; For he still reigns, And will bring low The proud-est foe That him dis-dains.
4. Sing forth Je-ho-vah's praise, Ye saints, that on him call! Him mag-ni-fy al-ways His ho-ly church-es all! In him re-joice, And there pro-claim His ho-ly Name With sound-ing voice.
5. My soul, bear thou thy part, Tri-umph in God a-bove; With a well-tu-ned heart Sing thou the songs of love; Thou art his own, Whose pre-cious blood Shed for thy good His love made known. A-MEN.

    6. Away, distrustful care!
       I have thy promise, Lord:
       To banish all despair,
       I have thine oath and word:
       And therefore I
       Shall see thy face
       And there thy grace
       Shall magnify.

    7. With thy triumphant flock,
       Then I shall numbered be;
       Built on th'eternal Rock,
       His glory we shall see.
       The heav'ns so high
       With praise shall ring
       And all shall sing
       In harmony.

# 18 THE GLORY OF GOD

*And every creature which is in heaven, and on the earth... heard I saying, Blessing, and honour, and glory, and power, be unto him that sitteth upon the throne...* **Rev. 5 : 13**

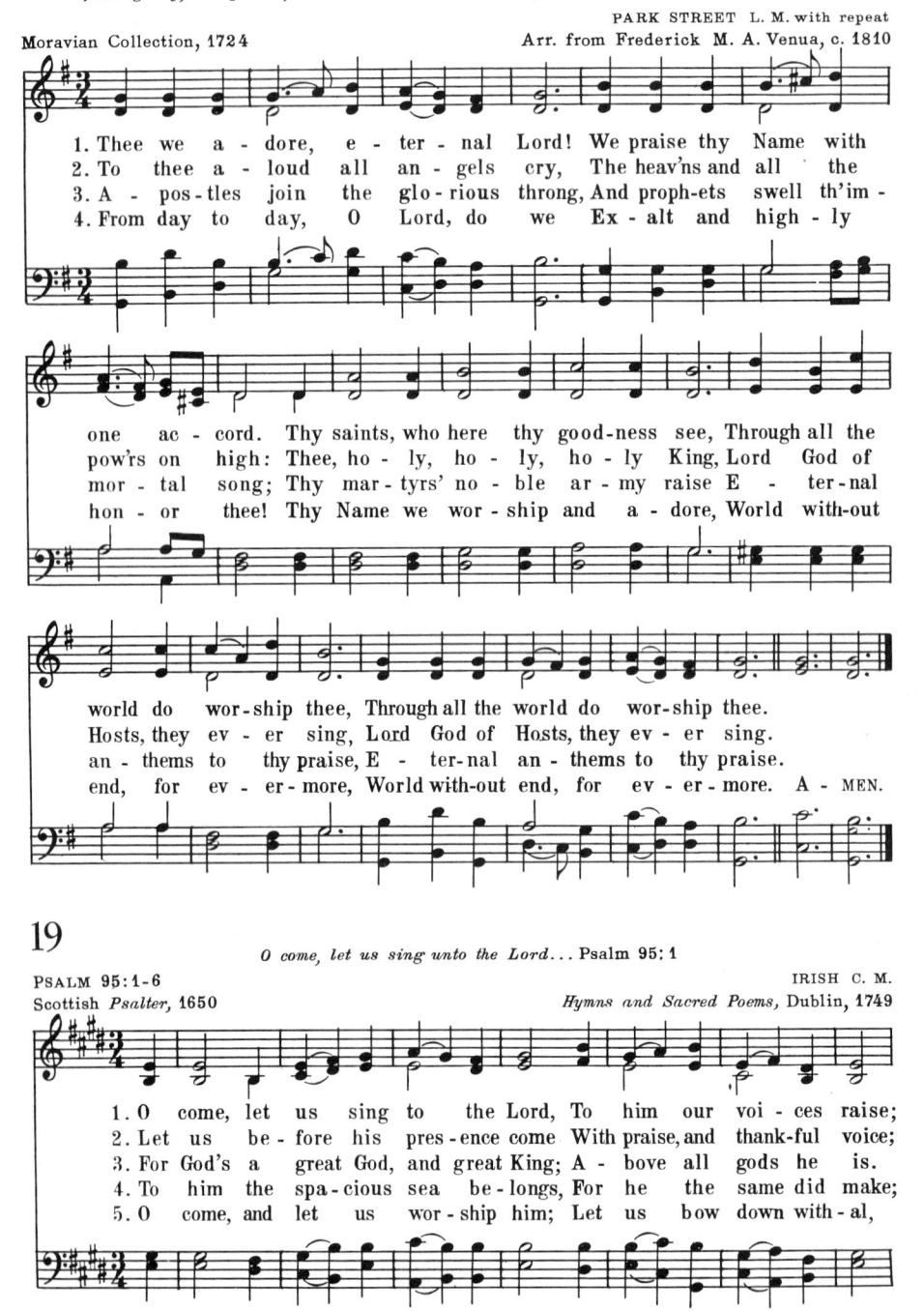

Moravian Collection, 1724

PARK STREET L. M. with repeat
Arr. from Frederick M. A. Venua, c. 1810

1. Thee we a - dore, e - ter - nal Lord! We praise thy Name with one ac - cord. Thy saints, who here thy good-ness see, Through all the world do wor-ship thee, Through all the world do wor-ship thee.
2. To thee a - loud all an - gels cry, The heav'ns and all the pow'rs on high: Thee, ho - ly, ho - ly, ho - ly King, Lord God of Hosts, they ev - er sing, Lord God of Hosts, they ev - er sing.
3. A - pos - tles join the glo - rious throng, And proph-ets swell th'im - mor - tal song; Thy mar - tyrs' no - ble ar - my raise E - ter - nal an - thems to thy praise, E - ter - nal an - thems to thy praise.
4. From day to day, O Lord, do we Ex - alt and high - ly hon - or thee! Thy Name we wor - ship and a - dore, World with - out end, for ev - er - more, World with-out end, for ev - er - more. A - MEN.

# 19

*O come, let us sing unto the Lord... Psalm 95: 1*

PSALM 95:1-6
Scottish *Psalter*, 1650

IRISH C. M.
*Hymns and Sacred Poems*, Dublin, 1749

1. O come, let us sing to the Lord, To him our voi - ces raise;
2. Let us be - fore his pres - ence come With praise, and thank - ful voice;
3. For God's a great God, and great King; A - bove all gods he is.
4. To him the spa - cious sea be - longs, For he the same did make;
5. O come, and let us wor - ship him; Let us bow down with - al,

# THE DIVINE PERFECTIONS

With joy-ful noise let us the Rock Of our sal-va-tion praise.
Let us sing psalms to him with grace, And make a joy-ful noise.
The depths of earth are in his hand; The heights of hills are his.
The dry land al-so from his hands Its form at first did take.
And on our knees be-fore the Lord, Our Mak-er, let us fall. A-MEN.

*For his mercy endureth forever.* Psalm 136:1

**20**

From PSALM 136
Isaac Watts, 1719

WARRINGTON L. M.
Ralph Harrison, 1784

1. Give to our God im-mor-tal praise; Mer-cy and truth are all his ways: Won-ders of grace to God be-long; Re-peat his mer-cies in your song.
2. Give to the Lord of lords re-nown; The King of kings with glo-ry crown: His mer-cies ev-er shall en-dure, When lords and kings are known no more.
3. He built the earth, he spread the sky, And fixed the star-ry lights on high: Won-ders of grace to God be-long; Re-peat his mer-cies in your song.
4. He fills the sun with morn-ing light; He bids the moon di-rect the night: His mer-cies ev-er shall en-dure, When suns and moons shall shine no more.
5. He sent his Son with pow'r to save From guilt, and dark-ness, and the grave: Won-ders of grace to God be-long; Re-peat his mer-cies in your song.
6. Through this vain world he guides our feet, And leads us to his heav'n-ly seat: His mer-cies ev-er shall en-dure, When this vain world shall be no more. A-MEN.

## 21 THE GLORY OF GOD

*I will make darkness light before them, and crooked things straight.* Isa. 42:16

HERMON C. M.

William Cowper, 1774  
Lowell Mason, 1832

1. God moves in a mys-te-rious way His won-ders to per - form;
2. Deep in un-fath-om-a-ble mines Of nev-er - fail - ing skill
3. Ye fear-ful saints, fresh cour-age take; The clouds ye so much dread
4. Judge not the Lord by fee-ble sense, But trust him for his grace;
5. His pur-pos-es will rip-en fast, Un - fold-ing ev - 'ry hour;
6. Blind un-be-lief is sure to err, And scan his work in vain;

He plants his foot-steps in the sea, And rides up-on the storm.
He treas-ures up his bright de-signs, And works his sov-ereign will.
Are big with mer-cy, and shall break In bless-ings on your head.
Be - hind a frown-ing prov-i-dence He hides a smil-ing face.
The bud may have a bit-ter taste, But sweet will be the flow'r.
God is his own in - ter-pre-ter, And he will make it plain. A - MEN.

## 22

*Thou, O Lord, remainest for ever; thy throne from generation to generation.* Lam. 5:19

WINDSOR C. M.

Isaac Watts, 1707  
St. 1, line 2, and st. 5, line 2, alt.

Melody arr. from Christopher Tye, 1533,  
in Wm. Daman's *Booke of Musicke,* 1591

1. Great God, how in - fi - nite art thou! How poor and weak are we!
2. Thy throne e - ter-nal a - ges stood, Ere seas or stars were made:
3. E - ter-ni - ty, with all its years, Stands pres-ent in thy view;
4. Our lives through var-ious scenes are drawn, And vexed with trif-ling cares;
5. Great God, how in - fi - nite art thou! How poor and weak are we!

Let the whole race of crea-tures bow, And pay their praise to thee.
Thou art the ev - er - liv-ing God, Were all the na-tions dead.
To thee there's noth-ing old ap-pears; To thee there's noth-ing new.
While thine e - ter - nal thought moves on Thine un-dis-turbed af-fairs.
Let the whole race of crea-tures bow, And pay their praise to thee. A - MEN.

St. 3, line 4, alt.

# INFINITE 23

*God is light, and in him is no darkness at all.* I John 1:5

Gregory Nazianzen, 325 - 390
Tr. by John Brownlie, 1859 - 1925

WAVERTON 6. 6. 6. 6. 8. 8.
Robert Jackson, 1876

1. O Light that knew no dawn, That shines to endless day, All things in earth and heav'n Are lustred by thy ray; No eye can to thy throne ascend, Nor mind thy brightness comprehend.
2. Thy grace, O Father, give, That I may serve in fear; Above all boons, I pray, Grant me thy voice to hear; From sin thy child in mercy free, And let me dwell in light with thee:
3. That, cleansed from stain of sin, I may meet homage give, And, pure in heart, behold Thy beauty while I live; Clean hands in holy worship raise, And thee, O Christ my Saviour, praise.
4. In supplication meek To thee I bend the knee; O Christ, when thou shalt come, In love remember me, And in thy kingdom, by thy grace, Grant me a humble servant's place.
5. Thy grace, O Father, give, I humbly thee implore; And let thy mercy bless Thy servant more and more. All grace and glory be to thee, From age to age eternally. A - MEN.

Words used by permission of Marshall, Morgan and Scott, Ltd.

# 24  THE GLORY OF GOD

*Lord, thou hast been our dwelling place in all generations.* Psalm 90:1

Edward H. Bickersteth, 1860

SCHUBERT 7. 6. 7. 6. D.
Arr. from Franz Schubert by W. W. Gilchrist, 1895

1. O God, the Rock of A - ges, Who ev - er - more hast been,
   What time the tem - pest ra - ges, Our dwell - ing place se - rene:
   Be - fore thy first cre - a - tions, O Lord, the same as now,
   To end - less gen - er - a - tions The Ev - er - last - ing Thou!

2. Our years are like the shad - ows On sun - ny hills that lie,
   Or grass - es in the mead - ows That blos - som but to die;
   A sleep, a dream, a sto - ry By stran - gers quick - ly told,
   An un - re - main - ing glo - ry Of things that soon are old.

3. O thou who canst not slum - ber, Whose light grows nev - er pale,
   Teach us a - right to num - ber Our years be - fore they fail;
   On us thy mer - cy light - en, On us thy good - ness rest,
   And let thy Spir - it bright - en The hearts thy - self hast blessed.

4. Lord, crown our faith's en - deav - or With beau - ty and with grace,
   Till, clothed in light for ev - er, We see thee face to face:
   A joy no lan - guage meas - ures; A foun - tain brim - ming o'er;
   An end - less flow of pleas - ures; An o - cean with - out shore. A - MEN.

# ETERNAL  25

*He will regard the prayer of the destitute... Psalm 102:17*

Psalm 102:17-28  
*The Psalter,* 1912  

REST L. M.  
William B. Bradbury, 1843

1. The Lord has heard and an-swered prayer And saved his peo-ple in dis-tress; This to the com-ing age de-clare, That they his ho-ly Name may bless.
2. The Lord, ex-alt-ed on his throne, Looked down from heav'n with pit-ying eye To still the low-ly cap-tive's moan And save his peo-ple doomed to die.
3. All men in Zi-on shall de-clare His gra-cious Name with one ac-cord, When kings and na-tions gath-er there To serve and wor-ship God the Lord.
4. Be-fore my jour-ney is com-plete My vig-or fails, my years de-cline; My God, O spare me, I en-treat; The days of life are whol-ly thine.
5. The earth and heav'ns shall pass a-way, Like ves-ture worn and laid a-side, But change-less thou shalt live for aye, Thy years for ev-er shall a-bide. A-MEN.

6. Thou, O Jehovah, shalt endure,  
Thy throne for ever is the same;  
And to all generations sure  
Shall be thy great memorial Name.

7. Thy servants' children shall remain  
For evermore before thy face;  
Enduring honor they shall gain,  
Established ever in thy grace.

# 26 (FIRST TUNE)          THE GLORY OF GOD

*Lord, thou hast been our dwelling place in all generations. Psalm 90:1*

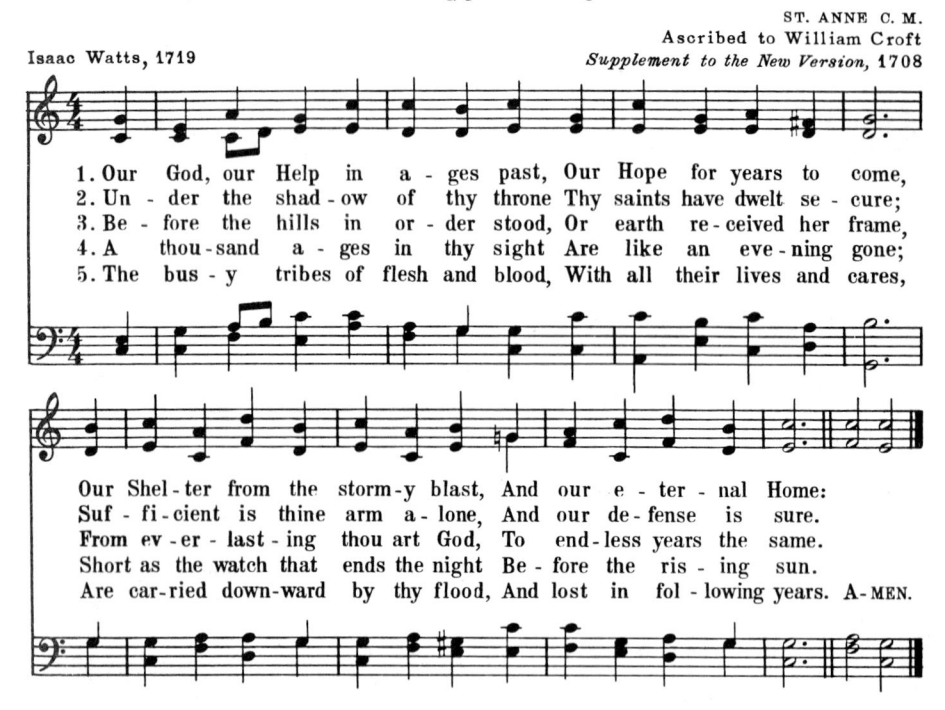

Isaac Watts, 1719

ST. ANNE C. M.
Ascribed to William Croft
*Supplement to the New Version, 1708*

1. Our God, our Help in a - ges past, Our Hope for years to come,
2. Un - der the shad - ow of thy throne Thy saints have dwelt se - cure;
3. Be - fore the hills in or - der stood, Or earth re - ceived her frame,
4. A thou - sand a - ges in thy sight Are like an eve - ning gone;
5. The bus - y tribes of flesh and blood, With all their lives and cares,

Our Shel - ter from the storm - y blast, And our e - ter - nal Home:
Suf - fi - cient is thine arm a - lone, And our de - fense is sure.
From ev - er - last - ing thou art God, To end - less years the same.
Short as the watch that ends the night Be - fore the ris - ing sun.
Are car - ried down - ward by thy flood, And lost in fol - lowing years. A-MEN.

6. Time, like an ever-rolling stream,
Bears all its sons away;
They fly forgotten, as a dream
Dies at the opening day.

7. Our God, our Help in ages past,
Our Hope for years to come;
Be thou our Guard while troubles last,
And our eternal Home.

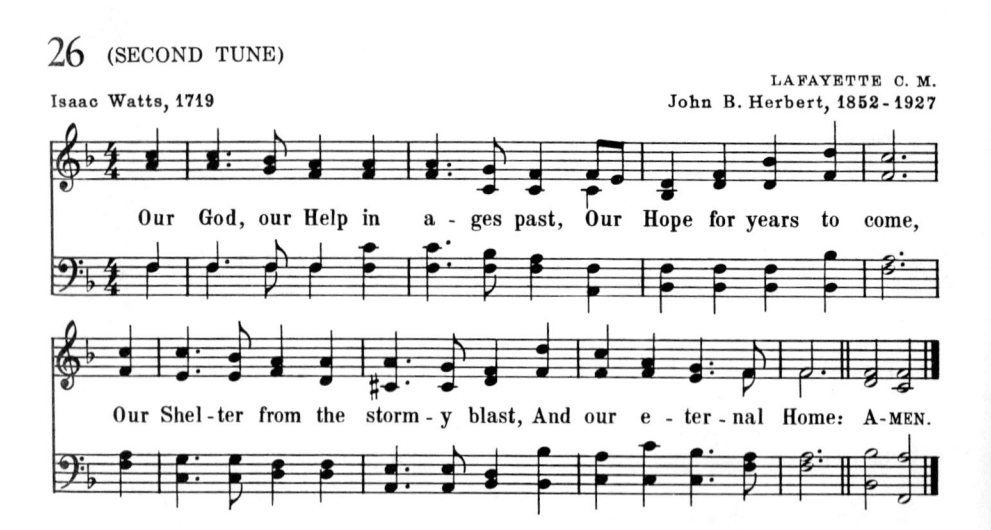

# 26 (SECOND TUNE)

Isaac Watts, 1719

LAFAYETTE C. M.
John B. Herbert, 1852-1927

Our God, our Help in a - ges past, Our Hope for years to come,

Our Shel - ter from the storm - y blast, And our e - ter - nal Home: A-MEN.

# UNCHANGEABLE

**27**

*His compassions fail not. They are new every morning: great is thy faithfulness.* Lam. 3: 22-23

Thomas O. Chisholm

FAITHFULNESS 11.10.11.10. with refrain

William M. Runyan

1. "Great is thy faith-ful-ness," O God my Fa-ther, There is no shad-ow of turn-ing with thee; Thou chang-est not, thy com-pas-sions, they fail not; As thou hast been thou for ev-er wilt be.
2. Sum-mer and win-ter, and spring-time and har-vest, Sun, moon and stars in their cours-es a-bove, Join with all na-ture in man-i-fold wit-ness To thy great faith-ful-ness, mer-cy and love.
3. Par-don for sin and a peace that en-dur-eth, Thine own dear pres-ence to cheer and to guide; Strength for to-day and bright hope for to-mor-row, Bless-ings all mine, with ten thou-sand be-side!

REFRAIN

"Great is thy faith-ful-ness! Great is thy faith-ful-ness!" Morn-ing by morn-ing new mer-cies I see: All I have need-ed thy hand hath pro-vid-ed—"Great is thy faith-ful-ness," Lord, un-to me! A-MEN.

Copyright, 1923. Renewal, 1951, by W. M. Runyan. Assigned to Hope Publishing Co. All rights reserved. Used by permission.

## 28                                                     THE GLORY OF GOD

*Hast thou not known? hast thou not heard, that the everlasting God, the Lord, the Creator of the ends of the earth, fainteth not, neither is weary?*    Isa. 40:28

Isaac Watts, 1707                                                 DUNDEE C. M.
Alt. in Scottish *Paraphrases,* 1781                              Scottish *Psalter,* 1615

1. Hast thou not known, hast thou not heard  That firm re-mains on high
    The ev-er-last-ing throne of him  Who formed the earth and sky?
2. Art thou a-fraid his pow'r shall fail  When comes thine e-vil day?
    And can an all-cre-at-ing arm  Grow wea-ry or de-cay?
3. Su-preme in wis-dom as in pow'r  The Rock of A-ges stands,
    Though him thou canst not see, nor trace  The work-ing of his hands.
4. He gives the con-quest to the weak,  Sup-ports the faint-ing heart;
    And cour-age in the e-vil hour  His heav'n-ly aids im-part.
5. Mere hu-man pow'r shall fast de-cay,  And youth-ful vig-or cease;
    But they who wait up-on the Lord  In strength shall still in-crease. A-MEN.

6. They with unwearied feet shall tread
   The path of life divine,
   With growing ardor onward move,
   With growing brightness shine.

7. On eagles' wings they mount, they soar—
   Their wings are faith and love—
   Till, past the cloudy regions here,
   They rise to heav'n above.

## 29

*O praise the Lord, all ye nations: praise him, all ye people.*    Psalm 117:1

Psalm 117                                                         ST. OSWALD 8.7.8.7.
United Presbyterian *Book of Psalms,* 1871                          John B. Dykes, 1857

1. Praise Je-ho-vah, all ye na-tions, All ye peo-ple, praise pro-claim;
2. Great to us hath been his mer-cy, Ev-er faith-ful is his word;

## UNCHANGEABLE

For his grace and lov-ing-kind-ness, O sing prais-es to his Name.
Through all a - ges it en - dur - eth. Hal - le - lu - jah, praise the Lord. A - MEN.

## 30

*O give thanks unto the Lord; for he is good: for his mercy endureth for ever.* Psalm 136:1

From PSALM 136  
John Milton, 1624, alt.

MONKLAND 7. 7. 7. 7.  
Anon., 1824; arr. John B. Wilkes, 1861

1. Let us, with a glad-some mind, Praise the Lord, for he is kind:
2. Let us blaze his Name a-broad, For of gods he is the God:
3. He with all-com-mand-ing might Filled the new-made world with light:
4. All things liv-ing he doth feed; His full hand sup-plies their need:
5. He his cho-sen race did bless In the waste-ful wil-der-ness:

REFRAIN

For his mer-cies aye en-dure, Ev - er faith-ful, ev - er sure. A - MEN.

6. He hath with a piteous eye
   Looked upon our misery:
   For his mercies aye endure,
   Ever faithful, ever sure.

7. Let us therefore warble forth
   His high majesty and worth:
   For his mercies aye endure,
   Ever faithful, ever sure.

# 31      THE GLORY OF GOD

*Who is like unto the Lord our God, who dwelleth on high, who humbleth himself to behold the things that are in heaven, and in the earth!*    Psalm 113:5-6

Frederick W. Faber, 1848

ST. ETHELDREDA C. M.
Thomas Turton, 1780-1864

1. My God, how won-der-ful thou art, Thy maj-es-ty how bright! How beau-ti-ful thy mer-cy-seat, In depths of burn-ing light!
2. How dread are thine e-ter-nal years, O ev-er-last-ing Lord, By ho-ly an-gels, day and night, In-ces-sant-ly a-dored!
3. O how I fear thee, liv-ing God, With deep-est, ten-d'rest fears; And wor-ship thee with trem-bling hope, And pen-i-ten-tial tears.
4. Yet I may love thee too, O Lord, Al-might-y as thou art; For thou hast stooped to ask of me The love of my poor heart. A-MEN.

5. No earthly father loves like thee,
    No mother half so mild
    Bears and forbears, as thou hast done
    With me, thy sinful child.

6. How wonderful, how beautiful,
    The sight of thee will be,
    Thine endless wisdom, boundless power,
    And aweful purity!

St. 2, line 3, and st. 6, line 2, alt.

# HIS BEING 32

*But without faith it is impossible to please him: for he that cometh to God must believe that he is...* Heb. 11:6

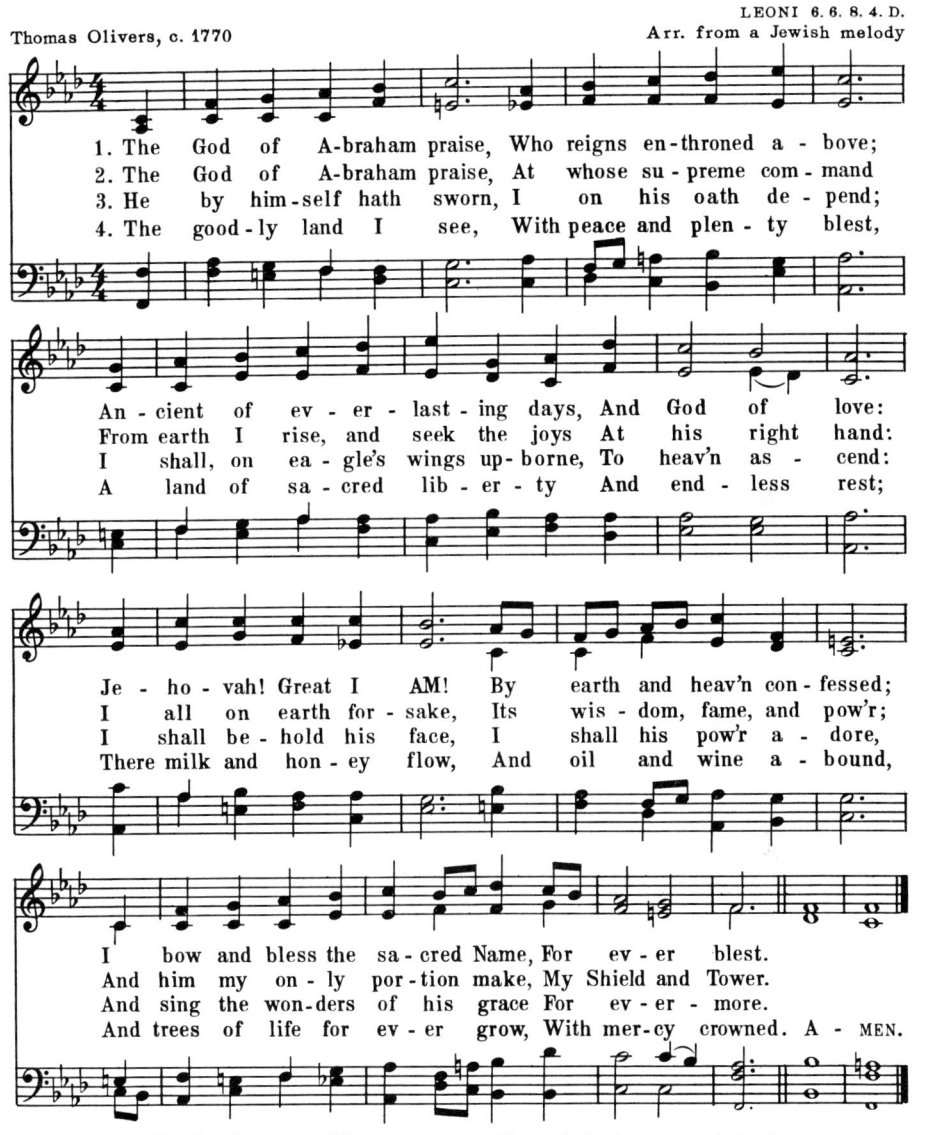

Thomas Olivers, c. 1770  
LEONI 6.6.8.4.D.  
Arr. from a Jewish melody

1. The God of A-braham praise, Who reigns en-throned a-bove;
2. The God of A-braham praise, At whose su-preme com-mand
3. He by him-self hath sworn, I on his oath de-pend;
4. The good-ly land I see, With peace and plen-ty blest,

An-cient of ev-er-last-ing days, And God of love:
From earth I rise, and seek the joys At his right hand:
I shall, on ea-gle's wings up-borne, To heav'n as-cend:
A land of sa-cred lib-er-ty And end-less rest;

Je-ho-vah! Great I AM! By earth and heav'n con-fessed;
I all on earth for-sake, Its wis-dom, fame, and pow'r;
I shall be-hold his face, I shall his pow'r a-dore,
There milk and hon-ey flow, And oil and wine a-bound,

I bow and bless the sa-cred Name, For ev-er blest.
And him my on-ly por-tion make, My Shield and Tower.
And sing the won-ders of his grace For ev-er-more.
And trees of life for ev-er grow, With mer-cy crowned. A-MEN.

5. There dwells the Lord our King,
   The Lord our Righteousness;
   Triumphant o'er the world and sin,
   The Prince of Peace
   On Zion's sacred height
   His kingdom still maintains,
   And glorious with his saints in light
   For ever reigns.

6. The whole triumphant host
   Give thanks to God on high;
   "Hail, Father, Son, and Holy Ghost!"
   They ever cry:
   Hail, Abraham's God and mine!
   I join the heavenly lays;
   All might and majesty are thine,
   And endless praise.

**33** THE GLORY OF GOD

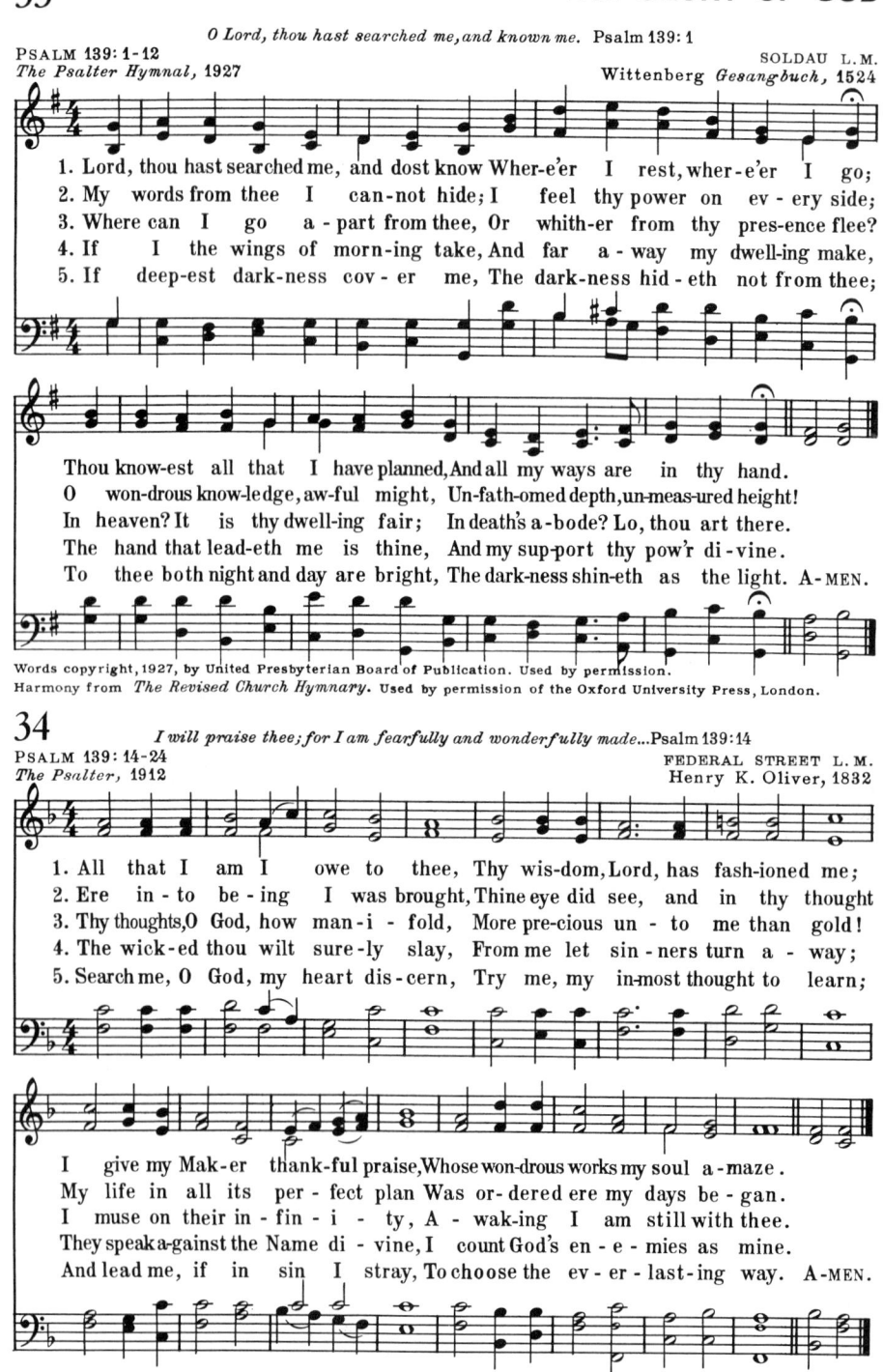

*O Lord, thou hast searched me, and known me.* Psalm 139:1

PSALM 139: 1-12
The Psalter Hymnal, 1927

SOLDAU L.M.
Wittenberg *Gesangbuch,* 1524

1. Lord, thou hast searched me, and dost know Wher-e'er I rest, wher-e'er I go;
2. My words from thee I can-not hide; I feel thy power on ev - ery side;
3. Where can I go a - part from thee, Or whith-er from thy pres-ence flee?
4. If I the wings of morn-ing take, And far a - way my dwell-ing make,
5. If deep-est dark-ness cov - er me, The dark-ness hid - eth not from thee;

Thou know-est all that I have planned, And all my ways are in thy hand.
O won-drous know-ledge, aw-ful might, Un-fath-omed depth, un-meas-ured height!
In heaven? It is thy dwell-ing fair; In death's a -bode? Lo, thou art there.
The hand that lead-eth me is thine, And my sup-port thy pow'r di-vine.
To thee both night and day are bright, The dark-ness shin-eth as the light. A-MEN.

Words copyright, 1927, by United Presbyterian Board of Publication. Used by permission.
Harmony from *The Revised Church Hymnary.* Used by permission of the Oxford University Press, London.

**34**

*I will praise thee; for I am fearfully and wonderfully made...* Psalm 139:14

PSALM 139: 14-24
The Psalter, 1912

FEDERAL STREET L.M.
Henry K. Oliver, 1832

1. All that I am I owe to thee, Thy wis-dom, Lord, has fash-ioned me;
2. Ere in - to be - ing I was brought, Thine eye did see, and in thy thought
3. Thy thoughts, O God, how man-i - fold, More pre-cious un - to me than gold!
4. The wick-ed thou wilt sure-ly slay, From me let sin - ners turn a - way;
5. Search me, O God, my heart dis-cern, Try me, my in-most thought to learn;

I give my Mak-er thank-ful praise, Whose won-drous works my soul a - maze.
My life in all its per - fect plan Was or- dered ere my days be - gan.
I muse on their in - fin - i - ty, A - wak-ing I am still with thee.
They speak a-gainst the Name di - vine, I count God's en - e - mies as mine.
And lead me, if in sin I stray, To choose the ev - er - last-ing way. A-MEN.

# HIS WISDOM   35

*Now unto the King eternal, immortal, invisible, the only wise God,*
*be honour and glory for ever and ever. Amen.* I Tim. 1:17

Walter Chalmers Smith, 1824-1908

JOANNA 11. 11. 11. 11.
Welsh hymn melody

1. Im - mor - tal, in - vis - i - ble, God on - ly wise,
2. Un - rest - ing, un - hast - ing, and si - lent as light,
3. Great Fa - ther of Glo - ry, pure Fa - ther of Light,

In light in - ac - ces - si - ble hid from our eyes,
Nor want - ing, nor wast - ing, Thou rul - est in might;
Thine an - gels a - dore thee, all veil - ing their sight;

Most bless - ed, most glo - rious, the An - cient of Days,
Thy jus - tice like moun - tains high soar - ing a - bove
All praise we would ren - der; O help us to see

Al - might - y, vic - to - rious, Thy great Name we praise.
Thy clouds which are foun - tains of good - ness and love.
'Tis on - ly the splen - dor of light hid - eth thee! A - MEN.

For a lower setting of this tune, see No. 279.

# 36 THE GLORY OF GOD

*Give unto the Lord, O ye mighty, give unto the Lord glory and strength.* Psalm 29:1

PSALM 29: 1-5, 9-11
St. 1, *The Psalter*, 1912
St. 2-4, United Presbyterian *Book of Psalms*, 1871, alt.

ADESTE FIDELES 12.11.12.11. with repeat
Unknown: probably 18th century
Adapted from Wade's *Cantus Diversi*, 1751

1. Now un-to Je-ho-vah, ye sons of the might-y, All glo-ry and strength and do-min-ion ac-cord; As-cribe to him glo-ry, and ren-der him hon-or. In beau-ty of ho-li-ness wor-ship the Lord, In beau-ty of ho-li-ness wor-ship the Lord.

2. The voice of Je-ho-vah comes down on the wa-ters; In thun-der the God of the glo-ry draws nigh. Lo, o-ver the waves of the wide-flow-ing wa-ters Je-ho-vah as King is en-throned on high! Je-ho-vah as King is en-throned on high!

3. The voice of Je-ho-vah is might-y, is might-y; The voice of Je-ho-vah in maj-es-ty speaks: The voice of Je-ho-vah the ce-dars is break-ing; Je-ho-vah the ce-dars of Le-ban-on breaks, Je-ho-vah the ce-dars of Le-ban-on breaks.

4. Each one, in his tem-ple, his glo-ry pro-claim-eth. He sat on the flood; he is King on his throne. Je-ho-vah all strength to his peo-ple im-part-eth; Je-ho-vah with peace ev-er bless-eth his own, Je-ho-vah with peace ev-er bless-eth his own. A-MEN.

# HIS POWER

**37**

*God is our refuge and strength, a very present help in trouble.* Psalm 46:1

PSALM 46  
*The Psalter*, 1912

MATERNA C. M. D.  
Samuel A. Ward, 1882

1. God is our Ref-uge and our Strength, Our ev-er pres-ent aid,
2. A riv-er flows whose streams make glad The cit-y of our God,
3. The na-tions raged, the king-doms moved, But when his voice was heard
4. O come, be-hold what won-drous works Je-ho-vah's hand has wrought;
5. Be still and know that I am God, O'er all ex-alt-ed high;

And, there-fore, though the earth re-move, We will not be a-fraid;
The ho-ly place where-in the Lord Most high has his a-bode;
The trou-bled earth was stilled to peace Be-fore his might-y word.
Come, see what des-o-la-tion great He on the earth has brought.
The sub-ject na-tions of the earth My Name shall mag-ni-fy.—

Though hills a-midst the seas be cast, Though foam-ing wa-ters roar,
Since God is in the midst of her, Un-moved her walls shall stand,
The Lord of Hosts is on our side, Our safe-ty to se-cure;
To ut-most ends of all the earth He caus-es war to cease;
The Lord of Hosts is on our side, Our safe-ty to se-cure;

Yea, though the might-y bil-lows shake The moun-tains on the shore.
For God will be her ear-ly help, When trou-ble is at hand.
The God of Ja-cob is for us A ref-uge strong and sure.
The weap-ons of the strong de-stroyed, He makes a-bid-ing peace.
The God of Ja-cob is for us A ref-uge strong and sure. A-MEN.

## 38      THE GLORY OF GOD

*And the heavens shall praise thy wonders, O Lord... Psalm 89:5*

PSALM 89:5, 13-18                                                                             SHEFFIELD C. M.
*The Book of Psalms,* Church of Scotland, 1886                           William Mather

1. The prais - es of thy won - ders, Lord, The heav - ens shall ex - press;
2. Thou hast an arm that's full of pow'r: Thy hand is great in might;
3. Jus - tice and judg - ment of thy throne Are made the dwell - ing - place;
4. O great - ly bless'd the peo - ple are The joy - ful sound that know;

And in the con - gre - ga - tion Of saints thy faith - ful - ness.
And thy right hand ex - ceed - ing - ly Ex - alt - ed is in height.
Mer - cy, ac - com - pan - y'd with truth, Shall go be - fore thy face.
In bright - ness of thy face, O Lord, They ev - er on shall go. A-MEN.

5. Because the glory of their strength
    Doth only stand in thee;
    And in thy favor shall our horn
    And pow'r exalted be.

6. For God is our defense; and he
    To us doth safety bring:
    The Holy One of Israel
    Is our almighty King.

## 39

*When Israel went out of Egypt, the house of Jacob
from a people of strange language... Psalm 114:1*

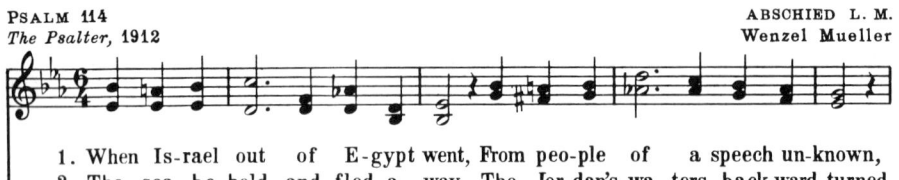

PSALM 114                                                                                ABSCHIED L. M.
*The Psalter,* 1912                                                              Wenzel Mueller

1. When Is - rael out of E - gypt went, From peo - ple of a speech un - known,
2. The sea be - held and fled a - way, The Jor - dan's wa - ters back - ward turned,
3. What ail - eth thee, O troub - led sea? Thou Jor - dan, why thy ri - ven tide?
4. O trem - ble, earth, be - fore the Lord, In pres - ence of Je - ho - vah fear,

## HIS POWER

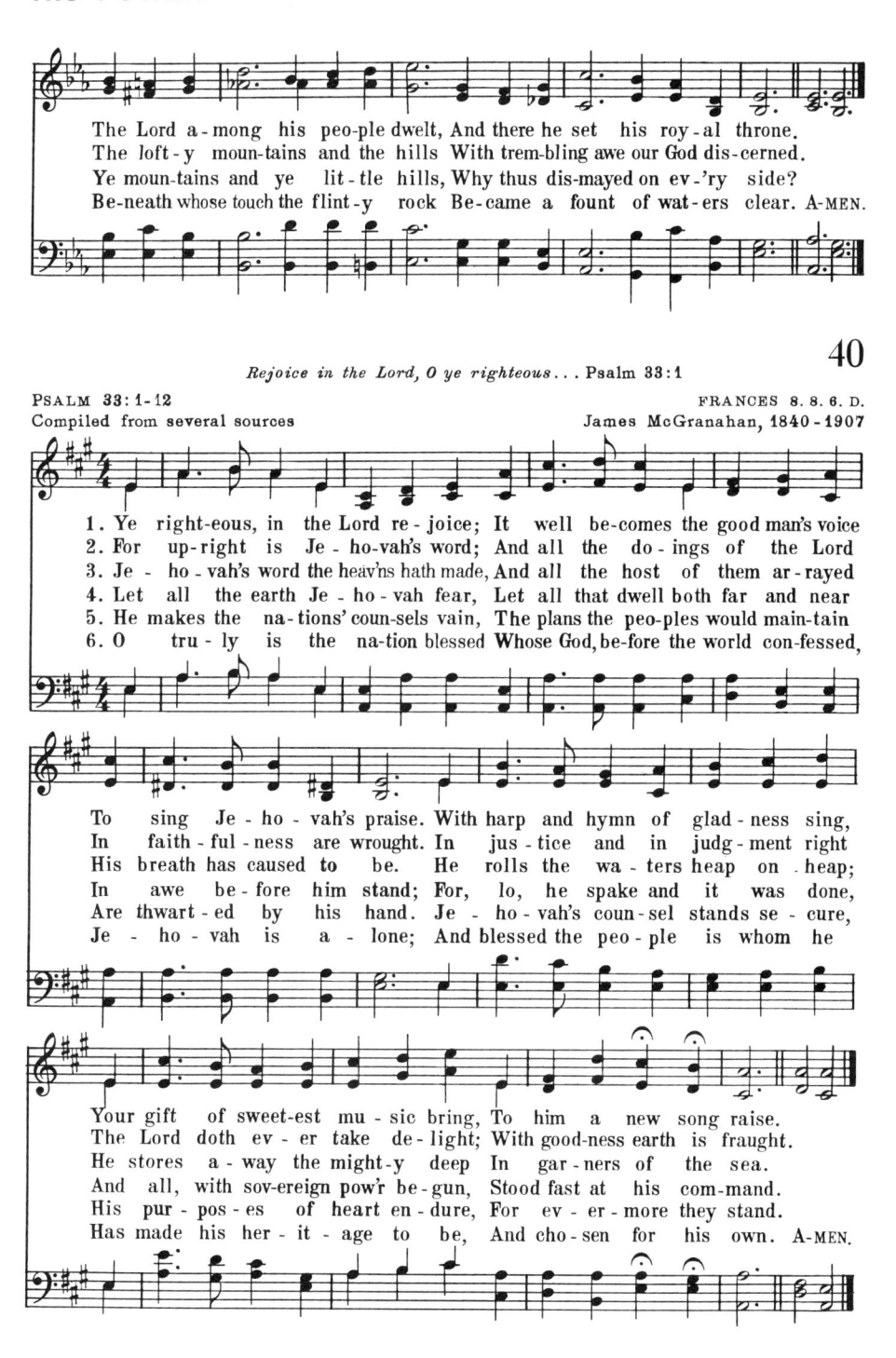

The Lord a-mong his peo-ple dwelt, And there he set his roy-al throne.
The loft-y moun-tains and the hills With trem-bling awe our God dis-cerned.
Ye moun-tains and ye lit-tle hills, Why thus dis-mayed on ev-'ry side?
Be-neath whose touch the flint-y rock Be-came a fount of wat-ers clear. A-MEN.

*Rejoice in the Lord, O ye righteous... Psalm 33:1*

**40**

PSALM 33:1-12  
Compiled from several sources

FRANCES 8.8.6.D.  
James McGranahan, 1840-1907

1. Ye right-eous, in the Lord re-joice; It well be-comes the good man's voice
2. For up-right is Je-ho-vah's word; And all the do-ings of the Lord
3. Je-ho-vah's word the heav'ns hath made, And all the host of them ar-rayed
4. Let all the earth Je-ho-vah fear, Let all that dwell both far and near
5. He makes the na-tions' coun-sels vain, The plans the peo-ples would main-tain
6. O tru-ly is the na-tion blessed Whose God, be-fore the world con-fessed,

To sing Je-ho-vah's praise. With harp and hymn of glad-ness sing,
In faith-ful-ness are wrought. In jus-tice and in judg-ment right
His breath has caused to be. He rolls the wa-ters heap on heap;
In awe be-fore him stand; For, lo, he spake and it was done,
Are thwart-ed by his hand. Je-ho-vah's coun-sel stands se-cure,
Je-ho-vah is a-lone; And blessed the peo-ple is whom he

Your gift of sweet-est mu-sic bring, To him a new song raise.
The Lord doth ev-er take de-light; With good-ness earth is fraught.
He stores a-way the might-y deep In gar-ners of the sea.
And all, with sov-ereign pow'r be-gun, Stood fast at his com-mand.
His pur-pos-es of heart en-dure, For ev-er-more they stand.
Has made his her-it-age to be, And cho-sen for his own. A-MEN.

# 41 THE GLORY OF GOD

*Thy way, O God, is in the sanctuary: who is so great a God as our God?* Psalm 77:13

PSALM 77:13-20
*The Psalter,* 1912

THE LORD'S PRAYER (VATER UNSER) 8.8.8.8.8.8.
Schumann's *Gesangbuch,* 1539

1. O God, most ho-ly are thy ways, And who like thee de-serves my praise? Thou on-ly do-est won-drous things, The whole wide world thy glo-ry sings; Thine out-stretched arm thy peo-ple saved, Though sore dis-tressed and long en-slaved.

2. O God, from thee the wa-ters fled, The depths were moved with might-y dread, The swell-ing clouds their tor-rents poured, And o'er the earth the tem-pest roared; 'Mid light-'ning's flash and thun-der's sound Great trem-bling shook the sol-id ground.

3. Thy way was in the sea, O God, Through might-y wa-ters, deep and broad; None un-der-stood but God a-lone, To man thy foot-steps were un-known; But safe thy peo-ple thou didst keep, Al-might-y Shep-herd of thy sheep. A-MEN.

# HIS HOLINESS

**42**

*And one cried unto another, and said, Holy, holy, holy, is the Lord of hosts: the whole earth is full of his glory.* Isa. 6:3

Richard Mant, 1837

EBENEZER 8. 7. 8. 7. D.
Thomas John Williams, 1890

1. Round the Lord in glo-ry seat-ed, Cher-u-bim and ser-a-phim
Filled his tem-ple, and re-peat-ed Each to each the al-ter-nate hymn:
"Lord, thy glo-ry fills the heav-en, Earth is with its ful-ness stored;
Un-to thee be glo-ry giv-en, Ho-ly, ho-ly, ho-ly Lord!"

2. Heav'n is still with glo-ry ring-ing, Earth takes up the an-gels' cry,
"Ho-ly, ho-ly, ho-ly," sing-ing, "Lord of Hosts, the Lord most high."
With his ser-aph train be-fore him, With his ho-ly church be-low,
Thus con-spire we to a-dore him, Bid we thus our an-them flow:

3. "Lord, thy glo-ry fills the heav-en, Earth is with its ful-ness stored;
Un-to thee be glo-ry giv-en, Ho-ly, ho-ly, ho-ly Lord!"
Thus thy glo-rious Name con-fess-ing, We a-dopt thine an-gels' cry,
"Ho-ly, ho-ly, ho-ly," bless-ing Thee, the Lord of Hosts most high. A-MEN.

Music copyright by Gwenlyn Evans, Ltd. Used by permission.

## 43 THE GLORY OF GOD

*The Lord reigneth; let the people tremble... Psalm 99:1*

From PSALM 99  
George Rawson, 1807-1889

ARDUDWY 8.7.8.7.8.7.  
John Roberts, 1822-1877

1. God the Lord is King: be-fore him Earth with all thy na-tions, wait!
2. God the Lord is King of glo-ry, Zi-on, tell the world his fame;
3. Laws di-vine to them were spo-ken From the pil-lar of the cloud;
4. But their Fa-ther God for-gave them When they sought his face once more:

Where the cher-u-bim a-dore him, Sit-teth he in roy-al state:
An-cient Is-ra-el, the sto-ry Of his faith-ful-ness pro-claim:
Sa-cred pre-cepts, quick-ly bro-ken! Fierce-ly then his ven-geance flowed:
Ev-er rea-dy was to save them, Ten-der-ly did he re-store:

He is ho-ly; He is ho-ly; Bless-ed, on-ly Po-ten-tate!
He is ho-ly; He is ho-ly; Ho-ly is his aw-ful Name.
He is ho-ly; He is ho-ly; To the dust their hearts were bowed.
He is ho-ly; He is ho-ly; We too will his grace im-plore. A-MEN.

## 44

*I will praise thee, O Lord, with my whole heart... Psalm 9:1*

PSALM 9:1-2, 7-11  
The Psalter, 1912

ROCKINGHAM OLD L. M.  
Arr. by Edward Miller, 1790

1. O Lord most high, with all my heart Thy won-drous works I will pro-claim;
2. The Lord, the ev-er-last-ing King, Is seat-ed on his judg-ment throne;
3. Je-ho-vah will a ref-uge prove, A ref-uge strong for all op-pressed,
4. All they, O Lord, that know thy Name Their con-fid-ence in thee will place,
5. Sing prais-es to the Lord most high, To him who doth in Zi-on dwell;

# HIS JUSTICE

I will be glad and give thee thanks And sing the prais-es of thy Name.
The right-eous Judge of all the world Will make his per-fect jus-tice known.
A safe re-treat, where wea-ry souls In troub-lous times may sure-ly rest.
For thou hast ne'er for-sak-en them Who earn-est-ly have sought thy face.
De-clare his might-y deeds a-broad, His deeds a-mong the na-tions tell. A-MEN.

45

*Help, Lord; for the godly man ceaseth; for the faith-
ful fail from among the children of men. Psalm 12:1*

PSALM 12     COLWYN BAY 8.8.6.D.
*The Psalter,* 1912     Thomas Joseph Linekar, b. 1858

1. O Lord, be thou my help-er true, For just and god-ly men are few;
2. The lips that speak, the truth to hide, The tongues of ar-ro-gance and pride,
3. Be-cause the poor are sore op-pressed, Be-cause the need-y are dis-tressed,
4. Je-ho-vah's prom-is-es are sure, His words are true, his words are pure

The faith-ful who can find? From truth and wis-dom men de-part,
That boast-ful words em-ploy, False-speak-ing tongues that boast their might,
And bit-ter are their cries, The Lord will be their help-er strong;
As sil-ver from the flame. Though base men walk on ev-'ry side,

With flat-tering lips and dou-ble heart They speak their e-vil mind.
That own no law, that know no right, Je-ho-vah will de-stroy.
To save them from con-tempt and wrong Je-ho-vah will a-rise.
His saints are safe, what-e'er be-tide, Pro-tect-ed by his Name. A-MEN.

Music used by permission of the Trustees of the *Church Hymnary.*

## 46 THE GLORY OF GOD

*O Lord God, to whom vengeance belongeth; O God, to whom vengeance belongeth, show thyself.* Psalm 94:1

PSALM 94: 1-5, 8-13, 17-22
*The Psalter,* 1912

BELOIT L. M.
Carl G. Reissiger, 1798-1859

1. O Lord, thou Judge of all the earth, To whom all
vengeance doth belong, A-rise and show thy
glo-ry forth, Re-quite the proud, con-demn the wrong.

2. How long, O Lord, in boast-ful pride Shall wick-ed
men tri-um-phant stand? How long shall they afflict thy saints And scorn thy wrath, thy dread-ful hand?

3. Be wise, ye fools and brut-ish men; Shall not he
see who formed the eye? Shall not he hear who
formed the ear, And judge, who reign-eth, God most high?

4. The Lord will judge in right-eous-ness, From him all
truth and knowl-edge flow; The fool-ish thoughts of
wick-ed men, How vain they are the Lord doth know.

5. That man is blest whom thou, O Lord, With chast-ening
hand dost teach thy will, For in the day when
sin-ners fall That man in peace a-bid-eth still.

6. Un-less the Lord had been my Help, My life had
quick-ly passed a-way; But when my foot had
al-most slipped, O Lord, thy mer-cy was my stay. A-MEN.

7. Amid the doubts that fill my mind
Thy comforts, Lord, bring joy to me;
Can wickedness, though throned in might,
Have fellowship, O Lord, with thee?

8. The wicked, in their might arrayed,
Against the righteous join their power,
But to the Lord I flee for help,
He is my Refuge and my Tower.

St. 2, line 4, alt.

# HIS JUSTICE 47

*Give ear to my words, O Lord, consider my meditation.* Psalm 5:1

PSALM 5  
*The Psalter,* 1912

REHOBOTH 7. 7. 7. 7. D.  
H. Vander Werp, 1911, alt.

1. O Je-ho-vah, hear my words, To my thoughts at-ten-tive be;
2. Thou, Je-ho-vah, art a God Who de-light-est not in sin;
3. In the ful-ness of thy grace To thy house I will re-pair;
4. False and faith-less are my foes, In their mouth no truth is found;
5. O let all that trust thy care Ev-er glad and joy-ful be;

Hear my cry, my King, my God, I will make my prayer to thee.
E - vil shall not dwell with thee, Nor the proud thy fa-vor win.
Bow-ing toward thy ho-ly place, In thy fear to wor-ship there.
Dead-ly are the words they speak, All their thoughts with sin a-bound.
Let them joy who love thy Name, Safe-ly guard-ed, Lord, by thee.

With the morn-ing light, O Lord, Thou shalt hear my voice a-rise,
E - vil - do - ers thou dost hate, Ly-ing tongues thou wilt de-feat;
Lead me in thy right-eous-ness, Let my foes as-sail in vain;
Bring, O God, their plans to naught, Hold them guilt-y in thy sight,
For a bless-ing from thy store To the right-eous thou wilt yield;

And ex-pect-ant I will bring Prayer as morn-ing sac-ri-fice.
God ab-hors the man who loves Vi - o - lence and base de-ceit.
Lest my feet be turned a - side, Make thy way be-fore me plain.
For a-gainst thee and thy law They have set them-selves to fight.
Thou wilt com-pass him a - bout With thy fa-vor as a shield. A - MEN.

## 48 THE GLORY OF GOD

*In the Lord put I my trust... Psalm 11:1*

PSALM 11:1-5, 7  
Compiled from several sources

AYLESBURY S. M.  
Harvey Camp

1. My trust is in the Lord: How say ye then to me,
2. Lo, sin-ners bend the bow With ar-row fixed for flight;
3. What can the right-eous do, What can for them a-vail,
4. The Lord in Zi-on dwells, The Lord is throned on high;
5. The Lord the right-eous proves; But those who scorn the right,
6. For right-eous is the Lord, He lov-eth right-eous-ness,

"Now, like a bird from per-il haste, And to your moun-tain flee"?
And stealth-i-ly in dark-ness go The true in heart to smite.
When all foun-da-tions are de-stroyed, And all the pil-lars fail?
His eyes be-hold the sons of men Their hearts and ways to try.
Who love de-ceit and vi-o-lence Are hate-ful in his sight.
And with a gra-cious coun-te-nance The up-right he will bless. A-MEN.

## 49

*Praise ye the Lord. Praise, O ye servants of the Lord, praise the name of the Lord.* Psalm 113:1

PSALM 113  
Josiah Conder, 1789-1855

ALCESTER 7. 7. 7. 7.  
Har. by Samuel S. Wesley, 1810-1876

1. Hal-le-lu-jah! Raise, O raise To our God the song of praise;
2. Bless-ed be for ev-er-more That dread Name which we a-dore:
3. O'er all na-tions God a-lone, High-er than the heav'ns his throne;
4. Yet to view the heav'ns he bends; Yea, to earth he con-des-cends;
5. He can raise the poor to stand With the princ-es of the land;
6. He the bro-ken spir-it cheers: Turns to joy the mourn-er's tears;

All his serv-ants join to sing God our Sav-iour and our King.
Round the world his praise be sung Through all lands, in ev-'ry tongue.
Who is like to God most high, In-fin-ite in maj-es-ty!
Pass-ing by the rich and great, For the low and des-o-late.
Wealth up-on the need-y show'r; Set him with the high in pow'r.
Such the won-ders of his ways; Praise his Name, for ev-er praise! A-MEN.

St. 5, line 4, alt.

# HIS GOODNESS     50

*Bless the Lord, O my soul, and forget not all his benefits.*   Psalm 103: 2

Joachim Neander, 1680
Tr. by Catherine Winkworth, 1863

LOBE DEN HERREN 14. 14. 4. 7. 8.
Stralsund *Gesangbuch*, 1665
Arr. in *Praxis Pietatis Melica*, 1668

1. Praise to the Lord, the Al-might-y, the King of cre - a - tion!
2. Praise to the Lord, who o'er all things so won-drous-ly reign - eth,
3. Praise to the Lord, who doth pros - per thy work and de - fend thee!
4. Praise thou the Lord, who with mar - vel - ous wis-dom hath made thee,
5. Praise to the Lord! O let all that is in me a - dore him!

O my soul, praise him, for he is thy health and sal - va - tion!
Shel - ters thee un - der his wings, yea, so gen - tly sus - tain - eth!
Sure - ly his good-ness and mer - cy here dai - ly at - tend thee;
Decked thee with health, and with lov - ing hand guid - ed and stayed thee.
All that hath life and breath, come now with prais - es be - fore him!

All ye who hear, Now to his tem - ple draw near,
Hast thou not seen How thy de - sires e'er have been
Pon - der a - new What the Al - might - y will do,
How oft in grief Hath not he brought thee re - lief,
Let the A - men Sound from his peo - ple a - gain;

Join me in glad ad - o - ra - tion.
Grant - ed in what he or - dain - eth?
If with his love he be - friend thee!
Spread - ing his wings to o'er - shade thee!
Glad - ly for aye we a - dore him. A - MEN.

## 51 THE GLORY OF GOD

*Surely goodness and mercy shall follow me all the days of my life: and I will dwell in the house of the Lord for ever.* Psalm 23:6

Joseph Addison, 1712
ST. PETER C. M.
Alexander R. Reinagle, 1836

1. When all thy mer-cies, O my God, My ri-sing soul sur-veys,
2. Un-num-bered com-forts to my soul Thy ten-der care be-stowed,
3. When worn with sick-ness, oft hast thou With health re-newed my face;
4. Ten thou-sand thou-sand pre-cious gifts My dai-ly thanks em-ploy;
5. Through ev-'ry per-iod of my life Thy good-ness I'll pur-sue;
6. Through all e-ter-ni-ty to thee A joy-ful song I'll raise;

Trans-port-ed with the view, I'm lost In won-der, love, and praise.
Be-fore my in-fant heart con-ceived From whom those com-forts flowed.
And, when in sins and sor-rows sunk, Re-vived my soul with grace.
Nor is the least a cheer-ful heart That tastes those gifts with joy.
And af-ter death, in dis-tant worlds, The glo-rious theme re-new.
For O, e-ter-ni-ty's too short To ut-ter all thy praise. A-MEN.

## 52

*Thy mercy, O Lord, is in the heavens; and thy faithfulness reacheth unto the clouds.* Psalm 36:5

Isaac Watts, 1719
ALSACE L. M.
Arr. from Ludwig van Beethoven, 1770-1827

1. High in the heav'ns, E-ter-nal God, Thy good-ness in full glo-ry shines;
2. For ev-er firm thy jus-tice stands, As moun-tains their foun-da-tions keep;
3. Thy prov-i-dence is kind and large, Both man and beast thy boun-ty share;
4. My God, how ex-cel-lent thy grace, Whence all our hope and com-fort spring!
5. From the pro-vis-ions of thy house We shall be fed with sweet re-past;
6. Life, like a foun-tain, rich and free, Springs from the pres-ence of my Lord;

Thy truth shall break through ev-'ry cloud That veils and dark-ens thy de-signs.
Wise are the won-ders of thy hands; Thy judg-ments are a might-y deep.
The whole cre-a-tion is thy charge, But saints are thy pe-cu-liar care.
The sons of Ad-am in dis-tress Fly to the shad-ow of thy wing.
There mer-cy like a riv-er flows, And brings sal-va-tion to our taste.
And in thy light our souls shall see The glo-ries prom-ised in thy Word. A-MEN.

# HIS GOODNESS 53

*Praise ye the Lord. Praise the Lord, O my soul.* Psalm 146:1

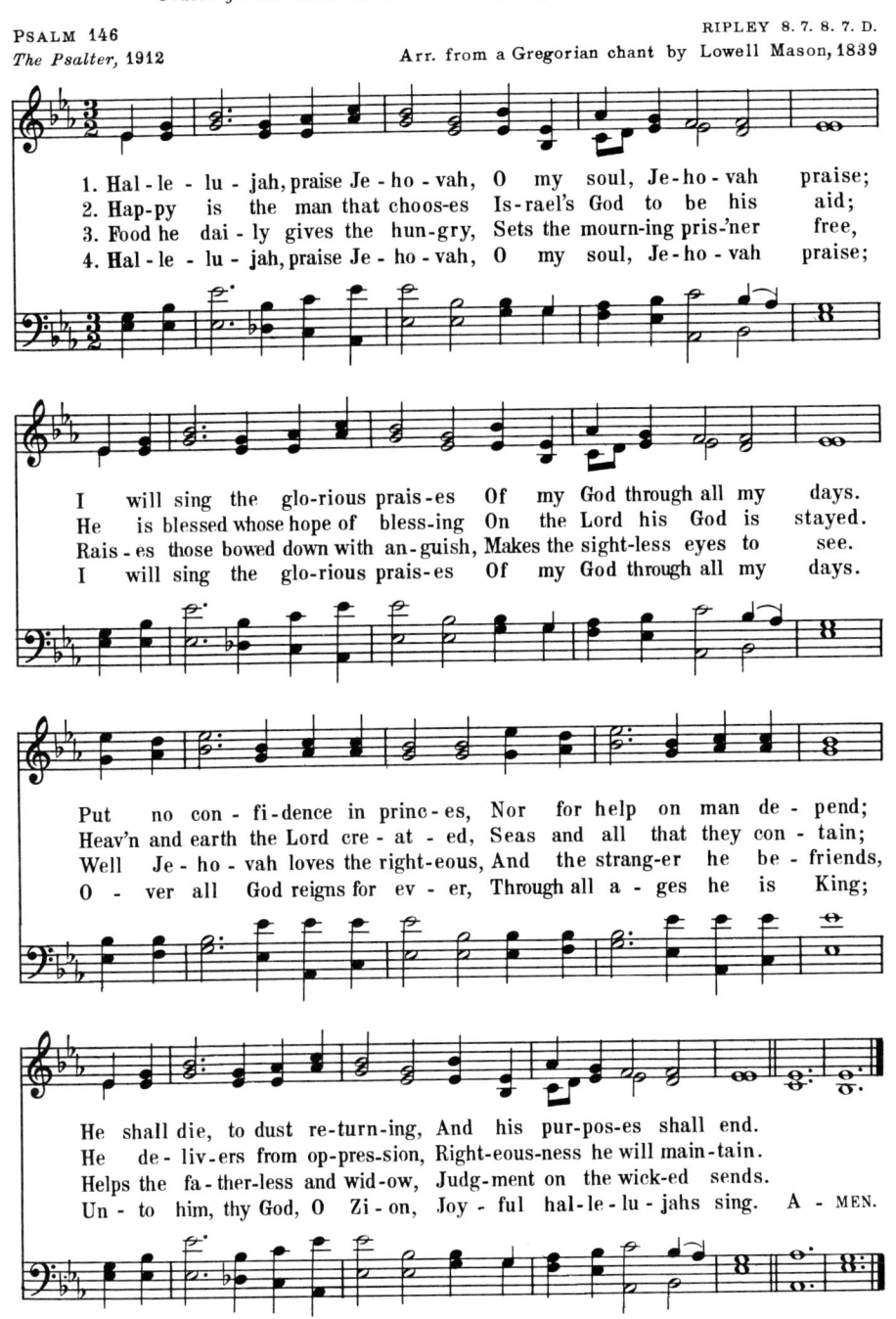

PSALM 146  
*The Psalter*, 1912

RIPLEY 8. 7. 8. 7. D.  
Arr. from a Gregorian chant by Lowell Mason, 1839

1. Hal - le - lu - jah, praise Je - ho - vah, O my soul, Je - ho - vah praise;
2. Hap - py is the man that choos - es Is - rael's God to be his aid;
3. Food he dai - ly gives the hun - gry, Sets the mourn - ing pris-'ner free,
4. Hal - le - lu - jah, praise Je - ho - vah, O my soul, Je - ho - vah praise;

I will sing the glo - rious prais - es Of my God through all my days.
He is blessed whose hope of bless - ing On the Lord his God is stayed.
Rais - es those bowed down with an - guish, Makes the sight - less eyes to see.
I will sing the glo - rious prais - es Of my God through all my days.

Put no con - fi - dence in princ - es, Nor for help on man de - pend;
Heav'n and earth the Lord cre - at - ed, Seas and all that they con - tain;
Well Je - ho - vah loves the right - eous, And the strang - er he be - friends,
O - ver all God reigns for ev - er, Through all a - ges he is King;

He shall die, to dust re - turn - ing, And his pur - pos - es shall end.
He de - liv - ers from op - pres - sion, Right - eous - ness he will main - tain.
Helps the fa - ther - less and wid - ow, Judg - ment on the wick - ed sends.
Un - to him, thy God, O Zi - on, Joy - ful hal - le - lu - jahs sing. A - MEN.

## 54 THE GLORY OF GOD

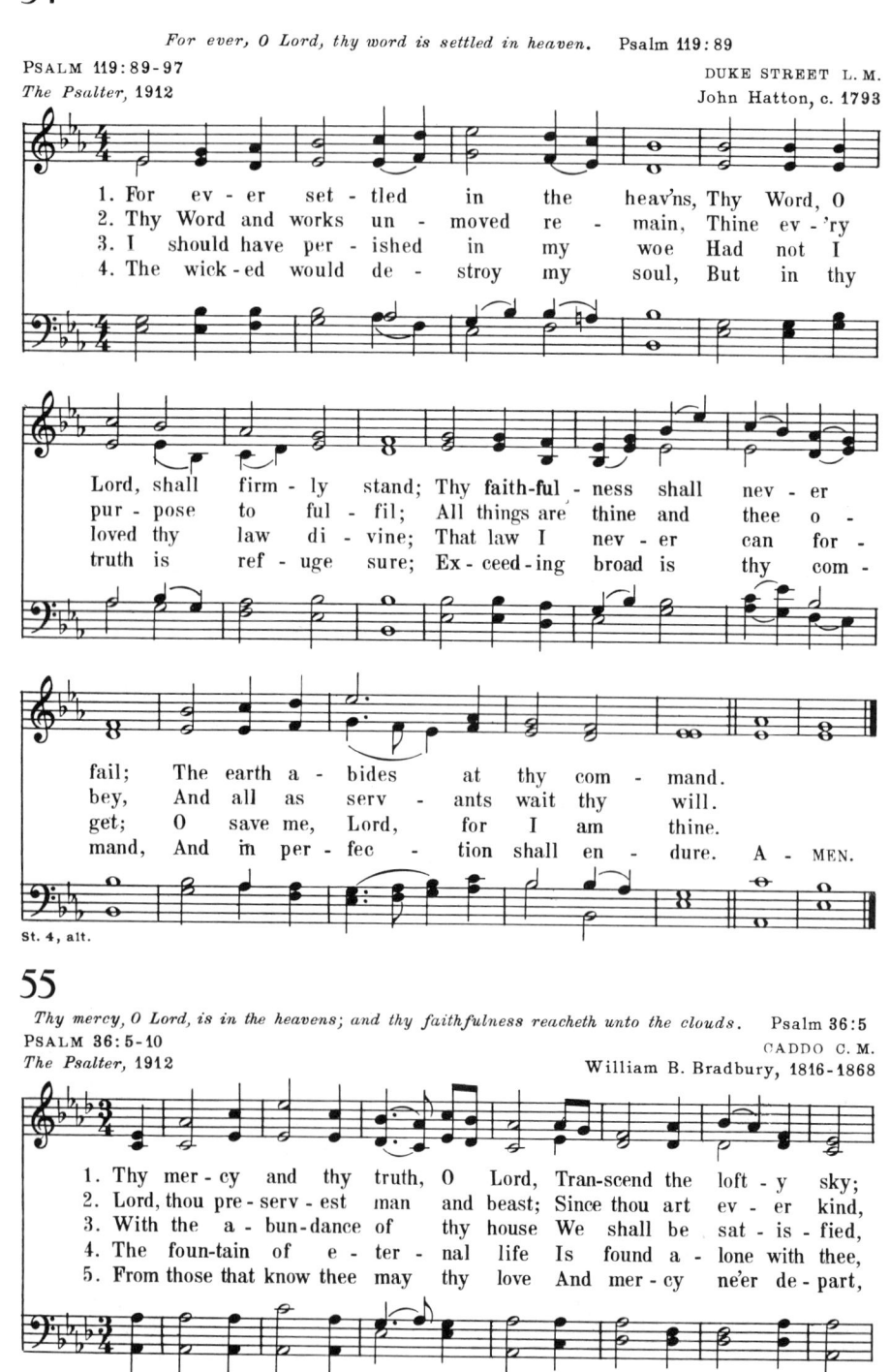

*For ever, O Lord, thy word is settled in heaven.* Psalm 119:89

PSALM 119:89-97
The Psalter, 1912

DUKE STREET L. M.
John Hatton, c. 1793

1. For ev-er set-tled in the heav'ns, Thy Word, O Lord, shall firm-ly stand; Thy faith-ful-ness shall nev-er fail; The earth a-bides at thy com-mand.
2. Thy Word and works un-moved re-main, Thine ev-'ry pur-pose to ful-fil; All things are thine and thee o-bey, And all as serv-ants wait thy will.
3. I should have per-ished in my woe Had not I loved thy law di-vine; That law I nev-er can for-get; O save me, Lord, for I am thine.
4. The wick-ed would de-stroy my soul, But in thy truth is ref-uge sure; Ex-ceed-ing broad is thy com-mand, And in per-fec-tion shall en-dure. A-MEN.

St. 4, alt.

## 55

*Thy mercy, O Lord, is in the heavens; and thy faithfulness reacheth unto the clouds.* Psalm 36:5

PSALM 36:5-10
The Psalter, 1912

CADDO C. M.
William B. Bradbury, 1816-1868

1. Thy mer-cy and thy truth, O Lord, Tran-scend the loft-y sky;
2. Lord, thou pre-serv-est man and beast; Since thou art ev-er kind,
3. With the a-bun-dance of thy house We shall be sat-is-fied,
4. The foun-tain of e-ter-nal life Is found a-lone with thee,
5. From those that know thee may thy love And mer-cy ne'er de-part,

## HIS TRUTH

Thy judg-ments are a might-y deep, And as the moun-tains high.
Be-neath the shad-ow of thy wings We may a ref - uge find.
From riv - ers of un - fail - ing joy Our thirst shall be sup-plied.
And in the bright-ness of thy light We clear - ly light shall see.
And may thy jus - tice still pro-tect And bless the up-right heart. A - MEN.

*In him was life; and the life was the light of men.* John 1:4

Ambrose of Milan, 340-397
Tr. compiled by Louis F. Benson, 1910

WINCHESTER NEW L. M.
*Musikalisches Handbuch*, Hamburg, 1690

56

1. O Splen-dor of God's glo - ry bright, From light e-ter - nal bring-ing light, Thou Light of light, light's liv - ing Spring, True Day, all days il - lu - min - ing:
2. Come, ver - y Sun of heav-en's love, In last - ing ra - diance from a - bove, And pour the Ho - ly Spir - it's ray On all we think or do to - day.
3. And now to thee our pray'rs as - cend, O Fa - ther, glo - rious with - out end; We plead with Sov - ereign Grace for pow'r To con-quer in temp - ta - tion's hour.
4. Con - firm our will to do the right, And keep our hearts from en - vy's blight; Let faith her ea - ger fires re - new, And hate the false, and love the true.
5. O joy - ful be the pass - ing day With thoughts as pure as morn - ing's ray, With faith like noon - tide shin - ing bright, Our souls un - shad-owed by the night.
6. Dawn's glo - ry gilds the earth and skies, Let him, our per - fect Morn, a - rise, The Word in God the Fa - ther one, The Fa - ther im - aged in the Son. A - MEN.

# 57                                        THE GLORY OF GOD

*Keep not thou silence, O God: hold not thy peace ... Psalm 83:1*

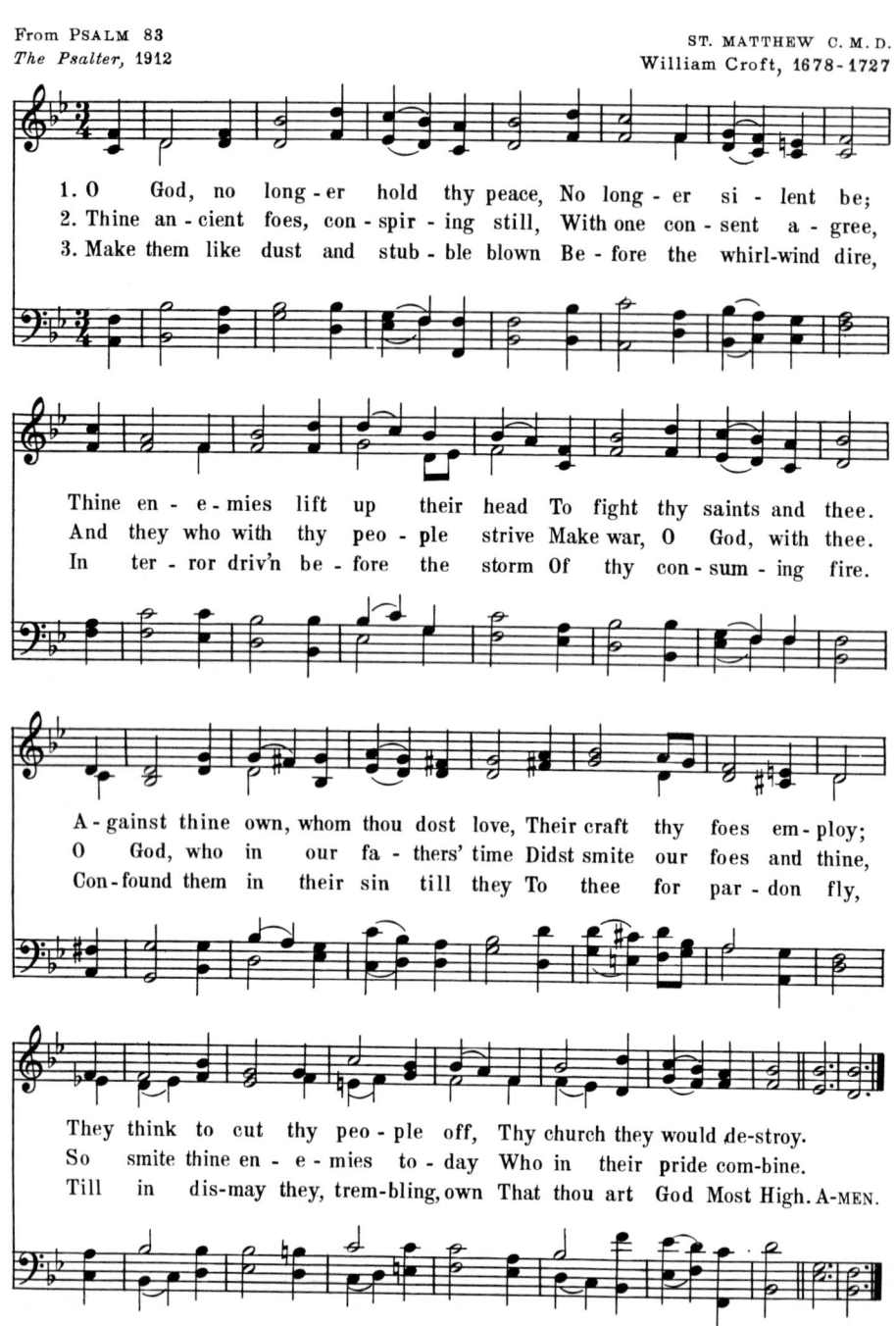

From PSALM 83                                          ST. MATTHEW C. M. D.
*The Psalter*, 1912                                       William Croft, 1678-1727

1. O God, no long-er hold thy peace, No long-er si-lent be; Thine en-e-mies lift up their head To fight thy saints and thee. A-gainst thine own, whom thou dost love, Their craft thy foes em-ploy; They think to cut thy peo-ple off, Thy church they would de-stroy.

2. Thine an-cient foes, con-spir-ing still, With one con-sent a-gree, And they who with thy peo-ple strive Make war, O God, with thee. O God, who in our fa-thers' time Didst smite our foes and thine, So smite thine en-e-mies to-day Who in their pride com-bine.

3. Make them like dust and stub-ble blown Be-fore the whirl-wind dire, In ter-ror driv'n be-fore the storm Of thy con-sum-ing fire. Con-found them in their sin till they To thee for par-don fly, Till in dis-may they, trem-bling, own That thou art God Most High. A-MEN.

# HIS SOVEREIGNTY

**58**

*The Lord God omnipotent reigneth.* Rev. 19:6

Josiah Conder, 1824

CHURCH TRIUMPHANT L. M.
James W. Elliott, 1874

1. The Lord is King! Lift up thy voice, O earth; and all ye heav'ns, re-joice:
2. The Lord is King! Who then shall dare Re-sist his will, dis-trust his care,
3. The Lord is King! Child of the dust, The Judge of all the earth is just;
4. A-like per-vad-ed by his eye, All parts of his do-min-ion lie;
5. One Lord, one em-pire, all se-cures; He reigns, and life and death are yours:

From world to world the joy shall ring, "The Lord om-nip-o-tent is King!"
Or mur-mur at his wise de-crees, Or doubt his roy-al prom-is-es?
Ho-ly and true are all his ways: Let ev-'ry crea-ture speak his praise.
This world of ours, and worlds un-seen, And thin the boun-da-ry be-tween.
Through earth and heav'n one song shall ring, "The Lord om-nip-o-tent is King!" A-MEN.

Music used by permission of Novello & Company, Ltd.

**59**

*The Lord reigneth; let the earth rejoice...* Psalm 97:1

From PSALM 97
*The Psalter*, 1912

BRYNTEG L. M.
John Ambrose Lloyd, 1815-1874

1. Je-ho-vah reigns; let earth be glad, And all the isles their joy make known;
2. Con-sum-ing fire de-stroys his foes, A-round the world his light-nings blaze;
3. The heav'ns his right-eous-ness pro-claim, Through earth his glo-ry shines a-broad;
4. Thy church re-joic-es to be-hold Thy judg-ments in the earth, O Lord;
5. All ye that tru-ly love the Lord, Hate sin, for he is just and pure;
6. For good men light and joy are sown To bless them in the har-vest-time;

With clouds and dark-ness he is clad, On truth and jus-tice rests his throne.
The trem-bling earth his pres-ence knows, The moun-tains melt be-fore his gaze.
From i-dol-wor-ship turn with shame And bow be-fore the liv-ing God.
Thy glo-ry to the world un-fold, Su-preme o'er all be thou a-dored.
To saints his help he will ac-cord And keep them in his love se-cure.
Ye saints, your joy in God make known And ev-er praise his Name sub-lime. A-MEN.

## 60 THE GLORY OF GOD

*The Lord reigneth, he is clothed with majesty... Psalm 93:1*

From PSALM 93
John Keble, 1839

REGENT SQUARE 8.7.8.7.8.7.
Henry Smart, 1867

1. God, the Lord, a King re-main-eth, Robed in his own glo-rious light;
2. In her ev-er-last-ing sta-tion Earth is poised, to swerve no more:
3. Lord, the wat-er-floods have lift-ed, O-cean floods have lift their roar;
4. With all tones of wat-ers blend-ing, Glo-rious is the break-ing deep;
5. Lord, the words thy lips are tell-ing Are the per-fect ver-i-ty:

God hath robed him, and he reign-eth; He hath gird-ed him with might.
Thou hast laid thy throne's foun-da-tion From all time where thought can soar.
Now they pause where they have drift-ed, Now they burst up-on the shore.
Glo-rious, beau-teous with-out end-ing, God who reigns on heav'n's high steep.
Of thine high e-ter-nal dwell-ing Ho-li-ness shall in-mate be.

Al-le-lu-ia! Al-le-lu-ia! God is King in depth and height.
Al-le-lu-ia! Al-le-lu-ia! Lord, thou art for ev-er-more.
Al-le-lu-ia! Al-le-lu-ia! For the o-cean's sound-ing store.
Al-le-lu-ia! Al-le-lu-ia! Songs of o-cean nev-er sleep.
Al-le-lu-ia! Al-le-lu-ia! Pure is all that lives with thee. A-MEN.

## 61

*O clap your hands, all ye people; shout unto God with the voice of triumph. Psalm 47:1*

From PSALM 47
The Psalter, 1912

TRURO L. M.
*Psalmodia Evangelica,* 1789

1. Re-joice, ye peo-ple, hom-age give, To God with voice of tri-umph sing;
2. He put-teth na-tions un-der us And mak-eth us tri-umph-ant stand;
3. God hath as-cend-ed with a shout, Je-ho-vah with the trump-et's sound;
4. Our God is King of all the earth, With thought-ful heart his praise make known;
5. To praise and serve our cov-'nant God The princ-es of the earth draw nigh;

For a higher setting of this tune, see No. 298.

# HIS SOVEREIGNTY

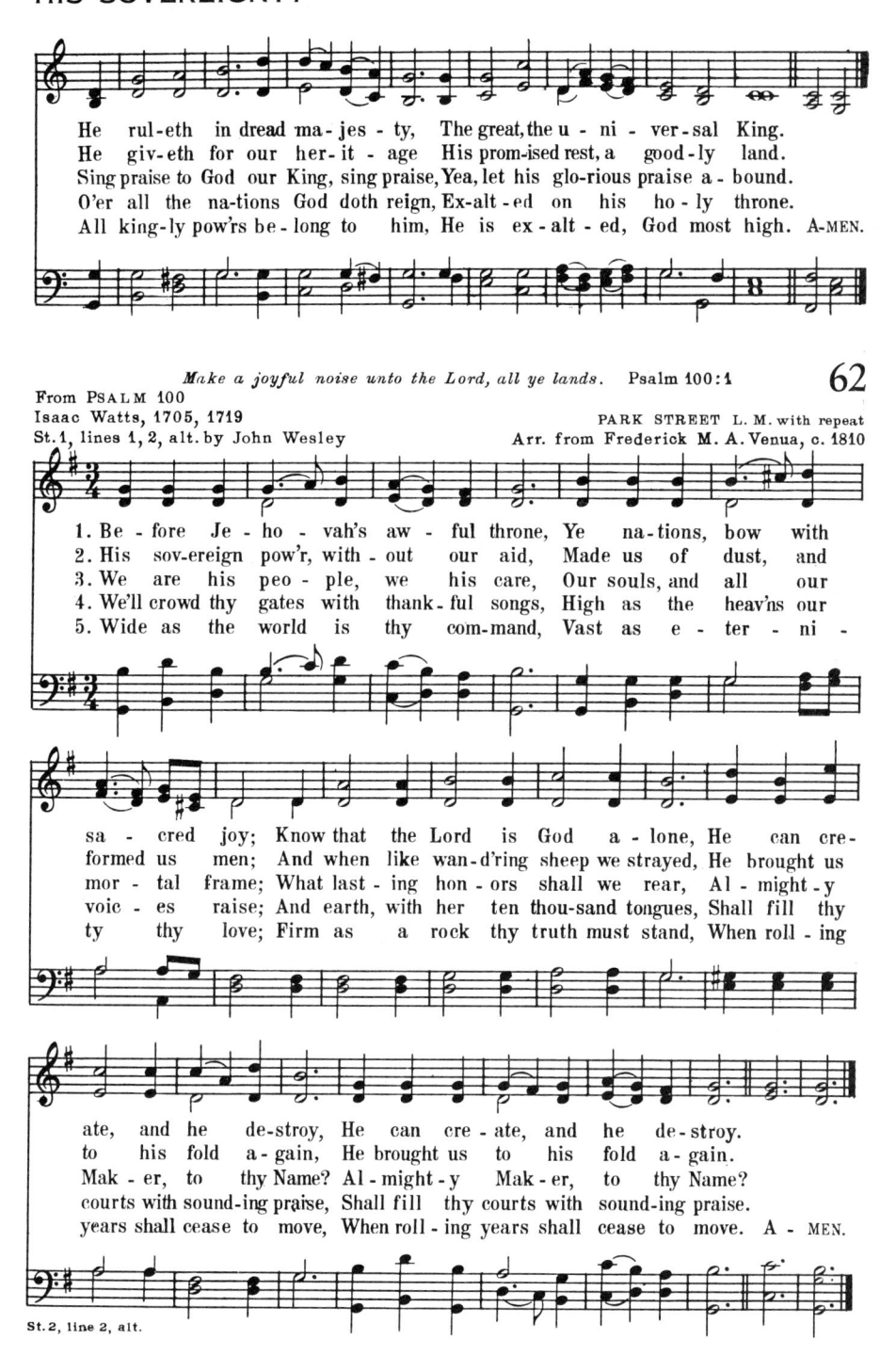

He rul-eth in dread ma-jes-ty, The great, the u-ni-ver-sal King.
He giv-eth for our her-it-age His prom-ised rest, a good-ly land.
Sing praise to God our King, sing praise, Yea, let his glo-rious praise a-bound.
O'er all the na-tions God doth reign, Ex-alt-ed on his ho-ly throne.
All king-ly pow'rs be-long to him, He is ex-alt-ed, God most high. A-MEN.

*Make a joyful noise unto the Lord, all ye lands.* Psalm 100:1

62

From PSALM 100
Isaac Watts, 1705, 1719
St. 1, lines 1, 2, alt. by John Wesley

PARK STREET L. M. with repeat
Arr. from Frederick M. A. Venua, c. 1810

1. Be-fore Je-ho-vah's aw-ful throne, Ye na-tions, bow with sa-cred joy; Know that the Lord is God a-lone, He can cre-ate, and he de-stroy, He can cre-ate, and he de-stroy.
2. His sov-ereign pow'r, with-out our aid, Made us of dust, and formed us men; And when like wan-d'ring sheep we strayed, He brought us to his fold a-gain, He brought us to his fold a-gain.
3. We are his peo-ple, we his care, Our souls, and all our mor-tal frame; What last-ing hon-ors shall we rear, Al-might-y Mak-er, to thy Name? Al-might-y Mak-er, to thy Name?
4. We'll crowd thy gates with thank-ful songs, High as the heav'ns our voic-es raise; And earth, with her ten thou-sand tongues, Shall fill thy courts with sound-ing praise, Shall fill thy courts with sound-ing praise.
5. Wide as the world is thy com-mand, Vast as e-ter-ni-ty thy love; Firm as a rock thy truth must stand, When roll-ing years shall cease to move, When roll-ing years shall cease to move. A-MEN.

St. 2, line 2, alt.

# 63 THE GLORY OF GOD

*In Judah is God known: his name is great in Israel.* Psalm 76:1

From PSALM 76
The Psalter, 1912

PRAISE, MY SOUL 8.7.8.7.8.7.
Sir John Goss, 1869

1. God is known a-mong his peo-ple, Ev-ery mouth his prais-es fill;
   From of old he has es-tab-lished His a-bode on Zi-on's hill;
   There he broke the sword and ar-row, Bade the noise of war be still.

2. Ex-cel-lent and glo-rious art thou, With thy tro-phies from the fray;
   Thou hast slain the val-iant-heart-ed, Wrapped in sleep of death are they;
   When thine an-ger once is ris-en, Who can stand in that dread day?

3. When from heav'n thy sen-tence sound-ed, All the earth in fear was still,
   While to save the meek and low-ly God in judg-ment wrought his will;
   E'en the wrath of man shall praise thee, Thy de-signs it shall ful-fil.

4. Vow and pay ye to Je-ho-vah, Him your God for ev-er own;
   All men, bring your gifts be-fore him, Wor-ship him, and him a-lone;
   Might-y kings o-bey and fear him, Princ-es bow be-fore his throne. A-MEN.

# 64

*The Lord reigneth, he is clothed with majesty...* Psalm 93:1

From PSALM 93
Tate and Brady's *New Version,* 1696, 1698

MENDON L.M.
German melody arr. by Samuel Dyer, 1828

1. With glo-ry clad, with strength ar-rayed, The Lord, that o'er all na-ture reigns,
2. How sure-ly stab-lished is thy throne, Which shall no change or per-iod see!
3. The floods, O Lord, lift up their voice, And toss the trou-bled waves on high;
4. Thy prom-ise, Lord, is ev-er sure, And they that in thy house would dwell,

# HIS SOVEREIGNTY

The world's foun-da-tions strong-ly laid, And the vast fab-ric still sus-tains.
For thou, O Lord, and thou a-lone, Art God from all e-ter-ni-ty.
But God a-bove can still their noise, And make the an-gry sea com-ply.
That hap-py sta-tion to se-cure, Must still in ho-li-ness ex-cel. A-MEN.

---

**65**

*O sing unto the Lord a new song: sing unto the Lord, all the earth.* Psalm 96:1

From PSALM 96
The Psalter, 1912

WESLEY 11.10.11.10.
Lowell Mason, 1830

1. Sing to the Lord, sing his praise, all ye peo-ples, New be your
2. Tell of his won-drous works, tell of his glo-ry, Till through the
3. Vain are the hea-then gods, i-dols and help-less; God made the
4. Give un-to God most high glo-ry and hon-or, Come with your
5. Make all the na-tions know God reigns for ev-er; Earth is es-
6. Let heav'n and earth be glad; waves of the o-cean, For-est and

song as new hon-ors ye pay; Sing of his maj-es-ty,
na-tions his Name is re-vered; Praise and ex-alt him, for
heav'ns, and his glo-ry they tell; Hon-or and maj-es-ty
off-'rings and hum-bly draw near; In ho-ly beau-ty now
tab-lished as he did de-cree; Right-eous and just is the
field, ex-ul-ta-tion ex-press; For God is com-ing, the

bless him for ev-er, Show his sal-va-tion from day to day.
he is al-might-y, God o-ver all let the Lord be feared.
shine out be-fore him, Beau-ty and strength in his tem-ple dwell.
wor-ship Je-ho-vah, Trem-ble be-fore him with god-ly fear.
King of the na-tions, Judg-ing the peo-ple with eq-ui-ty.
Judge of the na-tions, Com-ing to judge in his right-eous-ness. A-MEN.

## 66 THE GLORY OF GOD

*The earth is the Lord's, and the fulness thereof...* Psalm 24:1

From PSALM 24　　　　　　　　　　　　　　　　　　　　　　　MIRFIELD C. M.
The Psalter, 1912　　　　　　　　　　　　　　　　　　　　　　Arthur Cottman, 1872

1. The earth, with all that dwell there-in, With all its wealth un-told,
   Be-longs to God who found-ed it Up-on the seas of old.
2. What man shall stand be-fore the Lord On Zi-on's ho-ly hill?
   The clean of hand, the pure of heart, The just who do his will.
3. Lo, such are they that seek for God, And blest by him they live;
   To them his per-fect right-eous-ness The God of grace will give.
4. Ye ev-er-last-ing doors, give way, Lift up your heads, ye gates!
   For now, be-hold, to en-ter in The King of Glo-ry waits.
5. Who is this glo-rious King that comes To claim his sov-ereign right?
   It is the Lord om-nip-o-tent, All-con-quering in his might. A-MEN.

6. Ye everlasting doors, give way,
   Lift up your heads, ye gates!
   For now, behold, to enter in
   The King of Glory waits.

7. Who is this glorious King that comes
   To claim his rightful throne?
   The Lord of Hosts, he is the King
   Of Glory, God alone.

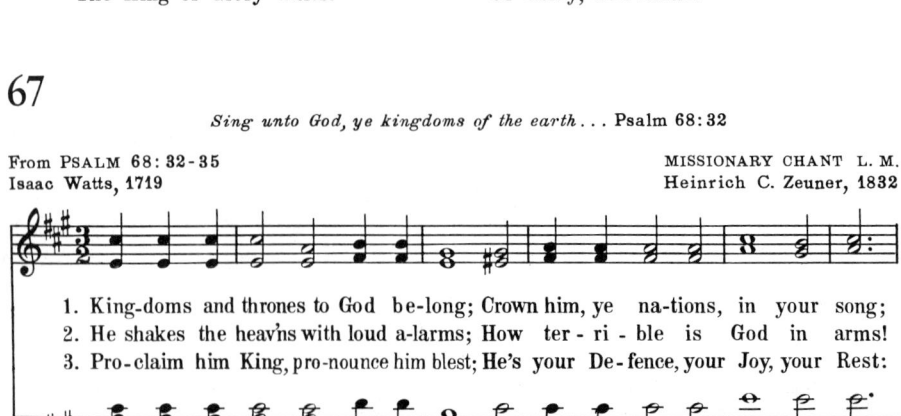

## 67

*Sing unto God, ye kingdoms of the earth...* Psalm 68:32

From PSALM 68: 32-35　　　　　　　　　　　　　　　　MISSIONARY CHANT L. M.
Isaac Watts, 1719　　　　　　　　　　　　　　　　　　Heinrich C. Zeuner, 1832

1. King-doms and thrones to God be-long; Crown him, ye na-tions, in your song;
2. He shakes the heav'ns with loud a-larms; How ter-ri-ble is God in arms!
3. Pro-claim him King, pro-nounce him blest; He's your De-fence, your Joy, your Rest:

# HIS SOVEREIGNTY

His won-drous names and pow'rs re-hearse; His hon-ors shall en-rich your verse.
In Is-rael are his mer-cies known; Is-rael is his pe-cu-liar throne.
When ter-rors rise, and na-tions faint, God is the strength of ev-ery saint. A-MEN.

*Not unto us, O Lord, not unto us, but unto thy name give glory,*
*for thy mercy, and for thy truth's sake.* Psalm 115:1

**68**

From PSALM 115:1-3, 9-14, 18
*The Psalter,* 1912

GAIRNEY BRIDGE 8.8.8.8.8.8.
Ernest R. Kroeger

1. Not un-to us, O Lord of heav'n, But un-to thee be glo-ry given;
2. Let Is-rael trust in God a-lone, The Lord whose grace and pow'r are known;
3. All ye that fear him and a-dore, The Lord in-crease you more and more;

In love and truth thou dost ful-fil The coun-sels of thy sov-ereign will;
To him your full al-le-giance yield, And he will be your Help and Shield;
Both great and small who him con-fess, You and your chil-dren he will bless.

Though na-tions fail thy pow'r to own, Yet thou dost reign, and thou a-lone.
All those who fear him God will bless, His saints have prov'd his faith-ful-ness.
Yea, we will ev-er bless his Name; Praise ye the Lord, his praise pro-claim. A-MEN.

# 69 THE GLORY OF GOD

*To the praise of the glory of his grace* ... Eph. 1:6

RIPLEY 8.7.8.7. D.

Francis Scott Key, 1817  
Arr. from a Gregorian chant by Lowell Mason, 1839

1. Lord, with glow-ing heart I'd praise thee For the bliss thy love be-stows,
2. Praise, my soul, the God that sought thee, Wretch-ed wan-d'rer far a-stray;
3. Praise thy Sav-iour God that drew thee To that cross, new life to give,
4. Lord, this bos-om's ar-dent feel-ing Vain-ly would my lips ex-press:

For the par-d'ning grace that saves me, And the peace that from it flows:
Found thee lost, and kind-ly brought thee From the paths of death a-way:
Held a blood-sealed par-don to thee, Bade thee look to him and live:
Low be-fore thy foot-stool kneel-ing, Deign thy sup-pliant's pray'r to bless:

Help, O God, my weak en-deav-or; This dull soul to rap-ture raise:
Praise, with love's de-vout-est feel-ing, Him who saw thy guilt-born fear,
Praise the grace whose threats a-larmed thee, Roused thee from thy fa-tal ease,
Let thy love, my soul's chief treas-ure, Love's pure flame with-in me raise;

Thou must light the flame, or nev-er Can my love be warmed to praise.
And, the light of hope re-veal-ing, Bade the blood-stain'd cross ap-pear.
Praise the grace whose prom-ise warm'd thee, Praise the grace that whis-pered peace.
And, since words can nev-er meas-ure, Let my life show forth thy praise. A-MEN.

# HIS LOVE AND GRACE 70

*Bless the Lord, all his works in all places of his dominion: bless the Lord, O my soul.* Psalm 103:22

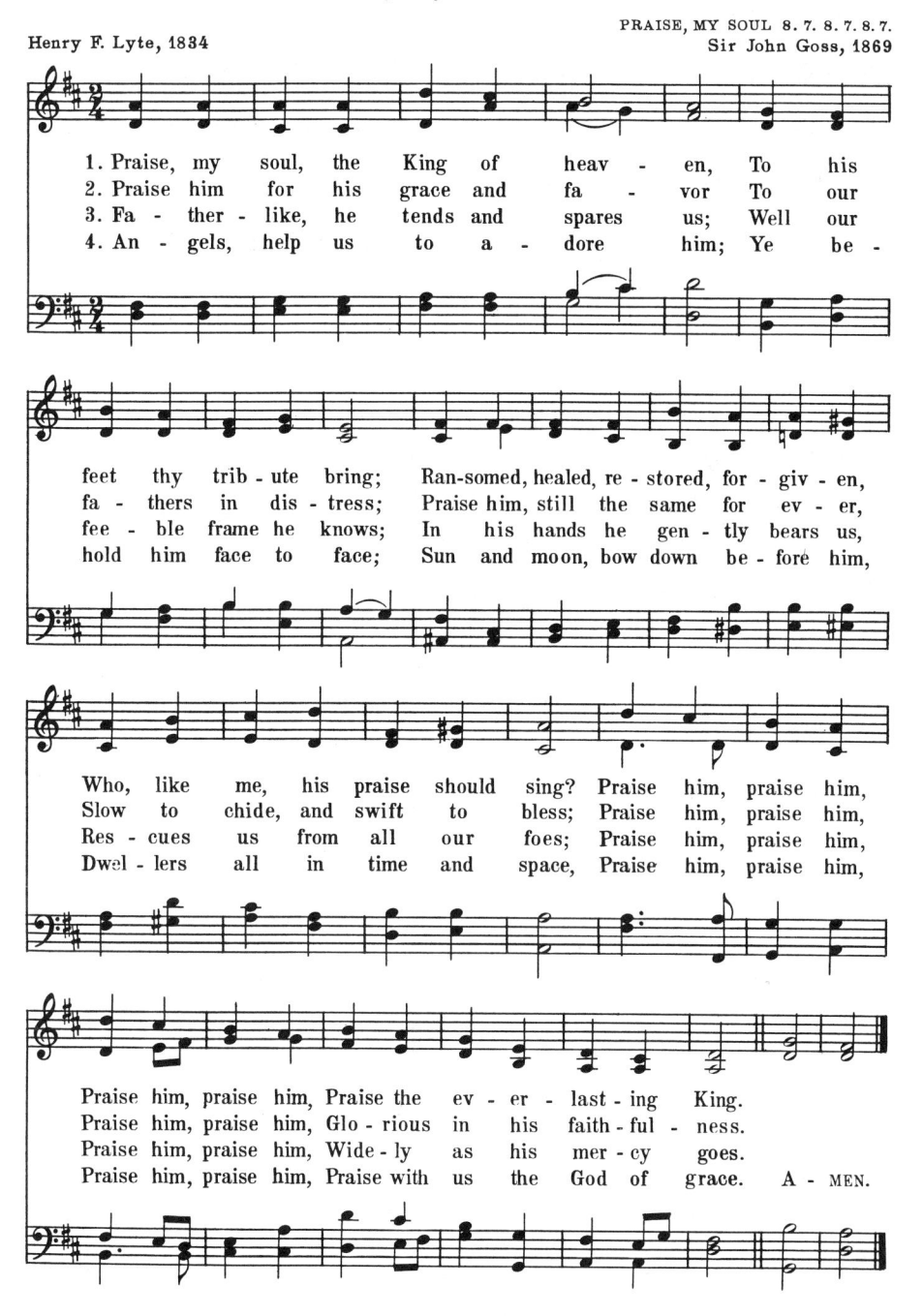

Henry F. Lyte, 1834

PRAISE, MY SOUL 8. 7. 8. 7. 8. 7.
Sir John Goss, 1869

1. Praise, my soul, the King of heav-en, To his feet thy trib-ute bring; Ran-somed, healed, re-stored, for-giv-en, Who, like me, his praise should sing? Praise him, praise him, Praise him, praise him, Praise the ev-er-last-ing King.
2. Praise him for his grace and fa-vor To our fa-thers in dis-tress; Praise him, still the same for ev-er, Slow to chide, and swift to bless; Praise him, praise him, Praise him, praise him, Glo-rious in his faith-ful-ness.
3. Fa-ther-like, he tends and spares us; Well our fee-ble frame he knows; In his hands he gen-tly bears us, Res-cues us from all our foes; Praise him, praise him, Praise him, praise him, Wide-ly as his mer-cy goes.
4. An-gels, help us to a-dore him; Ye be-hold him face to face; Sun and moon, bow down be-fore him, Dwel-lers all in time and space, Praise him, praise him, Praise him, praise him, Praise with us the God of grace. A-MEN.

## 71 THE GLORY OF GOD

*Who is a God like unto thee, that pardoneth iniquity?* Micah 7:18

Samuel Davies, 1723-1761
PATER OMNIUM 8.8.8.8.8.8.
Henry J. E. Holmes, 1875

1. Great God of wonders! all thy ways Are worthy of thyself divine; And the bright glories of thy grace Among thine other wonders shine: Who is a par-d'ning God like thee? Or who has grace so rich and free?
2. Pardon from an offended God! Pardon for sins of deepest dye! Pardon bestowed through Jesus' blood! Pardon that brings the rebel nigh! Who is a par-d'ning God like thee? Or who has grace so rich and free?
3. O may this glorious, matchless love, This God-like miracle of grace, Teach mortal tongues, like those above, To raise this song of lofty praise: Who is a par-d'ning God like thee? Or who has grace so rich and free? A-MEN.

St. 1, lines 3 and 4, alt.
Music used by permission of Miss Marjorie J. Holmes.

## 72

*Bless the Lord, O my soul: and all that is within me, bless his holy name.* Psalm 103:1

Isaac Watts, 1719
ST. MICHAEL S. M.
From the Geneva *Psalter*, 1543

1. O bless the Lord, my soul; Let all within me join,
2. O bless the Lord, my soul, Nor let his mercies lie
3. 'Tis he forgives thy sins, 'Tis he relieves thy pain,
4. He crowns thy life with love, When ransomed from the grave;
5. He fills the poor with good; He gives the suff'rers rest:
6. His wondrous works and ways He made by Moses known;

# HIS LOVE AND GRACE

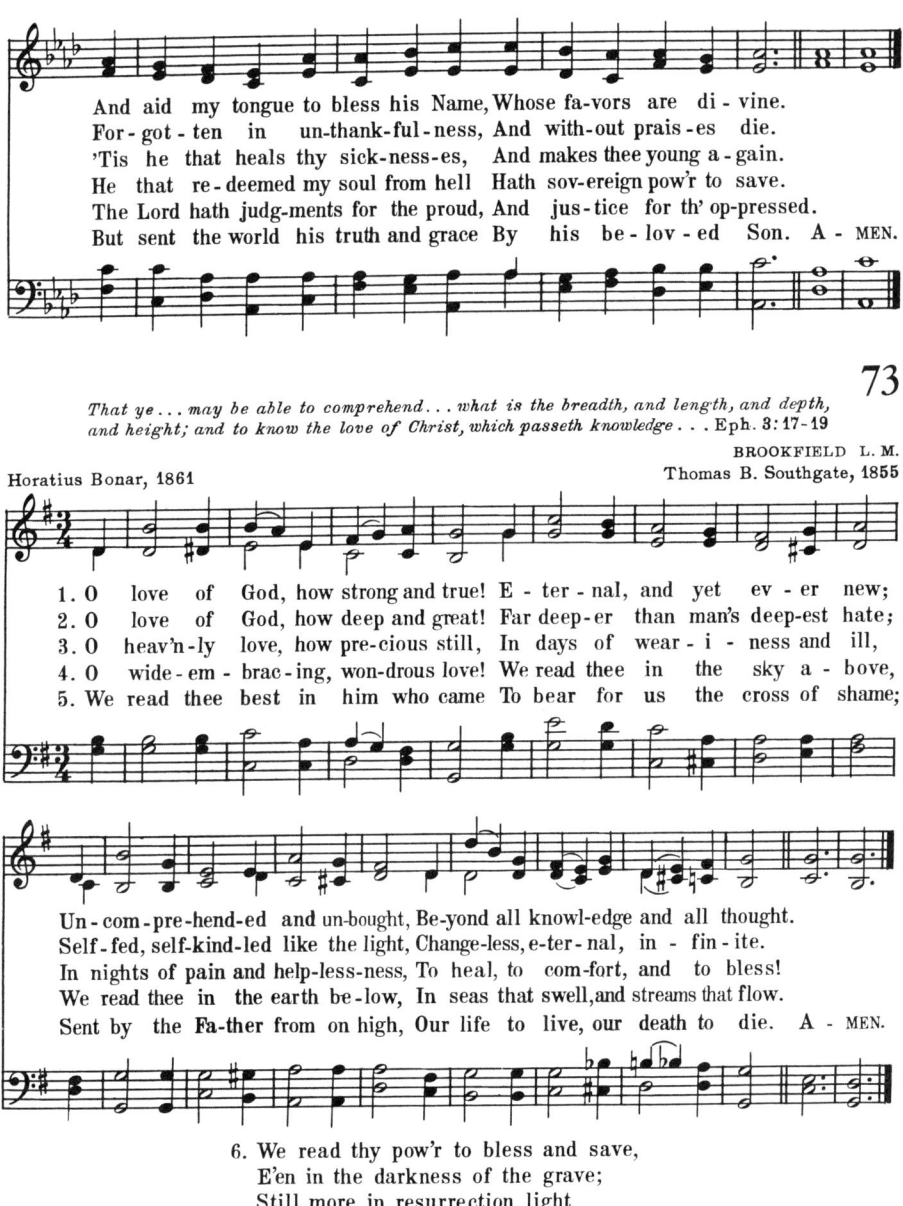

And aid my tongue to bless his Name, Whose fa-vors are di - vine.
For - got - ten in un-thank-ful-ness, And with-out prais - es die.
'Tis he that heals thy sick-ness-es, And makes thee young a - gain.
He that re-deemed my soul from hell Hath sov-ereign pow'r to save.
The Lord hath judg-ments for the proud, And jus-tice for th' op-pressed.
But sent the world his truth and grace By his be - lov - ed Son. A - MEN.

**73**

*That ye ... may be able to comprehend ... what is the breadth, and length, and depth, and height; and to know the love of Christ, which passeth knowledge ... Eph. 3: 17-19*

Horatius Bonar, 1861

BROOKFIELD L. M.
Thomas B. Southgate, 1855

1. O love of God, how strong and true! E - ter - nal, and yet ev - er new;
2. O love of God, how deep and great! Far deep-er than man's deep-est hate;
3. O heav'n-ly love, how pre-cious still, In days of wear - i - ness and ill,
4. O wide - em - brac - ing, won-drous love! We read thee in the sky a - bove,
5. We read thee best in him who came To bear for us the cross of shame;

Un - com - pre - hend - ed and un-bought, Be-yond all knowl-edge and all thought.
Self - fed, self-kind-led like the light, Change-less, e-ter - nal, in - fin - ite.
In nights of pain and help-less-ness, To heal, to com-fort, and to bless!
We read thee in the earth be-low, In seas that swell, and streams that flow.
Sent by the Fa-ther from on high, Our life to live, our death to die. A - MEN.

6. We read thy pow'r to bless and save,
E'en in the darkness of the grave;
Still more in resurrection light
We read the fulness of thy might.

7. O love of God, our shield and stay
Through all the perils of our way!
Eternal love, in thee we rest,
For ever safe, for ever blest.

# 74 THE GLORY OF GOD

*He that dwelleth in the secret place of the most High shall abide under the shadow of the Almighty.* Psalm 91:1

PSALM 91:1-6, 11-12, 14
Reformed Presbyterian *Book of Psalms*, 1940

UXBRIDGE L. M.
Lowell Mason, 1830

1. The man who once has found a-bode, With-in the se-cret place of God
2. I there-fore of the Lord will say, He is my Ref-uge and my Stay;
3. For he shall with his watch-ful care Pre-serve thee from the fow-ler's snare;
4. His out-spread pin-ions shall thee hide, Be-neath his wings shalt thou con-fide.
5. No night-ly ter-rors shall a-larm, No dead-ly shaft by day shall harm;

Shall with Al-might-y God a-bide, And in his shad-ow safe-ly hide.
My Cit-a-del of strength is he— My God in whom my trust shall be.
Yea, he shall be thy sure de-fense A-gainst the dead-ly pes-ti-lence.
His faith-ful-ness shall ev-er be A shield and buck-ler un-to thee.
Nor pes-ti-lence that walks by night, Nor plagues that waste in noon-day light. A-MEN.

6. Because his angels he commands
To bear thee safely in their hands,
To guard thy ways, lest left alone,
Thou dash thy foot against a stone.

7. Because he set his love on Me,
From danger I will set him free.
Because to him My Name is known,
On high I'll set him as Mine own.

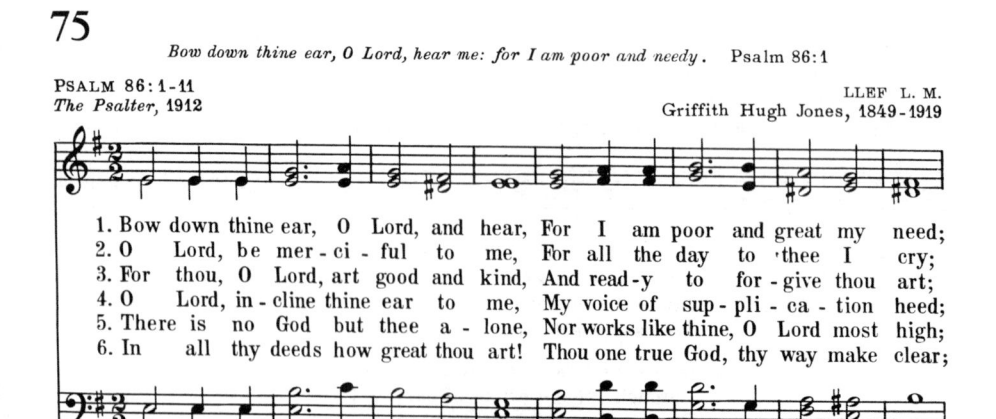

# 75

*Bow down thine ear, O Lord, hear me: for I am poor and needy.* Psalm 86:1

PSALM 86:1-11
The Psalter, 1912

LLEF L. M.
Griffith Hugh Jones, 1849-1919

1. Bow down thine ear, O Lord, and hear, For I am poor and great my need;
2. O Lord, be mer-ci-ful to me, For all the day to thee I cry;
3. For thou, O Lord, art good and kind, And read-y to for-give thou art;
4. O Lord, in-cline thine ear to me, My voice of sup-pli-ca-tion heed;
5. There is no God but thee a-lone, Nor works like thine, O Lord most high;
6. In all thy deeds how great thou art! Thou one true God, thy way make clear;

# HIS FAITHFULNESS

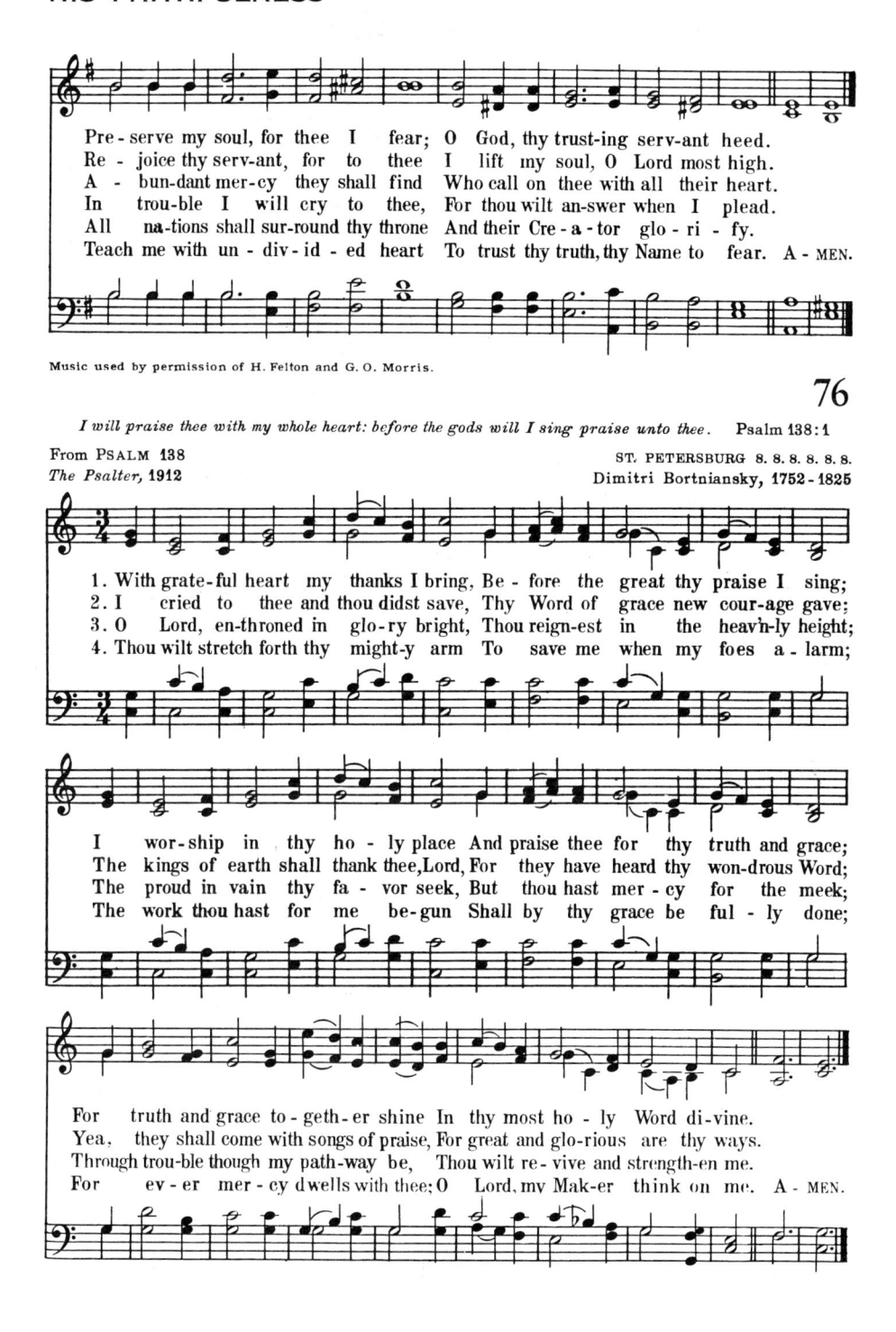

Pre - serve my soul, for thee I fear; O God, thy trust-ing serv-ant heed.
Re - joice thy serv-ant, for to thee I lift my soul, O Lord most high.
A - bun-dant mer-cy they shall find Who call on thee with all their heart.
In trou-ble I will cry to thee, For thou wilt an-swer when I plead.
All na-tions shall sur-round thy throne And their Cre - a - tor glo - ri - fy.
Teach me with un - div-id - ed heart To trust thy truth, thy Name to fear. A - MEN.

Music used by permission of H. Felton and G. O. Morris.

76

*I will praise thee with my whole heart: before the gods will I sing praise unto thee.* Psalm 138:1

From PSALM 138　　　　　　　　　　　　　　　　　　　　ST. PETERSBURG 8. 8. 8. 8. 8. 8.
*The Psalter,* 1912　　　　　　　　　　　　　　　　　　　Dimitri Bortniansky, 1752 - 1825

1. With grate-ful heart my thanks I bring, Be - fore the great thy praise I sing;
2. I cried to thee and thou didst save, Thy Word of grace new cour-age gave;
3. O Lord, en-throned in glo-ry bright, Thou reign-est in the heav'n-ly height;
4. Thou wilt stretch forth thy might-y arm To save me when my foes a - larm;

I wor-ship in thy ho - ly place And praise thee for thy truth and grace;
The kings of earth shall thank thee, Lord, For they have heard thy won-drous Word;
The proud in vain thy fa - vor seek, But thou hast mer - cy for the meek;
The work thou hast for me be-gun Shall by thy grace be ful - ly done;

For truth and grace to-geth-er shine In thy most ho - ly Word di-vine.
Yea, they shall come with songs of praise, For great and glo-rious are thy ways.
Through trou-ble though my path-way be, Thou wilt re - vive and strength-en me.
For ev - er mer - cy dwells with thee; O Lord, my Mak-er think on me. A - MEN.

**77** (FIRST TUNE)                                                    **THE GLORY OF GOD**

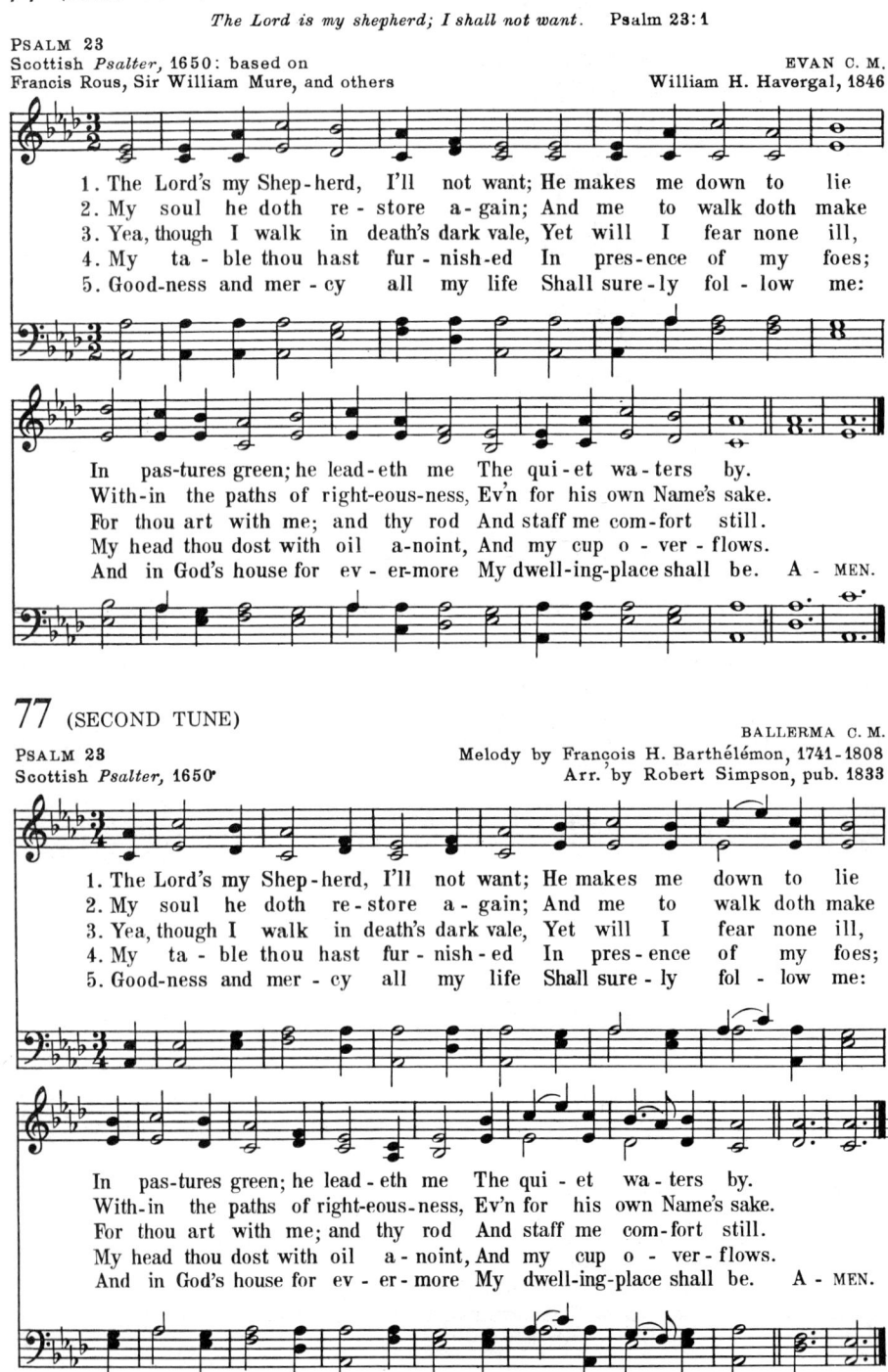

*The Lord is my shepherd; I shall not want.*    Psalm 23:1

PSALM 23  
Scottish *Psalter*, 1650: based on                                                           EVAN C. M.  
Francis Rous, Sir William Mure, and others                         William H. Havergal, 1846

1. The Lord's my Shep-herd, I'll not want; He makes me down to lie
2. My soul he doth re-store a-gain; And me to walk doth make
3. Yea, though I walk in death's dark vale, Yet will I fear none ill,
4. My ta-ble thou hast fur-nish-ed In pres-ence of my foes;
5. Good-ness and mer-cy all my life Shall sure-ly fol-low me:

In pas-tures green; he lead-eth me The qui-et wa-ters by.  
With-in the paths of right-eous-ness, Ev'n for his own Name's sake.  
For thou art with me; and thy rod And staff me com-fort still.  
My head thou dost with oil a-noint, And my cup o-ver-flows.  
And in God's house for ev-er-more My dwell-ing-place shall be. A - MEN.

**77** (SECOND TUNE)

                                                   BALLERMA C. M.  
PSALM 23                      Melody by François H. Barthélémon, 1741-1808  
Scottish *Psalter*, 1650                   Arr. by Robert Simpson, pub. 1833

1. The Lord's my Shep-herd, I'll not want; He makes me down to lie
2. My soul he doth re-store a-gain; And me to walk doth make
3. Yea, though I walk in death's dark vale, Yet will I fear none ill,
4. My ta-ble thou hast fur-nish-ed In pres-ence of my foes;
5. Good-ness and mer-cy all my life Shall sure-ly fol-low me:

In pas-tures green; he lead-eth me The qui-et wa-ters by.  
With-in the paths of right-eous-ness, Ev'n for his own Name's sake.  
For thou art with me; and thy rod And staff me com-fort still.  
My head thou dost with oil a-noint, And my cup o-ver-flows.  
And in God's house for ev-er-more My dwell-ing-place shall be. A - MEN.

# HIS FAITHFULNESS

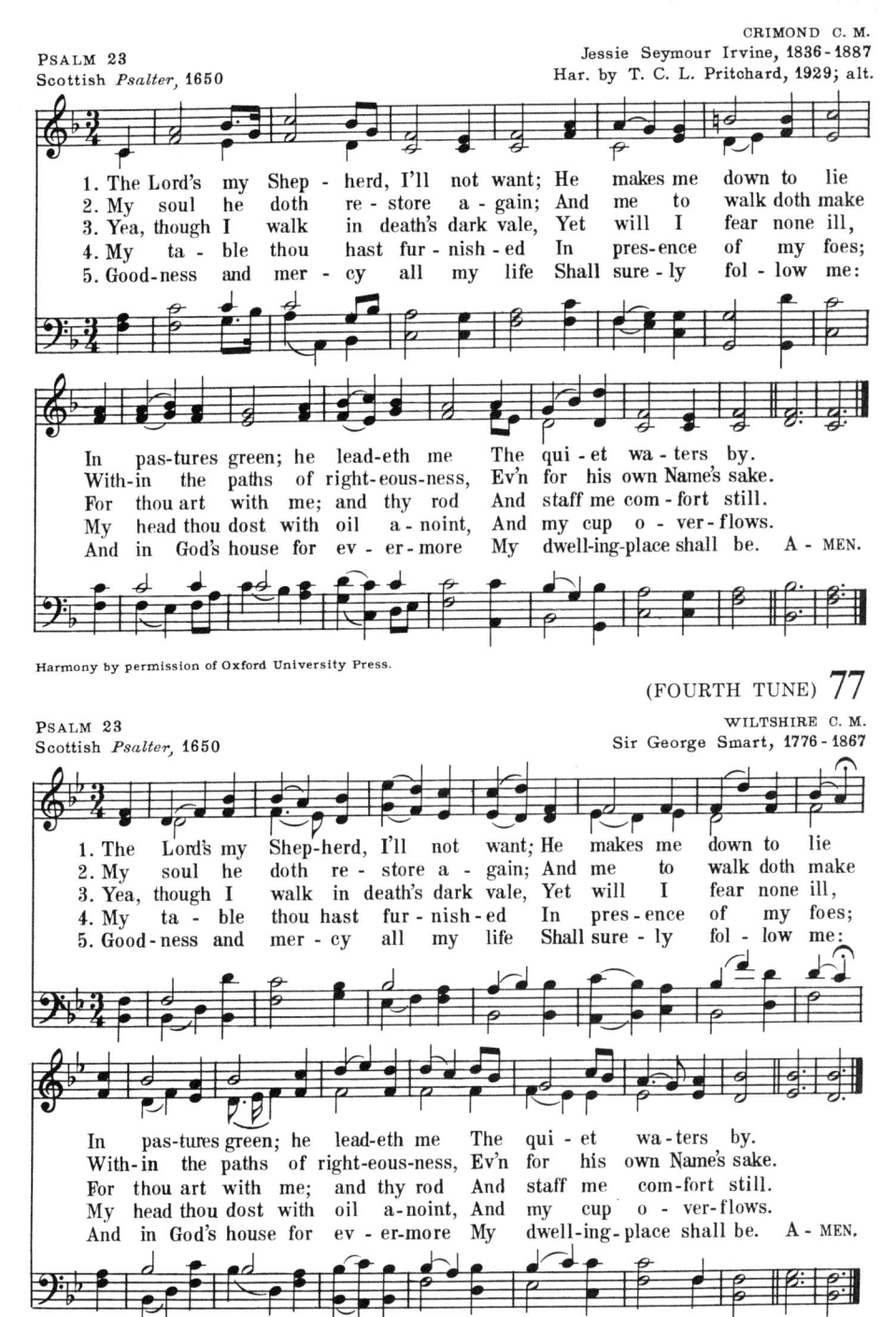

(THIRD TUNE) 77

CRIMOND C. M.
Jessie Seymour Irvine, 1836-1887
Har. by T. C. L. Pritchard, 1929; alt.

PSALM 23
Scottish *Psalter*, 1650

1. The Lord's my Shep-herd, I'll not want; He makes me down to lie
   In pas-tures green; he lead-eth me The qui-et wa-ters by.
2. My soul he doth re-store a-gain; And me to walk doth make
   With-in the paths of right-eous-ness, Ev'n for his own Name's sake.
3. Yea, though I walk in death's dark vale, Yet will I fear none ill,
   For thou art with me; and thy rod And staff me com-fort still.
4. My ta-ble thou hast fur-nish-ed In pres-ence of my foes;
   My head thou dost with oil a-noint, And my cup o-ver-flows.
5. Good-ness and mer-cy all my life Shall sure-ly fol-low me:
   And in God's house for ev-er-more My dwell-ing-place shall be. A-MEN.

Harmony by permission of Oxford University Press.

(FOURTH TUNE) 77

WILTSHIRE C. M.
Sir George Smart, 1776-1867

PSALM 23
Scottish *Psalter*, 1650

1. The Lord's my Shep-herd, I'll not want; He makes me down to lie
   In pas-tures green; he lead-eth me The qui-et wa-ters by.
2. My soul he doth re-store a-gain; And me to walk doth make
   With-in the paths of right-eous-ness, Ev'n for his own Name's sake.
3. Yea, though I walk in death's dark vale, Yet will I fear none ill,
   For thou art with me; and thy rod And staff me com-fort still.
4. My ta-ble thou hast fur-nish-ed In pres-ence of my foes;
   My head thou dost with oil a-noint, And my cup o-ver-flows.
5. Good-ness and mer-cy all my life Shall sure-ly fol-low me:
   And in God's house for ev-er-more My dwell-ing-place shall be. A-MEN.

## 78            THE GLORY OF GOD

*Under his wings shalt thou trust... Psalm 91:4*

From PSALM 91  
United Presbyterian *Bible Songs Hymnal*, 1927

UNDER HIS WINGS 11.10.11.10. with refrain  
Ira D. Sankey, 1840-1908

1. Un-der the care of my God, the Al-might-y, Safe in the se-cret place of the Most High! He is my Ref-uge, the Lord is my For-tress, Him I am trust-ing when trou-ble is nigh.
2. Be not a-fraid for the ter-ror of mid-night, Nor for the ar-row that hast-eth to slay; Fear not the pes-ti-lence walk-ing in dark-ness, Nor the de-stroy-er that wast-eth by day.
3. Seek the Most High for thy sure hab-i-ta-tion, Un-to Je-ho-vah for ref-uge now fly; There shall no e-vil be-fall thee nor harm thee, Un-to thy dwell-ing no plague shall come nigh.
4. Love thou the Lord, sure-ly he will de-liv-er; He will ex-alt thee and an-swer thy prayer; He will be with thee to hon-or and give thee Life with-out end, his sal-va-tion to share.

REFRAIN

Un-der his wings, un-der his wings, Safe in the ref-uge hide thee; Trust-ing his truth and faith-ful-ness, No e-vil can be-tide thee. A-MEN.

# HIS FAITHFULNESS 79

*But my God shall supply all your need according to his riches in glory by Christ Jesus.* Phil. 4:19

John Newton, 1779
*The New Christian Hymnal,* 1929

JOANNA 11. 11. 11. 11.
Welsh hymn melody

1. Though troubles assail us, and dangers affright,
Though friends should all fail us, and foes all unite,
Yet one thing secures us, whatever betide,
The promise assures us, "The Lord will provide."

2. The birds, without garner or storehouse, are fed;
From them let us learn to trust God for our bread:
His saints what is fitting shall ne'er be denied,
So long as 'tis written, "The Lord will provide."

3. When Satan assails us to stop up our path,
And courage all fails us, we triumph by faith.
He cannot take from us, though oft he has tried,
This heart-cheering promise, "The Lord will provide."

4. No strength of our own, and no goodness we claim;
Yet, since we have known of the Saviour's great Name,
In this our strong tower for safety we hide:
The Lord is our power, "The Lord will provide." A-MEN.

For a lower setting of this tune, see No. 279.

## 80 THE GLORY OF GOD

*Fear thou not; for I am with thee: be not dismayed; for I am thy God:*
*I will strengthen thee; yea, I will help thee . . .* Isa. 41:10

"K" in Rippon's *Selection*, 1787

ADESTE FIDELES 11. 11. 11. 11. with repeat
Unknown: probably 18th century

1. How firm a foun-da-tion, ye saints of the Lord, Is laid for your faith in his ex-cel-lent Word! What more can he say than to you he hath said, You who un-to Je-sus for ref-uge have fled? You who un-to Je-sus for ref-uge have fled?

2. "Fear not, I am with thee, O be not dis-mayed; I, I am thy God, and will still give thee aid; I'll strength-en thee, help thee, and cause thee to stand, Up-held by my right-eous, om-nip-o-tent hand, Up-held by my right-eous, om-nip-o-tent hand.

3. "When through the deep wa-ters I call thee to go, The riv-ers of woe shall not thee o-ver-flow; For I will be with thee thy trou-bles to bless, And sanc-ti-fy to thee thy deep-est dis-tress, And sanc-ti-fy to thee thy deep-est dis-tress.

4. "When through fier-y tri-als thy path-way shall lie, My grace, all-suf-fi-cient, shall be thy sup-ply; The flame shall not hurt thee; I on-ly de-sign Thy dross to con-sume, and thy gold to re-fine, Thy dross to con-sume, and thy gold to re-fine.

5. "E'en down to old age all my peo-ple shall prove My sov-ereign, e-ter-nal, un-change-a-ble love; And when hoar-y hairs shall their tem-ples a-dorn, Like lambs they shall still in my bo-som be borne, Like lambs they shall still in my bos-om be borne.

6. "The soul that on Je-sus hath leaned for re-pose, I will not, I will not de-sert to his foes; That soul, though all hell should en-deav-or to shake, I'll nev-er, no, nev-er, no, nev-er for-sake, I'll nev-er, no, nev-er, no, nev-er for-sake." A-MEN.

# HIS FAITHFULNESS

**81**

*God is our refuge and strength, a very present help in trouble.* Psalm 46:1

Martin Luther, 1529
Tr. by Frederick H. Hedge, 1853

EIN' FESTE BURG 8.7.8.7.6.6.6.6.7.
Martin Luther, 1529

1. A might-y For-tress is our God, A Bul-wark nev-er fail-ing;
2. Did we in our own strength con-fide, Our striv-ing would be los-ing;
3. And though this world, with dev-ils filled, Should threat-en to un-do us,
4. That Word a-bove all earth-ly powers, No thanks to them, a-bid-eth;

Our Help-er he a-mid the flood Of mor-tal ills pre-vail-ing.
Were not the right Man on our side, The Man of God's own choos-ing.
We will not fear, for God hath willed His truth to tri-umph through us.
The Spir-it and the gifts are ours Through him who with us sid-eth;

For still our an-cient foe Doth seek to work us woe; His craft and pow'r are
Dost ask who that may be? Christ Je-sus, it is he, Lord Sab-a-oth his
The prince of dark-ness grim, We trem-ble not for him; His rage we can en-
Let goods and kin-dred go, This mor-tal life al-so; The bod-y they may

great; And, armed with cru-el hate, On earth is not his e-qual.
Name, From age to age the same, And he must win the bat-tle.
dure, For lo! his doom is sure; One lit-tle word shall fell him.
kill: God's truth a-bid-eth still; His king-dom is for ev-er. A-MEN.

# 82 THE GLORY OF GOD

*I will lift up mine eyes unto the hills, from whence cometh my help.* Psalm 121:1

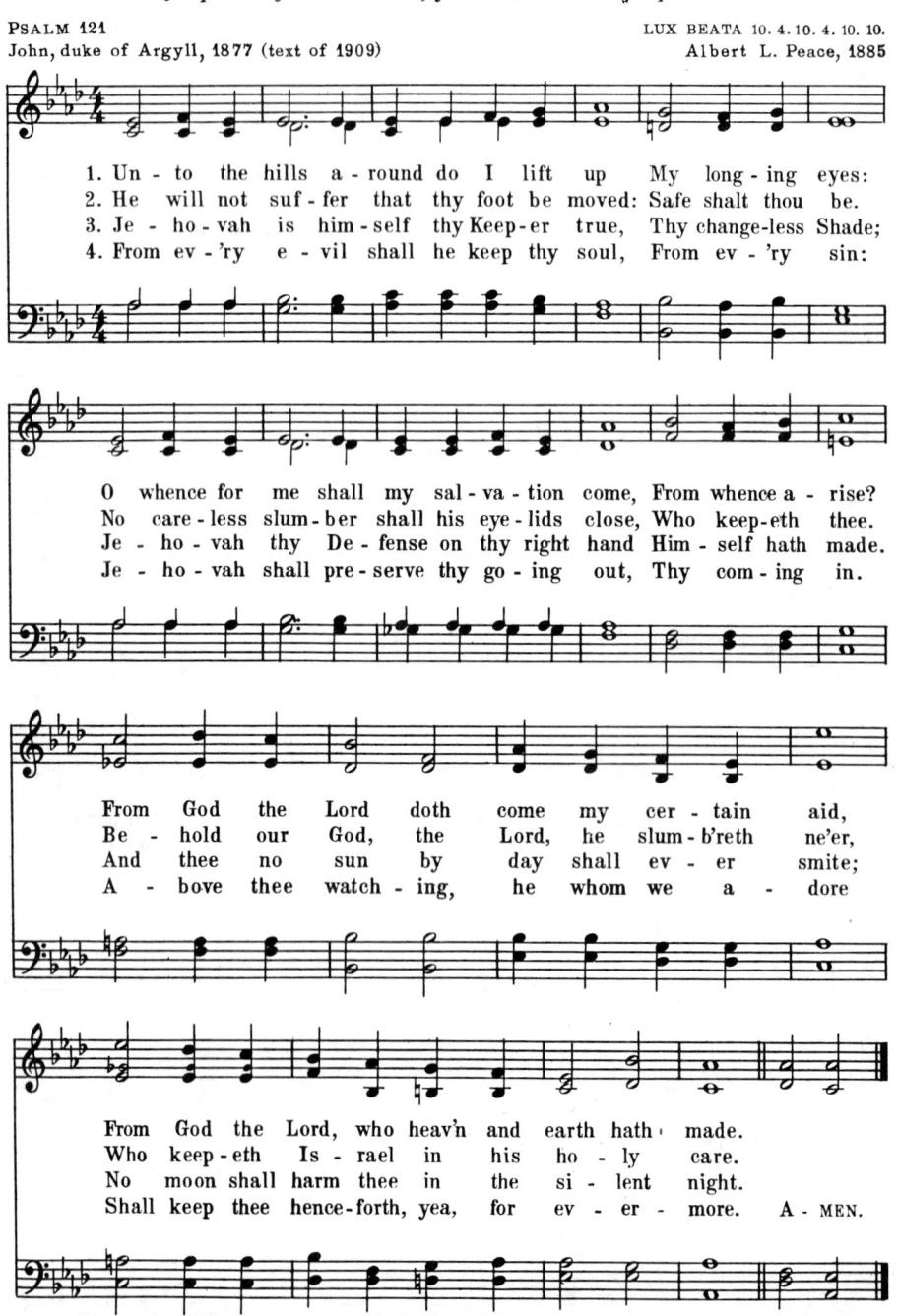

PSALM 121  
John, duke of Argyll, 1877 (text of 1909)

LUX BEATA 10. 4. 10. 4. 10. 10.  
Albert L. Peace, 1885

1. Un-to the hills a-round do I lift up My long-ing eyes:
2. He will not suf-fer that thy foot be moved: Safe shalt thou be.
3. Je-ho-vah is him-self thy Keep-er true, Thy change-less Shade;
4. From ev-'ry e-vil shall he keep thy soul, From ev-'ry sin:

O whence for me shall my sal-va-tion come, From whence a-rise?
No care-less slum-ber shall his eye-lids close, Who keep-eth thee.
Je-ho-vah thy De-fense on thy right hand Him-self hath made.
Je-ho-vah shall pre-serve thy go-ing out, Thy com-ing in.

From God the Lord doth come my cer-tain aid,
Be-hold our God, the Lord, he slum-b'reth ne'er,
And thee no sun by day shall ev-er smite;
A-bove thee watch-ing, he whom we a-dore

From God the Lord, who heav'n and earth hath made.
Who keep-eth Is-rael in his ho-ly care.
No moon shall harm thee in the si-lent night.
Shall keep thee hence-forth, yea, for ev-er-more. A-MEN.

# HIS FAITHFULNESS 83

*Our redeemer, the Lord of hosts is his name, the Holy One of Israel.* Isa. 47:4

Julia Cady Cory

KREMSER 12. 11. 12. 11.
Old Netherlands melody in
*The Collection*, Adrianus Valerius, 1625

1. We praise thee, O God, our Re - deem - er, Cre - a - tor,
2. We wor - ship thee, God of our fa - thers, we bless thee;
3. With voi - ces u - nit - ed our prais - es we of - fer,

In grate - ful de - vo - tion our trib - ute we bring.
Through life's storm and tem - pest our Guide hast thou been.
To thee, great Je - ho - vah, glad an - thems we raise.

We lay it be - fore thee, we kneel and a - dore thee,
When per - ils o'er - take us, es - cape thou wilt make us,
Thy strong arm will guide us, our God is be - side us,

We bless thy ho - ly Name, glad prais - es we sing.
And with thy help, O Lord, our bat - tles we win.
To thee, our great Re - deem - er, for ev - er be praise. A - MEN.

Words used by permission.

## 84 THE GLORY OF GOD

*O give thanks unto the Lord, for he is good: for his mercy endureth for ever.* Psalm 107:1

PSALM 107:1-9
Reformed Presbyterian *Book of Psalms*, 1940

NEWELL C. M. with repeat
William B. Bradbury, 1816-1868

1. O praise the Lord, for he is good, His mer-cies still en-dure; Thus say the
2. He gath-ered them from out the lands, From north, south, east and west. They strayed in
3. Their wea-ry soul with-in them faints When thirst and hun-ger press; In trou-ble
4. He made the way be-fore them straight, Him-self be-came their guide, That they might
5. O that men would Je-ho-vah praise For all his kind-ness shown, And for his
6. Be-cause the long-ing soul by him With food is sat-is-fied; The hun-gry

ran-somed of the Lord, From all their foes se-cure, From all their foes se-cure.
des-ert's path-less way, No cit-y found for rest, No cit-y found for rest.
then they cried to God, He saved them from dis-tress, He saved them from dis-tress.
to a cit-y go Where-in they might a-bide, Where-in they might a-bide.
works so won-der-ful Which he to men makes known! Which he to men makes known!
soul that looks to him With good-ness is sup-plied, With good-ness is sup-plied. A-MEN.

## 85

*Like as a father pitieth his children, so the Lord pitieth them that fear him.* Psalm 103:13

From PSALM 103:13-18
*The Psalter*, 1912

AVONDALE C. M.
Charles H. Gabriel, 1856-1932

1. The ten-der love a fa-ther has For all his chil-dren dear,
2. The Lord re-mem-bers we are dust, And all our frail-ty knows;
3. The flower is with-ered by the wind That smites with blight-ing breath;
4. Un-chang-ing is the love of God, From age to age the same,
5. Those who his gra-cious cov-'nant keep The Lord will ev-er bless;

Such love the Lord be-stows on them Who wor-ship him in fear.
Man's days are like the ten-der grass, And as the flower he grows.
So man is quick-ly swept a-way Be-fore the blast of death.
Dis-played to all who do his will And rev-er-ence his Name.
Their chil-dren's chil-dren shall re-joice To see his right-eous-ness. A-MEN.

# HIS FAITHFULNESS 86

*Now therefore, our God, we thank thee, and praise thy glorious name.* I Chron. 29:13

Martin Rinkart, c. 1636
Tr. by Catherine Winkworth, 1858

NUN DANKET 6.7.6.7.6.6.6.6.
Johann Crüger, 1647

1. Now thank we all our God With heart and hands and voic - es,
2. O may this boun - teous God Through all our life be near us,
3. All praise and thanks to God, The Fa - ther, now be giv - en,

Who won-drous things hath done, In whom his world re - joic - es;
With ev - er joy - ful hearts And bless-ed peace to cheer us;
The Son, and Him who reigns With them in high - est heav - en,

Who from our moth - ers' arms, Hath blessed us on our way
And keep us in his grace, And guide us when per - plexed,
The One E - ter - nal God Whom earth and heav'n a - dore;

With count-less gifts of love, And still is ours to - day.
And free us from all ills In this world and the next.
For thus it was, is now, And shall be ev - er - more. A - MEN.

## 87 THE HOLY TRINITY

*They rest not day and night, saying, Holy, holy, holy, Lord God Almighty... Rev. 4:8*

Reginald Heber, 1783-1826

NICAEA 11. 12. 12. 10.
John B. Dykes, 1861

1. Ho-ly, Ho-ly, Ho-ly, Lord God Al-might-y! Ear-ly in the morn-ing our song shall rise to thee; Ho-ly, Ho-ly, Ho-ly! Mer-ci-ful and Might-y! God in three Per-sons, bless-ed Trin-i-ty!
2. Ho-ly, Ho-ly, Ho-ly! All the saints a-dore thee, Cast-ing down their gold-en crowns a-round the glass-y sea; Cher-u-bim and ser-a-phim fall-ing down be-fore thee, Who wert, and art, and ev-er-more shalt be.
3. Ho-ly, Ho-ly, Ho-ly! Though the dark-ness hide thee, Though the eye of sin-ful man thy glo-ry may not see, On-ly thou art ho-ly; there is none be-side thee Per-fect in pow'r, in love, and pur-i-ty.
4. Ho-ly, Ho-ly, Ho-ly! Lord God Al-might-y! All thy works shall praise thy Name, in earth and sky and sea; Ho-ly, Ho-ly, Ho-ly! Mer-ci-ful and Might-y! God in three Per-sons, bless-ed Trin-i-ty! A-MEN.

## 88

*Holy, holy, holy, Lord God Almighty, which was, and is, and is to come. Rev. 4:8*

Edward Cooper, 1805

ANGELUS L. M.
*Heilige Seelenlust,*
Breslau, 1657

1. Fa-ther of heav'n, whose love pro-found A ran-som for our souls hath found,
2. Al-might-y Son, In-car-nate Word, Our Proph-et, Priest, Re-deem-er, Lord,
3. E-ter-nal Spir-it, by whose breath The soul is raised from sin and death,
4. Je-ho-vah! Fa-ther, Spir-it, Son, Mys-te-rious God-head, Three in One,

# THE HOLY TRINITY

Be-fore thy throne we sin-ners bend; To us thy par-d'ning love ex-tend.
Be-fore thy throne we sin-ners bend; To us thy sav-ing grace ex-tend.
Be-fore thy throne we sin-ners bend; To us thy quick-'ning pow'r ex-tend.
Be-fore thy throne we sin-ners bend; Grace, par-don, life, to us ex-tend. A-MEN.

*The grace of the Lord Jesus Christ, and the love of God, and the communion of the Holy Ghost, be with you all.* II Cor. 13:14

**89**

TRINITY 6. 6. 4. 6. 6. 6. 4.
Anon., c. 1757
Felice de Giardini, 1769

1. Come, thou Al - might-y King, Help us thy Name to sing,
2. Come, thou In - car-nate Word, Gird on thy might-y sword,
3. Come, Ho - ly Com-fort - er, Thy sa - cred wit - ness bear
4. To the great One in Three E - ter - nal prais-es be,

Help us to praise: Fa - ther, all - glo - ri - ous, O'er all vic -
Our prayer at - tend: Come, and thy peo - ple bless, And give thy
In this glad hour: Thou who al - might-y art, Now rule in
Hence ev - er - more. His sov-ereign maj - es - ty May we in

to - ri - ous, Come, and reign o - ver us, An-cient of Days.
Word suc-cess; Spir - it of Ho - li - ness, On us de-scend.
ev - ery heart, And ne'er from us de-part, Spir - it of pow'r.
glo - ry see, And to e - ter - ni - ty Love and a - dore. A - MEN.

## 90 THE HOLY TRINITY

*Holy, holy, holy is the Lord of hosts: the whole earth is full of his glory.* Isa. 6: 3

Anon. (Te Deum) 5th century
Tr. in Tate and Brady's *Supplement*, c. 1700

DUNDEE C. M.
Scottish *Psalter*, 1615

1. O God, we praise thee; and con-fess That thou the on-ly Lord
And Ev-er-last-ing Fa-ther art, By all the earth a-dored.

2. To thee all an-gels cry a-loud; To thee the pow'rs on high,
Both cher-u-bim and ser-a-phim, Con-tin-ual-ly do cry:

3. O ho-ly, ho-ly, ho-ly Lord, Whom heav'n-ly hosts o-bey,
The world is with the glo-ry filled Of thy maj-es-tic ray.

4. Th'a-pos-tles' glo-rious com-pan-y, And proph-ets crowned with light,
With all the mar-tyrs' no-ble host, Thy con-stant praise re-cite.

5. The ho-ly church through-out the world, O Lord, con-fess-es thee,
That thou E-ter-nal Fa-ther art, Of bound-less maj-es-ty;

6. Thine hon-ored, true, and on-ly Son; And Ho-ly Ghost, the Spring
Of nev-er-ceas-ing joy: O Christ, Of glo-ry thou art King. A-MEN.

## 91

*Holy Father, keep through thine own name those whom thou hast given me...* John 17:11

Martin Luther, 1541
Tr. by Catherine Winkworth, 1863

ERHALT UNS, HERR L. M.
*Geistliche Lieder*, Wittenberg, 1543

1. Lord, keep us stead-fast in thy Word; Curb those who fain by craft and sword
Would wrest the king-dom from thy Son And set at naught all he hath done.

2. Lord Je-sus Christ, thy pow'r make known, For thou art Lord of lords a-lone;
De-fend thy Chris-ten-dom that we May ev-er-more sing praise to thee.

3. O Com-fort-er of price-less worth, Send peace and u-ni-ty on earth.
Sup-port us in our fi-nal strife And lead us out of death to life. A-MEN.

# THE HOLY TRINITY 92

*Save us, O God of our salvation, and gather us together...*
*that we may give thanks to thy holy name... I Chron. 16:35*

Tr. from German version of
Latin hymn, *Gloria in Excelsis*

ALLEIN GOTT IN DER HÖH' 8.7.8.7.8.8.7.
*Geistliche Lieder,* Leipzig, 1539
Arr. by Felix Mendelssohn-Bartholdy, 1809-1847

1. All glory be to thee, Most High, To thee all ad-o-ration; In grace and truth thou draw-est nigh To of-fer us sal-va-tion; Thou show-est thy good will to men, And peace shall reign on earth a-gain; We praise thy Name for ev-er.

2. We praise, we wor-ship thee, we trust, And give thee thanks for ev-er, O Fa-ther, for thy rule is just And wise, and chang-es nev-er; Thy hand al-might-y o'er us reigns, Thou do-est what thy will or-dains; 'Tis well for us thou rul-est.

3. O Je-sus Christ, our God and Lord, Son of the Heav'n-ly Fa-ther, O thou who hast our peace re-stored, The stray-ing sheep dost gath-er, Thou Lamb of God, to thee on high Out of the depths we sin-ners cry: Have mer-cy on us, Je-sus!

4. O Ho-ly Spir-it, pre-cious gift, Thou Com-fort-er un-fail-ing, From Sa-tan's snares our souls up-lift, And let thy pow'r, a-vail-ing, A-vert our woes and calm our dread. For us the Sav-iour's blood was shed; We trust in thee to save us. A-MEN.

## 93     THE DECREES OF GOD

*O the depth of the riches both of the wisdom and knowledge of God! how unsearchable are his judgments, and his ways past finding out!* Rom. 11:33

CANONBURY L. M.

Ray Palmer, 1858     Arr. from Robert Schumann, 1839

1. Lord, my weak thought in vain would climb To search the star-ry vault pro-found; In vain would wing her flight sub-lime To find cre-a-tion's ut-most bound.

2. But weak-er yet that thought must prove To search thy great e-ter-nal plan, Thy sov-ereign coun-sels, born of love Long ag-es ere the world be-gan.

3. When my dim rea-son would de-mand Why that, or this, thou dost or-dain, By some vast deep I seem to stand, Whose se-crets I must ask in vain. A-MEN.

4. When doubts disturb my troubled breast,
And all is dark as night to me,
Here, as on solid rock, I rest,—
That so it seemeth good to thee.

5. Be this my joy, that evermore
Thou rulest all things at thy will;
Thy sovereign wisdom I adore,
And calmly, sweetly, trust thee still.

# THE DECREES OF GOD      94

*Shall not the Judge of all the earth do right?* Gen. 18:25

Samuel Rodigast, 1675
Tr. by Catherine Winkworth, 1829-1878

WAS GOTT TUT 8. 7. 8. 7. 4. 4. 8. 8.
Severus Gastorius, 1681

1. What-e'er my God or-dains is right: Ho - ly his will a - bid - eth;
2. What-e'er my God or-dains is right: He nev-er will de - ceive me;
3. What-e'er my God or-dains is right: Though now this cup, in drink-ing,
4. What-e'er my God or-dains is right: Here shall my stand be tak - en;

I will be still what-e'er he doth, And fol-low where he guid-eth:
He leads me by the prop-er path; I know he will not leave me:
May bit-ter seem to my faint heart, I take it, all un-shrink-ing;
Though sor-row, need, or death be mine, Yet am I not for-sak-en;

He is my God; Though dark my road, He holds me that I
I take, con - tent, What he hath sent; His hand can turn my
My God is true; Each morn a - new Sweet com - fort yet shall
My Fa - ther's care Is round me there; He holds me that I

shall not fall: Where-fore to him I leave it all.
griefs a - way, And pa - tient - ly I wait his day.
fill my heart, And pain and sor - row shall de - part.
shall not fall: And so to him I leave it all. A - MEN.

St. 3, lines 5 and 6, alt.

Harmony from *The Revised Church Hymnary* by permission of the Oxford University Press, London.

## 95 ELECTION

*He hath chosen us in him before the foundation of the world, that we should be holy and without blame before him... Eph. 1:4*

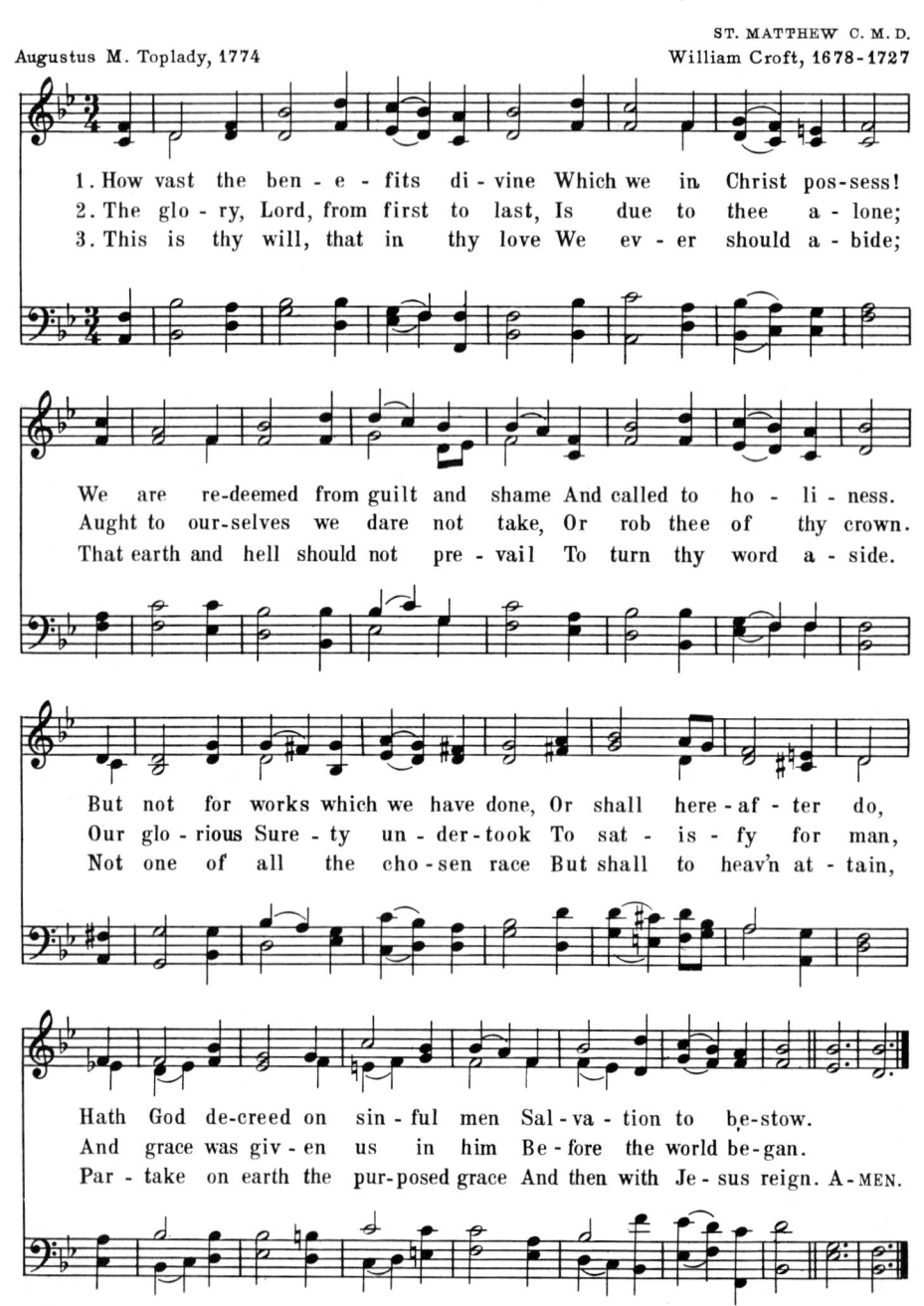

Augustus M. Toplady, 1774
ST. MATTHEW C. M. D.
William Croft, 1678-1727

1. How vast the ben-e-fits di-vine Which we in Christ pos-sess!
We are re-deemed from guilt and shame And called to ho-li-ness.
But not for works which we have done, Or shall here-af-ter do,
Hath God de-creed on sin-ful men Sal-va-tion to be-stow.

2. The glo-ry, Lord, from first to last, Is due to thee a-lone;
Aught to our-selves we dare not take, Or rob thee of thy crown.
Our glo-rious Sure-ty un-der-took To sat-is-fy for man,
And grace was giv-en us in him Be-fore the world be-gan.

3. This is thy will, that in thy love We ev-er should a-bide;
That earth and hell should not pre-vail To turn thy word a-side.
Not one of all the cho-sen race But shall to heav'n at-tain,
Par-take on earth the pur-posed grace And then with Je-sus reign. A-MEN.

Stanzas 1 and 3, revised

# ELECTION

96

*Ye have not chosen me, but I have chosen you... John 15:16*

Josiah Conder, 1836

SAVOY CHAPEL 7. 6. 7. 6. D.
J. Baptiste Calkin, 1887

1. 'Tis not that I did choose thee, For, Lord, that could not be;
   This heart would still refuse thee, Hadst thou not chosen me.
   Thou from the sin that stained me Hast cleansed and set me free;
   Of old thou hast ordained me, That I should live to thee.

2. 'Twas sov'reign mercy called me And taught my op'ning mind;
   The world had else enthralled me, To heav'nly glories blind.
   My heart owns none before thee, For thy rich grace I thirst;
   This knowing, if I love thee, Thou must have loved me first. A-MEN.

## 97 THE COVENANT OF GRACE

*Bless the Lord, O my soul: and all that is within me, bless his holy name.* Psalm 103:1

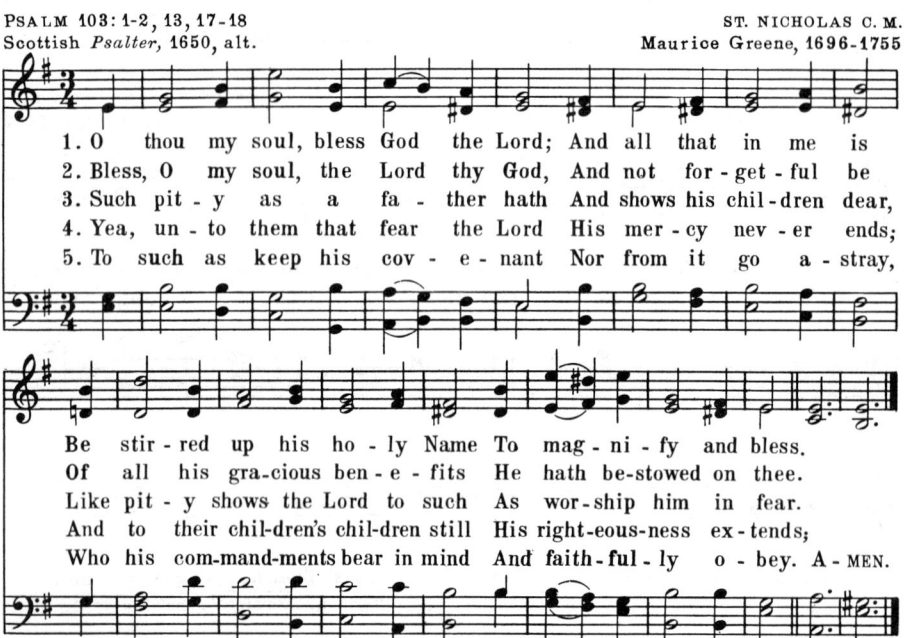

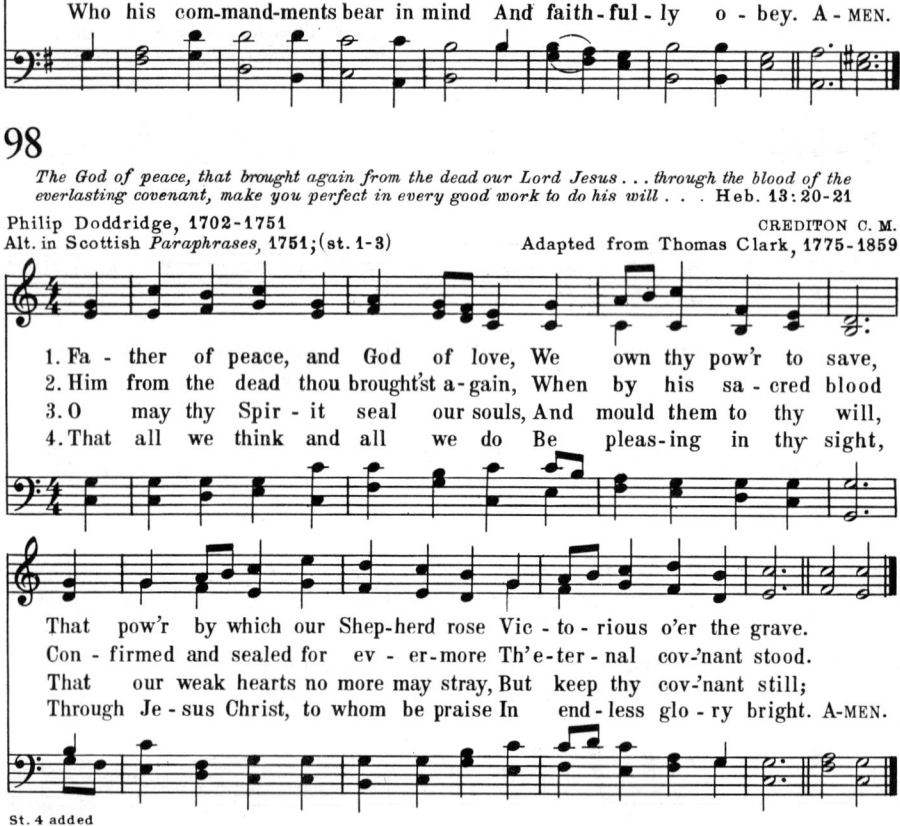

PSALM 103:1-2, 13, 17-18
Scottish *Psalter,* 1650, alt.

ST. NICHOLAS C. M.
Maurice Greene, 1696-1755

1. O thou my soul, bless God the Lord; And all that in me is
   Be stir-red up his ho-ly Name To mag-ni-fy and bless.
2. Bless, O my soul, the Lord thy God, And not for-get-ful be
   Of all his gra-cious ben-e-fits He hath be-stowed on thee.
3. Such pit-y as a fa-ther hath And shows his chil-dren dear,
   Like pit-y shows the Lord to such As wor-ship him in fear.
4. Yea, un-to them that fear the Lord His mer-cy nev-er ends;
   And to their chil-dren's chil-dren still His right-eous-ness ex-tends;
5. To such as keep his cov-e-nant Nor from it go a-stray,
   Who his com-mand-ments bear in mind And faith-ful-ly o-bey. A-MEN.

## 98

*The God of peace, that brought again from the dead our Lord Jesus . . . through the blood of the everlasting covenant, make you perfect in every good work to do his will . . .* Heb. 13:20-21

Philip Doddridge, 1702-1751
Alt. in Scottish *Paraphrases,* 1751; (st. 1-3)

CREDITON C. M.
Adapted from Thomas Clark, 1775-1859

1. Fa-ther of peace, and God of love, We own thy pow'r to save,
   That pow'r by which our Shep-herd rose Vic-to-rious o'er the grave.
2. Him from the dead thou brought'st a-gain, When by his sa-cred blood
   Con-firmed and sealed for ev-er-more Th'e-ter-nal cov'nant stood.
3. O may thy Spir-it seal our souls, And mould them to thy will,
   That our weak hearts no more may stray, But keep thy cov'nant still;
4. That all we think and all we do Be pleas-ing in thy sight,
   Through Je-sus Christ, to whom be praise In end-less glo-ry bright. A-MEN.

St. 4 added

# THE COVENANT OF GRACE 99

*He which hath begun a good work in you will perform it until the day of Jesus Christ.* Phil. 1:6

Augustus M. Toplady, 1740-1778

LLANGRISTIOLUS 8.8.8.8.D.
Joseph Parry, 1841-1903

1. A debt-or to mer-cy a-lone, Of cov-e-nant mer-cy I sing;
2. The work which his good-ness be-gan, The arm of his strength will com-plete;
3. My name from the palms of his hands E-ter-ni-ty will not e-rase;

Nor fear, with thy right-eous-ness on, My per-son and of-f'ring to bring.
His prom-ise is Yea and A-men, And nev-er was for-feit-ed yet.
Im-pressed on his heart it re-mains, In marks of in-del-i-ble grace.

The ter-rors of law and of God With me can have noth-ing to do;
Things fu-ture, nor things that are now, Nor all things be-low or a-bove,
Yes, I to the end shall en-dure, As sure as the earn-est is giv'n;

My Sav-iour's o-be-dience and blood Hide all my trans-gres-sions from view.
Can make him his pur-pose for-go, Or sev-er my soul from his love.
More hap-py, but not more se-cure, The glo-ri-fied spir-its in heav'n. A-MEN.

## 100 THE COVENANT OF GRACE

*Arise, O Lord, into thy rest; thou, and the ark of thy strength.* Psalm 132:8

From PSALM 132  
The Psalter, 1912

HERR JESU CHRIST L. M.  
Pensum Sacrum, 1648  
Arr. by Johann Sebastian Bach, 1685-1750

1. Arise, O Lord, our God, arise And enter now into thy rest; O let this house be thine abode, For ever with thy presence blest.
2. Thy gracious cov'nant, Lord, fulfil, Turn not away from us thy face; Establish thou Messiah's throne And let him reign within this place.
3. Thy Zion thou hast chosen, Lord, And thou hast said, I love her well, This is my constant resting place, And here will I delight to dwell.
4. I will abundantly provide For Zion's good, the Lord hath said; I will supply her daily need And satisfy her poor with bread. A-MEN.

## 101

*I will sing of the mercies of the Lord for ever . . .* Psalm 89:1

From PSALM 89:1-4, 28-29, 52  
The Psalter, 1912

MARYTON L. M.  
H. Percy Smith, 1874

1. My song for ever shall record The tender
2. I sing of mercies that endure, For ever
3. Behold God's truth and grace displayed, For he has
4. For him my mercy shall endure, My cov-'nant
5. Blessed be the Lord for evermore, Whose promise

# THE WORK OF CREATION

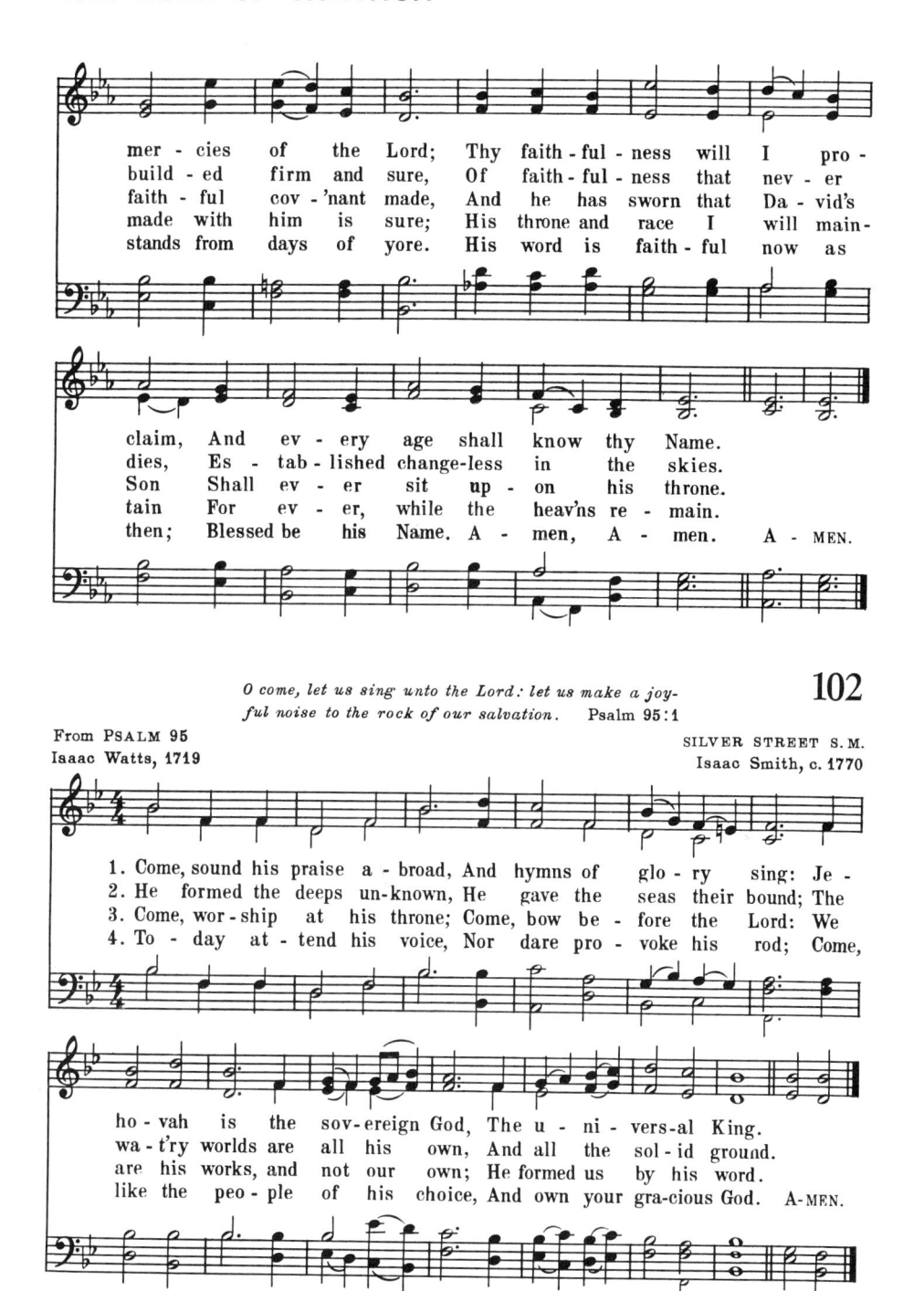

mer - cies of the Lord; Thy faith - ful - ness will I pro -
build - ed firm and sure, Of faith - ful - ness that nev - er
faith - ful cov - 'nant made, And he has sworn that Da - vid's
made with him is sure; His throne and race I will main -
stands from days of yore. His word is faith - ful now as

claim, And ev - ery age shall know thy Name.
dies, Es - tab - lished change-less in the skies.
Son Shall ev - er sit up - on his throne.
tain For ev - er, while the heav'ns re - main.
then; Blessed be his Name. A - men, A - men. A - MEN.

*O come, let us sing unto the Lord: let us make a joy-*
*ful noise to the rock of our salvation.* Psalm 95:1

**102**

From PSALM 95  
Isaac Watts, 1719

SILVER STREET S.M.  
Isaac Smith, c. 1770

1. Come, sound his praise a - broad, And hymns of glo - ry sing: Je -
2. He formed the deeps un - known, He gave the seas their bound; The
3. Come, wor - ship at his throne; Come, bow be - fore the Lord: We
4. To - day at - tend his voice, Nor dare pro - voke his rod; Come,

ho - vah is the sov-ereign God, The u - ni - vers-al King.
wa - t'ry worlds are all his own, And all the sol - id ground.
are his works, and not our own; He formed us by his word.
like the peo - ple of his choice, And own your gra-cious God. A-MEN.

# 103 THE WORK OF CREATION

*The heavens declare the glory of God; and the firmament sheweth his handywork.* Psalm 19:1

Joseph Addison, 1712  
CREATION L. M. D.  
Arr. from Franz Josef Haydn, 1798

1. The spa-cious firm-a-ment on high, With all the blue e-the-real sky, And span-gled heav'ns, a shin-ing frame, Their great O-rig-i-nal pro-claim. Th'un-wear-ied sun, from day to day, Does his Cre-a-tor's pow'r dis-play, And pub-lish-es to ev-'ry land The work of an al-might-y hand.

2. Soon as the eve-ning shades pre-vail, The moon takes up the won-drous tale, And night-ly to the lis-t'ning earth Re-peats the sto-ry of her birth; Whilst all the stars that round her burn, And all the plan-ets in their turn, Con-firm the ti-dings as they roll, And spread the truth from pole to pole.

3. What though in sol-emn si-lence all Move round this dark ter-res-trial ball? What though nor re-al voice nor sound A-midst their ra-diant orbs be found? In rea-son's ear they all re-joice, And ut-ter forth a glo-rious voice; For ev-er sing-ing, as they shine, "The hand that made us is di-vine." A-MEN.

# THE WORK OF CREATION  104

*The heavens declare the glory of God; and the firmament sheweth his handywork.* Psalm 19:1

From PSALM 19:1-6, 14  
Thomas R. Birks, 1874

FAITHFUL 7.6.7.6.D.  
Johann Sebastian Bach, 1685-1750

1. The heav'ns de-clare thy glo - ry, The fir - ma-ment thy pow'r;
2. The sun with roy - al splen-dor Goes forth to chant thy praise,
3. All heav'n on high re - joic - es To do its Mak - er's will;

Day un - to day the sto - ry Re - peats from hour to hour;
And moon - beams soft and ten - der Their gen - tler an - them raise;
The stars with sol - emn voic - es Re - sound thy prais - es still;

Night un - to night re - ply - ing, Pro - claims in ev - ery land,
O'er ev - ery tribe and na - tion The mu - sic strange is poured,
So let my whole be - hav - ior, Thoughts, words, and ac - tions be,

O Lord, with voice un - dy - ing, The won - ders of thy hand.
The song of all cre - a - tion To thee, cre - a - tion's Lord.
O Lord, my Strength, my Sav - iour, One cease - less song to thee. A-MEN.

## 105 THE WORK OF CREATION

*Praise ye the Lord. Praise ye the Lord from the heavens... Psalm 148:1*

PSALM 148:1-13
United Presbyterian *Bible Songs Hymnal,* 1927

KIRKPATRICK 8.7.8.7. D. with refrain
Willam J. Kirkpatrick, 1838-1921

1. Hal - le - lu - jah, praise Je - ho - vah, From the heav-ens praise his Name;
2. Let them prais - es give Je - ho - vah, They were made at his com - mand;
3. All ye fruit - ful trees and ce - dars, All ye hills and moun-tains high,

Praise Je - ho - vah in the high - est, All his an - gels, praise pro - claim.
Them for ev - er he es - tab - lish-ed, His de - cree shall ev - er stand.
Creep - ing things and beasts and cat - tle, Birds that in the heav - ens fly,

All his hosts, to - geth - er praise him, Sun and moon and stars on high;
From the earth, O praise Je - ho - vah, All ye seas, ye mon - sters all,
Kings of earth, and all ye peo - ple, Prin - ces great, earth's judg - es all;

Praise him, O ye heav'ns of heav - ens, And ye floods a - bove the sky.
Fire and hail and snow and va - pors, Storm-y winds that hear his call.
Praise his Name, young men and maid - ens, A - ged men, and chil-dren small.

# THE WORK OF CREATION

*Refrain*

Let them prais - es give Jeho - vah, For his Name a - lone is high, And his glo - ry is ex - alt - ed, And his glo - ry is ex - alt - ed, And his glo - ry is ex - alt - ed Far a - bove the earth and sky. A-MEN.

## 106 THE WORK OF CREATION

*The Lord made heaven and earth, the sea, and all that in them is...* Ex. 20:11

Isaac Watts, 1719

ORTONVILLE C. M. with repeat
Thomas Hastings, 1837

1. I sing th' almighty pow'r of God, That made the mountains rise, That spread the flowing seas abroad, And built the lofty skies, And built the lofty skies.
2. I sing the goodness of the Lord That filled the earth with food; He formed the creatures with his word, And then pronounced them good, And then pronounced them good.
3. Lord! how thy wonders are displayed Where'er I turn mine eye! If I survey the ground I tread, Or gaze upon the sky, Or gaze upon the sky! A-MEN.

4. There's not a plant or flower below
   But makes thy glories known;
   And clouds arise, and tempests blow,
   By order from thy throne,
   By order from thy throne.

5. Creatures as numerous as they be
   Are subject to thy care;
   There's not a place where we can flee,
   But God is present there,
   But God is present there.

# THE WORK OF CREATION 107

*O Lord our Lord, how excellent is thy name in all the earth!* Psalm 8:1

PSALM 8:1-6, 9  
The Psalter, 1912

THANKSGIVING 7.7.7.7. D.  
Walter Bond Gilbert, 1829-1910

1. Lord, our Lord, thy glo-rious Name All thy won-drous works pro-claim;  
In the heav'ns with ra-diant signs Ev - er-more thy glo - ry shines.  
In - fant lips thou dost or - dain Wrath and ven-geance to re - strain;  
Weak-est means ful - fil thy will, Might - y en - e-mies to still.

2. Moon and stars in shin - ing height Night-ly tell their Mak - er's might;  
When thy won-drous heav'ns I scan, Then I know how weak is man.  
What is man that he should be Loved and vis - it - ed by thee,  
Raised to an ex - alt - ed height, Crowned with hon-or in thy sight?

3. With do - min-ion crowned he stands O'er the crea-tures of thy hands;  
All to him sub - jec-tion yield In the sea and air and field.  
Lord, our Lord, thy glo - rious Name All thy won-drous works pro-claim;  
Thine the Name of match-less worth, Ex - cel - lent in all the earth. A-MEN.

## 108 THE WORK OF CREATION

*Praise ye the Lord ... praise him in the heights.* Psalm 148:1

From PSALM 148  
The Psalter, 1912

COLUMBIA 6.6.6.6.8.8.  
Leonard Cooper Blanton, 1951, alt.

1. Praise ye, praise ye the Lord In yon-der heav'n-ly height; Ye an-gels, all his hosts, In joy-ful praise u-nite; O sun and moon, de-clare his might, Show forth his praise, ye stars of light.

2. Praise him, ye high-est heav'ns, Praise him, ye clouds that roll, Cre-at-ed by his pow'r And un-der his con-trol, Ye heav'ns that stand e-ter-nal-ly, Es-tab-lished by his firm de-cree.

3. Ye crea-tures in the sea And crea-tures on the earth, Your might-y Mak-er praise And tell his match-less worth; Praise him, ye storm-y winds that blow, Ye fire and hail, ye rain and snow.

4. Ye hills and moun-tains, praise, Each tree and beast and bird; Ye kings and realms of earth, Now let your praise be heard; By high and low, by young and old, Be all his praise and glo-ry told.

5. By all let God be praised, For he a-lone is great; A-bove the earth and heav'n He reigns in glo-rious state; Praise him, ye saints, who know his grace And ev-er dwell be-fore his face. A-MEN.

Music copyright, 1951, by the composer. Used by permission.

# THE WORK OF CREATION  109

*Lord, thou art God, which hast made heaven, and earth, and the sea, and all that in them is.* **Acts 4:24**

Maltbie D. Babcock, 1901

TERRA BEATA S.M.D.
Franklin L. Sheppard, 1915
Arr. by Edward Shippen Barnes, 1926

1. This is my Father's world, And to my list'ning ears, All nature sings, and round me rings The music of the spheres. This is my Father's world: I rest me in the thought Of rocks and trees, of skies and seas; His hand the wonders wrought.

2. This is my Father's world, The birds their carols raise, The morning light, the lily white, Declare their Maker's praise. This is my Father's world: He shines in all that's fair; In the rustling grass I hear him pass, He speaks to me ev'ry-where.

3. This is my Father's world, O let me ne'er forget That though the wrong seems oft so strong, God is the Ruler yet. This is my Father's world: The battle is not done; Jesus who died shall be satisfied, And earth and heav'n be one. A-MEN.

Music copyright, 1927, by Edward Shippen Barnes.

## 110    GOD'S WORKS OF PROVIDENCE

*Bless the Lord, O my soul. O Lord my God, thou art very great.. Psalm 104:1*

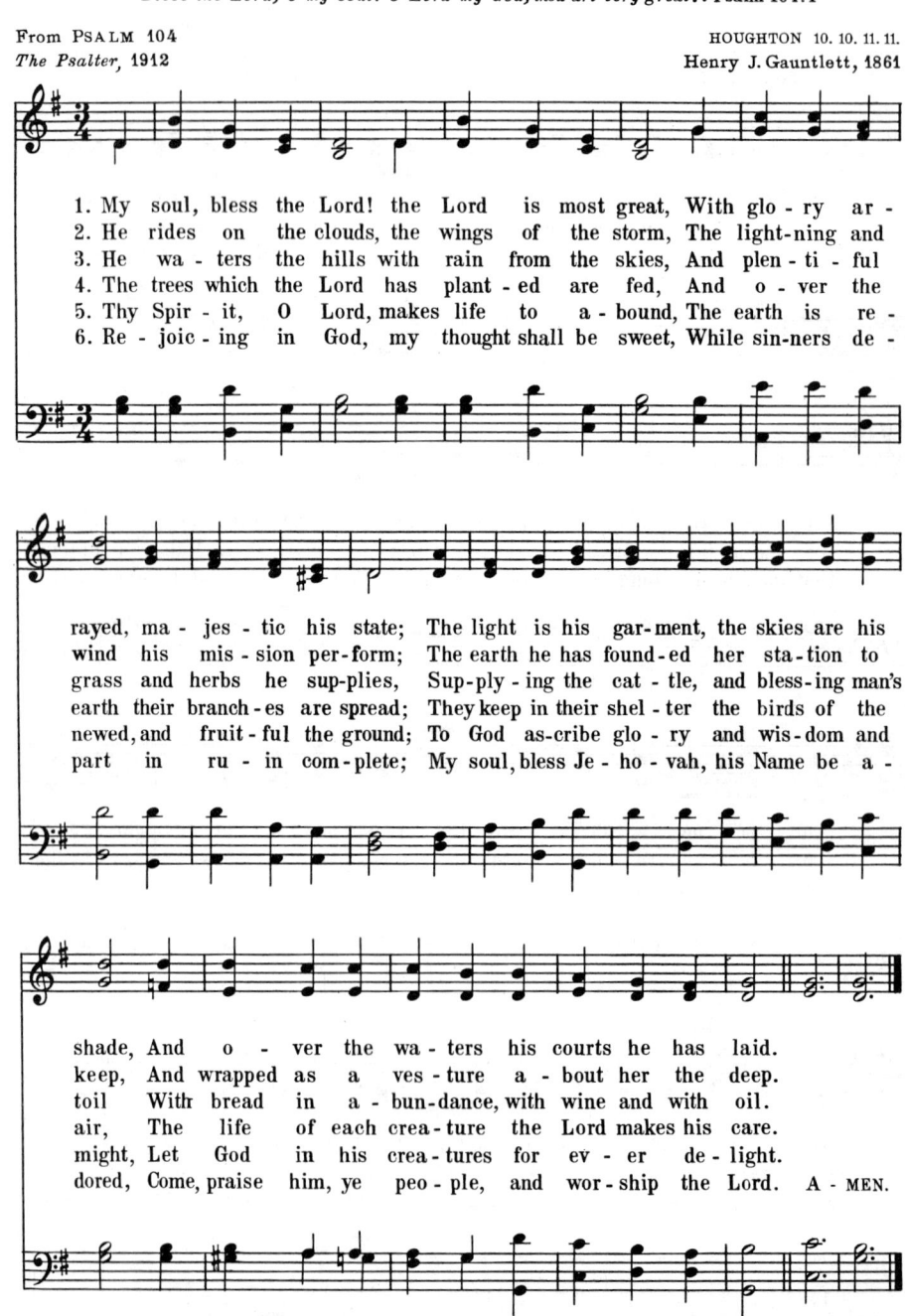

From PSALM 104  
*The Psalter,* 1912

HOUGHTON 10. 10. 11. 11.  
Henry J. Gauntlett, 1861

1. My soul, bless the Lord! the Lord is most great, With glo-ry ar-rayed, ma-jes-tic his state; The light is his gar-ment, the skies are his shade, And o-ver the wa-ters his courts he has laid.
2. He rides on the clouds, the wings of the storm, The light-ning and wind his mis-sion per-form; The earth he has found-ed her sta-tion to keep, And wrapped as a ves-ture a-bout her the deep.
3. He wa-ters the hills with rain from the skies, And plen-ti-ful grass and herbs he sup-plies, Sup-ply-ing the cat-tle, and bless-ing man's toil With bread in a-bun-dance, with wine and with oil.
4. The trees which the Lord has plant-ed are fed, And o-ver the earth their branch-es are spread; They keep in their shel-ter the birds of the air, The life of each crea-ture the Lord makes his care.
5. Thy Spir-it, O Lord, makes life to a-bound, The earth is re-newed, and fruit-ful the ground; To God as-cribe glo-ry and wis-dom and might, Let God in his crea-tures for ev-er de-light.
6. Re-joic-ing in God, my thought shall be sweet, While sin-ners de-part in ru-in com-plete; My soul, bless Je-ho-vah, his Name be a-dored, Come, praise him, ye peo-ple, and wor-ship the Lord. A-MEN.

# GOD'S WORKS OF PROVIDENCE 111

*Which by his strength setteth fast the mountains; being girded with power.* Psalm 65:6

From PSALM 65:6-13  
*The Psalter,* 1912

WEBB 7. 6. 7. 6. D.  
George J. Webb, 1837

1. Thy might sets fast the moun-tains; Strength girds thee ev - er - more  
To calm the rag - ing peo - ples And still the o - cean's roar.  
Thy maj - es - ty and great-ness Are through all lands con - fess'd,  
And joy on earth thou send-est A - far from east to west.

2. To bless the earth thou send - est From thine a - bun-dant store  
The wa - ters of the spring-time, En - rich - ing it once more.  
The seed by thee pro - vid - ed Is sown o'er hill and plain,  
And thou with gen - tle show - ers Dost bless the spring-ing grain.

3. The year with good thou crown-est, The earth thy mer - cy fills,  
The wil - der-ness is fruit - ful, And joy - ful are the hills;  
With corn the vales are cov-ered, The flocks in pas-tures graze;  
All na-ture joins in sing-ing A joy - ful song of praise. A - MEN.

## 112 GOD'S WORKS OF PROVIDENCE

*Thou crownest the year with thy goodness; and thy paths drop fatness.* Psalm 65:11

Anna L. Barbauld, 1772
Doxology, Charles Wesley, 1740

NUREMBERG 7.7.7.7.
Alt. from Johann R. Ahle, 1664

1. Praise to God, im-mor-tal praise, For the love that crowns our days;
2. Flocks that whit-en all the plain, Yel-low sheaves of rip-ened grain,
3. All that spring with boun-teous hand Scat-ters o'er the smil-ing land;
4. These to thee, my God, we owe, Source whence all our bless-ings flow;
5. Sing we to our God a-bove Praise e-ter-nal as his love;

Boun-teous Source of ev-ery joy, Let thy praise our tongues em-ploy.
Clouds that drop their fat-t'ning dews, Suns that tem-p'rate warmth dif-fuse;
All that lib-eral au-tumn pours From her rich o'er-flow-ing stores;
And for these my soul shall raise Grate-ful vows and sol-emn praise.
Praise him, all ye heav'n-ly host, Fa-ther, Son, and Ho-ly Ghost. A-MEN.

## 113

*Sing unto the Lord... who covereth the heaven with clouds, who prepareth rain for the earth... Psalm 147:7, 8*

From PSALM 147:7-8, 15-18
Isaac Watts, 1719

ST. MAGNUS C.M.
Jeremiah Clark, 1670-1707

1. With songs and hon-ors sound-ing loud Ad-dress the Lord on high;
2. He sends his show'rs of bless-ing down To cheer the plains be-low;
3. His stead-y coun-sels change the face Of the de-clin-ing year;
4. His hoar-y frost, his fleec-y snow, De-scend and clothe the ground;
5. He sends his word, and melts the snow; The fields no long-er mourn;
6. The chang-ing wind, the fly-ing cloud, O-bey his might-y word:

O-ver the heav'ns he spreads his cloud, And wa-ters veil the sky.
He makes the grass the moun-tains crown, And corn in val-leys grow.
He bids the sun cut short his race, And win-try days ap-pear.
The liq-uid streams for-bear to flow, In ic-y fet-ters bound.
He calls the warm-er gales to blow, And bids the spring re-turn.
With songs and hon-ors sound-ing loud Praise ye the sov-ereign Lord. A-MEN.

# GOD'S WORKS OF PROVIDENCE

114

*Praise waiteth for thee, O God, in Zion . . . Psalm 65:1*

From PSALM 65:1-4, 6-9, 11-13  
Henry F. Lyte, 1834  
St. 1, line 1, alt.

MIGDOL L.M.  
Lowell Mason, 1840

1. Praise, Lord, for thee in Zi - on waits; Prayer shall be - siege thy tem - ple gates: All flesh shall to thy throne re - pair, And find, through Christ, sal - va - tion there.
2. Our spir - its faint; our sins pre - vail; Leave not our trem - bling hearts to fail: O thou that hear - est prayer, de - scend, And still be found the sin - ner's Friend.
3. How blest thy saints! how safe - ly led, How sure - ly kept, how rich - ly fed! Sav - iour of all in earth and sea, How hap - py they who rest in thee!
4. Thy hand sets fast the might - y hills, Thy voice the trou - bled o - cean stills; Eve - ning and morn - ing hymn thy praise, And earth thy boun - ty wide dis - plays. A - MEN.

5. The year is with thy goodness crowned;  
Thy clouds drop wealth the world around;  
Through thee the deserts laugh and sing,  
And nature smiles, and owns her King.

6. Lord, on our souls thine influence pour;  
The moral waste within restore:  
O let thy love our spring-tide be,  
And make us all bear fruit to thee.

## 115 THE LORD JESUS CHRIST

*Whom have I in heaven but thee? and there is none
upon earth that I desire beside thee.* Psalm 73:25

Christina G. Rossetti, before 1893

ROSSETTI 8. 10. 10. 4.
William Jeater, 1907

1. None other Lamb, none other Name, None other
Hope in heav'n or earth or sea, None other Hiding-place
from guilt and shame, None beside thee!

2. My faith burns low, my hope burns low; Only my
heart's desire cries out in me By the deep thunder of
its want and woe, Cries out to thee.

3. Lord, thou art Life, though I be dead; Love's fire thou
art, however cold I be: Nor heav'n have I, nor place
to lay my head, Nor home, but thee. A-MEN.

## 116

*I am the way, the truth, and the life: no man cometh unto the Father, but by me.* John 14:6

George W. Doane, 1824

ARLINGTON C. M.
Arr. by Ralph Harrison, 1784,
from Thomas A. Arne, 1762

1. Thou art the Way: to thee alone From sin and death we flee;
2. Thou art the Truth: thy Word alone True wisdom can impart;
3. Thou art the Life: the rending tomb Proclaims thy conquering arm,
4. Thou art the Way, the Truth, the Life: Grant us that Way to know,

# THE ONLY MEDIATOR AND REDEEMER

And he who would the Father seek Must seek him, Lord, by thee.
Thou on-ly canst in-form the mind, And pur-i-fy the heart.
And those who put their trust in thee Nor death nor hell shall harm.
That Truth to keep, that Life to win, Whose joys e-ter-nal flow. A-MEN.

*He shall feed his flock like a shepherd: he shall gather the lambs with his arm . . . Isa. 40:11*

**117**

Ascribed to Clement of Alexandria, c. 200
Tr. by Henry M. Dexter, 1846

BRAUN 6. 6. 4. 6. 6. 6. 4.
Johann G. Braun, 1675

1. Shep-herd of ten-der youth, Guid-ing in love and truth
2. Thou art our ho-ly Lord, The all-sub-du-ing Word,
3. Thou art the Great High Priest, Thou hast pre-pared the feast
4. Ev-er be thou our Guide, Our Shep-herd and our Pride,
5. So now and till we die, Sound we thy prais-es high,

Through de-vious ways: Christ, our tri-um-phant King, We come thy
Heal-er of strife: Thou didst thy-self a-base, That from sin's
Of heav'n-ly love: While in our mor-tal pain, None calls on
Our Staff and Song: Je-sus, thou Christ of God, By thy per-
And joy-ful sing: In-fants, and the glad throng Who to thy

Name to sing; Hith-er our chil-dren bring, To shout thy praise.
deep dis-grace Thou might-est save our race, And give us life.
thee in vain: Help thou dost not dis-dain, Help from a-bove.
en-nial Word, Lead us where thou hast trod; Make our faith strong.
church be-long, U-nite to swell the song To Christ our King. A-MEN.

# 118. THE LORD JESUS CHRIST

*Jesus Christ: whom having not seen, ye love . . . I Peter 1: 7-8*

MEIRIONYDD 7. 6. 7. 6. D.
Welsh hymn melody
Ascribed to William Lloyd, 1840

Frances R. Havergal, 1870

1. O Saviour, precious Saviour, Whom yet unseen we love,
O Name of might and favor, All other names above;
We worship thee, we bless thee, To thee alone we sing;
We praise thee, and confess thee Our holy Lord and King.

2. O Bringer of salvation, Who wondrously hast wrought,
Thyself the revelation Of love beyond our thought;
We worship thee, we bless thee, To thee alone we sing;
We praise thee, and confess thee Our gracious Lord and King.

3. In thee all fulness dwelleth, All grace and power divine:
The glory that excelleth, O Son of God, is thine;
We worship thee, we bless thee, To thee alone we sing;
We praise thee, and confess thee Our glorious Lord and King.

4. O grant the consummation Of this our song above
In endless adoration, And everlasting love;
Then shall we praise and bless thee Where perfect praises ring,
And evermore confess thee Our Saviour and our King. A-MEN.

Music used by permission of the Executors of the late Dr. Basil Harwood.

# THE ONLY MEDIATOR AND REDEEMER 119

*The bridegroom cometh; go ye out to meet him.* Matt. 25:6

Paul Gerhardt, 1653, cento
Tr. composite

ST. THEODULPH 7. 6. 7. 6. D.
Melchior Teschner, c. 1615

1. O Lord, how shall I meet thee, How wel-come thee a-right?
   Thy peo-ple long to greet thee, My Hope, my heart's De-light!
   O, kin-dle, Lord, most ho-ly, Thy lamp with-in my breast
   To do in spir-it low-ly All that may please thee best.

2. Love caused thine in-car-na-tion, Love brought thee down to me;
   Thy thirst for my sal-va-tion Pro-cured my lib-er-ty.
   O love be-yond all tell-ing, That led thee to em-brace,
   In love all love ex-cel-ling, Our lost and fall-en race!

3. Re-joice, then, ye sad-heart-ed, Who sit in deep-est gloom,
   Who mourn o'er joys de-part-ed And trem-ble at your doom.
   De-spair not, he is near you, Yea, stand-ing at the door,
   Who best can help and cheer you And bids you weep no more.

4. Sin's debt, that fear-ful bur-den, Let not your souls dis-tress;
   Your guilt the Lord will par-don And cov-er by his grace.
   He comes, for men pro-cur-ing The peace of sin for-giv'n,
   For all God's sons se-cur-ing Their her-it-age in heav'n. A-MEN.

## 120 THE LORD JESUS CHRIST

*The dayspring from on high hath visited us.* Luke 1:78

Latin hymn, 7th or 8th century  
Tr. by John Chandler, 1837

BRADFORD C. M.  
Arr. from George Frederick Handel, 1741

1. O Christ, our hope, our heart's de-sire, Re-demp-tion's on - ly spring!
   Cre - a - tor of the world art thou, Its Sav-iour and its King.
2. How vast the mer - cy and the love Which laid our sins on thee,
   And led thee to a cru - el death, To set thy peo - ple free.
3. But now the bands of death are burst, The ran - som has been paid;
   And thou art on thy Fa - ther's throne, In glo - rious robes ar - rayed.
4. O Christ, be thou our last - ing joy, Our ev - er great re - ward!
   Our on - ly glo - ry may it be To glo - ry in the Lord. A - MEN.

## 121

*That ye ... may be able to comprehend ... what is the breadth, and length, and depth, and height; and to know the love of Christ ...* Eph. 3:17-19

Anon., Latin, 15th century  
Tr. by Benjamin Webb, 1854 (Text of 1871)

MELCOMBE L. M.  
Samuel Webbe, 1782

1. O, love, how deep, how broad, how high, How pass - ing thought and fan - ta - sy,
   That God, the Son of God, should take Our mor - tal form for mor-tals' sake!
2. For us bap-tized, for us he bore His ho - ly fast, and hun-gered sore,
   For us temp-ta-tions sharp he knew, For us the tempt-er o - ver-threw.
3. For us to wick-ed men be-trayed, Scourged, mocked, in crown of thorns ar-rayed;
   For us he bore the cross-'s death, For us at length gave up his breath.
4. For us he rose from death a - gain, For us he went on high to reign,
   For us he sent his Spir-it here To guide, to strength-en and to cheer.
5. All hon-or, laud, and glo - ry be, O Je - sus, vir - gin-born, to thee;
   Whom with the Fa - ther we a - dore, And Ho - ly Ghost, for ev - er - more. A-MEN.

# HIS DEITY

## 122

*We beheld his glory, the glory as of the only begotten of the Father... John 1:14*

Aurelius Clemens Prudentius, 348-413
Tr. by John Mason Neale, 1818-1866

PRAISE, MY SOUL 8. 7. 8. 7. 8. 7.
Sir John Goss, 1869

1. Of the Father's love be - got - ten Ere the worlds be-gan to be,
   He is Al - pha and O - me - ga, He the source, the end-ing he,
   Of the things that are, that have been, And that fu-ture years shall see.

2. This is he whom heav'n-taught sing - ers Sang of old with one ac - cord,
   Whom the Script-ures of the proph-ets Prom-ised in their faith-ful word;
   Now he shines, the long-ex - pect-ed; Let cre - a-tion praise its Lord.

3. O ye heights of heav'n, a - dore him; An - gel hosts, his prais-es sing;
   All do - min - ions, bow be - fore him, And ex - tol our God and King;
   Let no tongue on earth be si - lent, Ev-'ry voice in con - cert ring. A-MEN.

4. Thee let age and thee let manhood,
   Thee let boys in chorus sing;
   Matrons, virgins, little maidens,
   With glad voices answering;
   Let their guileless songs re-echo,
   And their heart its music bring.

5. Christ, to thee, with God the Father,
   And, O Holy Ghost, to thee,
   Hymn, and chant, and high thanksgiving,
   And unwearied praises be,
   Honor, glory, and dominion,
   And eternal victory.

## 123 THE LORD JESUS CHRIST

*The people that walked in darkness have seen a great light... Isa. 9:2*

John Morison, 1781, alt.

LOBT GOTT, IHR CHRISTEN C. M. with repeat
Nikolaus Herman, 1554

1. The peo - ple that in dark - ness sat A glo - rious light have seen; The light has shined on them who long In shades of death have been, In shades of death have been.
2. To hail thee, Sun of Right - eous - ness, The gath - 'ring na - tions come; They joy as when the reap - ers bear Their har - vest treas - ures home, Their har - vest treas - ures home.
3. For thou their bur - den dost re - move And break the ty - rant's rod, As in the day when Mid - ian fell Be - fore the sword of God, Be - fore the sword of God.
4. To us a Child of hope is born, To us a Son is giv'n, And on his shoul - der ev - er rests All pow'r in earth and heav'n, All pow'r in earth and heav'n.
5. His name shall be the Prince of Peace, The Ev - er - last - ing Lord, The Won - der - ful, the Coun - sel - lor, The God by all a - dored, The God by all a - dored. A - MEN.

6. His righteous government and pow'r
Shall over all extend;
On judgment and on justice based,
His reign shall have no end.

7. Lord Jesus, reign in us, we pray,
And make us thine alone,
Who with the Father ever art
And Holy Spirit, one.

# HIS DEITY 124

*That at the name of Jesus every knee should bow...and that every tongue should confess that Jesus Christ is Lord... Phil. 2:10, 11*

Caroline M. Noel, 1870
St. 3, line 4, alt.

ST. CEPHAS 6. 5. 6. 5. D.
Howard A. Crosbie, 1875

1. At the Name of Jesus Ev-'ry knee shall bow,
   Ev-'ry tongue con-fess him King of Glo-ry now.
   'Tis the Fa-ther's pleas-ure We should call him Lord,
   Who from the be-gin-ning Was the might-y Word.

2. At his voice cre-a-tion Sprang at once to sight,
   All the an-gel fac-es, All the hosts of light,
   Thrones and dom-i-na-tions, Stars up-on their way,
   All the heav'n-ly or-ders In their great ar-ray.

3. Hum-bled for a sea-son To re-ceive a Name
   From the lips of sin-ners Un-to whom he came,
   Faith-ful-ly he bore it Spot-less to the last,
   Brought it back vic-to-rious, When from death he passed.

4. In your hearts en-throne him; There let him sub-due
   All that is not ho-ly, All that is not true:
   Crown him as your Cap-tain In temp-ta-tion's hour:
   Let his will en-fold you In its light and pow'r.

5. Broth-ers, this Lord Je-sus Shall re-turn a-gain,
   With his Fa-ther's glo-ry, With his an-gel train;
   For all wreaths of em-pire Meet up-on his brow,
   And our hearts con-fess him King of Glo-ry now. A-MEN.

# 125 THE LORD JESUS CHRIST

*My heart is inditing a good matter: I speak of the things
which I have made touching the king... Psalm 45:1*

From PSALM 45:1-10
The Psalter, 1912

LEOMINSTER S.M.D.
George William Martin, 1862
Har. by Sir Arthur S. Sullivan, 1874

1. My heart doth o-ver-flow, A good-ly theme is mine;
My ea-ger tongue with joy-ful song Doth praise the King di-vine.
Su-preme-ly fair thou art, Thy lips with grace o'er-flow;
His rich-est bless-ings ev-er-more Doth God on thee be-stow.

2. Now gird thee with thy sword, O strong and might-y One,
In splen-did maj-es-ty ar-rayed, More glo-rious than the sun.
Tri-um-phant-ly ride forth For meek-ness, truth, and right;
Thine arm shall gain the vic-to-ry In won-drous deeds of might.

3. Thy strength shall o-ver-come All those that hate the King,
And un-der thy do-min-ion strong The na-tions thou shalt bring.
Thy roy-al throne, O God, For ev-er-more shall stand;
E-ter-nal truth and jus-tice wield The scep-tre in thy hand.

4. Since thou art sin-less found, The Lord, thy God con-fessed,
A-noint-eth thee with per-fect joy, Thou art su-preme-ly blessed.
Thy gar-ments breathe of myrrh And spic-es sweet and rare;
Glad strains of heav'n-ly mu-sic ring Through-out thy pal-ace fair.

5. A-mid thy glo-rious train Kings' daugh-ters wait-ing stand,
And fair-est gems be-deck thy bride, The queen at thy right hand.
O roy-al bride, give heed, And to my words at-tend;
For Christ, the King, for-sake the world And ev-'ry for-mer friend. A-MEN.

# HIS PRAISE 126

*I heard the voice of many angels round about the throne...*
*saying with a loud voice, Worthy is the Lamb... Rev. 5:11, 12*

Samuel Medley, 1789  
ARIEL 8.8.6.8.8.6.6.  
Arr. from Mozart by Lowell Mason, 1836

1. O could I speak the match-less worth,
2. I'd sing the pre-cious blood he spilt,
3. I'd sing the char-ac-ters he bears,
4. Well, the de-light-ful day will come

O could I sound the glo-ries forth, Which in my Sav-iour shine,
My ran-som from the dread-ful guilt, Of sin, and wrath Di-vine:
And all the forms of love he wears, Ex-alt-ed on his throne:
When my dear Lord will bring me home, And I shall see his face;

I'd soar, and touch the heav'n-ly strings, And vie with Ga-briel while he sings
I'd sing his glo-rious right-eous-ness, In which all-per-fect, heav'n-ly dress
In loft-iest songs of sweet-est praise, I would to ev-er-last-ing days
Then with my Sav-iour, Broth-er, Friend, A blest e-ter-ni-ty I'll spend,

In notes al-most di-vine, In notes al-most di-vine.
My soul shall ev-er shine, My soul shall ev-er shine.
Make all his glo-ries known, Make all his glo-ries known.
Tri-um-phant in his grace, Tri-um-phant in his grace. A-MEN.

# 127 THE LORD JESUS CHRIST

*Unto him that loved us, and washed us from our sins in his own blood... be glory and dominion... Rev. 1:5, 6*

John Newton, 1774

ALL SAINTS OLD 8. 7. 8. 7. 7. 7.
Darmstadt *Gesangbuch*, 1698

1. Let us love, and sing, and won-der, Let us praise the Sav-iour's name! He has hushed the law's loud thun-der, He has quenched Mount Sin-ai's flame; He has washed us with his blood, He has brought us nigh to God.
2. Let us love the Lord who bought us, Pit-ied us when en-e-mies, Called us by his grace, and taught us, Gave us ears and gave us eyes: He has washed us with his blood, He pre-sents our souls to God.
3. Let us sing, though fierce temp-ta-tion Threat-en hard to bear us down! For the Lord, our strong sal-va-tion, Holds in view the con-qu'ror's crown, He who washed us with his blood, Soon will bring us home to God.
4. Let us won-der; grace and jus-tice Join, and point to mer-cy's store; When through grace in Christ our trust is, Jus-tice smiles, and asks no more: He who washed us with his blood, Has se-cured our way to God.
5. Let us praise, and join the cho-rus Of the saints en-throned on high; Here they trust-ed him be-fore us, Now their prais-es fill the sky: "Thou hast washed us with thy blood; Thou art wor-thy, Lamb of God!" A-MEN.

*For a lower setting of this tune, see No. 602.*

# HIS PRAISE

**128**

*Worthy is the Lamb that was slain to receive power, and riches, and wisdom, and strength, and honour, and glory, and blessing.* Rev. 5:12

John Bakewell, 1757
Enlarged by Martin Madan, 1760
Alt. by Augustus M. Toplady, 1776

ST. HILDA 8. 7. 8. 7. D.
Sir Joseph Barnby, 1861

1. Hail, thou once de-spi-sed Je-sus, Hail, thou Gal-i-le-an King!
   Thou didst suf-fer to re-lease us: Thou didst free sal-va-tion bring.
   Hail, thou ag-on-iz-ing Sav-iour, Bear-er of our sin and shame!
   By thy mer-its we find fa-vor; Life is giv-en through thy Name.

2. Pas-chal Lamb, by God ap-point-ed, All our sins were on thee laid;
   By al-migh-ty Love a-noint-ed, Thou hast full a-tone-ment made:
   All thy peo-ple are for-giv-en Through the vir-tue of thy blood;
   O-pened is the gate of heav-en, Peace is made 'twixt man and God.

3. Je-sus, hail! en-throned in glo-ry, There for ev-er to a-bide;
   All the heav'n-ly hosts a-dore thee, Seat-ed at thy Fa-ther's side:
   There for sin-ners thou art plead-ing; There thou dost our place pre-pare;
   Ev-er for us in-ter-ced-ing, Till in glo-ry we ap-pear.

4. Wor-ship, hon-or, pow'r, and bless-ing Thou art wor-thy to re-ceive:
   Loud-est prais-es with-out ceas-ing, Meet it is for us to give.
   Help, ye bright an-gel-ic spir-its, Bring your sweet-est, no-blest lays;
   Help to sing our Sav-iour's mer-its, Help to chant Im-man-uel's praise. A-MEN.

## 129 THE LORD JESUS CHRIST

*Thou art fairer than the children of men... Psalm 45:2*

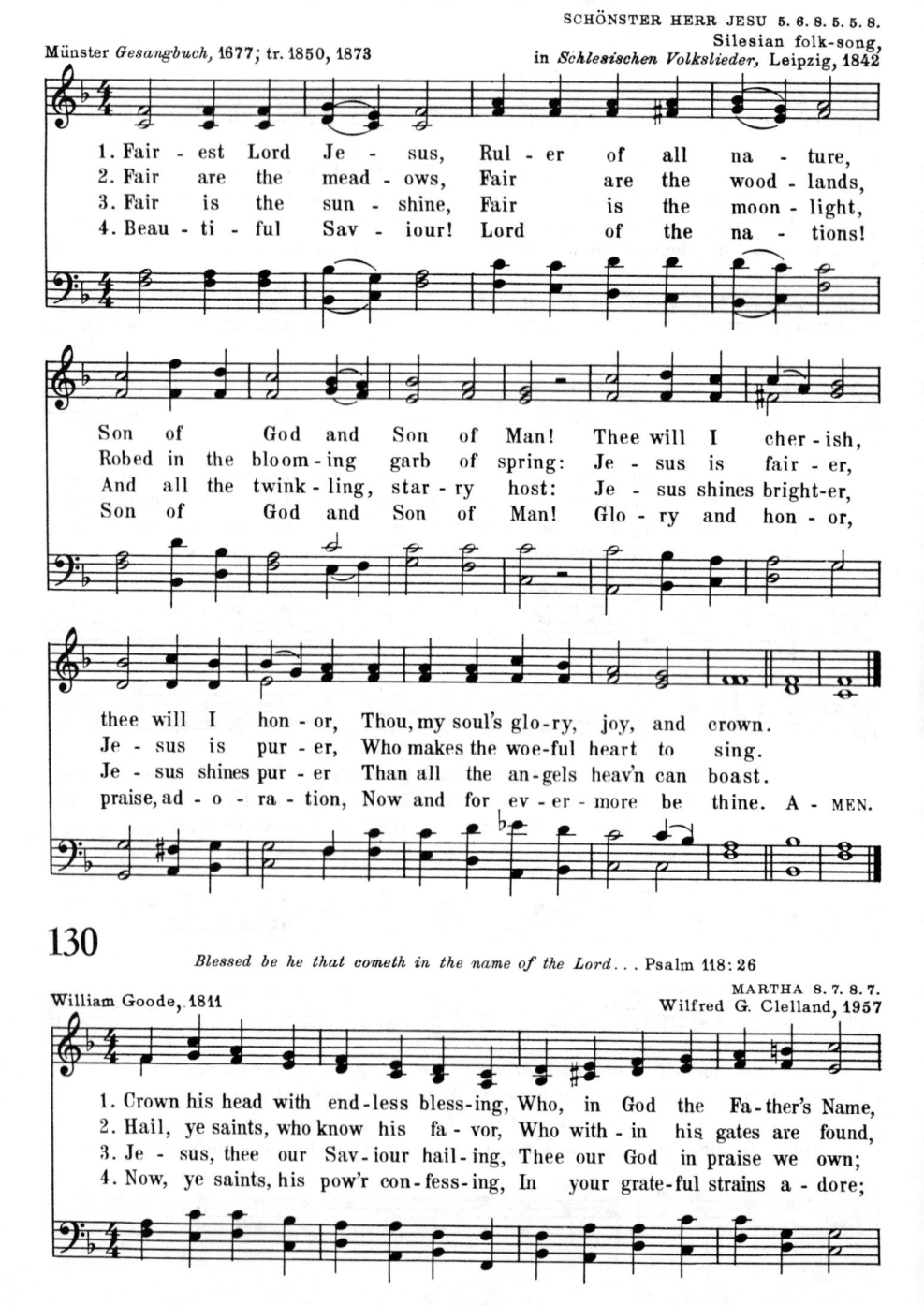

SCHÖNSTER HERR JESU 5.6.8.5.5.8.
Silesian folk-song,
Münster *Gesangbuch*, 1677; tr. 1850, 1873
in *Schlesischen Volkslieder*, Leipzig, 1842

1. Fairest Lord Jesus, Ruler of all nature,
Son of God and Son of Man!
thee will I honor, Thou, my soul's glory, joy, and crown.

2. Fair are the meadows, Fair are the woodlands,
Robed in the blooming garb of spring:
Jesus is fairer, Jesus is purer, Who makes the woeful heart to sing.

3. Fair is the sunshine, Fair is the moonlight,
And all the twinkling, starry host:
Jesus shines brighter, Jesus shines purer Than all the angels heav'n can boast.

4. Beautiful Saviour! Lord of the nations!
Son of God and Son of Man!
Glory and honor, praise, adoration, Now and for evermore be thine. A-MEN.

## 130

*Blessed be he that cometh in the name of the Lord... Psalm 118:26*

MARTHA 8.7.8.7.
William Goode, 1811
Wilfred G. Clelland, 1957

1. Crown his head with endless blessing, Who, in God the Father's Name,
2. Hail, ye saints, who know his favor, Who within his gates are found,
3. Jesus, thee our Saviour hailing, Thee our God in praise we own;
4. Now, ye saints, his pow'r confessing, In your grateful strains adore;

# HIS PRAISE

With com-pas-sions nev-er ceas-ing, Comes sal-va-tion to pro-claim.
Hail, ye saints, th' ex-alt-ed Sav-iour, Let his courts with praise re-sound.
High-est hon-ors, nev-er fail-ing, Rise e - ter - nal round thy throne.
For his mer-cy, nev-er ceas-ing, Flows, and flows for ev - er-more. A - MEN.

*His praise shall continually be in my mouth.* Psalm 34:1

**131**

Anon., German, c. 1800
Tr. by Edward Caswall, 1853, 1858

LAUDES DOMINI 6.6.6.D.
Sir Joseph Barnby, 1868

1. When morn-ing gilds the skies, My heart a - wak-ing cries
2. When sleep her balm de - nies, My si - lent spir - it sighs,
3. Does sad-ness fill my mind? A so - lace here I find,
4. In heav'n's e - ter - nal bliss The love - liest strain is this,
5. Let earth's wide cir - cle round In joy - ful notes re - sound,
6. Be this, while life is mine, My can - ti - cle di - vine,

May Je - sus Christ be praised: A - like at work and prayer
May Je - sus Christ be praised: When e - vil thoughts mo - lest,
May Je - sus Christ be praised: Or fades my earth - ly bliss?
May Je - sus Christ be praised: The pow'rs of dark - ness fear,
May Je - sus Christ be praised: Let air and sea and sky,
May Je - sus Christ be praised: Be this th' e - ter - nal song,

To Je - sus I re - pair; May Je - sus Christ be praised.
With this I shield my breast, May Je - sus Christ be praised.
My com - fort still is this, May Je - sus Christ be praised.
When this sweet chant they hear, May Je - sus Christ be praised.
From depth to height, re - ply, May Je - sus Christ be praised.
Through all the a - ges on, May Je - sus Christ be praised. A-MEN.

# 132 THE LORD JESUS CHRIST

*Christ came, who is over all, God blessed for ever.* Rom. 9:5

Joachim Neander, 1680
Tr. by William J. Schaefer, 1938

WUNDERBARER KÖNIG 6.6.8.6.6.8.3.3.6.6.
Joachim Neander, 1680

1. Won-drous King, all-glo-rious, Sov-'reign Lord vic-to-rious, O, re-ceive our
praise with fa - vor! From thee welled God's kind-ness Tho' we in our blind-ness
Strayed from thee, our bless-ed Sav - iour. Strength-en thou, Help us now;
Let our tongues be sing-ing, Thee our prais-es bring-ing.

2. Heav-ens, spread the sto - ry Of our Mak-er's glo-ry, All the pomp of
earth ob - scur - ing. Sun, thy rays be send-ing, Thy bright beams ex - pend-ing,
Light to all the earth as-sur - ing. Moon and star, Praise a - far
Him who glo - rious made you; The vast heav-ens aid you.

3. O my soul, re-joic-ing, Sing, thy prais-es voic-ing, Sing, with hymns of
faith a - dore him! All who here have be - ing, Shout, your voic-es free-ing,
Bow down in the dust be - fore him. He is God Sab - a - oth;
Praise a - lone the Sav - iour, Here and there for ev - er.

4. Hal - le - lu - jahs ren-der To the Lord most ten-der, Ye who know and
love the Sav - iour. Hal - le - lu - jahs sing ye, Ye re-deemed, O, bring ye
Hearts that yield him glad be - hav - ior. Blest are ye End - less - ly;
Sin - less there for ev - er, Ye shall laud him ev - er. A-MEN.

Words used by permission of Concordia Publishing House.

# HIS PRAISE

**133**

*And he leaping up stood, and walked, and entered with them into the temple, walking, and leaping, and praising God. Acts 3:8*

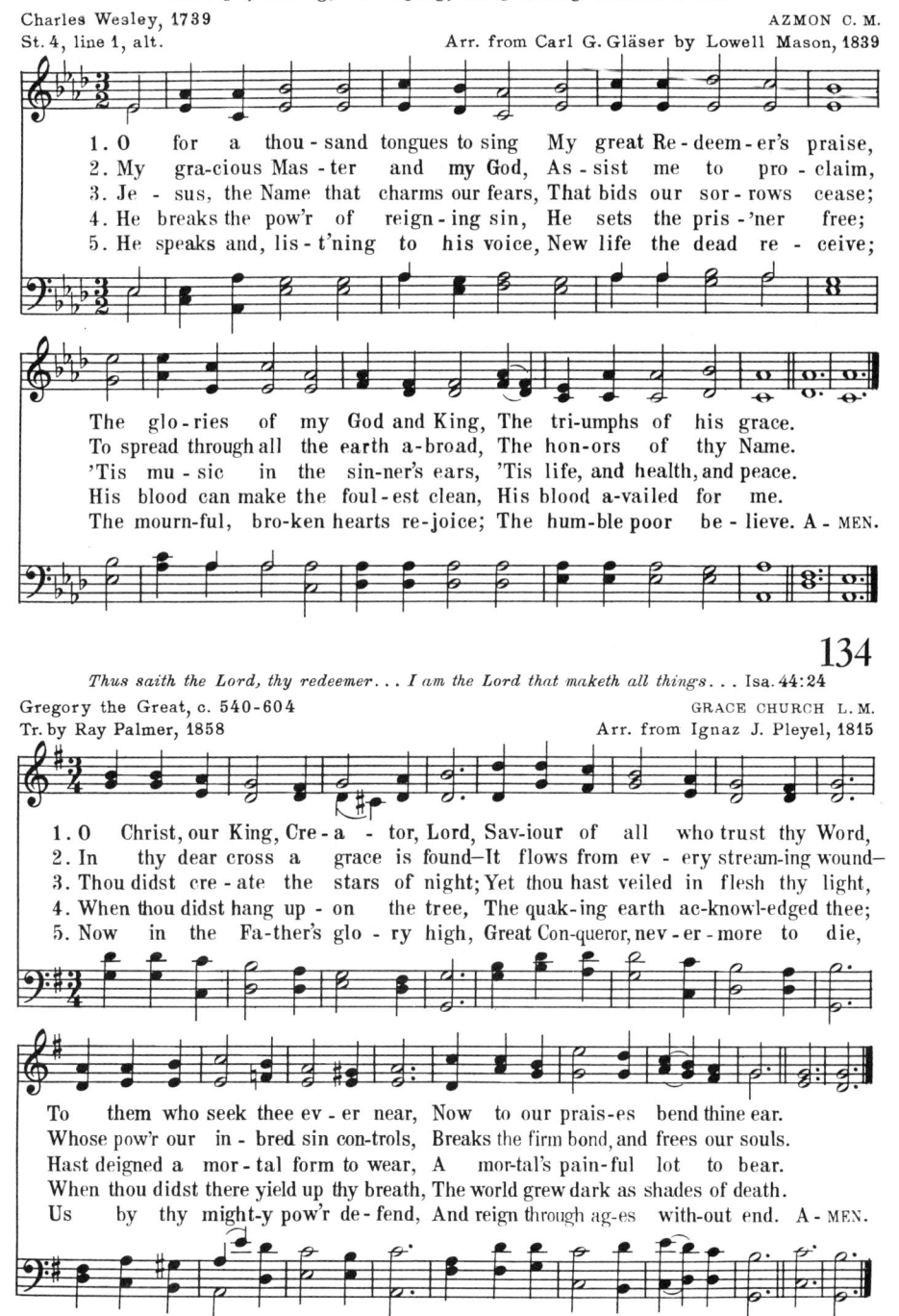

Charles Wesley, 1739
St. 4, line 1, alt.

AZMON C. M.
Arr. from Carl G. Gläser by Lowell Mason, 1839

1. O for a thou-sand tongues to sing My great Re-deem-er's praise,
2. My gra-cious Mas-ter and my God, As-sist me to pro-claim,
3. Je-sus, the Name that charms our fears, That bids our sor-rows cease;
4. He breaks the pow'r of reign-ing sin, He sets the pris-'ner free;
5. He speaks and, lis-t'ning to his voice, New life the dead re-ceive;

The glo-ries of my God and King, The tri-umphs of his grace.
To spread through all the earth a-broad, The hon-ors of thy Name.
'Tis mu-sic in the sin-ner's ears, 'Tis life, and health, and peace.
His blood can make the foul-est clean, His blood a-vailed for me.
The mourn-ful, bro-ken hearts re-joice; The hum-ble poor be-lieve. A-MEN.

**134**

*Thus saith the Lord, thy redeemer... I am the Lord that maketh all things... Isa. 44:24*

Gregory the Great, c. 540-604
Tr. by Ray Palmer, 1858

GRACE CHURCH L. M.
Arr. from Ignaz J. Pleyel, 1815

1. O Christ, our King, Cre-a-tor, Lord, Sav-iour of all who trust thy Word,
2. In thy dear cross a grace is found—It flows from ev-ery stream-ing wound—
3. Thou didst cre-ate the stars of night; Yet thou hast veiled in flesh thy light,
4. When thou didst hang up-on the tree, The quak-ing earth ac-knowl-edged thee;
5. Now in the Fa-ther's glo-ry high, Great Con-queror, nev-er-more to die,

To them who seek thee ev-er near, Now to our prais-es bend thine ear.
Whose pow'r our in-bred sin con-trols, Breaks the firm bond, and frees our souls.
Hast deigned a mor-tal form to wear, A mor-tal's pain-ful lot to bear.
When thou didst there yield up thy breath, The world grew dark as shades of death.
Us by thy might-y pow'r de-fend, And reign through ag-es with-out end. A-MEN.

## 135 THE LORD JESUS CHRIST

*Who gave himself for our sins, that he might deliver us from this present evil world... Gal. 1:4*

Strasbourg *Psalter,* 1545
TOULON 10. 10. 10. 10.
Geneva *Psalter,* 1551

1. I greet thee, who my sure Redeemer art,
2. Thou art the King of mercy and of grace,
3. Thou art the Life, by which alone we live,
4. Thou hast the true and perfect gentleness,
5. Our hope is in no other save in thee;

My only trust and Saviour of my heart,
Reigning omnipotent in ev'ry place:
And all our substance and our strength receive;
No harshness hast thou and no bitterness:
Our faith is built upon thy promise free;

Who pain didst undergo for my poor sake;
So come, O King, and our whole being sway;
O comfort us in death's approaching hour,
Make us to taste the sweet grace found in thee
O grant to us such stronger hope and sure

I pray thee from our hearts all cares to take.
Shine on us with the light of thy pure day.
Strong-hearted then to face it by thy pow'r.
And ever stay in thy sweet unity.
That we can boldly conquer and endure. A-MEN.

St. 3, lines 3 and 4, st. 5, lines 3 and 4, tr. alt.

# HIS PRAISE

**136**

*Our Lord and Saviour Jesus Christ. To him be glory both now and for ever.* II Peter 3:18

Charles Wesley, 1744  
St. 3, line 3, alt.

LYONS 10. 10. 11. 11.  
Arr. from J. Michael Haydn, 1737-1806

1. Ye servants of God, your Master proclaim, And publish abroad his wonderful Name; The Name, all-victorious, of Jesus extol; His kingdom is glorious, and rules over all.
2. God ruleth on high, almighty to save; And still he is nigh— his presence we have: The great congregation his triumph shall sing, Ascribing salvation to Jesus, our King.
3. Salvation to God who sits on the throne! Let all cry aloud and honor the Son: The praises of Jesus the angels proclaim, Fall down on their faces and worship the Lamb.
4. Then let us adore, and give him his right, All glory and pow'r, and wisdom and might, All honor and blessing, with angels above, And thanks never ceasing for infinite love. A-MEN.

St. 4, line 4, alt.

## 137 THE LORD JESUS CHRIST

*Joy shall be in heaven over one sinner that repenteth, more than over ninety and nine just persons, which need no repentance.* Luke 15:7

Elizabeth C. Clephane, 1868

THE NINETY AND NINE irregular with repeat

Ira D. Sankey, 1874

1. There were nine-ty and nine that safe-ly lay In the shel-ter of the fold, But one was out on the hills a-way, Far off from the gates of gold— A-way on the moun-tains wild and bare, A-way from the ten-der
2. "Lord, thou hast here thy nine-ty and nine; Are they not e-nough for thee?" But the Shep-herd made an-swer: "This of mine Has wan-dered a-way from me, And al-though the road be rough and steep, I go to the des-ert to
3. But none of the ran-somed ev - er knew How deep were the wa-ters crossed; Nor how dark was the night that the Lord passed thro' Ere he found his sheep that was lost. Out in the des-ert he heard its cry— Sick and help-less, and
4. "Lord, whence are those blood-drops all the way That mark out the moun-tain's track?" "They were shed for one who had gone a-stray Ere the Shep-herd could bring him back." "Lord, whence are thy hands so rent and torn?" "They're pierced to-night by
5. But all thro' the moun-tains, thun - der-riv'n, And up from the rock-y steep, There a-rose a glad cry to the gate of heav'n, "Re - joice! I have found my sheep!" And the an - gels ech-oed a-round the throne, "Re - joice, for the Lord brings

# HIS LOVE AND GRACE

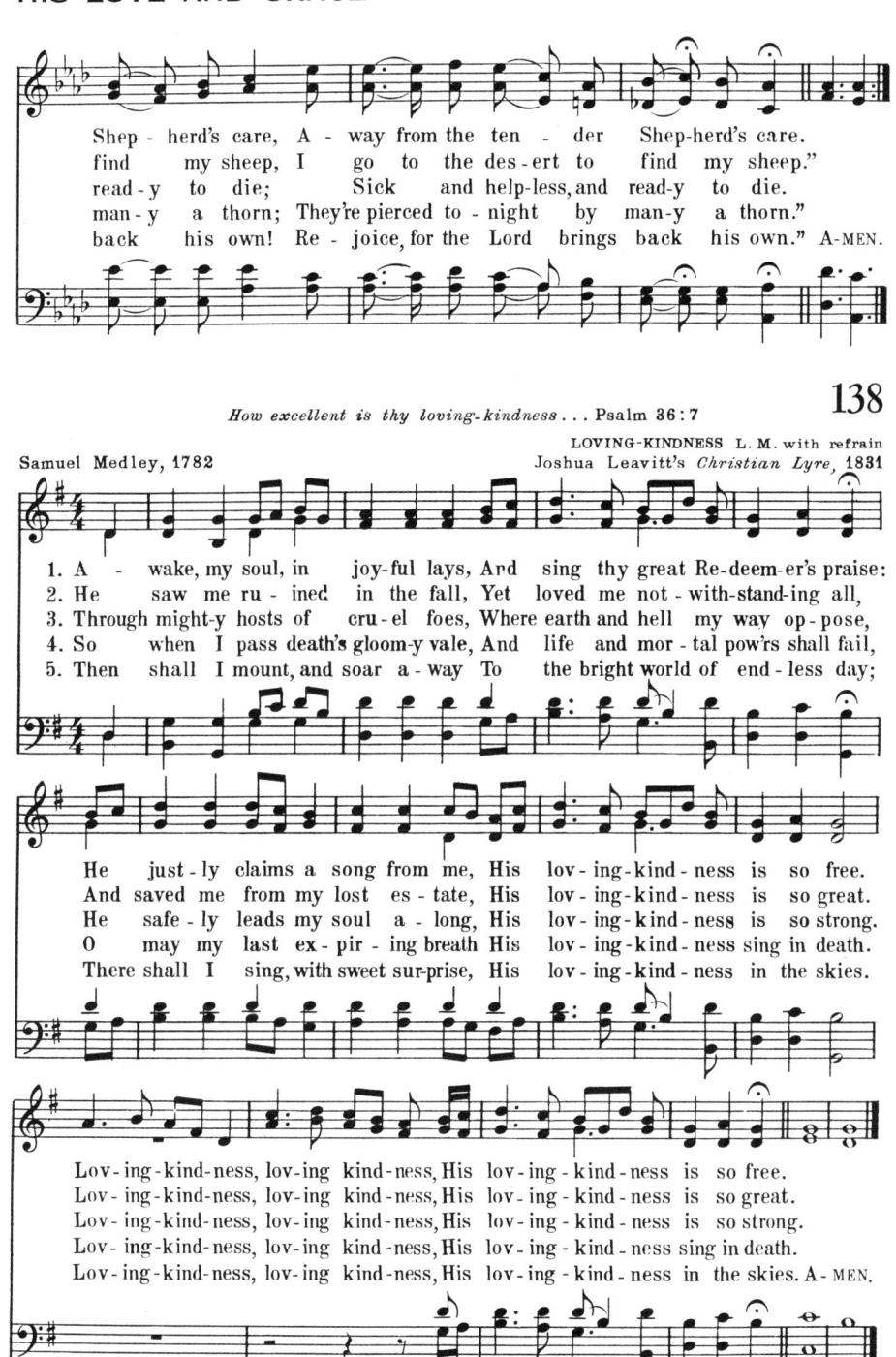

Shep - herd's care, A - way from the ten - der Shep-herd's care.
find my sheep, I go to the des - ert to find my sheep."
read - y to die; Sick and help-less, and read - y to die.
man - y a thorn; They're pierced to - night by man - y a thorn."
back his own! Re - joice, for the Lord brings back his own." A-MEN.

*How excellent is thy loving-kindness... Psalm 36:7*

## 138

LOVING-KINDNESS L. M. with refrain
Samuel Medley, 1782
Joshua Leavitt's *Christian Lyre*, 1831

1. A - wake, my soul, in joy-ful lays, And sing thy great Re-deem-er's praise:
2. He saw me ru - ined in the fall, Yet loved me not - with-stand-ing all,
3. Through might-y hosts of cru - el foes, Where earth and hell my way op - pose,
4. So when I pass death's gloom-y vale, And life and mor - tal pow'rs shall fail,
5. Then shall I mount, and soar a - way To the bright world of end - less day;

He just - ly claims a song from me, His lov - ing-kind - ness is so free.
And saved me from my lost es - tate, His lov - ing-kind - ness is so great.
He safe - ly leads my soul a - long, His lov - ing-kind - ness is so strong.
O may my last ex - pir - ing breath His lov - ing-kind - ness sing in death.
There shall I sing, with sweet sur-prise, His lov - ing-kind - ness in the skies.

Lov - ing-kind-ness, lov - ing kind - ness, His lov - ing - kind - ness is so free.
Lov - ing-kind-ness, lov - ing kind - ness, His lov - ing - kind - ness is so great.
Lov - ing-kind-ness, lov - ing kind - ness, His lov - ing - kind - ness is so strong.
Lov - ing-kind-ness, lov - ing kind - ness, His lov - ing - kind - ness sing in death.
Lov - ing-kind-ness, lov - ing kind - ness, His lov - ing - kind - ness in the skies. A-MEN.

# 139 THE LORD JESUS CHRIST

*Looking unto Jesus the author and finisher of our faith . . . Heb. 12:2*

Jean Sophia Pigott, 1876, alt.

RESTING 8. 7. 8. 5. D. with refrain
James Mountain, 1843-1933

1. Je - sus, I am rest - ing, rest-ing In the joy of what thou art;
   I am find - ing out the great-ness Of thy lov - ing heart.
   Thou hast bid me gaze up - on thee, As thy beau - ty fills my soul,
   For by thy trans - form - ing pow - er, Thou hast made me whole.

2. O how great thy lov - ing-kind-ness, Vast - er, broad - er than the sea!
   O how mar - vel - ous thy good-ness Lav - ished all on me!
   Yes, I rest in thee, Be - lov - ed, Know what wealth of grace is thine,
   Know thy cer - tain - ty of prom - ise And have made it mine.

3. Sim - ply trust - ing thee, Lord Je - sus, I be - hold thee as thou art,
   And thy love, so pure, so change-less, Sat - is - fies my heart;
   Sat - is - fies its deep-est long-ings, Meets, sup - plies its ev - 'ry need,
   Com - pass - eth me round with bless - ings: Thine is love in - deed.

4. Ev - er lift thy face up - on me As I work and wait for thee;
   Rest - ing 'neath thy smile, Lord Je - sus, Earth's dark shad - ows flee.
   Bright-ness of my Fa - ther's glo - ry, Sun - shine of my Fa - ther's face,
   Keep me ev - er trust - ing, rest - ing, Fill me with thy grace.

# HIS LOVE AND GRACE

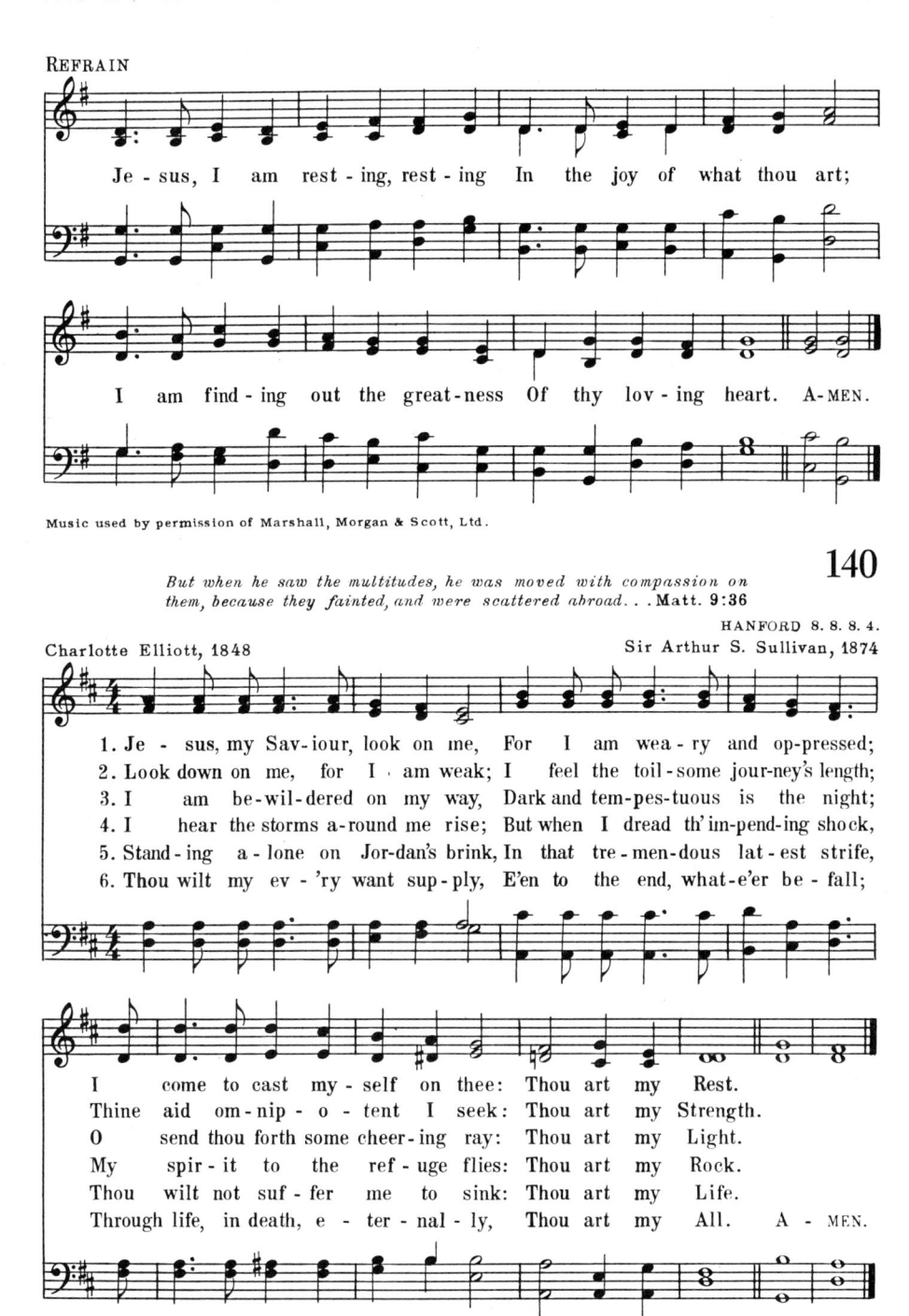

**REFRAIN**

Je-sus, I am rest-ing, rest-ing In the joy of what thou art;
I am find-ing out the great-ness Of thy lov-ing heart. A-MEN.

Music used by permission of Marshall, Morgan & Scott, Ltd.

*But when he saw the multitudes, he was moved with compassion on them, because they fainted, and were scattered abroad...Matt. 9:36*

**140**

HANFORD 8. 8. 8. 4.

Charlotte Elliott, 1848      Sir Arthur S. Sullivan, 1874

1. Je - sus, my Sav-iour, look on me, For I am wea-ry and op-pressed;
2. Look down on me, for I am weak; I feel the toil-some jour-ney's length;
3. I am be-wil-dered on my way, Dark and tem-pes-tuous is the night;
4. I hear the storms a-round me rise; But when I dread th' im-pend-ing shock,
5. Stand-ing a-lone on Jor-dan's brink, In that tre-men-dous lat-est strife,
6. Thou wilt my ev-'ry want sup-ply, E'en to the end, what-e'er be-fall;

I come to cast my-self on thee: Thou art my Rest.
Thine aid om-nip-o-tent I seek: Thou art my Strength.
O send thou forth some cheer-ing ray: Thou art my Light.
My spir-it to the ref-uge flies: Thou art my Rock.
Thou wilt not suf-fer me to sink: Thou art my Life.
Through life, in death, e-ter-nal-ly, Thou art my All. A-MEN.

## 141 THE LORD JESUS CHRIST

*The Lord is my shepherd; I shall not want.* Psalm 23:1

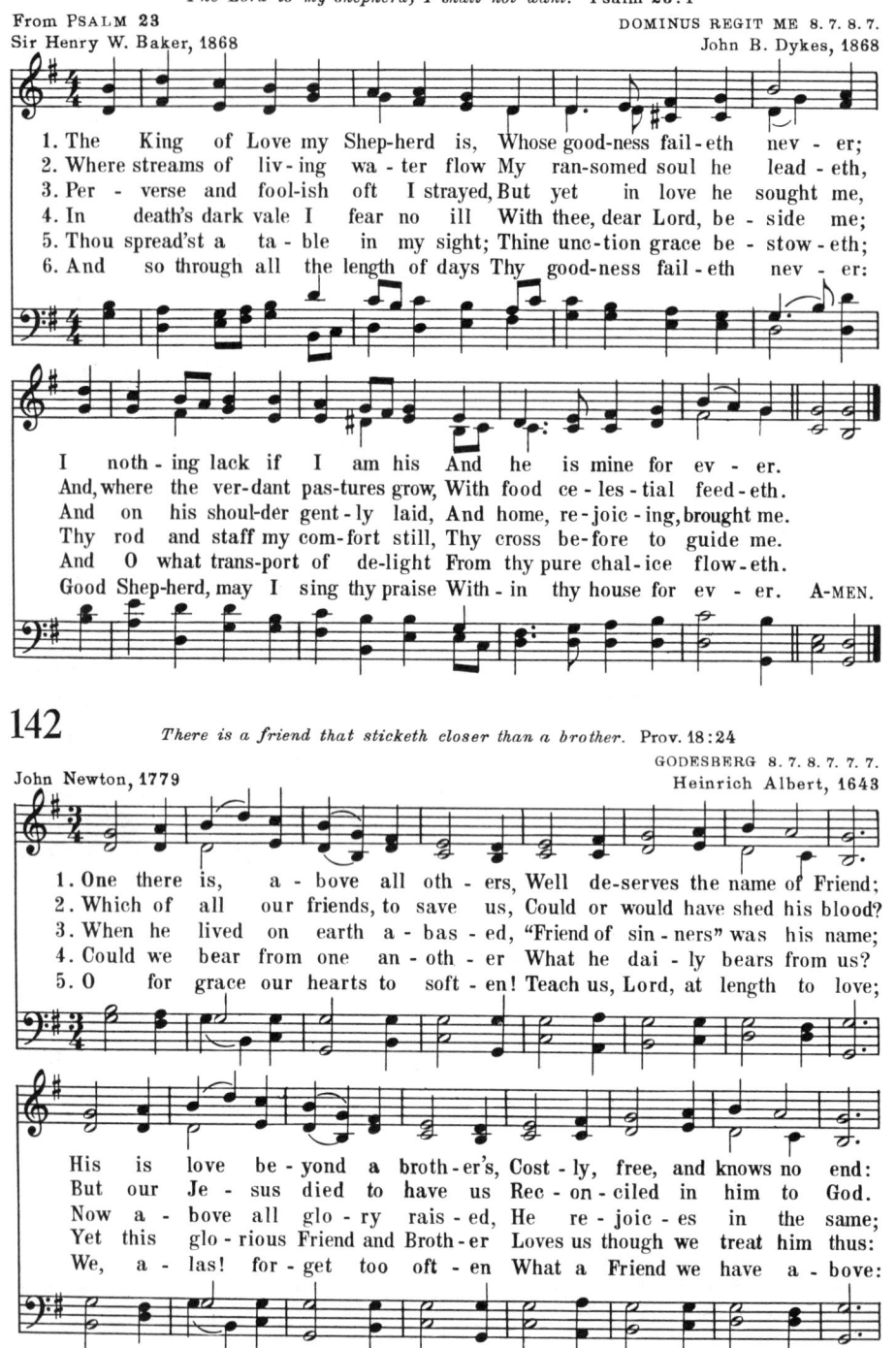

From PSALM 23
Sir Henry W. Baker, 1868

DOMINUS REGIT ME 8.7.8.7.
John B. Dykes, 1868

1. The King of Love my Shep-herd is, Whose good-ness fail-eth nev - er;
2. Where streams of liv-ing wa - ter flow My ran-somed soul he lead - eth,
3. Per - verse and fool-ish oft I strayed, But yet in love he sought me,
4. In death's dark vale I fear no ill With thee, dear Lord, be - side me;
5. Thou spread'st a ta - ble in my sight; Thine unc-tion grace be - stow-eth;
6. And so through all the length of days Thy good-ness fail - eth nev - er:

I noth - ing lack if I am his And he is mine for ev - er.
And, where the ver-dant pas-tures grow, With food ce - les - tial feed-eth.
And on his shoul-der gent - ly laid, And home, re-joic - ing, brought me.
Thy rod and staff my com-fort still, Thy cross be-fore to guide me.
And O what trans-port of de-light From thy pure chal-ice flow-eth.
Good Shep-herd, may I sing thy praise With - in thy house for ev - er. A-MEN.

## 142

*There is a friend that sticketh closer than a brother.* Prov. 18:24

John Newton, 1779

GODESBERG 8.7.8.7.7.7.
Heinrich Albert, 1643

1. One there is, a - bove all oth - ers, Well de-serves the name of Friend;
2. Which of all our friends, to save us, Could or would have shed his blood?
3. When he lived on earth a - based, "Friend of sin - ners" was his name;
4. Could we bear from one an - oth - er What he dai - ly bears from us?
5. O for grace our hearts to soft - en! Teach us, Lord, at length to love;

His is love be - yond a broth-er's, Cost - ly, free, and knows no end:
But our Je - sus died to have us Rec - on - ciled in him to God.
Now a - bove all glo - ry rais - ed, He re - joic - es in the same;
Yet this glo - rious Friend and Broth - er Loves us though we treat him thus:
We, a - las! for - get too oft - en What a Friend we have a - bove:

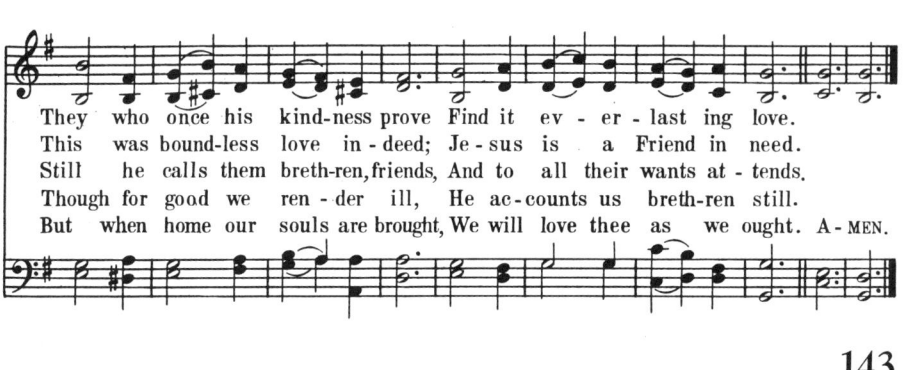

# HIS LOVE AND GRACE

They who once his kind-ness prove Find it ev - er - last ing love.
This was bound-less love in - deed; Je - sus is a Friend in need.
Still he calls them breth-ren, friends, And to all their wants at - tends.
Though for good we ren - der ill, He ac - counts us breth-ren still.
But when home our souls are brought, We will love thee as we ought. A - MEN.

*But we see Jesus... crowned with glory and honour... Heb. 2:9*

**143**

Samuel Stennett, 1787
St. 1, line 2, alt.

ORTONVILLE C. M. with repeat
Thomas Hastings, 1837

1. Ma - jes - tic sweet - ness sits en - throned Up - on the
2. No mor - tal can with him com - pare, A - mong the
3. He saw me plunged in deep dis - tress, He flew to
4. To him I owe my life and breath, And all the
5. To heav'n, the place of his a - bode, He brings my
6. Since from his boun - ty I re - ceive Such proofs of

Sav - iour's brow; His head with ra - diant glo - ries crowned, His
sons of men; Fair - er is he than all the fair That
my re - lief; For me he bore the shame - ful cross, And
joys I have; He makes me tri - umph o - ver death, And
wea - ry feet; Shows me the glo - ries of my God, And
love di - vine, Had I a thou - sand hearts to give, Lord,

lips with grace o'er - flow, His lips with grace o'er - flow.
fill the heav'n - ly train, That fill the heav'n - ly train.
car - ried all my grief, And car - ried all my grief.
saves me from the grave, And saves me from the grave.
makes my joys com - plete, And makes my joys com - plete.
they should all be thine, Lord, they should all be thine. A - MEN.

# 144 THE LORD JESUS CHRIST: HIS LOVE AND GRACE

*Thou shalt call his name Jesus: for he shall save his people from their sins.* Matt. 1:21

William Hunter, 1859

SYMPATHY 8. 7. 8. 7. with refrain
John Hart Stockton, 1813-1877

1. The great Phy-si-cian now is near, The sym-pa-thiz-ing Je-sus; He speaks the droop-ing heart to cheer; O hear the voice of Je-sus.
2. His Name dis-pels my guilt and fear, No oth-er Name but Je-sus; O how my soul de-lights to hear The pre-cious Name of Je-sus! Sweet-est note in ser-aph song,
3. And when to that bright world a-bove We rise to be with Je-sus, We'll sing a-round the throne of love His Name—the Name of Je-sus.

REFRAIN

Sweet-est Name on mor-tal tongue, Sweet-est car-ol ev-er sung, "Je-sus, bless-ed Je-sus." A-MEN.

# THE LORD JESUS CHRIST: HIS ADVENT         145

*Waiting for the consolation of Israel... Luke 2:25*

Charles Wesley, 1744

HYFRYDOL 8. 7. 8. 7. D.
Rowland Hugh Prichard, 1855

1. Come, thou long-expected Jesus, Born to set thy people free; From our fears and sins release us; Let us find our rest in thee. Is-rael's Strength and Consolation, Hope of all the earth thou art; Dear Desire of ev-'ry nation, Joy of ev-'ry long-ing heart.

2. Born thy people to deliver, Born a child, and yet a King, Born to reign in us forever, Now thy gracious kingdom bring. By thine own eternal Spirit Rule in all our hearts alone; By thine all-sufficient merit Raise us to thy glorious throne. A-MEN.

# 146                  THE LORD JESUS CHRIST

*Lift up your heads, O ye gates ... and the King of glory shall come in.*    Psalm 24:7

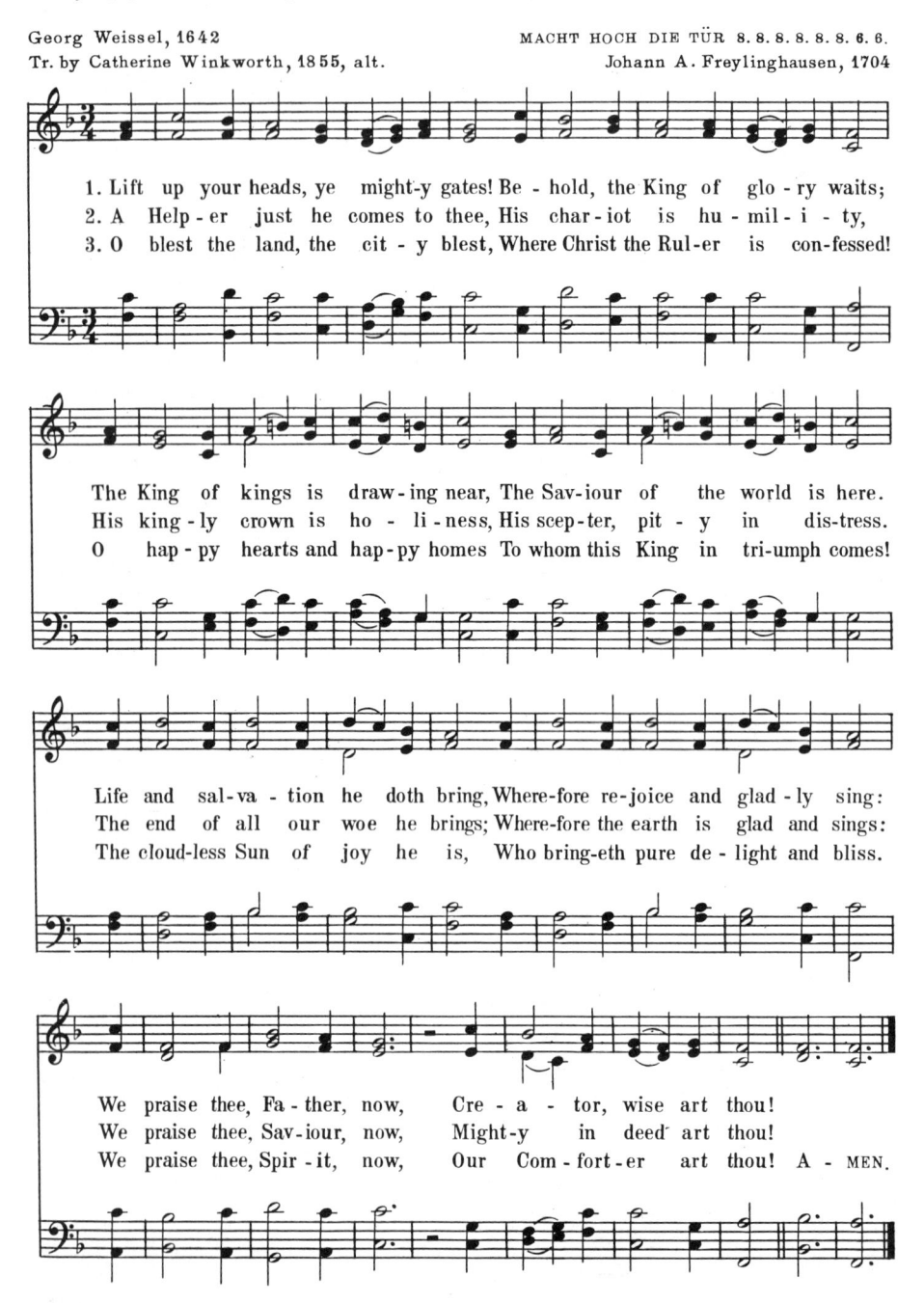

Georg Weissel, 1642                            MACHT HOCH DIE TÜR 8.8.8.8.8.8.6.6.
Tr. by Catherine Winkworth, 1855, alt.                  Johann A. Freylinghausen, 1704

1. Lift up your heads, ye mighty gates! Behold, the King of glory waits;
The King of kings is drawing near, The Saviour of the world is here.
Life and salvation he doth bring, Wherefore rejoice and gladly sing:
We praise thee, Father, now, Creator, wise art thou!

2. A Helper just he comes to thee, His chariot is humility,
His kingly crown is holiness, His scepter, pity in distress.
The end of all our woe he brings; Wherefore the earth is glad and sings:
We praise thee, Saviour, now, Mighty in deed art thou!

3. O blest the land, the city blest, Where Christ the Ruler is confessed!
O happy hearts and happy homes To whom this King in triumph comes!
The cloudless Sun of joy he is, Who bringeth pure delight and bliss.
We praise thee, Spirit, now, Our Comforter art thou! A-MEN.

## HIS ADVENT 147

*And the Redeemer shall come to Zion... Isa. 59:20*

Latin antiphons, 12th century. Latin hymn, 1710
Tr. by John Mason Neale, 1851

VENI EMMANUEL 8.8.8.8. with refrain
Ancient plain song, 13th century
Adapted by Thomas Helmore, 1856

1. O come, O come, Emmanuel, And ransom captive Israel, That mourns in lonely exile here, Until the Son of God appear.
2. O come, O come, thou Lord of might, Who to thy tribes, on Sinai's height, In ancient times didst give the law In cloud and majesty and awe.
3. O come, thou Rod of Jesse, free Thine own from Satan's tyranny; From depths of hell thy people save, And give them vict'ry o'er the grave.
4. O come, thou Day-spring from on high And cheer us by thy drawing nigh; Disperse the gloomy clouds of night, And death's dark shadows put to flight.
5. O come, thou Key of David, come And open wide our heav'nly home; Make safe the way that leads on high, And close the path to misery.

REFRAIN

Rejoice! Rejoice! Emmanuel Shall come to thee, O Israel. A-MEN.

St. 5, line 1, alt.

## 148 THE LORD JESUS CHRIST

*Comfort ye, comfort ye my people, saith your God.* Isa. 40:1

THIRSTING 8.7.8.7.7.7.8.8.
Louis Bourgeois, 1551

Johannes Olearius, 1671
Tr. by Catherine Winkworth, 1863

Harmony adapted from Dutch *Koraalboek*
of B. DeVries by Henry A. Bruinsma

1. Com-fort, com-fort ye my peo-ple, Speak ye peace, thus saith our God;
2. Yea, her sins our God will par-don, Blot-ting out each dark mis-deed;
3. For the her-ald's voice is cry-ing In the des-ert far and near,
4. Make ye straight what long was crook-ed, Make the rough-er plac-es plain;

Com-fort those who sit in dark-ness, Mourn-ing 'neath their sor-row's load.
All that well de-served his an-ger He no more will see or heed.
Bid-ding all men to re-pent-ance, Since the king-dom now is here.
Let your hearts be true and hum-ble, As be-fits his ho-ly reign.

Speak ye to Je-ru-sa-lem Of the peace that waits for them;
She hath suf-fered many a day Now her griefs have passed a-way;
O that warn-ing cry o-bey! Now pre-pare for God a way;
For the glo-ry of the Lord Now o'er earth is shed a-broad;

Tell her that her sins I cov-er, And her war-fare now is o-ver.
God will change her pin-ing sad-ness In-to ev-er-spring-ing glad-ness.
Let the val-leys rise to meet him, And the hills bow down to greet him.
And all flesh shall see the to-ken, That his word is nev-er bro-ken. A-MEN.

Music used by permission of the Publication Committee of the Christian Reformed Church.

# HIS ADVENT 149

*Make a joyful noise unto the Lord, all the earth... Psalm 98:4*

Isaac Watts, 1719

ANTIOCH C. M. with repeat
Lowell Mason, 1836
based on George Frederick Handel, 1742

1. Joy to the world! the Lord is come: Let earth re-ceive her King; Let ev-ery heart pre-pare him room, And heav'n and na-ture sing, And heav'n and na-ture sing, And heav'n, and heav'n and na-ture sing.
2. Joy to the earth! the Sav-iour reigns: Let men their songs em-ploy; While fields and floods, rocks, hills, and plains Re-peat the sound-ing joy, Re-peat the sound-ing joy, Re-peat, re-peat the sound-ing joy.
3. No more let sins and sor-rows grow, Nor thorns in-fest the ground; He comes to make his bless-ings flow Far as the curse is found, Far as the curse is found, Far as, far as the curse is found.
4. He rules the world with truth and grace, And makes the na-tions prove The glo-ries of his right-eous-ness, And won-ders of his love, And won-ders of his love, And won-ders, won-ders of his love. A-MEN.

# 150 THE LORD JESUS CHRIST

*And the Word was made flesh, and dwelt among us, and we beheld his glory... John 1:14*

Paul Gerhardt, 1653  
Tr. by Catherine Winkworth, 1858, alt.

WARUM SOLLT' ICH MICH DENN GRÄMEN  
8. 3. 3. 6. 8. 3. 3. 6.  
Johann G. Ebeling, 1666

1. All my heart this night re-joic-es As I hear Far and near
2. Forth to-day the Con-queror go-eth, Who the foe, Sin and woe,
3. Shall we still dread God's dis-plea-sure, Who, to save, Free-ly gave
4. He be-comes the Lamb that tak-eth Sin a-way And for aye
5. Hark! a voice from yon-der man-ger, Soft and sweet, Doth en-treat:

Sweet-est an-gel voic-es. "Christ is born," their choirs are sing-ing
Death and hell, o'er-throw-eth. God is man, man to de-liv-er;
His most cher-ished Trea-sure? To re-deem us, he hath giv-en
Full a-tone-ment mak-eth. For our life his own he ten-ders;
"Flee from woe and dan-ger. Breth-ren, from all ills that grieve you

Till the air Ev-'ry-where Now with joy is ring-ing.
His dear Son Now is one With our blood for ev-er.
His own Son From the throne Of his might in heav-en.
And our race, By his grace, Meet for glo-ry ren-ders.
You are freed; All you need I will sure-ly give you." A-MEN.

6. Come, then, banish all your sadness,
One and all,
Great and small;
Come with songs of gladness.
Love him who with love is glowing;
Hail the Star,
Near and far
Light and joy bestowing.

7. Dearest Lord, thee will I cherish.
Though my breath
Fail in death,
Yet I shall not perish,
But with thee abide for ever
There on high,
In that joy
Which can vanish never.

# HIS BIRTH 151

*Let us now go even unto Bethlehem, and see this*
*thing which is come to pass . . . Luke 2:15*

Anon., Latin, 18th century
Tr. by Frederick Oakeley, 1841
St. 1, lines 1 and 2, alt.

ADESTE FIDELES irregular
Unknown: probably 18th century

1. O come, all ye faith-ful, Joy-ful and tri-um-phant,
2. God of God, Light of Light;
3. Sing, choirs of an-gels; Sing in ex-ul-ta-tion,
4. Yea, Lord, we greet thee, Born this hap-py morn-ing:

O come ye, O come ye to Beth-le-hem;
Lo, he ab-hors not the Vir-gin's womb:
Sing, all ye cit-i-zens of heav'n a-bove;
Je-sus, to thee be glo-ry giv'n;

Come and be-hold him Born the King of an-gels;
Ver-y God, Be-got-ten, not cre-at-ed;
Glo-ry to God In the high-est;
Word of the Fa-ther, Late in flesh ap-pear-ing;

O come, let us a-dore him, O come, let us a-dore him, O come, let us a-dore him, Christ the Lord. A-MEN.

## 152     THE LORD JESUS CHRIST

*But thou, Bethlehem Ephratah, though thou be little... yet out of thee shall he come... whose goings forth have been from of old, from everlasting.* Micah 5:2

Phillips Brooks, 1868
ST. LOUIS 8.6.8.6.7.6.8.6.
Lewis H. Redner, 1868

1. O lit-tle town of Beth-le-hem, How still we see thee lie;
2. For Christ is born of Ma - ry; And gath-ered all a - bove,
3. How si - lent-ly, how si - lent-ly The won-drous gift is giv'n!
4. O ho - ly Child of Beth-le-hem, De-scend to us, we pray;

A - bove thy deep and dream-less sleep The si - lent stars go by:
While mor-tals sleep, the an - gels keep Their watch of won-d'ring love.
So God im - parts to hu - man hearts The bless-ings of his heav'n.
Cast out our sin, and en - ter in, Be born in us to - day.

Yet in thy dark streets shin - eth The ev - er - last - ing Light;
O morn-ing stars, to - geth - er Pro - claim the ho - ly birth;
No ear may hear his com - ing, But in this world of sin,
We hear the Christ-mas an - gels The great glad ti - dings tell;

The hopes and fears of all the years Are met in thee to-night.
And prais-es sing to God the King, And peace to men on earth.
Where meek souls will re-ceive him still, The dear Christ en-ters in.
O come to us, a - bide with us, Our Lord Em-man-u - el. A-MEN.

# HIS BIRTH 153

*And there shall come forth a rod out of the stem of Jesse,*
*and a Branch shall grow out of his roots.* Isa. 11:1

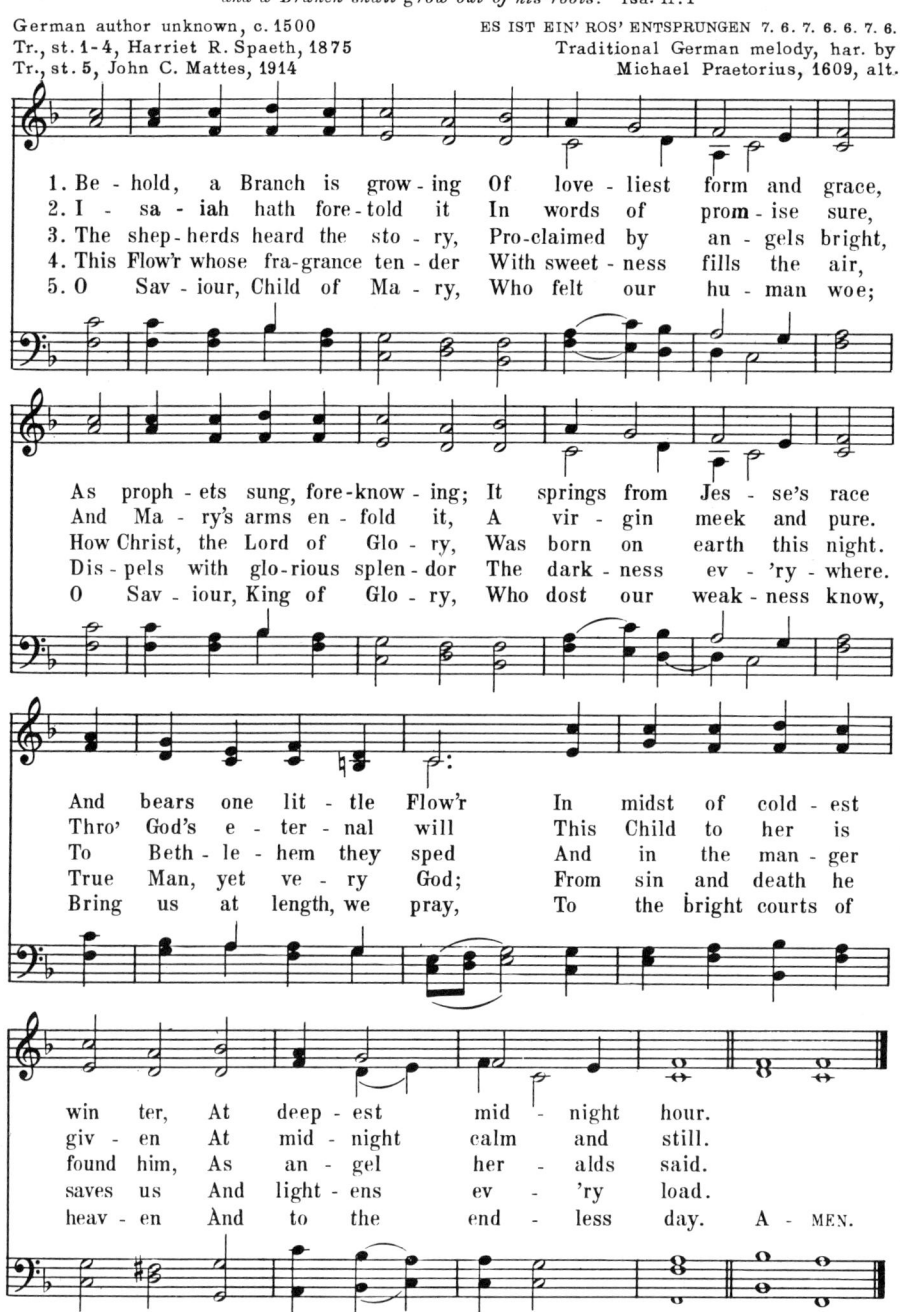

German author unknown, c. 1500  
Tr., st. 1-4, Harriet R. Spaeth, 1875  
Tr., st. 5, John C. Mattes, 1914

ES IST EIN' ROS' ENTSPRUNGEN 7. 6. 7. 6. 6. 7. 6.  
Traditional German melody, har. by  
Michael Praetorius, 1609, alt.

1. Behold, a Branch is growing Of loveliest form and grace,
   As prophets sung, foreknowing; It springs from Jesse's race
   And bears one little Flow'r In midst of coldest winter,
   At deepest midnight hour.

2. Isaiah hath foretold it In words of promise sure,
   And Mary's arms enfold it, A virgin meek and pure.
   Thro' God's eternal will This Child to her is given,
   At midnight calm and still.

3. The shepherds heard the story, Proclaimed by angels bright,
   How Christ, the Lord of Glory, Was born on earth this night.
   To Bethlehem they sped And in the manger found him,
   As angel heralds said.

4. This Flow'r whose fragrance tender With sweetness fills the air,
   Dispels with glorious splendor The darkness ev'rywhere.
   True Man, yet very God; From sin and death he saves us,
   And lightens ev'ry load.

5. O Saviour, Child of Mary, Who felt our human woe;
   O Saviour, King of Glory, Who dost our weakness know,
   Bring us at length, we pray, To the bright courts of heaven,
   And to the endless day. A-MEN.

Music used by permission of the Church Pension Fund, Protestant Episcopal Church.

## 154 THE LORD JESUS CHRIST

*When they saw the star, they rejoiced with exceeding great joy.* Matt. 2:10

William C. Dix, 1861  
DIX 7.7.7.7.7.7.  
Arr. from Conrad Kocher, 1838

1. As with glad-ness men of old Did the guid-ing star be-hold;
2. As with joy-ful steps they sped To that low-ly cra-dle-bed,
3. As they of-fered gifts most rare At that cra-dle rude and bare;
4. Ho-ly Je-sus, ev-'ry day Keep us in the nar-row way;
5. In the heav'n-ly coun-try bright Need they no cre-at-ed light;

As with joy they hailed its light, Lead-ing on-ward, beam-ing bright,
There to bend the knee be-fore Him whom heav'n and earth a-dore;
So may we with ho-ly joy, Pure, and free from sin's al-loy,
And, when earth-ly things are past, Bring our ran-somed souls at last
Thou its Light, its Joy, its Crown, Thou its Sun which goes not down;

So, most gra-cious God, may we Ev-er-more be led to thee.
So may we with will-ing feet Ev-er seek thy mer-cy-seat.
All our cost-liest treas-ures bring, Christ, to thee, our heav'n-ly King.
Where they need no star to guide, Where no clouds thy glo-ry hide.
There for ev-er may we sing Al-le-lu-ias to our King. A-MEN.

St. 2, line 2, st. 3, line 2, alt.

## 155

*For ye know the grace of our Lord Jesus Christ, that, though he was rich, yet for your sakes he became poor...* II Cor. 8:9

Martin Luther, 1524  
Tr. in *Sabbath Hymn Book*, 1858  
CANONBURY L. M.  
Arr. from Robert Schumann, 1839

1. All praise to thee, E-ter-nal Lord, Clothed in a garb of flesh and blood;
2. Once did the skies be-fore thee bow; A Vir-gin's arms con-tain thee now:
3. A lit-tle Child, thou art our Guest, That wea-ry ones in thee may rest;
4. Thou com-est in the dark-some night To make us chil-dren of the light,
5. All this for us thy love hath done; By this to thee our love is won:

**HIS BIRTH**

Choos-ing a man-ger for thy throne, While worlds on worlds are thine a-lone.
An-gels who did in thee re-joice Now lis-ten for thine in-fant voice.
For-lorn and low-ly is thy birth, That we may rise to heav'n from earth.
To make us, in the realms di-vine, Like thine own an-gels round thee shine.
For this we tune our cheer-ful lays, And shout our thanks in cease-less praise. A-MEN.

*And there were... shepherds abiding in the field,
keeping watch over their flock by night.* Luke 2:8

## 156

CHRISTMAS C. M. with repeat
Nahum Tate, 1700
George Frederick Handel, 1728

1. While shep-herds watched their flocks by night,
2. "Fear not," said he— for might-y dread
3. "To you, in Da-vid's town this day,
4. "The heav'n-ly Babe you there shall find

All seat-ed on the ground, The an-gel of the Lord came down,
Had seized their trou-bled mind— "Glad ti-dings of great joy I bring
Is born of Da-vid's line, The Sav-iour, who is Christ, the Lord,
To hu-man view dis-played, All mean-ly wrapped in swath-ing bands,

And glo-ry shone a-round, And glo-ry shone a-round.
To you and all man-kind, To you and all man-kind.
And this shall be the sign: And this shall be the sign:
And in a man-ger laid, And in a man-ger laid." A-MEN.

5. Thus spake the seraph, and forthwith
   Appeared a shining throng
   Of angels praising God, who thus
   Addressed their joyful song:

6. "All glory be to God on high,
   And to the earth be peace:
   Good will henceforth, from heav'n to men,
   Begin and never cease!"

# 157 THE LORD JESUS CHRIST

*And, lo, the angel of the Lord came upon them, and the glory of the Lord shone round about them...Luke 2:9*

Edmund H. Sears, 1850

CAROL C. M. D.
Richard S. Willis, 1850

1. It came up-on the mid-night clear, That glo-rious song of old,
2. Still through the clo-ven skies they come, With peace-ful wings un-furled,
3. And ye, be-neath life's crush-ing load, Whose forms are bend-ing low,
4. For lo, the days are hast-'ning on, By proph-et bards fore-told,

From an-gels bend-ing near the earth To touch their harps of gold:
And still their heav'n-ly mu-sic floats O'er all the wea-ry world:
Who toil a-long the climb-ing way With pain-ful steps and slow,
When with the ev-er-cir-cling years Comes round the age of gold;

"Peace on the earth, good will to men, From heav'n's all-gra-cious King:"
A-bove its sad and low-ly plains They bend on hov-'ring wing,
Look now! for glad and gold-en hours Come swift-ly on the wing:
When peace shall o-ver all the earth Its an-cient splen-dors fling,

The world in sol-emn still-ness lay, To hear the an-gels sing.
And ev-er o'er its Bab-el-sounds The bless-ed an-gels sing.
O rest be-side the wea-ry road, And hear the an-gels sing.
And the whole world give back the song Which now the an-gels sing. A-MEN.

# HIS BIRTH

**158**

*Let this mind be in you, which was also in Christ Jesus: who... humbled himself... Phil. 2:5-8*

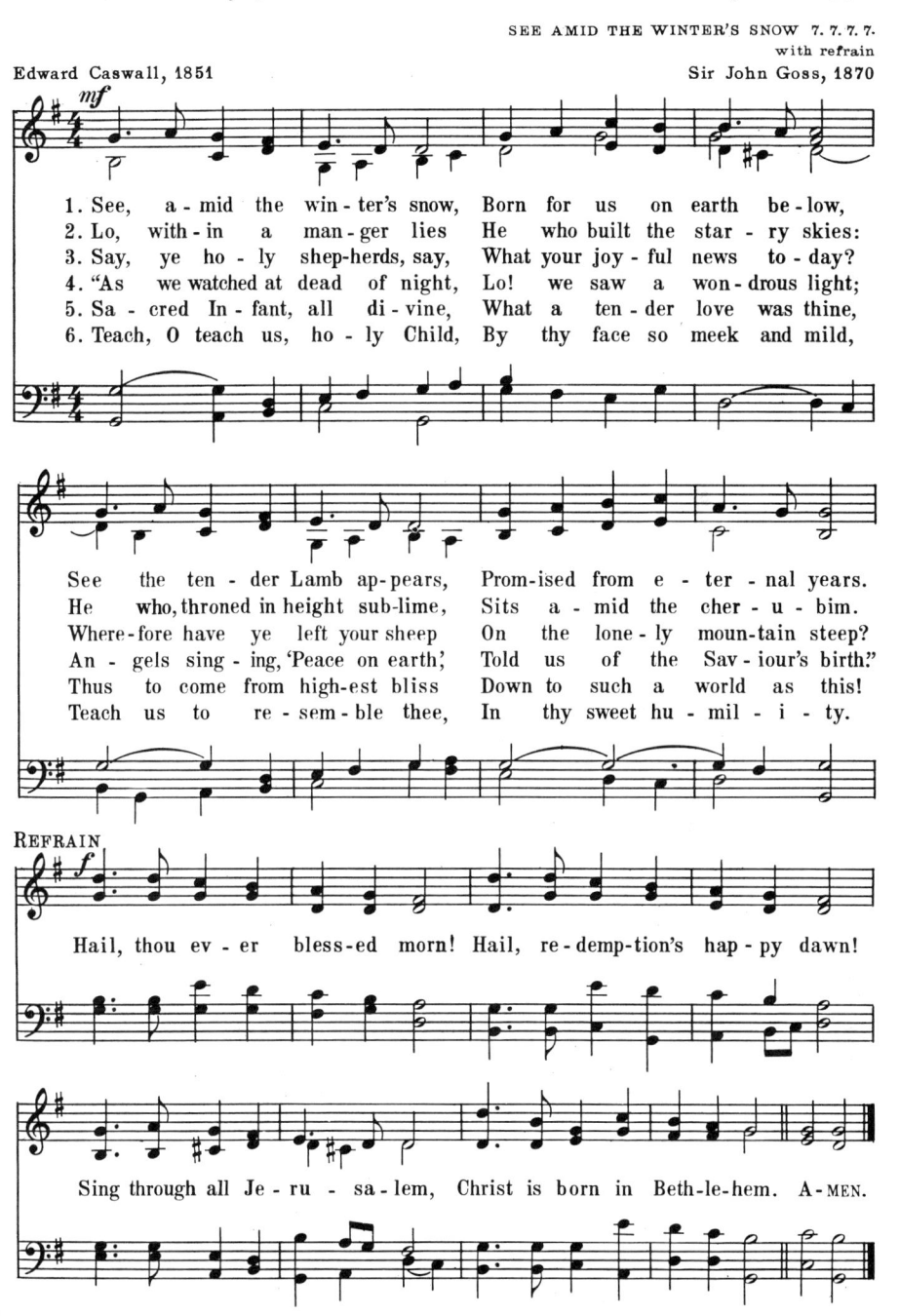

SEE AMID THE WINTER'S SNOW 7. 7. 7. 7.
with refrain

Edward Caswall, 1851                        Sir John Goss, 1870

1. See, a-mid the win-ter's snow, Born for us on earth be-low,
   See the ten-der Lamb ap-pears, Prom-ised from e-ter-nal years.
2. Lo, with-in a man-ger lies He who built the star-ry skies:
   He who, throned in height sub-lime, Sits a-mid the cher-u-bim.
3. Say, ye ho-ly shep-herds, say, What your joy-ful news to-day?
   Where-fore have ye left your sheep On the lone-ly moun-tain steep?
4. "As we watched at dead of night, Lo! we saw a won-drous light;
   An-gels sing-ing, 'Peace on earth,' Told us of the Sav-iour's birth."
5. Sa-cred In-fant, all di-vine, What a ten-der love was thine,
   Thus to come from high-est bliss Down to such a world as this!
6. Teach, O teach us, ho-ly Child, By thy face so meek and mild,
   Teach us to re-sem-ble thee, In thy sweet hu-mil-i-ty.

**REFRAIN**

Hail, thou ev-er bless-ed morn! Hail, re-demp-tion's hap-py dawn!
Sing through all Je-ru-sa-lem, Christ is born in Beth-le-hem. A-MEN.

## 159     THE LORD JESUS CHRIST

*Unto you is born this day in the city of David a Saviour, which is Christ the Lord.* Luke 2:11

Medieval Latin  
Tr. by John Mason Neale, 1853

IN DULCI JUBILO 6. 6. 7. 7. 7. 8. 5. 5.  
14th century melody; har. by W. D., 1918

**With marked rhythm**

1. Good Christian men, rejoice, With heart, and soul, and voice;
2. Good Christian men, rejoice, With heart, and soul, and voice;
3. Good Christian men, rejoice, With heart, and soul, and voice;

Give ye heed to what we say: Jesus Christ is born to-day;  
Now ye hear of endless bliss: Jesus Christ was born for this!  
Now ye need not fear the grave: Jesus Christ was born to save!

Earth and heav'n before him bow, And he is in the manger now.  
He hath oped the heav'nly door, And man is blessed evermore.  
Calls you one and calls you all To gain his everlasting hall.

Christ is born to-day! Christ is born to-day!  
Christ was born for this! Christ was born for this!  
Christ was born to save! Christ was born to save! A-MEN.

St. 1, line 3, alt.

# HIS BIRTH

## 160

*Fear not: for, behold, I bring you good tidings of great joy... Luke 2:10*

GOD REST YOU MERRY 8. 6. 8. 6. 8. 6. with refrain

English traditional carol  
English traditional melody

1. God rest you mer - ry, gen - tle - men, Let noth - ing you dis - may,
2. From God our heav'n - ly Fa - ther, A bless - ed an - gel came;
3. 'Fear not then,' said the an - gel, 'Let noth - ing you af - fright,
4. The shep - herds at those tid - ings Re - joic - ed much in mind,

Re - mem - ber Christ our Sav - iour Was born on Christ - mas day,
And un - to cer - tain shep - herds Brought tid - ings of the same:
This day is born a Sav - iour Of a pure vir - gin bright,
And left their flocks a - feed - ing, In temp - est, storm, and wind:

To save us all from Sa - tan's pow'r When we were gone a - stray;
How that in Beth - le - hem was born The Son of God by name.
To free all those who trust in him From Sa - tan's pow'r and might.'
And went to Beth - le - hem straight-way, The Son of God to find.

REFRAIN

O tid - ings of com - fort and joy, com - fort and joy,

O tid - ings of com - fort and joy. A - MEN.

# THE LORD JESUS CHRIST

## 161

*And they came with haste, and found Mary, and Joseph, and the babe lying in a manger.* Luke 2:16

Joseph Mohr, 1818
Tr. unknown

STILLE NACHT irregular
Franz Gruber, 1818

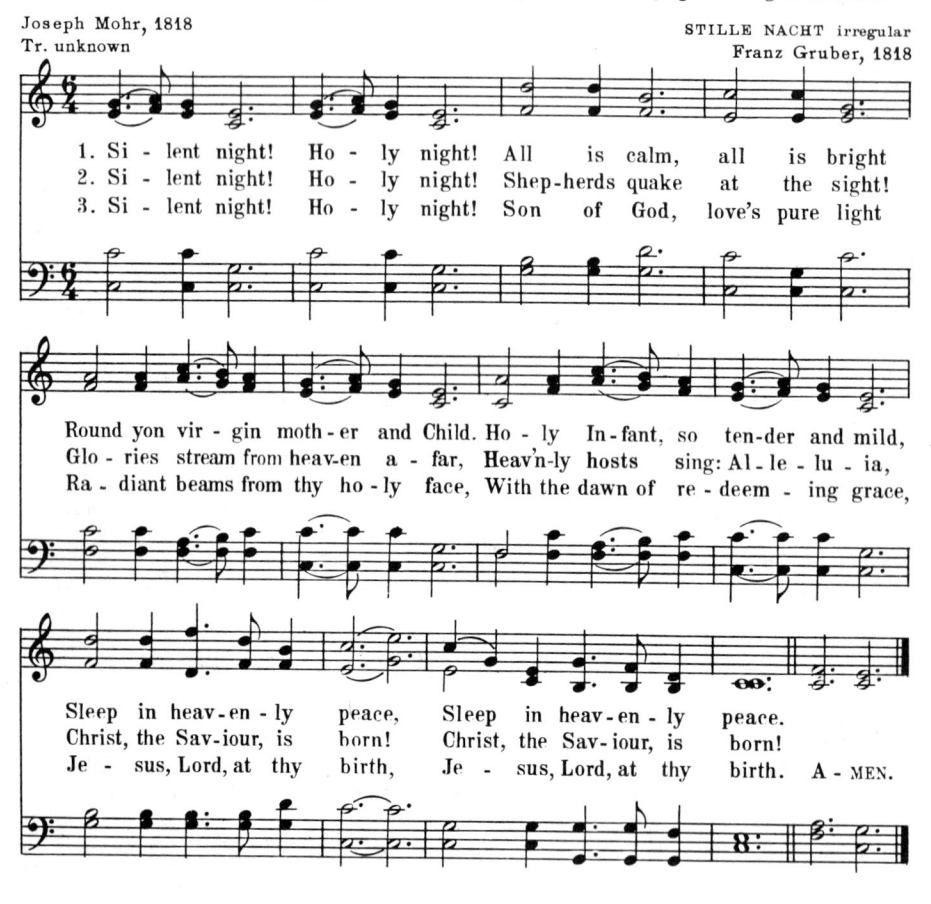

1. Si - lent night! Ho - ly night! All is calm, all is bright
2. Si - lent night! Ho - ly night! Shep-herds quake at the sight!
3. Si - lent night! Ho - ly night! Son of God, love's pure light

Round yon vir - gin moth - er and Child. Ho - ly In - fant, so ten-der and mild,
Glo - ries stream from heav-en a - far, Heav'n-ly hosts sing: Al - le - lu - ia,
Ra - diant beams from thy ho - ly face, With the dawn of re - deem - ing grace,

Sleep in heav - en - ly peace, Sleep in heav - en - ly peace.
Christ, the Sav-iour, is born! Christ, the Sav-iour, is born!
Je - sus, Lord, at thy birth, Je - sus, Lord, at thy birth. A - MEN.

## 162

*The Spirit of the Lord God is upon me; because the Lord hath anointed me to preach good tidings unto the meek . . .* Isa. 61:1

Philip Doddridge, 1735

ST. SAVIOUR C. M.
Frederick G. Baker, 1876

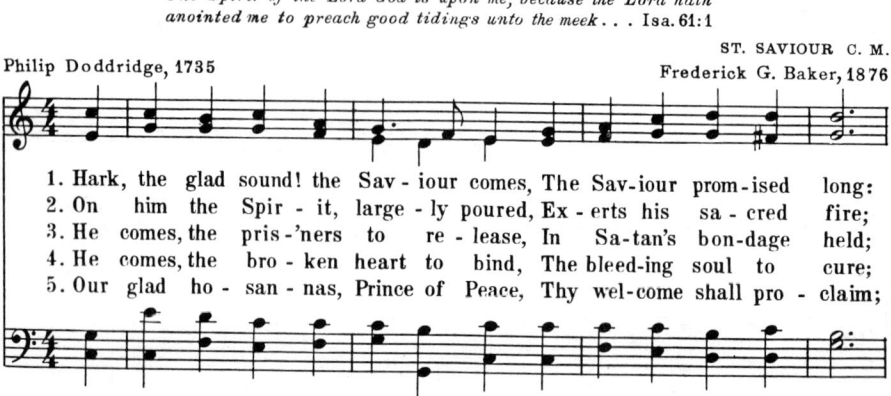

1. Hark, the glad sound! the Sav - iour comes, The Sav-iour prom-ised long:
2. On him the Spir - it, large - ly poured, Ex - erts his sa - cred fire;
3. He comes, the pris -'ners to re - lease, In Sa-tan's bon-dage held;
4. He comes, the bro - ken heart to bind, The bleed-ing soul to cure;
5. Our glad ho - san - nas, Prince of Peace, Thy wel-come shall pro - claim;

# HIS BIRTH

Let ev-'ry heart pre-pare a throne, And ev-'ry voice a song.
Wis-dom and might, and zeal and love, His ho-ly breast in-spire.
The gates of brass be-fore him burst, The i-ron fet-ters yield.
And with the treas-ures of his grace To en-rich the hum-ble poor.
And heav'n's e-ter-nal arch-es ring With thy be-lov-ed Name. A-MEN.

*Unto us a child is born, unto us a son is given... Isa. 9:6*

**163**

John Morison, 1781, alt.

ZERAH C. M. with repeat
Lowell Mason, 1837

1. To us a Child of hope is born, To us a Son is giv'n,
2. His Name shall be the Prince of Peace, For ev-er-more a-dored,
3. His pow'r, in-creas-ing, still shall spread, His reign no end shall know;
4. To us a Child of hope is born, To us a Son is giv'n,

Him shall the tribes of earth o-bey, Him all the hosts of heav'n;
The Won-der-ful, the Coun-sel-lor, The great and might-y Lord;
Jus-tice shall guard his throne a-bove, And peace a-bound be-low;
The Won-der-ful, the Coun-sel-lor, The might-y Lord of heav'n;

Him shall the tribes of earth o-bey, Him all the hosts of heav'n.
The Won-der-ful, the Coun-sel-lor, The great and might-y Lord.
Jus-tice shall guard his throne a-bove, And peace a-bound be-low.
The Won-der-ful, the Coun-sel-lor, The might-y Lord of heav'n. A-MEN.

## 164 THE LORD JESUS CHRIST

*They saw the young child ... and fell down, and worshipped him... Matt. 2:11*

James Montgomery, 1816
Doxology added

REGENT SQUARE 8.7.8.7.8.7.
Henry Smart, 1867

1. An - gels, from the realms of glo - ry, Wing your flight o'er all the earth;
2. Shep-herds, in the fields a - bid - ing, Watch-ing o'er your flocks by night,
3. Sag - es, leave your con - tem - pla - tions, Bright-er vis - ions beam a - far;
4. Saints, be - fore the al - tar bend - ing, Watch-ing long in hope and fear,
5. All cre - a - tion, join in prais - ing God the Fa - ther, Spir - it, Son;

Ye who sang cre - a - tion's sto - ry, Now pro-claim Mes - si - ah's birth:
God with man is now re - sid - ing, Yon - der shines the in - fant Light:
Seek the great De - sire of na - tions; Ye have seen his na - tal star:
Sud - den - ly the Lord, de-scend-ing, In his tem - ple shall ap - pear:
Ev - er-more your voic - es rais - ing To th' E - ter - nal Three in One:

Come and wor-ship, come and wor-ship, Wor-ship Christ, the new-born King.
Come and wor-ship, come and wor-ship, Wor-ship Christ, the new-born King.
Come and wor-ship, come and wor-ship, Wor-ship Christ, the new-born King.
Come and wor-ship, come and wor-ship, Wor-ship Christ, the new-born King.
Come and wor-ship, come and wor-ship, Wor-ship Christ, the new-born King. A-MEN.

For a lower setting of this tune, see No. 60

## 165

*And the Word was made flesh, and dwelt among us... John 1:14*

Ambrose of Milan, 340-397
Tr. by Martin Luther, 1524
Tr. by William M. Reynolds, 1860, alt.

NUN KOMM, DER HEIDEN HEILAND 7.7.7.7.
Adapted from *Geistliches Gesangbüchlein,*
Wittenberg, 1524

1. Sav - iour of the na - tions, come, Vir - gin's Son, make here thy home!
2. Not of flesh and blood the Son, Off - spring of the Ho - ly One;
3. Won-drous birth! O won-drous Child Of the vir - gin un - de - filed!
4. From the Fa - ther forth he came And re - turn-eth to the same,
5. Thou, the Fa - ther's on - ly Son, Hast o'er sin the vic - t'ry won.
6. Praise to God the Fa - ther sing, Praise to God the Son, our King,

## HIS BIRTH

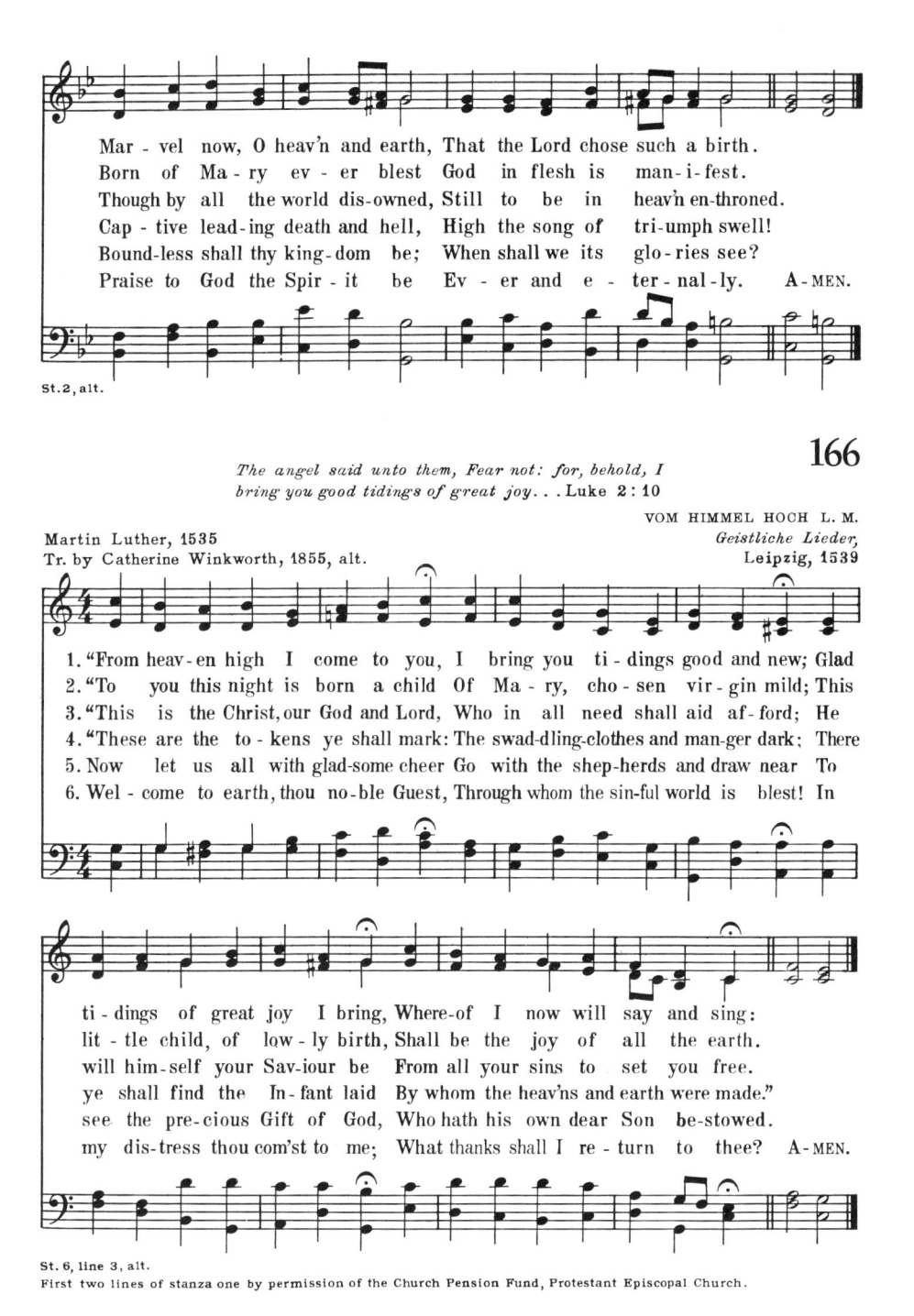

Mar - vel now, O heav'n and earth, That the Lord chose such a birth.
Born of Ma - ry ev - er blest God in flesh is man - i - fest.
Though by all the world dis-owned, Still to be in heav'n en-throned.
Cap - tive lead-ing death and hell, High the song of tri-umph swell!
Bound-less shall thy king-dom be; When shall we its glo-ries see?
Praise to God the Spir - it be Ev - er and e - ter - nal - ly. A-MEN.

St. 2, alt.

### 166

*The angel said unto them, Fear not: for, behold, I bring you good tidings of great joy... Luke 2:10*

Martin Luther, 1535
Tr. by Catherine Winkworth, 1855, alt.

VOM HIMMEL HOCH L. M.
*Geistliche Lieder,*
Leipzig, 1539

1. "From heav-en high I come to you, I bring you ti - dings good and new; Glad
2. "To you this night is born a child Of Ma - ry, cho - sen vir - gin mild; This
3. "This is the Christ, our God and Lord, Who in all need shall aid af - ford; He
4. "These are the to - kens ye shall mark: The swad-dling-clothes and man-ger dark; There
5. Now let us all with glad-some cheer Go with the shep-herds and draw near To
6. Wel - come to earth, thou no-ble Guest, Through whom the sin-ful world is blest! In

ti - dings of great joy I bring, Where-of I now will say and sing:
lit - tle child, of low - ly birth, Shall be the joy of all the earth.
will him-self your Sav-iour be From all your sins to set you free.
ye shall find the In - fant laid By whom the heav'ns and earth were made."
see the pre - cious Gift of God, Who hath his own dear Son be-stowed.
my dis-tress thou com'st to me; What thanks shall I re - turn to thee? A-MEN.

St. 6, line 3, alt.
First two lines of stanza one by permission of the Church Pension Fund, Protestant Episcopal Church.

## 167 THE LORD JESUS CHRIST

*For we have seen his star in the east, and are come to worship him.* Matt. 2:2

Reginald Heber, 1811

MORNING STAR 11. 10. 11. 10.
James P. Harding, 1892

1. Bright-est and best of the sons of the morn-ing,
2. Cold on his cra-dle the dew-drops are shin-ing;
3. Say, shall we yield him, in cost-ly de-vo-tion,
4. Vain-ly we of-fer each am-ple ob-la-tion,
5. Bright-est and best of the sons of the morn-ing,

Dawn on our dark-ness, and lend us thine aid;
Low lies his head with the beasts of the stall;
O-dours of E-dom, and off-'rings di-vine,
Vain-ly with gifts would his fa-vor se-cure;
Dawn on our dark-ness, and lend us thine aid;

Star of the East, the hor-i-zon a-dorn-ing,
An-gels a-dore him in slum-ber re-clin-ing,
Gems of the moun-tain and pearls of the o-cean,
Rich-er by far is the heart's ad-o-ra-tion;
Star of the East, the hor-i-zon a-dorn-ing,

Guide where our in-fant Re-deem-er is laid.
Mak-er and Mon-arch, and Lord o-ver all.
Myrrh from the for-est or gold from the mine?
Dear-er to God are the prayers of the poor.
Guide where our in-fant Re-deem-er is laid. A-MEN.

St. 2, line 4, alt.

# HIS BIRTH

**168**

*Glory to God in the highest, and on earth peace among men in whom he is well pleased.* Luke 2:14 (R. V.)

Charles Wesley, 1739, alt.

MENDELSSOHN 7. 7. 7. 7. D. with refrain
Arr. from Mendelssohn
by William H. Cummings, 1856

1. Hark! the her - ald an - gels sing, "Glo - ry to the new - born King;
2. Christ, by high - est heav'n a - dored, Christ, the Ev - er - last - ing Lord!
3. Hail, the heav'n-born Prince of Peace! Hail, the Sun of Right-eous - ness!

Peace on earth, and mer - cy mild, God and sin - ners rec - on - ciled!"
Late in time be - hold him come, Off - spring of the Vir - gin's womb.
Light and life to all he brings, Ris'n with heal - ing in his wings.

Joy - ful, all ye na - tions, rise, Join the tri - umph of the skies;
Veiled in flesh the God - head see; Hail th' In - car - nate De - i - ty,
Mild he lays his glo - ry by, Born that man no more may die,

With th' an - gel - ic host pro - claim, "Christ is born in Beth - le - hem!"
Pleased as man with men to dwell, Je - sus, our Em - man - u - el.
Born to raise the sons of earth, Born to give them sec - ond birth.

REFRAIN

Hark! the her - ald an - gels sing, "Glo - ry to the new-born King." A - MEN.

Music used by permission of Novello & Company, Ltd.

# 169 THE LORD JESUS CHRIST

*He was in the world, and the world was made by him, and the world knew him not.* John 1:10

William Walsham How, 1823-1897

EIFIONYDD 8.7.8.7. D.
John Ambrose Lloyd, the elder, 1815-1874

1. Who is this so weak and help-less, Child of low-ly He-brew maid,
2. Who is this, a Man of Sor-rows, Walk-ing sad-ly life's hard way,
3. Who is this? be-hold him shed-ding Drops of blood up-on the ground!
4. Who is this that hang-eth dy-ing While the rude world scoffs and scorns,

Rude-ly in a sta-ble shel-tered, Cold-ly in a man-ger laid?
Home-less, wea-ry, sigh-ing, weep-ing O-ver sin and Sa-tan's sway?
Who is this, de-spised, re-ject-ed, Mocked, in-sult-ed, beat-en, bound?
Num-bered with the mal-e-fac-tors, Torn with nails, and crowned with thorns?

'Tis the Lord of all cre-a-tion, Who this won-drous path hath trod;
'Tis our God, our glo-rious Sav-iour, Who a-bove the star-ry sky
'Tis our God, who gifts and grac-es On his Church now pour-eth down;
'Tis the God who ev-er liv-eth 'Mid the shin-ing ones on high,

He is God from ev-er-last-ing, And to ev-er-last-ing God.
Now for us a place pre-par-eth, Where no tear can dim the eye.
Who shall smite in ho-ly ven-geance All his foes be-neath his throne.
In the glo-rious gold-en cit-y, Reign-ing ev-er-last-ing-ly. A-MEN.

## HIS LIFE, MINISTRY, AND OBEDIENCE        170

*Though he was rich, yet for your sakes he became poor, that ye through his poverty might be rich.* II Cor. 8:9

Emily E. S. Elliott, 1864, alt.

MARGARET irregular
T. Richard Matthews, 1876

1. Thou dost reign on high With a king-ly crown, Yet thou cam-est to earth for me, And in Beth-lehem's home Was there found no room For thy ho-ly na-tiv-i-ty: O come to my heart, Lord Je-sus, There is room in my heart for thee.

2. Heav-en's arch-es rang When the an-gels sang, Pro-claim-ing thy roy-al de-gree; But of low-ly birth Didst thou come to earth, And in great hu-mil-i-ty: O come to my heart, Lord Je-sus, There is room in my heart for thee.

3. The fox-es found rest, And the birds their nest, In the shade of the for-est tree; But thy couch was the sod, O thou Son of God, In the des-erts of Gal-i-lee: O come to my heart, Lord Je-sus, There is room in my heart for thee.

4. Thou cam-est, O Lord, With the liv-ing word That should set thy peo-ple free; But with mock-ing scorn, And with crown of thorn, They bore thee to Cal-va-ry: O come to my heart, Lord Je-sus, Thy cross is my on-ly plea.

5. When heav'n's arch-es shall ring, And her choirs shall sing, At thy com-ing to vic-to-ry, Let thy voice call me home, Say-ing, "Yet there is room, There is room at my side for thee." And my heart shall re-joice, Lord Je-sus, When thou com-est and call-est for me. A-MEN.

St. 1, lines 1-4, alt.

## THE LORD JESUS CHRIST

**171**

*He that saith he abideth in him ought himself also so to walk, even as he walked.* I John 2:6

Isaac Watts, 1709

FEDERAL STREET L. M.
Henry K. Oliver, 1832

1. My dear Redeemer and my Lord, I read my duty in thy Word;
   But in thy life the law appears Drawn out in living characters.
2. Such was thy truth, and such thy zeal, Such def'rence to thy Father's will,
   Such love, and meekness so divine, I would transcribe and make them mine.
3. Cold mountains and the midnight air Witnessed the fervor of thy prayer;
   The desert thy temptations knew, Thy conflict and thy vic'try too.
4. Be thou my pattern; make me bear More of thy gracious image here:
   Then God the Judge shall own my name Amongst the foll'wers of the Lamb. A-MEN.

**172**

*Tell ye the daughter of Sion, Behold, thy King cometh unto thee, meek, and sitting upon an ass...* Matt. 21:5

Henry H. Milman, 1827
St. 1, line 3, alt.

ST. DROSTANE L. M.
John B. Dykes, 1862

1. Ride on! ride on in majesty! Hark! all the tribes Hosanna cry;
   O Saviour meek, pursue thy road With palms and scattered garments strowed.
2. Ride on! ride on in majesty! In lowly pomp ride on to die:
   O Christ, thy triumphs now begin O'er captive death and conquered sin.
3. Ride on! ride on in majesty! The winged squadrons of the sky
   Look down with sad and wond'ring eyes To see th' approaching sacrifice.
4. Ride on! ride on in majesty! Thy last and fiercest strife is nigh;
   The Father on his sapphire throne Expects his own Anointed Son.
5. Ride on! ride on in majesty! In lowly pomp ride on to die;
   Bow thy meek head to mortal pain, Then take, O God, thy pow'r and reign. A-MEN.

# HIS LIFE, MINISTRY, AND OBEDIENCE  173

*Blessed is the King of Israel that cometh in the name of the Lord.* John 12:13

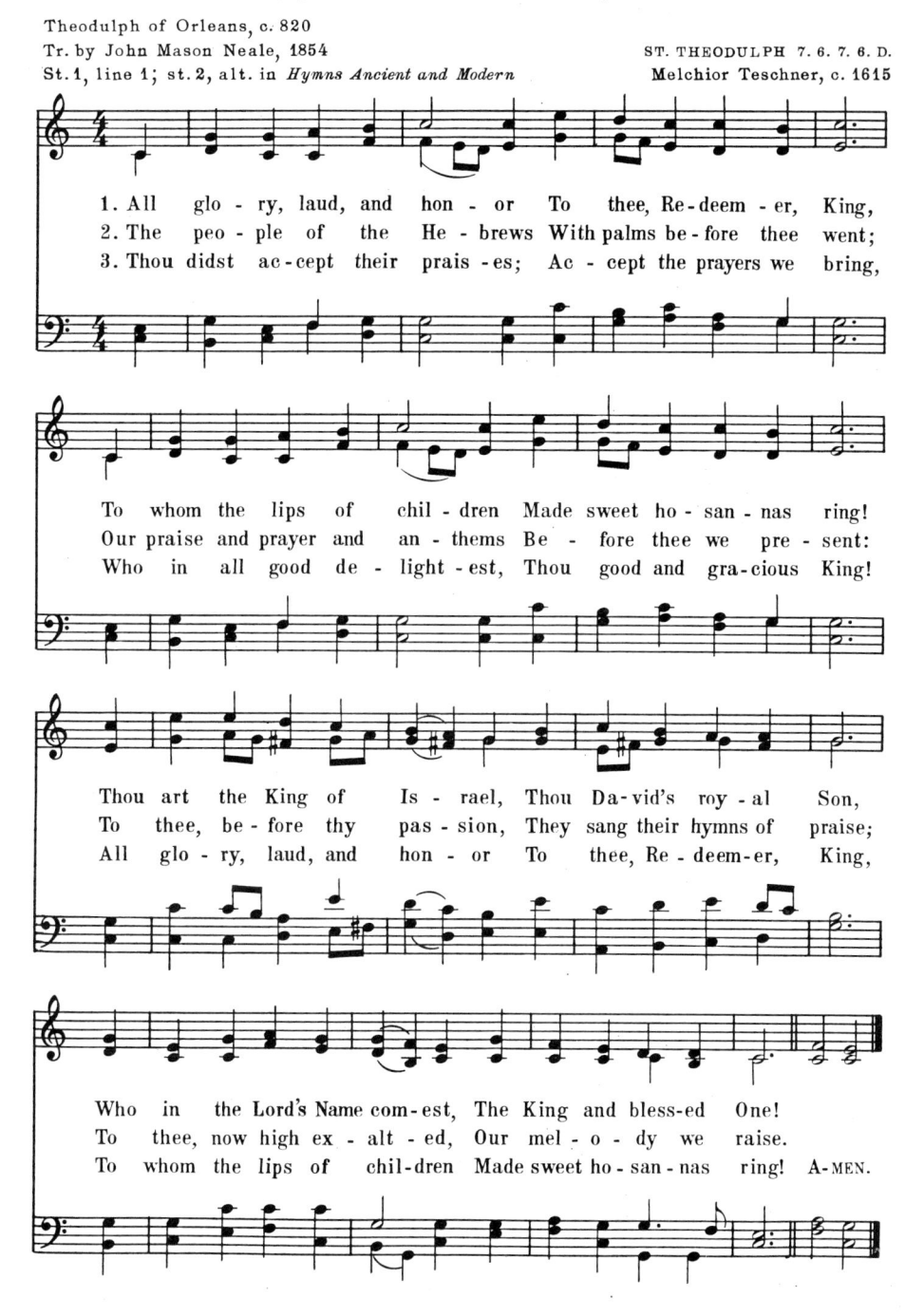

Theodulph of Orleans, c. 820
Tr. by John Mason Neale, 1854
St. 1, line 1; st. 2, alt. in *Hymns Ancient and Modern*

ST. THEODULPH 7. 6. 7. 6. D.
Melchior Teschner, c. 1615

1. All glo-ry, laud, and hon-or To thee, Re-deem-er, King,
2. The peo-ple of the He-brews With palms be-fore thee went;
3. Thou didst ac-cept their prais-es; Ac-cept the prayers we bring,

To whom the lips of chil-dren Made sweet ho-san-nas ring!
Our praise and prayer and an-thems Be-fore thee we pre-sent:
Who in all good de-light-est, Thou good and gra-cious King!

Thou art the King of Is-rael, Thou Da-vid's roy-al Son,
To thee, be-fore thy pas-sion, They sang their hymns of praise;
All glo-ry, laud, and hon-or To thee, Re-deem-er, King,

Who in the Lord's Name com-est, The King and bless-ed One!
To thee, now high ex-alt-ed, Our mel-o-dy we raise.
To whom the lips of chil-dren Made sweet ho-san-nas ring! A-MEN.

# 174 THE LORD JESUS CHRIST

*That through death he might destroy him that had the power of death . . . Heb. 2:14*

Venantius H. C. Fortunatus, c. 530-609  
Tr. by Augustus Nelson

UPP, MIN TUNGA 4. 4. 7. 4. 4. 7. 4. 4. 7.  
Swedish *Koralbok,* 1697

1. Praise the Saviour Now and ever; Praise him, all beneath the skies; Prostrate lying, Suff'ring, dying On the cross, a sacrifice. Vict'ry gaining, Life obtaining, Now in glory he doth rise.
2. Man's work faileth, Christ's availeth; He is all our righteousness; He, our Saviour, Has for ever Set us free from dire distress. Through his merit We inherit Light and peace and happiness.
3. Sin's bonds severed; We're deliv-ered; Christ has bruised the serpent's head; Death no longer Is the stronger; Hell itself is captive led. Christ has risen From death's pris-on; O'er the tomb he light has shed.
4. For his favor, Praise for ever Unto God the Father sing; Praise the Saviour, Praise him ever, Son of God, our Lord and King. Praise the Spirit; Through Christ's merit, He doth us salvation bring. A-MEN.

# HIS ATONING WORK

## 175

*A man of sorrows, and acquainted with grief... Isa. 53:3*

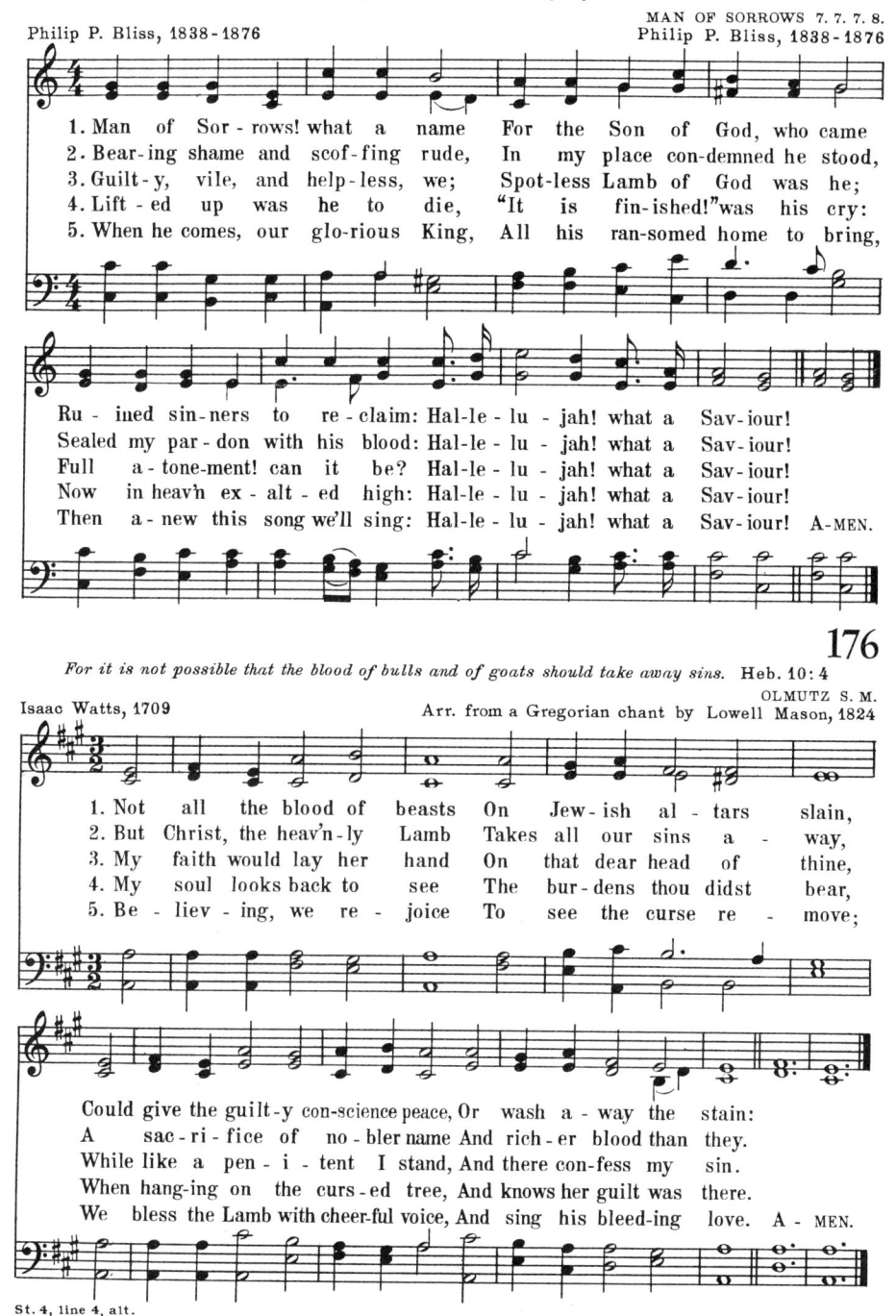

Philip P. Bliss, 1838-1876

MAN OF SORROWS 7. 7. 7. 8.
Philip P. Bliss, 1838-1876

1. Man of Sor-rows! what a name For the Son of God, who came
2. Bear-ing shame and scof-fing rude, In my place con-demned he stood,
3. Guilt-y, vile, and help-less, we; Spot-less Lamb of God was he;
4. Lift-ed up was he to die, "It is fin-ished!" was his cry:
5. When he comes, our glo-rious King, All his ran-somed home to bring,

Ru-ined sin-ners to re-claim: Hal-le-lu-jah! what a Sav-iour!
Sealed my par-don with his blood: Hal-le-lu-jah! what a Sav-iour!
Full a-tone-ment! can it be? Hal-le-lu-jah! what a Sav-iour!
Now in heav'n ex-alt-ed high: Hal-le-lu-jah! what a Sav-iour!
Then a-new this song we'll sing: Hal-le-lu-jah! what a Sav-iour! A-MEN.

## 176

*For it is not possible that the blood of bulls and of goats should take away sins. Heb. 10:4*

Isaac Watts, 1709

OLMUTZ S. M.
Arr. from a Gregorian chant by Lowell Mason, 1824

1. Not all the blood of beasts On Jew-ish al-tars slain,
2. But Christ, the heav'n-ly Lamb Takes all our sins a-way,
3. My faith would lay her hand On that dear head of thine,
4. My soul looks back to see The bur-dens thou didst bear,
5. Be-liev-ing, we re-joice To see the curse re-move;

Could give the guilt-y con-science peace, Or wash a-way the stain:
A sac-ri-fice of no-bler name And rich-er blood than they.
While like a pen-i-tent I stand, And there con-fess my sin.
When hang-ing on the curs-ed tree, And knows her guilt was there.
We bless the Lamb with cheer-ful voice, And sing his bleed-ing love. A-MEN.

St. 4, line 4, alt.

# 177          THE LORD JESUS CHRIST

*And a man shall be as an hiding place from the wind, and a covert from the tempest... as the shadow of a great rock in a weary land.* Isa. 32:2

Elizabeth C. Clephane, 1872     ST. CHRISTOPHER 7. 6. 8. 6. 8. 6. 8. 6.
Frederick C. Maker, 1881

1. Be-neath the cross of Je-sus I fain would take my stand,—
   The shad-ow of a might-y Rock With-in a wea-ry land;
   A home with-in the wil-der-ness, A rest up-on the way,
   From the burn-ing of the noon-tide heat, And the bur-den of the day.

2. Up-on the cross of Je-sus Mine eye at times can see
   The ver-y dy-ing form of One Who suf-fered there for me:
   And from my strick-en heart with tears Two won-ders I con-fess,—
   The won-ders of re-deem-ing love And my own worth-less-ness.

3. I take, O cross, thy shad-ow For my a-bid-ing-place:
   I ask no oth-er sun-shine than The sun-shine of his face;
   Con-tent to let the world go by, To know no gain nor loss;
   My sin-ful self my on-ly shame, My glo-ry, all the cross. A-MEN.

# HIS SUFFERING

178

*He was wounded for our transgressions, he was bruised for our iniquities...* Isa. 53:5

Ascribed to Bernard of Clairvaux, 1091-1153
Tr. by Paul Gerhardt, 1656
Tr. by James Waddell Alexander, 1830

PASSION CHORALE 7. 6. 7. 6. D.
Hans Leo Hassler, 1601
har. by Johann Sebastian Bach, 1729

1. O sacred Head, now wounded, With grief and shame weighed down;
Now scornfully surrounded With thorns, thine only crown;
O sacred Head, what glory, What bliss till now was thine!
Yet, though despised and gory, I joy to call thee mine.

2. What thou, my Lord, hast suffered Was all for sinners' gain:
Mine, mine was the transgression, But thine the deadly pain.
Lo, here I fall, my Saviour! 'Tis I deserve thy place;
Look on me with thy favor, Vouchsafe to me thy grace.

3. What language shall I borrow To thank thee, dearest Friend,
For this thy dying sorrow, Thy pity without end?
O make me thine forever; And should I fainting be,
Lord, let me never, never Outlive my love to thee.

4. Be near when I am dying, O show thy cross to me;
And for my succor flying, Come, Lord, to set me free:
These eyes, new faith receiving, From Jesus shall not move;
For he who dies believing, Dies safely, through thy love. A-MEN.

## 179 (FIRST TUNE) — THE LORD JESUS CHRIST

*He hath borne our griefs, and carried our sorrows: yet we did esteem him stricken, smitten of God, and afflicted.* Isa. 53:4

Johann Heermann, 1630
Tr. *Yattendon Hymnal*, 1899

ISTE CONFESSOR 11. 11. 11. 5.
Rouen church melody
har. by Healey Willan, 1880-

1. Ah, ho-ly Je-sus, how hast thou of-fend-ed, That man to judge thee hath in hate pre-tend-ed? By foes de-rid-ed, by thine own re-ject-ed, O most af-flict-ed.
2. Who was the guilt-y? who brought this up-on thee? A-las, my trea-son, Je-sus, hath un-done thee. 'Twas I, Lord Je-sus, I it was de-nied thee: I cru-ci-fied thee.
3. Lo, the good Shep-herd for the sheep is of-fered: The slave hath sin-ned, and the Son hath suf-fered: For man's a-tone-ment, while he noth-ing heed-eth, God in-ter-ced-eth.
4. For me, kind Je-sus, was thine in-car-na-tion, Thy mor-tal sor-row, and thy life's ob-la-tion: Thy death of an-guish and thy bit-ter pas-sion, For my sal-va-tion.
5. There-fore, kind Je-sus, since I can-not pay thee, I do a-dore thee, and will ev-er pray thee Think on thy pit-y and thy love un-swerv-ing, Not my de-serv-ing. A-MEN.

Music used by permission of the arranger.

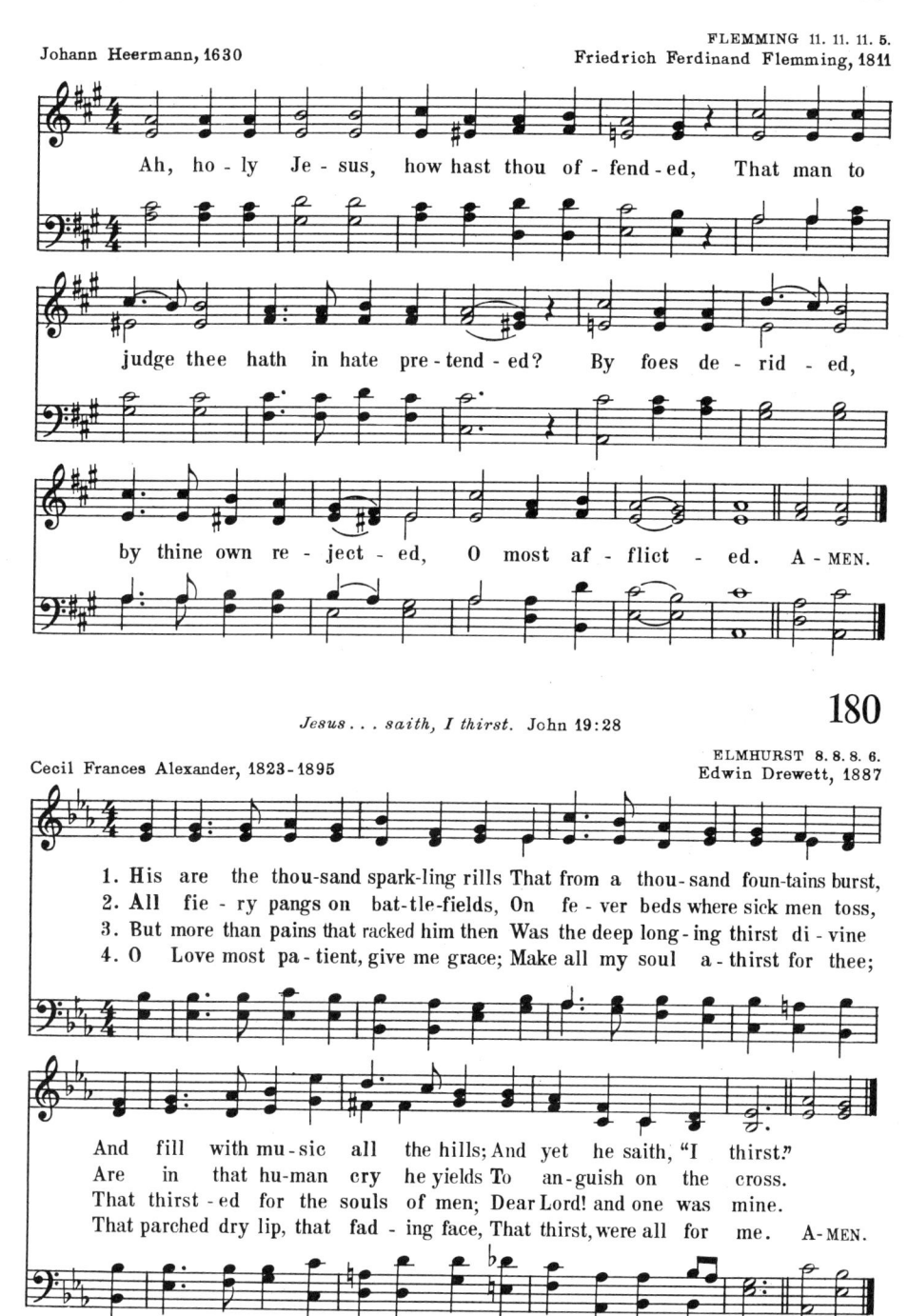

# HIS SUFFERING

(SECOND TUNE) **179**

Johann Heermann, 1630

FLEMMING 11. 11. 11. 5.
Friedrich Ferdinand Flemming, 1811

Ah, ho-ly Je-sus, how hast thou of-fend-ed, That man to judge thee hath in hate pre-tend-ed? By foes de-rid-ed, by thine own re-ject-ed, O most af-flict-ed. A-MEN.

**180**

*Jesus... saith, I thirst.* John 19:28

Cecil Frances Alexander, 1823-1895

ELMHURST 8. 8. 8. 6.
Edwin Drewett, 1887

1. His are the thou-sand spark-ling rills That from a thou-sand foun-tains burst,
2. All fie-ry pangs on bat-tle-fields, On fe-ver beds where sick men toss,
3. But more than pains that racked him then Was the deep long-ing thirst di-vine
4. O Love most pa-tient, give me grace; Make all my soul a-thirst for thee;

And fill with mu-sic all the hills; And yet he saith, "I thirst."
Are in that hu-man cry he yields To an-guish on the cross.
That thirst-ed for the souls of men; Dear Lord! and one was mine.
That parched dry lip, that fad-ing face, That thirst, were all for me. A-MEN.

## 181 THE LORD JESUS CHRIST

*He had done no violence, neither was any deceit in his mouth.*
*Yet it pleased the Lord to bruise him... Isa. 53:9-10*

Johann Heermann, 1630
Tr. by Catherine Winkworth, 1863, alt.

HERZLIEBSTER JESU 11. 11. 11. 5.
Johann Crüger, 1640

1. O dearest Jesus, what law hast thou broken
That such sharp sentence should on thee be spoken?
Of what great crime hast thou to make confession,
What dark transgression?

2. They crown thy head with thorns, they smite, they scourge thee;
With cruel mockings to the cross they urge thee;
Gall to drink, they still decry thee;
They crucify thee.

3. Whence come these sorrows, whence this mortal anguish?
It is my sins for which thou, Lord, must languish;
Yea, all the wrath, the woe, thou dost inherit,
This I do merit.

4. What punishment so strange is suffered yonder!
The Shepherd dies for sheep that loved to wander;
The Master pays the debt his servants owe him,
Who would not know him.

5. The sinless Son of God must die in sadness;
The sinful child of man may live in gladness;
Man forfeited his life and is acquitted,—
God is committed. A-MEN.

## 182

*And he... went, as he was wont, to the mount of Olives... Luke 22:39*

William B. Tappan, 1822

OLIVE'S BROW L.M.
William B. Bradbury, 1853

1. 'Tis midnight; and on Olive's brow
The star is dimmed that lately shone:

2. 'Tis midnight; and, from all removed,
Emmanuel wrestles lone with fears:

3. 'Tis midnight; and, for others' guilt,
The Man of Sorrows weeps in blood:

4. 'Tis midnight; from the heav'nly plains
Is borne the song that angels know:

# HIS SUFFERING

'Tis mid-night; in the gar-den now The suf-f'ring Sav-iour prays a-lone.
E'en the dis-ci-ple that he loved Heeds not his Mas-ter's grief and tears.
Yet he that hath in an-guish knelt Is not for-sak-en by his God.
Un-heard by mor-tals are the strains That sweet-ly soothe the Sav-iour's woe. A-MEN.

*My God, my God, why hast thou forsaken me?* Mark 15:34

**183**

John Ellerton, 1875

ARFON 7. 7. 7. 7. 7. 7.
Welsh hymn melody

1. Throned up-on the aw-ful tree, King of grief, I watch with thee.
2. Si-lent through those three dread hours, Wrest-ling with the e-vil pow'rs,
3. Hark, that cry that peals a-loud Up-ward through the whelm-ing cloud!
4. Lord, should fear and an-guish roll Dark-ly o'er my sin-ful soul,

Dark-ness veils thine an-guished face: None its lines of woe can trace:
Left a-lone with hu-man sin, Gloom a-round thee and with-in,
Thou, the Fa-ther's on-ly Son, Thou, his own A-noint-ed One,
Thou, who once wast thus be-reft That thine own might ne'er be left,

None can tell what pangs un-known Hold thee si-lent and a-lone.
Till th'ap-point-ed time is nigh, Till the Lamb of God may die.
Thou dost ask him—can it be?— "Why hast Thou for-sak-en Me?"
Teach me by that bit-ter cry In the gloom to know thee nigh. A-MEN.

## 184 THE LORD JESUS CHRIST

*Jesus ... suffered without the gate. Let us go forth therefore unto him without the camp, bearing his reproach.* Heb. 13:12-13

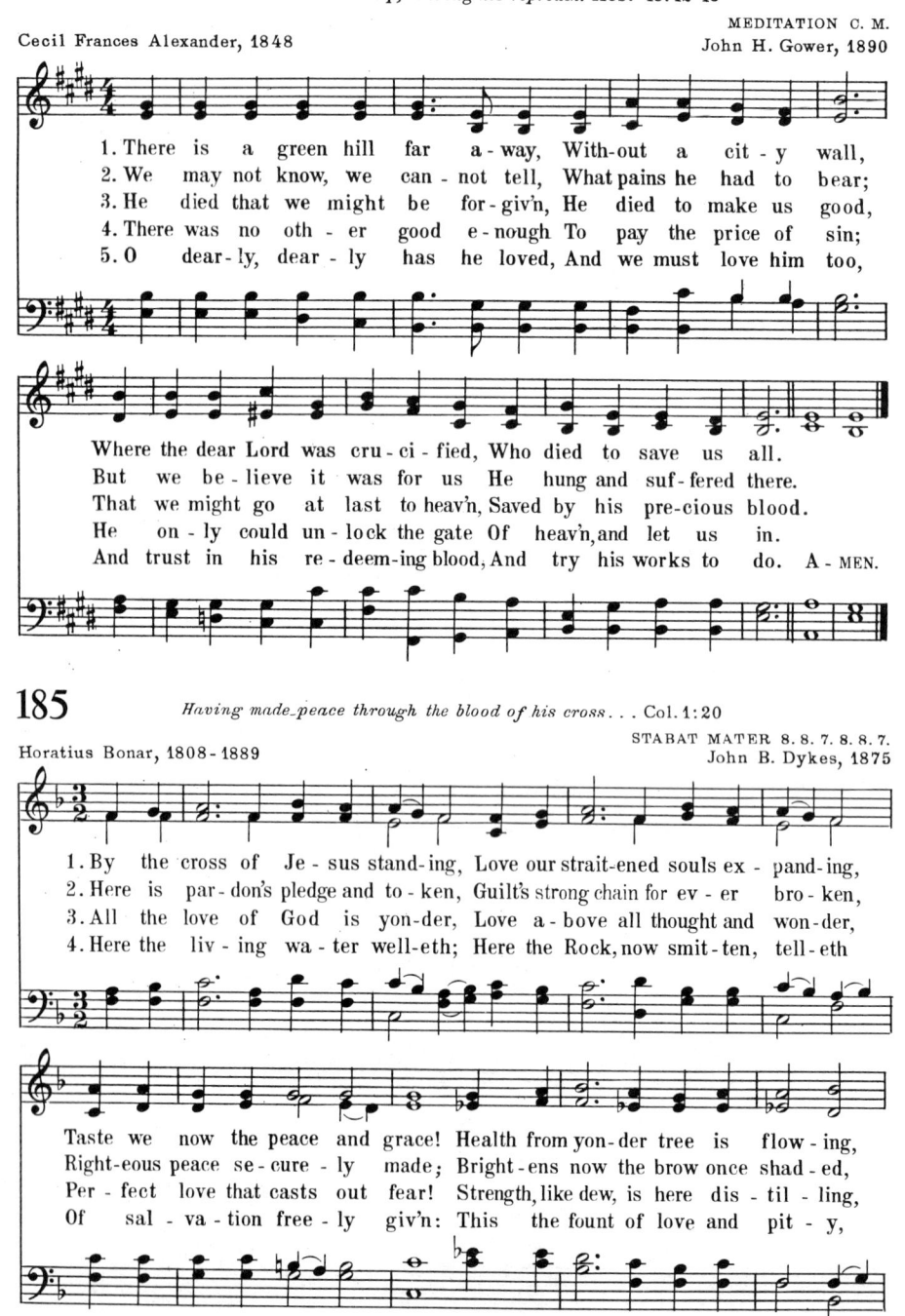

Cecil Frances Alexander, 1848  
MEDITATION C. M.  
John H. Gower, 1890

1. There is a green hill far away, Without a city wall,
2. We may not know, we cannot tell, What pains he had to bear;
3. He died that we might be for-giv'n, He died to make us good,
4. There was no other good enough To pay the price of sin;
5. O dearly, dearly has he loved, And we must love him too,

Where the dear Lord was crucified, Who died to save us all.
But we believe it was for us He hung and suffered there.
That we might go at last to heav'n, Saved by his precious blood.
He only could unlock the gate Of heav'n, and let us in.
And trust in his redeeming blood, And try his works to do. A-MEN.

## 185

*Having made peace through the blood of his cross...* Col. 1:20

Horatius Bonar, 1808-1889  
STABAT MATER 8.8.7.8.8.7.  
John B. Dykes, 1875

1. By the cross of Jesus standing, Love our strait-ened souls expanding,
2. Here is pardon's pledge and token, Guilt's strong chain for ever broken,
3. All the love of God is yonder, Love above all thought and wonder,
4. Here the living water welleth; Here the Rock, now smitten, telleth

Taste we now the peace and grace! Health from yonder tree is flowing,
Righteous peace securely made; Brightens now the brow once shaded,
Perfect love that casts out fear! Strength, like dew, is here distilling,
Of salvation freely giv'n: This the fount of love and pity,

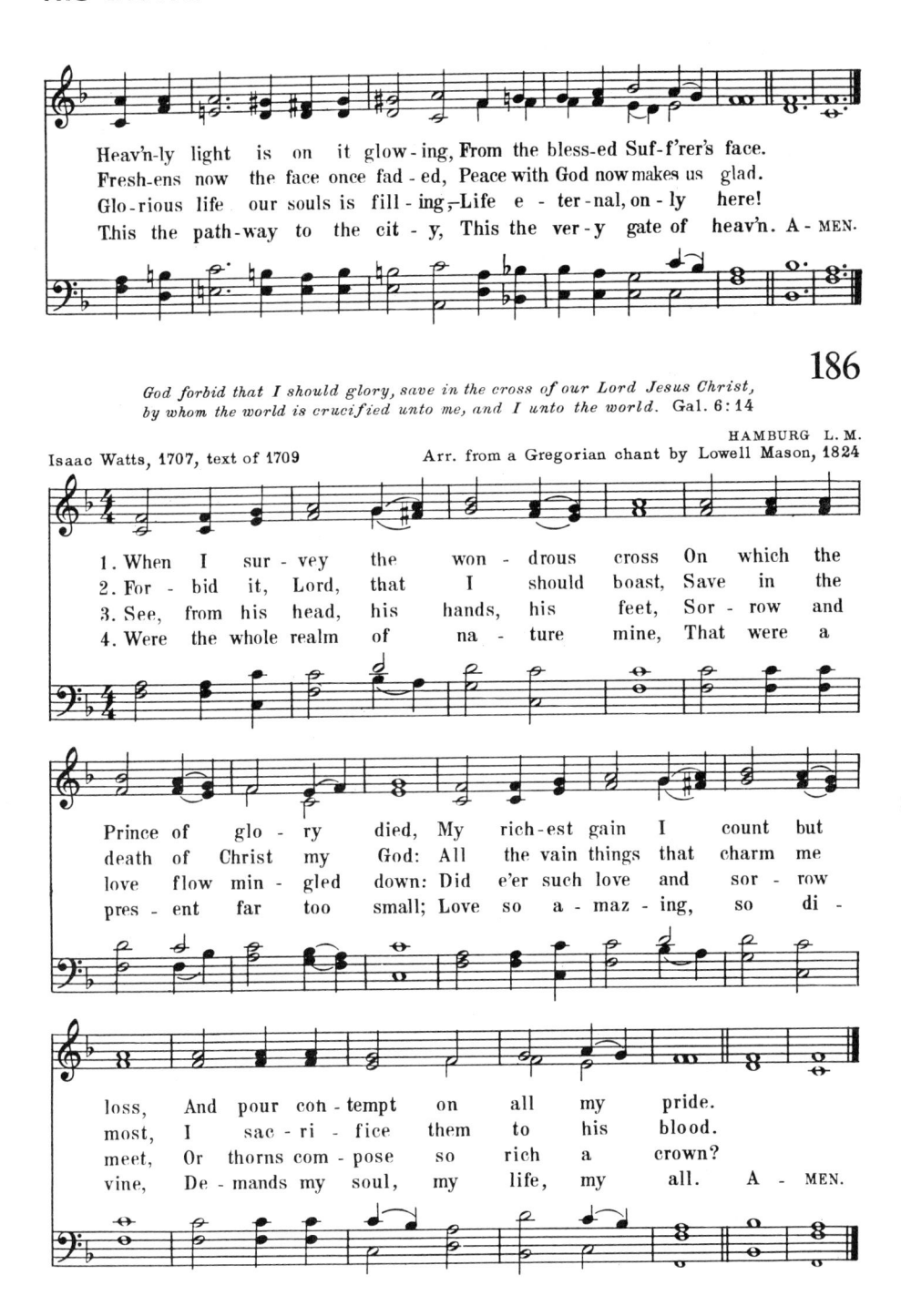

# HIS DEATH

Heav'n-ly light is on it glow-ing, From the bless-ed Suf-f'rer's face.
Fresh-ens now the face once fad-ed, Peace with God now makes us glad.
Glo-rious life our souls is fill-ing, Life e-ter-nal, on-ly here!
This the path-way to the cit-y, This the ver-y gate of heav'n. A-MEN.

**186**

*God forbid that I should glory, save in the cross of our Lord Jesus Christ, by whom the world is crucified unto me, and I unto the world. Gal. 6:14*

Isaac Watts, 1707, text of 1709

HAMBURG L. M.
Arr. from a Gregorian chant by Lowell Mason, 1824

1. When I sur-vey the won-drous cross On which the Prince of glo-ry died, My rich-est gain I count but loss, And pour con-tempt on all my pride.
2. For-bid it, Lord, that I should boast, Save in the death of Christ my God: All the vain things that charm me most, I sac-ri-fice them to his blood.
3. See, from his head, his hands, his feet, Sor-row and love flow min-gled down: Did e'er such love and sor-row meet, Or thorns com-pose so rich a crown?
4. Were the whole realm of na-ture mine, That were a pres-ent far too small; Love so a-maz-ing, so di-vine, De-mands my soul, my life, my all. A-MEN.

## 187. THE LORD JESUS CHRIST

*Jesus ... said, It is finished: and he bowed his head, and gave up the ghost.* John 19:30

Jonathan Evans, 1784; alt.
BRYN CALFARIA 8. 7. 8. 7. 4. 4. 4. 7. 7.
William Owen, 1814-1893

1. Hark! the voice of love and mer-cy Sounds a-loud from Cal-va-ry;
2. "It is fin-ished!" O what pleas-ure Do these pre-cious words af-ford;
3. Fin-ished all the types and shad-ows Of the ce-re-mo-nial law;
4. Tune your harps a-new, ye ser-aphs, Join to sing the glo-rious theme;

See, it rends the rocks a-sun-der, Shakes the earth, and veils the sky:
Heav'n-ly bless-ings, with-out meas-ure, Flow to us from Christ the Lord:
Fin-ished all that God had prom-ised; Death and hell no more shall awe:
All in earth, and all in heav-en, Join to praise Em-man-uel's Name:

"It is fin-ished!" "It is fin-ished!" "It is fin-ished!"
"It is fin-ished!" "It is fin-ished!" "It is fin-ished!"
"It is fin-ished!" "It is fin-ished!" "It is fin-ished!"
Al-le-lu-ia! Al-le-lu-ia! Al-le-lu-ia!

Hear the dy-ing Sav-iour cry; Hear the dy-ing Sav-iour cry.
Saints the dy-ing words re-cord; Saints the dy-ing words re-cord.
Saints, from hence your com-fort draw; Saints, from hence your com-fort draw.
Glo-ry to the bleed-ing Lamb! Glo-ry to the bleed-ing Lamb! A-MEN.

# HIS DEATH 188

*In that day there shall be a fountain opened ... for sin and for uncleanness.* Zech. 13:1

William Cowper, 1771

FOUNTAIN 8. 6. 8. 6. 6. 6. 8. 6.
Lowell Mason, 1830

1. There is a foun-tain filled with blood, Drawn from Im-man-uel's veins;
2. The dy-ing thief re-joiced to see That foun-tain in his day;
3. E'er since by faith I saw the stream Thy flow-ing wounds sup-ply,
4. Dear dy-ing Lamb, thy pre-cious blood Shall nev-er lose its power,

And sin-ners, plunged be-neath that flood, Lose all their guilt-y stains:
And there have I, as vile as he, Washed all my sins a-way:
Re-deem-ing love has been my theme, And shall be till I die:
Till all the ran-somed church of God Be saved, to sin no more:

Lose all their guilt-y stains, Lose all their guilt-y stains;
Washed all my sins a-way, Washed all my sins a-way;
And shall be till I die, And shall be till I die;
Be saved, to sin no more, Be saved, to sin no more;

And sin-ners, plunged be-neath that flood, Lose all their guilt-y stains.
And there have I, as vile as he, Washed all my sins a-way.
Re-deem-ing love has been my theme, And shall be till I die.
Till all the ran-somed church of God Be saved, to sin no more. A-MEN.

See also AZMON, No. 133

## 189 THE LORD JESUS CHRIST

*Blessed are they whose iniquities are forgiven, and whose sins are covered.* Rom. 4:7

Walter Shirley, 1770
Based on James Allen, 1757

CROSS OF JESUS 8.7.8.7.
Sir John Stainer, 1887

1. Sweet the moments, rich in blessing, Which before the cross I spend, Life, and health, and peace possessing, From the sinner's dying friend.
2. Here I rest, in wonder viewing All my sins on Jesus laid, Here I see redemption flowing From the sacrifice he made.
3. Here I find the dawn of heaven, While upon the cross I gaze, See my trespasses forgiven, And my songs of triumph raise.
4. O that, near the cross abiding, I may to the Saviour cleave, Nought with him my heart dividing, All for him content to leave. A-MEN.

## 190

*Forasmuch as ye know that ye were not redeemed with corruptible things...but with the precious blood of Christ...* I Peter 1:18, 19

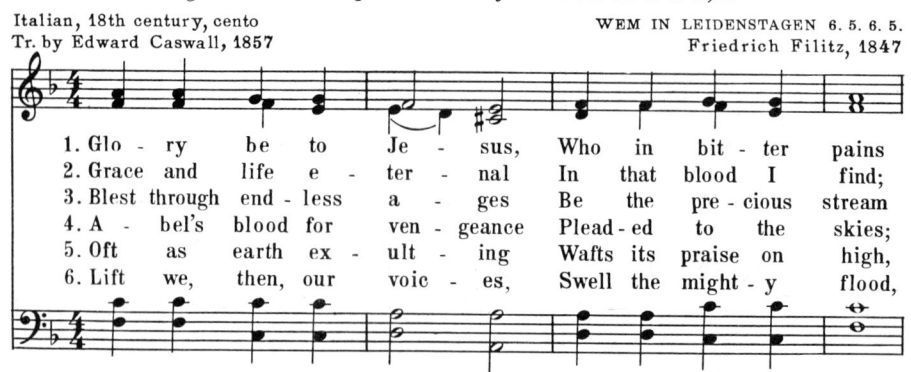

Italian, 18th century, cento
Tr. by Edward Caswall, 1857

WEM IN LEIDENSTAGEN 6.5.6.5.
Friedrich Filitz, 1847

1. Glory be to Jesus, Who in bitter pains
2. Grace and life eternal In that blood I find;
3. Blest through endless ages Be the precious stream
4. Abel's blood for vengeance Pleaded to the skies;
5. Oft as earth exulting Wafts its praise on high,
6. Lift we, then, our voices, Swell the mighty flood,

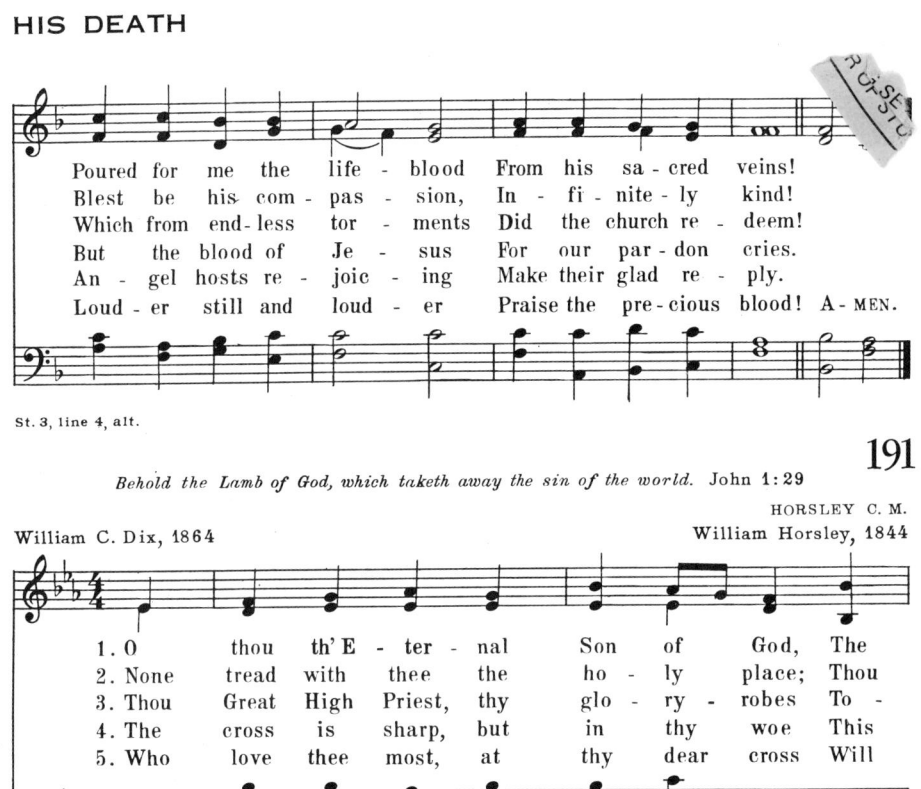

# HIS DEATH

Poured for me the life-blood From his sa-cred veins!
Blest be his com-pas-sion, In-fi-nite-ly kind!
Which from end-less tor-ments Did the church re-deem!
But the blood of Je-sus For our par-don cries.
An-gel hosts re-joic-ing Make their glad re-ply.
Loud-er still and loud-er Praise the pre-cious blood! A-MEN.

St. 3, line 4, alt.

*Behold the Lamb of God, which taketh away the sin of the world.* John 1:29

William C. Dix, 1864

HORSLEY C. M.
William Horsley, 1844

191

1. O thou th' E-ter-nal Son of God, The Lamb for sin-ners slain, We wor-ship, while thy head is bowed In a-go-ny and pain.
2. None tread with thee the ho-ly place; Thou suf-fer-est a-lone; Thine is the per-fect sac-ri-fice, Which on-ly can a-tone.
3. Thou Great High Priest, thy glo-ry-robes To-day are laid a-side; And hu-man sor-rows, Son of Man, Thy God-head seem to hide.
4. The cross is sharp, but in thy woe This is the light-est part; Our sin it is which pierc-es thee, And breaks thy sa-cred heart.
5. Who love thee most, at thy dear cross Will tru-est, Lord, a-bide; Make thou that cross our on-ly hope, O Je-sus cru-ci-fied. A-MEN.

# 192 THE LORD JESUS CHRIST

*We did esteem him stricken, smitten of God, and afflicted.* Isa. 53:4

Thomas Kelly, 1804

O MEIN JESU, ICH MUSS STERBEN 8.7.8.7. D.
*Geistliche Volkslieder*, Paderborn, 1850

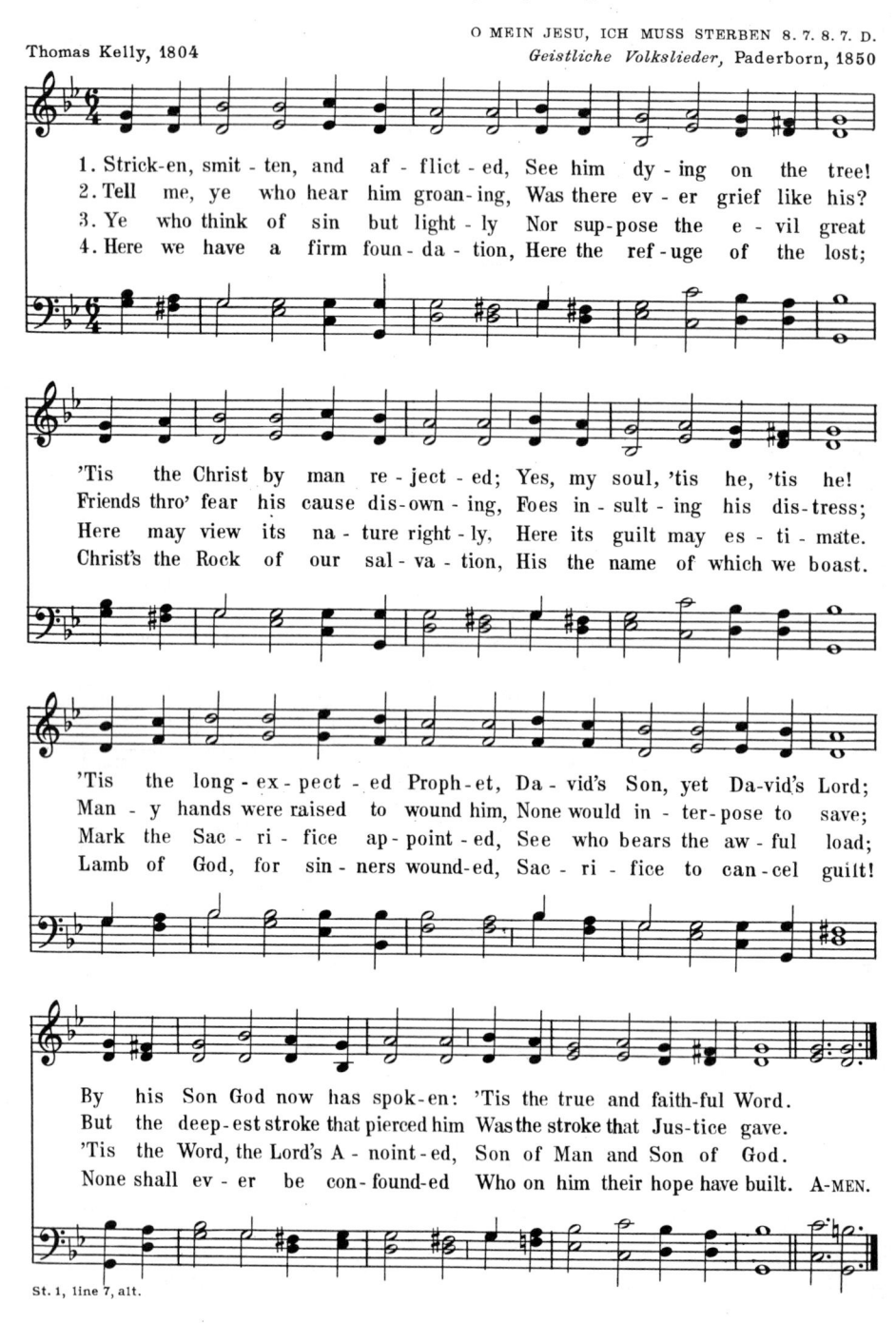

1. Strick-en, smit-ten, and af-flict-ed, See him dy-ing on the tree!
'Tis the Christ by man re-ject-ed; Yes, my soul, 'tis he, 'tis he!
'Tis the long-ex-pect-ed Proph-et, Da-vid's Son, yet Da-vid's Lord;
By his Son God now has spok-en: 'Tis the true and faith-ful Word.

2. Tell me, ye who hear him groan-ing, Was there ev-er grief like his?
Friends thro' fear his cause dis-own-ing, Foes in-sult-ing his dis-tress;
Man-y hands were raised to wound him, None would in-ter-pose to save;
But the deep-est stroke that pierced him Was the stroke that Jus-tice gave.

3. Ye who think of sin but light-ly Nor sup-pose the e-vil great
Here may view its na-ture right-ly, Here its guilt may es-ti-mate.
Mark the Sac-ri-fice ap-point-ed, See who bears the aw-ful load;
'Tis the Word, the Lord's A-noint-ed, Son of Man and Son of God.

4. Here we have a firm foun-da-tion, Here the ref-uge of the lost;
Christ's the Rock of our sal-va-tion, His the name of which we boast.
Lamb of God, for sin-ners wound-ed, Sac-ri-fice to can-cel guilt!
None shall ev-er be con-found-ed Who on him their hope have built. A-MEN.

St. 1, line 7, alt.

# HIS DEATH

### 193

*Surely he hath borne our griefs, and carried our sorrows: yet we did esteem him stricken, smitten of God, and afflicted. Isa. 53:4*

Arthur T. Russell, 1851

MEIRIONYDD 7. 6. 7. 6. D.
Welsh hymn melody
Ascribed to William Lloyd, 1840

1. O Jesus, we adore thee, Upon the cross, our King!
We bow our hearts before thee, Thy gracious Name we sing.
That Name hath brought salvation, That Name in life our stay,
Our peace, our consolation, When life shall fade away.

2. Yet doth the world disdain thee, Still passing by the cross;
Lord, may our hearts retain thee; All else we count but loss.
Ah, Lord, our sins arraigned thee, And nailed thee to the tree:
Our pride, our Lord, disdained thee; Yet deign our hope to be.

3. O glorious King, we bless thee, No longer pass thee by;
O Jesus, we confess thee The Son enthroned on high.
Lord, grant to us remission; Life through thy death restore;
Yea, grant us the fruition Of life for evermore. A-MEN.

Music used by permission of the Executors of the late Dr. Basil Harwood.

## 194 THE LORD JESUS CHRIST

*Looking unto Jesus...who for the joy that was set before him endured the cross...and is set down at the right hand of the throne of God.* Heb. 12:2

Venantius H.C. Fortunatus, c. 530-609
Tr. by William Mair, 1830-1920, and A.W. Wotherspoon, b. 1853

ARDUDWY 8.7.8.7.8.7.
John Roberts, 1822-1877

1. Sing, my tongue, how glorious battle Glorious victory became;
And above the cross, his trophy, Tell the triumph and the fame:
Tell how he, the earth's Redeemer, By his death for man o'ercame.

2. Thirty years fulfilled among us— Perfect life in low estate—
Born for this, and self-surrendered, To his passion dedicate,
On the cross the Lamb is lifted, For his people immolate.

3. Unto God be laud and honor: To the Father, to the Son,
To the mighty Spirit, glory— Ever Three and ever One:
Pow'r and glory in the highest While eternal ages run. A-MEN.

Words used by permission.

## 195

*He was wounded for our transgressions, he was bruised for our iniquities...* Isa. 53:5

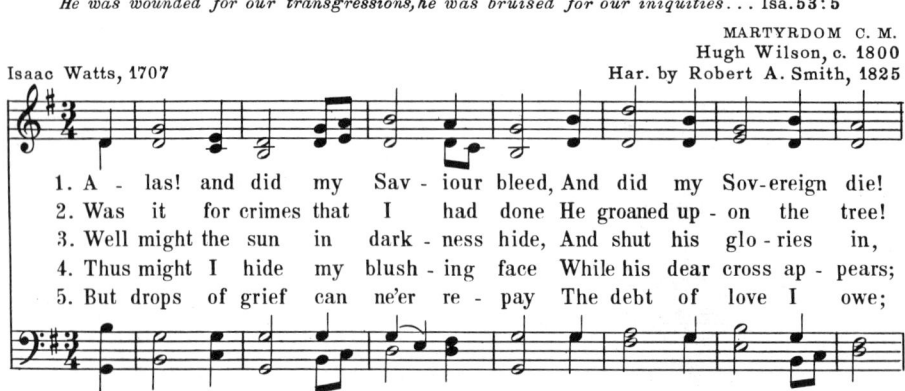

Isaac Watts, 1707

MARTYRDOM C. M.
Hugh Wilson, c. 1800
Har. by Robert A. Smith, 1825

1. Alas! and did my Saviour bleed, And did my Sov'reign die!
2. Was it for crimes that I had done He groaned upon the tree!
3. Well might the sun in darkness hide, And shut his glories in,
4. Thus might I hide my blushing face While his dear cross appears;
5. But drops of grief can ne'er repay The debt of love I owe;

# HIS DEATH

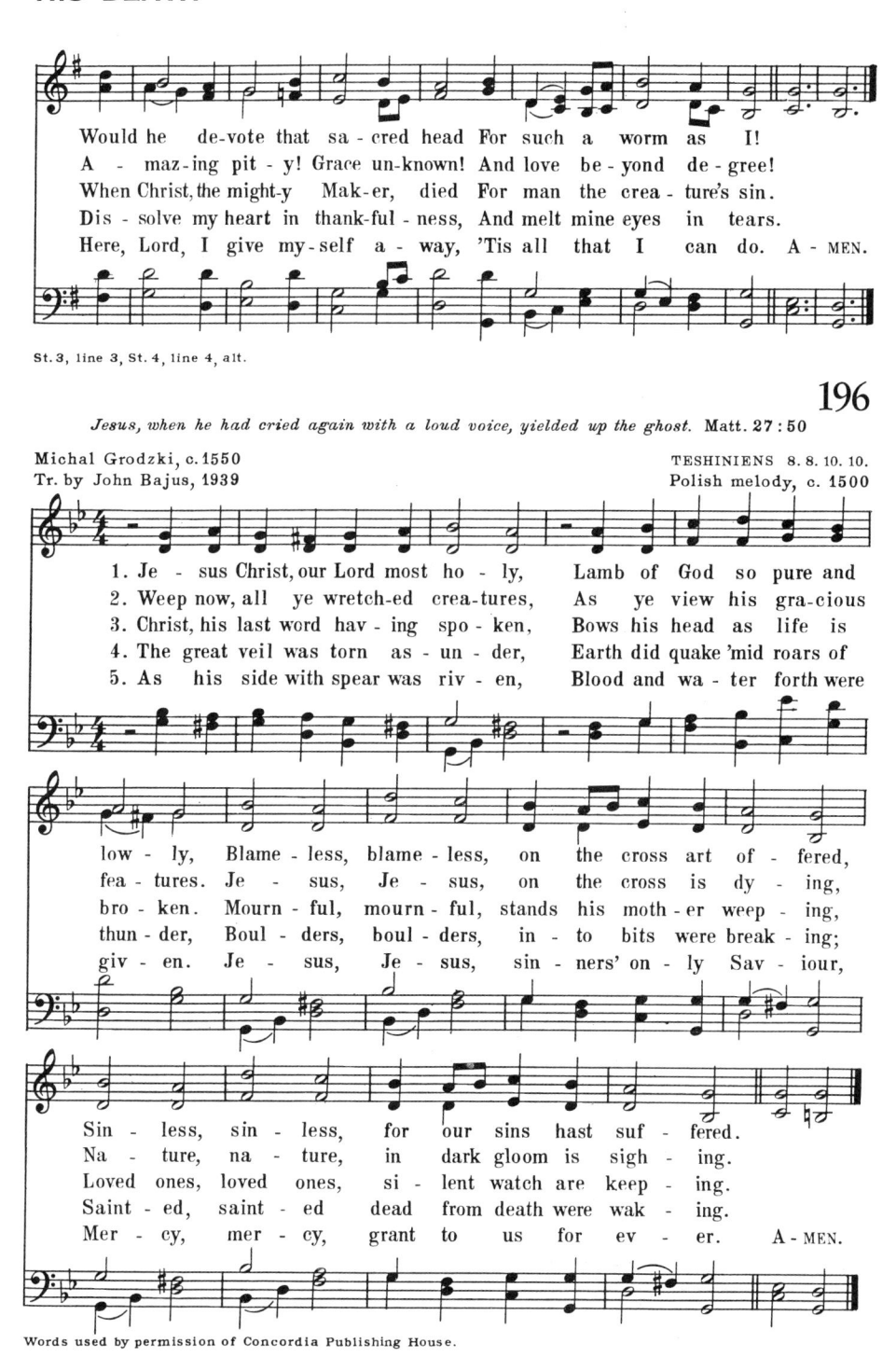

Would he de-vote that sa-cred head For such a worm as I!
A-maz-ing pit-y! Grace un-known! And love be-yond de-gree!
When Christ, the might-y Mak-er, died For man the crea-ture's sin.
Dis-solve my heart in thank-ful-ness, And melt mine eyes in tears.
Here, Lord, I give my-self a-way, 'Tis all that I can do. A-MEN.

St. 3, line 3, St. 4, line 4, alt.

*Jesus, when he had cried again with a loud voice, yielded up the ghost.* Matt. 27:50

**196**

Michal Grodzki, c. 1550  TESHINIENS 8. 8. 10. 10.
Tr. by John Bajus, 1939  Polish melody, c. 1500

1. Je-sus Christ, our Lord most ho-ly, Lamb of God so pure and low-ly, Blame-less, blame-less, on the cross art of-fered, Sin-less, sin-less, for our sins hast suf-fered.
2. Weep now, all ye wretch-ed crea-tures, As ye view his gra-cious fea-tures. Je-sus, Je-sus, on the cross is dy-ing, Na-ture, na-ture, in dark gloom is sigh-ing.
3. Christ, his last word hav-ing spo-ken, Bows his head as life is bro-ken. Mourn-ful, mourn-ful, stands his moth-er weep-ing, Loved ones, loved ones, si-lent watch are keep-ing.
4. The great veil was torn as-un-der, Earth did quake 'mid roars of thun-der, Boul-ders, boul-ders, in-to bits were break-ing; Saint-ed, saint-ed dead from death were wak-ing.
5. As his side with spear was riv-en, Blood and wa-ter forth were giv-en. Je-sus, Je-sus, sin-ners' on-ly Sav-iour, Mer-cy, mer-cy, grant to us for ev-er. A-MEN.

Words used by permission of Concordia Publishing House.

## 197 THE LORD JESUS CHRIST

*Behold, Jesus met them, saying, All hail.* Matt. 28:9

John of Damascus, 8th century
Tr. by John Mason Neale, 1862
St. 1, line 1, alt.

LANCASHIRE 7. 6. 7. 6. D.
Henry Smart, 1836

1. The day of res-ur-rec-tion! Earth, tell it out a-broad;
2. Our hearts be pure from e-vil, That we may see a-right
3. Now let the heav'ns be joy-ful, Let earth her song be-gin;

The Pass-o-ver of glad-ness, The Pass-o-ver of God.
The Lord in rays e-ter-nal Of res-ur-rec-tion-light;
Let the round world keep tri-umph, And all that is there-in;

From death to life e-ter-nal, From this world to the sky,
And, lis-tening to his ac-cents, May hear, so calm and plain,
In-vis-i-ble and vis-i-ble, Their notes let all things blend,

Our Christ hath brought us o-ver With hymns of vic-to-ry.
His own "All hail!" and hear-ing, May raise the vic-tor strain.
For Christ the Lord hath ris-en, Our Joy that hath no end. A-MEN.

# HIS RESURRECTION 198

*Go quickly, and tell his disciples that he is risen from the dead... Matt. 28:7*

St. 1, anon.; St. 2-3, Arnold's
*Compleat Psalmodist*, 1740;
St. 4, Charles Wesley, 1740; alt.

EASTER HYMN 7.7.7.7. with alleluias
From *Lyra Davidica*, 1708; alt.

1. Jesus Christ is risen today, Alleluia!
2. Hymns of praise then let us sing, Alleluia!
3. But the pains which he endured, Alleluia!
4. Sing we to our God above, Alleluia!

Our triumphant holy day, Alleluia!
Unto Christ our heav'nly King, Alleluia!
Our salvation have procured; Alleluia!
Praise eternal as his love; Alleluia!

Who did once, upon the cross, Alleluia!
Who endured the cross and grave, Alleluia!
Now above the sky he's King, Alleluia!
Praise him, all ye heav'nly host, Alleluia!

Suffer to redeem our loss. Alleluia!
Sinners to redeem and save. Alleluia!
Where the angels ever sing. Alleluia!
Father, Son, and Holy Ghost. Alleluia! A-MEN.

## 199 THE LORD JESUS CHRIST

*Now is Christ risen from the dead, and become the firstfruits of them that slept.* I Cor. 15:20

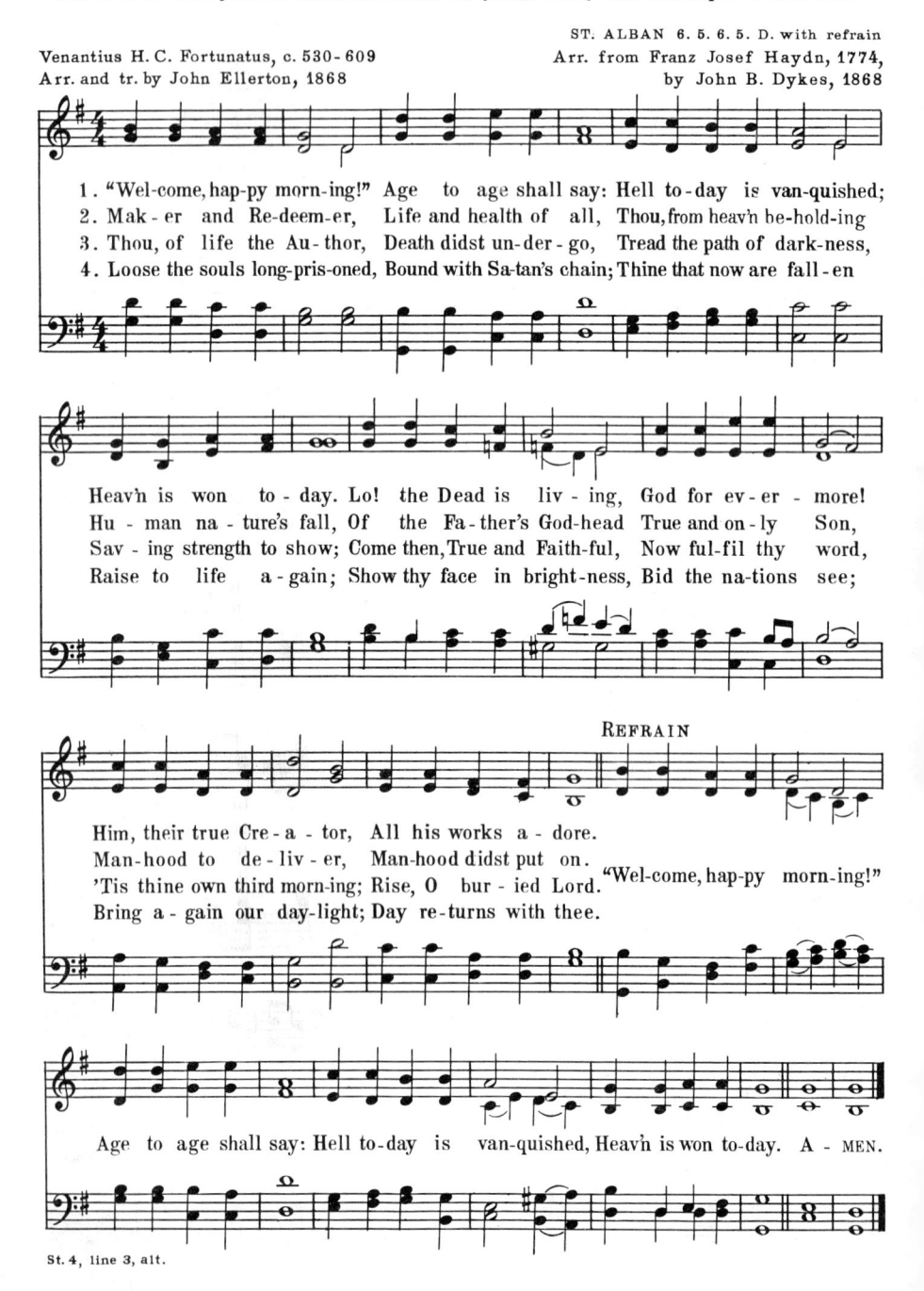

Venantius H. C. Fortunatus, c. 530-609
Arr. and tr. by John Ellerton, 1868

ST. ALBAN 6. 5. 6. 5. D. with refrain
Arr. from Franz Josef Haydn, 1774,
by John B. Dykes, 1868

1. "Wel-come, hap-py morn-ing!" Age to age shall say: Hell to-day is van-quished;
2. Mak-er and Re-deem-er, Life and health of all, Thou, from heav'n be-hold-ing
3. Thou, of life the Au-thor, Death didst un-der-go, Tread the path of dark-ness,
4. Loose the souls long-pris-oned, Bound with Sa-tan's chain; Thine that now are fall-en

Heav'n is won to-day. Lo! the Dead is liv-ing, God for ev-er-more!
Hu-man na-ture's fall, Of the Fa-ther's God-head True and on-ly Son,
Sav-ing strength to show; Come then, True and Faith-ful, Now ful-fil thy word,
Raise to life a-gain; Show thy face in bright-ness, Bid the na-tions see;

REFRAIN

Him, their true Cre-a-tor, All his works a-dore.
Man-hood to de-liv-er, Man-hood didst put on. "Wel-come, hap-py morn-ing!"
'Tis thine own third morn-ing; Rise, O bur-ied Lord.
Bring a-gain our day-light; Day re-turns with thee.

Age to age shall say: Hell to-day is van-quished, Heav'n is won to-day. A-MEN.

St. 4, line 3, alt.

# HIS RESURRECTION

**200**

*I will sing unto the Lord, for he hath triumphed gloriously... Ex. 15:1*

John of Damascus, 8th century  
Tr. by John Mason Neale, 1853

ST. KEVIN 7. 6. 7. 6. D.  
Sir Arthur S. Sullivan, 1872

1. Come, ye faith-ful, raise the strain Of tri-umph-ant glad-ness;
2. 'Tis the spring of souls to-day; Christ hath burst his pris-on,
3. Now the queen of sea-sons, bright With the day of splen-dor,
4. Nei-ther might the gates of death, Nor the tomb's dark por-tal,

God hath brought his Is-ra-el In-to joy from sad-ness;  
And from three days' sleep in death As a sun hath ris-en;  
With the roy-al feast of feasts, Comes its joy to ren-der;  
Nor the watch-ers, nor the seal Hold thee as a mor-tal:

Loosed from Pha-raoh's bit-ter yoke Ja-cob's sons and daugh-ters;  
All the win-ter of our sins, Long and dark, is fly-ing  
Comes to glad Je-ru-sa-lem, Who with true af-fec-tion  
But to-day a-midst the twelve Thou didst stand, be-stow-ing

Led them with un-moist-ened foot Through the Red Sea wa-ters.  
From his light, to whom we give Laud and praise un-dy-ing.  
Wel-comes in un-wea-ried strains Je-sus' res-ur-rec-tion.  
That thy peace, which ev-er-more Pass-eth hu-man know-ing. A-MEN.

# 201 THE LORD JESUS CHRIST

*Ought not Christ to have suffered these things, and to enter into his glory?* Luke 24:26

Anon. (Latin)  
Tr. by Francis Pott, 1861

PALESTRINA 8.8.8. with alleluias  
Arr. from Giovanni P. da Palestrina, 1591

Al - le - lu - ia! Al - le - lu - ia! Al - le - lu - ia!

1. The strife is o'er, the bat-tle done; The vic-to-ry of life is won;
2. The pow'rs of death have done their worst, But Christ their le-gions hath dis-persed:
3. The three sad days have quick-ly sped; He ris - es glo - rious from the dead:
4. He closed the yawn - ing gates of hell; The bars from heav'n's high por-tals fell:
5. Lord, by the stripes which wound-ed thee, From death's dread sting thy serv-ants free,

The song of tri-umph has be-gun. Al-le-lu-ia!
Let shouts of ho-ly joy out-burst. Al-le-lu-ia!
All glo-ry to our ris-en Head! Al-le-lu-ia!
Let hymns of praise his tri-umphs tell. Al-le-lu-ia!
That we may live and sing to thee, Al-le-lu-ia! A-MEN.

# 202

*And having spoiled principalities and powers, he made a show of them openly, triumphing over them...* Col. 2:15

Cento, based on John Mason Neale, 1854

WALTHAM L. M.  
J. Baptiste Calkin, 1872

1. Lift up, lift up your voic-es now; The whole wide world re-joic-es now:
2. In vain with stone the cave they barr'd; In vain the watch kept ward and guard:
3. He binds in chains the an-cient foe; A count-less host he frees from woe,
4. And all he did, and all he bare, He gives us as our own to share;
5. O Vic - tor, aid us in the fight, And lead through death to realms of light:
6. Thy flock, from sin and death set free, Glad al-le-lu-ias raise to thee;

## HIS RESURRECTION

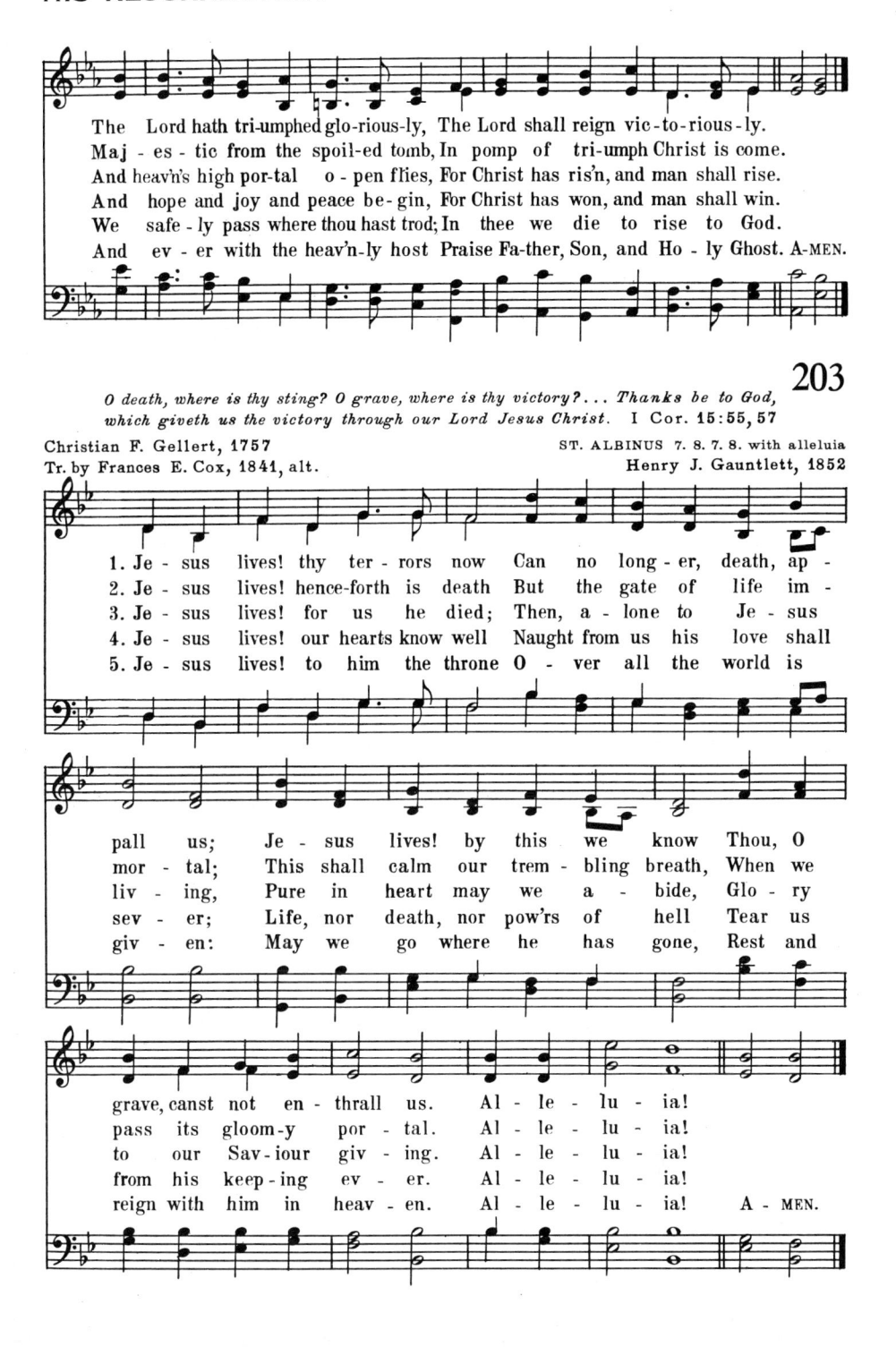

The Lord hath triumphed glo-rious-ly, The Lord shall reign vic-to-rious-ly.
Maj - es - tic from the spoil-ed tomb, In pomp of tri-umph Christ is come.
And heav'n's high por-tal o - pen flies, For Christ has ris'n, and man shall rise.
And hope and joy and peace be-gin, For Christ has won, and man shall win.
We safe - ly pass where thou hast trod; In thee we die to rise to God.
And ev - er with the heav'n-ly host Praise Fa-ther, Son, and Ho - ly Ghost. A-MEN.

*O death, where is thy sting? O grave, where is thy victory?... Thanks be to God, which giveth us the victory through our Lord Jesus Christ.* I Cor. 15:55, 57

Christian F. Gellert, 1757
Tr. by Frances E. Cox, 1841, alt.

ST. ALBINUS 7. 8. 7. 8. with alleluia
Henry J. Gauntlett, 1852

**203**

1. Je - sus lives! thy ter - rors now Can no long - er, death, ap -
2. Je - sus lives! hence-forth is death But the gate of life im -
3. Je - sus lives! for us he died; Then, a - lone to Je - sus
4. Je - sus lives! our hearts know well Naught from us his love shall
5. Je - sus lives! to him the throne O - ver all the world is

pall us; Je - sus lives! by this we know Thou, O
mor - tal; This shall calm our trem - bling breath, When we
liv - ing, Pure in heart may we a - bide, Glo - ry
sev - er; Life, nor death, nor pow'rs of hell Tear us
giv - en: May we go where he has gone, Rest and

grave, canst not en - thrall us. Al - le - lu - ia!
pass its gloom-y por - tal. Al - le - lu - ia!
to our Sav - iour giv - ing. Al - le - lu - ia!
from his keep - ing ev - er. Al - le - lu - ia!
reign with him in heav - en. Al - le - lu - ia! A - MEN.

## 204                           THE LORD JESUS CHRIST

*But now is Christ risen from the dead, and become the firstfruits of them that slept.* I Cor. 15: 20

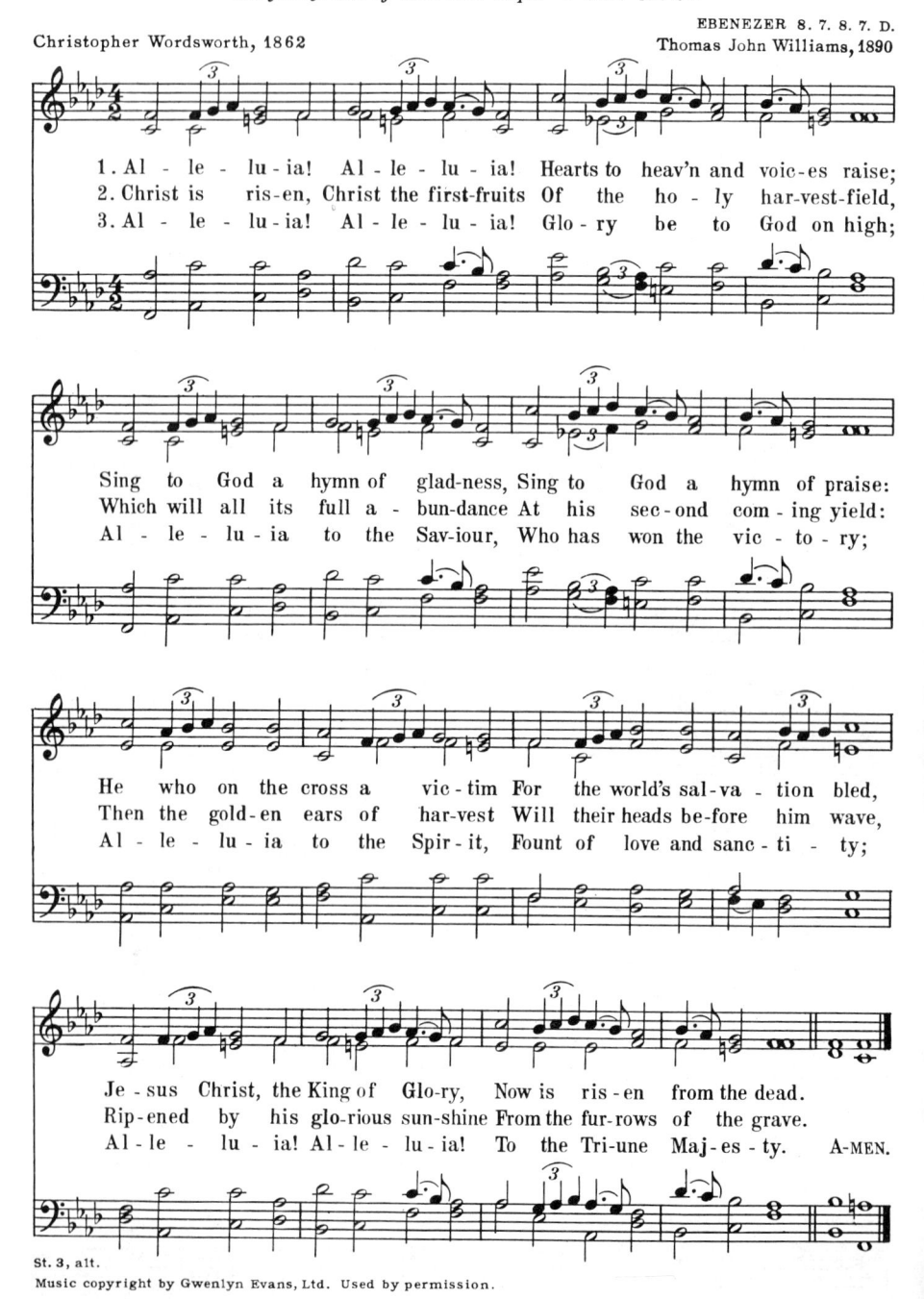

Christopher Wordsworth, 1862                 EBENEZER 8. 7. 8. 7. D.
                                          Thomas John Williams, 1890

1. Al - le - lu - ia! Al - le - lu - ia! Hearts to heav'n and voic-es raise;
Sing to God a hymn of glad-ness, Sing to God a hymn of praise:
He who on the cross a vic-tim For the world's sal-va-tion bled,
Je-sus Christ, the King of Glo-ry, Now is ris-en from the dead.

2. Christ is ris-en, Christ the first-fruits Of the ho-ly har-vest-field,
Which will all its full a-bun-dance At his sec-ond com-ing yield:
Then the gold-en ears of har-vest Will their heads be-fore him wave,
Rip-ened by his glo-rious sun-shine From the fur-rows of the grave.

3. Al - le - lu - ia! Al - le - lu - ia! Glo-ry be to God on high;
Al - le - lu - ia to the Sav-iour, Who has won the vic-to-ry;
Al - le - lu - ia to the Spir-it, Fount of love and sanc-ti-ty;
Al - le - lu - ia! Al - le - lu - ia! To the Tri-une Maj-es-ty. A-MEN.

St. 3, alt.
Music copyright by Gwenlyn Evans, Ltd. Used by permission.

# HIS RESURRECTION

## 205

*Thanks be to God, which giveth us the victory through our Lord Jesus Christ.* I Cor. 15:57

Charles Wesley, 1739

LLANFAIR 7. 7. 7. 7. with alleluias
Robert Williams, 1817

1. "Christ the Lord is risen to-day," Alleluia!
2. Vain the stone, the watch, the seal; Alleluia!
3. Lives again our glorious King; Alleluia!
4. Soar we now where Christ has led, Alleluia!
5. Hail, the Lord of earth and heav'n! Alleluia!

Sons of men and angels say; Alleluia!
Christ has burst the gates of hell: Alleluia!
Where, O death, is now thy sting? Alleluia!
Following our exalted Head; Alleluia!
Praise to thee by both be giv'n; Alleluia!

Raise your joys and triumphs high; Alleluia!
Death in vain forbids his rise; Alleluia!
Once he died, our souls to save; Alleluia!
Made like him, like him we rise; Alleluia!
Thee we greet triumphant now; Alleluia!

*In unison*

Sing, ye heav'ns, and earth, reply; Alleluia!
Christ hath opened Paradise. Alleluia!
Where thy victory, O grave? Alleluia!
Ours the cross, the grave, the skies. Alleluia!
Hail, the Resurrection Thou! Alleluia! A-MEN.

Harmony from *The Revised Church Hymnary* by permission of the Oxford University Press, London.

## 206. THE LORD JESUS CHRIST

*The angel of the Lord descended from heaven, and came and rolled back the stone from the door... Matt. 28:2*

Robert Lowry, 1874

CHRIST AROSE 11.10. with refrain
Robert Lowry

1. Low in the grave he lay— Jesus, my Saviour, Waiting the coming day—
2. Vainly they watch his bed— Jesus, my Saviour; Vainly they seal the dead—
3. Death cannot keep his prey— Jesus, my Saviour; He tore the bars away—

**REFRAIN** *Faster*

Jesus, my Lord.
Jesus, my Lord. Up from the grave he arose,
Jesus, my Lord.
 He arose!

With a mighty triumph o'er his foes.
 He arose!
He arose a victor from the dark domain, And he lives for ever with his saints to reign. He arose! He arose! Hallelujah! Christ arose! A-MEN.
 He arose! He arose!

# HIS RESURRECTION 207

*Whom God hath raised up, having loosed the pains of death: because it was not possible that he should be holden of it.* Acts 2:24

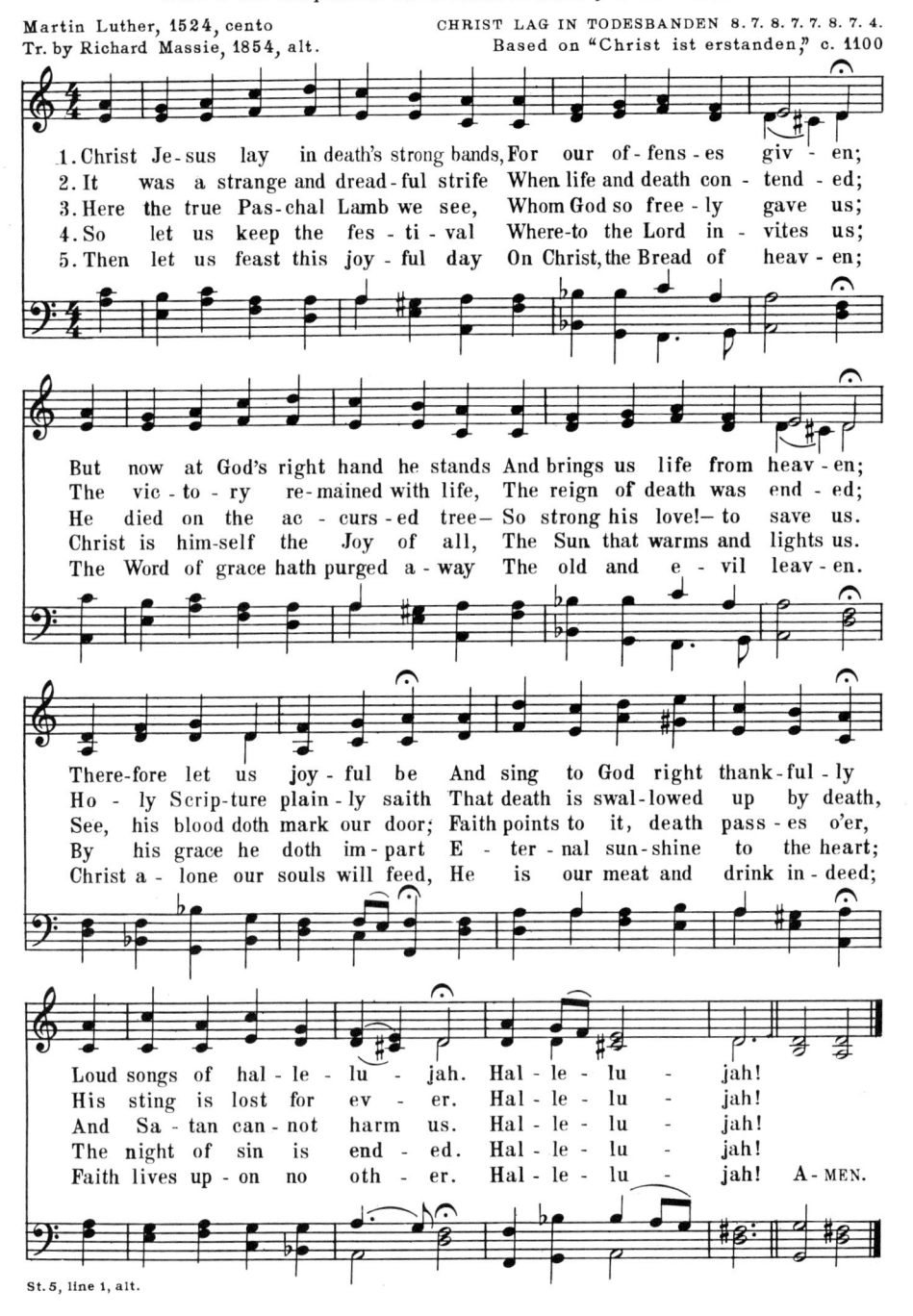

Martin Luther, 1524, cento
Tr. by Richard Massie, 1854, alt.

CHRIST LAG IN TODESBANDEN 8. 7. 8. 7. 7. 8. 7. 4.
Based on "Christ ist erstanden," c. 1100

1. Christ Je-sus lay in death's strong bands, For our of-fens-es giv-en;
2. It was a strange and dread-ful strife When life and death con-tend-ed;
3. Here the true Pas-chal Lamb we see, Whom God so free-ly gave us;
4. So let us keep the fes-ti-val Where-to the Lord in-vites us;
5. Then let us feast this joy-ful day On Christ, the Bread of heav-en;

But now at God's right hand he stands And brings us life from heav-en;
The vic-to-ry re-mained with life, The reign of death was end-ed;
He died on the ac-curs-ed tree— So strong his love!— to save us.
Christ is him-self the Joy of all, The Sun that warms and lights us.
The Word of grace hath purged a-way The old and e-vil leav-en.

There-fore let us joy-ful be And sing to God right thank-ful-ly
Ho-ly Scrip-ture plain-ly saith That death is swal-lowed up by death,
See, his blood doth mark our door; Faith points to it, death pass-es o'er,
By his grace he doth im-part E-ter-nal sun-shine to the heart;
Christ a-lone our souls will feed, He is our meat and drink in-deed;

Loud songs of hal-le-lu-jah. Hal-le-lu-jah!
His sting is lost for ev-er. Hal-le-lu-jah!
And Sa-tan can-not harm us. Hal-le-lu-jah!
The night of sin is end-ed. Hal-le-lu-jah!
Faith lives up-on no oth-er. Hal-le-lu-jah! A-MEN.

St. 5, line 1, alt.

# 208 THE LORD JESUS CHRIST

*Did not our heart burn within us, while he talked with us by the way, and while he opened to us the scriptures?* Luke 24:32

Patrick Miller Kirkland, b. 1857

KIRKLAND 6. 5. 6. 5. D.
David Evans, 1874-1948

1. Jesus, Lord, Redeemer, Once for sinners slain,
   Crucified in weakness, Raised in pow'r, to reign,
   Dwelling with the Father, Endless in thy days,
   Unto thee be glory, Honor, blessing, praise.

2. Faithful ones, communing, Toward the close of day,
   Desolate and weary, Met thee in the way.
   So, when sun is setting, Come to us, and show
   All the truth; and in us Make our hearts to glow.

3. In the upper chamber, Where the ten, in fear,
   Gathered sad and troubled, There thou didst appear.
   So, O Lord, this evening, Bid our sorrows cease;
   Breathing on us, Saviour, Say, "I give you peace." A-MEN.

Words used by permission of the Misses Kirkland, 3 Lingdale Road, West Kirby, Wirral, Cheshire, England.
Music from *The Revised Church Hymnary* by permission of the Oxford University Press, London.

# HIS RESURRECTION

## 209

*He is not here: for he is risen, as he said... Matt. 28:6*

Thomas Hastings, 1831  
HASTINGS 8.6.8.6.8.8.  
Thomas Hastings, 1831

1. How calm and beau-ti-ful the morn That gilds the sa-cred tomb, Where Christ the cru-ci-fied was borne, And veiled in mid-night gloom! O weep no more the Sav-iour slain; The Lord is risen; he lives a-gain.

2. Ye mourn-ing saints, dry ev-'ry tear For your de-part-ed Lord; Be-hold the place, he is not here, The tomb is all un-barred; The gates of death were closed in vain: The Lord is risen; he lives a-gain.

3. Now cheer-ful to the house of prayer Your ear-ly foot-steps bend; The Sav-iour will him-self be there, Your Ad-vo-cate and Friend: Once by the law your hopes were slain, But now in Christ ye live a-gain.

4. How tran-quil now the ris-ing day! 'Tis Je-sus still ap-pears, A ris-en Lord to chase a-way Your un-be-liev-ing fears: O weep no more your com-forts slain; The Lord is risen; he lives a-gain.

5. And when the shades of eve-ning fall, When life's last hour draws nigh, If Je-sus shine up-on the soul, How bliss-ful then to die! Since he has risen that once was slain, Ye die in Christ to live a-gain. A-MEN.

## 210 THE LORD JESUS CHRIST

*God is gone up with a shout, the Lord with the sound of a trumpet.* Psalm 47:5

Gottfried W. Sacer, 1661, cento
Tr. by Frances E. Cox, 1841, alt.

AUS MEINES HERZENS GRUNDE 7. 6. 7. 6. 6. 7. 7. 6.
*Neu Catechismus-Gesangbüchlein,*
Hamburg, 1598

1. Lo, God to heav'n as-cend-eth! Through-out its re-gions vast
With shouts tri-um-phant blend-eth The trum-pet's thrill-ing blast:
Sing praise to Christ the Lord; Sing praise with ex-ul-ta-tion,
King of each hea-then na-tion, The God of hosts a-dored!

2. With joy is heav'n re-sound-ing Christ's glad re-turn to see;
Be-hold the saints sur-round-ing The Lord who set them free.
Bright myr-iads, throng-ing, come; The cher-ub band re-joic-es,
And loud se-raph-ic voic-es All wel-come Je-sus home.

3. Our place he is pre-par-ing; To heav'n we, too, shall rise,
With him his glo-ry shar-ing, Be where our Treas-ure lies.
Be-stir thy-self, my soul! Where Je-sus Christ has en-tered,
There let thy hope be cen-tered; Press on-ward toward the goal.

4. Let all our thoughts be wing-ing To where thou didst as-cend,
And let our hearts be sing-ing: "We seek thee, Christ, our Friend,
Thee, God's ex-alt-ed Son, Our Life, and Way to heav-en,
To whom all pow-er is giv'n, Our Joy and Hope and Crown." A-MEN.

# HIS ASCENSION  211

*Thou hast ascended on high, thou hast led captivity captive* ... Psalm 68:18

Christopher Wordsworth, 1862

ST. ASAPH 8. 7. 8. 7. D.
William S. Bambridge, 1872

1. See, the Con-queror mounts in tri-umph; See the King in roy-al state,
2. Who is this that comes in glo-ry, With the trump of ju-bi-lee?
3. Thou hast raised our hu-man na-ture In the clouds to God's right hand;

Rid-ing on the clouds, his char-iot, To his heav'n-ly pal-ace gate:
Lord of bat-tles, God of ar-mies, He has gained the vic-to-ry;
There we sit in heav'n-ly plac-es, There with thee in glo-ry stand:

Hark! the choirs of an-gel voic-es Joy-ful Al-le-lu-ias sing
He who on the cross did suf-fer, He who from the grave a-rose,
Je-sus reigns, a-dored by an-gels, Man with God is on the throne;

And the por-tals high are lift-ed To re-ceive their heav'n-ly King.
He has van-quished sin and Sa-tan, He by death has spoiled his foes.
Might-y Lord, in thine as-cen-sion We by faith be-hold our own. A-MEN.

## 212 THE LORD JESUS CHRIST

*Why stand ye gazing up into heaven? this same Jesus, which is taken up from you into heaven, shall so come in like manner as ye have seen him go into heaven.* Acts 1:11

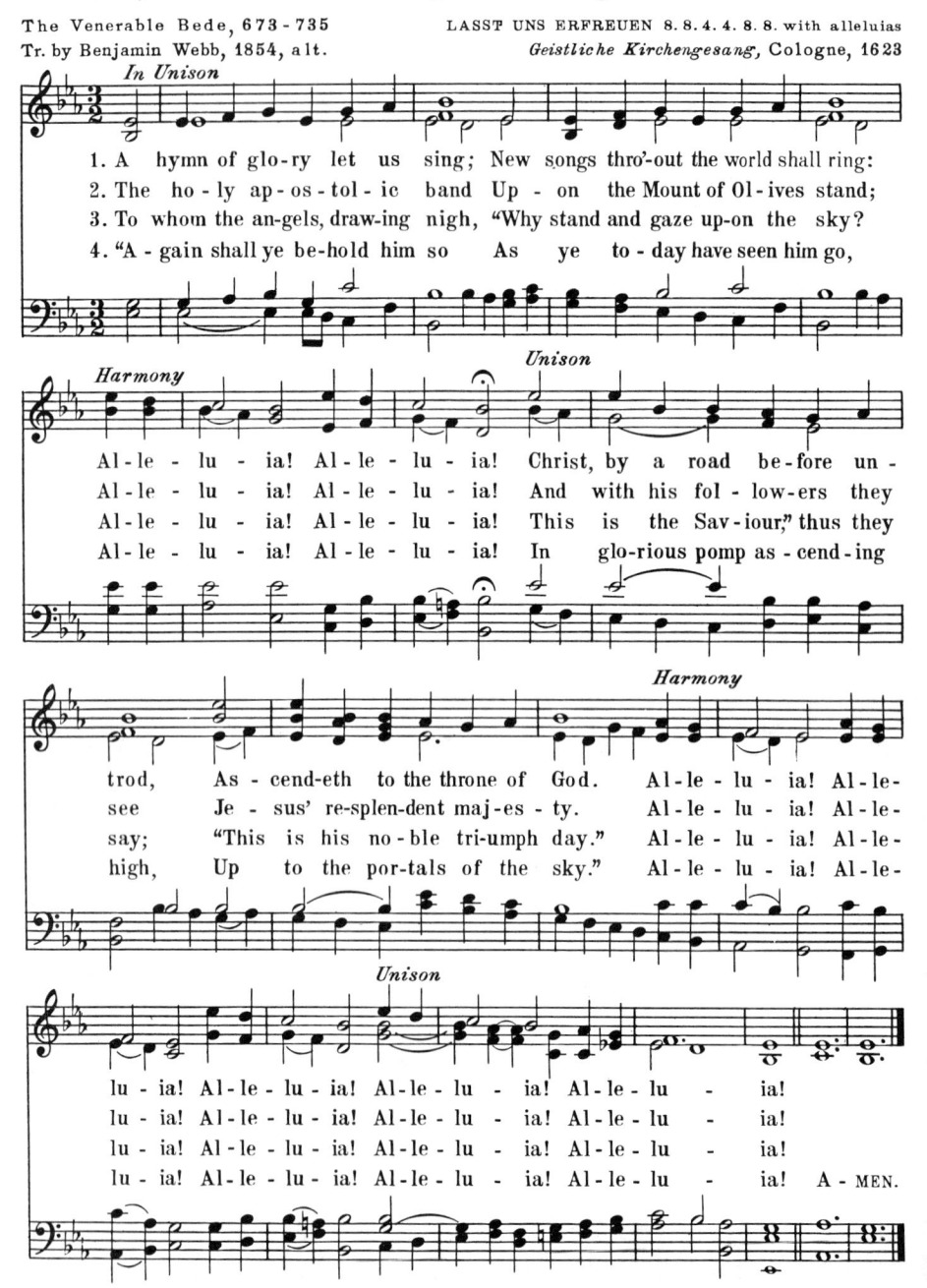

The Venerable Bede, 673-735
Tr. by Benjamin Webb, 1854, alt.

LASST UNS ERFREUEN 8.8.4.4.8.8. with alleluias
*Geistliche Kirchengesang,* Cologne, 1623

1. A hymn of glo-ry let us sing; New songs thro'-out the world shall ring:
2. The ho-ly ap-os-tol-ic band Up-on the Mount of Ol-ives stand;
3. To whom the an-gels, draw-ing nigh, "Why stand and gaze up-on the sky?
4. "A-gain shall ye be-hold him so As ye to-day have seen him go,

Al-le-lu-ia! Al-le-lu-ia! Christ, by a road be-fore un-
Al-le-lu-ia! Al-le-lu-ia! And with his fol-low-ers they
Al-le-lu-ia! Al-le-lu-ia! This is the Sav-iour," thus they
Al-le-lu-ia! Al-le-lu-ia! In glo-rious pomp as-cend-ing

trod, As-cend-eth to the throne of God. Al-le-lu-ia! Al-le-
see Je-sus' re-splen-dent maj-es-ty. Al-le-lu-ia! Al-le-
say; "This is his no-ble tri-umph day." Al-le-lu-ia! Al-le-
high, Up to the por-tals of the sky." Al-le-lu-ia! Al-le-

lu-ia! Al-le-lu-ia! Al-le-lu-ia! Al-le-lu-ia!
lu-ia! Al-le-lu-ia! Al-le-lu-ia! Al-le-lu-ia!
lu-ia! Al-le-lu-ia! Al-le-lu-ia! Al-le-lu-ia!
lu-ia! Al-le-lu-ia! Al-le-lu-ia! Al-le-lu-ia! A-MEN.

Harmony from *Songs of Praise* by permission of the Oxford University Press, London

# HIS ASCENSION

### 213

*For Christ is ... entered ... into heaven itself, now to appear in the presence of God for us.* Heb. 9:24

Frances R. Havergal, 1871

HERMAS 6. 5. 6. 5. D. with refrain
Frances R. Havergal, 1871

1. Gold-en harps are sound-ing, An-gel voic-es ring, Pearl-y gates are o-pened, O-pened for the King: Christ, the King of glo-ry, Je-sus, King of love, Is gone up in tri-umph To his throne a-bove.
2. He who came to save us, He who bled and died, Now is crowned with glo-ry At his Fa-ther's side. Nev-er more to suf-fer, Nev-er more to die, Je-sus, King of glo-ry, Is gone up on high.
3. Pray-ing for his chil-dren In that bless-ed place, Call-ing them to glo-ry, Send-ing them his grace; His bright home pre-par-ing, Faith-ful ones, for you; Je-sus ev-er liv-eth, Ev-er lov-eth too.

**REFRAIN**

All his work is end-ed, Joy-ful-ly we sing; Je-sus hath as-cend-ed: Glo-ry to our King! A-MEN.

## 214 THE LORD JESUS CHRIST

*I go to prepare a place for you.* John 14:2

Cecil Frances Alexander, 1852, 1858

MIRFIELD C. M.
Arthur Cottman, 1872

1. The gold-en gates are lift-ed up, The doors are o-pened wide;
   The King of Glo-ry is gone in Un-to his Fa-ther's side.
2. Thou art gone up be-fore us, Lord, To make for us a place,
   That we may be where now thou art, And look up-on God's face.
3. And ev-er on our earth-ly path A gleam of glo-ry lies,
   A light still breaks be-hind the cloud That veiled thee from our eyes.
4. Lift up our hearts, lift up our minds: Let thy dear grace be giv'n,
   That, while we wan-der here be-low, Our treas-ure be in heav'n;
5. That where thou art, at God's right hand, Our hope, our love, may be:
   Dwell thou in us, that we may dwell For ev-er-more in thee. A-MEN.

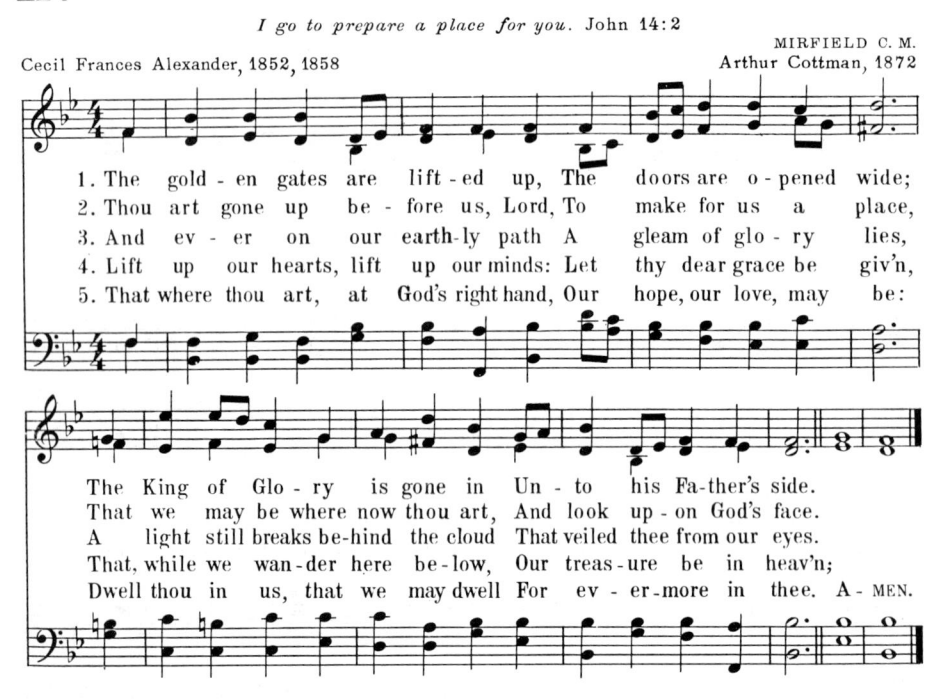

## 215

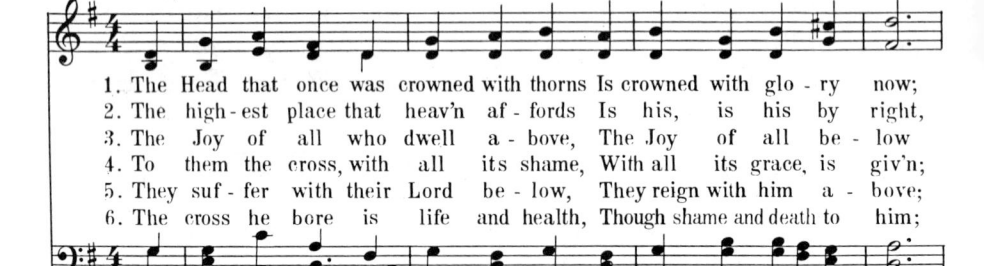

*God hath made that same Jesus, whom ye have crucified, both Lord and Christ.* Acts 2:36

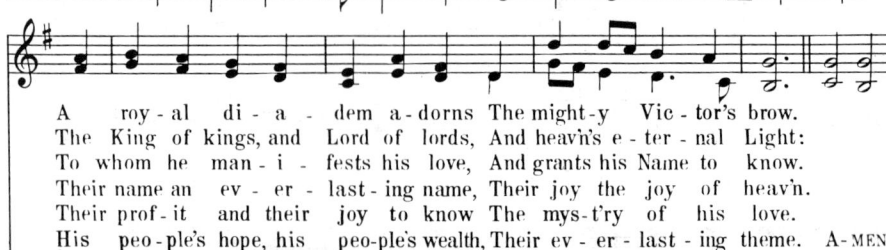

Thomas Kelly, 1820

ST. MAGNUS C. M.
Jeremiah Clark, 1670-1707

1. The Head that once was crowned with thorns Is crowned with glo-ry now;
   A roy-al di-a-dem a-dorns The might-y Vic-tor's brow.
2. The high-est place that heav'n af-fords Is his, is his by right,
   The King of kings, and Lord of lords, And heav'n's e-ter-nal Light:
3. The Joy of all who dwell a-bove, The Joy of all be-low
   To whom he man-i-fests his love, And grants his Name to know.
4. To them the cross, with all its shame, With all its grace, is giv'n;
   Their name an ev-er-last-ing name, Their joy the joy of heav'n.
5. They suf-fer with their Lord be-low, They reign with him a-bove,
   Their prof-it and their joy to know The mys-t'ry of his love.
6. The cross he bore is life and health, Though shame and death to him;
   His peo-ple's hope, his peo-ple's wealth, Their ev-er-last-ing theme. A-MEN.

# HIS EXALTATION 216

*On his head were many crowns... Rev. 19:12*

Matthew Bridges, 1851

DIADEMATA S. M. D.
Sir George J. Elvey, 1868

1. Crown him with man-y crowns, The Lamb up-on his throne;
2. Crown him the Lord of love; Be-hold his hands and side,
3. Crown him the Lord of peace; Whose pow'r a scep-ter sways
4. Crown him the Lord of years, The Po-ten-tate of time;

Hark! how the heav'n-ly an-them drowns All mu-sic but its own:
Rich wounds, yet vis-i-ble a-bove, In beau-ty glo-ri-fied:
From pole to pole, that wars may cease, Ab-sorbed in prayer and praise:
Cre-a-tor of the roll-ing spheres, In-ef-fa-bly sub-lime:

A-wake, my soul, and sing Of him who died for thee,
No an-gel in the sky Can ful-ly bear that sight,
His reign shall know no end; And round his pierc-ed feet
All hail, Re-deem-er, hail! For thou hast died for me:

And hail him as thy match-less King Through all e-ter-ni-ty.
But down-ward bends his burn-ing eye At mys-ter-ies so bright.
Fair flowers of Par-a-dise ex-tend Their fra-grance ev-er sweet.
Thy praise shall nev-er, nev-er fail Through-out e-ter-ni-ty. A-MEN.

## 217 THE LORD JESUS CHRIST

*Wherefore God also hath highly exalted him, and given him a name which is above every name.* Phil. 2:9

Thomas Kelly, 1809

CORONAE 8. 7. 8. 7. 4. 7.
William H. Monk, 1871

1. Look, ye saints, the sight is glo-rious: See the Man of Sor-rows now;
2. Crown the Sav-iour, an-gels, crown him; Rich the tro-phies Je-sus brings;
3. Sin-ners in de-ri-sion crowned him, Mock-ing thus the Sav-iour's claim;
4. Hark! those bursts of ac-cla-ma-tion! Hark! those loud tri-um-phant chords!

From the fight re-turned vic-to-rious, Ev-'ry knee to him shall bow:
In the seat of pow'r en-throne him, While the vault of heav-en rings:
Saints and an-gels crowd a-round him, Own his ti-tle, praise his Name:
Je-sus takes the high-est sta-tion; O what joy the sight af-fords!

Crown him! crown him! Crowns be-come the Vic-tor's brow.
Crown him! crown him! Crown the Sav-iour King of kings.
Crown him! crown him! Spread a-broad the Vic-tor's fame!
Crown him! crown him! King of kings, and Lord of lords. A-MEN.

## 218 (FIRST TUNE)

*Wherefore God also hath highly exalted him, and given him a name which is above every name: that at the name of Jesus every knee should bow...* Phil. 2:9-10

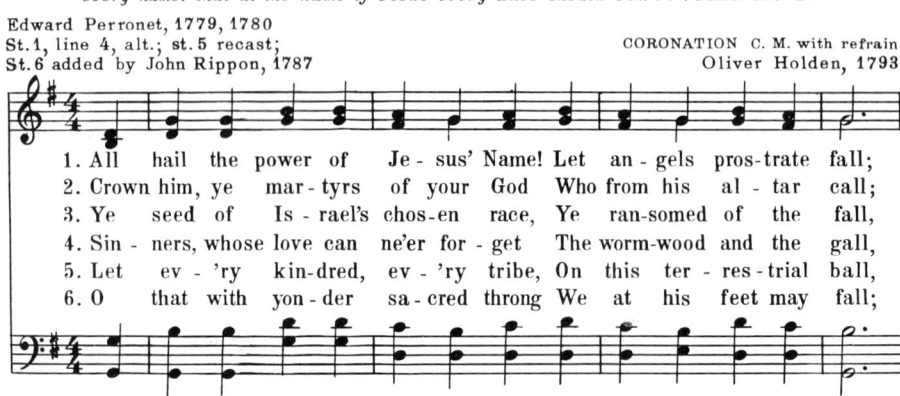

Edward Perronet, 1779, 1780
St.1, line 4, alt.; st.5 recast;
St.6 added by John Rippon, 1787

CORONATION C. M. with refrain
Oliver Holden, 1793

1. All hail the power of Je-sus' Name! Let an-gels pros-trate fall;
2. Crown him, ye mar-tyrs of your God Who from his al-tar call;
3. Ye seed of Is-rael's chos-en race, Ye ran-somed of the fall,
4. Sin-ners, whose love can ne'er for-get The worm-wood and the gall,
5. Let ev-'ry kin-dred, ev-'ry tribe, On this ter-res-trial ball,
6. O that with yon-der sa-cred throng We at his feet may fall;

## HIS EXALTATION

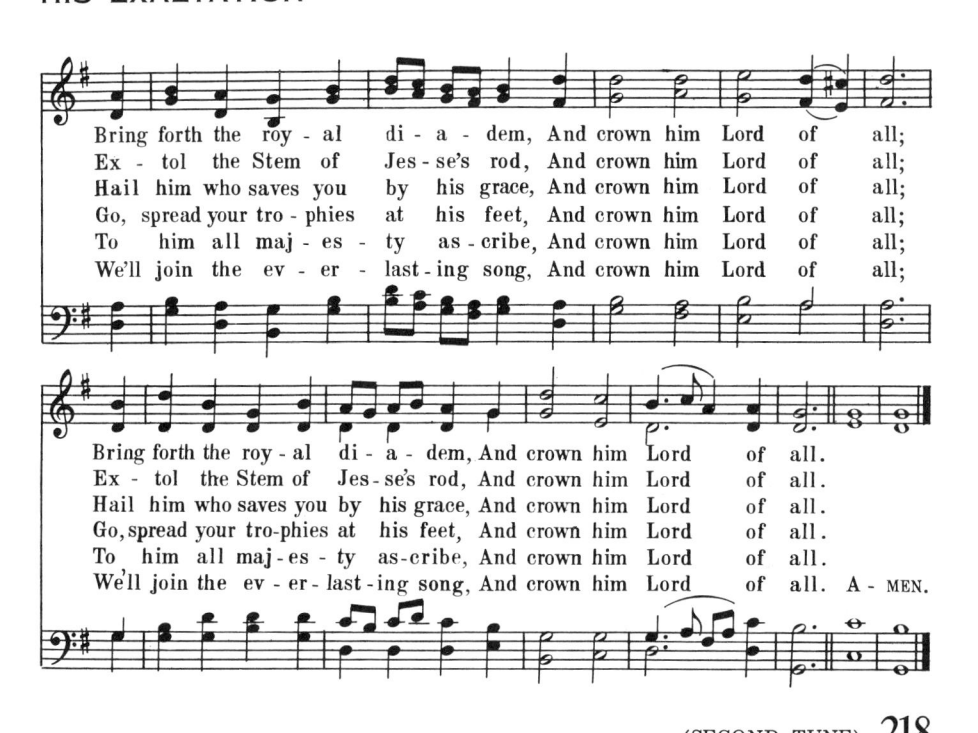

Bring forth the roy-al di - a - dem, And crown him Lord of all;
Ex - tol the Stem of Jes - se's rod, And crown him Lord of all;
Hail him who saves you by his grace, And crown him Lord of all;
Go, spread your tro - phies at his feet, And crown him Lord of all;
To him all maj - es - ty as - cribe, And crown him Lord of all;
We'll join the ev - er - last - ing song, And crown him Lord of all;

Bring forth the roy - al di - a - dem, And crown him Lord of all.
Ex - tol the Stem of Jes - se's rod, And crown him Lord of all.
Hail him who saves you by his grace, And crown him Lord of all.
Go, spread your tro-phies at his feet, And crown him Lord of all.
To him all maj - es - ty as-cribe, And crown him Lord of all.
We'll join the ev - er - last - ing song, And crown him Lord of all. A - MEN.

(SECOND TUNE) 218

Edward Perronet, 1779, 1780, alt.

MILES LANE C. M. with repeat
William Shrubsole, 1779

All hail the power of Je - sus' Name! Let an - gels
pros - trate fall; Bring forth the roy - al di - a - dem,
And crown him, crown him, crown him, crown him Lord of all! A - MEN.

**218** (THIRD TUNE)            **THE LORD JESUS CHRIST**

Edward Perronet, 1779, 1780, alt.

DIADEM C. M. irregular with refrain
James Ellor

1. All hail the power of Jesus' Name! Let angels prostrate fall,
2. Crown him, ye martyrs of your God Who from his altar call,
3. Ye seed of Israel's chosen race, Ye ransomed of the fall,
4. Sinners, whose love can ne'er forget The wormwood and the gall,
5. Let ev'ry kindred, ev'ry tribe On this terrestrial ball,
6. O that with yonder sacred throng We at his feet may fall,

Let angels prostrate fall; Bring forth the royal diadem,
Who from his altar call; Extol the Stem of Jesse's rod,
Ye ransomed of the fall, Hail him who saves you by his grace,
The wormwood and the gall, Go, spread your trophies at his feet,
On this terrestrial ball, To him all majesty ascribe,
We at his feet may fall! We'll join the everlasting song,

And crown . . . . . . . . . . him, crown him,
And crown him, crown him, crown him, crown . . . . . . . .

crown him, crown him, And crown him Lord of all!
. . . . . . . him, And crown him Lord of all.

A-MEN.

# HIS EXALTATION

**219**

*Worthy is the Lamb that was slain to receive power, and riches, and wisdom, and strength, and honour, and glory, and blessing. Rev. 5:12*

Horatius Bonar, 1866, alt.

O QUANTA QUALIA 10. 10. 10. 10.
La Feillée's *Méthode du Plain Chant*, 1808

1. Bless-ing and hon-or and glo-ry and power,
   Wis-dom and rich-es and strength ev-er-more
   Give ye to him who our bat-tle hath won,
   Whose are the King-dom, the crown, and the throne.

2. Sound-eth the heav'n of the heav'ns with his Name;
   Ring-eth the earth with his glo-ry and fame;
   O-cean and moun-tain, stream, for-est, and flower
   Ech-o his prais-es and tell of his power.

3. Ev-er as-cend-eth the song and the joy;
   Ev-er de-scend-eth the love from on high;
   Bless-ing and hon-or and glo-ry and praise—
   This is the theme of the hymns that we raise.

4. Give we the glo-ry and praise to the Lamb;
   Take we the robe and the harp and the palm;
   Sing we the song of the Lamb that was slain,
   Dy-ing in weak-ness, but ris-ing to reign. A-MEN.

Harmony from *The Revised Church Hymnary* by permission of the Oxford University Press, London

## 220 THE LORD JESUS CHRIST

*Lord . . . thou hast the words of eternal life.* John 6:68

St. 1-3, Tobias Clausnitzer, 1663
St. 4, anon., 1707
Tr. by Catherine Winkworth, 1858
Tr., st. 4, anon.

LIEBSTER JESU 7.8.7.8.8.8.
Johann R. Ahle, 1664

1. Bless-ed Jesus, at thy word We are gath-ered all to hear thee; Let our hearts and souls be stirred Now to seek and love and fear thee, By thy teach-ings, sweet and ho-ly, Drawn from earth to love thee sole-ly.
2. All our knowl-edge, sense, and sight Lie in deep-est dark-ness shroud-ed Till thy Spir-it breaks our night With the beams of truth un-cloud-ed. Thou a-lone to God canst win us; Thou must work all good with-in us.
3. Glo-rious Lord, thy-self im-part, Light of Light, from God pro-ceed-ing; O-pen thou our ears and heart, Help us by thy Spir-it's plead-ing; Hear the cry thy peo-ple rais-es, Hear and bless our prayers and prais-es.
4. Fa-ther, Son, and Ho-ly Ghost, Praise to thee and ad-o-ra-tion! Grant that we thy Word may trust And ob-tain true con-so-la-tion While we here be-low must wan-der, Till we sing thy prais-es yon-der. A-MEN.

# HIS PROPHETIC OFFICE

## 221

*Come unto me, all ye that labour and are heavy laden, and I will give you rest.* Matt. 11:28

Horatius Bonar, 1846

VOX DILECTI C. M. D.
John B. Dykes, 1868

1. I heard the voice of Jesus say, "Come unto me and rest;
   Lay down, thou weary one, lay down Thy head upon my breast."
   I came to Jesus as I was, Weary and worn and sad,
   I found in him a resting-place, And he has made me glad.

2. I heard the voice of Jesus say, "Behold, I freely give
   The living water; thirsty one, Stoop down and drink, and live."
   I came to Jesus, and I drank Of that life-giving stream;
   My thirst was quenched, my soul revived, And now I live in him.

3. I heard the voice of Jesus say, "I am this dark world's Light;
   Look unto me, thy morn shall rise, And all thy day be bright."
   I looked to Jesus, and I found In him my Star, my Sun;
   And in that light of life I'll walk, Till trav'ling days are done. A-MEN.

## 222 THE LORD JESUS CHRIST

*Christ being come an high priest . . . by his own blood he entered in once into the holy place, having obtained eternal redemption for us.* Heb. 9:11, 12

Isaac Watts, 1709, cento

BEVAN 6. 6. 6. 6. 8. 8.
Sir John Goss, 1853

1. Jesus, my great High Priest, Offered his blood and died;
My guilty conscience seeks No sacrifice beside.
His pow'rful blood did once atone, And now it pleads before the Throne.

2. To this dear Surety's hand Will I commit my cause;
He answers and fulfils His Father's broken laws.
Behold my soul at freedom set; My Surety paid the dreadful debt.

3. My Advocate appears For my defense on high;
The Father bows his ears And lays his thunder by.
Not all that hell or sin can say Shall turn his heart, his love, away.

4. Should all the hosts of death And pow'rs of hell unknown
Put their most dreadful forms Of rage and mischief on,
I shall be safe, for Christ displays His conqu'ring pow'r and guardian grace. A-MEN.

St. 4, line 6, alt.

# HIS PRIESTLY INTERCESSION                                                 223

*Wherefore he is able also to save them to the uttermost that come unto God by him, seeing he ever liveth to make intercession for them.* Heb. 7:25

LENOX 6.6.6.6.8.8.
Charles Wesley, 1742　　　　　　　　　　　　　　　　　　　　Louis Edson, 1782

1. A-rise, my soul, a-rise, Shake off thy guilt-y fears:
   The bleed-ing Sac-ri-fice In my be-half ap-pears:
   Be-fore the Throne my Sure-ty stands, Be-fore the Throne my
   Sure-ty stands, My name is writ-ten on his hands.

2. He ev-er lives a-bove, For me to in-ter-cede,
   His all-re-deem-ing love, His pre-cious blood to plead;
   His blood a-toned for ev-'ry race, His blood a-toned for
   ev-'ry race, And sprin-kles now the throne of grace.

3. Five bleed-ing wounds he bears, Re-ceived on Cal-va-ry;
   They pour ef-fect-ual prayers, They strong-ly plead for me;
   For-give him, O for-give, they cry, For-give him, O for-
   give, they cry, Nor let that ran-somed sin-ner die!

4. My God is rec-on-ciled; His par-d'ning voice I hear;
   He owns me for his child, I can no long-er fear;
   With con-fid-ence I now draw nigh, With con-fid-ence I
   now draw nigh, And "Fa-ther, Ab-ba, Fa-ther!" cry. A - MEN.

St. 2, line 5, alt.

# 224                         THE LORD JESUS CHRIST

*In his days shall the righteous flourish; and abundance of peace so long as the moon endureth.* Psalm 72:7

James Montgomery, 1821, 1828                     AURELIA 7.6.7.6.D.
                                                                   Samuel S. Wesley, 1864

1. Hail to the Lord's Anointed, Great David's greater Son!
Hail, in the time appointed, His reign on earth begun!
He comes to break oppression, To set the captive free,
To take away transgression, And rule in equity.

2. He comes with succor speedy To those who suffer wrong;
To help the poor and needy, And bid the weak be strong;
To give them songs for sighing, Their darkness turn to light,
Whose souls, condemned and dying, Were precious in his sight.

3. He shall come down like showers Upon the fruitful earth;
And love, joy, hope, like flowers, Spring in his path to birth;
Before him on the mountains Shall peace, the herald, go;
And righteousness, in fountains, From hill to valley flow.

4. O'er ev'ry foe victorious, He on his throne shall rest,
From age to age more glorious, All-blessing and all-blessed;
The tide of time shall never His covenant remove;
His Name shall stand for ever — That Name to us is Love. A-MEN.

# HIS KINGLY OFFICE 225

*Let all the angels of God worship him.* Heb. 1:6

Thomas Kelly, 1806

HARWELL 8. 7. 8. 7. 7. 7. with alleluias
Lowell Mason, 1840

1. Hark! ten thou-sand harps and voic-es Sound the note of praise a-bove;
2. King of glo-ry, reign for ev-er, Thine an ev-er-last-ing crown;
3. Sav-iour, hast-en thine ap-pear-ing; Bring, O bring the glo-rious day,

Je-sus reigns, and heav'n re-joic-es; Je-sus reigns, the God of love:
Noth-ing from thy love shall sev-er Those whom thou hast made thine own:
When, the aw-ful sum-mons hear-ing, Heav'n and earth shall pass a-way:

See, he sits on yon-der throne; Je-sus rules the world a-lone.
Hap-py ob-jects of thy grace, Des-tined to be-hold thy face.
Then with gold-en harps we'll sing, "Glo-ry, glo-ry to our King!"

Al-le-lu-ia! Al-le-lu-ia! Al-le-lu-ia! A-men. A-MEN.

## 226 THE LORD JESUS CHRIST

*When he had by himself purged our sins, he sat down on the right hand of the Majesty on high.* Heb. 1:3

Charles Wesley, 1746
St. 1, line 3, alt.

ARTHUR'S SEAT 6.6.6.6.8.8.
Arr. from Sir John Goss by Uzziah C. Burnap, 1874

1. Rejoice, the Lord is King: Your Lord and King adore;
Rejoice, give thanks and sing, And triumph evermore: Lift up your heart, lift up your voice; Rejoice, again I say, rejoice.

2. Jesus, the Saviour, reigns, The God of truth and love;
When he had purged our stains, He took his seat above: Lift up your heart, lift up your voice; Rejoice, again I say, rejoice.

3. His kingdom cannot fail, He rules o'er earth and heav'n;
The keys of death and hell Are to our Jesus giv'n: Lift up your heart, lift up your voice; Rejoice, again I say, rejoice.

4. He sits at God's right hand Till all his foes submit,
And bow to his command, And fall beneath his feet: Lift up your heart, lift up your voice; Rejoice, again I say, rejoice. A-MEN.

## 227

*Why do the heathen rage, and the people imagine a vain thing?* Psalm 2:1

From PSALM 2
The Psalter, 1912

UXBRIDGE L. M.
Lowell Mason, 1830

1. O wherefore do the nations rage, And kings and rulers strive in vain,

2. Their strength is weakness in the sight Of him who sits enthroned above;

3. By God's decree his Son receives The nations for his heritage;

4. Be wise, ye rulers of the earth, And serve the Lord with godly fear;

5. Delay not, lest his anger rise, And ye should perish in your way;

## HIS KINGLY OFFICE

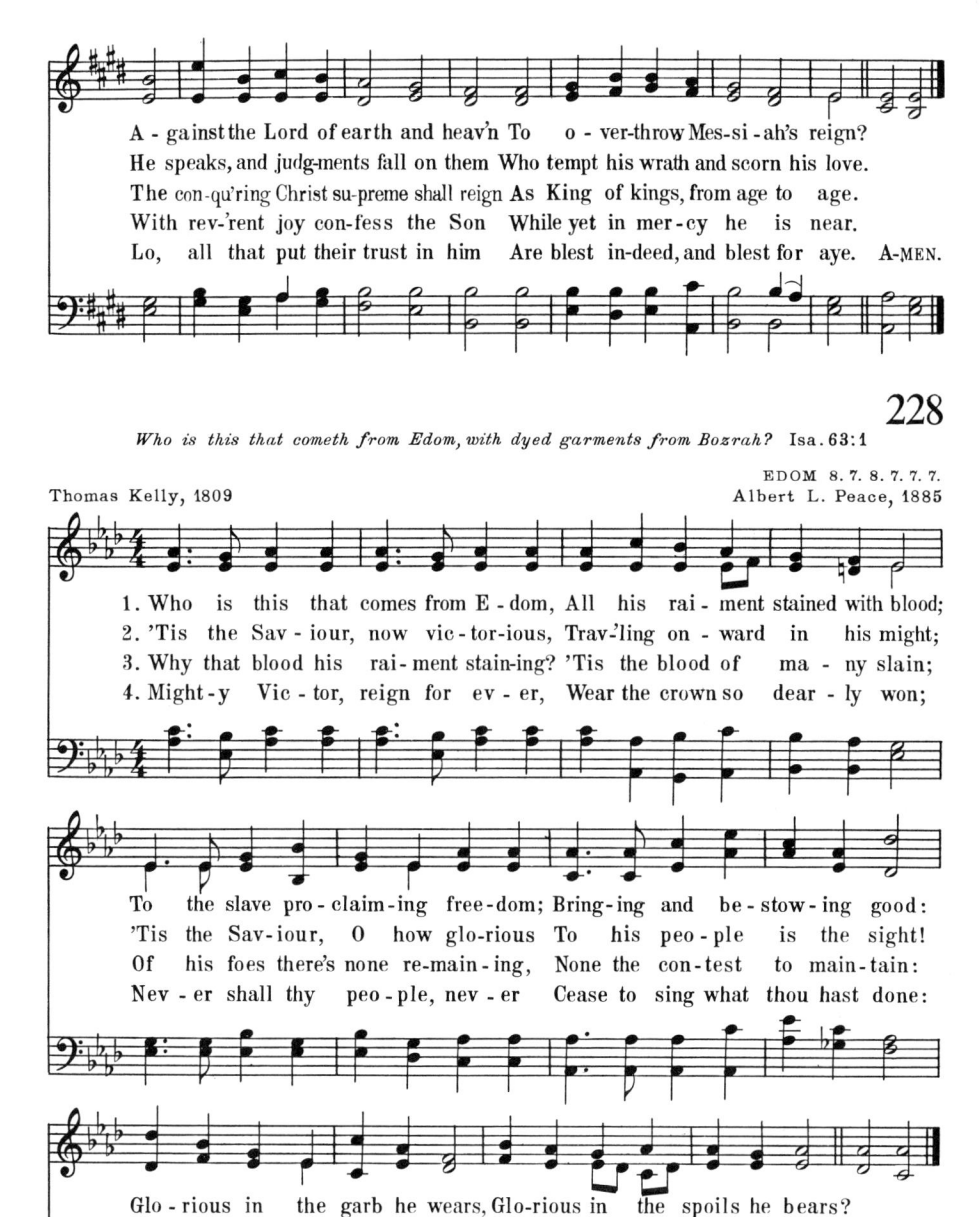

A - gainst the Lord of earth and heav'n To o - ver-throw Mes-si - ah's reign?
He speaks, and judg-ments fall on them Who tempt his wrath and scorn his love.
The con-qu'ring Christ su-preme shall reign As King of kings, from age to age.
With rev-'rent joy con-fess the Son While yet in mer-cy he is near.
Lo, all that put their trust in him Are blest in-deed, and blest for aye. A-MEN.

### 228

*Who is this that cometh from Edom, with dyed garments from Bozrah?* Isa. 63:1

Thomas Kelly, 1809

EDOM 8. 7. 8. 7. 7. 7.
Albert L. Peace, 1885

1. Who is this that comes from E - dom, All his rai - ment stained with blood;
2. 'Tis the Sav - iour, now vic - tor-ious, Trav-'ling on - ward in his might;
3. Why that blood his rai - ment stain-ing? 'Tis the blood of ma - ny slain;
4. Might - y Vic - tor, reign for ev - er, Wear the crown so dear - ly won;

To the slave pro - claim-ing free-dom; Bring-ing and be - stow-ing good:
'Tis the Sav-iour, O how glo-rious To his peo - ple is the sight!
Of his foes there's none re - main-ing, None the con-test to main-tain:
Nev - er shall thy peo - ple, nev - er Cease to sing what thou hast done:

Glo - rious in the garb he wears, Glo-rious in the spoils he bears?
Je - sus now is strong to save, Might-y to re - deem the slave.
Fall'n they are, no more to rise, All their glo - ry pros-trate lies.
Thou hast fought thy peo-ple's foes; Thou wilt heal thy peo-ple's woes. A-MEN.

# 229 THE LORD JESUS CHRIST

*The Lord said unto my Lord, Sit thou at my right hand,
until I make thine enemies thy footstool.* Psalm 110:1

PSALM 110     LORD OF MIGHT 8. 7. 8. 7. 8. 8. 7.
Irish *Psalter*, 1898     Arthur Page, b. 1846

1. Un-to my Lord Je-ho-vah said, "At my right hand I throne thee,
Till at thy feet, in tri-umph laid, Thy foes their rul-er own thee." From Zi-on shall Je-ho-vah send Thy scep-ter, till be-fore thee bend The knees of proud re-bel-lion.

2. Thy saints, to greet thy day of might, In ho-ly rai-ment mus-ter;
As dew-drops in the morn-ing light Thy youths a-round thee clus-ter. Je-ho-vah sware and made de-cree, "Thou, King of Right-eous-ness, shalt be A roy-al Priest for ev-er."

3. The Lord at thy right hand shall bring On rul-ers des-o-la-tion;
The Lord shall smite each hea-then king, And judge each reb-el na-tion. He, swift-ly march-ing in his wrath, Shall quaff the brook up-on his path, And lift his head in glo-ry. A-MEN.

# HIS KINGLY OFFICE  230

*Give the king thy judgments, O God, and thy righteousness unto the king's son.* Psalm 72:1

PSALM 72:1-4; 7-8; 11; 18-19  
Reformed Presbyterian *Book of Psalms*, 1940

OSTEND C. M. D.  
Lowell Mason, 1792-1872  
Harmonized by Wilfred G. Clelland, 1958

1. O God, thy judgments give the King, His Son thy right-eous-ness; With
2. The peo-ple's poor ones he shall judge, The need-y's chil-dren bless; And
3. His large and great do-min-ion shall From sea to sea ex-tend; It
4. Now bless-ed be the Lord our God, The God of Is-ra-el, For

right he shall thy peo-ple judge, Thy poor with up-right-ness. And
he will break in piec-es those Who would the poor op-press. The
from the Riv-er shall reach forth To earth's re-mot-est end. Yea,
he a-lone doth won-drous works In glo-ry that ex-cel. And

then the moun-tains shall bring forth To all the peo-ple peace; The
just shall flour-ish in his days, And pros-per in his reign; And
kings shall all be-fore him bow, All na-tions shall o-bey; He'll
bless-ed be his glo-rious Name To all e-ter-ni-ty. The

hills be-cause of right-eous-ness Their bless-ing shall in-crease.
while the moon en-dures he shall A-bun-dant peace main-tain.
save the need-y when he cries, The poor who hath no stay.
whole earth let his glo-ry fill; A-men, so let it be. A-MEN.

# 231 THE LORD JESUS CHRIST

*Behold, the bridegroom cometh; go ye out to meet him.* Matt. 25:6

Philipp Nicolai, 1599
Tr. by Catherine Winkworth, 1858, 1863

WACHET AUF 8. 9. 8. 8. 9. 8. 6. 6. 4. 8. 8.
Philipp Nicolai, 1599

1. "Wake, a-wake, for night is fly - ing," The watch-men on the heights are cry - ing; "A - wake, Je - ru - sa - lem, at last!" Mid-night hears the wel-come voic - es, And at the thrill - ing cry re - joic - es: "Come forth, ye vir - gins, night is past! The Bride-groom comes; a - wake, Your lamps with glad-ness take;

2. Zi - on hears the watch-men sing - ing, And all her heart with joy is spring - ing; She wakes, she ris - es from her gloom: For her Lord comes down all - glo - rious, The Strong in grace, in truth Vic - to - rious, Her Star is ris'n, her Light is come! Ah, come, thou bless - ed Lord, O Je - sus, Son of God,

3. Now let all the heav'ns a - dore thee, And men and an - gels sing be - fore thee, With harp and cym - bal's clear-est tone; Of one pearl each shin-ing por - tal, Where we are with the choir im - mor - tal Of an - gels round thy daz - zling throne; Nor eye hath seen, nor ear Hath yet at - tained to hear

# HIS SECOND COMING AND JUDGMENT

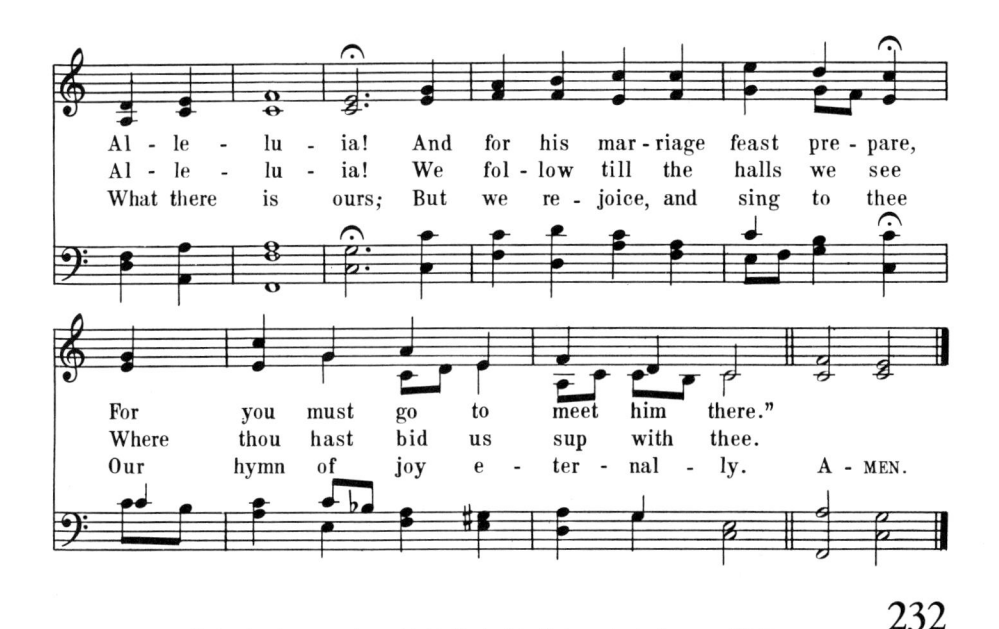

Al - le - lu - ia! And for his mar-riage feast pre - pare,
Al - le - lu - ia! We fol - low till the halls we see
What there is ours; But we re - joice, and sing to thee

For you must go to meet him there."
Where thou hast bid us sup with thee.
Our hymn of joy e - ter - nal - ly. A - MEN.

**232**

*Take heed, as unto a light that shineth in a dark place, until the day dawn and the day star arise in your hearts.* II Peter 1:19

Sir Edward Denny, 1842

EAGLEY C. M.
James Walch, 1860

1. Light of the lone - ly pil - grim's heart, Star of the com - ing day,
2. Come, bless-ed Lord, bid ev - 'ry shore And an-sw'ring is - land sing
3. Bid the whole earth, re - spon - sive now To the bright world a - bove,
4. Lord, Lord, thy fair cre - a - tion groans, The air, the earth, the sea,
5. Come, then, with all thy quick-'ning pow'r, With one a - wak-'ning smile,
6. Thine was the cross, with all its fruits Of grace and peace Di - vine:

A - rise, and with thy morn-ing beams Chase all our griefs a - way.
The prais-es of thy roy - al Name, And own thee as their King.
Break forth in rapt-urous strains of joy In mem-'ry of thy love.
In u - ni - son with all our hearts, And calls a - loud for thee.
And bid the ser - pent's trail no more Thy beau-teous realms de-file.
Be thine the crown of glo - ry now, The palm of vic - t'ry thine. A - MEN.

## 233 THE LORD JESUS CHRIST

*Behold, the bridegroom cometh; go ye out to meet him.* Matt. 25:6

Laurentius Laurenti, 1700
Tr. by Sarah B. Findlater, 1854

LANCASHIRE 7. 6. 7. 6. D.
Henry Smart, 1836

1. Re-joice, all ye be-liev-ers, And let your lights ap-pear;
   The eve-ning is ad-vanc-ing, And dark-er night is near:
   The Bride-groom is a-ris-ing, And soon he draw-eth nigh;
   Up, pray, and watch, and wres-tle: At mid-night comes the cry.

2. See that your lamps are burn-ing; Re-plen-ish them with oil;
   And wait for your sal-va-tion, The end of earth-ly toil.
   The watch-ers on the moun-tain Pro-claim the Bride-groom near,
   Go meet him as he com-eth, With Al-le-lu-ias clear.

3. Ye saints, who here in pa-tience Your cross and suf-f'rings bore,
   Shall live and reign for ev-er, When sor-row is no more:
   A-round the throne of glo-ry The Lamb ye shall be-hold,
   In tri-umph cast be-fore him Your di-a-dems of gold.

4. Our Hope and Ex-pec-ta-tion, O Je-sus, now ap-pear;
   A-rise, thou Sun so longed for, O'er this be-night-ed sphere.
   With hearts and hands up-lift-ed, We plead, O Lord, to see
   The day of earth's re-demp-tion That brings us un-to thee. A-MEN.

# HIS SECOND COMING AND JUDGMENT 234

*Ten thousand times ten thousand . . . saying with a loud voice, Worthy is the Lamb that was slain to receive power . . . Rev. 5:11-12*

Henry Alford, 1867　　　　　　　　　　　　　　　　ALFORD 7. 6. 8. 6. D.
　　　　　　　　　　　　　　　　　　　　　　　　　John B. Dykes, 1875

1. Ten thou-sand times ten thou-sand In spark-ling rai - ment bright,
2. What rush of al - le - lu - ias Fills all the earth and sky!
3. O then what rap-tured greet-ings On Can - aan's hap - py shore;
4. Bring near thy great sal - va - tion, Thou Lamb for sin - ners slain;

The ar - mies of the ran-somed saints Throng up the steeps of light:
What ring - ing of a thou-sand harps Be-speaks the tri - umph nigh!
What knit-ting sev - ered friend-ships up Where part-ings are no more!
Fill up the roll of thine e - lect, Then take thy pow'r, and reign:

'Tis fin-ished, all is fin-ished, Their fight with death and sin:
O day, for which cre - a - tion And all its tribes were made;
Then eyes with joy shall spar-kle, That brimmed with tears of late;
Ap - pear, De - sire of na - tions, Thine ex - iles long for home;

Fling o - pen wide the gold - en gates, And let the vic - tors in.
O joy, for all its form - er woes A thou-sand fold re-paid!
Or - phans no long - er fa - ther-less, Nor wi - dows des - o - late.
Show in the heav'n thy prom-ised sign; Thou Prince and Sav-iour, come. A-MEN.

# 235 THE LORD JESUS CHRIST

*Behold, he cometh with clouds; and every eye shall see him... Rev. 1:7*

Frances R. Havergal, 1872
BEVERLEY 8. 7. 8. 8. 7. 7. 7. 7.
William H. Monk, 1875

1. Thou art com-ing, O my Sav-iour, Thou art com-ing, O my King, In thy beau-ty all re-splen-dent; In thy glo-ry all tran-scend-ent; Well may we re-joice and sing: Com-ing! in the open-ing east Her-ald bright-ness slow-ly swells; Com-ing! O my

2. Thou art com-ing, thou art com-ing; We shall meet thee on thy way, We shall see thee, we shall know thee, We shall bless thee, we shall show thee All our hearts could nev-er say: What an an-them that will be, Ring-ing out our love to thee, Pour-ing out our

3. O the joy to see thee reign-ing, Thee, my own be-lov-ed Lord! Ev-'ry tongue thy Name con-fess-ing, Wor-ship, hon-or, glo-ry, bless-ing Brought to thee with glad ac-cord; Thee, my Mas-ter and my Friend, Vin-di-cat-ed and en-throned; Un-to earth's re-

# HIS SECOND COMING AND JUDGMENT

glo - rious Priest, Hear we not thy gold - en bells?
rap - ture sweet At thine own all - glo - rious feet.
mot - est end Glo - ri - fied, a - dored, and owned. A - MEN.

## 236

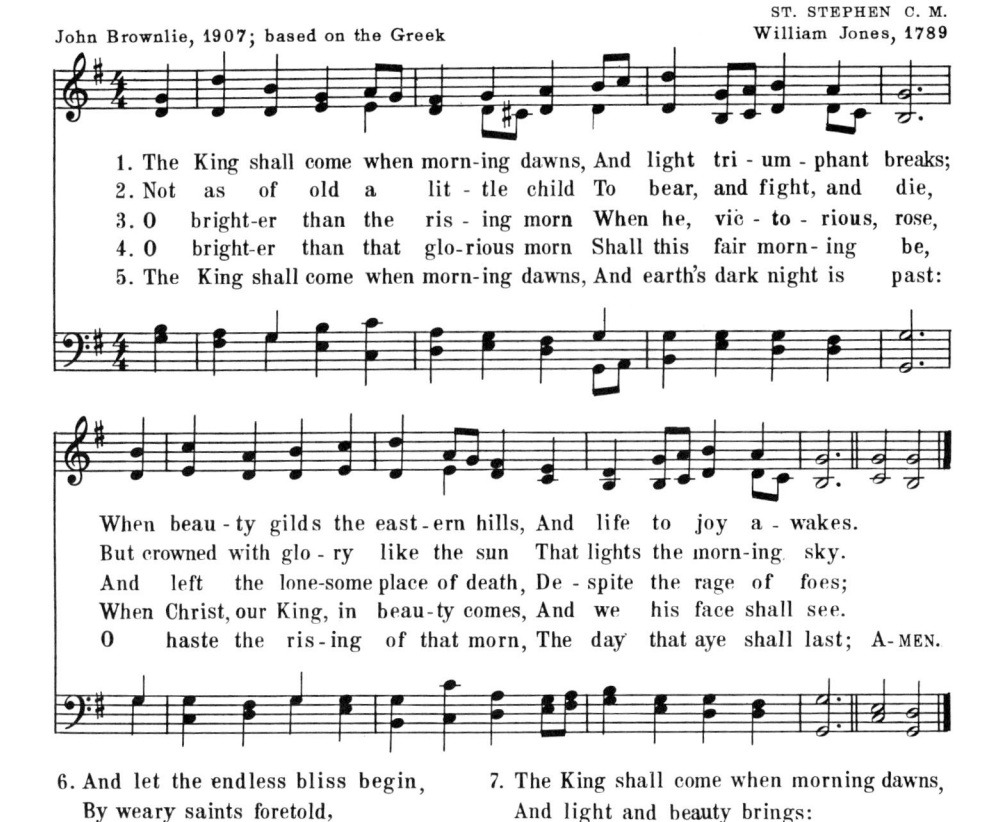

*Surely I come quickly... Even so, come, Lord Jesus.* Rev. 22:20

John Brownlie, 1907; based on the Greek

ST. STEPHEN C. M.
William Jones, 1789

1. The King shall come when morn-ing dawns, And light tri - um - phant breaks;
2. Not as of old a lit - tle child To bear, and fight, and die,
3. O bright-er than the ris - ing morn When he, vic - to - rious, rose,
4. O bright-er than that glo-rious morn Shall this fair morn - ing be,
5. The King shall come when morn-ing dawns, And earth's dark night is past:

When beau - ty gilds the east-ern hills, And life to joy a - wakes.
But crowned with glo - ry like the sun That lights the morn-ing sky.
And left the lone-some place of death, De - spite the rage of foes;
When Christ, our King, in beau-ty comes, And we his face shall see.
O haste the ris-ing of that morn, The day that aye shall last; A-MEN.

6. And let the endless bliss begin,
By weary saints foretold,
When right shall triumph over wrong,
And truth shall be extolled.

7. The King shall come when morning dawns,
And light and beauty brings;
Hail, Christ the Lord! thy people pray,
Come quickly, King of kings.

Words from *Hymns of the Russian Church.* Used by permission of the Oxford University Press, London.

## 237 THE LORD JESUS CHRIST

*Behold, he cometh with clouds; and every eye shall see him... Rev. 1:7*

St. 1-2, 5, Charles Wesley, 1758
St. 3-4, John Cennick, 1752
Arr. and alt. by Martin Madan, 1760

HOLYWOOD 8.7.8.7.8.7.
J. F. Wade's *Cantus Diversi*, 1751

1. Lo! he comes, with clouds descending, Once for favored sinners slain; Thousand thousand saints attending Swell the triumph of his train: Alleluia! God appears on earth to reign.

2. Ev'ry eye shall now behold him, Robed in dreadful majesty; Those who set at naught and sold him, Pierced, and nailed him to the tree, Deeply wailing, Shall the true Messiah see.

3. Ev'ry island, sea, and mountain, Heav'n and earth, shall flee away; All who hate him must, confounded, Hear the trump proclaim the day; Come to judgment! Come to judgment, come away!

4. Now Redemption, long expected, See in solemn pomp appear! All his saints, by man rejected, Now shall meet him in the air: Alleluia! See the day of God appear!

5. Yea, Amen! let all adore thee, High on thine eternal throne; Saviour, take the pow'r and glory, Claim the kingdom for thine own: O come quickly; Alleluia! come, Lord, come. A-MEN.

# HIS SECOND COMING AND JUDGMENT 238

*Looking for that blessed hope, and the glorious appearing
of the great God and our Saviour Jesus Christ.* Titus 2:13

John Ross Macduff, 1818-1895

NEANDER 8. 7. 8. 7. 8. 7.
Joachim Neander, 1680

1. Christ is coming! let creation From her groans and travail cease; Let the glorious proclamation Hope restore and faith increase: Christ is coming! Christ is coming! Come, thou blessed Prince of Peace.
2. Earth can now but tell the story Of thy bitter cross and pain; She shall yet behold thy glory, When thou comest back to reign: Christ is coming! Christ is coming! Let each heart repeat the strain.
3. Long thine exiles have been pining, Far from rest, and home, and thee: But, in heav'nly vestures shining, They their loving Lord shall see: Christ is coming! Christ is coming! Haste the joyous jubilee.
4. With that blessed hope before us, Let no harp remain unstrung; Let the mighty advent chorus Onward roll from tongue to tongue: "Christ is coming! Christ is coming! Come, Lord Jesus, quickly come!" A-MEN.

# 239 THE LORD JESUS CHRIST

*The mighty God, even the Lord, hath spoken... Psalm 50:1*

PSALM 50:1-6  
Based on Scottish *Psalter*, 1650

DIADEMATA S. M. D.  
Sir George J. Elvey, 1868

1. The might-y God, the Lord, Hath spok-en un-to all;  
From ris-ing to the set-ting sun, He un-to earth doth call.  
From Zi-on, his own hill, Where per-fect beau-ty dwells,  
Je-ho-vah hath his glo-ry shown, In bright-ness that ex-cels.

2. Our God shall sure-ly come, And si-lence shall not keep;  
Be-fore him fire shall waste, and storms Tem-pes-tuous round him sweep.  
He to the heav'ns a-bove Shall then send forth his call,  
And like-wise to the earth, that he May judge his peo-ple all.

3. "To-geth-er let my saints Un-to me gath-ered be,  
Those that by sac-ri-fice have made A cov-e-nant with me."  
Then shall the heav'ns de-clare His right-eous-ness a-broad;  
Be-cause the Lord him-self is judge, Yea, none is judge, but God. A-MEN.

# HIS SECOND COMING AND JUDGMENT  240

*For the Lord himself shall descend from heaven with a shout, with the voice of the archangel, and with the trump of God... I Thess. 4:16*

St. 1, anon., 1802
St. 2-4, William B. Collyer, 1812
Alt. by Thomas Cotterill, 1820

LUTHER'S HYMN 8.7.8.7.8.8.7.
Melody by Martin Luther, 1483-1546;
*Geistliche Lieder,* Wittenberg, 1535

1. Great God, what do I see and hear! The end of things cre-at-ed!
2. The dead in Christ shall first a-rise, At the last trum-pet's sound-ing,
3. But sin-ners, filled with guilt-y fears, Be-hold his wrath pre-vail-ing;
4. Great God, what do I see and hear! The end of things cre-at-ed!

The Judge of man-kind doth ap-pear On clouds of glo-ry seat-ed!
Caught up to meet him in the skies, With joy their Lord sur-round-ing;
For they shall rise, and find their tears And sighs are un-a-vail-ing:
The Judge of man-kind doth ap-pear, On clouds of glo-ry seat-ed!

The trum-pet sounds; the graves re-store The dead which they con-
No gloom-y fears their souls dis-may; His pres-ence sheds e-
The day of grace is past and gone; Trem-bling they stand be-
Be-neath his cross I view the day When heav'n and earth shall

tained be-fore: Pre-pare, my soul, to meet him.
ter-nal day On those pre-pared to meet him.
fore the throne, All un-pre-pared to meet him.
pass a-way, And thus pre-pare to meet him. A-MEN.

## 241 THE LORD JESUS CHRIST

*For the trumpet shall sound, and the dead shall be raised . . . I Cor. 15:52*

John Newton, 1774

ST. AUSTIN 8. 7. 8. 7. 4. 7.
Arr. from a Gregorian chant for the
*Bristol Tune Book,* 1876

1. Day of judg-ment! day of won-ders! Hark! the trum-pet's aw - ful sound,
2. See the Judge, our na-ture wear-ing, Clothed in maj - es - ty di-vine;
3. At his call the dead a - wak - en, Rise to life from earth and sea;
4. But to those who have con-fess - ed, Loved and served the Lord be - low,

Loud - er than a thou-sand thun-ders, Shakes the vast cre - a - tion round.
You who long for his ap - pear-ing Then shall say, This God is mine!
All the pow'rs of na - ture, shak - en By his looks, pre-pare to flee.
He will say, Come near, ye bless-ed, See the king-dom I be - stow;

How the sum-mons Will the sin - ner's heart con - found!
Gra-cious Sav - iour, Own me in that day as thine.
Care-less sin - ner, What will then be - come of thee?
You for ev - er Shall my love and glo - ry know. A - MEN.

## 242

*But the day of the Lord will come as a thief in the night; in the which the heavens shall pass away with a great noise . . . II Peter 3:10*

Thomas of Celano, 13th century
Tr. by Sir Walter Scott, 1805

ST. CROSS L. M.
John B. Dykes, 1861

1. That day of wrath, that dread-ful day When heav'n and earth shall pass a - way!
2. When, shriv-el-ling like a parch-ed scroll, The flam-ing heav'ns to - geth-er roll;
3. O on that day, that wrath-ful day When man to judg-ment wakes from clay,

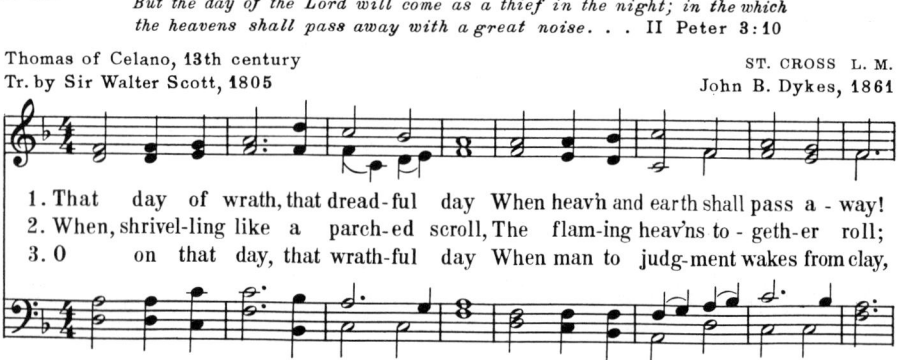

# HIS SECOND COMING AND JUDGMENT

What pow'r shall be the sinner's stay? How shall he meet that dreadful day?
When louder yet, and yet more dread, Swells the high trump that wakes the dead;
Be thou the trembling sinner's stay, Though heav'n and earth shall pass away. A-MEN.

## 243

*Behold, I come quickly; and my reward is with me... Rev. 22:12*

Lawrence Tuttiett, 1854
MELITA 8.8.8.8.8.8.
John B. Dykes, 1861

1. O quickly come, dread Judge of all; For, awful though thine advent be,
2. O quickly come, great King of all; Reign all around us, and within;
3. O quickly come, true Life of all; For death is mighty all around;
4. O quickly come, sure Light of all; For gloomy night broods o'er our way;

All shadows from the truth will fall, And falsehood die, in sight of thee:
Let sin no more our souls enthral, Let pain and sorrow die with sin:
On ev-'ry home his shadows fall, On ev-'ry heart his mark is found:
And weakly souls begin to fall With weary watching for the day:

O quickly come; for doubt and fear Like clouds dissolve when thou art near.
O quickly come; for thou alone Canst make thy scattered people one.
O quickly come; for grief and pain Can never cloud thy glorious reign.
O quickly come; for round thy throne No eye is blind, no night is known. A-MEN.

## 244 THE HOLY SPIRIT

*Strengthened with might by his Spirit in the inner man. Eph. 3:16*

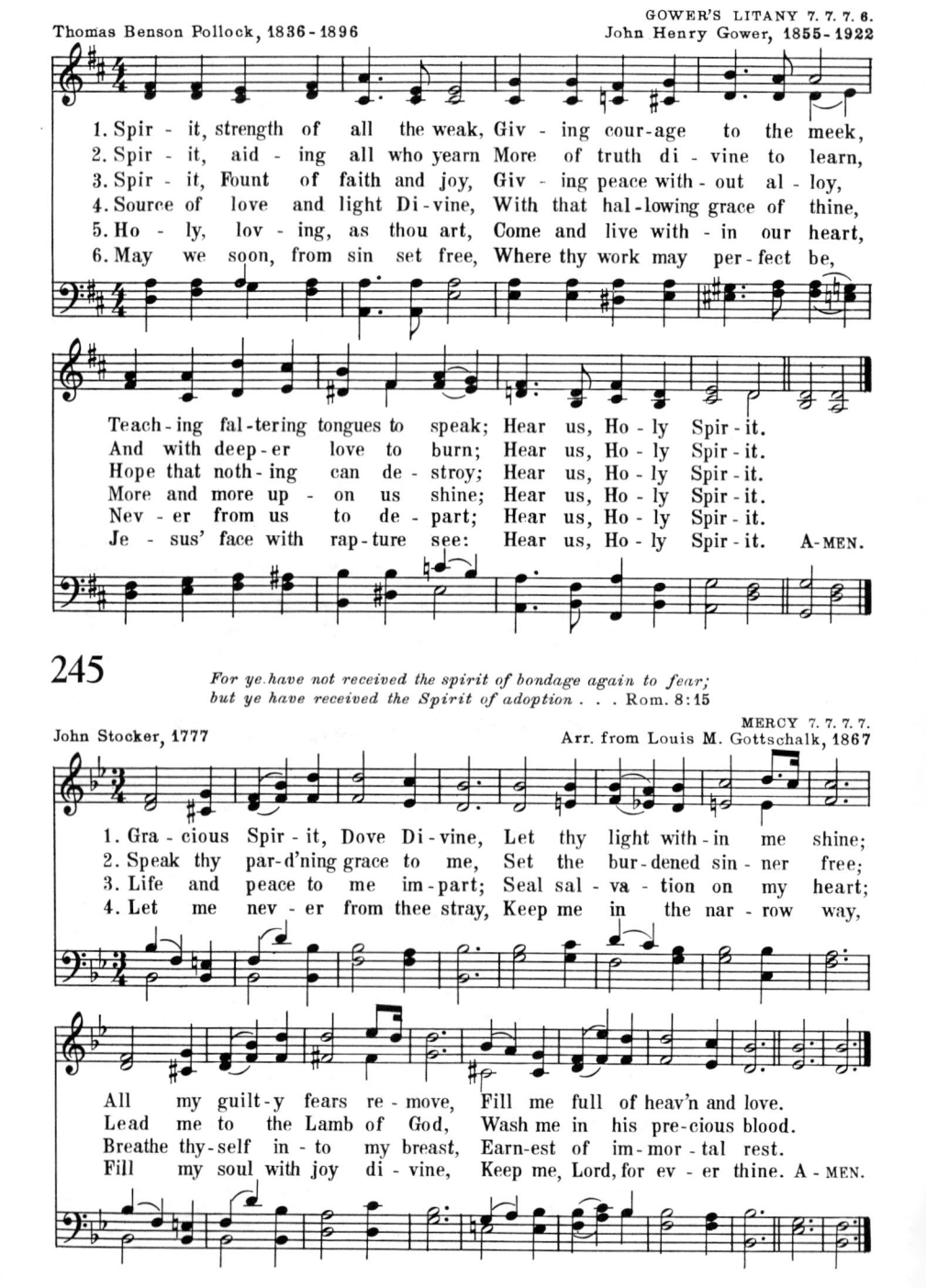

Thomas Benson Pollock, 1836-1896

GOWER'S LITANY 7. 7. 7. 6.
John Henry Gower, 1855-1922

1. Spirit, strength of all the weak, Giving courage to the meek,
   Teaching faltering tongues to speak; Hear us, Holy Spirit.
2. Spirit, aiding all who yearn More of truth divine to learn,
   And with deeper love to burn; Hear us, Holy Spirit.
3. Spirit, Fount of faith and joy, Giving peace without alloy,
   Hope that nothing can destroy; Hear us, Holy Spirit.
4. Source of love and light Divine, With that hallowing grace of thine,
   More and more upon us shine; Hear us, Holy Spirit.
5. Holy, loving, as thou art, Come and live within our heart,
   Never from us to depart; Hear us, Holy Spirit.
6. May we soon, from sin set free, Where thy work may perfect be,
   Jesus' face with rapture see: Hear us, Holy Spirit. A-MEN.

## 245

*For ye have not received the spirit of bondage again to fear;
but ye have received the Spirit of adoption . . . Rom. 8:15*

John Stocker, 1777

MERCY 7. 7. 7. 7.
Arr. from Louis M. Gottschalk, 1867

1. Gracious Spirit, Dove Divine, Let thy light within me shine;
   All my guilty fears remove, Fill me full of heav'n and love.
2. Speak thy pard'ning grace to me, Set the burdened sinner free;
   Lead me to the Lamb of God, Wash me in his precious blood.
3. Life and peace to me impart; Seal salvation on my heart;
   Breathe thyself into my breast, Earnest of immortal rest.
4. Let me never from thee stray, Keep me in the narrow way,
   Fill my soul with joy divine, Keep me, Lord, for ever thine. A-MEN.

# THE HOLY SPIRIT 246

*The kingdom of God is ... righteousness, and peace, and joy in the Holy Ghost.* Rom. 14:17

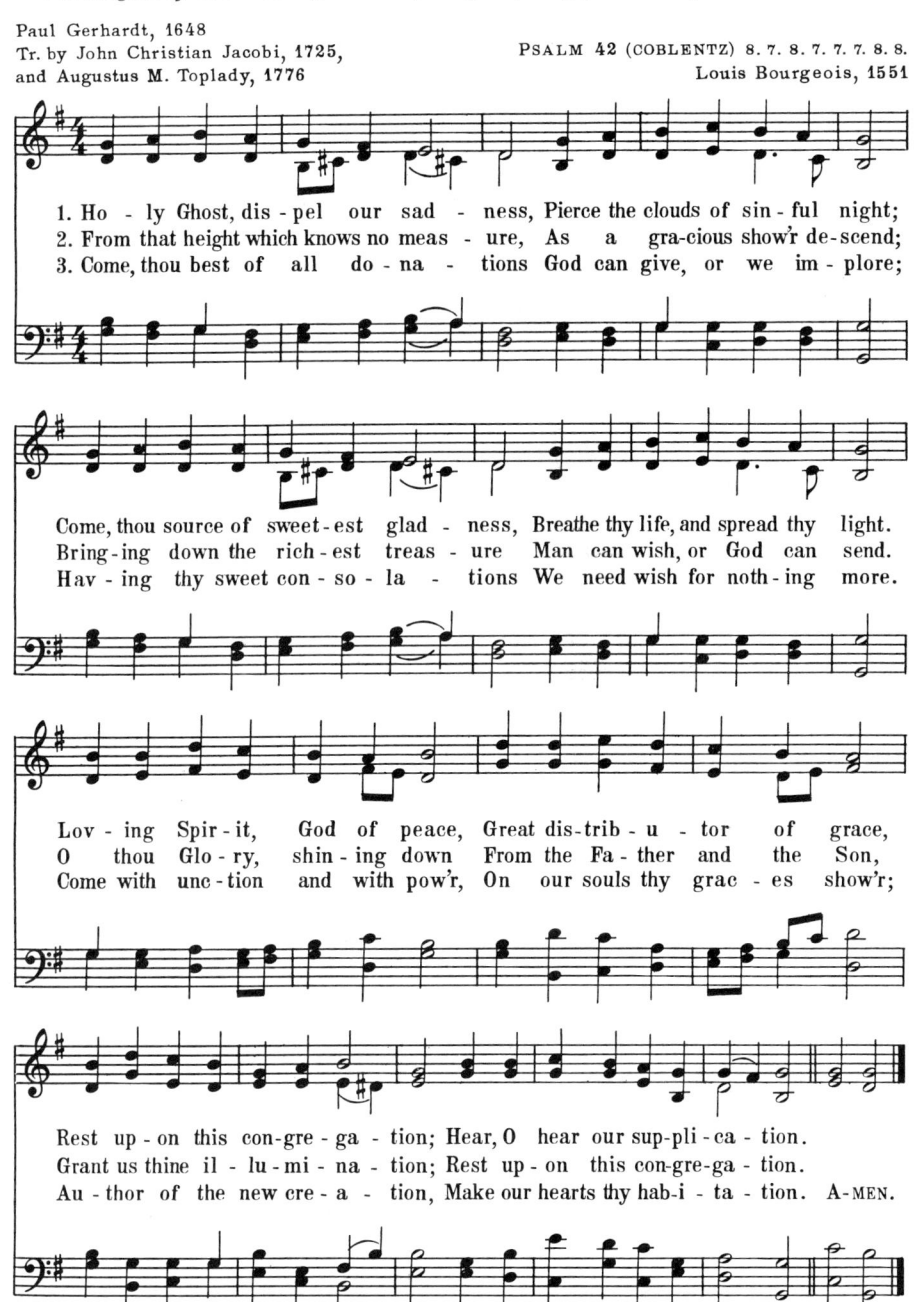

Paul Gerhardt, 1648
Tr. by John Christian Jacobi, 1725,
and Augustus M. Toplady, 1776

PSALM 42 (COBLENTZ) 8. 7. 8. 7. 7. 7. 8. 8.
Louis Bourgeois, 1551

1. Ho - ly Ghost, dis - pel our sad - ness, Pierce the clouds of sin - ful night;
2. From that height which knows no meas - ure, As a gra-cious show'r de-scend;
3. Come, thou best of all do - na - tions God can give, or we im - plore;

Come, thou source of sweet-est glad - ness, Breathe thy life, and spread thy light.
Bring-ing down the rich-est treas - ure Man can wish, or God can send.
Hav - ing thy sweet con - so - la - tions We need wish for noth-ing more.

Lov - ing Spir - it, God of peace, Great dis-trib - u - tor of grace,
O thou Glo - ry, shin - ing down From the Fa - ther and the Son,
Come with unc - tion and with pow'r, On our souls thy grac - es show'r;

Rest up - on this con-gre - ga - tion; Hear, O hear our sup-pli - ca - tion.
Grant us thine il - lu - mi - na - tion; Rest up - on this con-gre-ga - tion.
Au - thor of the new cre - a - tion, Make our hearts thy hab-i - ta - tion. A-MEN.

## 247 THE HOLY SPIRIT

*I will pray the Father, and he shall give you another Comforter, that he may abide with you for ever; even the Spirit of truth . . . John 14:16-17*

Heinrich Held, c. 1664
Tr. by Charles W. Schaeffer, 1866, alt.

LUX PRIMA 8. 7. 8. 7. 7. 7.
Charles F. Gounod, 1872

1. Come, O come, thou quick'ning Spir-it, God from all e - ter - ni - ty!
2. Grant our hearts in full - est meas-ure Wis-dom, coun-sel, pu - ri - ty,
3. Show us, Lord, the path of bless-ing; When we tres - pass on our way,
4. Ho - ly Spir - it, strong and might-y, Thou who mak-est all things new,

May thy pow - er nev - er fail us; Dwell with - in us con - stant - ly.
That we ev - er may be seek-ing On - ly that which pleas-eth thee.
Cast, O Lord, our sins be-hind thee And be with us day by day.
Make thy work with - in us per - fect And the e - vil foe sub-due.

Then shall truth and life and light Ban - ish all the gloom of night.
Let thy knowl-edge spread and grow, Work-ing er - ror's o - ver-throw.
Should we stray, O Lord, re - call; Work re - pent - ance when we fall.
Grant us weap - ons for the strife And with vic - t'ry crown our life. A-MEN.

St. 2, line 3, alt.

## 248

*The Spirit also helpeth our infirmities . . . Rom. 8:26*

George Rawson, 1807-1889

IRENE 7. 7. 7. 5.
Clement C. Scholefield, 1839-1904

1. Come to our poor na - ture's night, With thy bless-ed in-ward light,
2. We are sin - ful—cleanse us, Lord; Sick and faint—thy strength af - ford;
3. Like the dew thy peace dis - til; Guide, sub-due our way-ward will,
4. With us, for us, in - ter - cede, And, with voice-less groan-ings, plead
5. In us Ab - ba, Fa - ther! cry, Earn-est of the bliss on high,
6. Search for us the depths of God; Up-wards by the star - ry road,

# THE HOLY SPIRIT

Ho - ly Ghost, the In - fin - ite, Com - fort - er Di - vine.
Lost— un - til by thee re - stored, Com - fort - er Di - vine.
Things of Christ un - fold - ing still, Com - fort - er Di - vine.
Our un - ut - ter - a - ble need, Com - fort - er Di - vine.
Seal of im - mor - tal - i - ty, Com - fort - er Di - vine.
Bear us to thy high a - bode, Com - fort - er Di - vine. A - MEN.

## 249

*The love of God is shed abroad in our hearts by the Holy Ghost... Rom. 5:5*

Anon., Latin, 13th century  
Tr. by Ray Palmer, 1858

BRAUN 6.6.4.6.6.6.4.  
Johann G. Braun, 1675

1. Come, Ho - ly Ghost, in love Shed on us from a - bove
2. Come, ten - d'rest Friend and best, Our most de - light - ful Guest,
3. Come, Light se - rene, and still Our in - most bos - oms fill;
4. Ex - alt our low de - sires; Ex - tin - guish pas - sion's fires;
5. Come, all the faith - ful bless: Let all who Christ con - fess

Thine own bright ray: Di - vine - ly good thou art; Thy sa - cred
With sooth - ing pow'r: Rest, which the wea - ry know; Shade, 'mid the
Dwell in each breast: We know no dawn but thine; Send forth thy
Heal ev - 'ry wound: Our stub - born spir - its bend, Our i - cy
His praise em - ploy; Give vir - tue's rich re - ward; Vic - to - rious

gifts im - part To glad - den each sad heart: O come to - day.
noon - tide glow; Peace, when deep griefs o'er - flow—Cheer us this hour.
beams di - vine On our dark souls to shine, And make us blest.
cold - ness end, Our de - vious steps at - tend, While heav'nward bound.
death ac - cord, And, with our glo - rious Lord, E - ter - nal joy. A - MEN.

# THE HOLY SPIRIT

## 250

*That Christ may dwell in your hearts by faith... Eph. 3:17*

Isaac Watts, 1709

FEDERAL STREET L. M.
Henry K. Oliver, 1832

1. Come, dear-est Lord, de-scend and dwell By faith and love in ev-'ry breast; Then shall we know and taste and feel The joys that can-not be ex-pressed.
2. Come, fill our hearts with in-ward strength; Make our en-larg-ed souls pos-sess And learn the height, and breadth, and length Of thine un-meas-ur-a-ble grace.
3. Now to the God whose pow'r can do More than our thoughts or wish-es know, Be ev-er-last-ing hon-ors done By all the church, through Christ his Son. A-MEN.

## 251

*In whom ye also are builded together for an habitation of God through the Spirit. Eph. 2:22*

Anon., Latin, 10th century
Tr. cento

GRACE CHURCH L. M.
Arr. from Ignaz J. Pleyel, 1815

1. Come, O Cre-a-tor Spir-it blest, And in our hearts take up thy rest;
2. Thou art the Com-fort-er, we cry, Sent to the earth from God Most High,
3. Bring-ing from heav'n our sev'n-fold dow'r, Sign of our God's right hand of pow'r,
4. Make our dull minds with rap-ture glow, Let hu-man hearts with love o'er-flow;
5. Far from our souls the foe re-pel, Grant us in peace hence-forth to dwell;
6. Show us the Fa-ther, Ho-ly One, Help us to know th' E-ter-nal Son;

# THE HOLY SPIRIT

Spir-it of grace, with heav'n-ly aid Come to the souls whom thou hast made.
Foun-tain of life and Fire of love, And our A-noint-ing from a-bove.
O bless-ed Spir-it, prom-ised long, Thy com-ing wakes the heart to song.
And, when our fee-ble flesh would fail, May thine im-mor-tal strength pre-vail.
Ill shall not come, nor harm be-tide, If on-ly thou wilt be our Guide.
Spir-it Di-vine, for ev-er-more Thee will we trust and thee a-dore. A-MEN.

## 252

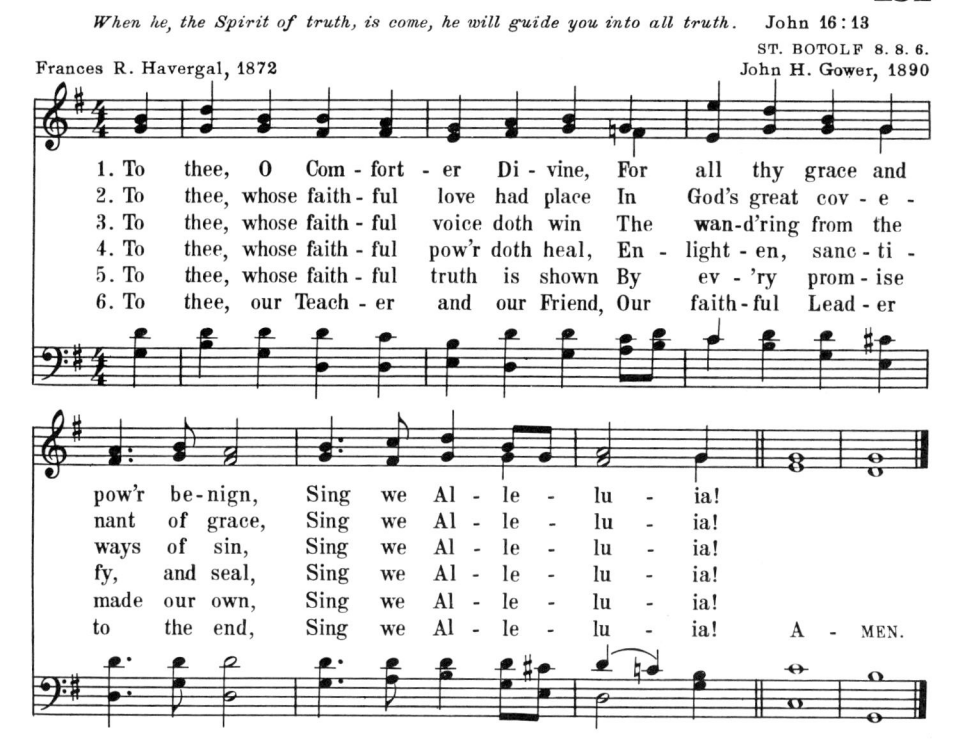

*When he, the Spirit of truth, is come, he will guide you into all truth.* John 16:13

Frances R. Havergal, 1872

ST. BOTOLF 8. 8. 6.
John H. Gower, 1890

1. To thee, O Com-fort-er Di-vine, For all thy grace and pow'r be-nign, Sing we Al-le-lu-ia!
2. To thee, whose faith-ful love had place In God's great cov-e-nant of grace, Sing we Al-le-lu-ia!
3. To thee, whose faith-ful voice doth win The wan-d'ring from the ways of sin, Sing we Al-le-lu-ia!
4. To thee, whose faith-ful pow'r doth heal, En-light-en, sanc-ti-fy, and seal, Sing we Al-le-lu-ia!
5. To thee, whose faith-ful truth is shown By ev-'ry prom-ise made our own, Sing we Al-le-lu-ia!
6. To thee, our Teach-er and our Friend, Our faith-ful Lead-er to the end, Sing we Al-le-lu-ia! A-MEN.

7. To thee, by Jesus Christ sent down,
Of all his gifts the sum and crown,
Sing we Alleluia!

8. To thee, who art with God the Son
And God the Father ever One,
Sing we Alleluia!

## 253 THE HOLY SPIRIT

*I will pour out of my Spirit upon all flesh... Acts 2:17*

MENDON L. M.

James Montgomery, 1823

German melody arr. by Samuel Dyer, 1828

1. O Spirit of the living God, In all thy plen-i-tude of grace,
Wher-e'er the foot of man hath trod, Descend on our a-pos-tate race.

2. Give tongues of fire and hearts of love To preach the rec-on-cil-ing word;
Give pow'r and unc-tion from a-bove, When-e'er the joy-ful sound is heard.

3. Be darkness, at thy com-ing, light; Con-fu-sion, or-der in thy path;
Souls with-out strength in-spire with might; Bid mer-cy tri-umph o-ver wrath.

4. O Spirit of the Lord, pre-pare All the round earth her God to meet;
Breathe thou a-broad like morn-ing air, Till hearts of stone be-gin to beat. A-MEN.

5. Baptize the nations; far and nigh
The triumphs of the cross record;
The Name of Jesus glorify,
Till every kindred call him Lord.

6. God from eternity hath willed
All flesh shall his salvation see:
So be the Father's love fulfilled,
The Saviour's sufferings crowned through thee.

## 254

*When the Comforter is come, whom I will send unto you from the Father, even the Spirit of truth... he shall testify of me. John 15:26*

CAMBERWELL S. M.

Joseph Hart, 1712-1768

Har. by Samuel S. Wesley, 1810-1876

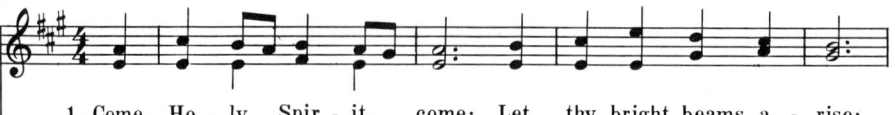

1. Come, Holy Spirit, come; Let thy bright beams a-rise;
2. Cheer our des-pond-ing hearts, Thou heav'n-ly Par-a-clete;
3. Re-vive our droop-ing faith; Our doubts and fears re-move;
4. Con-vince us of our sin; Then lead to Je-sus' blood,

# THE HOLY SPIRIT

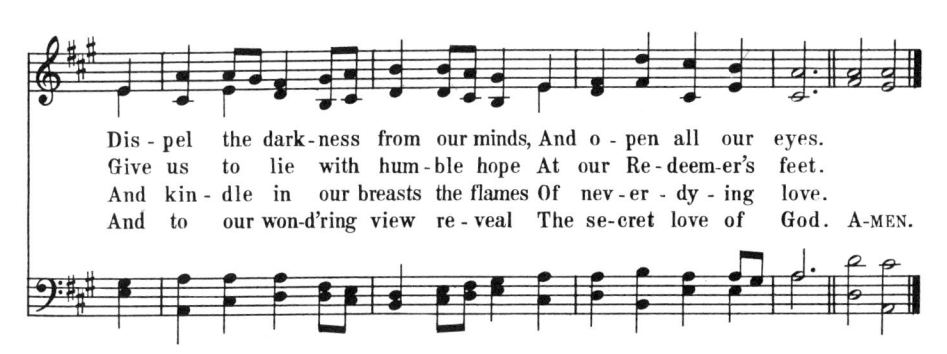

Dis - pel    the dark - ness from our minds, And o - pen all    our    eyes.
Give us    to    lie    with hum - ble hope At our Re - deem - er's    feet.
And kin - dle in    our breasts the flames Of nev - er - dy - ing    love.
And    to    our won-d'ring view re - veal The se - cret love of    God. A-MEN.

5. 'Tis thine to cleanse the heart,
To sanctify the soul,
To pour fresh life in every part,
And new create the whole.

6. Dwell, therefore, in our hearts;
Our minds from bondage free;
Then we shall know and praise and love
The Father, Son, and Thee.

## 255

*And I will put my spirit within you, and cause you to walk in my statutes, and ye shall keep my judgments, and do them.* Ezek. 36:27

Cecil Frances Alexander, 1823-1895

SOLDAU L. M.
Wittenberg *Gesangbuch,* 1524

1. Spir - it    of    God, that moved of old    Up - on the wa - ters' dark-ened face,
2. Thou that    art pow'r and peace com-bined, All high-est strength, all pur - est    love,
3. Come, give us still thy pow'r-ful aid,    And urge us on, and make us thine;
4. Nor    let    us quench thy sev'n-fold light; But still with soft - est breath-ings stir

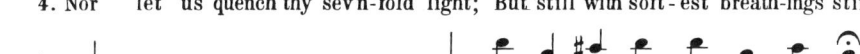

Come, when our faith-less hearts are cold, And stir them with an    in-ward grace.
The    rush-ing of    the might-y wind, The brood-ing of    the gen - tle    dove.
Nor    leave the hearts that once were made Fit temp-les for thy grace di - vine.
Our    way-ward souls, and lead us right, O    Ho - ly Ghost, the Com-fort - er. A-MEN.

Harmony from *The Revised Church Hymnary.* Used by permission of the Oxford University Press, London.

# 256                                                                 THE HOLY SCRIPTURES

*Lord, evermore give us this bread.* John 6:34

Mary A. Lathbury, 1877                                              BREAD OF LIFE 6.4.6.4.D.
William F. Sherwin, 1826-1888

1. Break thou the bread of life, Dear Lord, to me,
   As thou didst break the loaves Beside the sea;
   Throughout the sacred page I seek thee, Lord,
   My spirit pants for thee, O living Word.

2. Bless thou the truth, dear Lord, To me, to me,
   As thou didst bless the bread By Galilee;
   Then shall all bondage cease, All fetters fall;
   And I shall find my peace, My All in all.

3. Thou art the Bread of Life, O Lord, to me,
   Thy holy Word the truth That saveth me;
   Give me to eat and live With thee above;
   Teach me to love thy truth, For thou art love.

4. O send thy Spirit, Lord, Now unto me,
   That he may touch mine eyes, And make me see:
   Show me the truth concealed Within thy Word,
   And in thy Book revealed I see the Lord. A-MEN.

St. 1, line 3, alt.

# THE HOLY SCRIPTURES 257

*Open thou mine eyes, that I may behold wondrous things out of thy law.* Psalm 119:18

Edwin Hodder, 1863

SERAPH C. M. D.
Gottfried W. Fink, 1842

1. Thy Word is like a gar-den, Lord, With flow-ers bright and fair;
And ev-ery one who seeks may pluck A love-ly clus-ter there.
Thy Word is like a deep, deep mine; And jew-els rich and rare
Are hid-den in its might-y depths For ev-ery search-er there.

2. Thy Word is like a star-ry host: A thou-sand rays of light
Are seen to guide the trav-el-er, And make his path-way bright.
Thy Word is like an ar-mor-y, Where sol-diers may re-pair,
And find, for life's long bat-tle day, All need-ful weap-ons there.

3. O may I love thy pre-cious Word, May I ex-plore the mine,
May I its fra-grant flow-ers glean, May light up-on me shine.
O may I find my ar-mor there, Thy Word my trust-y sword;
I'll learn to fight with ev-ery foe The bat-tle of the Lord. A-MEN.

## 258 THE HOLY SCRIPTURES

*But the Comforter, which is the Holy Ghost... he shall... bring all things to your remembrance, whatsoever I have said unto you.* John 14:26

William Cowper, 1779
ORTONVILLE C. M. with repeat
Thomas Hastings, 1837

1. The Spir-it breathes up-on the Word, And brings the truth to sight; Pre-cepts and prom-is-es af-ford A sanc-ti-fy-ing light, A sanc-ti-fy-ing light.
2. A glo-ry gilds the sa-cred page, Maj-es-tic, like the sun: It gives a light to ev-ery age; It gives, but bor-rows none, It gives, but bor-rows none.
3. The Hand that gave it still sup-plies The gra-cious light and heat: His truths up-on the na-tions rise; They rise, but nev-er set, They rise, but nev-er set.
4. Let ev-er-last-ing thanks be thine For such a bright dis-play As makes a world of dark-ness shine With beams of heav'n-ly day, With beams of heav'n-ly day.
5. My soul re-joic-es to pur-sue The steps of him I love, Till glo-ry break up-on my view In bright-er worlds a-bove, In bright-er worlds a-bove. A-MEN.

## 259

*For his merciful kindness is great toward us: and the truth of the Lord endureth forever...* Psalm 117:2

Anne Steele, 1760
BEATITUDO C. M.
John B. Dykes, 1875

1. Fa-ther of mer-cies, in thy Word What end-less glo-ry shines;
2. Here may the wretch-ed sons of want Ex-haust-less rich-es find;
3. Here the Re-deem-er's wel-come voice Spreads heav'n-ly peace a-round;
4. O may these heav'n-ly pag-es be My ev-er dear de-light;
5. Di-vine In-struct-or, gra-cious Lord, Be thou for ev-er near;

# THE HOLY SCRIPTURES

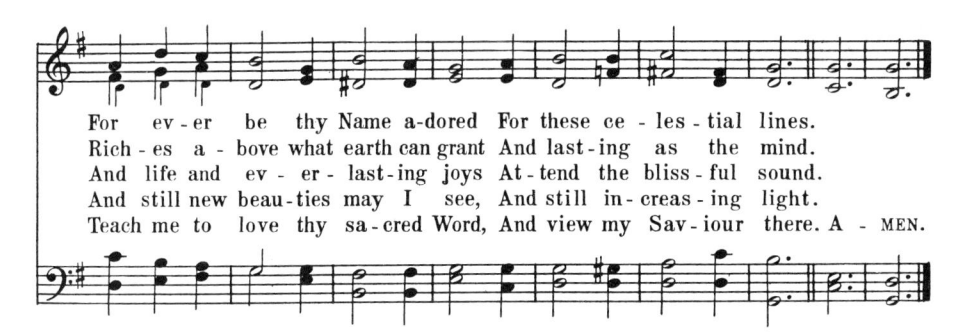

For ev-er be thy Name a-dored For these ce-les-tial lines.
Rich-es a-bove what earth can grant And last-ing as the mind.
And life and ev-er-last-ing joys At-tend the bliss-ful sound.
And still new beau-ties may I see, And still in-creas-ing light.
Teach me to love thy sa-cred Word, And view my Sav-iour there. A-MEN.

## 260

*Deal bountifully with thy servant, that I may live, and keep thy word.* Psalm 119:17

From PSALM 119:17-24　　　　　　　　　　　　　　ST. MARTIN'S C. M.
*The Psalter*, 1912　　　　　　　　　　　　　　William Tans'ur, 1740

1. Thy serv-ant, blessed by thee, shall live And keep thy Word with awe; Lord o-pen thou mine eyes to see The won-ders of thy law.
2. A pil-grim in the earth am I, Thy will to me re-veal; To know thy truth my spir-it yearns, Con-sumed with ar-dent zeal.
3. Thou dost re-buke the proud, O Lord, Who hate thy ho-ly Name; But since I keep thy right-eous law, De-liv-er me from shame.
4. I on thy stat-utes med-i-tate, Though e-vil men de-ride; Thy faith-ful Word is my de-light, My coun-se-lor and guide. A-MEN.

## 261 THE HOLY SCRIPTURES

*The voice of my beloved! behold, he cometh...* Song of Solomon 2:8

Thomas T. Lynch, 1855

KIRBY BEDON 6. 6. 4. 6. 6. 6. 4.
Edward Bunnett, 1887

1. Christ in his Word draws near; Hush, moan-ing voice of fear, He bids thee cease; With songs sin-cere and sweet Let us a-rise, and meet Him who comes forth to greet Our souls with peace.
2. Ris - ing a - bove thy care, Meet him as in the air, O wea-ry heart; Put on joy's sa-cred dress; Lo, as he comes to bless, Quite from thy wea - ri - ness Set free thou art.
3. For works of love and praise He brings thee sum-mer days, Warm days and bright; Win - ter is past and gone, Now he, sal - va - tion's Sun, Shin - eth on ev - ery one With mer - cy's light.
4. From the bright sky a - bove, Clad in his robes of love, 'Tis he, our Lord! Dim earth it - self grows clear, As his light draw-eth near: O let us hush and hear His ho - ly Word. A - MEN.

## 262

*To testify the gospel of the grace of God.* Acts 20:24

St. 1-2, Benjamin Beddome, 1787;
St. 3-5 alt. by Thomas Cotterill, 1819

GERMANY L. M.
William Gardiner's *Sacred Melodies*, 1815

1. God, in the gos - pel of his Son, Makes his e - ter - nal coun-sels known;
2. Here sin - ners of a hum - ble frame May taste his grace, and learn his Name;
3. The pris-'ner here may break his chains; The wea - ry rest from all his pains;
4. Here faith re - veals to mor - tal eyes A bright-er world be - yond the skies;
5. O grant us grace, Al - might-y Lord, To read and mark thy ho - ly Word;

## THE HOLY SCRIPTURES

Where love in all its glo-ry shines, And truth is drawn in fair-est lines.
May read, in char-ac-ters of blood, The wis-dom, pow'r, and grace of God.
The cap-tive feel his bon-dage cease; The mourn-er find the way of peace.
Here shines the light which guides our way From earth to realms of end-less day.
Its truths with meek-ness to re-ceive, And by its ho-ly pre-cepts live. A-MEN.

### 263

*The heavens declare the glory of God; and the firmament sheweth his handywork.* Psalm 19:1

From PSALM 19  
Isaac Watts, 1719

UXBRIDGE L. M.  
Lowell Mason, 1830

1. The heav'ns de-clare thy glo-ry, Lord; In ev-'ry star thy wis-dom shines;
2. The roll-ing sun, the chang-ing light, And nights and days, thy pow'r con-fess;
3. Sun, moon, and stars con-vey thy praise Round the whole earth, and nev-er stand;
4. Nor shall thy spread-ing gos-pel rest Till through the world thy Truth has run;

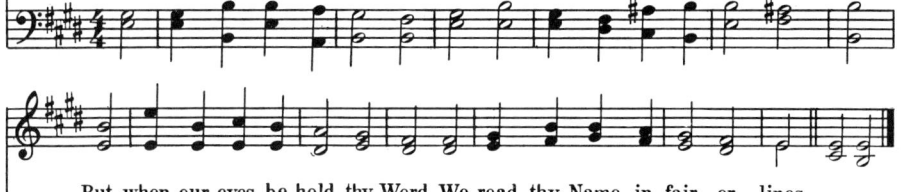

But when our eyes be-hold thy Word, We read thy Name in fair-er lines.
But the blest vol-ume thou hast writ Re-veals thy jus-tice and thy grace.
So when thy truth be-gan its race, It touched and glanced on ev-'ry land.
Till Christ has all the na-tions blessed That see the light, or feel the sun. A-MEN.

5. Great Sun of Righteousness, arise;
Bless the dark world with heav'nly light:
Thy gospel makes the simple wise,
Thy laws are pure, thy judgments right.

6. Thy noblest wonders here we view
In souls renewed, and sins forgiv'n:
Lord, cleanse my sins, my soul renew,
And make thy Word my guide to heav'n.

## 264 THE HOLY SCRIPTURES

*Wherewithal shall a young man cleanse his way? by taking heed thereto according to thy word.* Psalm 119:9

PSALM 119:9-16
The Psalter, 1912

DUANE STREET L.M.D.
George Coles, 1792-1858

1. How shall the young direct their way? What light shall be their perfect guide? Thy Word, O Lord, will safely lead, If in its wisdom they confide. Sincerely I have sought thee, Lord, O let me not from thee depart; To know thy will and keep from sin Thy Word I cherish in my heart.

2. O blessed Lord, teach me thy law, Thy righteous judgments I declare; Thy testimonies make me glad, For they are wealth beyond compare. Upon thy precepts and thy ways My heart will meditate with awe; Thy Word shall be my chief delight, And I will not forget thy law. A-MEN.

# THE HOLY SCRIPTURES

## 265

*Thy word is a lamp unto my feet, and a light unto my path.* Psalm 119:105

BELMONT C. M.

John Fawcett, 1782 — Arr. from William Gardiner, 1812

1. How pre-cious is the book di-vine, By in-spir-a-tion giv-en;
2. It sweet-ly cheers our droop-ing hearts, In this dark vale of tears;
3. This lamp, through all the te-dious night Of life, shall guide our way,

Bright as a lamp its doc-trines shine, To guide our souls to heav'n.
Life, light, and joy it still im-parts, And quells our ris-ing fears.
Till we be-hold the clear-er light Of an e-ter-nal day. A-MEN.

## 266

*The law of the Lord is perfect, converting the soul: the testimony of the Lord is sure, making wise the simple.* Psalm 19:7

ST. CYPRIAN 6.6.6.6.

Sir Henry W. Baker, 1861 — Richard R. Chope, 1862

1. Lord, thy Word a-bid-eth, And our foot-steps guid-eth;
2. When our foes are near us, Then thy Word doth cheer us;
3. When the storms are o'er us, And dark clouds be-fore us,
4. Who can tell the pleas-ure, Who re-count the treas-ure,
5. Word of mer-cy, giv-ing Suc-cor to the liv-ing;
6. O that we, dis-cern-ing Its most ho-ly learn-ing,

Who its truth be-liev-eth Light and joy re-ceiv-eth.
Word of con-so-la-tion, Mes-sage of sal-va-tion.
Then its light di-rect-eth, And our way pro-tect-eth.
By thy Word im-part-ed To the sim-ple-heart-ed?
Word of life, sup-ply-ing Com-fort to the dy-ing!
Lord, may love and fear thee, Ev-er-more be near thee. A-MEN.

# 267 — THE HOLY SCRIPTURES

*The entrance of thy words giveth light; it giveth understanding unto the simple.* Psalm 119:130

William Walsham How, 1867
MUNICH 7. 6. 7. 6. D.
Meiningen *Gesangbuch*, 1693

1. O Word of God Incarnate, O Wisdom from on high,
   O Truth unchanged, unchanging, O Light of our dark sky;
   We praise thee for the radiance That from the hallowed page,
   A lantern to our foot-steps, Shines on from age to age.

2. The church from her dear Master Received the gift divine,
   And still that light she lifteth O'er all the earth to shine.
   It is the golden casket, Where gems of truth are stored;
   It is the heav'n-drawn picture Of Christ, the living Word.

3. It floateth like a banner Before God's host unfurled;
   It shineth like a beacon Above the darkling world.
   It is the chart and compass That o'er life's surging sea,
   'Mid mists and rocks and quick-sands, Still guides, O Christ, to thee.

4. O make thy church, dear Saviour, A lamp of purest gold,
   To bear before the nations Thy true light, as of old.
   O teach thy wand'ring pilgrims By this their path to trace,
   Till, clouds and darkness ended, They see thee face to face. A-MEN.

# THE CHURCH OF CHRIST

268

*Thus saith the Lord God, Behold, I lay in Zion for a foundation a stone, a tried stone, a precious corner stone, a sure foundation . . . Isa. 28:16*

Anon., Latin, 7th century
Tr. by John Mason Neale, 1851
Alt. in *Hymns Ancient and Modern*, 1861

REGENT SQUARE 8.7.8.7.8.7.
Henry Smart, 1867

1. Christ is made the sure Foun-da-tion, Christ the Head and Cor-ner-stone,
2. All that ded-i-cat-ed cit-y, Dear-ly loved of God on high,
3. To this tem-ple, where we call thee, Come, O Lord of hosts, to-day:
4. Here vouch-safe to all thy serv-ants What they ask of thee to gain,
5. Laud and hon-or to the Fa-ther, Laud and hon-or to the Son,

Cho-sen of the Lord and pre-cious, Bind-ing all the church in one;
In ex-ul-tant ju-bi-la-tion Pours per-pet-ual mel-o-dy;
With thy wont-ed lov-ing-kind-ness Hear thy peo-ple as they pray;
What they gain from thee for ev-er With the bless-ed to re-tain,
Laud and hon-or to the Spir-it, Ev-er Three and ev-er One,

Ho-ly Zi-on's help for ev-er, And her con-fi-dence a-lone.
God the One in Three a-dor-ing In glad hymns e-ter-nal-ly.
And thy full-est ben-e-dic-tion Shed with-in its walls al-way.
And here-af-ter in thy glo-ry Ev-er-more with thee to reign.
One in might, and One in glo-ry, While un-end-ing a-ges run. A-MEN.

# 269 THE CHURCH OF CHRIST

*Glorious things are spoken of thee, O city of God.* Psalm 87:3

John Newton, 1779

AUSTRIAN HYMN 8. 7. 8. 7. D.
Franz Josef Haydn, 1797

1. Glo-rious things of thee are spok-en, Zi-on, cit-y of our God;
2. See, the streams of liv-ing wa-ters, Spring-ing from e-ter-nal love,
3. Round each hab-i-ta-tion hov-'ring, See the cloud and fire ap-pear
4. Sav-iour, if of Zi-on's ci-ty I, through grace, a mem-ber am,

He whose word can-not be bro-ken Formed thee for his own a-bode:
Well sup-ply thy sons and daugh-ters, And all fear of want re-move:
For a glo-ry and a cov-'ring, Show-ing that the Lord is near:
Let the world de-ride or pit-y, I will glo-ry in thy Name:

On the Rock of A-ges found-ed, What can shake thy sure re-pose?
Who can faint, while such a riv-er Ev-er flows their thirst t' as-suage?
Thus de-riv-ing from their ban-ner Light by night and shade by day,
Fad-ing is the world-ling's pleas-ure, All his boast-ed pomp and show;

With sal-va-tion's walls sur-round-ed, Thou may'st smile at all thy foes.
Grace which, like the Lord, the giv-er, Nev-er fails from age to age.
Safe they feed up-on the man-na Which he gives them when they pray.
Sol-id joys and last-ing treas-ure None but Zi-on's chil-dren know. A-MEN.

# THE CHURCH OF CHRIST  270

*Jesus Christ himself being the chief corner stone. Eph. 2:20*

Samuel J. Stone, 1866  
AURELIA 7. 6. 7. 6. D.  
Samuel S. Wesley, 1864

1. The church-'s one Foun-da-tion Is Je-sus Christ her Lord;  
She is his new cre-a-tion By wa-ter and the Word:  
From heav'n he came and sought her To be his ho-ly bride;  
With his own blood he bought her, And for her life he died.

2. E-lect from ev-'ry na-tion, Yet one o'er all the earth,  
Her char-ter of sal-va-tion One Lord, one faith, one birth;  
One ho-ly Name she bless-es, Par-takes one ho-ly food,  
And to one hope she press-es, With ev-'ry grace en-dued.

3. Though with a scorn-ful won-der Men see her sore op-pressed,  
By schi-sms rent as-un-der, By her-e-sies dis-tressed,  
Yet saints their watch are keep-ing, Their cry goes up, "How long?"  
And soon the night of weep-ing Shall be the morn of song.

4. The church shall nev-er per-ish! Her dear Lord to de-fend,  
To guide, sus-tain and cher-ish, Is with her to the end;  
Though there be those that hate her, And false sons in her pale,  
A-gainst or foe or trait-or She ev-er shall pre-vail.

5. 'Mid toil and trib-u-la-tion, And tu-mult of her war,  
She waits the con-sum-ma-tion Of peace for ev-er-more;  
Till with the vi-sion glo-rious Her long-ing eyes are blest,  
And the great church vic-to-rious Shall be the church at rest.

6. Yet she on earth hath u-nion With God the Three in One,  
And mys-tic sweet com-mun-ion With those whose rest is won:  
O hap-py ones and ho-ly! Lord, give us grace that we,  
Like them, the meek and low-ly, On high may dwell with thee. A-MEN.

## 271 THE CHURCH OF CHRIST

*A certain man made a great supper, and bade many.* Luke 14:16

Isaac Watts, 1707
ST. COLUMBA C. M.
Old Irish hymn melody

1. How sweet and aw-ful is the place
2. While all our hearts and all our songs
3. "Why was I made to hear thy voice,
4. 'Twas the same love that spread the feast
5. Pit-y the na-tions, O our God,
6. We long to see thy church-es full,

With Christ with-in the doors, While ev-er-last-ing
Join to ad-mire the feast, Each of us cry, with
And en-ter while there's room, When thous-ands make a
That sweet-ly drew us in; Else we had still re-
Con-strain the earth to come; Send thy vic-to-rious
That all the cho-sen race May, with one voice and

love dis-plays The choic-est of her stores.
thank-ful tongues, "Lord, why was I a guest?"
wretch-ed choice, And rath-er starve than come?"
fused to taste, And per-ished in our sin.
Word a-broad, And bring the strang-ers home.
heart and soul, Sing thy re-deem-ing grace. A-MEN.

St. 4, line 2, alt.

## 272

*And it shall come to pass in the last days, that the mountain of the Lord's house shall be established in the top of the mountains*...Isa. 2:2

Scottish *Paraphrases*, 1781
GLASGOW C. M.
Moore's *Psalm-Singer's Pocket Companion*, 1756

1. Be-hold! the moun-tain of the Lord In lat-ter days shall rise
2. To this the joy-ful na-tions round, All tribes and tongues, shall flow;
3. The beam that shines from Zi-on hill Shall light-en ev-'ry land;
4. A-mong the na-tions he shall judge; His judg-ments truth shall guide;
5. Come then, O house of Ja-cob, come To wor-ship at his shrine;

# THE CHURCH OF CHRIST

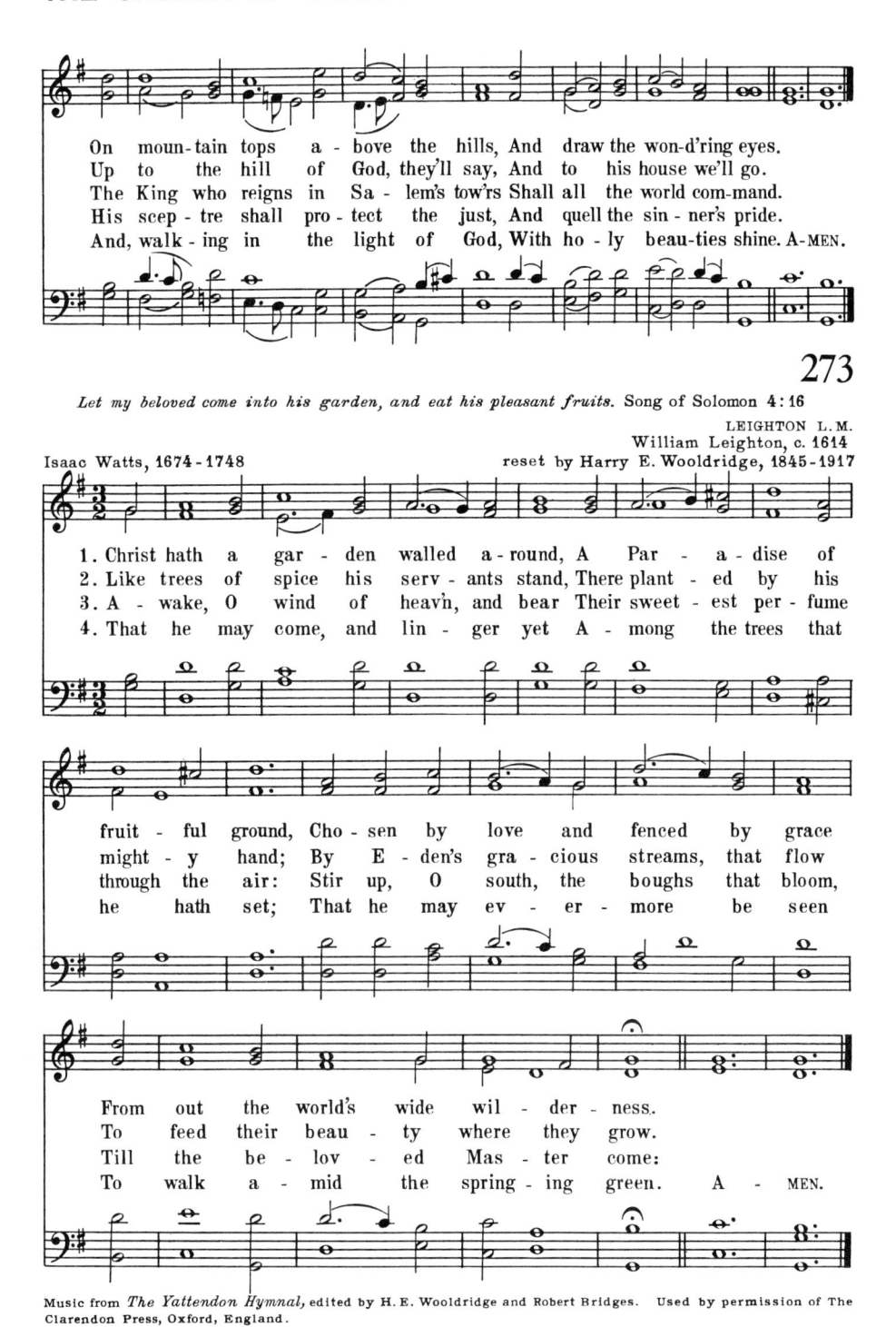

On moun-tain tops a - bove the hills, And draw the won-d'ring eyes.
Up to the hill of God, they'll say, And to his house we'll go.
The King who reigns in Sa - lem's tow'rs Shall all the world com-mand.
His scep - tre shall pro - tect the just, And quell the sin - ner's pride.
And, walk - ing in the light of God, With ho - ly beau - ties shine. A-MEN.

**273**

*Let my beloved come into his garden, and eat his pleasant fruits.* Song of Solomon 4:16

LEIGHTON L.M.
William Leighton, c. 1614
reset by Harry E. Wooldridge, 1845-1917

Isaac Watts, 1674-1748

1. Christ hath a gar - den walled a - round, A Par - a - dise of
2. Like trees of spice his serv - ants stand, There plant - ed by his
3. A - wake, O wind of heav'n, and bear Their sweet - est per - fume
4. That he may come, and lin - ger yet A - mong the trees that

fruit - ful ground, Cho - sen by love and fenced by grace
might - y hand; By E - den's gra - cious streams, that flow
through the air: Stir up, O south, the boughs that bloom,
he hath set; That he may ev - er - more be seen

From out the world's wide wil - der - ness.
To feed their beau - ty where they grow.
Till the be - lov - ed Mas - ter come:
To walk a - mid the spring - ing green. A - MEN.

Music from *The Yattendon Hymnal,* edited by H. E. Wooldridge and Robert Bridges. Used by permission of The Clarendon Press, Oxford, England.

## 274 THE CHURCH OF CHRIST

*Arise, shine; for thy light is come, and the glory of the Lord is risen upon thee... And the Gentiles shall come to thy light, and kings to the brightness of thy rising.* Isa. 60:1, 3

Thomas Hastings, 1831

WESLEY 11. 10. 11. 10.
Lowell Mason, 1830

1. Hail to the brightness of Zion's glad morning!
   Joy to the lands that in darkness have lain!
   Hushed be the accents of sorrow and mourning;
   Zion in triumph begins her mild reign.

2. Hail to the brightness of Zion's glad morning!
   Long by the prophets of Israel foretold!
   Hail to the millions from bondage returning!
   Gentiles and Jews the blest vision behold.

3. Lo, in the desert rich flowers are springing,
   Streams ever copious are gliding along;
   Loud from the mountain tops echoes are ringing,
   Wastes rise in verdure, and mingle in song.

4. See, from all lands, from the isles of the ocean,
   Praise to Jehovah ascending on high;
   Fall'n are the engines of war and commotion,
   Shouts of salvation are rending the sky. A-MEN.

# THE CHURCH OF CHRIST 275

*As the mountains are round about Jerusalem, so the Lord is round about his people from henceforth even for ever.* Psalm 125:2

Thomas Kelly, 1806  
ZION 8.7.8.7.4.7. with repeat  
Thomas Hastings, 1830

1. Zi-on stands by hills sur-round-ed, Zi-on, kept by pow'r di-vine;  
All her foes shall be con-found-ed, Though the world in arms com-bine;  
Hap-py Zi-on, What a fa-vored lot is thine!  
Hap-py Zi-on, What a fa-vored lot is thine!

2. Ev-'ry hu-man tie may per-ish; Friend to friend un-faith-ful prove;  
Moth-ers cease their own to cher-ish; Heav'n and earth at last re-move;  
But no chang-es Can at-tend Je-ho-vah's love,  
But no chang-es Can at-tend Je-ho-vah's love.

3. In the fur-nace God may prove thee, Thence to bring thee forth more bright,  
But can nev-er cease to love thee; Thou art pre-cious in his sight;  
God is with thee— God, thine ev-er-last-ing light,  
God is with thee— God, thine ev-er-last-ing light. A-MEN.

## 276 THE CHURCH OF CHRIST

*I was glad when they said unto me, Let us go into the house of the Lord.* Psalm 122:1

From PSALM 122
Tate and Brady's *New Version*, 1696; 1698

ARNOLD C. M.
Samuel Arnold, 1740-1802

1. O 'twas a joyful sound to hear Our tribes devoutly say, Up, Israel! to the temple haste, And keep your festal day.
2. At Salem's courts we must appear With our assembled pow'rs, In strong and beauteous order ranged, Like her united tow'rs.
3. O pray we then for Salem's peace; For they shall prosp'rous be, Thou holy city of our God, Who bear true love to thee.
4. May peace within thy sacred walls A constant guest be found; With plenty and prosperity Thy palaces be crowned.
5. For my dear brethren's sake, and friends No less than brethren dear, I'll pray, May peace in Salem's tow'rs A constant guest appear.
6. But most of all I'll seek thy good, And ever wish thee well, For Zion and the temple's sake, Where God vouchsafes to dwell. A-MEN.

## 277

*We have a strong city; salvation will God appoint for walls and bulwarks.* Isa. 26:1

Adapted from Isaac Watts, 1707,
as in *Scottish Paraphrases*, 1781

IRISH C. M.
*Hymns and Sacred Poems*, Dublin, 1749

1. How glorious Zion's courts appear, The city of our God!
2. Its walls, defended by his grace, No pow'r shall e'er o'erthrow,
3. Lift up the everlasting gates, The doors wide open fling!
4. Trust in the Lord, for ever trust, And banish all your fears;

# THE CHURCH OF CHRIST

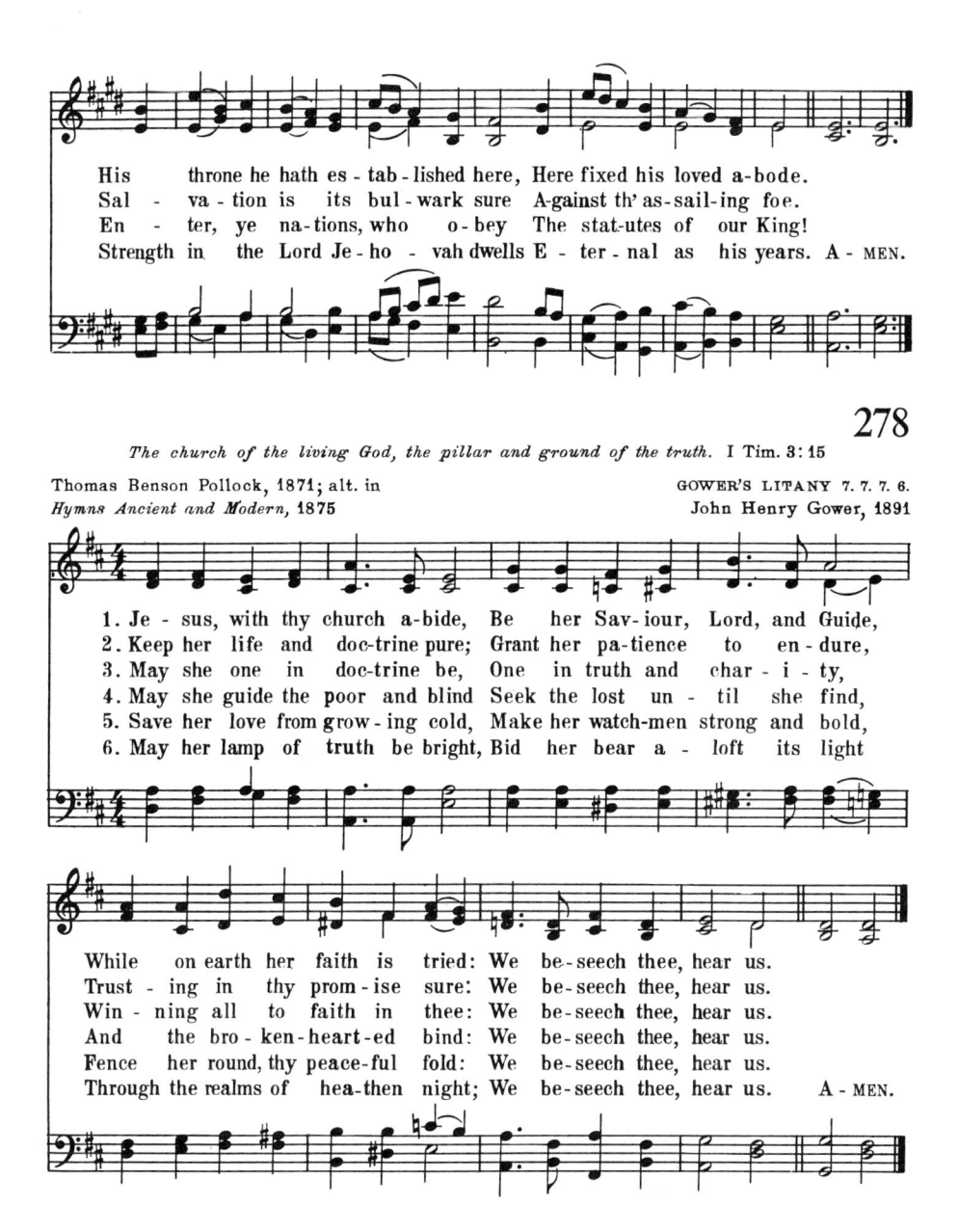

His throne he hath es-tab-lished here, Here fixed his loved a-bode.
Sal - va - tion is its bul-wark sure A-gainst th' as-sail-ing foe.
En - ter, ye na-tions, who o-bey The stat-utes of our King!
Strength in the Lord Je-ho-vah dwells E-ter-nal as his years. A-MEN.

**278**

*The church of the living God, the pillar and ground of the truth.* I Tim. 3:15

Thomas Benson Pollock, 1871; alt. in
*Hymns Ancient and Modern,* 1875

GOWER'S LITANY 7. 7. 7. 6.
John Henry Gower, 1891

1. Je - sus, with thy church a-bide, Be her Sav-iour, Lord, and Guide,
2. Keep her life and doc-trine pure; Grant her pa-tience to en-dure,
3. May she one in doc-trine be, One in truth and char - i - ty,
4. May she guide the poor and blind Seek the lost un - til she find,
5. Save her love from grow-ing cold, Make her watch-men strong and bold,
6. May her lamp of truth be bright, Bid her bear a-loft its light

While on earth her faith is tried: We be-seech thee, hear us.
Trust - ing in thy prom-ise sure: We be-seech thee, hear us.
Win - ning all to faith in thee: We be-seech thee, hear us.
And the bro-ken-heart-ed bind: We be-seech thee, hear us.
Fence her round, thy peace-ful fold: We be-seech thee, hear us.
Through the realms of hea-then night; We be-seech thee, hear us. A - MEN.

7. Arm her soldiers with the cross,
   Brave to suffer toil or loss,
   Counting earthly gain but dross:
   We beseech thee, hear us.

8. May she holy triumphs win,
   Overthrow the hosts of sin,
   Gather all the nations in:
   We beseech thee, hear us.

## 279 THE CHURCH OF CHRIST

*Give ear, O Shepherd of Israel, thou that leadest Joseph like a flock... Psalm 80:1*

From PSALM 80: 1-3, 8-9, 16-19　　　　　　　　　　　　　　　　JOANNA 11. 11. 11. 11.
Associate Reformed Presbyterian *Psalter*, 1931　　　　　　　　　Welsh hymn melody

1. O thou who the Shepherd of Israel art,
2. In Ephraim's, Manasseh's and Benjamin's sight,
3. From Egypt's dark border a vine thou didst take;
4. The axe hews it down; it is burned in the fire;
5. No more shall we wander, delighting in shame;

Give ear to our pray'r and thy favor impart;
O come thou and save us; awake in thy might.
Destroying the heathen didst room for it make.
They perish, rebuked in thy terrible ire.
Revive us, O Lord, we will call on thy Name.

Thou leader of Joseph, thou guide of his way,
O God, give us favor, restore to thy grace;
Where planted it grew at thy sov-'reign command,
O lay then thy hand on the Man of thy might,
O Lord God of Hosts, us restore to thy grace.

'Mid cherubim dwelling, thy glory display.
And then we shall live in the light of thy face.
With roots deeply set and boughs filling the land.
The Son of Man made to stand strong in thy sight.
And then we shall live in the light of thy face. A-MEN.

For a higher setting of this tune, see No. 79

## THE CHURCH OF CHRIST (FIRST TUNE) 280

*Lord, I have loved the habitation of thy house, and
the place where thine honour dwelleth.* Psalm 26:8

Timothy Dwight, 1800

VENI S. M.
Sir John Stainer, 1890

1. I love thy King-dom, Lord, The house of thine a-bode,
2. I love thy church, O God: Her walls be-fore thee stand,
3. For her my tears shall fall, For her my prayers as-cend;
4. Be-yond my high-est joy I prize her heav'n-ly ways,
5. Je-sus, thou Friend Di-vine, Our Sav-iour and our King,
6. Sure as thy truth shall last, To Zi-on shall be giv'n

The church our blest Re-deem-er saved With his own pre-cious blood.
Dear as the ap-ple of thine eye, And grav-en on thy hand.
To her my cares and toils be giv'n, Till toils and cares shall end.
Her sweet com-mun-ion, sol-emn vows, Her hymns of love and praise.
Thy hand from ev-'ry snare and foe Shall great de-liv-'rance bring.
The bright-est glo-ries earth can yield, And bright-er bliss of heav'n. A-MEN.

(SECOND TUNE) 280

Timothy Dwight, 1800

SHIRLAND S. M.
Samuel Stanley, 1805

I love thy King-dom, Lord, The house of thine a-bode,

The church our blest Re-deem-er saved With his own pre-cious blood. A-MEN.

## 281

THE CHURCH

*That they may rest from their labours; and their works do follow them.* Rev. 14:13

SARUM 10. 10. 10. 4. 4.

William Walsham How, 1864; text of 1875

Sir Joseph Barnby, 1868

1. For all the saints who from their la - bors rest, Who thee by
2. Thou wast their Rock, their For - tress, and their Might; Thou, Lord, their
3. O may thy sol - diers, faith - ful, true, and bold, Fight as the
4. The gold - en eve - ning bright-ens in the west; Soon, soon to
5. But lo! there breaks a yet more glo - rious day; The saints tri -
6. From earth's wide bounds, from o - cean's far - thest coast, Through gates of

faith be - fore the world con - fessed, Thy Name, O Je - sus,
Cap - tain in the well - fought fight; Thou, in the dark - ness
saints who no - bly fought of old, And win with them the
faith - ful war - riors comes their rest; Sweet is the calm of
umph - ant rise in bright ar - ray; The King of Glo - ry
pearl streams in the count - less host, Sing - ing to Fa - ther,

be for ev - er blest. Al - le - lu - ia! Al - le - lu - ia!
drear, their one true Light. Al - le - lu - ia! Al - le - lu - ia!
vic - tor's crown of gold. Al - le - lu - ia! Al - le - lu - ia!
Par - a - dise the blest. Al - le - lu - ia! Al - le - lu - ia!
pass - es on his way. Al - le - lu - ia! Al - le - lu - ia!
Son, and Ho - ly Ghost, Al - le - lu - ia! Al - le - lu - ia! A - MEN.

## 282

*Inasmuch as ye have done it unto one of the least of these my brethren, ye have done it unto me.* Matt. 25:40

Philip Doddridge, 1702-1751, and others

ST. FRANCES C. M.
George Augustus Löhr, 1821-1897

1. Foun - tain of good, to own thy love Our thank - ful hearts in - cline;
2. But thou hast need - y breth - ren here, Par - tak - ers of thy grace,
3. And in their ac - cents of dis - tress Thy plead - ing voice is heard;
4. Thy face with rev - 'rence and with love We in thy poor would see;

# THE COMMUNION OF SAINTS

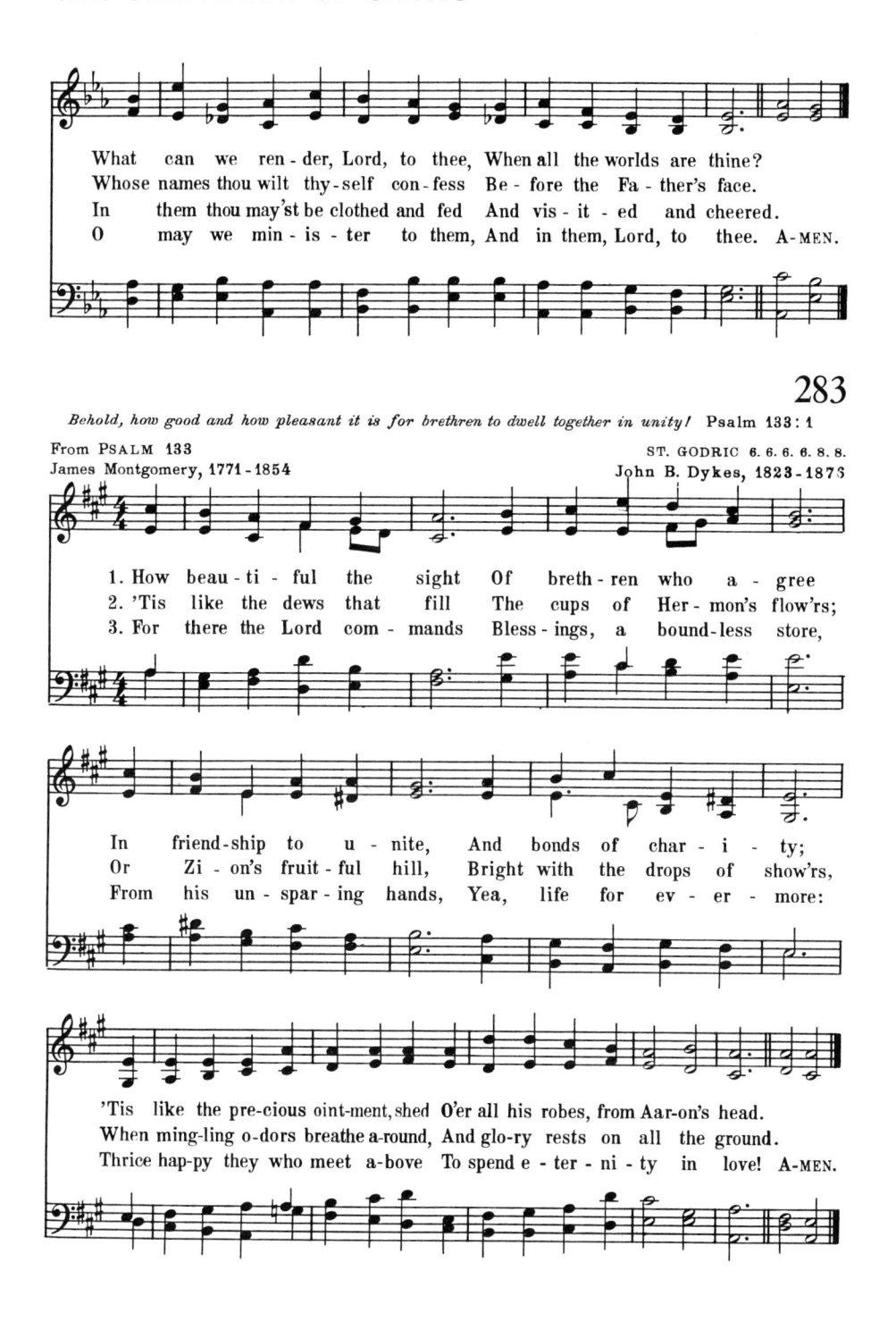

What can we ren-der, Lord, to thee, When all the worlds are thine?
Whose names thou wilt thy-self con-fess Be-fore the Fa-ther's face.
In them thou may'st be clothed and fed And vis-it-ed and cheered.
O may we min-is-ter to them, And in them, Lord, to thee. A-MEN.

## 283

*Behold, how good and how pleasant it is for brethren to dwell together in unity!* Psalm 133:1

From PSALM 133
James Montgomery, 1771-1854

ST. GODRIC 6.6.6.6.8.8.
John B. Dykes, 1823-1876

1. How beau-ti-ful the sight Of breth-ren who a-gree
2. 'Tis like the dews that fill The cups of Her-mon's flow'rs;
3. For there the Lord com-mands Bless-ings, a bound-less store,

In friend-ship to u-nite, And bonds of char-i-ty;
Or Zi-on's fruit-ful hill, Bright with the drops of show'rs,
From his un-spar-ing hands, Yea, life for ev-er-more:

'Tis like the pre-cious oint-ment, shed O'er all his robes, from Aar-on's head.
When ming-ling o-dors breathe a-round, And glo-ry rests on all the ground.
Thrice hap-py they who meet a-bove To spend e-ter-ni-ty in love! A-MEN.

# 284

THE CHURCH

*Be thou faithful unto death, and I will give thee a crown of life.* Rev. 2:10

Joseph the hymnographer, 9th century
Arr. and tr. by John Mason Neale, 1862
St. 1, line 5, alt.

ST. KEVIN 7. 6. 7. 6. D.
Sir Arthur S. Sullivan, 1872

1. Let our choir new anthems raise, Wake the morn with gladness;
God himself to joy and praise Turns the martyrs' sadness:
Bright the day that won their crown, Opened heav'n's bright portal,
As they laid the mortal down And put on th' immortal.

2. Never flinched they from the flame, From the torture never;
Vain the foeman's sharpest aim, Satan's best endeavor:
For by faith they saw the land Decked in all its glory,
Where triumphant now they stand With the victor's story.

3. Faith they had that knew not shame, Love that could not languish;
And eternal hope o'ercame Momentary anguish.
Up and follow, Christian men! Press through toil and sorrow;
Spurn the night of fear, and then, O the glorious morrow! A-MEN.

# THE COMMUNION OF SAINTS (FIRST TUNE) 285

*For ye are all one in Christ Jesus.* Gal. 3:28

John Fawcett, 1782

BOYLSTON S. M.
Lowell Mason, 1832

1. Blest be the tie that binds Our hearts in Chris-tian love:
2. Be-fore our Fa-ther's throne We pour our ar-dent prayers;
3. We share our mu-tual woes, Our mu-tual bur-dens bear,
4. When we as-un-der part, It gives us in-ward pain;
5. This glo-rious hope re-vives Our cour-age by the way,
6. From sor-row, toil and pain, And sin, we shall be free;

The fel-low-ship of kin-dred minds Is like to that a-bove.
Our fears, our hopes, our aims, are one, Our com-forts and our cares.
And oft-en for each oth-er flows The sym-pa-thiz-ing tear.
But we shall still be joined in heart, And hope to meet a-gain,
While each in ex-pec-ta-tion lives, And longs to see the day.
And per-fect love and friend-ship reign Through all e-ter-ni-ty. A-MEN.

(SECOND TUNE) 285

John Fawcett, 1782

DENNIS S. M.
Arr. from Hans G. Nägeli by Lowell Mason, 1845

Blest be the tie that binds Our hearts in Chris-tian love:
The fel-low-ship of kin-dred minds Is like to that a-bove. A-MEN.

# THE CHURCH

*I will instruct thee and teach thee in the way which thou shalt go: I will guide thee with mine eye.* Psalm 32:8

Anon., 1625; tr. by
Theodore Baker, 1851-1934

KREMSER 12. 11. 12. 11.
Old Netherlands melody,
in *The Collection,* Adrianus Valerius, 1625

1. We gather together to ask the Lord's blessing;
   He chastens and hastens his will to make known;
   The wicked oppressing now cease from distressing:
   Sing praises to his Name; he forgets not his own.

2. Beside us to guide us, our God with us joining,
   Ordaining, maintaining his Kingdom divine;
   So from the beginning the fight we were winning:
   Thou, Lord, wast at our side: all glory be thine!

3. We all do extol thee, thou Leader triumphant,
   And pray that thou still our Defender wilt be.
   Let thy congregation escape tribulation:
   Thy Name be ever prais'd! O Lord, make us free! A-MEN.

# THE COVENANT PEOPLE 287

*Lord, thou hast been our dwelling place in all generations.* Psalm 90:1

Thomas H. Gill, 1864

THE GOLDEN CHAIN 8. 7. 8. 7. 8. 8. 7.
Sir Joseph Barnby, 1887

1. Lord, thou hast been our dwell-ing-place In ev - 'ry gen - er - a - tion;
2. Our cleav-ing sins we oft have wept, And oft thy pa-tience prov - ed;
3. No, noth-ing from those arms of love Shall thine own peo-ple sev - er;

Thy peo - ple still have known thy grace, And blessed thy con - so - la - tion:
But still thy faith we fast have kept, Thy Name we still have lov - ed;
Our Help - er nev - er will re - move, Our God will fail us nev - er.

Through ev - 'ry age thou heard'st our cry; Through ev - 'ry age we
And thou hast kept and loved us well, Hast grant - ed us in
Thy peo - ple, Lord, have dwelt in thee, Our dwell - ing place thou

found thee nigh, Our Strength and our Sal - va - tion.
thee to dwell, Un - shak - en, un - re - mov - ed.
still wilt be For ev - er and for ev - er. A - MEN.

## 288 THE CHURCH

*Praise ye the Lord. Sing unto the Lord a new song, and his praise in the congregation of saints.* Psalm 149:1

From PSALM 149
The Psalter, 1912

LAUDATE DOMINUM 5.5.5.5.6.5.6.5.
Charles Hubert Hastings Parry, 1848-1918

1. O praise ye the Lord And sing a new song,
   Amid all his saints His praises prolong;
   The praise of their Maker His people shall sing,
   And children of Zion Rejoice in their King.

2. With timbrel and harp And joyful acclaim,
   With gladness and mirth, Sing praise to his Name;
   For God in his people His pleasure doth seek,
   With robes of salvation He clotheth the meek.

3. In glory exult, Ye saints of the Lord;
   With songs in the night High praises accord;
   Go forth in his service, Be strong in his might
   To conquer all evil And stand for the right.

4. For this is his word: His saints shall not fail,
   But over the earth Their pow'r shall prevail;
   All kingdoms and nations Shall yield to their sway.
   To God give the glory And praise him for aye. A-MEN.

Music used by permission of Novello & Company, Ltd.

# THE COVENANT PEOPLE 289

*Happy is that people, whose God is the Lord.* Psalm 144:15

From PSALM 144:12-15  
The Psalter, 1912

SHORTLE 8. 8. 6. D. with repeat  
Charles G. Goodrich, b. 1869

1. O people blest, whose sons in youth, In sturdy strength and noble truth, Like plants in vigor spring; Whose daughters fair, a queenly race, Are like the cornerstones that grace The palace of a king, The palace of a king.

2. O people blest, when flock and field Their rich, abundant increase yield, And blessings multiply; When plenty all thy children share, And no invading foe is there, And no distressful cry, And no distressful cry.

3. O happy people, favored land, To whom the Lord with liberal hand Has thus his goodness shown; Yea, surely is that people blest By whom Jehovah is confessed To be their God alone, To be their God alone. A-MEN.

St. 1, line 1;  
St. 2, lines 1 and 4, alt.

## 290 THE CHURCH

*When the Lord turned again the captivity of Zion, we were like them that dream.* Psalm 126:1

From PSALM 126  
The Psalter, 1912  

ARTHUR'S SEAT 6.6.6.6.8.8.  
Arr. from Sir John Goss by Uzziah C. Burnap, 1874

1. When in his might the Lord A-rose to set us free,
And Zi-on was re-stored From her cap-tiv-i-ty, In trans-ports then of
joy and mirth We praised the Lord of all the earth.

2. The na-tions saw with fear The might of God dis-played,
When he at last drew near To give his peo-ple aid; Great things for us the
Lord has wrought, And glad-ness to our hearts has brought.

3. A-gain re-fresh us, Lord, With thy re-viv-ing love,
And be thy bless-ing poured In mer-cy from a-bove; By grace re-vive our
hearts a-gain, As streams re-freshed by co-pious rain.

4. Al-though with bit-ter tears The sow-er bears his seed,
When har-vest time ap-pears He shall be glad in-deed; For they that in the
sow-ing weep Shall yet in joy and glad-ness reap. A-MEN.

## 291

*Except the Lord build the house, they labor in vain that build it...* Psalm 127:1

From PSALM 127  
The Psalter, 1912  

ROSE HILL L. M.  
Joseph E. Sweetser, 1825-1873

1. Un-less the Lord the house shall build, The wea-ry build-ers toil in vain;
2. In vain you rise ere morn-ing break, And late your night-ly vig-ils keep,
3. Lo, chil-dren are a great re-ward, A gift from God in ve-ry truth;
4. And blest the man whose age is cheered By stal-wart sons and daugh-ters fair;

# THE COVENANT PEOPLE

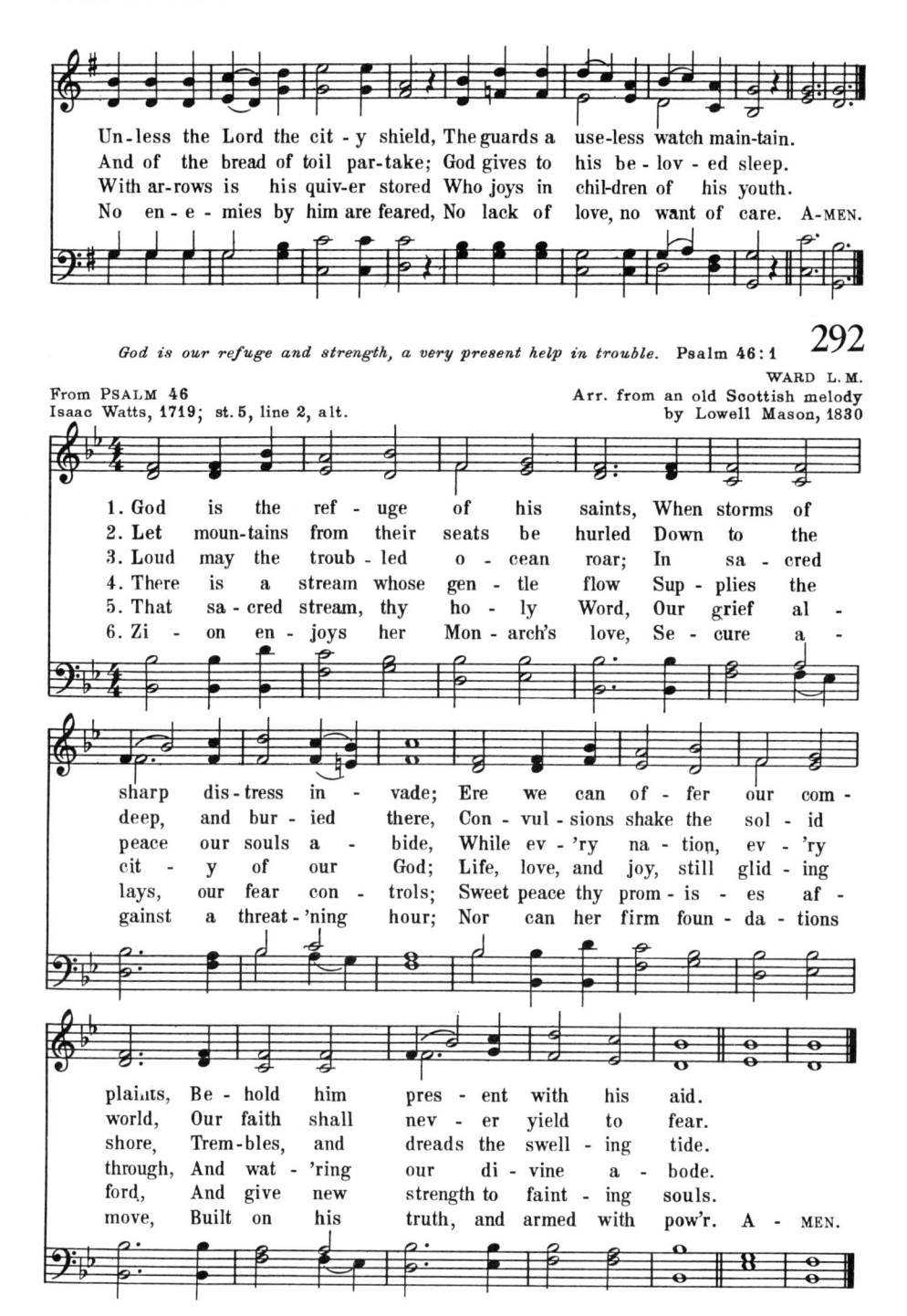

Un-less the Lord the cit-y shield, The guards a use-less watch main-tain.
And of the bread of toil par-take; God gives to his be-lov-ed sleep.
With ar-rows is his quiv-er stored Who joys in chil-dren of his youth.
No en-e-mies by him are feared, No lack of love, no want of care. A-MEN.

---

*God is our refuge and strength, a very present help in trouble.* Psalm 46:1

## 292

WARD L.M.

From PSALM 46
Isaac Watts, 1719; st. 5, line 2, alt.

Arr. from an old Scottish melody
by Lowell Mason, 1830

1. God is the ref-uge of his saints, When storms of sharp dis-tress in-vade; Ere we can of-fer our com-plaints, Be-hold him pres-ent with his aid.
2. Let moun-tains from their seats be hurled Down to the deep, and bur-ied there, Con-vul-sions shake the sol-id world, Our faith shall nev-er yield to fear.
3. Loud may the troub-led o-cean roar; In sa-cred peace our souls a-bide, While ev-'ry na-tion, ev-'ry shore, Trem-bles, and dreads the swell-ing tide.
4. There is a stream whose gen-tle flow Sup-plies the cit-y of our God; Life, love, and joy, still glid-ing through, And wat-'ring our di-vine a-bode.
5. That sa-cred stream, thy ho-ly Word, Our grief al-lays, our fear con-trols; Sweet peace thy prom-is-es af-ford, And give new strength to faint-ing souls.
6. Zi-on en-joys her Mon-arch's love, Se-cure a-gainst a threat-'ning hour; Nor can her firm foun-da-tions move, Built on his truth, and armed with pow'r. A-MEN.

# 293 THE CHURCH

*Give ear, O my people, to my law: incline your ears to the words of my mouth.* Psalm 78:1

From PSALM 78:1-7  
Isaac Watts, 1719

DUNDEE C. M.  
The Scottish *Psalter*, 1615

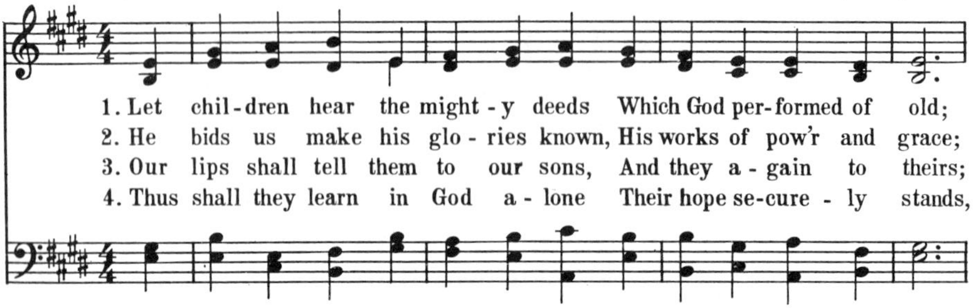

1. Let chil-dren hear the might-y deeds Which God per-formed of old;
2. He bids us make his glo-ries known, His works of pow'r and grace;
3. Our lips shall tell them to our sons, And they a-gain to theirs;
4. Thus shall they learn in God a-lone Their hope se-cure-ly stands,

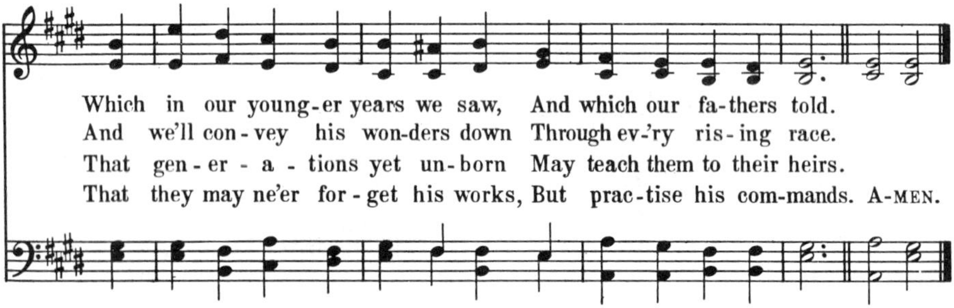

Which in our young-er years we saw, And which our fa-thers told.
And we'll con-vey his won-ders down Through ev-'ry ris-ing race.
That gen-er-a-tions yet un-born May teach them to their heirs.
That they may ne'er for-get his works, But prac-tise his com-mands. A-MEN.

# 294

*For he cometh, for he cometh to judge the earth: he shall judge the world with righteousness, and the people with his truth.* Psalm 96:13

John Milton, 1608-1674

ST. MAGNUS C. M.  
Jeremiah Clark, 1670-1707

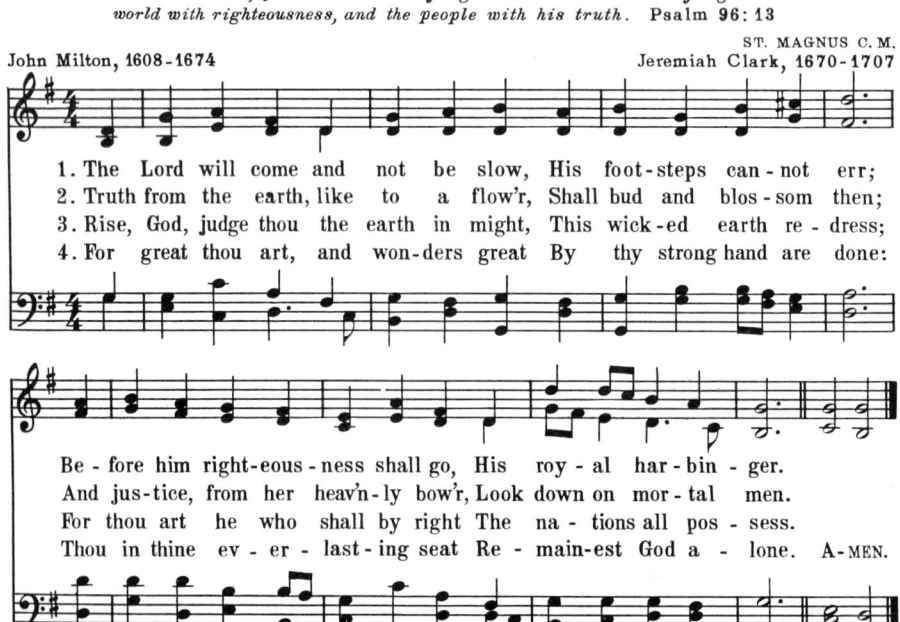

1. The Lord will come and not be slow, His foot-steps can-not err;
2. Truth from the earth, like to a flow'r, Shall bud and blos-som then;
3. Rise, God, judge thou the earth in might, This wick-ed earth re-dress;
4. For great thou art, and won-ders great By thy strong hand are done:

Be-fore him right-eous-ness shall go, His roy-al har-bin-ger.
And jus-tice, from her heav'n-ly bow'r, Look down on mor-tal men.
For thou art he who shall by right The na-tions all pos-sess.
Thou in thine ev-er-last-ing seat Re-main-est God a-lone. A-MEN.

# THE KINGDOM OF GOD  295

*All the ends of the world shall remember and turn unto the Lord: and all the kindreds of the nations shall worship before thee.* Psalm 22:27

From PSALM 22:27-30
*The Psalter,* 1912

VISION L. M. with refrain
William H. Doane, 1832-1916

1. The ends of all the earth shall hear And turn un-to the Lord in fear; All kin-dreds of the earth shall own And wor-ship him as God a-lone.
2. For his the king-dom, his of right, He rules the na-tions by his might; All earth to him her hom-age brings, The Lord of lords, the King of kings.
3. Both rich and poor, both bond and free, Shall wor-ship him on bend-ed knee, And chil-dren's chil-dren shall pro-claim The glo-rious hon-or of his Name.

REFRAIN

All earth to him her hom-age brings, The Lord of lords, the King of kings. A-MEN.

# THE CHURCH

## 296

*As long as I am in the world, I am the light of the world.* John 9:5

Johann Heermann, 1630
Tr. by Catherine Winkworth, 1858

BRESLAU L. M.
Alt. from *As hymnodus sacer*, Leipzig, 1625

1. O Christ, our true and on-ly Light, Il-lu-mine those who sit in night;
   Let those a-far now hear thy voice, And in thy fold with us re-joice.
2. And all who else have strayed from thee, O gen-tly seek; thy heal-ing be
   To ev-'ry wound-ed con-science giv'n; And let them al-so share thy heav'n.
3. O make the deaf to hear thy Word; And teach the dumb to speak, dear Lord,
   Who dare not yet the faith a-vow, Though se-cret-ly they hold it now.
4. Shine on the dark-ened and the cold; Re-call the wan-d'rers from thy fold;
   U-nite those now who walk a-part; Con-firm the weak and doubt-ing heart.
5. So they with us may ev-er-more Such grace with won-d'ring thanks a-dore,
   And end-less praise to thee be giv'n By all the church in earth and heav'n. A-MEN.

## 297

*O Lord, revive thy work in the midst of the years...* Hab. 3:2

Albert Midlane, 1858

HOLY ROOD S. M.
Arthur H. Brown, 1863

1. Re-vive thy work, O Lord, Thy might-y arm make bare;
   Speak with the voice that wakes the dead, And make thy peo-ple hear.
2. Re-vive thy work, O Lord, Dis-turb this sleep of death;
   Quick-en the smoul-d'ring em-bers now By thine al-might-y breath.
3. Re-vive thy work, O Lord, Cre-ate soul-thirst for thee;
   And hun-g'ring for the Bread of Life O may our spir-its be.
4. Re-vive thy work, O Lord, Ex-alt thy pre-cious Name;
   And, by the Ho-ly Ghost, our love For thee and thine in-flame.
5. Re-vive thy work, O Lord, Give pen-te-cos-tal show'rs:
   The glo-ry shall be all thine own, The bless-ing, Lord, be ours. A-MEN.

Music used by permission of the Oxford University Press, London.

# THE KINGDOM OF GOD                                                298

*And they shall bring all your brethren... out of all nations... Isa. 66:20*

Benjamin Beddome, 1769

TRURO L. M.
*Psalmodia Evangelica*, 1789

1. Shout, for the bless-ed Je-sus reigns; Through dis-tant lands his tri-umphs spread;
   And sin-ners, freed from end-less pains, Own him their Sav-iour and their Head.
2. He calls his cho-sen from a-far, They all at Zi-on's gates ar-rive;
   Those who were dead in sin be-fore By sov-ereign grace are made a-live.
3. Gen-tiles and Jews his laws o-bey; Na-tions re-mote their of-f'rings bring,
   And un-con-strained their hom-age pay To their ex-alt-ed God and King.
4. O may his ho-ly church in-crease, His Word and Spir-it still pre-vail,
   While an-gels cel-e-brate his praise, And saints his grow-ing glo-ries hail.
5. Loud hal-le-lu-jahs to the Lamb, From all be-low, and all a-bove!
   In loft-y songs ex-alt his Name, In songs as last-ing as his love. A-MEN.

*For a lower setting of this tune see No. 61.*

299

*He that goeth forth and weepeth, bearing precious seed, shall doubtless come again with rejoicing, bringing his sheaves with him.* Psalm 126:6

James Montgomery, 1819

SILVER STREET S. M.
Isaac Smith, c. 1770

1. Sow in the morn thy seed, At eve hold not thy hand; To
   doubt and fear give thou no heed, Broad-cast it o'er the land.
2. Thou know'st not which may thrive, The late or ear-ly sown, God
   keeps his pre-cious seed a-live, When and wher-ev-er strown.
3. Thou canst not toil in vain; Cold, heat, and moist, and dry, Shall
   fos-ter and ma-ture the grain For gar-ners in the sky.
4. Thence, when the glo-rious end, The day of God is come, The
   an-gel-reap-ers shall de-scend, And heav'n cry, "Har-vest Home." A-MEN.

St. 2, line 3, alt.

# 300

THE CHURCH

*The kingdoms of this world are become the kingdoms of our Lord, and of his Christ . . .* Rev. 11:15

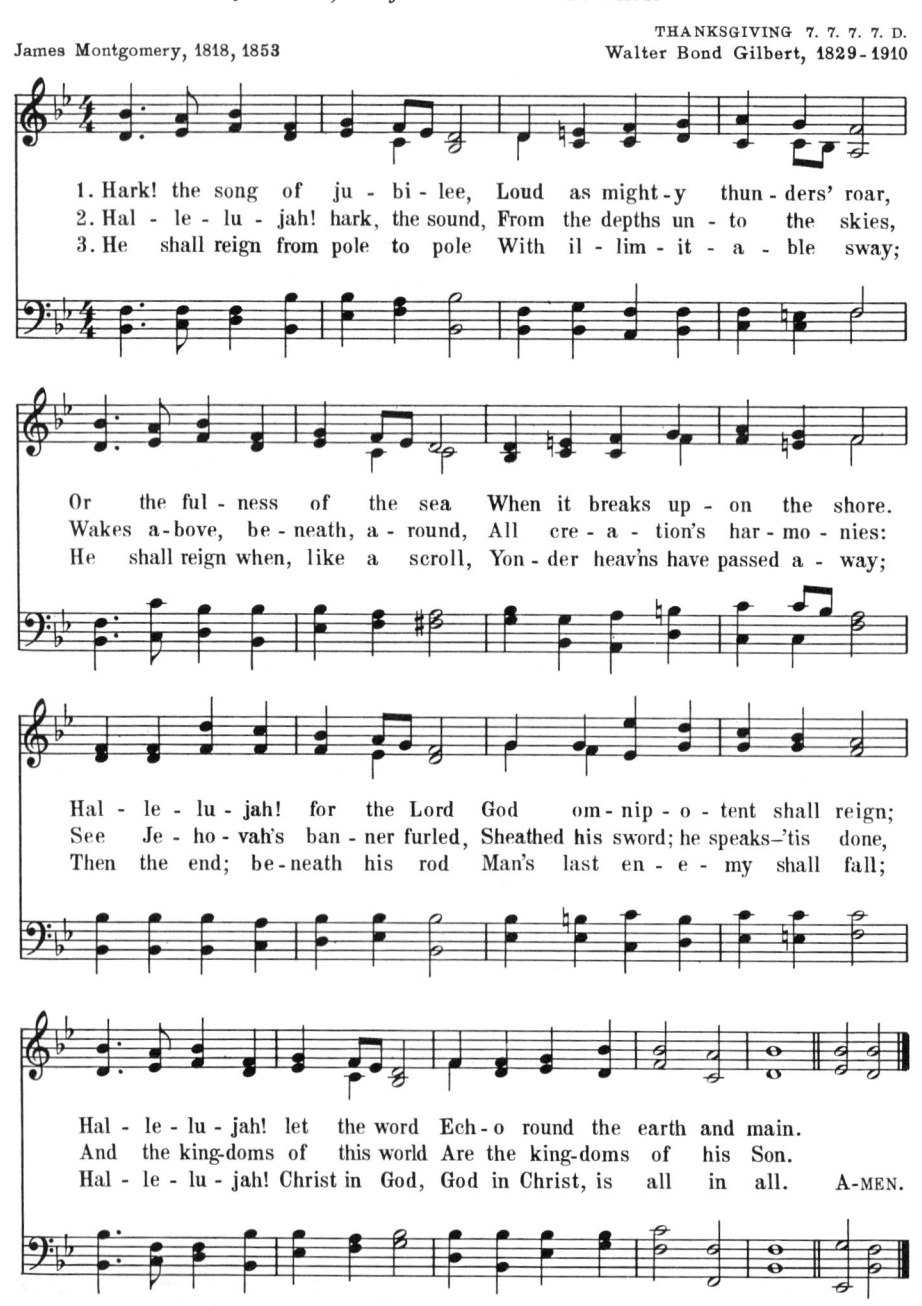

James Montgomery, 1818, 1853

THANKSGIVING 7. 7. 7. 7. D.
Walter Bond Gilbert, 1829-1910

1. Hark! the song of ju-bi-lee, Loud as might-y thun-ders' roar,
Or the ful-ness of the sea When it breaks up-on the shore.
Hal-le-lu-jah! for the Lord God om-nip-o-tent shall reign;
Hal-le-lu-jah! let the word Ech-o round the earth and main.

2. Hal-le-lu-jah! hark, the sound, From the depths un-to the skies,
Wakes a-bove, be-neath, a-round, All cre-a-tion's har-mo-nies:
See Je-ho-vah's ban-ner furled, Sheathed his sword; he speaks—'tis done,
And the king-doms of this world Are the king-doms of his Son.

3. He shall reign from pole to pole With il-lim-it-a-ble sway;
He shall reign when, like a scroll, Yon-der heav'ns have passed a-way;
Then the end; be-neath his rod Man's last en-e-my shall fall;
Hal-le-lu-jah! Christ in God, God in Christ, is all in all. A-MEN.

# THE KINGDOM OF GOD 301

*Give ear, O my people, to my law: incline your ears to the words of my mouth.* Psalm 78:1

From PSALM 78  
The Psalter, 1912

HANOVER (CROFT) 10. 10. 11. 11.  
William Croft, 1678-1727

1. My peo-ple, give ear, at-tend to my word, In par-a-bles new deep truths shall be heard; The won-der-ful sto-ry our fa-thers made known To chil-dren suc-ceed-ing by us must be shown.
2. In-struct-ing our sons we glad-ly re-cord The prais-es, the works, the might of the Lord, For he has com-mand-ed that what he has done Be passed in tra-di-tion from fa-ther to son.
3. Let chil-dren thus learn from his-to-ry's light To hope in our God and walk in his sight, The God of their fa-thers to fear and o-bey, And ne'er like their fa-thers to turn from his way.
4. The sto-ry be told, to warn and re-strain, Of hearts that were hard, re-bel-lious, and vain, Of sol-diers who fal-tered when bat-tle was near, Who kept not God's cov-'nant nor walked in his fear.
5. God's won-der-ful works to them he had shown, His mar-vel-ous deeds their fa-thers had known; He made for their path-way the wa-ters di-vide, His glo-ri-ous pil-lar of cloud was their guide.
6. Un-harmed through the sea, where per-ished their foe, He caused them with ease and safe-ty to go; His ho-ly land gain-ing, in peace they were brought To dwell in the moun-tain the Lord's hand had bought. A-MEN.

7. He gave them the land, a heritage fair;
   The nations that dwelt in wickedness there
   He drove out before them with great overthrow,
   And gave to his people the tents of the foe.

8. His servant he called, a shepherd of sheep,
   From tending his flock, the people to keep;
   So David, their shepherd, with wisdom and might
   Protected and fed them and led them aright.

## 302 THE LORD'S HOUSE

*Blessed are they that dwell in thy house: they will be still praising thee.* Psalm 84:4

From PSALM 84
Isaac Watts, 1719; st. 4 arr.

DARWALL'S 148th 6.6.6.6.8.8.
John Darwall, 1770

1. Lord of the worlds above, How pleasant and how fair The dwellings of thy love, Thine earthly temples, are: To thine abode my heart aspires, With warm desires to see my God.
2. O happy souls that pray Where God appoints to hear! O happy men that pay Their constant service there! They praise thee still; and happy they That love the way to Zion's hill.
3. They go from strength to strength, Through this dark vale of tears, Till each arrives at length, Till each in heav'n appears: O glorious seat, when God, our King, Shall thither bring our willing feet!
4. God is our Sun and Shield, Our Light and our Defence; With gifts his hands are filled; We draw our blessings thence. Thrice happy he, O God of hosts, Whose spirit trusts alone in thee. A-MEN.

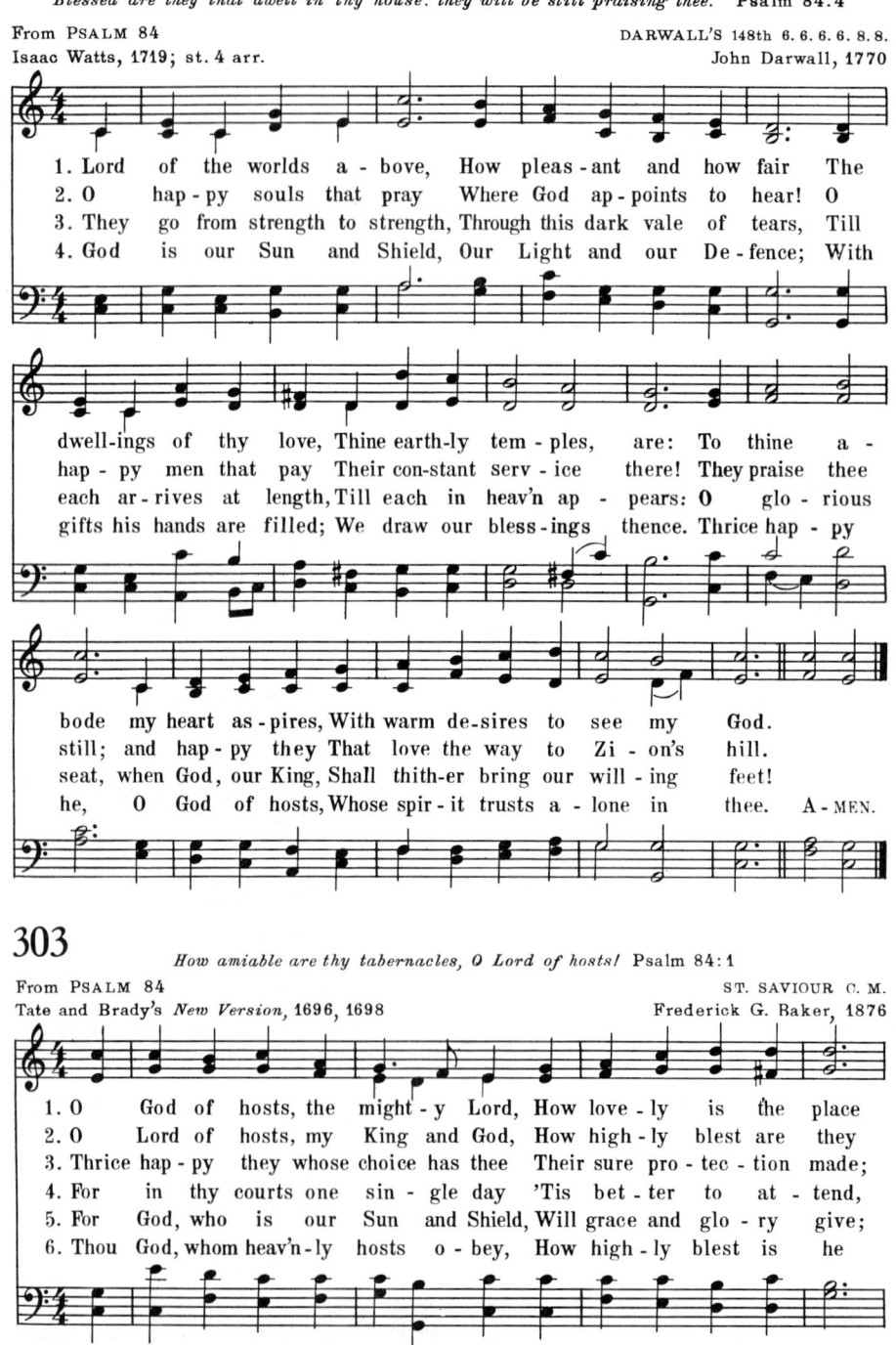

## 303

*How amiable are thy tabernacles, O Lord of hosts!* Psalm 84:1

From PSALM 84
Tate and Brady's *New Version*, 1696, 1698

ST. SAVIOUR C. M.
Frederick G. Baker, 1876

1. O God of hosts, the mighty Lord, How lovely is the place
2. O Lord of hosts, my King and God, How highly blest are they
3. Thrice happy they whose choice has thee Their sure protection made;
4. For in thy courts one single day 'Tis better to attend,
5. For God, who is our Sun and Shield, Will grace and glory give;
6. Thou God, whom heav'nly hosts obey, How highly blest is he

# THE LORD'S HOUSE

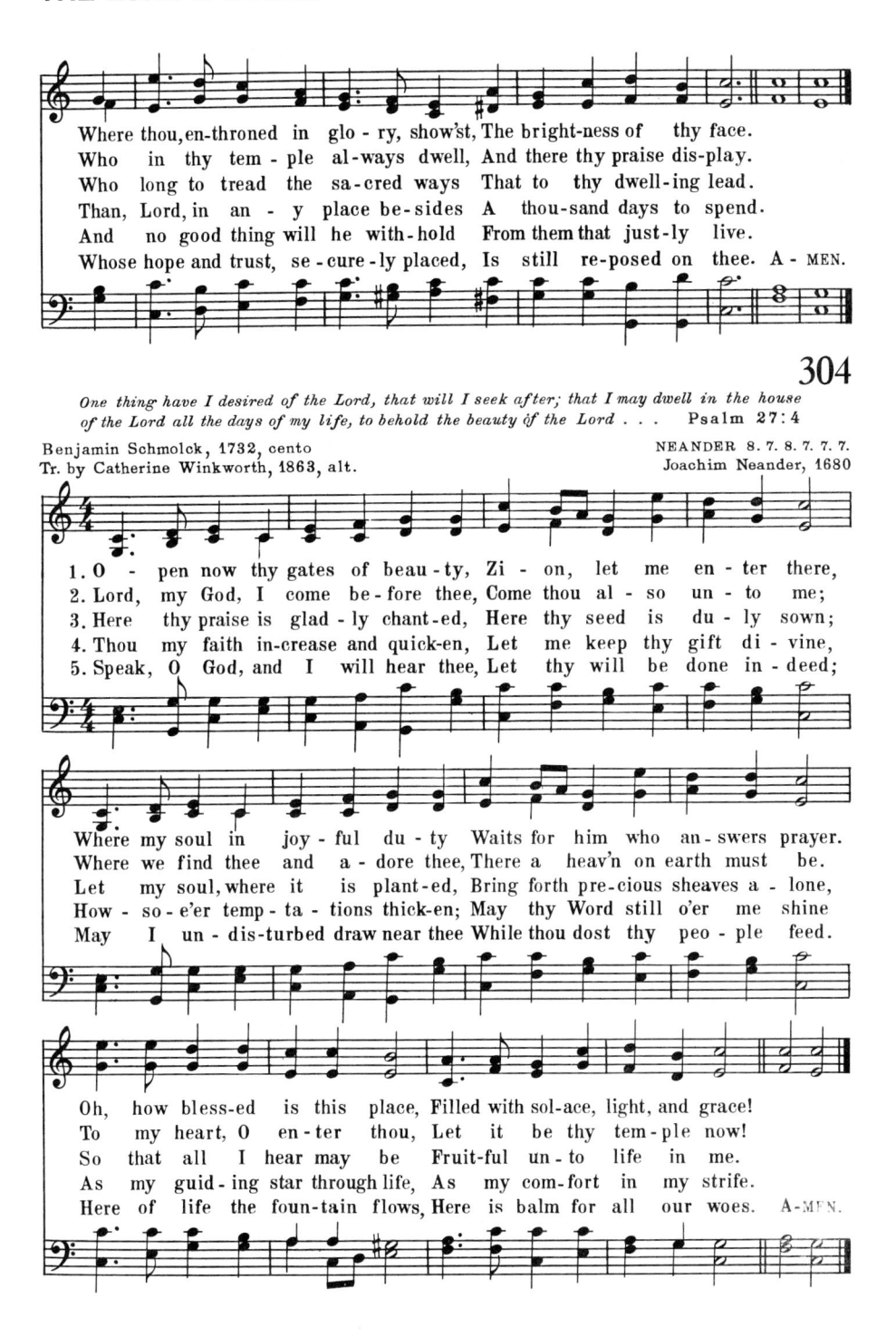

Where thou, en-throned in glo - ry, show'st, The bright-ness of thy face.
Who in thy tem - ple al-ways dwell, And there thy praise dis-play.
Who long to tread the sa-cred ways That to thy dwell-ing lead.
Than, Lord, in an - y place be-sides A thou-sand days to spend.
And no good thing will he with-hold From them that just-ly live.
Whose hope and trust, se-cure-ly placed, Is still re-posed on thee. A - MEN.

304

*One thing have I desired of the Lord, that will I seek after; that I may dwell in the house of the Lord all the days of my life, to behold the beauty of the Lord . . . Psalm 27:4*

Benjamin Schmolck, 1732, cento
Tr. by Catherine Winkworth, 1863, alt.

NEANDER 8. 7. 8. 7. 7. 7.
Joachim Neander, 1680

1. O - pen now thy gates of beau-ty, Zi - on, let me en - ter there,
2. Lord, my God, I come be-fore thee, Come thou al - so un - to me;
3. Here thy praise is glad - ly chant-ed, Here thy seed is du - ly sown;
4. Thou my faith in-crease and quick-en, Let me keep thy gift di - vine,
5. Speak, O God, and I will hear thee, Let thy will be done in - deed;

Where my soul in joy - ful du - ty Waits for him who an-swers prayer.
Where we find thee and a - dore thee, There a heav'n on earth must be.
Let my soul, where it is plant-ed, Bring forth pre-cious sheaves a - lone,
How - so - e'er temp - ta - tions thick-en; May thy Word still o'er me shine
May I un - dis-turbed draw near thee While thou dost thy peo - ple feed.

Oh, how bless-ed is this place, Filled with sol-ace, light, and grace!
To my heart, O en - ter thou, Let it be thy tem-ple now!
So that all I hear may be Fruit-ful un - to life in me.
As my guid-ing star through life, As my com-fort in my strife.
Here of life the foun-tain flows, Here is balm for all our woes. A - MEN.

## 305 THE LORD'S HOUSE

*How amiable are thy tabernacles, O Lord of hosts!* Psalm 84:1

From PSALM 84
Associate Reformed Presbyterian *Psalter*, 1931

LLANGLOFFAN 7. 6. 7. 6. D.
Welsh hymn melody

1. O Lord of Hosts, how love-ly the place where thou dost dwell!
2. Blest who thy house in-hab-it, they ev-er give thee praise;
3. O hear, Lord God of Ja-cob, to me an an-swer yield;
4. Our sun and shield, Je-ho-vah, will grace and glo-ry give;

Thy tab-er-nac-les ho-ly in pleas-ant-ness ex-cel.
Blest all whom thou dost strength-en, who love the sa-cred ways.
The face of thine A-noint-ed, be-hold, O God, our shield.
No good will he de-ny them that up-right-ly do live.

My soul is long-ing, faint-ing, Je-ho-vah's courts to see;
So they from strength un-wear-ied go for-ward un-to strength,
One day ex-cels a thou-sand if spent thy courts with-in;
O God of Hosts, Je-ho-vah, how blest is ev-'ry one

My heart and flesh are cry-ing, O liv-ing God, for thee.
Till they ap-pear in Zi-on be-fore the Lord at length.
I'll choose thy thresh-old, rath-er than dwell in tents of sin.
Who con-fid-ence re-pos-es on thee, O Lord, a-lone. A-MEN.

St. 1, line 1, alt.

# THE LORD'S HOUSE 306

*Praise waiteth for thee, O God, in Sion: and unto thee shall the vow be performed.* Psalm 65:1

From PSALM 65:1-5
*The Psalter,* 1912

NYLAND 7. 6. 7. 6. D.
Traditional Finnish melody, har. by
David Evans, 1927

1. Praise waits for thee in Zi - on; all men shall wor - ship there
And pay their vows be - fore thee, O God who hear - est prayer.
Our sins rise up a - gainst us, pre - vail - ing day by day,
But thou wilt show us mer - cy and take their guilt a - way.

2. How blest the man thou call - est and bring - est near to thee,
That in thy courts for ev - er his dwell - ing place may be;
He shall with - in thy tem - ple be sat - is - fied with grace,
And filled with all the good - ness of thy most ho - ly place.

3. O God of our sal - va - tion, since thou dost love the right,
Thou wilt an an - swer send us in won - drous deeds of might.
In all earth's hab - i - ta - tions, on all the bound - less sea,
Man finds no sure re - li - ance, no peace, a - part from thee. A-MEN.

Harmony from *The Revised Church Hymnary,* by permission of the Oxford University Press, London.

# 307 THE LORD'S HOUSE

*We have thought of thy lovingkindness, O God, in the midst of thy temple.* Psalm 48:9

From PSALM 48:9-14  
United Presbyterian *Book of Psalms*, 1871

ST. JOHN 6.6.6.6.8.8.  
*Congregational Church Music*, 1853

1. With-in thy tem-ple, Lord, We on thy mer-cies dwell; Far as thy Name is known, There doth thy praise ex-cel: Thy prais-es sound through ev-'ry land, And right thy scep-tre shall com-mand.
2. Let Zi-on's mount re-joice, Let Ju-dah's daugh-ters praise The Lord with cheer-ful voice, For judg-ment he dis-plays; Go round the walls on Zi-on's mount, Go round her splen-dors to re-count.
3. The tow'rs of Zi-on tell, Her pal-ac-es sur-vey, Mark all her bul-warks well, And to your chil-dren say: This God for ev-er shall a-bide, Ev'n un-to death, our God and guide. A-MEN.

St. 2, line 1, alt.

# 308

*How dreadful is this place! this is none other but the house of God...* Gen. 28:17

Gerhard Tersteegen, 1729  
Tr. by John Wesley, 1739, alt. and arr.

PENITENCE L. M.  
*St. Albans Tune Book*, 1875

1. Lo! God is here: let us a-dore, And own how dread-ful is this place;
2. Lo! God is here, whom day and night U-nit-ed choirs of an-gels praise;
3. Al-might-y Fa-ther, may our praise Thy courts with grate-ful fra-grance fill;
4. To Fa-ther, Son, and Ho-ly Ghost, The God whom earth and heav'n a-dore,

# THE LORD'S HOUSE

Let all with-in us feel his pow'r, And hum-bly bow be-fore his face.
To him, en-thron'd a-bove all height, The host of heav'n their an-thems raise.
Still may we stand be-fore thy face, Still hear and do thy sov-ereign will.
From men and from the an-gel host Be praise and glo-ry ev-er-more. A-MEN.

*For where two or three are gathered together in my name, there am I in the midst of them.* Matt. 18:20

**309**

WARRINGTON L. M.
William Cowper, 1769
Ralph Harrison, 1784

1. Je-sus, wher-e'er thy peo-ple meet, There they be-hold thy mer-cy-seat; Wher-e'er they seek thee, thou art found, And ev-'ry place is hal-lowed ground.
2. For thou, with-in no walls con-fined, In-hab-it-est the hum-ble mind; Such ev-er bring thee where they come, And go-ing, take thee to their home.
3. Dear Shep-herd of thy cho-sen few, Thy for-mer mer-cies here re-new; Here to our wait-ing hearts pro-claim The sweet-ness of thy sav-ing Name.
4. Here may we prove the pow'r of prayer To strength-en faith and sweet-en care, To teach our faint de-sires to rise, And bring all heav'n be-fore our eyes.
5. Lord, we are few, but thou art near; Nor short thine arm, nor deaf thine ear; O rend the heav'ns, come quick-ly down, And make a thou-sand hearts thine own. A-MEN.

# 310 THE LORD'S HOUSE

*I am the living bread which came down from heaven... John 6:51*

Horatius Bonar, 1855

MORECAMBE 10. 10. 10. 10.
Frederick C. Atkinson, c. 1870

1. Here, O my Lord, I see thee face to face;
   Here would I touch and handle things unseen,
   Here grasp with firmer hand th' eternal grace,
   And all my weariness upon thee lean.

2. Here would I feed upon the bread of God,
   Here drink with thee the royal wine of heaven;
   Here would I lay aside each earthly load,
   Here taste afresh the calm of sin forgiven.

3. This is the hour of banquet and of song;
   This is the heav'nly table spread for me:
   Here let me feast, and, feasting, still prolong
   The brief, bright hour of fellowship with thee.

4. I have no help but thine, nor do I need
   Another arm save thine to lean upon:
   It is enough, my Lord, enough indeed;
   My strength is in thy might, thy might alone.

5. Mine is the sin, but thine the righteousness;
   Mine is the guilt, but thine the cleansing blood;
   Here is my robe, my refuge, and my peace,
   Thy blood, thy righteousness, O Lord my God. A-MEN.

# THE OPENING OF WORSHIP 311

*Who is a God like unto thee, that pardoneth iniquity... he retaineth not his anger for ever, because he delighteth in mercy.* Micah 7:18

Lady Lucy E. G. Whitmore, 1824  
St. 3, line 2; st. 4, line 4, alt.

LONGWOOD 10. 10. 10. 10.  
Sir Joseph Barnby, 1872

1. Fa-ther, a-gain in Jesus' Name we meet,
And bow in pen-i-tence beneath thy feet:
A-gain to thee our fee-ble voic-es raise,
To sue for mer-cy, and to sing thy praise.

2. O we would bless thee for thy cease-less care,
And all thy works from day to day de-clare:
Is not our life with hour-ly mer-cies crowned?
Does not thine arm en-cir-cle us a-round?

3. A-las, un-worth-y of thy bound-less love,
Too oft with care-less feet from thee we rove;
But now, en-cour-aged by thy voice, we come,
Re-turn-ing sin-ners to a Fa-ther's home.

4. O by that Name in whom all ful-ness dwells,
O by that love which ev-'ry love ex-cels,
O by that blood so free-ly shed for sin,
O-pen blest mer-cy's gate, and take us in. A-MEN.

## 312 THE OPENING OF WORSHIP

*Let us come before his presence with thanksgiving, and make a joyful noise unto him with psalms. Psalm 95:2*

Author unknown, 1651
Tr. by Catherine Winkworth, 1863, alt.

HERR JESU CHRIST L. M.
*Pensum Sacrum*, 1648
Arr. by Johann Sebastian Bach, 1685-1750

1. Lord Jesus Christ, be present now, Our hearts in true devotion bow, Thy Spirit send with grace divine, And let thy truth within us shine.
2. Unseal our lips to sing thy praise, Our souls to thee in worship raise, Make strong our faith, increase our light That we may know thy Name aright:
3. Until we join the hosts that cry, "Holy art thou, O Lord, most high!" And in the light of that blest place For e'er behold thee face to face.
4. Glory to God the Father, Son, And Holy Spirit, Three in One! To thee, O blessed Trinity, Be praise throughout eternity! A-MEN.

## 313

*Having...boldness to enter into the holiest by the blood of Jesus...Let us draw near with a true heart... Heb. 10:19,22*

James Montgomery, 1812

ST. AUSTELL 7. 7. 7. 7.
Arthur H. Brown, 1876

1. To thy temple I repair; Lord, I love to worship there,
2. While thy glorious praise is sung, Touch my lips, unloose my tongue,
3. While the prayers of saints ascend, God of love, to mine attend;
4. While I hearken to thy law, Fill my soul with humble awe,
5. While thy ministers proclaim Peace and pardon in thy Name,
6. From thy house when I return, May my heart within me burn,

# THE OPENING OF WORSHIP

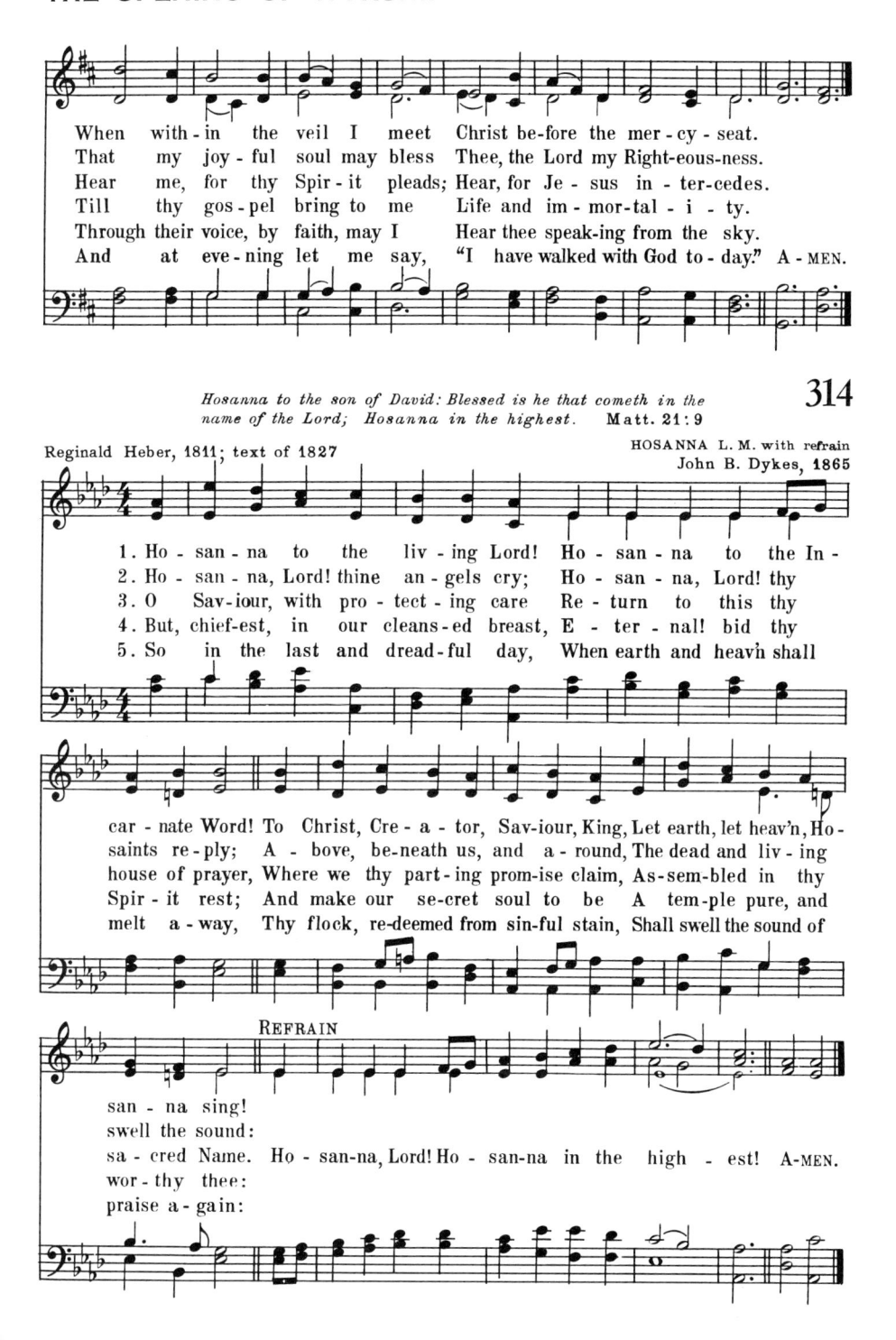

When with-in the veil I meet Christ be-fore the mer-cy-seat.
That my joy-ful soul may bless Thee, the Lord my Right-eous-ness.
Hear me, for thy Spir-it pleads; Hear, for Je-sus in-ter-cedes.
Till thy gos-pel bring to me Life and im-mor-tal-i-ty.
Through their voice, by faith, may I Hear thee speak-ing from the sky.
And at eve-ning let me say, "I have walked with God to-day." A-MEN.

---

*Hosanna to the son of David: Blessed is he that cometh in the name of the Lord; Hosanna in the highest.* Matt. 21:9

## 314

Reginald Heber, 1811; text of 1827

HOSANNA L. M. with refrain
John B. Dykes, 1865

1. Ho-san-na to the liv-ing Lord! Ho-san-na to the In-car-nate Word! To Christ, Cre-a-tor, Sav-iour, King, Let earth, let heav'n, Ho-san-na sing!
2. Ho-san-na, Lord! thine an-gels cry; Ho-san-na, Lord! thy saints re-ply; A-bove, be-neath us, and a-round, The dead and liv-ing swell the sound:
3. O Sav-iour, with pro-tect-ing care Re-turn to this thy house of prayer, Where we thy part-ing prom-ise claim, As-sem-bled in thy sa-cred Name.
4. But, chief-est, in our cleans-ed breast, E-ter-nal! bid thy Spir-it rest; And make our se-cret soul to be A tem-ple pure, and wor-thy thee:
5. So in the last and dread-ful day, When earth and heav'n shall melt a-way, Thy flock, re-deemed from sin-ful stain, Shall swell the sound of praise a-gain:

REFRAIN

Ho-san-na, Lord! Ho-san-na in the high-est! A-MEN.

# 315 THE OPENING OF WORSHIP

*The Lord is in his holy temple: let all the earth keep silence before him.* Hab. 2:20

Gerhard Tersteegen, 1729
Tr. by Frederick W. Foster
and John Miller, 1789

WUNDERBARER KÖNIG 6.6.8.6.6.8.3.3.6.6.
Joachim Neander, 1680

1. God himself is with us: Let us now adore him, And with awe appear before him. God is in his temple—All within keep silence, Prostrate lie with deepest rev-'rence. Him alone God we own, Him, our God and Saviour; Praise his Name for ever.

2. God himself is with us: Hear the harps resounding! See the crowds the throne surrounding! "Holy, Holy, Holy"—Hear the hymn ascending, Angels, saints, their voices blending! Bow thine ear To us here: Hear, O Christ, the praises That thy church now raises. A-MEN.

# THE CLOSE OF WORSHIP 316

*Peace I leave with you, my peace I give unto you ... John 14:27*

John Ellerton, 1866; text of 1868  
ELLERS 10. 10. 10. 10.  
Edward J. Hopkins, 1869

1. Sav-iour, a-gain to thy dear Name we raise
2. Grant us thy peace up-on our home-ward way;
3. Grant us thy peace, Lord, through the com-ing night;
4. Grant us thy peace through-out our earth-ly life,

With one ac-cord our part-ing hymn of praise;
With thee be-gan, with thee shall end the day:
Turn thou for us its dark-ness in-to light;
Our balm in sor-row, and our stay in strife;

We stand to bless thee ere our wor-ship cease;
Guard thou the lips from sin, the hearts from shame,
From harm and dan-ger keep thy chil-dren free,
Then, when thy voice shall bid our con-flict cease,

Then, low-ly kneel-ing, wait thy word of peace.
That in this house have called up-on thy Name.
For dark and light are both a-like to thee.
Call us, O Lord, to thine e-ter-nal peace. A-MEN.

## 317 THE CLOSE OF WORSHIP

*He that receiveth seed into the good ground is he that heareth the word, and understandeth it; which also beareth fruit... Matt. 13:23*

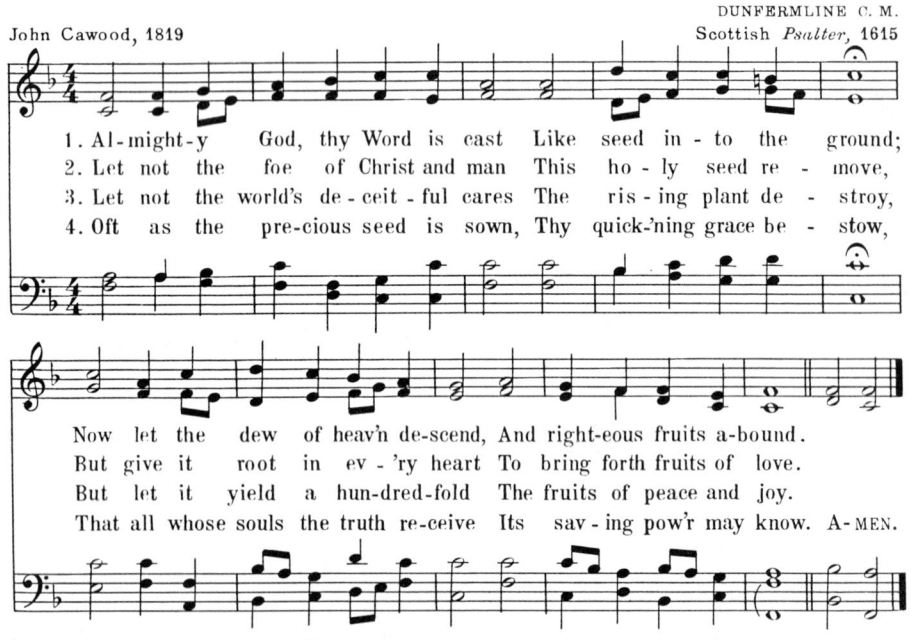

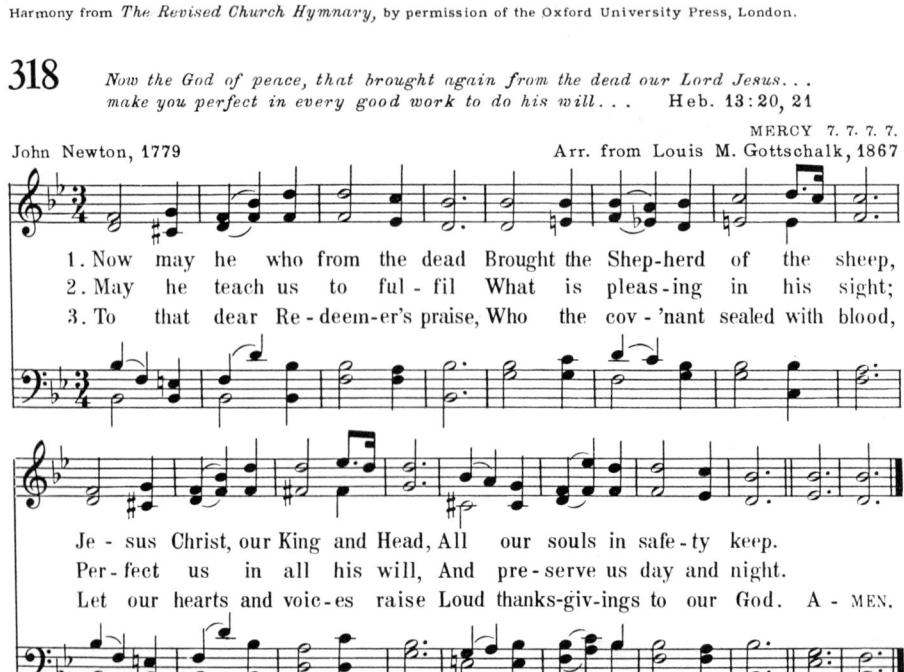

John Cawood, 1819
DUNFERMLINE C. M.
Scottish *Psalter*, 1615

1. Al-might-y God, thy Word is cast Like seed in-to the ground;
2. Let not the foe of Christ and man This ho-ly seed re-move,
3. Let not the world's de-ceit-ful cares The ris-ing plant de-stroy,
4. Oft as the pre-cious seed is sown, Thy quick-'ning grace be-stow,

Now let the dew of heav'n de-scend, And right-eous fruits a-bound.
But give it root in ev-'ry heart To bring forth fruits of love.
But let it yield a hun-dred-fold The fruits of peace and joy.
That all whose souls the truth re-ceive Its sav-ing pow'r may know. A-MEN.

Harmony from *The Revised Church Hymnary*, by permission of the Oxford University Press, London.

## 318

*Now the God of peace, that brought again from the dead our Lord Jesus... make you perfect in every good work to do his will... Heb. 13:20, 21*

John Newton, 1779
MERCY 7. 7. 7. 7.
Arr. from Louis M. Gottschalk, 1867

1. Now may he who from the dead Brought the Shep-herd of the sheep,
2. May he teach us to ful-fil What is pleas-ing in his sight;
3. To that dear Re-deem-er's praise, Who the cov-'nant sealed with blood,

Je-sus Christ, our King and Head, All our souls in safe-ty keep.
Per-fect us in all his will, And pre-serve us day and night.
Let our hearts and voic-es raise Loud thanks-giv-ings to our God. A-MEN.

# THE CLOSE OF WORSHIP 319

*The Lord bless thee, and keep thee.* Num. 6:24

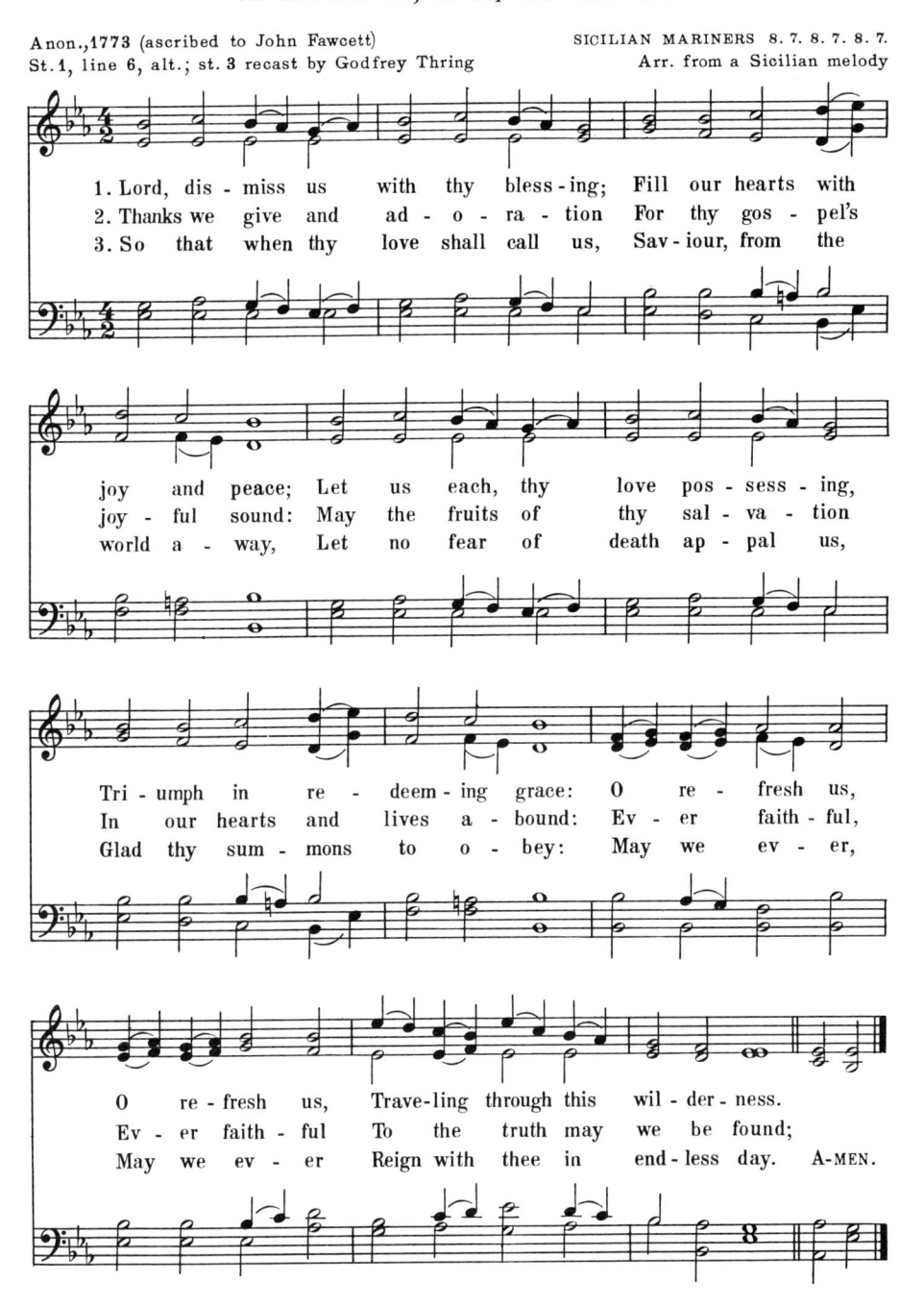

Anon., 1773 (ascribed to John Fawcett)  
St. 1, line 6, alt.; st. 3 recast by Godfrey Thring

SICILIAN MARINERS 8. 7. 8. 7. 8. 7.  
Arr. from a Sicilian melody

1. Lord, dis-miss us with thy bless-ing; Fill our hearts with joy and peace; Let us each, thy love pos-sess-ing, Tri-umph in re-deem-ing grace: O re-fresh us, O re-fresh us, Trave-ling through this wil-der-ness.

2. Thanks we give and ad-o-ra-tion For thy gos-pel's joy-ful sound: May the fruits of thy sal-va-tion In our hearts and lives a-bound: Ev-er faith-ful, Ev-er faith-ful, To the truth may we be found;

3. So that when thy love shall call us, Sav-iour, from the world a-way, Let no fear of death ap-pal us, Glad thy sum-mons to o-bey: May we ev-er, May we ev-er, Reign with thee in end-less day. A-MEN.

## 320 THE LORD'S DAY

*And it shall come to pass ... from one sabbath to another, shall all flesh come to worship before me, saith the Lord.* Isa. 66:23

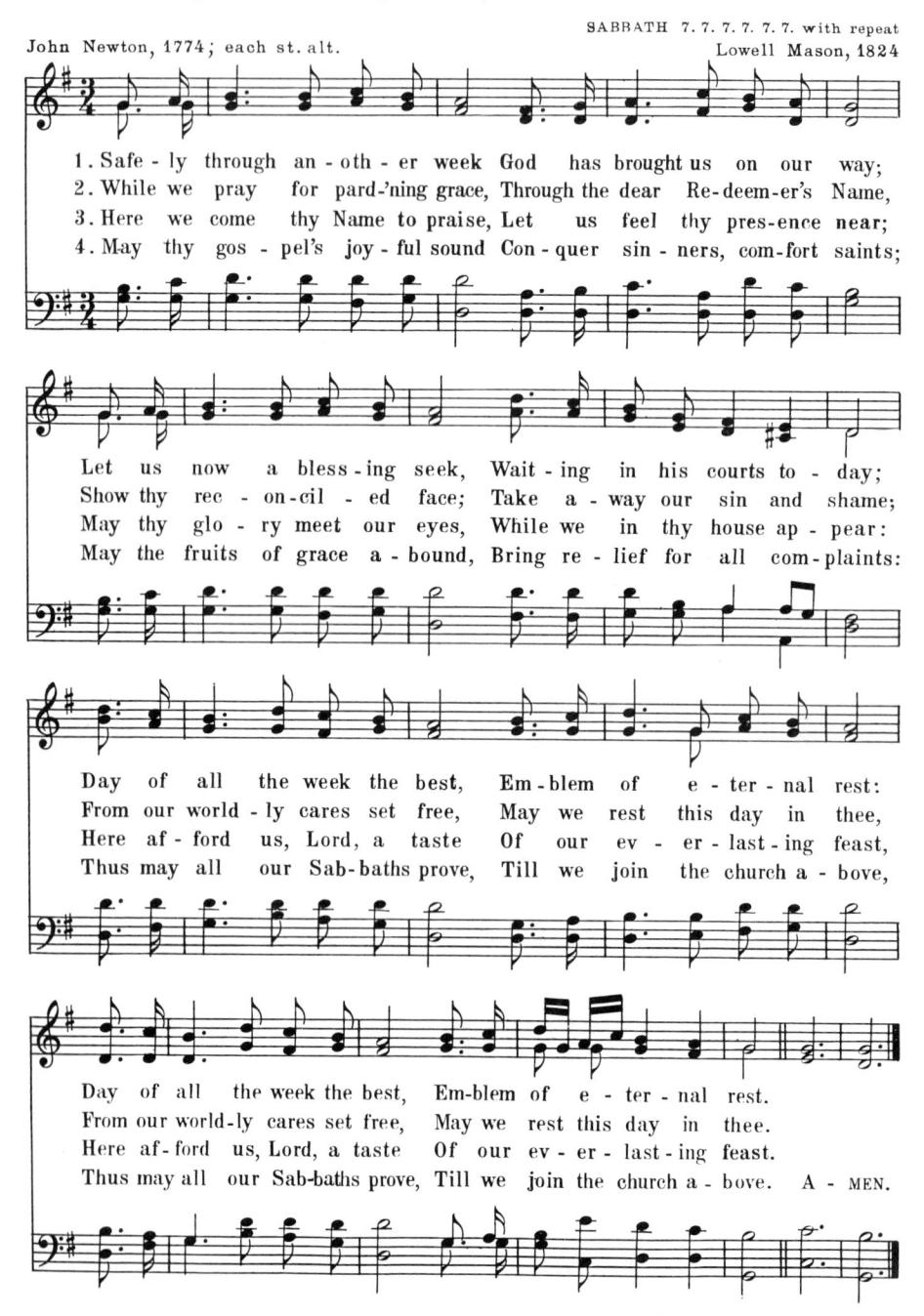

John Newton, 1774; each st. alt.
SABBATH 7. 7. 7. 7. 7. 7. with repeat
Lowell Mason, 1824

1. Safe - ly through an - oth - er week God has brought us on our way;
2. While we pray for pard-'ning grace, Through the dear Re-deem-er's Name,
3. Here we come thy Name to praise, Let us feel thy pres-ence near;
4. May thy gos - pel's joy - ful sound Con - quer sin - ners, com-fort saints;

Let us now a bless-ing seek, Wait - ing in his courts to - day;
Show thy rec - on-cil - ed face; Take a - way our sin and shame;
May thy glo - ry meet our eyes, While we in thy house ap - pear:
May the fruits of grace a - bound, Bring re - lief for all com - plaints:

Day of all the week the best, Em - blem of e - ter - nal rest:
From our world - ly cares set free, May we rest this day in thee,
Here af - ford us, Lord, a taste Of our ev - er - last - ing feast,
Thus may all our Sab-baths prove, Till we join the church a - bove,

Day of all the week the best, Em-blem of e - ter - nal rest.
From our world-ly cares set free, May we rest this day in thee.
Here af-ford us, Lord, a taste Of our ev - er - last - ing feast.
Thus may all our Sab-baths prove, Till we join the church a - bove. A - MEN.

# THE LORD'S DAY          321

*And call the sabbath a delight, the holy of the Lord... Isa. 58:13*

MENDEBRAS 7. 6. 7. 6. D.
Christopher Wordsworth, 1862
Arr. from a German melody by Lowell Mason, 1839

1. O day of rest and glad-ness, O day of joy and light,
2. On thee, at the cre - a - tion, The light first had its birth;
3. Thou art a port pro - tect - ed From storms that round us rise;
4. To - day on wea - ry na-tions The heav'n-ly man - na falls:
5. New grac - es ev - er gain-ing From this our day of rest,

O balm of care and sad-ness, Most beau - ti - ful, most bright;
On thee, for our sal - va - tion, Christ rose from depths of earth;
A gar - den in - ter - sect - ed With streams of Par - a - dise;
To ho - ly con - vo - ca - tions The sil - ver trum-pet calls,
We reach the rest re - main - ing To spir - its of the blest.

On thee the high and low - ly, Through a - ges joined in tune,
On thee our Lord, vic - to - rious, The Spir - it sent from heav'n;
Thou art a cool - ing foun-tain In life's dry, drea - ry sand;
Where gos - pel light is glow-ing With pure and ra - diant beams,
To Ho - ly Ghost be prais - es, To Fa - ther, and to Son;

Sing Ho - ly, Ho - ly, Ho - ly, To the great God Tri - une.
And thus on thee, most glo-rious, A trip - le light was giv'n.
From thee, like Pis-gah's moun-tain, We view our prom-ised land.
And liv - ing wa - ter flow-ing With soul-re - fresh-ing streams.
The church her voice up - rais - es To thee, blest Three in One.  A - MEN.

# 322    THE LORD'S DAY

*For the Son of man is Lord even of the sabbath day.* Matt. 12:8

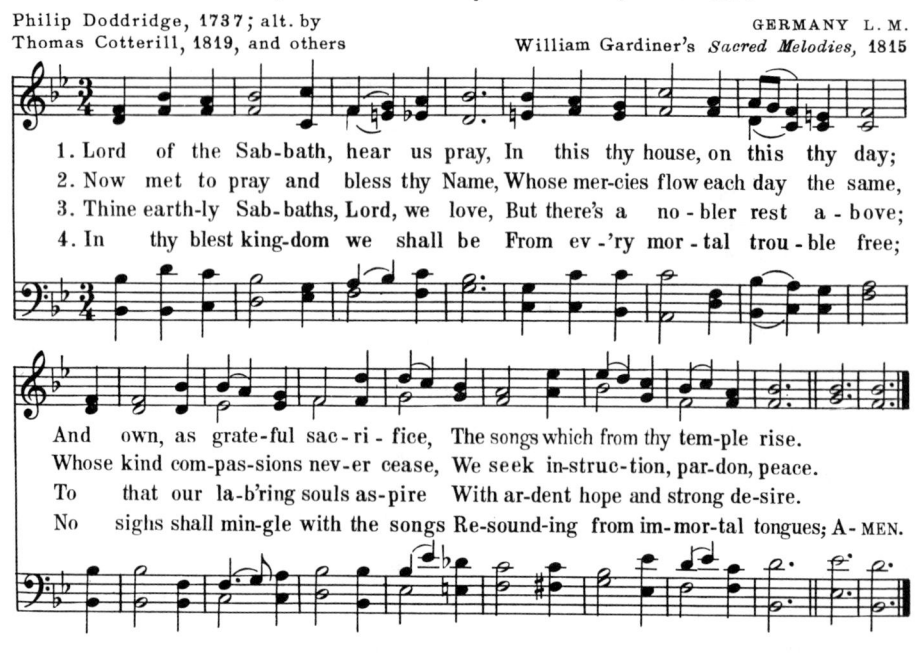

Philip Doddridge, 1737; alt. by  
Thomas Cotterill, 1819, and others  
GERMANY L. M.  
William Gardiner's *Sacred Melodies*, 1815

1. Lord of the Sabbath, hear us pray, In this thy house, on this thy day;
   And own, as grateful sacrifice, The songs which from thy temple rise.
2. Now met to pray and bless thy Name, Whose mercies flow each day the same,
   Whose kind compassions never cease, We seek instruction, pardon, peace.
3. Thine earthly Sabbaths, Lord, we love, But there's a nobler rest above,
   To that our lab'ring souls aspire With ardent hope and strong desire.
4. In thy blest kingdom we shall be From ev'ry mortal trouble free;
   No sighs shall mingle with the songs Resounding from immortal tongues; A-MEN.

5. No rude alarms of raging foes;
   No cares to break the long repose;
   No midnight shade, no waning moon,
   But sacred, high, eternal noon.

6. O long-expected day, begin,
   Dawn on these realms of woe and sin!
   Break, morn of God, upon our eyes;
   And let the world's true Sun arise!

# 323

*There remaineth therefore a sabbath rest for the people of God. (A.S.V.)* Heb. 4:9

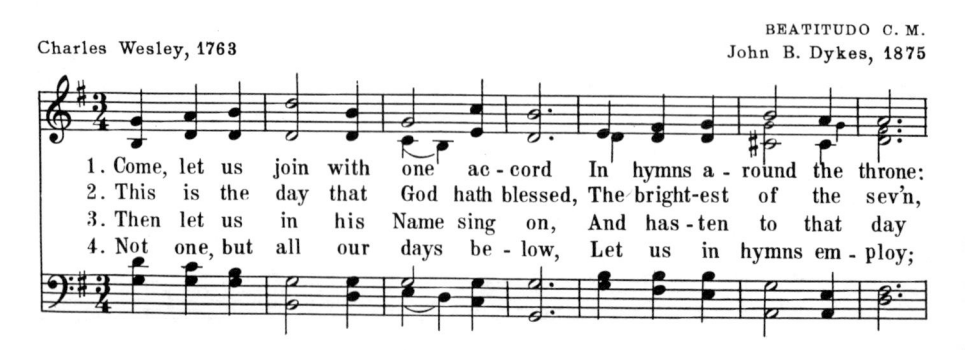

Charles Wesley, 1763  
BEATITUDO C. M.  
John B. Dykes, 1875

1. Come, let us join with one accord In hymns around the throne:
2. This is the day that God hath blessed, The brightest of the sev'n,
3. Then let us in his Name sing on, And hasten to that day
4. Not one, but all our days below, Let us in hymns employ;

# THE LORD'S DAY

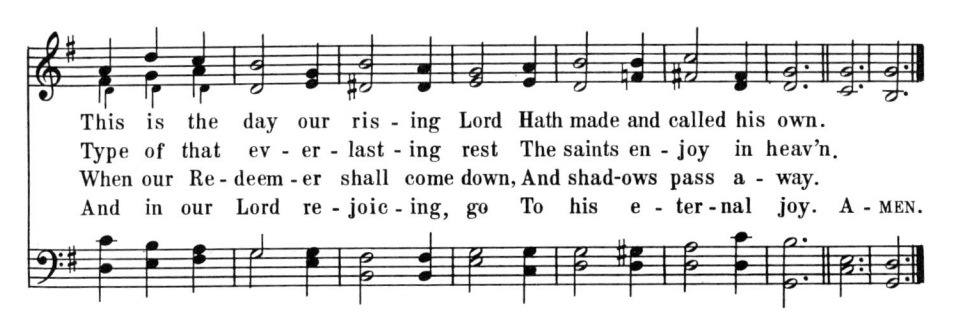

This is the day our ris-ing Lord Hath made and called his own.
Type of that ev-er-last-ing rest The saints en-joy in heav'n.
When our Re-deem-er shall come down, And shad-ows pass a-way.
And in our Lord re-joic-ing, go To his e-ter-nal joy. A-MEN.

**324**

*And upon the first day of the week... the disciples came together to break bread... Acts 20:7*

William Walsham How, 1871

WINCHESTER NEW L. M.
*Musikalisches Handbuch*, Hamburg, 1690

1. This day at thy cre-at-ing word First o'er the earth the light was poured: O Lord, this day up-on us shine And fill our souls with light di-vine.
2. This day the Lord for sin-ners slain In might vic-to-rious rose a-gain: O Je-sus, may we rais-ed be From death of sin to life in thee!
3. This day the Ho-ly Spir-it came With fi-ery tongues of clo-ven flame: O Spir-it, fill our hearts this day With grace to hear and grace to pray.
4. O day of light and life and grace, From earth-ly toil sweet rest-ing-place, Thy hal-lowed hours, blest gift of love, Give we a-gain to God a-bove.
5. All praise to God the Fa-ther be, All praise, e-ter-nal Son, to thee, Whom, with the Spir-it, we a-dore For ev-er and for ev-er-more. A-MEN.

# 325 THE LORD'S DAY

*The sabbath was made for man... Therefore the Son of man is Lord also of the sabbath.* Mark 2:27, 28

"Hayward," in Dobell's *Selections*, 1806

LISCHER 6.6.6.6.8.8. with repeat
Arr. from F. J. C. Schneider
by Lowell Mason, 1841

1. Welcome, delightful morn, Thou day of sacred rest!
   I hail thy kind return, Lord, make these moments blest;
   From the low train of mortal toys I soar to reach immortal joys,
   I soar to reach immortal joys.

2. Now may the King descend, And fill his throne of grace;
   Thy scepter, Lord, extend, While saints address thy face;
   Let sinners feel thy quick-'ning Word, And learn to know and fear the Lord,
   And learn to know and fear the Lord.

3. Descend, celestial Dove, With all thy quick-'ning pow'rs;
   Disclose a Saviour's love, And bless these sacred hours;
   Then shall my soul new life obtain, Nor Sabbaths e'er be spent in vain,
   Nor Sabbaths e'er be spent in vain. A-MEN.

# THE LORD'S DAY 326

*This is the day which the Lord hath made; we will rejoice and be glad in it.* Psalm 118:24

ARLINGTON C. M.
Arr. by Ralph Harrison, 1784,
from Thomas A. Arne, 1762

Isaac Watts, 1719

1. This is the day the Lord hath made; He calls the hours his own;
2. To-day he rose and left the dead, And Satan's empire fell;
3. Hosanna to th'anointed King, To David's holy Son!
4. Blest be the Lord, who comes to men With messages of grace;
5. Hosanna in the highest strains The church on earth can raise!

Let heav'n rejoice, let earth be glad, And praise surround the throne.
To-day the saints his triumphs spread, And all his wonders tell.
Help us, O Lord; descend and bring Salvation from the throne.
Who comes in God his Father's Name To save our sinful race.
The highest heav'ns in which he reigns Shall give him nobler praise. A-MEN.

---

# 327

*And God said, Let there be light: and there was light... And the evening and the morning were the first day.* Gen. 1:3, 5

GREENWOOD S. M.

John Ellerton, 1867

Joseph E. Sweetser, 1849

1. This is the day of light: Let there be light to-day;
2. This is the day of rest: Our failing strength renew;
3. This is the day of peace: Thy peace our spirits fill;
4. This is the day of prayer: Let earth to heav'n draw near:
5. This is the first of days: Send forth thy quick'ning breath,

O Day-spring, rise upon our night, And chase its gloom away.
On weary brain and troubled breast Shed thou thy fresh'ning dew.
Bid thou the blasts of discord cease, The waves of strife be still.
Lift up our hearts to seek thee there; Come down to meet us here.
And wake dead souls to love and praise, O Vanquisher of death! A-MEN.

## 328 MORNING

*His compassions fail not. They are new every morning: great is thy faithfulness.* Lam. 3:22, 23

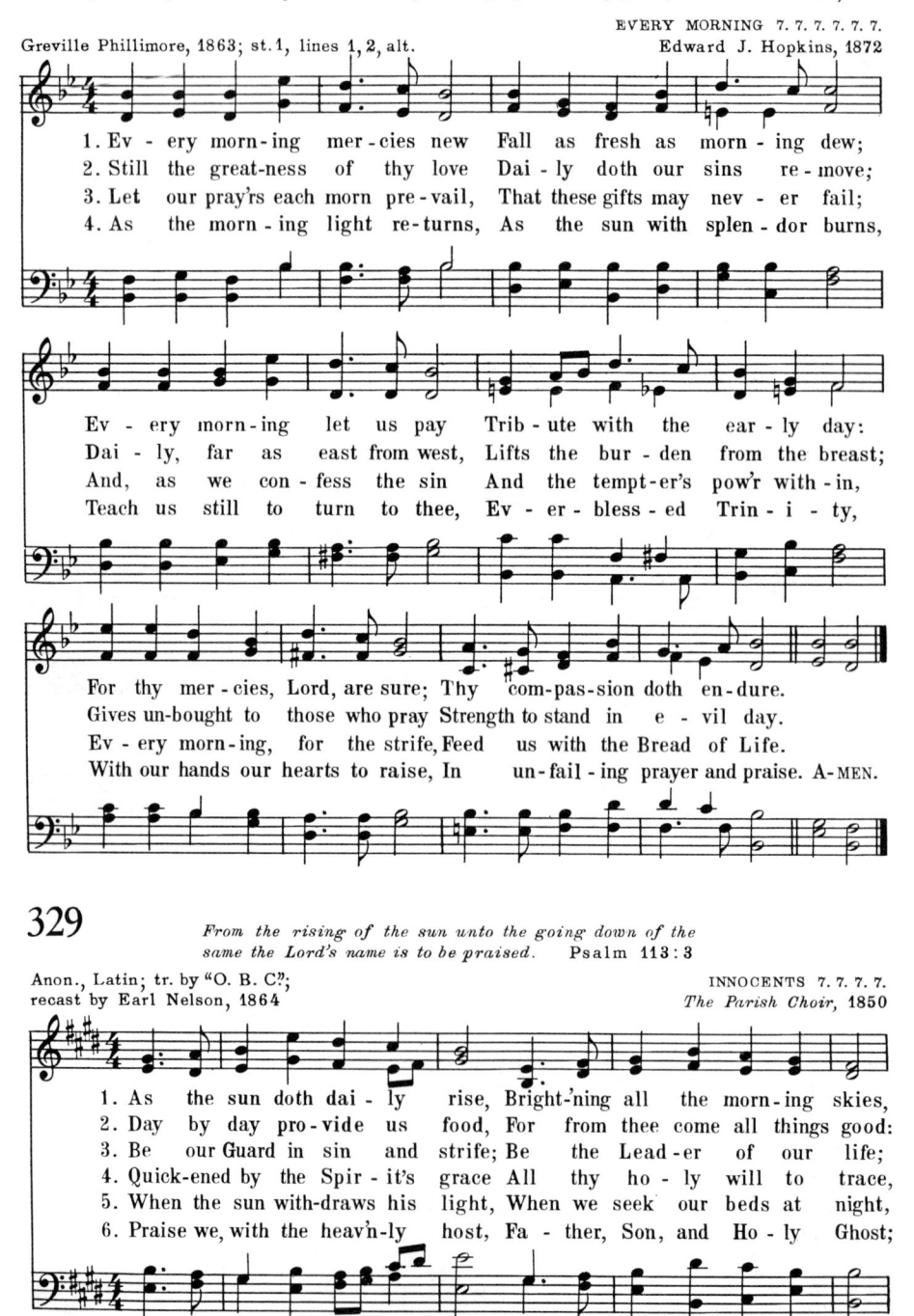

Greville Phillimore, 1863; st.1, lines 1, 2, alt.
EVERY MORNING 7. 7. 7. 7. 7. 7.
Edward J. Hopkins, 1872

1. Ev-ery morn-ing mer-cies new Fall as fresh as morn-ing dew;
2. Still the great-ness of thy love Dai-ly doth our sins re-move;
3. Let our pray'rs each morn pre-vail, That these gifts may nev-er fail;
4. As the morn-ing light re-turns, As the sun with splen-dor burns,

Ev-ery morn-ing let us pay Trib-ute with the ear-ly day:
Dai-ly, far as east from west, Lifts the bur-den from the breast;
And, as we con-fess the sin And the tempt-er's pow'r with-in,
Teach us still to turn to thee, Ev-er-bless-ed Trin-i-ty,

For thy mer-cies, Lord, are sure; Thy com-pas-sion doth en-dure.
Gives un-bought to those who pray Strength to stand in e-vil day.
Ev-ery morn-ing, for the strife, Feed us with the Bread of Life.
With our hands our hearts to raise, In un-fail-ing prayer and praise. A-MEN.

## 329

*From the rising of the sun unto the going down of the same the Lord's name is to be praised.* Psalm 113:3

Anon., Latin; tr. by "O. B. C."; recast by Earl Nelson, 1864
INNOCENTS 7. 7. 7. 7.
*The Parish Choir,* 1850

1. As the sun doth dai-ly rise, Bright-'ning all the morn-ing skies,
2. Day by day pro-vide us food, For from thee come all things good:
3. Be our Guard in sin and strife; Be the Lead-er of our life;
4. Quick-ened by the Spir-it's grace All thy ho-ly will to trace,
5. When the sun with-draws his light, When we seek our beds at night,
6. Praise we, with the heav'n-ly host, Fa-ther, Son, and Ho-ly Ghost;

## MORNING

So to thee with one ac-cord Lift we up our hearts, O Lord!
Strength un-to our souls af-ford From thy liv-ing Bread, O Lord!
Lest like sheep we stray a-broad, Stay our way-ward feet, O Lord!
While we dai-ly search thy Word, Wis-dom true im-part, O Lord!
Thou, by sleep-less hosts a-dored, Hear the pray'r of faith, O Lord!
Thee would we with one ac-cord Praise and mag-ni-fy, O Lord! A-MEN.

*The dayspring from on high hath visited us, to give light to them that sit in darkness... Luke 1:78, 79*

### 330

Charles Wesley, 1740

LUX PRIMA 7. 7. 7. 7. 7. 7.
Charles F. Gounod, 1872

1. Christ, whose glo-ry fills the skies, Christ the true, the on-ly Light,
2. Dark and cheer-less is the morn Un-ac-com-pan-ied by thee;
3. Vis-it, then, this soul of mine; Pierce the gloom of sin and grief;

Sun of Right-eous-ness, a-rise, Tri-umph o'er the shades of night;
Joy-less is the day's re-turn Till thy mer-cy's beams I see;
Fill me, Ra-dianc-y Di-vine; Scat-ter all my un-be-lief;

Day-spring from on high, be near; Day-star, in my heart ap-pear.
Till they in-ward light im-part, Glad my eyes and warm my heart.
More and more thy-self dis-play, Shin-ing to the per-fect day. A-MEN.

## 331 MORNING

*I myself will awake early. I will praise thee, O Lord, among the people . . . Psalm 57:8, 9*

Thomas Ken, 1695; text of 1709
MORNING HYMN L. M.
François H. Barthélémon, 1791

1. A-wake, my soul, and with the sun Thy dai-ly stage of du-ty run:
2. By in-fluence of the light Di-vine Let thine own light to oth-ers shine;
3. All praise to thee, who safe hast kept, And hast re-freshed me whilst I slept:
4. Lord, I my vows to thee re-new, Dis-perse my sins as morn-ing dew;
5. Praise God from whom all bless-ings flow; Praise him, all crea-tures here be-low;

Shake off dull sloth, and joy-ful rise To pay thy morn-ing sac-ri-fice.
Re-flect all heav'n's pro-pi-tious rays In ar-dent love and cheer-ful praise.
Grant, Lord, when I from death shall wake, I may of end-less light par-take.
Guard my first springs of thought and will, And with thy-self my spir-it fill.
Praise him a-bove, ye heav'n-ly host: Praise Fa-ther, Son, and Ho-ly Ghost. A-MEN.

## 332

*My voice shalt thou hear in the morning, O Lord; in the morning will I direct my prayer unto thee, and will look up. Psalm 5:3*

From PSALM 5
Isaac Watts, 1719
WARWICK C. M.
Samuel Stanley, 1800

1. Lord, in the morn-ing thou shalt hear My voice as-cend-ing high;
2. Up to the heav'ns, where Christ is gone To plead for all his saints,
3. Thou art a God be-fore whose sight The wick-ed shall not stand;
4. But to thy house will I re-sort, To taste thy mer-cies there;
5. O may thy Spir-it guide my feet In ways of right-eous-ness;

# MORNING

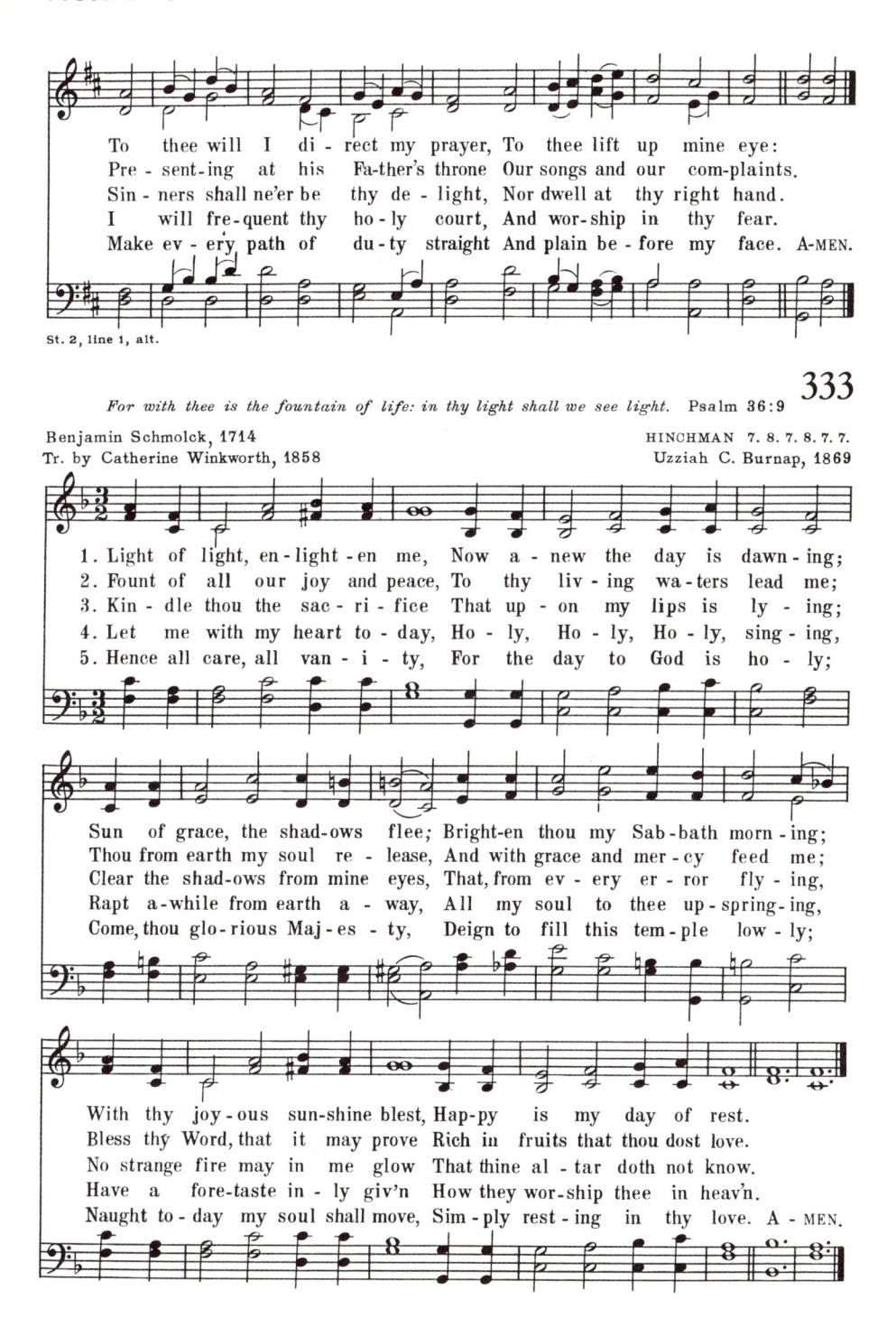

To thee will I di - rect my prayer, To thee lift up mine eye:
Pre - sent-ing at his Fa-ther's throne Our songs and our com-plaints.
Sin - ners shall ne'er be thy de - light, Nor dwell at thy right hand.
I will fre - quent thy ho - ly court, And wor - ship in thy fear.
Make ev - ery path of du - ty straight And plain be - fore my face. A-MEN.

St. 2, line 1, alt.

*For with thee is the fountain of life: in thy light shall we see light.* Psalm 36:9

**333**

Benjamin Schmolck, 1714
Tr. by Catherine Winkworth, 1858

HINCHMAN 7. 8. 7. 8. 7. 7.
Uzziah C. Burnap, 1869

1. Light of light, en - light - en me, Now a - new the day is dawn - ing;
2. Fount of all our joy and peace, To thy liv - ing wa - ters lead me;
3. Kin - dle thou the sac - ri - fice That up - on my lips is ly - ing;
4. Let me with my heart to - day, Ho - ly, Ho - ly, Ho - ly, sing - ing,
5. Hence all care, all van - i - ty, For the day to God is ho - ly;

Sun of grace, the shad - ows flee; Bright-en thou my Sab - bath morn - ing;
Thou from earth my soul re - lease, And with grace and mer - cy feed me;
Clear the shad - ows from mine eyes, That, from ev - ery er - ror fly - ing,
Rapt a - while from earth a - way, All my soul to thee up - spring - ing,
Come, thou glo - rious Maj - es - ty, Deign to fill this tem - ple low - ly;

With thy joy - ous sun - shine blest, Hap - py is my day of rest.
Bless thy Word, that it may prove Rich in fruits that thou dost love.
No strange fire may in me glow That thine al - tar doth not know.
Have a fore - taste in - ly giv'n How they wor - ship thee in heav'n.
Naught to - day my soul shall move, Sim - ply rest - ing in thy love. A - MEN.

## 334 MORNING

*Awake up, my glory . . . I myself will awake early. I will praise thee, O Lord, among the people . . .* Psalm **57: 8, 9**

F. R. L. von Canitz, 1700
Tr. by Henry J. Buckoll, 1841; st. 5, alt.

HAYDN 8. 4. 7. 8. 4. 7.
Arr. from Franz Josef Haydn, 1791

1. Come, my soul, thou must be wak-ing; Now is break-ing
2. Thou too hail the light re - turn-ing; Read-y burn-ing
3. Pray that he may pros - per ev - er Each en - deav-or,
4. Think that he thy ways be - hold-eth; He un - fold-eth
5. On - ly God's free gifts a - buse not, Light re - fuse not,

O'er the earth an - oth - er day: Come to him who made this splen-dor;
Be the in - cense of thy pow'rs; For the night is safe - ly end - ed,
Ev - ery fault that lurks with-in; Ev - ery stain of shame glossed o - ver
When thine aim is good and true; But that he may ev - er thwart thee,
But his Spir - it's voice o - bey; Thou with him shalt dwell, be - hold-ing

See thou ren - der All thy fee - ble powers can pay.
God hath tend - ed With his care thy help - less hours.
And con - vert thee, When thou e - vil wouldst pur - sue.
Can dis - cov - er, And dis - cern each deed of sin.
Light en - fold - ing All things in un - cloud - ed day. A - MEN.

# EVENING

## 335

*We know that he abideth in us, by the Spirit which he hath given us.* I John 3:24

Henry F. Lyte, 1847

EVENTIDE (MONK) 10. 10. 10. 10.
William H. Monk, 1861

1. A-bide with me: fast falls the e-ven-tide; The dark-ness deep-ens; Lord, with me a-bide: When oth-er help-ers fail, and com-forts flee, Help of the help-less, O a-bide with me.
2. Swift to its close ebbs out life's lit-tle day; Earth's joys grow dim, its glo-ries pass a-way; Change and de-cay in all a-round I see; O thou who chang-est not, a-bide with me.
3. I need thy pres-ence ev-ery pass-ing hour; What but thy grace can foil the tempt-er's pow'r? Who like thy-self my guide and stay can be? Through cloud and sun-shine, O a-bide with me.
4. I fear no foe, with thee 'at hand to bless: Ills have no weight, and tears no bit-ter-ness. Where is death's sting? where, grave, thy vic-to-ry? I tri-umph still, if thou a-bide with me.
5. Hold thou thy cross be-fore my clos-ing eyes; Shine through the gloom, and point me to the skies: Heav'n's morn-ing breaks, and earth's vain shad-ows flee: In life, in death, O Lord, a-bide with me. A-MEN.

## 336 EVENING

*And at even, when the sun did set, they brought unto him all that were diseased ... and he healed many ... Mark 1:32, 34*

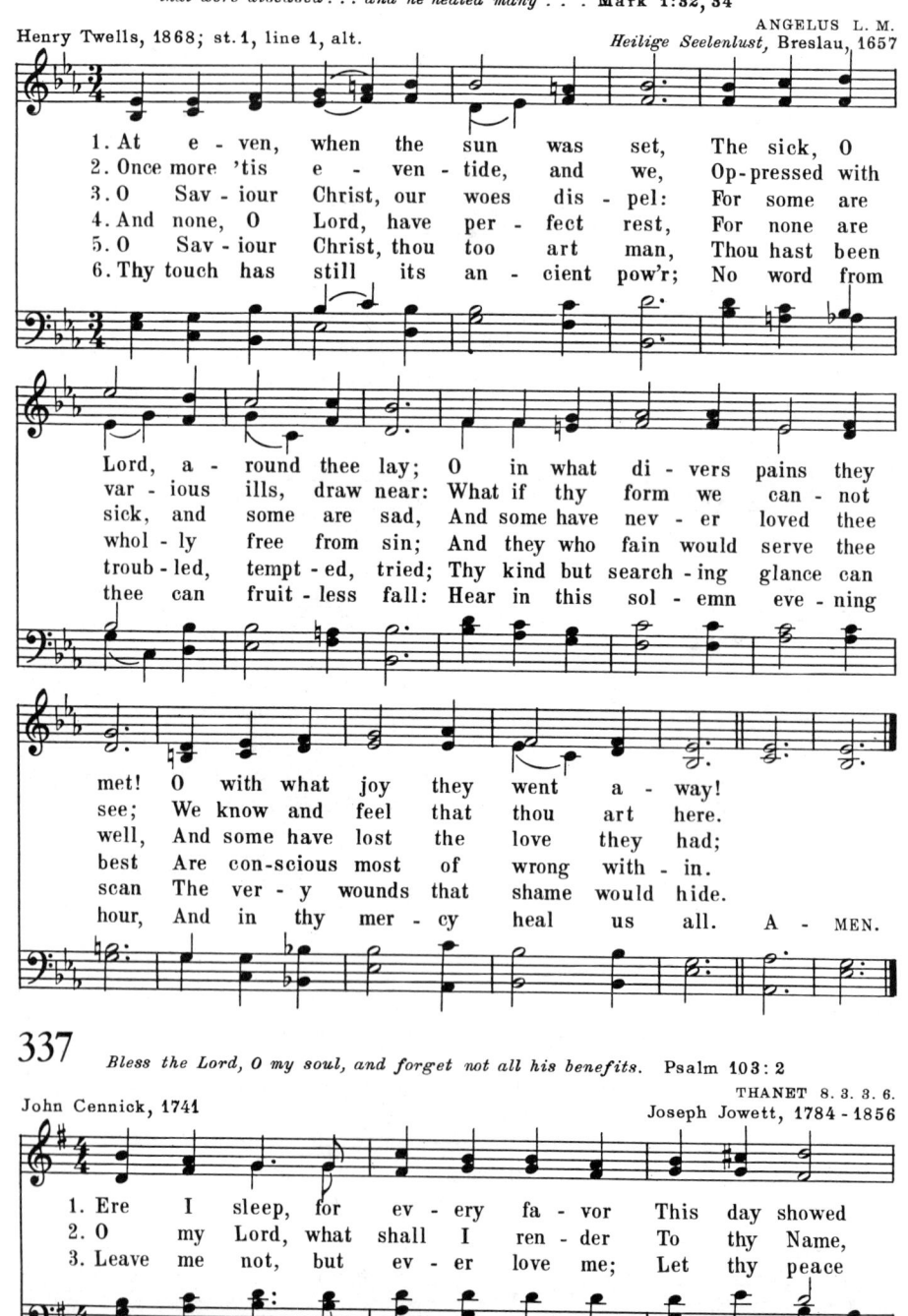

Henry Twells, 1868; st. 1, line 1, alt.

ANGELUS L. M.
*Heilige Seelenlust*, Breslau, 1657

1. At e - ven, when the sun was set, The sick, O Lord, a - round thee lay; O in what di - vers pains they met! O with what joy they went a - way!
2. Once more 'tis e - ven - tide, and we, Op - pressed with var - ious ills, draw near: What if thy form we can - not see; We know and feel that thou art here.
3. O Sav - iour Christ, our woes dis - pel: For some are sick, and some are sad, And some have nev - er loved thee well, And some have lost the love they had;
4. And none, O Lord, have per - fect rest, For none are whol - ly free from sin; And they who fain would serve thee best Are con-scious most of wrong with - in.
5. O Sav - iour Christ, thou too art man, Thou hast been troub - led, tempt - ed, tried; Thy kind but search - ing glance can scan The ver - y wounds that shame would hide.
6. Thy touch has still its an - cient pow'r; No word from thee can fruit - less fall: Hear in this sol - emn eve - ning hour, And in thy mer - cy heal us all. A - MEN.

## 337

*Bless the Lord, O my soul, and forget not all his benefits. Psalm 103:2*

John Cennick, 1741

THANET 8. 3. 3. 6.
Joseph Jowett, 1784 - 1856

1. Ere I sleep, for ev - ery fa - vor This day showed
2. O my Lord, what shall I ren - der To thy Name,
3. Leave me not, but ev - er love me; Let thy peace

EVENING

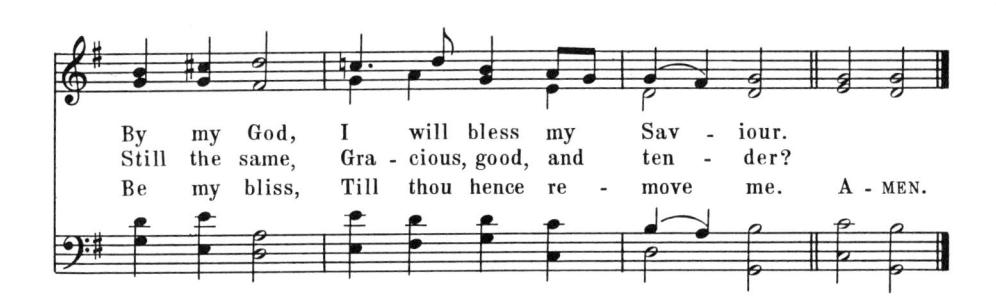

By my God, I will bless my Sav-iour.
Still the same, Gra-cious, good, and ten-der?
Be my bliss, Till thou hence re-move me. A-MEN.

*From the rising of the sun unto the going down of the same the Lord's name is to be praised.* Psalm 113:3

338

ST. CLEMENT 9. 8. 9. 8.

John Ellerton, 1870    Clement C. Scholefield, 1874

1. The day thou ga-vest, Lord, is end-ed, The dark-ness falls at thy be-hest; To thee our morn-ing hymns as-cend-ed, Thy praise shall hal-low now our rest.
2. We thank thee that thy church, un-sleep-ing While earth rolls on-ward in-to light, Through all the world her watch is keep-ing, And rests not now by day or night.
3. As o'er each con-ti-nent and is-land The dawn leads on an-oth-er day, The voice of prayer is nev-er si-lent, Nor dies the strain of praise a-way.
4. The sun, that bids us rest, is wak-ing Our breth-ren 'neath the west-ern sky, And hour by hour fresh lips are mak-ing Thy won-drous do-ings heard on high.
5. So be it, Lord; thy Throne shall nev-er, Like earth's proud em-pires, pass a-way: But stand, and rule, and grow for ev-er, Till all thy crea-tures own thy sway. A-MEN.

## 339 EVENING

*For God, who commanded the light to shine out of darkness, hath shined in our hearts... II Cor. 4:6*

Ambrose of Milan, 340-397
Tr. by John Mason Neale, 1852, alt.

O HEILIGE DREIFALTIGKEIT L. M.
Nikolaus Herman, 1560

1. O Trin-i-ty, most bless-ed Light, O U-ni-ty of sov-'reign might, As now the fi-ery sun de-parts, Shed thou thy beams with-in our hearts.
2. To thee our morn-ing song of praise, To thee our eve-ning prayer we raise; Thee may our glo-ry ev-er-more In low-ly rev-er-ence a-dore.
3. All praise to God the Fa-ther be, All praise, e-ter-nal Son, to thee, Whom with the Spir-it we a-dore For ev-er and for ev-er-more. A-MEN.

## 340

*Thou shalt not be afraid for the terror by night... Psalm 91:5*

James Edmeston, 1820

EVENING PRAYER 8. 7. 8. 7.
George C. Stebbins, 1878

1. Sav-iour, breathe an eve-ning bless-ing, Ere re-pose our spir-its seal;
2. Though de-struc-tion walk a-round us, Though the ar-row past us fly,
3. Though the night be dark and drea-ry, Dark-ness can-not hide from thee;
4. Should swift death this night o'er-take us, And our couch be-come our tomb,

# EVENING

Sin and want we come confessing: Thou canst save, and thou canst heal.
Angel-guards from thee surround us; We are safe if thou art nigh.
Thou art he who, never weary, Watchest where thy people be.
May the morn in heav'n awake us, Clad in light and deathless bloom. A-MEN.

*I will both lay me down in peace, and sleep: for thou,
Lord, only makest me dwell in safety. Psalm 4:8*

**341**

Thomas Ken, 1695; text of 1709

TALLIS' EVENING HYMN L. M.
Alt. from Thomas Tallis, 1560

1. All praise to thee, my God, this night, For all the blessings of the light;
2. Forgive me, Lord, for thy dear Son, The ills that I this day have done;
3. O may my soul on thee repose, And with sweet sleep mine eyelids close;
4. When in the night I sleepless lie, My soul with heav'nly thoughts supply;

Keep me, O keep me, King of kings, Beneath thine own almighty wings.
That with the world, myself, and thee, I, ere I sleep, at peace may be.
Sleep that may me more vig'rous make To serve my God when I awake.
Let no ill dreams disturb my rest, No pow'rs of darkness me molest. A-MEN.

5. O when shall I in endless day
   For ever chase dark sleep away,
   And hymns with the supernal choir
   Incessant sing, and never tire!

6. Praise God from whom all blessings flow;
   Praise him, all creatures here below;
   Praise him above, ye heav'nly host:
   Praise Father, Son, and Holy Ghost.

## 342
**EVENING**

*I will both lay me down in peace, and sleep: for thou,
Lord, only makest me dwell in safety.* Psalm 4:8

Ascribed to Anatolius, 7th century
Tr. by John Mason Neale, 1853, 1862

ST. ANATOLIUS (BROWN) 7. 6. 7. 6. 8. 8.
Arthur H. Brown, 1862

1. The day is past and o-ver: All thanks, O Lord, to thee;
   I pray thee that of-fense-less The hours of dark may be.
   O Jesus, keep me in thy sight,
   And save me through the com-ing night.

2. The toils of day are o-ver: I raise the hymn to thee,
   And ask that free from per-il The hours of night may be.
   O Jesus, keep me in thy sight,
   And guard me through the com-ing night.

3. Lord, that in death I sleep not, And lest my foe should say,
   "I have pre-vailed a-gainst him," Light-en mine eyes, I pray:
   O Jesus, keep me in thy sight,
   And guard me through the com-ing night.

4. Be thou my soul's Pre-serv-er, O God, for thou dost know
   How man-y are the per-ils Through which I have to go.
   Lov-er of men, O hear my call,
   And guard and save me from them all. A-MEN.

St. 2, line 4, alt.
Music used by permission of the Oxford University Press, London

# EVENING

## 343

*Holy, holy, holy, is the Lord of hosts: the whole earth is full of his glory.* Isa. 6:3

Mary A. Lathbury, 1877
EVENING PRAISE 7.7.7.7.4. with refrain
William F. Sherwin, 1877

1. Day is dy-ing in the west; Heav'n is touch-ing earth with rest;
Wait and wor-ship while the night Sets her eve-ning lamps a-light
Through all the sky.

2. While the deep-'ning shad-ows fall, Light of light, on whom we call
Through the glo-ry and the grace Of the stars that veil thy face,
Our hearts as-cend.

3. And when fad-ing from our sight Pass the stars, the day, the night,
Lord of Glo-ry, on our eyes Let e-ter-nal morn-ing rise,
And shad-ows end.

**Refrain**

Ho-ly, Ho-ly, Ho-ly, Lord God of hosts! Heav'n and earth are full of thee! Heav'n and earth are prais-ing thee, O Lord Most High. A-MEN.

St. 2, line 2; st. 3, lines 1 and 3, alt.
Words and music used by permission of the Chautauqua Institution, Chautauqua, New York.

# 344 EVENING

*The Lord will command his lovingkindness in the daytime, and in the night his song shall be with me...* Psalm 42:8

Reginald Heber, 1827, st. 1
William Mercer, 1864, st. 2
Richard Whately, 1787-1863, st. 3

WYNNSTAY 8.4.8.4.8.8.8.4.
John Ambrose Lloyd, 1815-1874

1. God, that mad-est earth and heav-en, Dark-ness and light,
2. And, when morn a-gain shall call us To run life's way,
3. Guard us wak-ing, guard us sleep-ing; And, when we die,

Who the day for toil hast giv-en, For rest the night;
May we still, what-e'er be-fall us, Thy will o-bey.
May we, in thy might-y keep-ing, All peace-ful lie:

May thine an-gel-guards de-fend us, Slum-ber sweet thy mer-cy send us,
From the pow'r of e-vil hide us, In the nar-row path-way guide us,
When the last dread trump shall wake us, Do not thou, O God, for-sake us,

Ho-ly dreams and hopes at-tend us, This live-long night.
Nor thy smile be e'er de-nied us The live-long day.
But to reign in glo-ry take us With thee on high. A-MEN.

# EVENING 345

*Seek the Lord, till he come and rain righteousness upon you.* Hosea 10:12

CAMBRIA 6. 4. 6. 4. 6. 6. 6. 4.
Welsh hymn melody,
from the *Bristol Tune Book,* 1876

Fanny J. Crosby, 1876

1. Here from the world we turn, Jesus to seek;
   Here may his loving voice Tenderly speak!
   Jesus, our dearest Friend, While at thy feet we bend,
   O let thy smile descend! 'Tis thee we seek.

2. Come, Holy Comforter, Presence Divine,
   Now in our longing hearts Graciously shine;
   O for thy mighty pow'r! O for a blessed show'r,
   Filling this hallowed hour With joy divine!

3. Saviour, thy work revive: Here may we see
   Those who are dead in sin Quickened by thee;
   Come to our hearts to-night, Make ev'ry burden light;
   Cheer thou our waiting sight; We long for thee. A-MEN.

## 346

EVENING

*Yea, the darkness hideth not from thee; but the night shineth as the day: the darkness and the light are both alike to thee.* Psalm 139:12

HURSLEY L. M.

John Keble, 1820     Alt. from *Katholisches Gesangbuch,* Vienna, c. 1774

1. Sun of my soul, thou Sav-iour dear, It is not night if thou be near; O may no earth-born cloud a-rise To hide thee from thy serv-ant's eyes.
2. When the soft dews of kind-ly sleep My wea-ry eye-lids gen-tly steep, Be my last thought, how sweet to rest For ev-er on my Sav-iour's breast.
3. A-bide with me from morn till eve, For with-out thee I can-not live; A-bide with me when night is nigh, For with-out thee I dare not die.
4. If some poor wan-d'ring child of thine Have spurned to-day the voice Di-vine, Now, Lord, the gra-cious work be-gin; Let him no more lie down in sin.
5. Watch by the sick; en-rich the poor With bless-ings from thy bound-less store; Be ev-ery mourn-er's sleep to-night, Like in-fant's slum-bers, pure and light.
6. Come near and bless us when we wake, Ere through the world our way we take, Till in the o-cean of thy love We lose our-selves in heav'n a-bove. A - MEN.

## 347

*In the night his song shall be with me, and my prayer unto the God of my life.* Psalm 42:8

SEYMOUR 7. 7. 7. 7.

George W. Doane, 1824     Arr. from Carl Maria von Weber, 1826

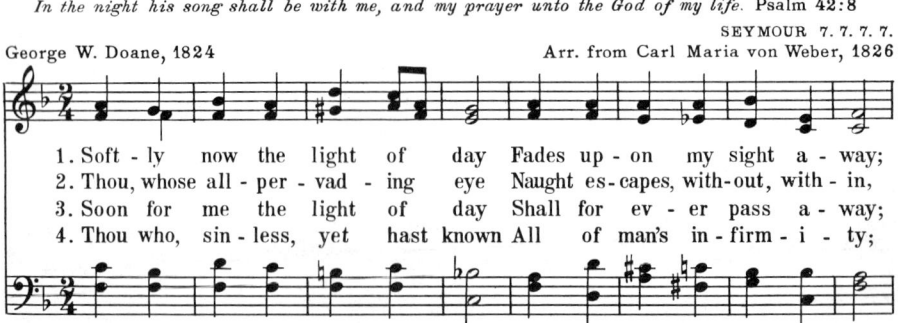

1. Soft-ly now the light of day Fades up-on my sight a-way;
2. Thou, whose all-per-vad-ing eye Naught es-capes, with-out, with-in,
3. Soon for me the light of day Shall for ev-er pass a-way;
4. Thou who, sin-less, yet hast known All of man's in-firm-i-ty;

# EVENING

Free from care, from labor free, Lord, I would commune with thee.
Pardon each infirmity, Open fault, and secret sin.
Then, from sin and sorrow free, Take me, Lord, to dwell with thee.
Then, from thine eternal throne, Jesus, look with pitying eye. A-MEN.

## 348

*Behold, bless ye the Lord, all ye servants of the Lord, which by night stand in the house of the Lord.* Psalm 134:1

From PSALM 134
Lambertus J. Lamberts, 1928

THE OLD HUNDREDTH L. M.
Louis Bourgeois, 1551

1. O bless our God with one accord, Ye faithful servants of the Lord, Who in his house do stand by night; And praise him there with all your might.
2. Lift up your hands, in prayer draw nigh Unto his sanctuary high; Bless ye the Lord, kneel at his feet, And worship him with reverence meet.
3. Jehovah bless thee from above, From Zion in his boundless love, Our God, who heav'n and earth did frame; Blest be his great and holy Name. A-MEN.

Words used by permission of the Publication Committee of the Christian Reformed Church.

# 349 EVENING

*How excellent is thy lovingkindness, O God! therefore the children of men put their trust under the shadow of thy wings.* Psalm 36:7

James D. Burns, 1856
AURELIA 7.6.7.6.D.
Samuel S. Wesley, 1864

1. This night, O Lord, we bless thee For thy pro-tect-ing care,
And, ere we rest, ad-dress thee In low-ly, fer-vent prayer:
From e-vil and temp-ta-tion De-fend us through the night,
And round our hab-i-ta-tion Be thou a wall of light.

2. On thee our whole re-li-ance From day to day we cast,
To thee, with firm af-fi-ance, Would cleave from first to last;
To thee, through Je-sus' mer-it, For need-ful grace we come,
And trust that thy good Spir-it Will guide us safe-ly home.

3. What may be on the mor-row Our fore-sight can-not see;
But be it joy or sor-row, We know it comes from thee.
And noth-ing can take from us, Wher-e'er our steps may move,
The staff of thy sure prom-ise, The shield of thy true love. A-MEN.

BAPTISM                                                                 350

*And he took them up in his arms, put his hands upon them, and blessed them.*   Mark. 10:16

Philip Doddridge, 1755                                       SOHO C. M.
                                              Sir Joseph Barnby, 1881

1. See Is-rael's gen-tle Shep-herd stand With all - en - gag - ing charms;
2. "Per-mit them to ap-proach," he cries, "Nor scorn their hum - ble name;
3. We bring them, Lord, in thank-ful hands, And yield them up to thee;

Hark! how he calls the ten-der lambs, And folds them in his arms.
For 'twas to bless such souls as these The Lord of an-gels came."
Joy-ful that we our-selves are thine, Thine let our off-spring be.   A-MEN.

                                                                        351
*For the promise is unto you, and to your children...*   Acts 2:39

Thomas Haweis, 1808; alt. 1817                            ABERGELE C. M.
                                              John Ambrose Lloyd, 1873

1. Our chil-dren, Lord, in faith and pray'r, We now de-vote to thee; Let
2. Such help-less babes thou didst em-brace, While dwell-ing here be-low; To
3. In ear-ly days their hearts se-cure From world-ly snares, we pray; O

them thy cov-'nant mer-cies share, And thy sal - va - tion see.
us and ours, O God of grace, The same com-pas-sion show.
let them to the end en-dure In ev - ery right-eous way. A - MEN.

## 352 BAPTISM

*Suffer the little children to come unto me, and forbid them not: for of such is the kingdom of God.* Mark 10:14

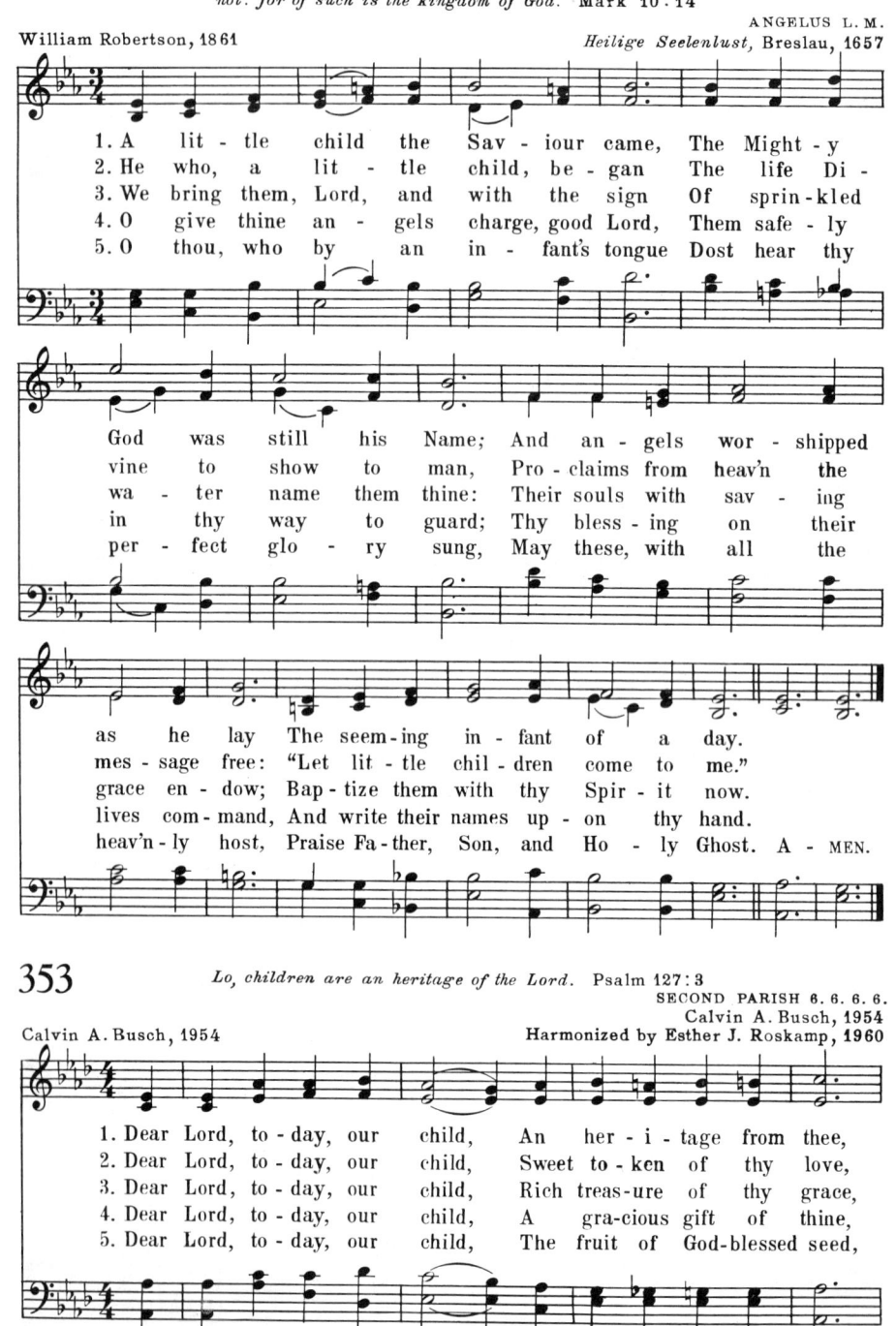

William Robertson, 1861

ANGELUS L. M.
*Heilige Seelenlust*, Breslau, 1657

1. A little child the Saviour came, The Mighty God was still his Name; And angels worshipped as he lay The seeming infant of a day.
2. He who, a little child, began The life Divine to show to man, Proclaims from heav'n the message free: "Let little children come to me."
3. We bring them, Lord, and with the sign Of sprinkled water name them thine: Their souls with saving grace endow; Baptize them with thy Spirit now.
4. O give thine angels charge, good Lord, Them safely in thy way to guard; Thy blessing on their lives command, And write their names upon thy hand.
5. O thou, who by an infant's tongue Dost hear thy perfect glory sung, May these, with all the heav'nly host, Praise Father, Son, and Holy Ghost. A-MEN.

## 353

*Lo, children are an heritage of the Lord.* Psalm 127:3

SECOND PARISH 6. 6. 6. 6.
Calvin A. Busch, 1954
Harmonized by Esther J. Roskamp, 1960

Calvin A. Busch, 1954

1. Dear Lord, to-day, our child, An heritage from thee,
2. Dear Lord, to-day, our child, Sweet token of thy love,
3. Dear Lord, to-day, our child, Rich treasure of thy grace,
4. Dear Lord, to-day, our child, A gracious gift of thine,
5. Dear Lord, to-day, our child, The fruit of God-blessed seed,

**BAPTISM**

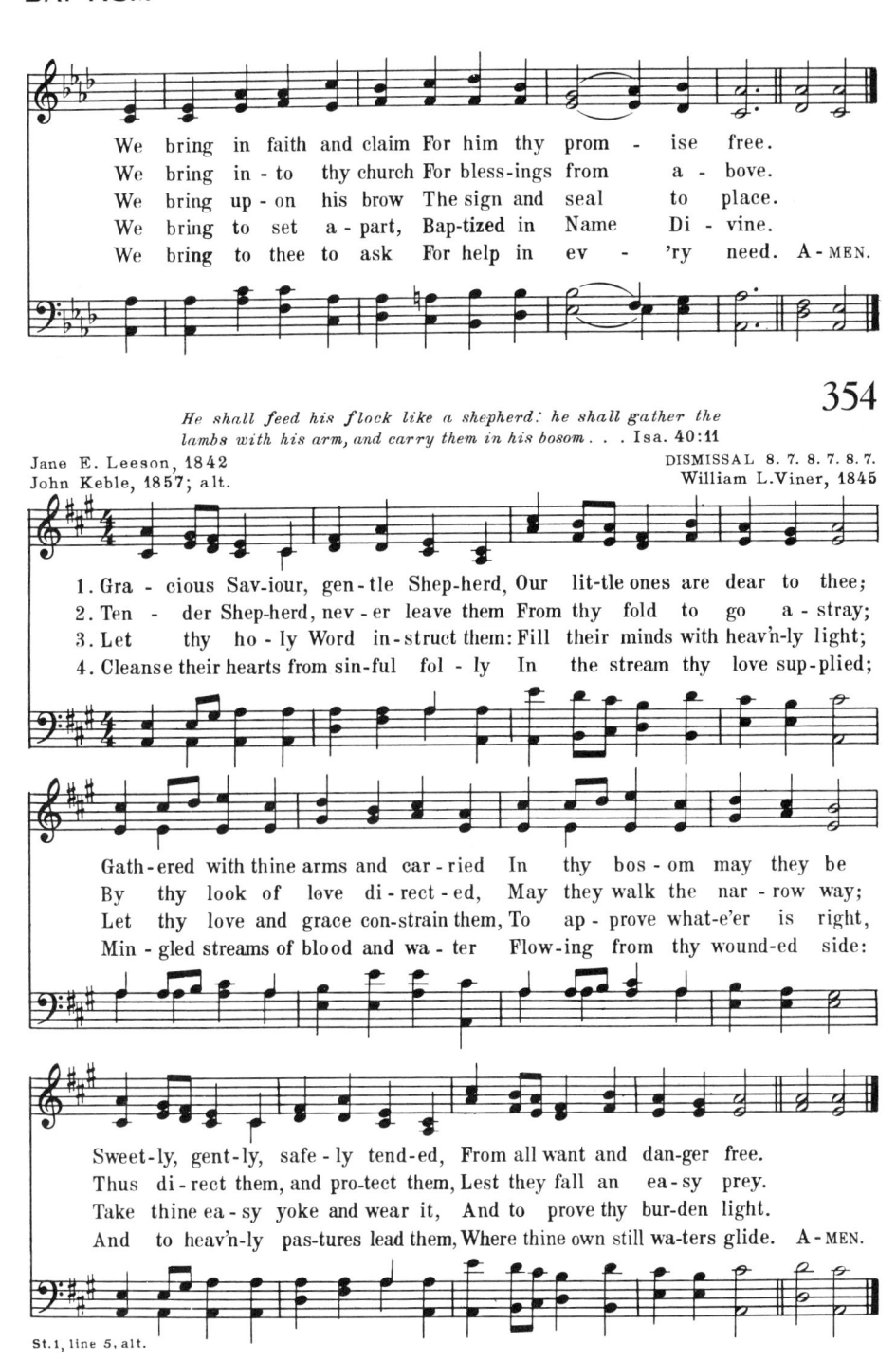

We bring in faith and claim For him thy prom - ise free.
We bring in - to thy church For bless-ings from a - bove.
We bring up - on his brow The sign and seal to place.
We bring to set a - part, Bap-tized in Name Di - vine.
We bring to thee to ask For help in ev - 'ry need. A-MEN.

## 354

*He shall feed his flock like a shepherd: he shall gather the lambs with his arm, and carry them in his bosom . . . Isa. 40:11*

Jane E. Leeson, 1842
John Keble, 1857; alt.

DISMISSAL 8. 7. 8. 7. 8. 7.
William L. Viner, 1845

1. Gra - cious Sav-iour, gen - tle Shep-herd, Our lit-tle ones are dear to thee;
2. Ten - der Shep-herd, nev - er leave them From thy fold to go a - stray;
3. Let thy ho - ly Word in-struct them: Fill their minds with heav'n-ly light;
4. Cleanse their hearts from sin-ful fol - ly In the stream thy love sup-plied;

Gath-ered with thine arms and car - ried In thy bos - om may they be
By thy look of love di - rect - ed, May they walk the nar - row way;
Let thy love and grace con-strain them, To ap - prove what-e'er is right,
Min - gled streams of blood and wa - ter Flow-ing from thy wound-ed side:

Sweet-ly, gent-ly, safe - ly tend - ed, From all want and dan-ger free.
Thus di - rect them, and pro-tect them, Lest they fall an ea - sy prey.
Take thine ea - sy yoke and wear it, And to prove thy bur-den light.
And to heav'n-ly pas-tures lead them, Where thine own still wa-ters glide. A-MEN.

St. 1, line 5, alt.

## 355     BAPTISM

*If ye be Christ's, then are ye Abraham's seed, and heirs according to the promise.* Gal. **3:29**

Heinrich of Laufenberg, 15th century
Tr. by Catherine Winkworth, 1869

CHRYSOSTOM 8. 8. 8. 8. 8. 8.
Sir Joseph Barnby, 1872

1. Lord Jesus Christ, our Lord most dear, As thou wast once an infant here, So give this child of thine, we pray, Thy grace and blessing day by day. O holy Jesus, Lord Divine, We pray thee guard this child of thine. A-MEN.
2. As in thy heav'nly Kingdom, Lord, All things obey thy sacred Word, Do thou thy mighty succour give, And shield this child by morn and eve.
3. Their watch let angels round him keep Wher-e'er he be, a-wake, asleep; Thy saving grace on him bestow That he in thee may live and grow.

St. 3, lines 4 and 5, alt.

*The following hymns are also appropriate:*

I think when I read that sweet story of old.....650
O Spirit of the living God..................253
Shepherd of tender youth...................117
When he cometh, when he cometh...........651

# THE LORD'S SUPPER 356

*Father, I have sinned against heaven, and in thy sight,
and am no more worthy to be called thy son.* Luke 15:21

Edward H. Bickersteth, 1872

COMMUNION 10. 10. 10. 10.
Arr. from Felix Mendelssohn-Bartholdy, 1835

1. Not worthy, Lord! to gather up the crumbs
With trembling hand that from thy table fall,
A weary, heavy-laden sinner comes
To plead thy promise and obey thy call.

2. I am not worthy to be thought thy child,
Nor sit the last and lowest at thy board;
Too long a wand'rer and too oft beguiled,
I only ask one reconciling word.

3. One word from thee, my Lord, one smile, one look,
And I could face the cold, rough world again;
And with that treasure in my heart could brook
The wrath of devils and the scorn of men.

4. I hear thy voice; thou bidd'st me come and rest;
I come, I kneel, I clasp thy piercèd feet;
Thou bidd'st me take my place, a welcome guest
Among thy saints, and of thy banquet eat.

5. My praise can only breathe itself in prayer,
My prayer can only lose itself in thee;
Dwell thou for ever in my heart, and there,
Lord, let me sup with thee; sup thou with me. A-MEN.

## 357 THE LORD'S SUPPER

*As often as ye eat this bread, and drink this cup, ye do shew the Lord's death till he come.* I Cor. 11:26

Edward H. Bickersteth, 1862

AJALON (REDHEAD No. 76) 7. 7. 7. 7. 7. 7.
Richard Redhead, 1853

1. Till he come! O let the words Lin-ger on the trem-bling chords;
Let the lit-tle while be-tween In their gold-en light be seen;
Let us think how heav'n and home Lie be-yond that "Till he come."

2. When the wea-ry ones we love En-ter on their rest a-bove,
Seems the earth so poor and vast, All our life-joy o-ver-cast?
Hush, be ev-ery mur-mur dumb: It is on-ly till he come.

3. Clouds and con-flicts round us press: Would we have one sor-row less?
All the sharp-ness of the cross, All that tells the world is loss,
Death and dark-ness, and the tomb, On-ly whis-per "Till he come."

4. See, the feast of love is spread, Drink the wine, and break the bread:
Sweet me-mo-rials,—till the Lord Call us round his heav'n-ly board;
Some from earth, from glo-ry some, Sev-ered on-ly till he come. A-MEN.

## 358

*My flesh is meat indeed, and my blood is drink indeed.* John 6:55

Reginald Heber, 1827

EUCHARISTIC HYMN 9. 8. 9. 8.
John S. B. Hodges, 1869

1. Bread of the world in mer-cy bro-ken, Wine of the soul in mer-cy shed,
2. Look on the heart by sor-row bro-ken, Look on the tears by sin-ners shed;

# THE LORD'S SUPPER

By whom the words of life were spo-ken, And in whose death our sins are dead;
And be thy feast to us the to-ken That by thy grace our souls are fed. A-MEN.

## 359

*The Lord Jesus the same night in which he was betrayed took bread.* I Cor. 11:23

John Morison, in  
Scottish *Paraphrases*, 1781

ROCKINGHAM OLD L. M.  
Arr. by Edward Miller, 1790

1. 'Twas on that night when doomed to know The ea-ger rage of ev-ery foe, That night in which he was be-trayed, The Sav-iour of the world took bread;
2. And, aft-er thanks and glo-ry given To him that rules in earth and heav'n, That sym-bol of his flesh he broke, And thus to all his fol-l'wers spoke:
3. "My bro-ken bod-y thus I give For you, for all. Take, eat, and live. And oft the sa-cred rite re-new That brings my sav-ing love to view."
4. Then in his hands the cup he raised, And God a-new he thanked and praised, While kind-ness in his bos-om glowed, And from his lips sal-va-tion flowed.
5. "My blood I thus pour forth," he cries, "To cleanse the soul in sin that lies; In this the cov-e-nant is sealed, And heav'n's e-ter-nal grace re-vealed." A-MEN.

## 360 THE LORD'S SUPPER

*This do in remembrance of me.* Luke 22:19

James Montgomery, 1825
DALEHURST C. M.
Arthur Cottman, 1874

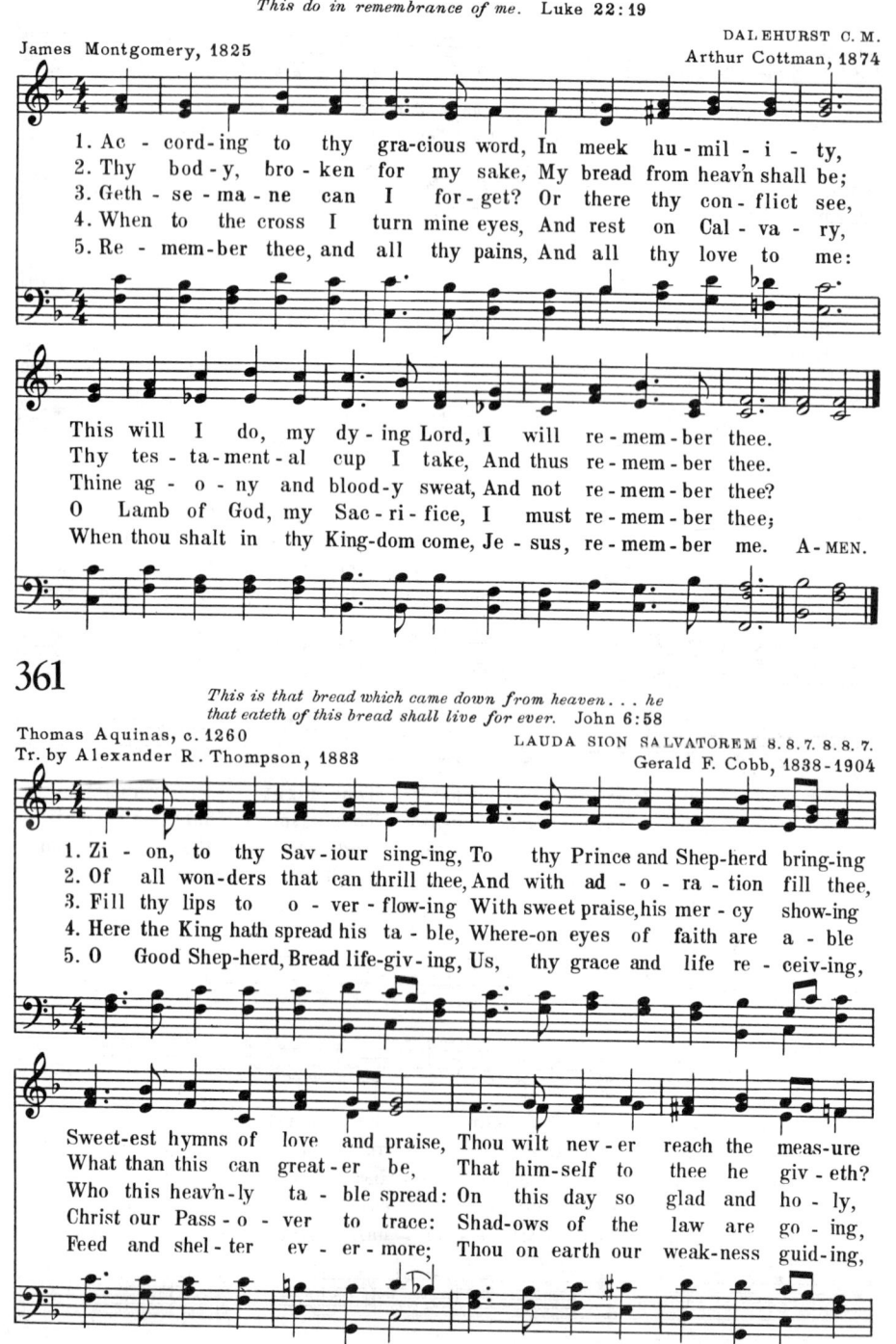

1. Ac-cord-ing to thy gra-cious word, In meek hu-mil-i-ty,
2. Thy bod-y, bro-ken for my sake, My bread from heav'n shall be;
3. Geth-se-ma-ne can I for-get? Or there thy con-flict see,
4. When to the cross I turn mine eyes, And rest on Cal-va-ry,
5. Re-mem-ber thee, and all thy pains, And all thy love to me:

This will I do, my dy-ing Lord, I will re-mem-ber thee.
Thy tes-ta-ment-al cup I take, And thus re-mem-ber thee.
Thine ag-o-ny and blood-y sweat, And not re-mem-ber thee?
O Lamb of God, my Sac-ri-fice, I must re-mem-ber thee;
When thou shalt in thy King-dom come, Je-sus, re-mem-ber me. A-MEN.

## 361

*This is that bread which came down from heaven... he that eateth of this bread shall live for ever.* John 6:58

Thomas Aquinas, c. 1260
Tr. by Alexander R. Thompson, 1883
LAUDA SION SALVATOREM 8.8.7.8.8.7.
Gerald F. Cobb, 1838-1904

1. Zi-on, to thy Sav-iour sing-ing, To thy Prince and Shep-herd bring-ing
2. Of all won-ders that can thrill thee, And with ad-o-ra-tion fill thee,
3. Fill thy lips to o-ver-flow-ing With sweet praise, his mer-cy show-ing
4. Here the King hath spread his ta-ble, Where-on eyes of faith are a-ble
5. O Good Shep-herd, Bread life-giv-ing, Us, thy grace and life re-ceiv-ing,

Sweet-est hymns of love and praise, Thou wilt nev-er reach the meas-ure
What than this can great-er be, That him-self to thee he giv-eth?
Who this heav'n-ly ta-ble spread: On this day so glad and ho-ly,
Christ our Pass-o-ver to trace: Shad-ows of the law are go-ing,
Feed and shel-ter ev-er-more; Thou on earth our weak-ness guid-ing,

# THE LORD'S SUPPER

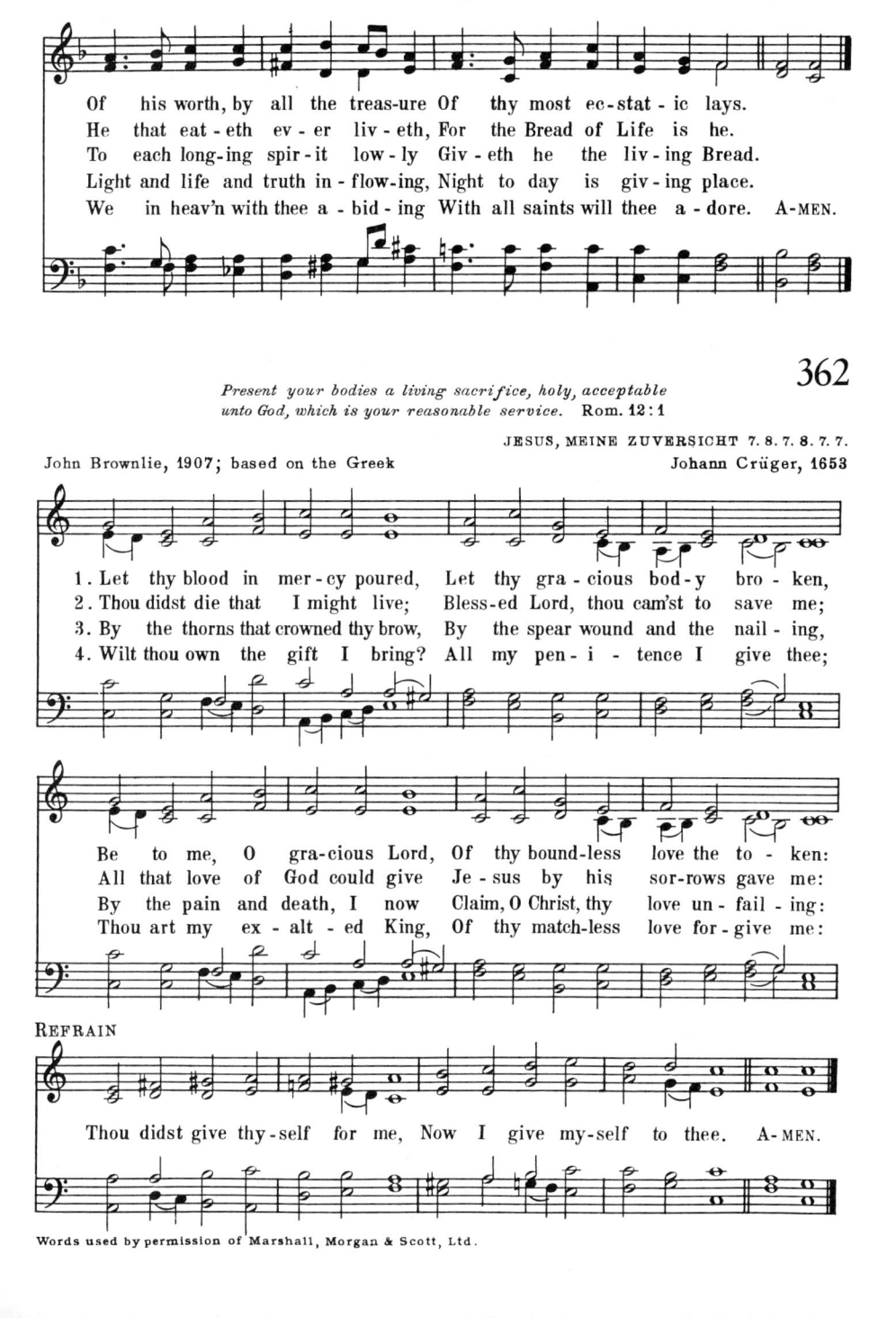

Of his worth, by all the treas-ure Of thy most ec-stat-ic lays.
He that eat-eth ev-er liv-eth, For the Bread of Life is he.
To each long-ing spir-it low-ly Giv-eth he the liv-ing Bread.
Light and life and truth in-flow-ing, Night to day is giv-ing place.
We in heav'n with thee a-bid-ing With all saints will thee a-dore. A-MEN.

**362**

*Present your bodies a living sacrifice, holy, acceptable unto God, which is your reasonable service.* Rom. 12:1

John Brownlie, 1907; based on the Greek

JESUS, MEINE ZUVERSICHT 7.8.7.8.7.7.
Johann Crüger, 1653

1. Let thy blood in mer-cy poured, Let thy gra-cious bod-y bro-ken,
2. Thou didst die that I might live; Bless-ed Lord, thou cam'st to save me;
3. By the thorns that crowned thy brow, By the spear wound and the nail-ing,
4. Wilt thou own the gift I bring? All my pen-i-tence I give thee;

Be to me, O gra-cious Lord, Of thy bound-less love the to-ken:
All that love of God could give Je-sus by his sor-rows gave me:
By the pain and death, I now Claim, O Christ, thy love un-fail-ing:
Thou art my ex-alt-ed King, Of thy match-less love for-give me:

REFRAIN

Thou didst give thy-self for me, Now I give my-self to thee. A-MEN.

Words used by permission of Marshall, Morgan & Scott, Ltd.

## 363 THE LORD'S SUPPER

*And when they had sung an hymn, they went out into the mount of Olives.* Matt. 26:30

Aaron R. Wolfe, 1858

SCHUMANN S. M.
Mason and Webb's *Cantica Laudis*,
Boston, 1850

1. A part-ing hymn we sing A-round thy ta-ble, Lord;
2. Here have we seen thy face, And felt thy pres-ence here;
3. The pur-chase of thy blood, By sin no lon-ger led,
4. In self-for-get-ting love Be our com-mun-ion shown,

A-gain our grate-ful trib-ute bring, Our sol-emn vows re-cord.
So may the sav-or of thy grace In word and life ap-pear.
The path our dear Re-deem-er trod May we re-joic-ing tread.
Un-til we join the church a-bove, And know as we are known. A-MEN.

## 364

*Our fathers ... did all eat the same spiritual meat; and did all drink the same spiritual drink: for they drank of that spiritual Rock ... and that Rock was Christ.* I Cor. 10:1-4

St. 1-3, Anon; st. 4-5, James Montgomery, 1825

ST. AGNES C. M.
John B. Dykes, 1866

1. Shep-herd of souls, re-fresh and bless Thy cho-sen pil-grim flock
2. Hun-gry and thirst-y, faint and weak, As thou when here be-low,
3. We would not live by bread a-lone, But by that Word of grace,
4. Be known to us in break-ing bread, But do not then de-part;
5. There sup with us in love Di-vine; Thy bod-y and thy blood,

With man-na in the wil-der-ness, With wa-ter from the rock.
Our souls the joys ce-les-tial seek Which from thy sor-rows flow.
In strength of which we trav-el on To our a-bid-ing place.
Sav-iour, a-bide with us, and spread Thy ta-ble in our heart.
That liv-ing bread, that heav'n-ly wine, Be our im-mor-tal food. A-MEN.

# THE LORD'S SUPPER

365

*For... Christ our passover is sacrificed for us.* I Cor. 5:7

Anon., Latin 6th century  
Tr. by Robert Campbell, 1849; alt.

ST. GEORGE'S, WINDSOR 7.7.7.7. D.  
Sir George J. Elvey, 1859

1. At the Lamb's high feast we sing Praise to our vic-to-rious King,
   Who hath washed us in the tide Flow-ing from his pierc-ed side;
   Praise we him whose love di-vine Gives his sa-cred blood for wine,
   Gives his bod-y for the feast, Christ the Vic-tim, Christ the Priest.

2. Where the pas-chal blood is poured, Death's dark an-gel sheathes his sword;
   Is-rael's hosts tri-um-phant go Through the wave that drowns the foe.
   Praise we Christ, whose blood was shed, Pas-chal Vic-tim, Pas-chal Bread;
   With sin-cer-i-ty and love Eat we man-na from a-bove.

3. Might-y Vic-tim from the sky, Pow'rs of hell be-neath thee lie;
   Death is con-quered in the fight, Thou hast brought us life and light:
   Hymns of glo-ry and of praise, Ris-en Lord, to thee we raise;
   Ho-ly Fa-ther, praise to thee, With the Spir-it, ev-er be. A-MEN.

*The following hymns are also appropriate:*

Here, O my Lord, I see thee face to face......310  
Jesus, thou Joy of loving hearts............549

See also *Index*: PREPARATORY SERVICES

## 366 THE CHURCH

*Inasmuch as ye have done it unto one of the least of these my brethren, ye have done it unto me.* Matt. 25:40

Godfrey Thring, 1877
ELMHURST 8.8.8.6.
Edwin Drewett, 1887

1. O God of mercy, God of might, In love and pity infinite,
   Teach us, as ever in thy sight, To live our life to thee.
2. And thou who cam'st on earth to die, That fallen man might live thereby,
   O hear us, for to thee we cry In hope, O Lord, to thee.
3. Teach us the lesson thou hast taught, To feel for those thy blood hath bought;
   That every word and deed and thought May work a work for thee.
4. For they are brethren, far and wide, Since thou, O Lord, for them hast died;
   Then teach us, what-so-e'er betide, To love them all in thee.
5. In sickness, sorrow, want, or care, Whate'er it be, 'tis ours to share;
   May we, when help is needed, there Give help as unto thee. A-MEN.

St. 4, lines 1 and 2, alt.

## 367

*All things come of thee, and of thine own have we given thee.* I Chron. 29:14

William Walsham How, 1864
SCHUMANN S. M.
Mason and Webb's *Cantica Laudis*,
Boston, 1850

1. We give thee but thine own, Whate'er the gift may be:
   All that we have is thine alone, A trust, O Lord, from thee.
2. May we thy bounties thus As stewards true receive,
   And gladly, as thou blessest us, To thee our first-fruits give.
3. O hearts are bruised and dead, And homes are bare and cold,
   And lambs for whom the Shepherd bled Are straying from the fold.
4. And we believe thy Word, Though dim our faith may be,
   Whate'er for thine we do, O Lord, We do it unto thee. A-MEN.

STEWARDSHIP 368

*God loveth a cheerful giver.* II Cor. 9:7

Robert Murray, 1898

BEECHER 8.7.8.7.D.
John Zundel, 1870

1. Lord, thou lov'st the cheer-ful giv-er, Who with o-pen heart and hand
2. We are thine, thy mer-cy sought us, Found us in death's dread-ful way,
3. Blest by thee with gifts and grac-es, May we heed thy church-'s call;
4. Sav-iour, thou hast free-ly giv-en All the bless-ings we en-joy,

Bless-es free-ly, as a riv-er That re-fresh-es all the land.
To the fold in safe-ty brought us, Nev-er more from thee to stray.
Glad-ly in all times and plac-es Give to thee who giv-est all.
Earth-ly store and bread of heav-en, Love and peace with-out al-loy;

Grant us then the grace of giv-ing With a spir-it large and free,
Thine own life thou free-ly gav-est As an off-'ring on the cross
Thou hast bought us, and no long-er Can we claim to be our own;
Hum-bly now we bow be-fore thee, And our all to thee re-sign;

That our life and all our liv-ing We may con-se-crate to thee.
For each sin-ner whom thou sav-est From e-ter-nal shame and loss.
Ev-er free and ev-er strong-er, We shall serve thee, Lord, a-lone.
For the king-dom, pow'r, and glo-ry, Are, O Lord, for ev-er thine. A-MEN.

## 369                                                           THE CHURCH

*His foundation is in the holy mountains.*    Psalm 87:1

From PSALM 87                                         CAERSALEM 8. 7. 8. 7. 4. 4. 4. 7.
*The Psalter,* 1912                                                Robert Edwards, 1837

1. Zion, founded on the mountains, God, thy Maker, loves thee well; He has chosen thee, most precious, He delights in thee to dwell; God's own city, God's own city, God's own city, Who can all thy glory tell?

2. Heathen lands and hostile peoples Soon shall come the Lord to know; Nations born again in Zion Shall the Lord's salvation show; God Almighty, God Almighty, God Almighty, Shall on Zion strength bestow.

3. When the Lord shall count the nations, Sons and daughters he shall see, Born to endless life in Zion, And their joyful song shall be: "Blessed Zion, blessed Zion, blessed Zion, All our fountains are in thee." A-MEN.

See also ZION, No. 275
Harmony from *The Revised Church Hymnary,* by permission of the Oxford University Press, London.

# MISSIONS

## 370

*Shew forth his salvation from day to day. Declare his glory among the heathen... Psalm 96:2-3*

Priscilla J. Owens, 1829-1899

JESUS SAVES 7. 6. 7. 6. 7. 7. 7. 6.

William J. Kirkpatrick, 1838-1921

1. We have heard the joyful sound: Jesus saves! Jesus saves!
2. Waft it on the rolling tide: Jesus saves! Jesus saves!
3. Sing above the battle strife, Jesus saves! Jesus saves!
4. Give the winds a mighty voice, Jesus saves! Jesus saves!

Spread the tidings all around: Jesus saves! Jesus saves!
Tell to sinners far and wide: Jesus saves! Jesus saves!
By his death and endless life, Jesus saves! Jesus saves!
Let the nations now rejoice— Jesus saves! Jesus saves!

Bear the news to ev'ry land, Climb the steeps and cross the waves;
Sing, ye islands of the sea; Ech-o back, ye ocean caves;
Sing it softly through the gloom, When the heart for mercy craves;
Shout salvation full and free, Highest hills and deepest caves;

Onward! 'tis our Lord's command; Jesus saves! Jesus saves!
Earth shall keep her jubilee: Jesus saves! Jesus saves!
Sing in triumph o'er the tomb— Jesus saves! Jesus saves!
This our song of victory— Jesus saves! Jesus saves! A-MEN.

## 371 THE CHURCH

*Repentance and remission of sins should be preached in his name among all nations... Luke 24:47*

Samuel Wolcott, 1869
BRAUN 6.6.4.6.6.6.4.
Johann G. Braun, 1675

1. Christ for the world we sing; The world to Christ we bring
   With lov-ing zeal; The poor and them that mourn, The faint and
   o-ver-borne, Sin-sick and sor-row-worn, Whom Christ doth heal.

2. Christ for the world we sing; The world to Christ we bring
   With fer-vent pray'r; The way-ward and the lost, By rest-less
   pas-sions tossed, Re-deemed at count-less cost From dark des-pair.

3. Christ for the world we sing; The world to Christ we bring
   With one ac-cord; With us the work to share, With us reproach to dare, With us the cross to bear, For Christ our Lord.

4. Christ for the world we sing; The world to Christ we bring
   With joy-ful song; The new-born souls whose days, Re-claimed from
   er-ror's ways, In-spired with hope and praise, To Christ be-long. A-MEN.

## 372

*Awake, awake, put on strength, O arm of the Lord... Isa. 51:9*

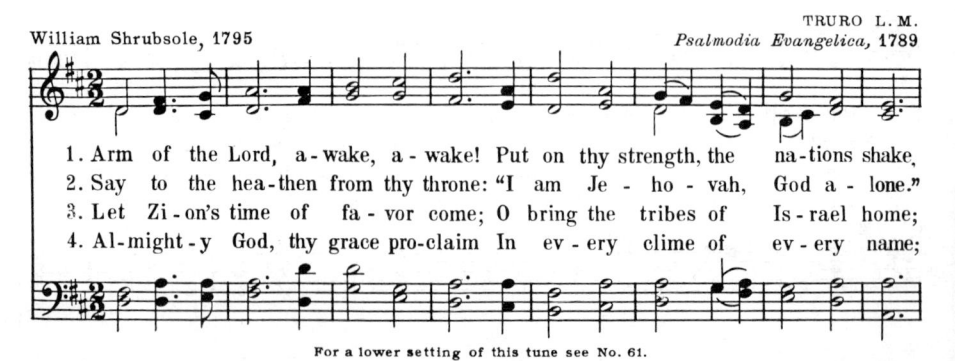

William Shrubsole, 1795
TRURO L. M.
*Psalmodia Evangelica*, 1789

1. Arm of the Lord, a-wake, a-wake! Put on thy strength, the na-tions shake.
2. Say to the hea-then from thy throne: "I am Je-ho-vah, God a-lone."
3. Let Zi-on's time of fa-vor come; O bring the tribes of Is-rael home;
4. Al-might-y God, thy grace pro-claim In ev-ery clime of ev-ery name;

For a lower setting of this tune see No. 61.

# MISSIONS

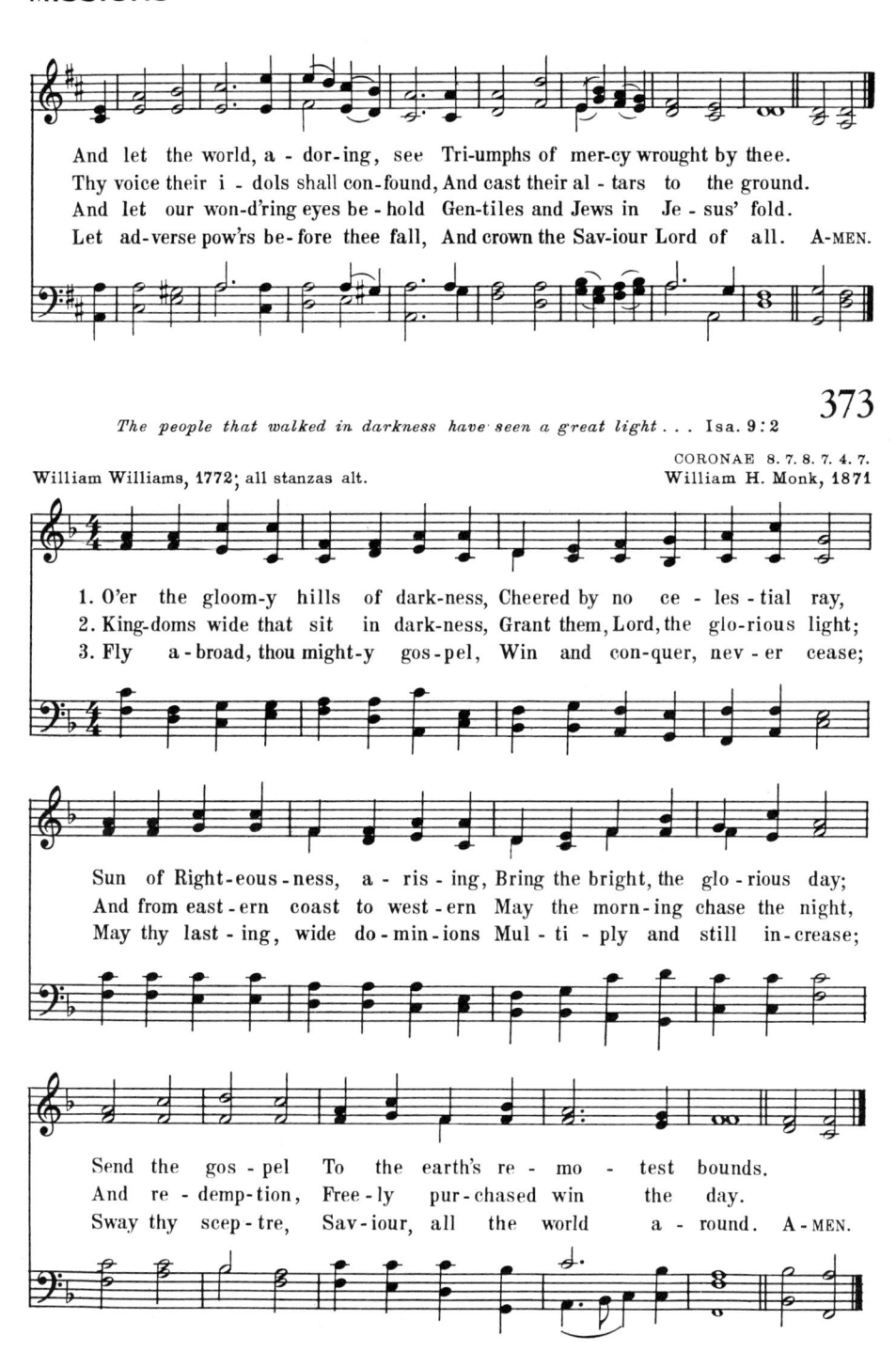

And let the world, a-dor-ing, see Tri-umphs of mer-cy wrought by thee.
Thy voice their i-dols shall con-found, And cast their al-tars to the ground.
And let our won-d'ring eyes be-hold Gen-tiles and Jews in Je-sus' fold.
Let ad-verse pow'rs be-fore thee fall, And crown the Sav-iour Lord of all. A-MEN.

### 373

*The people that walked in darkness have seen a great light... Isa. 9:2*

William Williams, 1772; all stanzas alt.

CORONAE 8. 7. 8. 7. 4. 7.
William H. Monk, 1871

1. O'er the gloom-y hills of dark-ness, Cheered by no ce-les-tial ray,
2. King-doms wide that sit in dark-ness, Grant them, Lord, the glo-rious light;
3. Fly a-broad, thou might-y gos-pel, Win and con-quer, nev-er cease;

Sun of Right-eous-ness, a-ris-ing, Bring the bright, the glo-rious day;
And from east-ern coast to west-ern May the morn-ing chase the night,
May thy last-ing, wide do-min-ions Mul-ti-ply and still in-crease;

Send the gos-pel To the earth's re-mo-test bounds.
And re-demp-tion, Free-ly pur-chased win the day.
Sway thy scep-tre, Sav-iour, all the world a-round. A-MEN.

## 374                                                             THE CHURCH

*He shall have dominion also from sea to sea, and from the river unto the ends of the earth.* Psalm 72:8

From PSALM 72                                   PARK STREET L. M. with repeat
Isaac Watts, 1719                         Arr. from Frederick M. A. Venua, c. 1810

1. Jesus shall reign wher-e'er the sun Does his successive journeys run; His kingdom stretch from shore to shore, Till moons shall wax and wane no more, Till moons shall wax and wane no more.
2. For him shall endless prayer be made, And praises throng to crown his head; His Name, like sweet perfume, shall rise With every morning sacrifice, With every morning sacrifice.
3. People and realms of every tongue Dwell on his love with sweetest song; And infant voices shall proclaim Their early blessings on his Name, Their early blessings on his Name.
4. Blessings abound wher-e'er he reigns; The pris-'ner leaps to lose his chains, The weary find eternal rest, And all the sons of want are blest, And all the sons of want are blest.
5. Let every creature rise and bring Peculiar honors to our King, Angels descend with songs again, And earth repeat the loud A-men, And earth repeat the loud A-men. A-MEN.

## 375

*Arise, O God, judge the earth: for thou shalt inherit all nations.* Psalm 82:8

Ralph Wardlaw, 1800                                         LABAN S. M.
                                                             Lowell Mason, 1830

1. O Lord our God, arise! The cause of truth maintain,
2. Thou Prince of life, arise! Nor let thy glory cease;
3. Thou Holy Ghost, arise! Expand thy quick-'ning wing,
4. All on the earth, arise! To God the Saviour sing;

# MISSIONS

And wide o'er all the peo-pled world Ex-tend thy bless-ed reign.
Far spread the con-quests of thy grace, And bless the earth with peace.
And o'er a dark and ru-ined world Let light and or-der spring.
From shore to shore, from earth to heav'n, Let ech-oing an-thems ring. A-MEN.

*And God said, Let there be light: and there was light.* Gen. 1:3

**376**

DENBIGH 6. 6. 4. 6. 6. 6. 4.
John Marriott, c. 1813; st. 4, line 1, alt.
Welsh melody

1. Thou, whose al-might-y word Cha-os and dark-ness heard, And took their flight, Hear us, we hum-bly pray; And, where the gos-pel's day Sheds not its glo-rious ray, Let there be light.
2. Thou, who didst come to bring On thy re-deem-ing wing Heal-ing and sight, Health to the sick in mind, Sight to the in-ly blind, O now to all man-kind Let there be light.
3. Spir-it of truth and love, Life-giv-ing, ho-ly Dove, Speed forth thy flight; Move o'er the wa-ters' face, Bear-ing the lamp of grace, And in earth's dark-est place Let there be light.
4. Ho-ly and bless-ed Three, Glo-ri-ous Trin-i-ty, Wis-dom, Love, Might! Bound-less as o-cean's tide, Roll-ing in full-est pride, Through the world far and wide Let there be light. A-MEN.

See also BRAUN, No. 371

# 377                                                                 THE CHURCH

*There is no man that hath left house, or brethren... for my sake, and the gospel's, but he shall receive an hundredfold now... and in the world to come eternal life.*   Mark 10:29-30

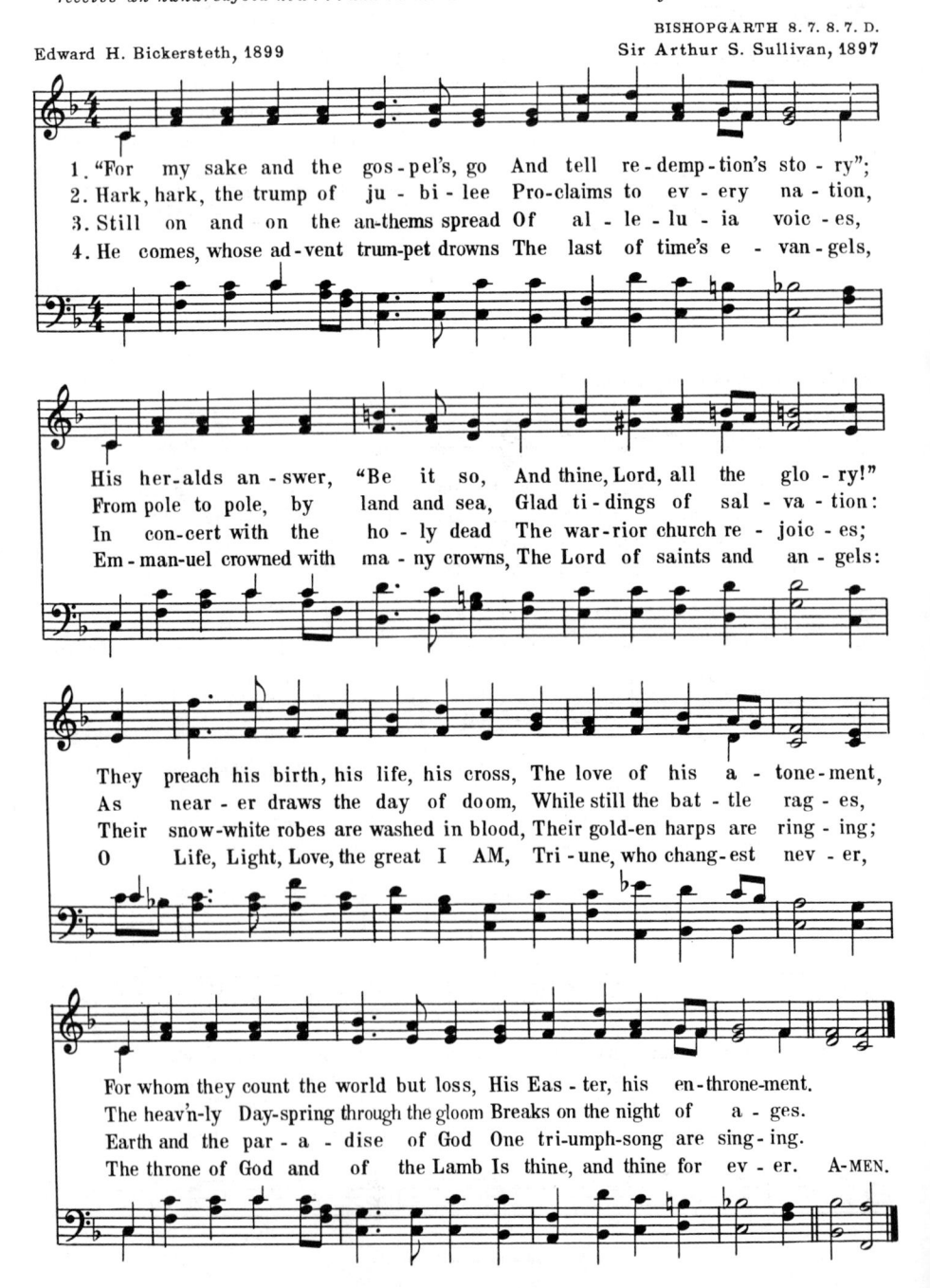

BISHOPGARTH 8. 7. 8. 7. D.
Edward H. Bickersteth, 1899                                                     Sir Arthur S. Sullivan, 1897

1. "For my sake and the gos-pel's, go And tell re-demp-tion's sto-ry";
2. Hark, hark, the trump of ju-bi-lee Pro-claims to ev-ery na-tion,
3. Still on and on the an-thems spread Of al-le-lu-ia voic-es,
4. He comes, whose ad-vent trum-pet drowns The last of time's e-van-gels,

His her-alds an-swer, "Be it so, And thine, Lord, all the glo-ry!"
From pole to pole, by land and sea, Glad ti-dings of sal-va-tion:
In con-cert with the ho-ly dead The war-rior church re-joic-es;
Em-man-uel crowned with ma-ny crowns, The Lord of saints and an-gels:

They preach his birth, his life, his cross, The love of his a-tone-ment,
As near-er draws the day of doom, While still the bat-tle rag-es,
Their snow-white robes are washed in blood, Their gold-en harps are ring-ing;
O Life, Light, Love, the great I AM, Tri-une, who chang-est nev-er,

For whom they count the world but loss, His Eas-ter, his en-throne-ment.
The heav'n-ly Day-spring through the gloom Breaks on the night of a-ges.
Earth and the par-a-dise of God One tri-umph-song are sing-ing.
The throne of God and of the Lamb Is thine, and thine for ev-er. A-MEN.

## MISSIONS

### 378

*Thou hast given a banner to them that fear thee, that it may be displayed because of the truth.* Psalm 60:4

George W. Doane, 1848

WALTHAM L. M.
J. Baptiste Calkin, 1872

1. Fling out the ban-ner! let it float Sky-ward and sea-ward, high and wide;
2. Fling out the ban-ner! an-gels bend In anx-ious si-lence o'er the sign,
3. Fling out the ban-ner! hea-then lands Shall see from far the glo-rious sight,
4. Fling out the ban-ner! sin-sick souls, That sink and per-ish in the strife,
5. Fling out the ban-ner! let it float Sky-ward and sea-ward, high and wide,
6. Fling out the ban-ner! wide and high, Sea-ward and sky-ward, let it shine:

The sun that lights its shin-ing folds, The cross on which the Sav-iour died.
And vain-ly seek to com-pre-hend The won-der of the love Di-vine.
And na-tions, crowd-ing to be born, Bap-tize their spir-its in its light.
Shall touch in faith its ra-diant hem And spring im-mor-tal in-to life.
Our glo-ry, on-ly in the cross; Our on-ly hope, the Cru-ci-fied!
Nor skill, nor might, nor mer-it ours; We con-quer on-ly in that sign. A-MEN.

### 379

*How beautiful upon the mountains are the feet of him that bringeth good tidings, that publisheth peace . . .* Isa. 52:7

Mary C. Gates, 1890

ELMHURST 8.8.8.6.
Edwin Drewett, 1887

1. Send thou, O Lord, to ev-'ry place Swift mes-sen-gers be-fore thy face,
2. Send men whose eyes have seen the King, Men in whose ears his sweet words ring;
3. To bring good news to souls in sin; The bruis'd and bro-ken hearts to win;
4. Gird each one with the Spir-it's sword, The sword of thine own death-less Word;
5. Raise up, O Lord the Ho-ly Ghost, From this broad land a might-y host,

The her-alds of thy won-drous grace, Where thou thy-self wilt come.
Send such thy lost ones home to bring; Send them where thou wilt come.
In ev-'ry place to bring them in Where thou thy-self wilt come.
And make them con-qu'rors, con-qu'ring Lord, Where thou thy-self wilt come.
Their war cry, "We will seek the lost Where thou, O Christ, wilt come." A-MEN.

## 380 THE CHURCH

*As ye go, preach... Matt. 10:7*

Bourne H. Draper, 1803
St. 1, lines 1,3, st. 2, line 2, alt.

MISSIONARY CHANT L. M.
Heinrich C. Zeuner, 1832

1. Ye Chris-tian her-alds, go pro-claim Sal - va-tion through Em-man-uel's Name!
2. God shield you with a wall of fire, With flam-ing zeal your breasts in - spire,
3. And when our la-bors all are o'er, Then we shall meet to part no more;

To dis-tant climes the ti-dings bear, And plant the Rose of Shar - on there.
Bid rag-ing winds their fu - ry cease, And hush the tem-pests in - to peace.
Meet with the blood-bought throng to fall, And crown our Je-sus Lord of all. A - MEN.

## 381

*Make a joyful noise unto God, all ye lands.* Psalm 66:1

From PSALM 66:1-7
The Psalter, 1912

MILES LANE C. M. with repeat
William Shrubsole, 1779
Arr. from *The New Christian Hymnal*, 1929

1. All lands, to God in joy-ful sounds A-loft your voic-es raise; Sing forth the hon-or
2. Say ye to God, how ter - ri-ble In all thy works art thou! To thee thy foes by
3. Yea, all the earth shall wor-ship thee, And un-to thee shall sing; To thy great Name shall
4. O come, be-hold the works of God, His might-y do - ings see; In deal - ing with the
5. He led in safe-ty through the flood The peo-ple of his choice, He turned the sea to
6. He rules for ev - er by his might, His eyes the na-tions try; Let not the proud, re-

of his Name, And glo-rious make his praise, And glo-rious make his praise.
thy great pow'r Shall be con-strained to bow, Shall be con-strained to bow.
songs of joy With loud ho-san-nas ring, With loud ho-san - nas ring.
sons of men Most won-der-ful is he, Most won-der-ful is he.
sol - id ground; In him let us re - joice, In him let us re - joice.
bel - lious ones Ex-alt them-selves on high, Ex - alt them-selves on high. A-MEN.

*See also WINDSOR, No. 22*

# MISSIONS

**382**

*Go ye therefore, and make disciples of all the nations...*
*and lo, I am with you always... Matt. 28:19, 20 (A.S.V.)*

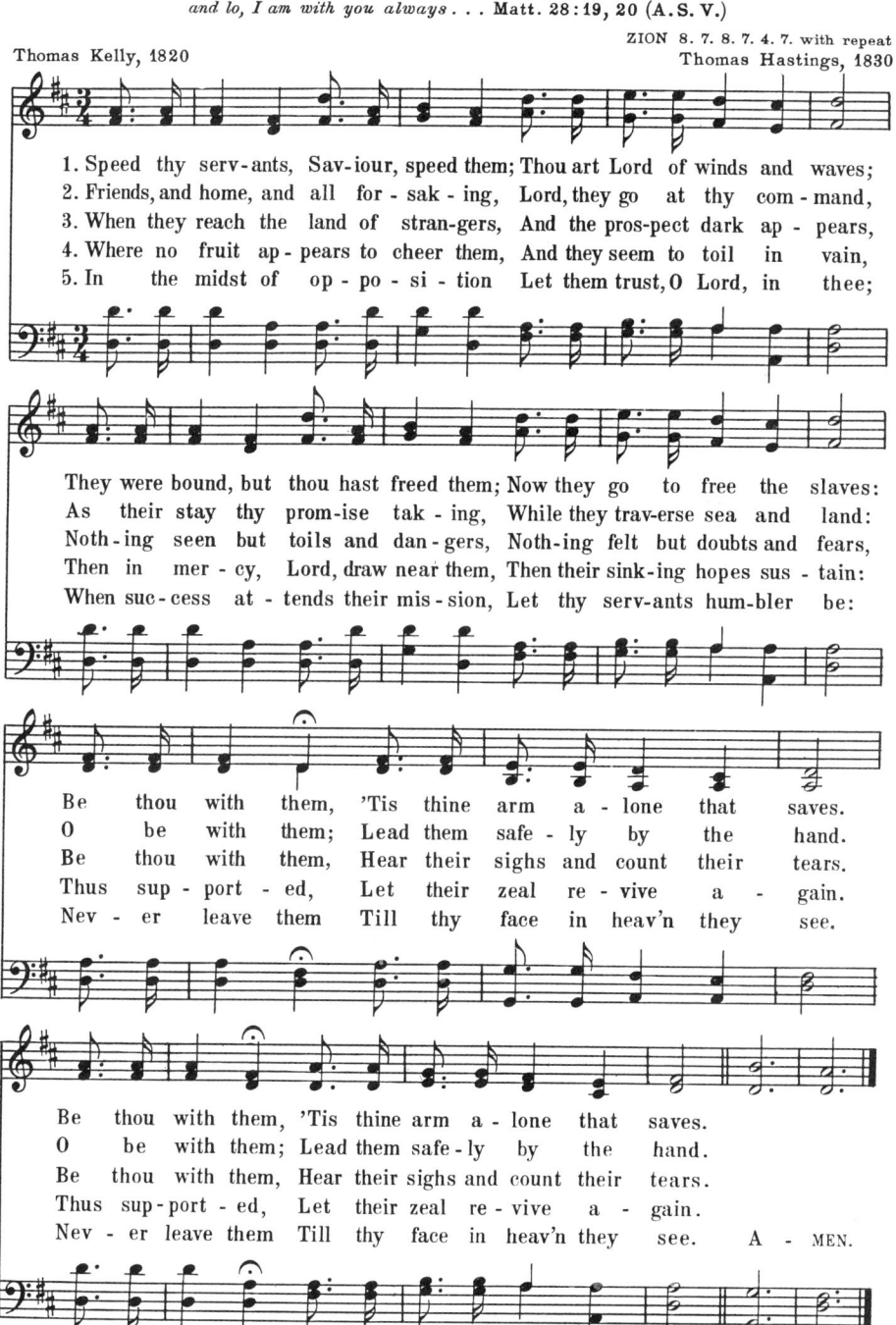

Thomas Kelly, 1820

ZION 8. 7. 8. 7. 4. 7. with repeat
Thomas Hastings, 1830

1. Speed thy serv-ants, Sav-iour, speed them; Thou art Lord of winds and waves;
2. Friends, and home, and all for-sak-ing, Lord, they go at thy com-mand,
3. When they reach the land of stran-gers, And the pros-pect dark ap-pears,
4. Where no fruit ap-pears to cheer them, And they seem to toil in vain,
5. In the midst of op-po-si-tion Let them trust, O Lord, in thee;

They were bound, but thou hast freed them; Now they go to free the slaves:
As their stay thy prom-ise tak-ing, While they trav-erse sea and land:
Noth-ing seen but toils and dan-gers, Noth-ing felt but doubts and fears,
Then in mer-cy, Lord, draw near them, Then their sink-ing hopes sus-tain:
When suc-cess at-tends their mis-sion, Let thy serv-ants hum-bler be:

Be thou with them, 'Tis thine arm a-lone that saves.
O be with them; Lead them safe-ly by the hand.
Be thou with them, Hear their sighs and count their tears.
Thus sup-port-ed, Let their zeal re-vive a-gain.
Nev-er leave them Till thy face in heav'n they see.

Be thou with them, 'Tis thine arm a-lone that saves.
O be with them; Lead them safe-ly by the hand.
Be thou with them, Hear their sighs and count their tears.
Thus sup-port-ed, Let their zeal re-vive a-gain.
Nev-er leave them Till thy face in heav'n they see. A-MEN.

# 383 THE CHURCH

*Come over ... and help us.* Acts 16:9

MISSIONARY HYMN 7. 6. 7. 6. D.
Reginald Heber, 1819 — Lowell Mason, 1823

1. From Greenland's icy mountains, From India's coral strand,
Where Afric's sunny fountains Roll down their golden sand,
From many an ancient river, From many a palmy plain,
They call us to deliver Their land from error's chain.

2. What though the spicy breezes Blow soft o'er Ceylon's isle;
Though ev'ry prospect pleases, And only man is vile:
In vain with lavish kindness The gifts of God are strown;
The heathen in his blindness Bows down to wood and stone.

3. Can we, whose souls are lighted With wisdom from on high,
Can we to men benighted The lamp of life deny?
Salvation! O salvation! The joyful sound proclaim,
Till each remotest nation Has learned Messiah's Name.

4. Waft, waft, ye winds, his story, And you, ye waters, roll,
Till like a sea of glory It spreads from pole to pole;
Till o'er our ransomed nature The Lamb for sinners slain,
Redeemer, King, Creator, In bliss returns to reign. A-MEN.

# MISSIONS 384

*I will break in pieces the gates of brass, and cut in sunder the bars of iron.* Isa. 45:2

James Montgomery, 1843; st. 4, lines 2, 3, alt.

ALL SAINTS NEW C. M. D.
Henry S. Cutler, 1872

1. Lift up your heads, ye gates of brass, Ye bars of i-ron, yield,
And let the King of Glo-ry pass; The cross is in the field:
That ban-ner, bright-er than the star That leads the train of night,
Shines on their march, and guides from far His serv-ants to the fight.

2. A ho-ly war those serv-ants wage; Mys-ter-ious-ly at strife,
The pow'rs of heav'n and hell en-gage For more than death or life.
Ye ar-mies of the liv-ing God, His sac-ra-men-tal host,
Where hal-lowed foot-steps nev-er trod Take your ap-point-ed post:

3. Though few and small and weak your bands, Strong in your Cap-tain's strength
Go to the con-quest of all lands; All must be his at length.
Those spoils at his vic-to-rious feet You shall re-joice to lay,
And lay your-selves, as tro-phies meet, In his great judg-ment-day.

4. O fear not, faint not, halt not now; In Je-sus' Name be strong;
To him shall all the na-tions bow, And sing with you this song:
"Up-lift-ed are the gates of brass, The bars of i-ron yield;
Be-hold the King of Glo-ry pass; The cross has won the field." A-MEN.

# 385 THE CHURCH

*God be merciful unto us, and bless us; and cause his face to shine upon us.* Psalm 67:1

Psalm 67
*The Psalter*, 1912

MEIRIONYDD 7. 6. 7. 6. D.
Welsh hymn melody
Ascribed to William Lloyd, 1840

1. O God, to us show mercy And bless us in thy grace;
Cause thou to shine upon us The brightness of thy face;
That so thy way most holy On earth may soon be known,
And unto ev'ry people Thy saving grace be shown.

2. O God, let all men praise thee, Let all the nations sing;
In ev'ry land let praises And songs of gladness ring;
For thou shalt judge the people In truth and righteousness,
And through the earth the nations Shall thy just rule confess.

3. O God, let people praise thee, Let all the nations sing,
For earth in rich abundance To us her fruit shall bring.
The Lord our God shall bless us, Our God shall blessing send,
And all the earth shall fear him To its remotest end. A-MEN.

Music used by permission of the Executors of the late Dr. Basil Harwood.

# MISSIONS 386

*The Lord shall arise upon thee, and his glory shall be seen upon thee.* Isa. 60:2

William Hurn, 1813, alt.

LISCHER 6. 6. 6. 6. 8. 8. with repeat
Arr. from F. J. C. Schneider
by Lowell Mason, 1841

1. A - rise, O God, and shine In all thy sav - ing might,
2. Bring dis - tant na - tions near To sing thy glo - rious praise;
3. Send forth thy glo - rious pow'r, That Gen - tiles all may see,
4. To God, the on - ly wise, The one im - mor - tal King,

And pros - per each de - sign To spread thy glo - rious light:
Let ev - 'ry peo - ple hear And learn thy ho - ly ways:
And earth pres - ent her store In con - verts born to thee:
Let hal - le - lu - jahs rise From ev - 'ry liv - ing thing:

Let heal - ing streams of mer - cy flow, That all the earth thy
Reign, might - y God, as - sert thy cause, And gov - ern by thy
God, our own God, thy church O bless, And fill the world with
Let all that breathe, on ev - 'ry coast, Praise Fa - ther, Son, and

truth may know, That all the earth thy truth may know.
right - eous laws, And gov - ern by thy right - eous laws.
right - eous - ness, And fill the world with right - eous - ness.
Ho - ly Ghost, Praise Fa - ther, Son, and Ho - ly Ghost. A-MEN.

St. 3, line 3, alt.

# 387          THE CHURCH

*I will declare what he hath done for my soul.* Psalm 66:16

I LOVE TO TELL THE STORY 7.6.7.6. D. with refrain

Katherine Hankey, 1866          William G. Fischer, 1869

1. I love to tell the story Of unseen things above,
Of Jesus and his glory, Of Jesus and his love.
I love to tell the story, Because I know 'tis true;
It satisfies my longings As nothing else could do.

2. I love to tell the story; More wonderful it seems
Than all the golden fancies Of all our golden dreams.
I love to tell the story, It did so much for me;
And that is just the reason I tell it now to thee.

3. I love to tell the story; 'Tis pleasant to repeat
What seems, each time I tell it, More wonderfully sweet.
I love to tell the story, For some have never heard
The message of salvation From God's own holy Word.

4. I love to tell the story; For those who know it best
Seem hungering and thirsting To hear it, like the rest.
And when, in scenes of glory, I sing the new, new song,
'Twill be the old, old story, That I have loved so long.

# THE FREE OFFER OF THE GOSPEL

**REFRAIN**

I love to tell the story, 'Twill be my theme in glory
To tell the old, old story Of Jesus and his love. A-MEN.

*Today if ye will hear his voice, harden not your hearts.* Heb. 4:7

**388**

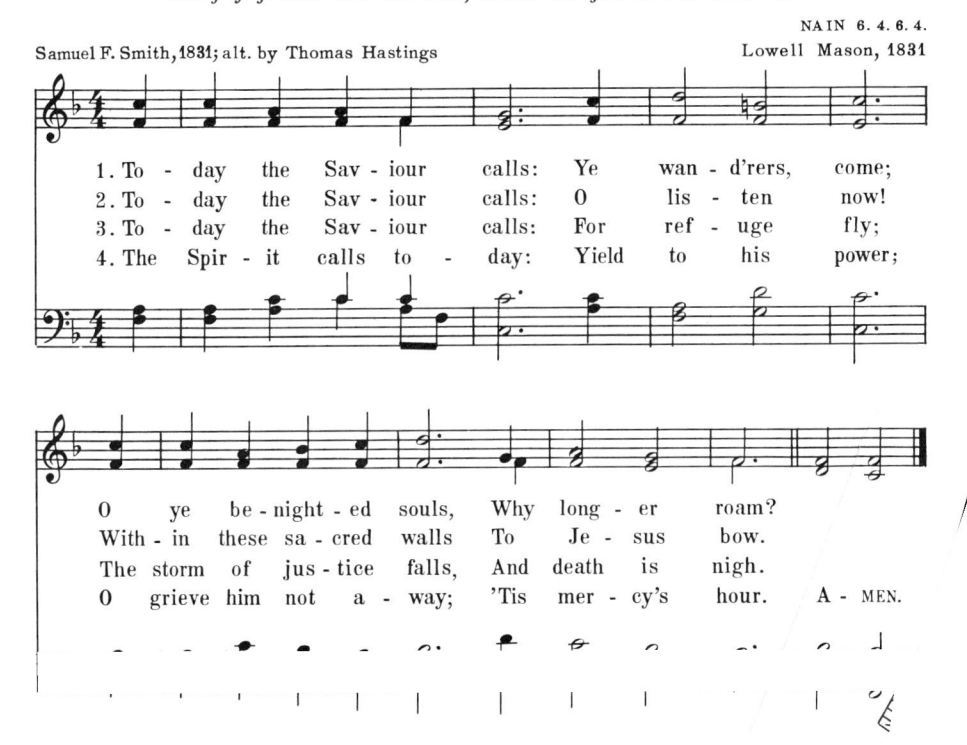

NAIN 6. 6. 4. 6. 4.

Samuel F. Smith, 1831; alt. by Thomas Hastings     Lowell Mason, 1831

1. To-day the Saviour calls: Ye wan-d'rers, come;
   O ye be-night-ed souls, Why long-er roam?
2. To-day the Saviour calls: O lis-ten now!
   With-in these sa-cred walls To Je-sus bow.
3. To-day the Saviour calls: For ref-uge fly;
   The storm of jus-tice falls, And death is nigh.
4. The Spir-it calls to-day: Yield to his power;
   O grieve him not a-way; 'Tis mer-cy's hour. A-MEN.

389 (FIRST TUNE)          THE CHURCH

*Come unto me, all ye that labour and are heavy laden, and I will give you rest.*    Matt. 11:28

John Mason Neale, 1862; st. 7, line 3, alt.      STEPHANOS 8.5.8.3.    Sir Henry W. Baker, 1868

1. Art thou wea-ry, art thou lan-guid, Art thou sore dis-tress'd?
2. Hath he marks to lead me to him, If he be my Guide?
3. Is there di-a-dem, as Mon-arch, That his brow a-dorns?
4. If I find him, if I fol-low, What his guer-don here?
5. If I still hold close-ly to him, What hath he at last?

"Come to me," saith One, "and, com-ing, Be at rest."
"In his feet and hands are wound-prints, And his side."
"Yea, a crown, in ver-y sure-ty, But of thorns."
"Man-y a sor-row, man-y a la-bor, Many a tear."
"Sor-row van-quished, la-bor end-ed, Jor-dan passed." A-MEN.

       6. If I ask him to receive me,
          Will he say me nay?
          "Not till earth and not till heaven
          Pass away."

       7. Finding, following, keeping, struggling,
          Is he sure to bless?
          "Saints, apostles, prophets, martyrs,
          Answer, 'Yes.'"

389 (SECOND TUNE)

John Mason Neale, 1862       BULLINGER 8.5.8.3.    Ethelbert W. Bullinger, 1874

Art thou wea-ry, art thou lan-guid, Art thou sore dis-tress'd?

# THE FREE OFFER OF THE GOSPEL

"Come to me," saith One, "and, com-ing, Be . . . at rest." A-MEN.

*Come unto me, all ye that labour and are heavy la-
den... Take my yoke upon you ... Matt. 11:28, 29*

**390**

ST. AUSTIN 8. 7. 8. 7. 4. 7.
Arr. from a Gregorian chant for the
*Bristol Tune Book,* 1876

Joseph Swain, 1792

1. Come, ye souls by sin af-flict-ed, Bowed with fruit-less sor-row down;
2. Take his ea-sy yoke and wear it; Love will make o-be-dience sweet;
3. Bless-ed are the eyes that see him, Blest the ears that hear his voice;
4. Sweet as home to pil-grims wea-ry, Light to new-ly o-pened eyes,

By the bro-ken law con-vict-ed, Through the cross be-hold the crown;
Christ will give you strength to bear it, While his wis-dom guides your feet
Bless-ed are the souls that trust him, And in him a-lone re-joice:
Or full springs in des-erts drea-ry, Is the rest the cross sup-plies:

Look to Je-sus; Mer-cy flows through him a-lone.
Safe to glo-ry, Where his ran-somed cap-tives meet.
His com-mand-ments Then be-come their hap-py choice.
All who taste it Shall to rest im-mor-tal rise. A-MEN.

# 391 THE CHURCH

*Come unto me... Matt. 11:28*

Henry Burton, 1878
SOMETHING FOR JESUS 6.4.6.4.6.6.6.4.
Robert Lowry, 1872

1. Come, for the feast is spread, Hark to the call;
   Come to the Living Bread, Offered to all.
   Come to his house of wine, Low on his breast recline,
   All that he has is thine; Come, sinner, come.

2. Come where the fountain flows, River of life;
   Healing for all thy woes, Doubting, and strife.
   Millions have been supplied, No one was e'er denied,
   Come to the crimson tide; Come, sinner, come.

3. Come to the throne of grace, Boldly draw near;
   He who would win the race Must tarry here.
   Whate'er thy want may be, Here is the grace for thee,
   Jesus thine only plea; Come, Christian, come. A-MEN.

# THE FREE OFFER OF THE GOSPEL 392

*The Lord hath anointed me... to proclaim the acceptable year of the Lord... Isa. 61:1,2*

Charles Wesley, 1750
LENOX 6.6.6.6.8.8.
Louis Edson, 1782

1. Blow ye the trum - pet, blow! The glad - ly sol - emn sound
2. Je - sus, our great High Priest, Hath full a - tone - ment made;
3. Ex - tol the Lamb of God; The sac - ri - fi - cial Lamb;
4. Ye slaves of sin and hell, Your lib - er - ty re - ceive;
5. Ye who have sold for nought Your her - it - age a - bove,
6. The gos - pel trum - pet hear, The news of heav'n - ly grace;

Let all the na - tions know, To earth's re - mot - est bound:
Ye wea - ry spir - its, rest; Ye mourn - ful souls, be glad:
Re - demp - tion through his blood Through-out the world pro - claim:
And safe in Je - sus dwell, And blest in Je - sus live:
Re - ceive it back un - bought, The gift of Je - sus' love:
And, saved from earth, ap - pear Be - fore your Sav - iour's face:

REFRAIN

The year of ju - bi - lee is come; Re - turn, ye ran - somed sin - ners, home; Re - turn, ye ran - somed sin - ners, home. A - MEN.

St. 3, line 2, alt.

## 393 THE CHURCH

*I am not come to call the righteous, but sinners to repentance.* Matt. 9:13

Joseph Hart, 1759, alt.
CAERSALEM 8.7.8.7.4.4.4.7.
Robert Edwards, 1837

1. Come, ye sinners, poor and wretch-ed, Weak and wound-ed, sick and sore; Je-sus read-y stands to save you, Full of pit-y joined with pow'r: He is a-ble, He is a-ble, He is a-ble, He is will-ing; doubt no more.

2. Come, ye need-y, come and wel-come, God's free boun-ty glo-ri-fy; True be-lief and true re-pent-ance, Ev-'ry grace that brings you nigh, With-out mon-ey, With-out mon-ey, With-out mon-ey, Come to Je-sus Christ and buy.

3. Come, ye wea-ry, heav-y la-den, Bruised and bro-ken by the fall; If you tar-ry till you're bet-ter, You will nev-er come at all: Not the right-eous, Not the right-eous, Not the right-eous—Sin-ners Je-sus came to call.

4. Let not con-science make you lin-ger, Nor of fit-ness fond-ly dream; All the fit-ness he re-quir-eth Is to feel your need of him; This he gives you, This he gives you, This he gives you; 'Tis the Spir-it's ris-ing beam.

5. Lo! th' in-car-nate God, as-cend-ed, Pleads the mer-it of his blood; Ven-ture on him, ven-ture whol-ly, Let no oth-er trust in-trude: None but Je-sus, None but Je-sus, None but Je-sus Can do help-less sin-ners good. A-MEN.

Harmony from *The Revised Church Hymnary*, by permission of the Oxford University Press, London.

# THE FREE OFFER OF THE GOSPEL 394

*This man receiveth sinners... Luke 15:2*

Erdmann Neumeister, 1718
Tr., cento

JESUS NIMMT DIE SÜNDER AN 7. 8. 7. 8. 7. 7.
Erdmann Neumeister, 1718
Harmonized by Esther J. Roskamp, 1960

1. "Jesus sinners doth receive:" Word of surest consolation;
   Word all sorrow to relieve, Word of pardon, peace, salvation!
   Naught like this can comfort give: "Jesus sinners doth receive."

2. On God's grace we have no claim, Yet to us his pledge is given;
   He hath sworn by his own Name, Open are the gates of heaven.
   Take to heart this word and live: "Jesus sinners doth receive."

3. When a helpless lamb doth stray, After it, the Shepherd, pressing
   Thro' each dark and dang'rous way, Brings it back, his own possessing.
   Jesus seeks thee, O believe: "Jesus sinners doth receive." A-MEN.

4. Oh, how blest it is to know:
   Were as scarlet my transgression,
   It shall be as white as snow
   By thy blood and bitter passion;
   For these words I now believe:
   "Jesus sinners doth receive."

5. Now my conscience is at peace,
   From the Law I stand acquitted;
   Christ hath purchased my release
   And my every sin remitted.
   Naught remains my soul to grieve—
   "Jesus sinners doth receive."

## 395 THE FREE OFFER OF THE GOSPEL

*Come unto me . . . Matt. 11:28*

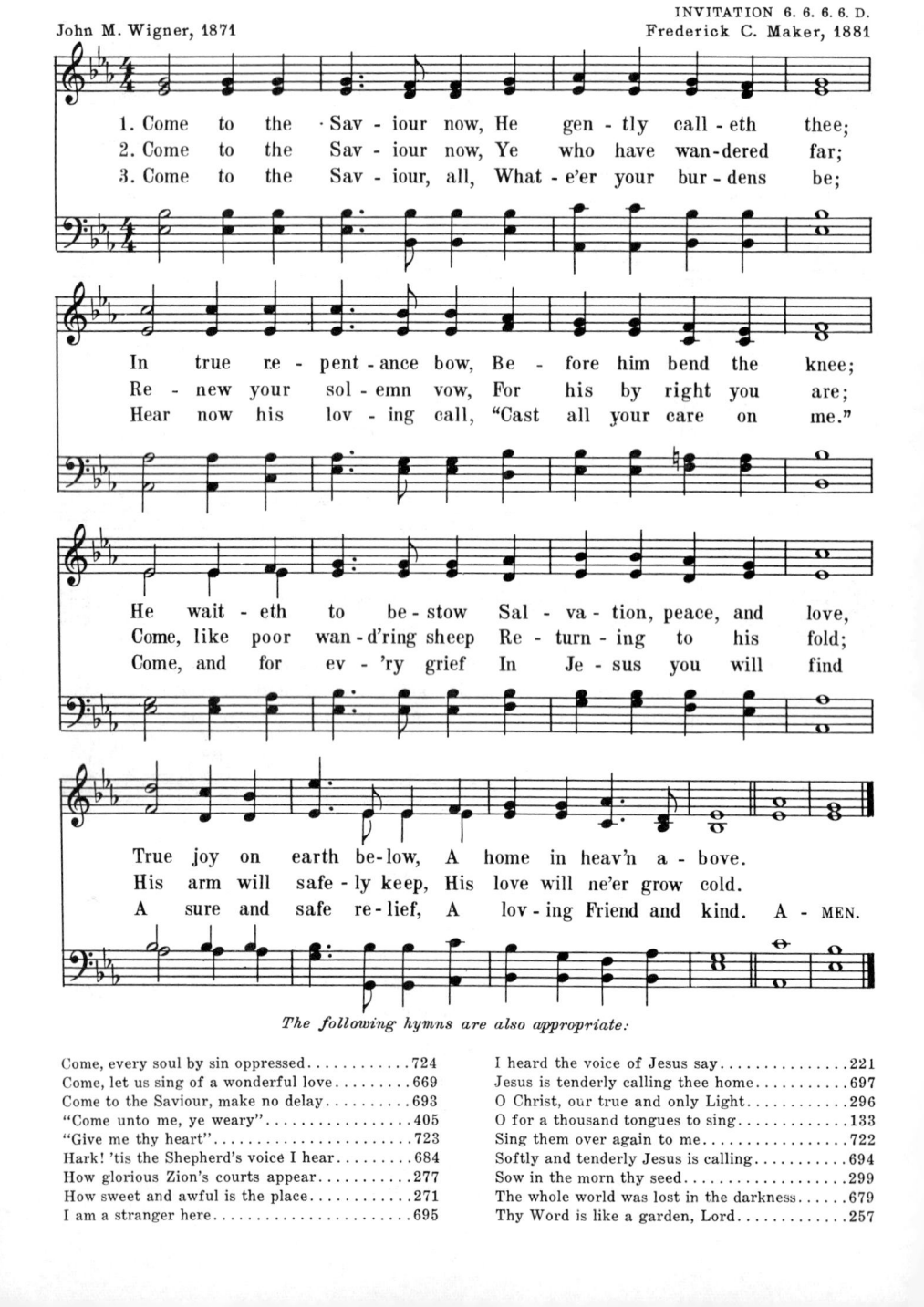

INVITATION 6. 6. 6. 6. D.
John M. Wigner, 1871
Frederick C. Maker, 1881

1. Come to the Saviour now, He gently calleth thee;
In true repentance bow, Before him bend the knee;
He waiteth to bestow Salvation, peace, and love,
True joy on earth below, A home in heav'n above.

2. Come to the Saviour now, Ye who have wandered far;
Renew your solemn vow, For his by right you are;
Come, like poor wan-d'ring sheep Returning to his fold;
His arm will safely keep, His love will ne'er grow cold.

3. Come to the Saviour, all, What-e'er your burdens be;
Hear now his loving call, "Cast all your care on me."
Come, and for ev'ry grief In Jesus you will find
A sure and safe relief, A loving Friend and kind. A-MEN.

*The following hymns are also appropriate:*

| | |
|---|---|
| Come, every soul by sin oppressed............724 | I heard the voice of Jesus say...............221 |
| Come, let us sing of a wonderful love........669 | Jesus is tenderly calling thee home..........697 |
| Come to the Saviour, make no delay..........693 | O Christ, our true and only Light............296 |
| "Come unto me, ye weary"....................405 | O for a thousand tongues to sing.............133 |
| "Give me thy heart".........................723 | Sing them over again to me...................722 |
| Hark! 'tis the Shepherd's voice I hear.........684 | Softly and tenderly Jesus is calling..........694 |
| How glorious Zion's courts appear...........277 | Sow in the morn thy seed....................299 |
| How sweet and awful is the place............271 | The whole world was lost in the darkness......679 |
| I am a stranger here........................695 | Thy Word is like a garden, Lord.............257 |

# THE CHRISTIAN LIFE

396

*All we like sheep have gone astray; we have turned every one to his own way; and the Lord hath laid on him the iniquity of us all.* Isa. 53:6

Horatius Bonar, 1843

LEBANON S. M. D.
John Zundel, 1855

1. I was a wan-d'ring sheep, I did not love the fold;
2. The Shepherd sought his sheep, The Father sought his child;
3. Jesus my Shepherd is; 'Twas he that loved my soul,
4. I was a wan-d'ring sheep, I would not be con-trolled;

I did not love my Shepherd's voice, I would not be con-trolled.
They followed me o'er vale and hill, O'er des-erts waste and wild:
'Twas he that washed me in his blood, 'Twas he that made me whole;
But now I love my Shepherd's voice, I love, I love the fold.

I was a way-ward child, I did not love my home;
They found me nigh to death, Fam-ished and faint and lone;
'Twas he that sought the lost, That found the wan-d'ring sheep,
I was a way-ward child, I once pre-ferred to roam;

I did not love my Father's voice, I loved a-far to roam.
They bound me with the bands of love, They saved the wan-d'ring one.
'Twas he that brought me to the fold, 'Tis he that still doth keep.
But now I love my Father's voice, I love, I love his home. A-MEN.

## 397 (FIRST TUNE) — THE CHRISTIAN LIFE

*We love him, because he first loved us.* I John 4:19

Anon., c. 1904
PEACE 10. 10. 10. 6.
George W. Chadwick, 1893

1. I sought the Lord, and af-ter-ward I knew He moved my soul to seek him, seek-ing me; It was not I that found, O Sav-iour true, No, I was found of thee.
2. Thou didst reach forth thy hand and mine en-fold; I walked and sank not on the storm-vexed sea,— 'Twas not so much that I on thee took hold, As thou, dear Lord, on me.
3. I find, I walk, I love, but, O the whole Of love is but my an-swer, Lord, to thee; For thou wert long be-fore-hand with my soul, Al-ways thou lov-edst me. A-MEN.

## 397 (SECOND TUNE)

Anon., c. 1904
ARTAVIA 10. 10. 10. 6.
Edward J. Hopkins, 1887

1. I sought the Lord, and af-ter-ward I knew He moved my
2. Thou didst reach forth thy hand and mine en-fold; I walked and
3. I find, I walk, I love, but, O the whole Of love is

# SALVATION BY GRACE

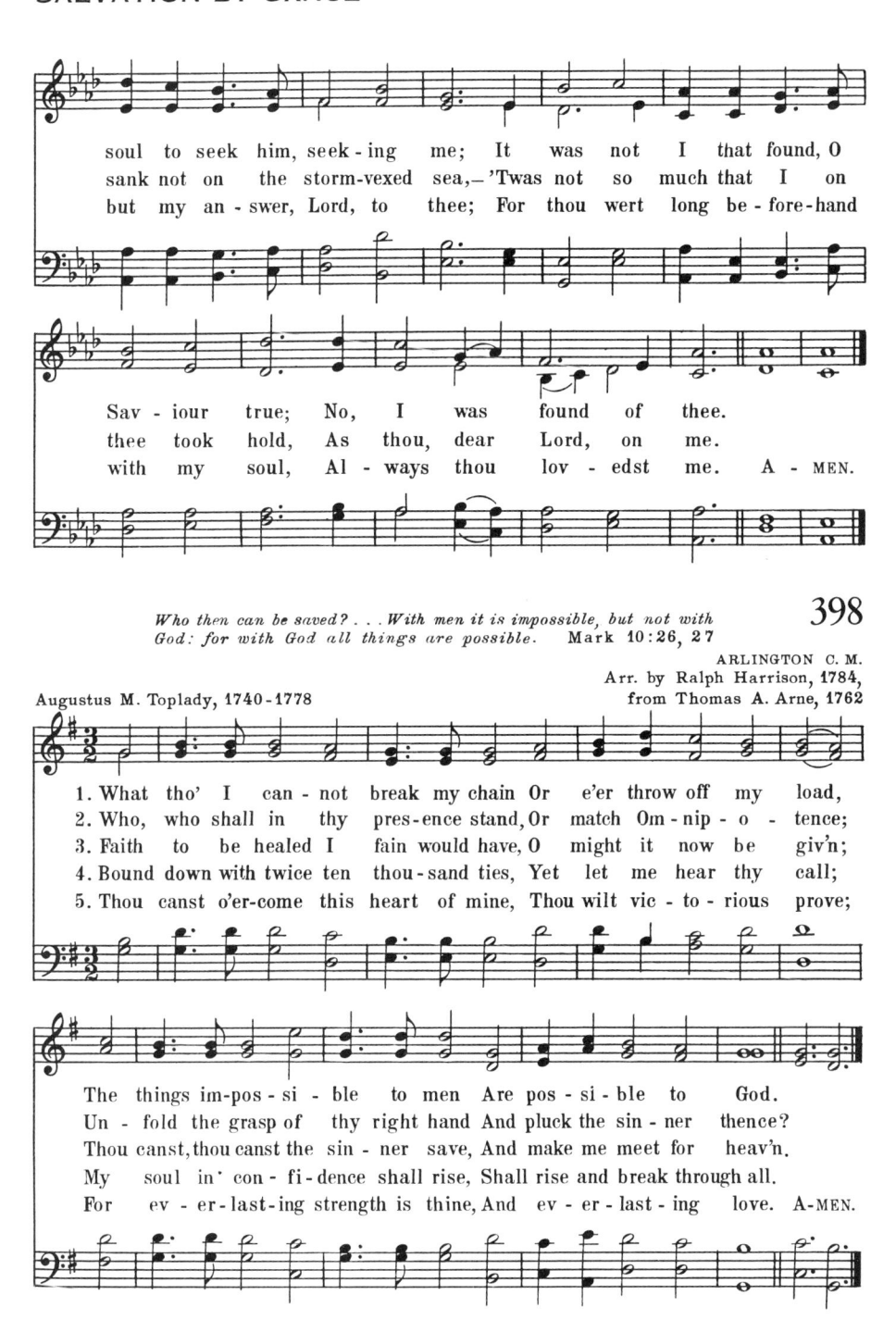

soul to seek him, seek-ing me; It was not I that found, O
sank not on the storm-vexed sea,—'Twas not so much that I on
but my an-swer, Lord, to thee; For thou wert long be-fore-hand

Sav-iour true; No, I was found of thee.
thee took hold, As thou, dear Lord, on me.
with my soul, Al-ways thou lov-edst me. A-MEN.

*Who then can be saved?...With men it is impossible, but not with God: for with God all things are possible.* Mark 10:26, 27

**398**

ARLINGTON C. M.
Arr. by Ralph Harrison, 1784,
from Thomas A. Arne, 1762

Augustus M. Toplady, 1740-1778

1. What tho' I can-not break my chain Or e'er throw off my load,
2. Who, who shall in thy pres-ence stand, Or match Om-nip-o-tence;
3. Faith to be healed I fain would have, O might it now be giv'n;
4. Bound down with twice ten thou-sand ties, Yet let me hear thy call;
5. Thou canst o'er-come this heart of mine, Thou wilt vic-to-rious prove;

The things im-pos-si-ble to men Are pos-si-ble to God.
Un-fold the grasp of thy right hand And pluck the sin-ner thence?
Thou canst, thou canst the sin-ner save, And make me meet for heav'n.
My soul in con-fi-dence shall rise, Shall rise and break through all.
For ev-er-last-ing strength is thine, And ev-er-last-ing love. A-MEN.

# 399 THE CHRISTIAN LIFE

*For by grace are ye saved through faith; and that not of yourselves: it is the gift of God: not of works, lest any man should boast.* Eph. 2:8-9

Christian L. Scheidt, 1742, cento
Tr., composite

AUS GNADEN SOLL ICH SELIG WERDEN
9.8.9.8.8.8.
Justin H. Knecht, 1796

1. By grace I'm saved, grace free and boundless; My soul, believe and doubt it not. Why stagger at this word of promise? Hath Scripture ever falsehood taught? Nay; then this word must true remain: By grace thou, too, shalt heav'n obtain.
2. By grace! None dare lay claim to merit; Our works and conduct have no worth. God in his love sent our Redeemer, Christ Jesus, to this sinful earth; His death did for our sins atone, And we are saved by grace alone.
3. By grace! O, mark this word of promise When thou art by thy sins oppressed, When Satan plagues thy troubled conscience, And when thy heart is seeking rest. What reason cannot comprehend God by his grace to thee doth send.
4. By grace! This ground of faith is certain; So long as God is true, it stands. What saints have penned by inspiration, What in his Word our God commands, What our whole faith must rest upon, Is grace alone, grace in his Son. A-MEN.

# SALVATION BY GRACE 400

*Then Samuel... called the name of it Ebenezer, saying, Hitherto hath the Lord helped us.* I Samuel 7:12

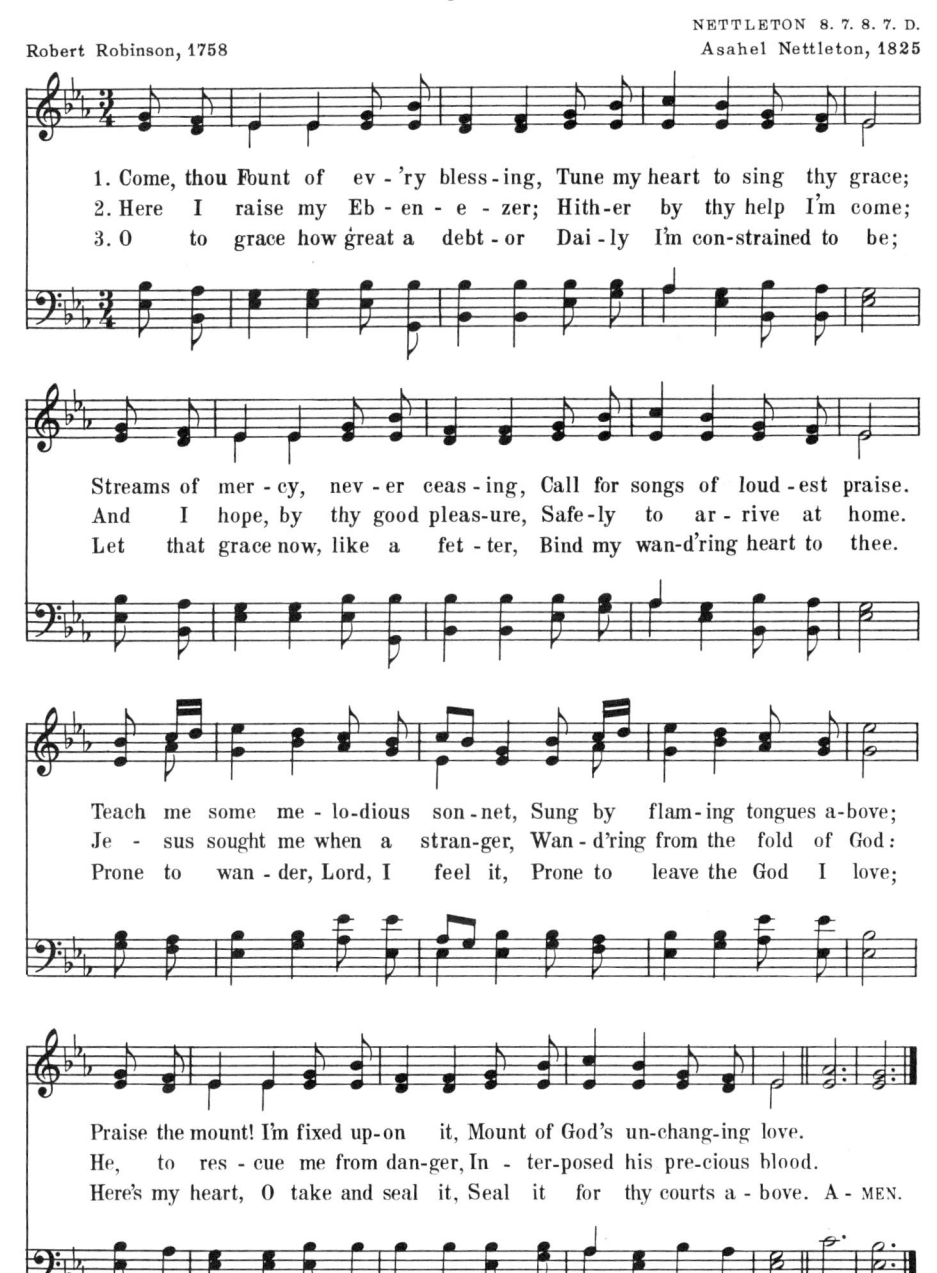

Robert Robinson, 1758

NETTLETON 8. 7. 8. 7. D.
Asahel Nettleton, 1825

1. Come, thou Fount of ev-'ry bless-ing, Tune my heart to sing thy grace;
2. Here I raise my Eb-en-e-zer; Hith-er by thy help I'm come;
3. O to grace how great a debt-or Dai-ly I'm con-strained to be;

Streams of mer-cy, nev-er ceas-ing, Call for songs of loud-est praise.
And I hope, by thy good pleas-ure, Safe-ly to ar-rive at home.
Let that grace now, like a fet-ter, Bind my wan-d'ring heart to thee.

Teach me some me-lo-dious son-net, Sung by flam-ing tongues a-bove;
Je-sus sought me when a stran-ger, Wan-d'ring from the fold of God:
Prone to wan-der, Lord, I feel it, Prone to leave the God I love;

Praise the mount! I'm fixed up-on it, Mount of God's un-chang-ing love.
He, to res-cue me from dan-ger, In-ter-posed his pre-cious blood.
Here's my heart, O take and seal it, Seal it for thy courts a-bove. A-MEN.

## 401 THE CHRISTIAN LIFE

*God ... hath quickened us together with Christ ... that ... he might show the exceeding riches of his grace ... Eph. 2:4-7*

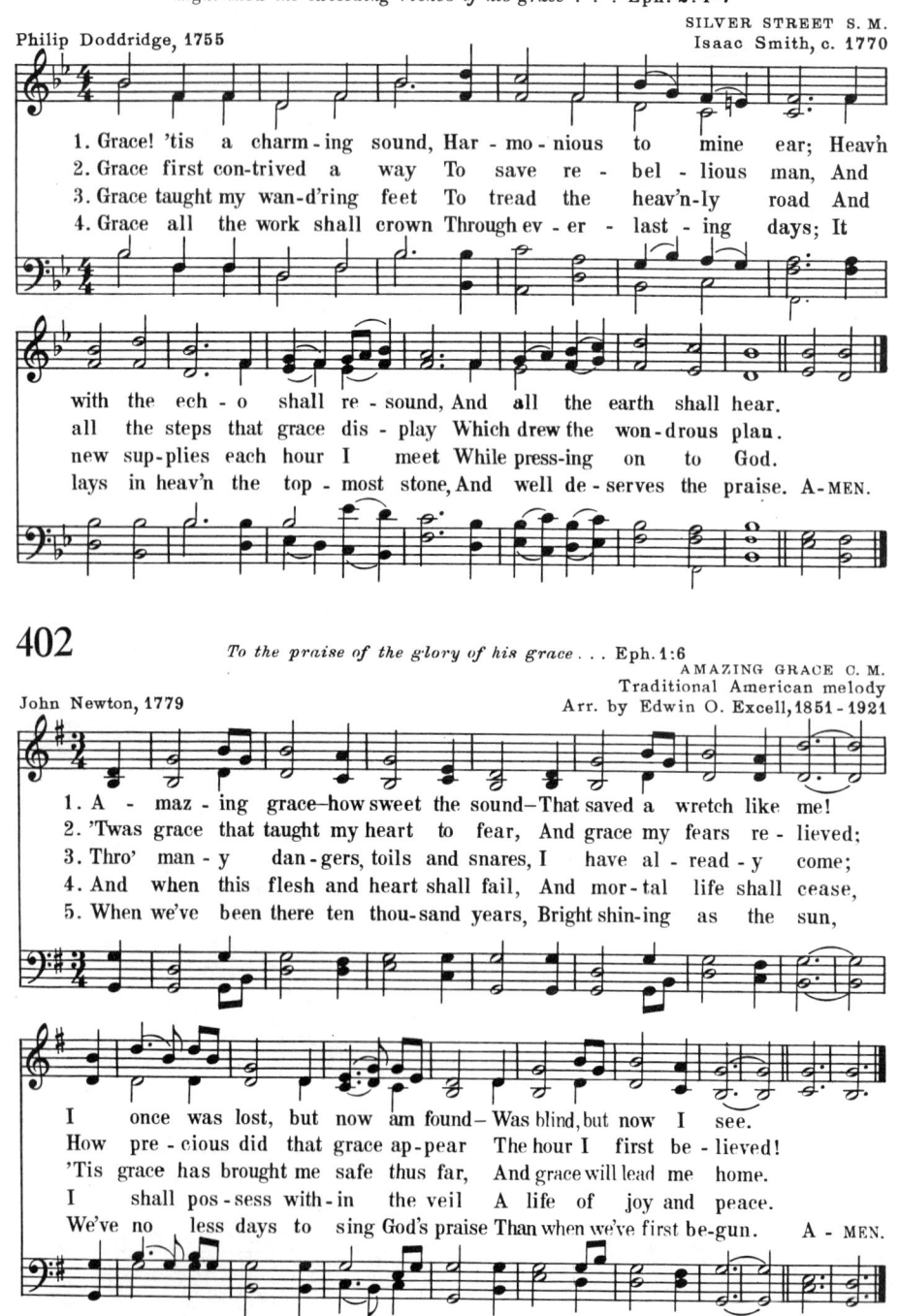

Philip Doddridge, 1755

SILVER STREET S. M.
Isaac Smith, c. 1770

1. Grace! 'tis a charm-ing sound, Har-mo-nious to mine ear; Heav'n with the ech-o shall re-sound, And all the earth shall hear.
2. Grace first con-trived a way To save re-bel-lious man, And all the steps that grace dis-play Which drew the won-drous plan.
3. Grace taught my wan-d'ring feet To tread the heav'n-ly road And new sup-plies each hour I meet While press-ing on to God.
4. Grace all the work shall crown Through ev-er-last-ing days; It lays in heav'n the top-most stone, And well de-serves the praise. A-MEN.

## 402

*To the praise of the glory of his grace ... Eph. 1:6*

John Newton, 1779

AMAZING GRACE C. M.
Traditional American melody
Arr. by Edwin O. Excell, 1851-1921

1. A-maz-ing grace—how sweet the sound—That saved a wretch like me! I once was lost, but now am found—Was blind, but now I see.
2. 'Twas grace that taught my heart to fear, And grace my fears re-lieved; How pre-cious did that grace ap-pear The hour I first be-lieved!
3. Thro' man-y dan-gers, toils and snares, I have al-read-y come; 'Tis grace has brought me safe thus far, And grace will lead me home.
4. And when this flesh and heart shall fail, And mor-tal life shall cease, I shall pos-sess with-in the veil A life of joy and peace.
5. When we've been there ten thou-sand years, Bright shin-ing as the sun, We've no less days to sing God's praise Than when we've first be-gun. A-MEN.

# SALVATION BY GRACE 403

*Not by works of righteousness which we have done, but according to his mercy he saved us ... Titus 3:5*

Horatius Bonar, 1861; alt.

LEOMINSTER S. M. D.
George William Martin, 1862
Har. by Sir Arthur S. Sullivan, 1874

1. Not what my hands have done Can save my guilt-y soul;
   Not what my toil-ing flesh has borne Can make my spir-it whole.
   Not what I feel or do Can give me peace with God;
   Not all my prayers and sighs and tears Can bear my aw-ful load.

2. Thy work a-lone, O Christ, Can ease this weight of sin;
   Thy blood a-lone, O Lamb of God, Can give me peace with-in.
   Thy love to me, O God, Not mine, O Lord, to thee,
   Can rid me of this dark un-rest, And set my spir-it free.

3. Thy grace a-lone, O God, To me can par-don speak;
   Thy pow'r a-lone, O Son of God, Can this sore bond-age break.
   No oth-er work, save thine, No oth-er blood will do;
   No strength, save that which is di-vine, Can bear me safe-ly through.

4. I bless the Christ of God; I rest on love di-vine;
   And with un-fal-t'ring lip and heart, I call this Sav-iour mine.
   His cross dis-pels each doubt; I bur-y in his tomb
   Each thought of un-be-lief and fear, Each lin-g'ring shade of gloom.

5. I praise the God of grace; I trust his truth and might;
   He calls me his, I call him mine, My God, my joy, my light.
   'Tis he who sav-eth me, And free-ly par-don gives;
   I love be-cause he lov-eth me, I live be-cause he lives. A-MEN.

404                          THE CHRISTIAN LIFE

*And Saul, yet breathing out threatenings and slaughter against the disciples of the Lord... Acts 9:1*

John Ellerton, 1871                MUNICH 7. 6. 7. 6. D.
                                 Meiningen *Gesangbuch*, 1693

1. We sing the glorious conquest Before Damascus gate,
   When Saul, the church's spoiler, Came breathing threats and hate;
   The rav'ning wolf rushed forward Full early to the prey;
   But lo! the Shepherd met him, And bound him fast today.

2. O glory most excelling That smote across his path!
   O light that pierced and blinded The zealot in his wrath!
   O voice that spake unto him The calm, reproving word!
   O love that sought and held him The bond-man of his Lord!

3. O Wisdom or-d'ring all things In order strong and sweet,
   What nobler spoil was ever Cast at the victor's feet?
   What wiser master-builder E'er wrought at thine employ
   Than he, till now so furious Thy building to destroy?

4. Lord, teach thy church the lesson, Still in her darkest hour
   Of weakness and of danger, To trust thy hidden pow'r:
   Thy grace by ways mysterious The wrath of man can bind,
   And in thy boldest foeman Thy chosen saint can find. A-MEN.

St. 2, line 5, alt.

# CALLING 405

*Come unto me, all ye that labour and are heavy laden, and I will give you rest.* Matt. 11:28

William C. Dix, 1867

LLANGLOFFAN 7. 6. 7. 6. D.
Welsh hymn melody

1. "Come un-to me, ye wea-ry, And I will give you rest."
2. "Come un-to me, dear chil-dren, And I will give you light."
3. "Come un-to me, ye faint-ing, And I will give you life."
4. "And who-so-ev-er com-eth I will not cast him out."

O bless-ed voice of Je-sus Which comes to hearts op-pressed!
O lov-ing voice of Je-sus Which comes to cheer the night!
O peace-ful voice of Je-sus Which comes to end our strife!
O pa-tient love of Je-sus Which drives a-way our doubt;

It tells of ben-e-dic-tion, Of par-don, grace, and peace,
Our hearts were filled with sad-ness, And we had lost our way;
The foe is stern and ea-ger, The fight is fierce and long;
Which calls us, ver-y sin-ners, Un-wor-thy though we be

Of joy that hath no end-ing, Of love which can-not cease.
But morn-ing brings us glad-ness, And songs the break of day.
But thou hast made us might-y, And strong-er than the strong.
Of love so free and bound-less, To come, dear Lord, to thee! A-MEN.

## 406 THE CHRISTIAN LIFE: CALLING

*I came not to call the righteous, but sinners to repentance.* Mark 2:17

WELCOME VOICE S. M. with refrain

Lewis Hartsough, 1872  
Lewis Hartsough, 1872

1. I hear thy wel-come voice That calls me, Lord, to thee For cleans-ing in thy pre-cious blood That flowed on Cal-va-ry.
2. Though com-ing weak and vile, Thou dost my strength as-sure; Thou dost my vile-ness full-y cleanse, Till spot-less all and pure.
3. 'Tis Je-sus calls me on To per-fect faith and love, To per-fect hope, and peace, and trust, For earth and heav'n a-bove.
4. 'Tis Je-sus who con-firms The bless-ed work with-in, By add-ing grace to wel-comed grace, Where reigned the pow'r of sin.
5. And he the wit-ness gives To loy-al hearts and free, That ev-'ry prom-ise is ful-filled, If faith but brings the plea.

REFRAIN

I am com-ing, Lord; Com-ing now to thee: Wash me, cleanse me, in the blood That flowed on Cal-va-ry. A-MEN.

# THE CHRISTIAN LIFE: REPENTANCE

## 407

*And the publican...smote upon his breast, saying, God be merciful to me a sinner.* Luke 18:13

Thomas Raffles, 1831

AVONDALE C. M.
Charles H. Gabriel, 1856-1932

1. Lord, like the pub-li-can I stand, And lift my heart to thee;
2. I smite up-on my anx-ious breast, O'er-whelmed with ag-o-ny;
3. My guilt, my shame, I all con-fess: I have no hope nor plea
4. Here at thy cross I still would wait, Nor from its shel-ter flee,

Thy par-d'ning grace, O God, com-mand, Be mer-ci-ful to me.
O save my soul by sin op-pressed, Be mer-ci-ful to me.
But Je-sus' blood and right-eous-ness: Be mer-ci-ful to me.
Till thou, O God, in mer-cy great, Art mer-ci-ful to me. A-MEN.

## 408

*O Lord, rebuke me not in thy wrath: neither chasten me in thy hot displeasure.* Psalm 38:1

From PSALM 38
The Psalter, 1912

ALICE 8. 7. 8. 7.
Robert Roberts, b. 1863

1. In thy wrath and hot dis-pleas-ure, Chas-ten not thy serv-ant, Lord;
2. Heav-y is my trib-u-la-tion, Sore my pun-ish-ment has been;
3. With my bur-den of trans-gres-sion Heav-y la-den, o-ver-borne;
4. Weak and wound-ed, I im-plore thee; Lord, to me thy mer-cy show;
5. Dark-ness gath-ers, foes as-sail me, But I an-swer not a word;

Let thy mer-cy, with-out meas-ure, Help and peace to me af-ford.
Bro-ken by thine in-dig-na-tion, I am trou-bled by my sin.
Hum-bled low I make con-fes-sion, For my fol-ly now I mourn.
All my pray'r is now be-fore thee, All my trou-ble thou dost know.
All my friends de-sert and fail me, On-ly thou my cry hast heard. A-MEN.

Music used by permission.

6. Lord, in thee am I confiding;
Thou wilt answer when I call,
Lest my foes, the good deriding,
Triumph in thy servant's fall.

7. Lord, my God, do not forsake me,
Let me know that thou art near,
Under thy protection take me,
As my Saviour now appear.

# 409 THE CHRISTIAN LIFE

*I said, Lord, be merciful unto me: heal my soul; for I have sinned against thee.* Psalm 41:4

Magnus B. Landstad, 1861
Tr. by Carl Döving, 1909

THE LORD'S PRAYER (VATER UNSER) 8.8.8.8.8.8.
Schumann's *Gesangbuch*, 1539

1. Be-fore thee, God, who know-est all, With grief and shame I pros-trate fall. I see my sins a-gainst thee, Lord, The sins of thought, of deed, and word. They press me sore; I cry to thee: O God, be mer-ci-ful to me!

2. O Lord, my God, to thee I pray: O cast me not in wrath a-way! Let thy good Spir-it ne'er de-part, But let him draw to thee my heart That tru-ly pen-i-tent I be: O God, be mer-ci-ful to me!

3. O Je-sus, let thy pre-cious blood Be to my soul a cleans-ing flood. Turn not, O Lord, thy guest a-way, But grant that jus-ti-fied I may Go to my house at peace with thee: O God, be mer-ci-ful to me! A-MEN.

Words reprinted from *The Lutheran Hymnary* by permission of the Augsburg Publishing House.

# REPENTANCE 410

*I have gone astray like a lost sheep; seek thy servant...* Psalm 119:176

VESPER HYMN 8. 7. 8. 7. D.
Arr. by Sir John A. Stevenson
from Dimitri Bortniansky, 1818

Ray Palmer, 1864

1. Take me, O my Father, take me; Take me, save me, through thy Son;
That which thou wouldst have me, make me, Let thy will in me be done.
Long from thee my foot-steps stray-ing, Thorn-y proved the way I trod;
Wea-ry come I now, and pray-ing, Take me to thy love, my God.

2. Fruit-less years with grief re-call-ing, Hum-bly I con-fess my sin;
At thy feet, O Fa-ther, fall-ing, To thy house-hold take me in.
Free-ly now to thee I prof-fer This re-lent-ing heart of mine;
Free-ly life and soul I of-fer, Gift un-worth-y love like thine.

3. Once the world's Re-deem-er, dy-ing, Bore our sins up-on the tree;
On that sac-ri-fice re-ly-ing, Now I look in hope to thee:
Fa-ther, take me; all for-giv-ing, Fold me to thy lov-ing breast;
In thy love for ev-er liv-ing I must be for ev-er blest. A-MEN.

## 411                                                                 THE CHRISTIAN LIFE

*If we confess our sins, he is faithful and just to forgive us our sins, and to cleanse us from all unrighteousness.* I John 1:9

KEDRON 6. 4. 6. 4. 6. 6. 4.

Horatius Bonar, 1866                                                           Ann B. Spratt, 1866

1. No, not despairingly Come I to thee; No, not distrustingly Bend I the knee: Sin hath gone over me, Yet is this still my plea, Jesus hath died.
2. Lord, I confess to thee Sadly my sin; All I am tell I thee, All I have been: Purge thou my sin away, Wash thou my soul this day; Lord, make me clean.
3. Faithful and just art thou, Forgiving all; Loving and kind art thou When poor ones call: Lord, let the cleansing blood, Blood of the Lamb of God, Pass o'er my soul.
4. Then all is peace and light This soul within; Thus shall I walk with thee, The loved Unseen; Leaning on thee, my God, Guided along the road, Nothing between. A-MEN.

## 412

*Thou art a God ready to pardon, gracious and merciful, slow to anger, and of great kindness...* Neh. 9:17

SOUTHWELL S. M.

Sir Henry W. Baker, 1868                                             William Daman, 1579

1. Out of the deep I call To thee, O Lord, to thee.
2. Out of the deep I cry, The woeful deep of sin,
3. Out of the deep of fear And dread of coming shame;
4. Lord, there is mercy now, As ever was, with thee.

## REPENTANCE

Before thy throne of grace I fall; Be merciful to me.
Of evil done in days gone by, Of evil now within;
All night till morning watch is near I plead the precious Name.
Before thy throne of grace I bow; Be merciful to me. A-MEN.

*Create in me a clean heart, O God; and renew a right spirit within me.* Psalm 51:10

From PSALM 51     HAMBURG L. M.
Isaac Watts, 1719     Arr. from a Gregorian chant by Lowell Mason, 1824

413

1. O thou that hear'st when sinners cry, Though all my crimes before thee lie, Behold them not with angry look, But blot their mem'ry from thy book.
2. Create my nature pure within, And form my soul averse to sin; Let thy good Spirit ne'er depart, Nor hide thy presence from my heart.
3. I cannot live without thy light, Cast out and banished from thy sight; Thy holy joys, my God, restore, And guard me, that I fall no more.
4. A broken heart, my God, my King, Is all the sacrifice I bring; The God of grace will ne'er despise A broken heart for sacrifice.
5. My soul lies humbled in the dust, And owns thy dreadful sentence just: Look down, O Lord, with pitying eye, And save the soul condemned to die.
6. Then will I teach the world thy ways; Sinners shall learn thy sovereign grace; I'll lead them to my Saviour's blood, And they shall praise a pard'ning God. A-MEN.

# 414 THE CHRISTIAN LIFE

*And unto...the church of the Laodiceans write...Behold, I stand at the door, and knock: if any man hear my voice, and open the door, I will come in to him, and will sup with him, and he with me.* Rev. 3:14, 20

ST. EDITH 7. 6. 7. 6. D.
Justin H. Knecht, 1799, and
Edward Husband, 1871

William Walsham How, 1867

1. O Jesus, thou art standing Outside the fast-closed door,
   In lowly patience waiting To pass the threshold o'er:
   Shame on us, Christian brothers, His Name and sign who bear,
   O shame, thrice shame upon us, To keep him standing there!

2. O Jesus, thou art knocking; And lo, that hand is scarred,
   And thorns thy brow encircle, And tears thy face have marred:
   O love that passeth knowledge, So patiently to wait!
   O sin that hath no equal, So fast to bar the gate!

3. O Jesus, thou art pleading In accents meek and low,
   "I died for you, My children, And will ye treat Me so?"
   O Lord, with shame and sorrow We open now the door;
   Dear Saviour, enter, enter, And leave us nevermore. A-MEN.

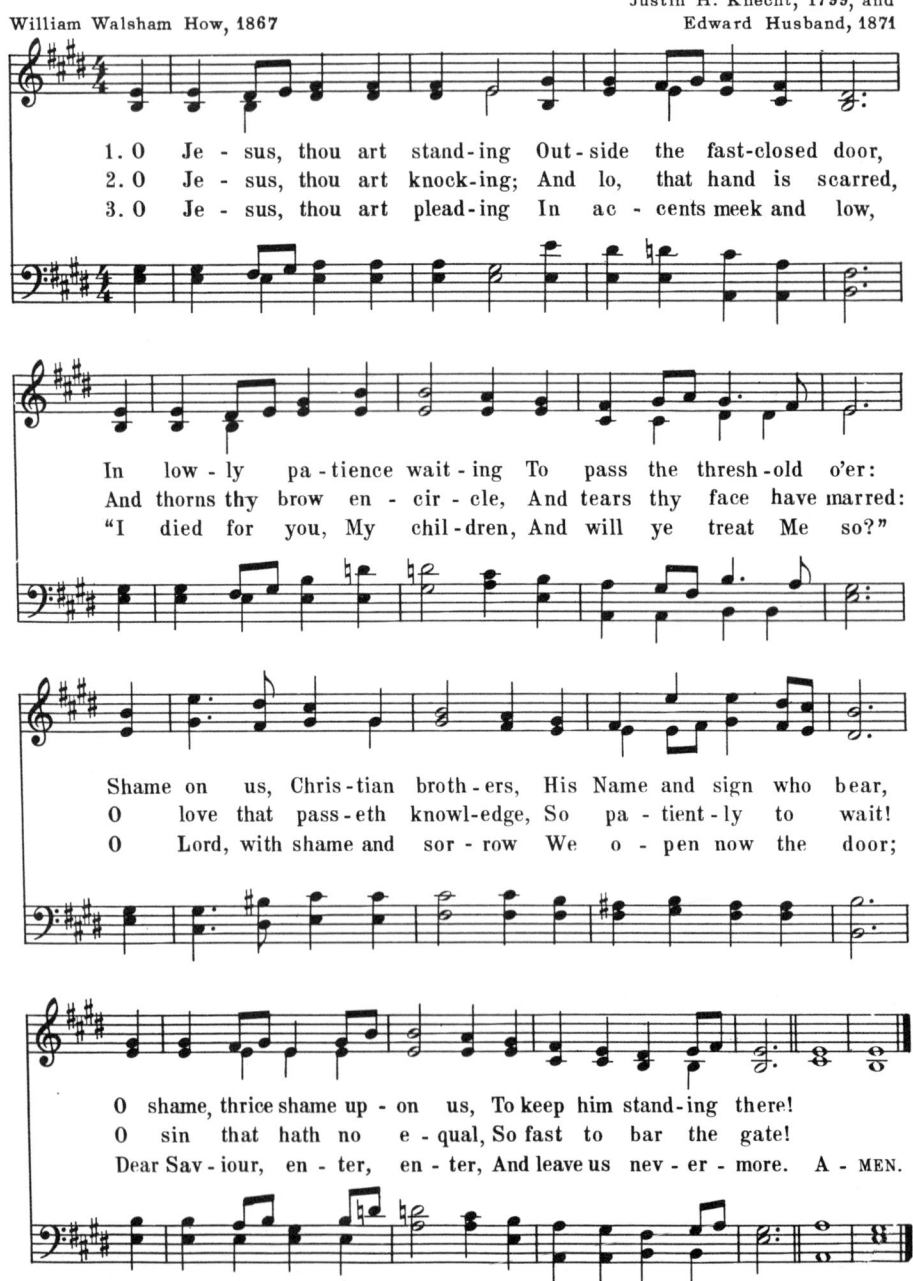

# REPENTANCE 415

*Have mercy upon me, O God, according to thy lovingkindness... Psalm 51:1*

From PSALM 51:1-15　　　　　　　　　AJALON (REDHEAD No. 76) 7. 7. 7. 7. 7. 7.
*The Psalter,* 1912　　　　　　　　　　　　　　　Richard Redhead, 1853

1. God, be mer-ci-ful to me, On thy grace I rest my plea;
2. My trans-gres-sions I con-fess, Grief and guilt my soul op-press;
3. I am e-vil, born in sin; Thou de-sir-est truth with-in.
4. Bro-ken, hum-bled to the dust By thy wrath and judg-ment just,

Plen-teous in com-pas-sion thou, Blot out my trans-gres-sions now;
I have sinned a-gainst thy grace And pro-voked thee to thy face;
Thou a-lone my Sav-iour art, Teach thy wis-dom to my heart;
Let my con-trite heart re-joice And in glad-ness hear thy voice;

Wash me, make me pure with-in, Cleanse, O cleanse me from my sin.
I con-fess thy judg-ment just, Speech-less, I thy mer-cy trust.
Make me pure, thy grace be-stow, Wash me whit-er than the snow.
From my sins O hide thy face, Blot them out in bound-less grace. A-MEN.

5. Gracious God, my heart renew,
Make my spirit right and true;
Cast me not away from thee,
Let thy Spirit dwell in me;
Thy salvation's joy impart,
Stedfast make my willing heart.

6. Sinners then shall learn from me
And return, O God, to thee;
Saviour, all my guilt remove,
And my tongue shall sing thy love;
Touch my silent lips, O Lord,
And my mouth shall praise accord.

## 416 THE CHRISTIAN LIFE

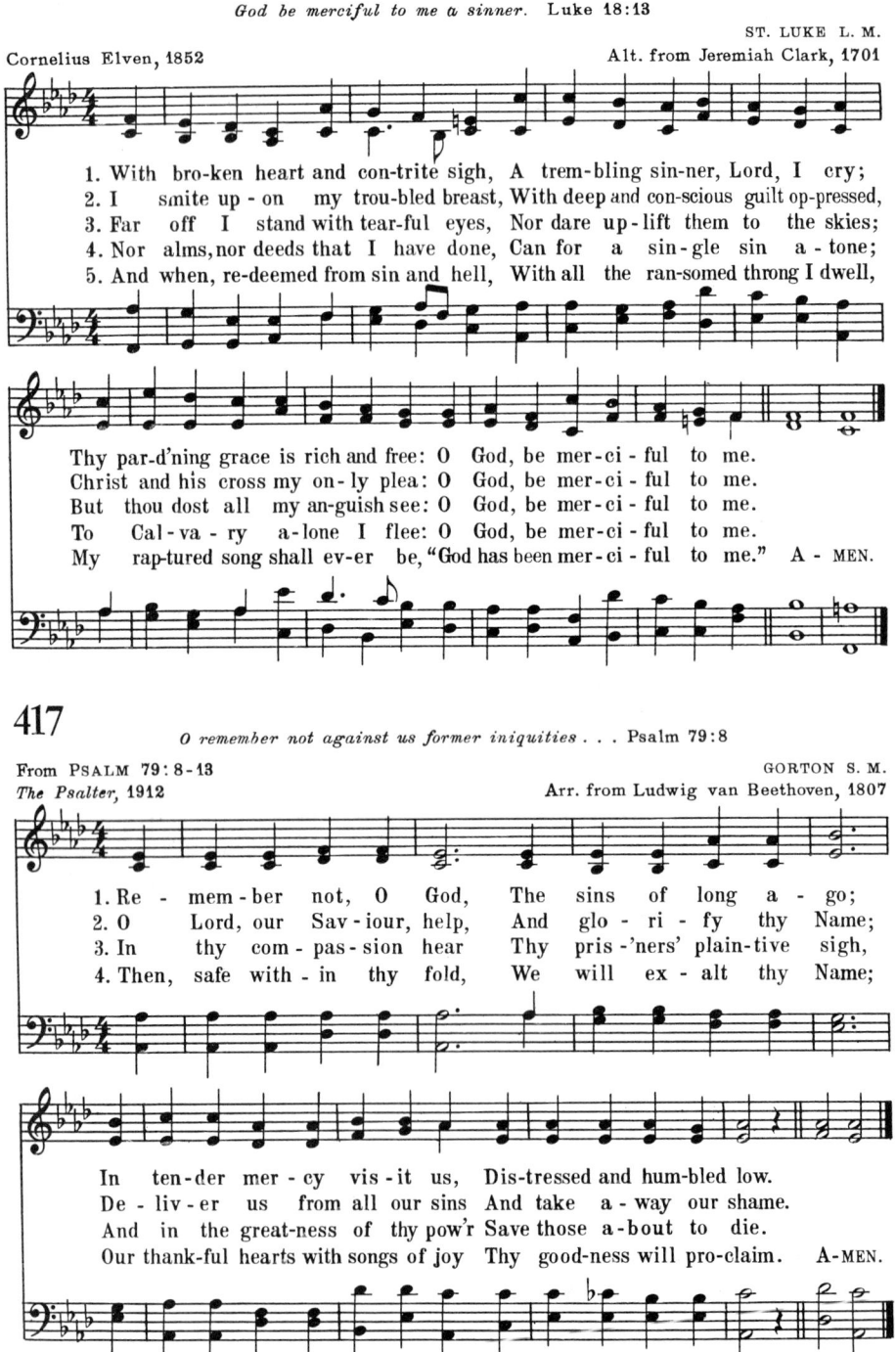

*God be merciful to me a sinner.* Luke 18:13

Cornelius Elven, 1852

ST. LUKE L. M.
Alt. from Jeremiah Clark, 1701

1. With broken heart and contrite sigh, A trembling sinner, Lord, I cry;
2. I smite upon my troubled breast, With deep and conscious guilt oppressed,
3. Far off I stand with tearful eyes, Nor dare uplift them to the skies.
4. Nor alms, nor deeds that I have done, Can for a single sin atone;
5. And when, redeemed from sin and hell, With all the ransomed throng I dwell,

Thy pard'ning grace is rich and free: O God, be merciful to me.
Christ and his cross my only plea: O God, be merciful to me.
But thou dost all my anguish see: O God, be merciful to me.
To Calvary alone I flee: O God, be merciful to me.
My raptured song shall ever be, "God has been merciful to me." A-MEN.

## 417

*O remember not against us former iniquities . . .* Psalm 79:8

From PSALM 79:8-13
The Psalter, 1912

GORTON S. M.
Arr. from Ludwig van Beethoven, 1807

1. Remember not, O God, The sins of long ago;
2. O Lord, our Saviour, help, And glorify thy Name;
3. In thy compassion hear Thy pris'ners' plaintive sigh,
4. Then, safe within thy fold, We will exalt thy Name;

In tender mercy visit us, Distressed and humbled low.
Deliver us from all our sins And take away our shame.
And in the greatness of thy pow'r Save those about to die.
Our thankful hearts with songs of joy Thy goodness will proclaim. A-MEN.

# REPENTANCE 418

*We have dealt very corruptly against thee, and have not kept the commandments... which thou commandedst thy servant Moses.* Neh. 1: 7

Thomas Benson Pollock, 1889

ST. CHRYSOSTOM 8. 8. 8. 8. 8. 8.
Sir Joseph Barnby, 1872

1. We have not known thee as we ought, Nor learned thy wisdom, grace, and pow'r; The things of earth have filled our thought, And trifles of the passing hour. Lord, give us light thy truth to see, And make us wise in knowing thee.

2. We have not feared thee as we ought, Nor bowed beneath thine awful eye, Nor guarded deed, and word, and thought, Remembering that God was nigh. Lord, give us faith to know thee near, And grant the grace of holy fear.

3. We have not loved thee as we ought, Nor cared that we are loved by thee; Thy presence we have coldly sought, And feebly longed thy face to see. Lord, give a pure and loving heart To feel and own the love thou art.

4. We have not served thee as we ought; Alas! the duties left undone, The work with little fervor wrought, The battles lost, or scarcely won! Lord, give the zeal, and give the might, For thee to toil, for thee to fight.

5. When shall we know thee as we ought, And fear, and love, and serve aright! When shall we, out of trial brought, Be perfect in the land of light! Lord, may we day by day prepare To see thy face, and serve thee there. A-MEN.

# 419 THE CHRISTIAN LIFE

*Lord, to whom shall we go? thou hast the words of eternal life.* John 6:68

MEIRIONYDD 7. 6. 7. 6. D.
Welsh hymn melody
Frederick Whitfield, 1855
Ascribed to William Lloyd, 1840

1. I need thee, precious Jesus, For I am full of sin;
   My soul is dark and guilty, My heart is dead within.
   I need the cleansing fountain Where I can always flee,
   The blood of Christ most precious, The sinner's perfect plea.

2. I need thee, precious Jesus, For I am very poor;
   A stranger and a pilgrim, I have no earthly store.
   I need the love of Jesus To cheer me on my way,
   To guide my doubting footsteps, To be my strength and stay.

3. I need thee, precious Jesus, And hope to see thee soon,
   Encircled with the rainbow And seated on thy throne.
   There, with thy blood-bought children, My joy shall ever be,
   To sing my Jesus' praises, To gaze, O Lord, on thee. A-MEN.

Music used by permission of the Executors of the late Dr. Basil Harwood.

# FAITH IN CHRIST 420

*In God is my salvation and my glory: the rock of my strength, and my refuge, is in God.* **Psalm 62:7**

Herbert Booth

BRYN CALFARIA 8.7.8.7.4.4.4.7.7.
William Owen, 1814-1893

1. Bless-ed Lord, in thee is ref-uge, Safe-ty for my trem-bling soul;
Pow'r to lift my head when droop-ing 'Midst the an-gry bil-lows' roll.
I will trust thee, I will trust thee, I will trust thee;
All my life thou shalt con-trol; All my life thou shalt con-trol.

2. In the past, too, un-be-liev-ing, 'Midst the tem-pest I have been,
And my heart has slow-ly trust-ed What my eyes have nev-er seen.
Bless-ed Je-sus, Bless-ed Je-sus, Bless-ed Je-sus,
Teach me on thine arm to lean; Teach me on thine arm to lean.

3. O, for trust that brings the tri-umph When de-feat seems strange-ly near;
O, for faith that chang-es fight-ing In-to vic-t'ry's ring-ing cheer!
Faith tri-um-phant, Faith tri-um-phant, Faith tri-um-phant,
Know-ing not de-feat nor fear; Know-ing not de-feat nor fear. A-MEN.

**421** (FIRST TUNE)          THE CHRISTIAN LIFE

*And that Rock was Christ.*   I Cor. 10:4

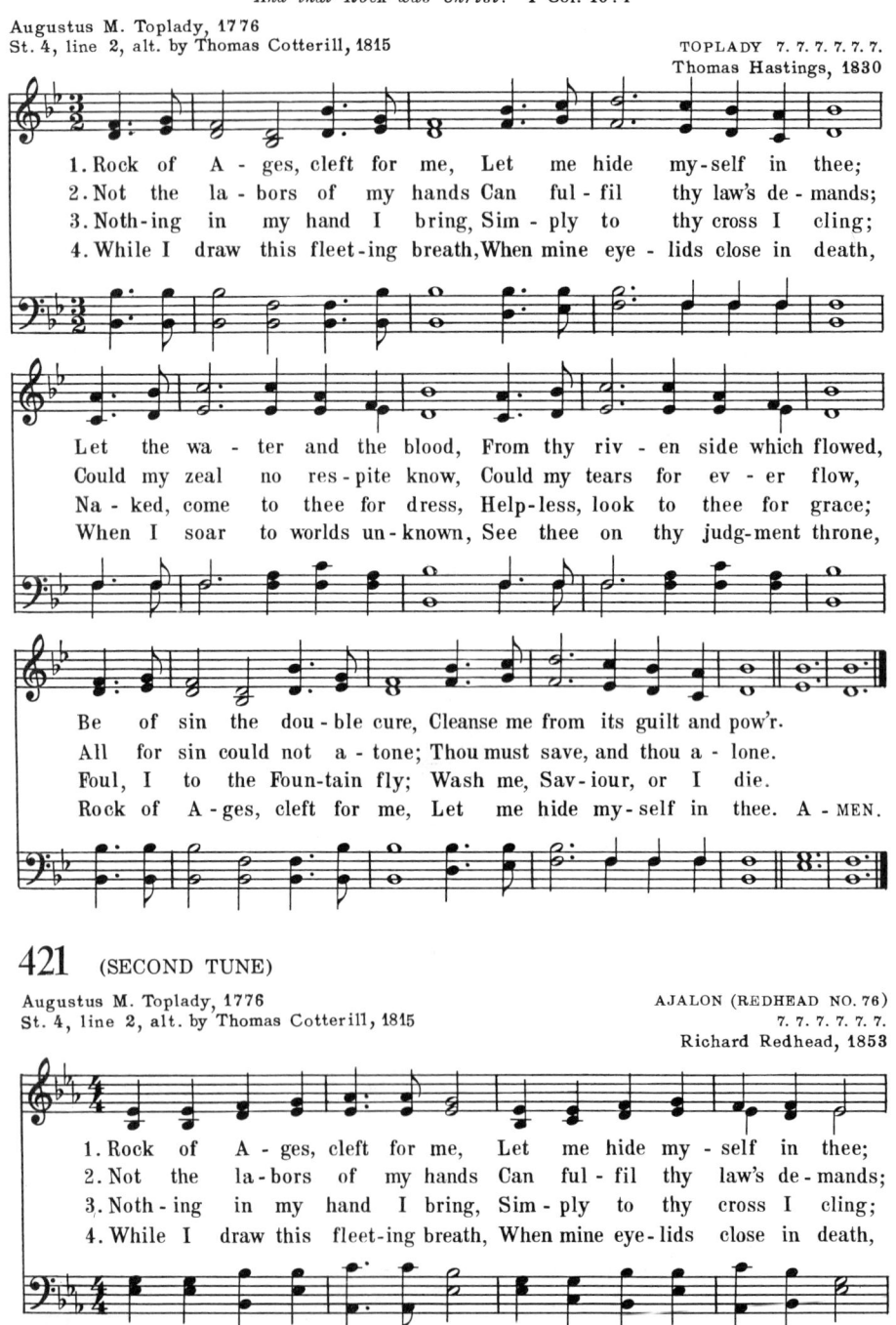

Augustus M. Toplady, 1776
St. 4, line 2, alt. by Thomas Cotterill, 1815

TOPLADY 7. 7. 7. 7. 7. 7.
Thomas Hastings, 1830

1. Rock of A - ges, cleft for me, Let me hide my-self in thee;
2. Not the la - bors of my hands Can ful - fil thy law's de - mands;
3. Noth-ing in my hand I bring, Sim - ply to thy cross I cling;
4. While I draw this fleet-ing breath, When mine eye - lids close in death,

Let the wa - ter and the blood, From thy riv - en side which flowed,
Could my zeal no res - pite know, Could my tears for ev - er flow,
Na - ked, come to thee for dress, Help-less, look to thee for grace;
When I soar to worlds un - known, See thee on thy judg-ment throne,

Be of sin the dou - ble cure, Cleanse me from its guilt and pow'r.
All for sin could not a - tone; Thou must save, and thou a - lone.
Foul, I to the Foun-tain fly; Wash me, Sav - iour, or I die.
Rock of A - ges, cleft for me, Let me hide my - self in thee. A - MEN.

**421** (SECOND TUNE)

Augustus M. Toplady, 1776
St. 4, line 2, alt. by Thomas Cotterill, 1815

AJALON (REDHEAD NO. 76)
7. 7. 7. 7. 7. 7.
Richard Redhead, 1853

1. Rock of A - ges, cleft for me, Let me hide my - self in thee;
2. Not the la - bors of my hands Can ful - fil thy law's de - mands;
3. Noth - ing in my hand I bring, Sim - ply to thy cross I cling;
4. While I draw this fleet-ing breath, When mine eye - lids close in death,

# FAITH IN CHRIST

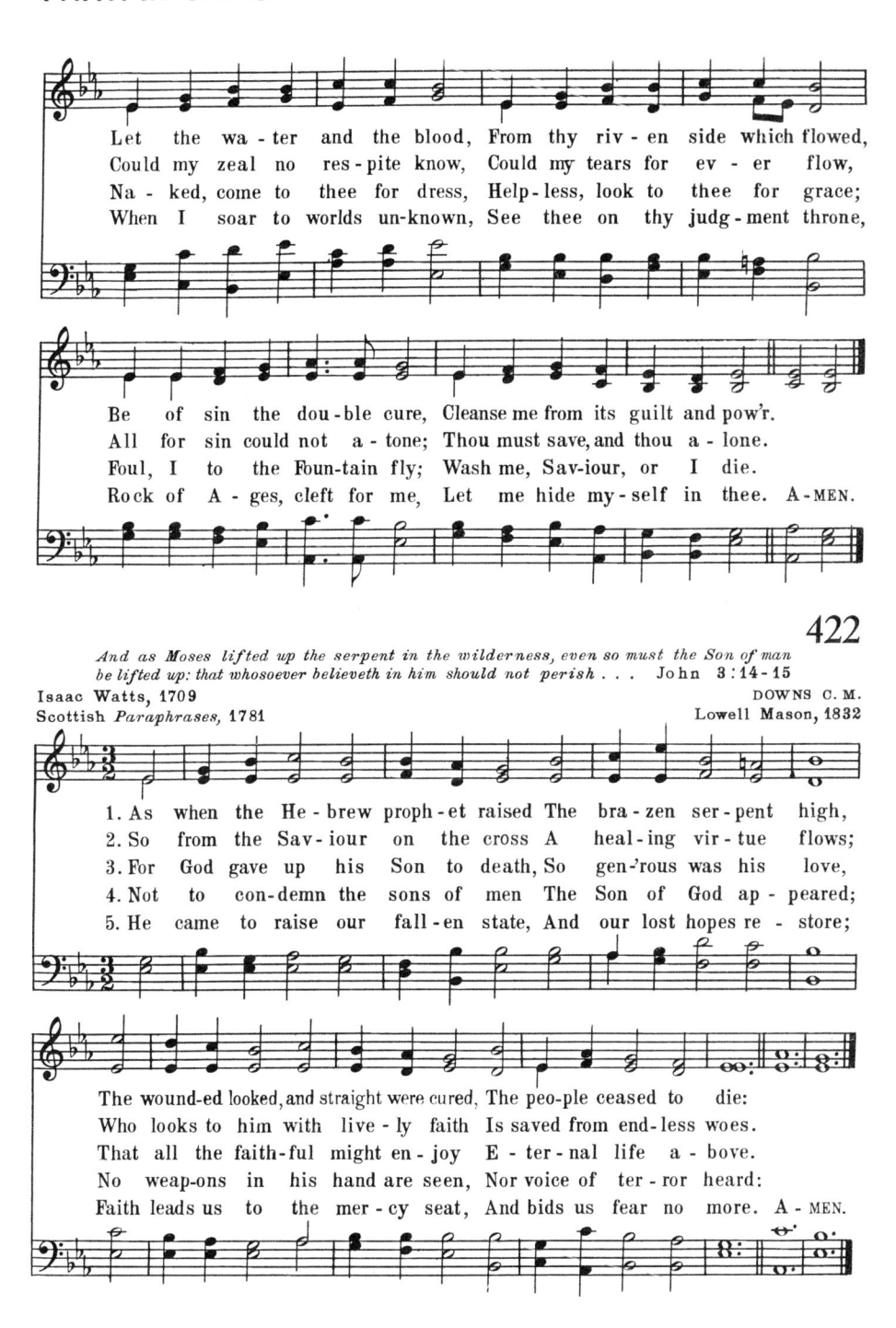

Let the wa-ter and the blood, From thy riv-en side which flowed,
Could my zeal no res-pite know, Could my tears for ev-er flow,
Na-ked, come to thee for dress, Help-less, look to thee for grace;
When I soar to worlds un-known, See thee on thy judg-ment throne,

Be of sin the dou-ble cure, Cleanse me from its guilt and pow'r.
All for sin could not a-tone; Thou must save, and thou a-lone.
Foul, I to the Foun-tain fly; Wash me, Sav-iour, or I die.
Rock of A-ges, cleft for me, Let me hide my-self in thee. A-MEN.

422

*And as Moses lifted up the serpent in the wilderness, even so must the Son of man be lifted up: that whosoever believeth in him should not perish* ... John 3:14-15

Isaac Watts, 1709  
Scottish *Paraphrases*, 1781  

DOWNS C. M.  
Lowell Mason, 1832

1. As when the He-brew proph-et raised The bra-zen ser-pent high,
2. So from the Sav-iour on the cross A heal-ing vir-tue flows;
3. For God gave up his Son to death, So gen-'rous was his love,
4. Not to con-demn the sons of men The Son of God ap-peared;
5. He came to raise our fall-en state, And our lost hopes re-store;

The wound-ed looked, and straight were cured, The peo-ple ceased to die:
Who looks to him with live-ly faith Is saved from end-less woes.
That all the faith-ful might en-joy E-ter-nal life a-bove.
No weap-ons in his hand are seen, Nor voice of ter-ror heard;
Faith leads us to the mer-cy seat, And bids us fear no more. A-MEN.

## 423 THE CHRISTIAN LIFE

*Seeing then that we have a great high priest. Let us therefore come boldly unto the throne of grace... Heb. 4:14,16*

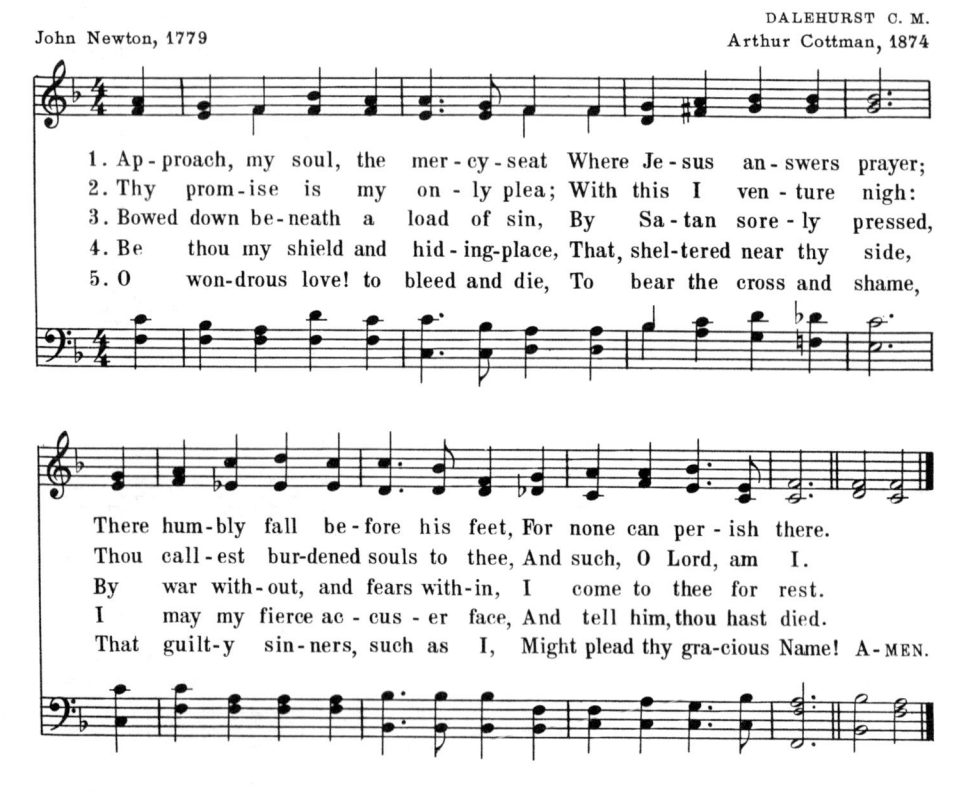

John Newton, 1779

DALEHURST C. M.
Arthur Cottman, 1874

1. Ap-proach, my soul, the mer-cy-seat Where Je-sus an-swers prayer;
2. Thy prom-ise is my on-ly plea; With this I ven-ture nigh:
3. Bowed down be-neath a load of sin, By Sa-tan sore-ly pressed,
4. Be thou my shield and hid-ing-place, That, shel-tered near thy side,
5. O won-drous love! to bleed and die, To bear the cross and shame,

There hum-bly fall be-fore his feet, For none can per-ish there.
Thou call-est bur-dened souls to thee, And such, O Lord, am I.
By war with-out, and fears with-in, I come to thee for rest.
I may my fierce ac-cus-er face, And tell him, thou hast died.
That guilt-y sin-ners, such as I, Might plead thy gra-cious Name! A-MEN.

## 424

*I know whom I have believed, and am persuaded that he is able to keep that which I have committed unto him against that day. II Tim. 1:12*

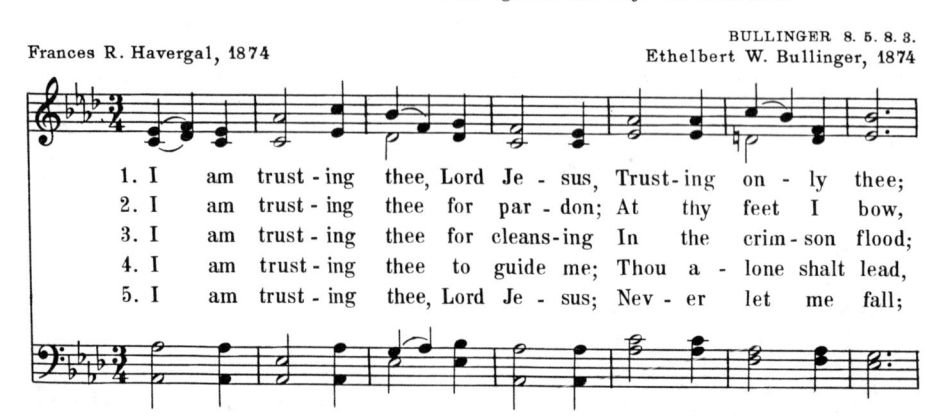

Frances R. Havergal, 1874

BULLINGER 8. 5. 8. 3.
Ethelbert W. Bullinger, 1874

1. I am trust-ing thee, Lord Je-sus, Trust-ing on-ly thee;
2. I am trust-ing thee for par-don; At thy feet I bow,
3. I am trust-ing thee for cleans-ing In the crim-son flood;
4. I am trust-ing thee to guide me; Thou a-lone shalt lead,
5. I am trust-ing thee, Lord Je-sus; Nev-er let me fall;

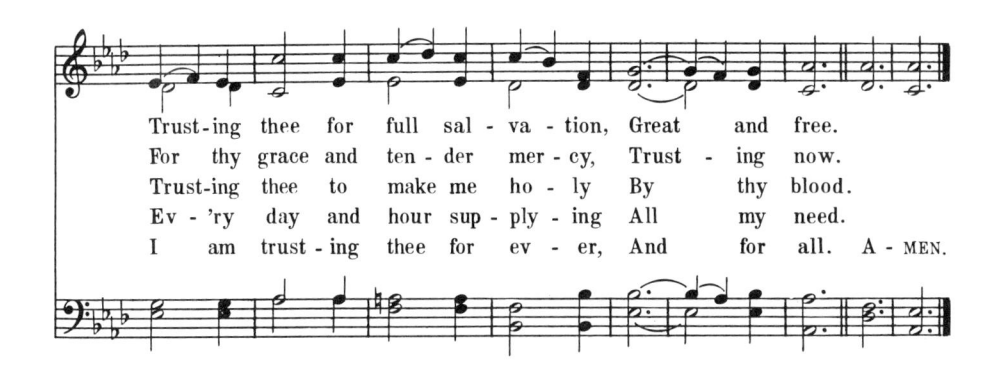

# FAITH IN CHRIST

Trust-ing thee for full sal - va - tion, Great and free.
For thy grace and ten - der mer - cy, Trust - ing now.
Trust-ing thee to make me ho - ly By thy blood.
Ev - 'ry day and hour sup - ply - ing All my need.
I am trust - ing thee for ev - er, And for all. A - MEN.

*Whosoever shall be ashamed of me and of my words, of him shall the Son of man be ashamed . . . Luke 9:26*

**425**

Joseph Grigg, 1765
Alt. by Benjamin Francis, 1787

BROOKFIELD L. M.
Thomas B. Southgate, 1855

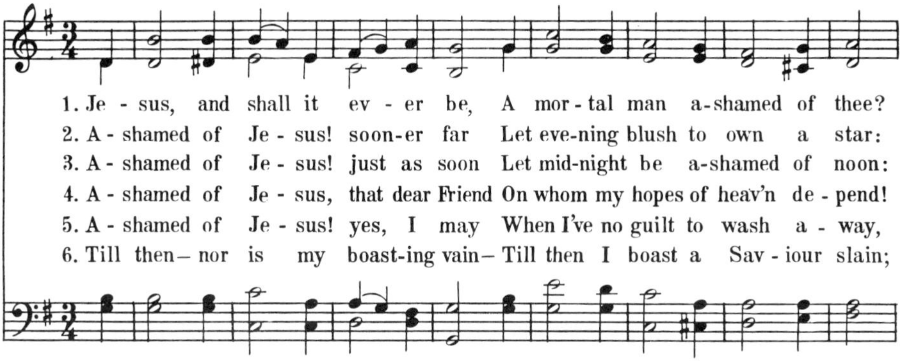

1. Je - sus, and shall it ev - er be, A mor - tal man a-shamed of thee?
2. A - shamed of Je - sus! soon-er far Let eve-ning blush to own a star:
3. A - shamed of Je - sus! just as soon Let mid-night be a-shamed of noon:
4. A - shamed of Je - sus, that dear Friend On whom my hopes of heav'n de - pend!
5. A - shamed of Je - sus! yes, I may When I've no guilt to wash a - way,
6. Till then— nor is my boast-ing vain— Till then I boast a Sav - iour slain;

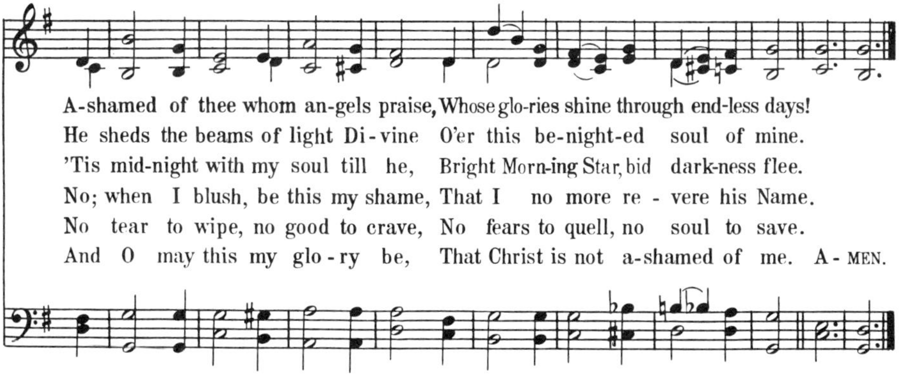

A-shamed of thee whom an-gels praise, Whose glo-ries shine through end-less days!
He sheds the beams of light Di - vine O'er this be-night-ed soul of mine.
'Tis mid-night with my soul till he, Bright Morn-ing Star, bid dark-ness flee.
No; when I blush, be this my shame, That I no more re - vere his Name.
No tear to wipe, no good to crave, No fears to quell, no soul to save.
And O may this my glo - ry be, That Christ is not a-shamed of me. A - MEN.

# 426 THE CHRISTIAN LIFE

*The peace of God ... shall keep your hearts and minds through Christ Jesus.* Phil. 4:7

STELLA 8. 8. 8. 8. 8. 8.

Charles Wesley, 1749      Old melody, arr. in *Easy Hymn Tunes*, 1851

1. Thou hidden source of calm repose, Thou all-sufficient love divine, My help and refuge from my foes, Secure I am, if thou art mine: And lo! from sin, and grief, and shame I hide me, Jesus, in thy Name.

2. Thy mighty Name salvation is, And keeps my happy soul above; Comfort it brings, and pow'r, and peace, And joy, and everlasting love: To me, with thy dear Name, are giv'n Pardon, and holiness, and heav'n.

3. Jesus, my all in all thou art; My rest in toil, my ease in pain, The medicine of my broken heart, In war my peace, in loss my gain, My smile beneath the tyrant's frown, In shame my glory and my crown:

4. In want my plentiful supply, In weakness my almighty pow'r, In bonds my perfect liberty, My light in Satan's darkest hour, My help and stay when-e'er I call, My life in death, my heav'n, my all. A-MEN.

Music used by permission of the Congregational Union of England and Wales.

# FAITH IN CHRIST

(FIRST TUNE) 427

*Who shall separate us from the love of Christ? shall tribulation, or distress, or persecution, or famine, or nakedness, or peril, or sword?* Rom. 8:35

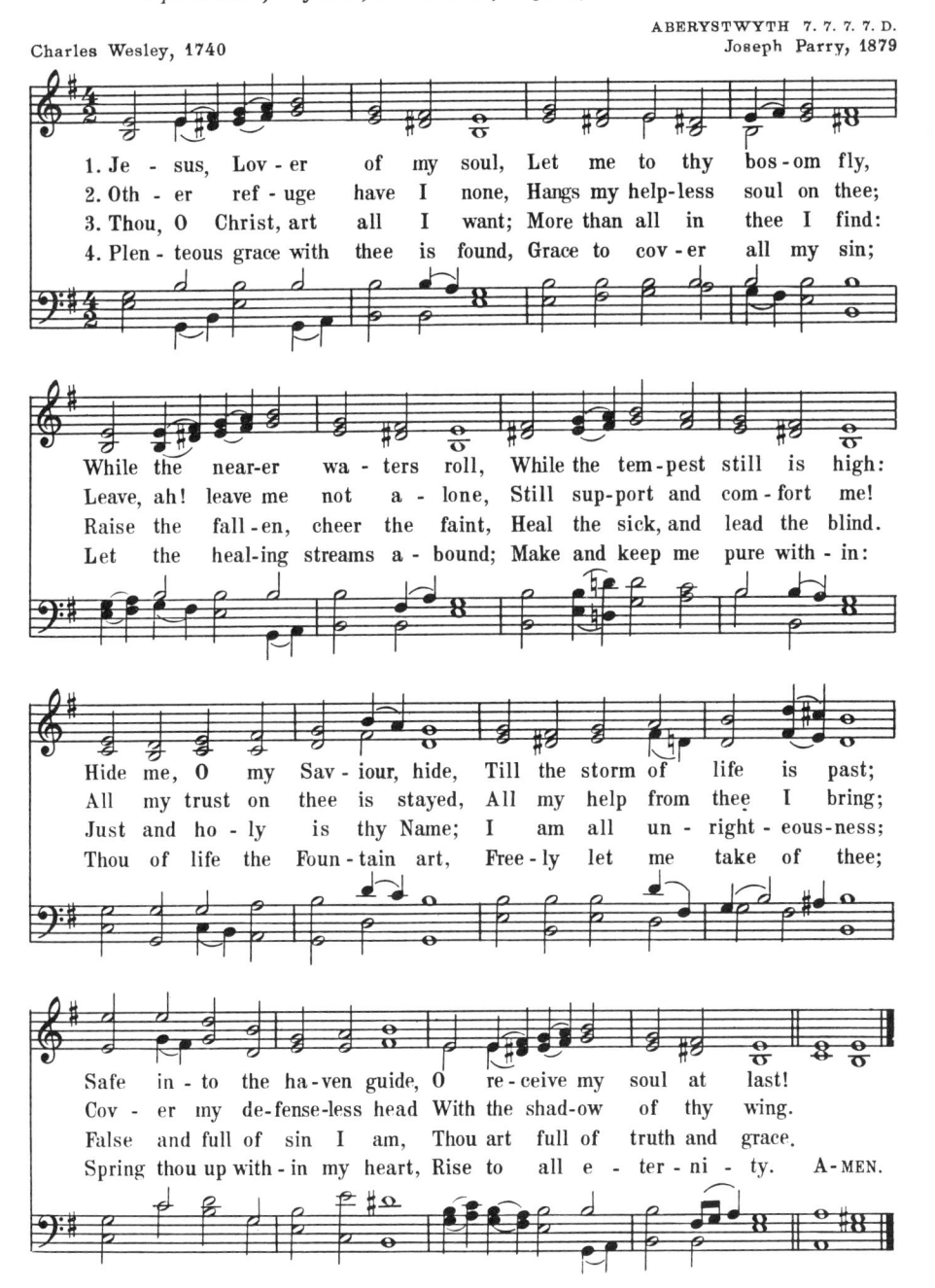

Charles Wesley, 1740

ABERYSTWYTH 7. 7. 7. 7. D.
Joseph Parry, 1879

1. Jesus, Lover of my soul, Let me to thy bosom fly,
While the nearer waters roll, While the tempest still is high:
Hide me, O my Saviour, hide, Till the storm of life is past;
Safe into the haven guide, O receive my soul at last!

2. Other refuge have I none, Hangs my helpless soul on thee;
Leave, ah! leave me not alone, Still support and comfort me!
All my trust on thee is stayed, All my help from thee I bring;
Cover my defenseless head With the shadow of thy wing.

3. Thou, O Christ, art all I want; More than all in thee I find:
Raise the fallen, cheer the faint, Heal the sick, and lead the blind.
Just and holy is thy Name; I am all unrighteousness;
False and full of sin I am, Thou art full of truth and grace.

4. Plenteous grace with thee is found, Grace to cover all my sin;
Let the healing streams abound; Make and keep me pure within:
Thou of life the Fountain art, Freely let me take of thee;
Spring thou up within my heart, Rise to all eternity. A-MEN.

**427** (SECOND TUNE)            THE CHRISTIAN LIFE

*For thou hast been a strength . . . to the needy in his distress, a refuge from the storm, a shadow from the heat.* Isa. 25:4

MARTYN 7. 7. 7. 7. D.
Simeon B. Marsh, 1834
Harmonized by Rhys Thomas, 1916

Charles Wesley, 1740

1. Jesus, Lover of my soul, Let me to thy bosom fly,
   While the nearer waters roll, While the tempest still is high:
   Hide me, O my Saviour, hide, Till the storm of life is past;
   Safe into the haven guide, O receive my soul at last!

2. Other refuge have I none, Hangs my helpless soul on thee;
   Leave, ah! leave me not alone, Still support and comfort me!
   All my trust on thee is stayed, All my help from thee I bring;
   Cover my defenseless head With the shadow of thy wing.

3. Thou, O Christ, art all I want; More than all in thee I find:
   Raise the fallen, cheer the faint, Heal the sick, and lead the blind.
   Just and holy is thy Name; I am all unrighteousness;
   False and full of sin I am, Thou art full of truth and grace.

4. Plenteous grace with thee is found, Grace to cover all my sin;
   Let the healing streams abound; Make and keep me pure within:
   Thou of life the Fountain art, Freely let me take of thee;
   Spring thou up within my heart, Rise to all eternity. A-MEN.

# FAITH IN CHRIST

(THIRD TUNE) 427

*And a man shall be as an hiding place from the wind, and a covert from the tempest.* Isa. 32:2

Charles Wesley, 1740

REFUGE 7. 7. 7. 7. D.
Joseph P. Holbrook, 1862

1. Je - sus, Lov - er of my soul, Let me to thy bos - om fly,
2. Oth - er ref - uge have I none, Hangs my help - less soul on thee;
3. Thou, O Christ, art all I want; More than all in thee I find:
4. Plen - teous grace with thee is found, Grace to cov - er all my sin;

While the near - er wa - ters roll, While the tem - pest still is high:
Leave, ah! leave me not a - lone, Still sup - port and com - fort me!
Raise the fall - en, cheer the faint, Heal the sick, and lead the blind.
Let the heal - ing streams a - bound; Make and keep me pure with - in:

Hide me, O my Sav - iour, hide, Till the storm of life is past;
All my trust on thee is stayed, All my help from thee I bring;
Just and ho - ly is thy Name; I am all un - right-eous - ness;
Thou of life the Foun - tain art, Free - ly let me take of thee;

Safe in - to the ha - ven guide, O re - ceive my soul at last!
Cov - er my de - fense-less head With the shad - ow of thy wing.
False and full of sin I am, Thou art full of truth and grace.
Spring thou up with - in my heart, Rise to all e - ter - ni - ty. A - MEN.

## 428 THE CHRISTIAN LIFE

*Lord, I believe; help thou mine unbelief.* Mark 9:24

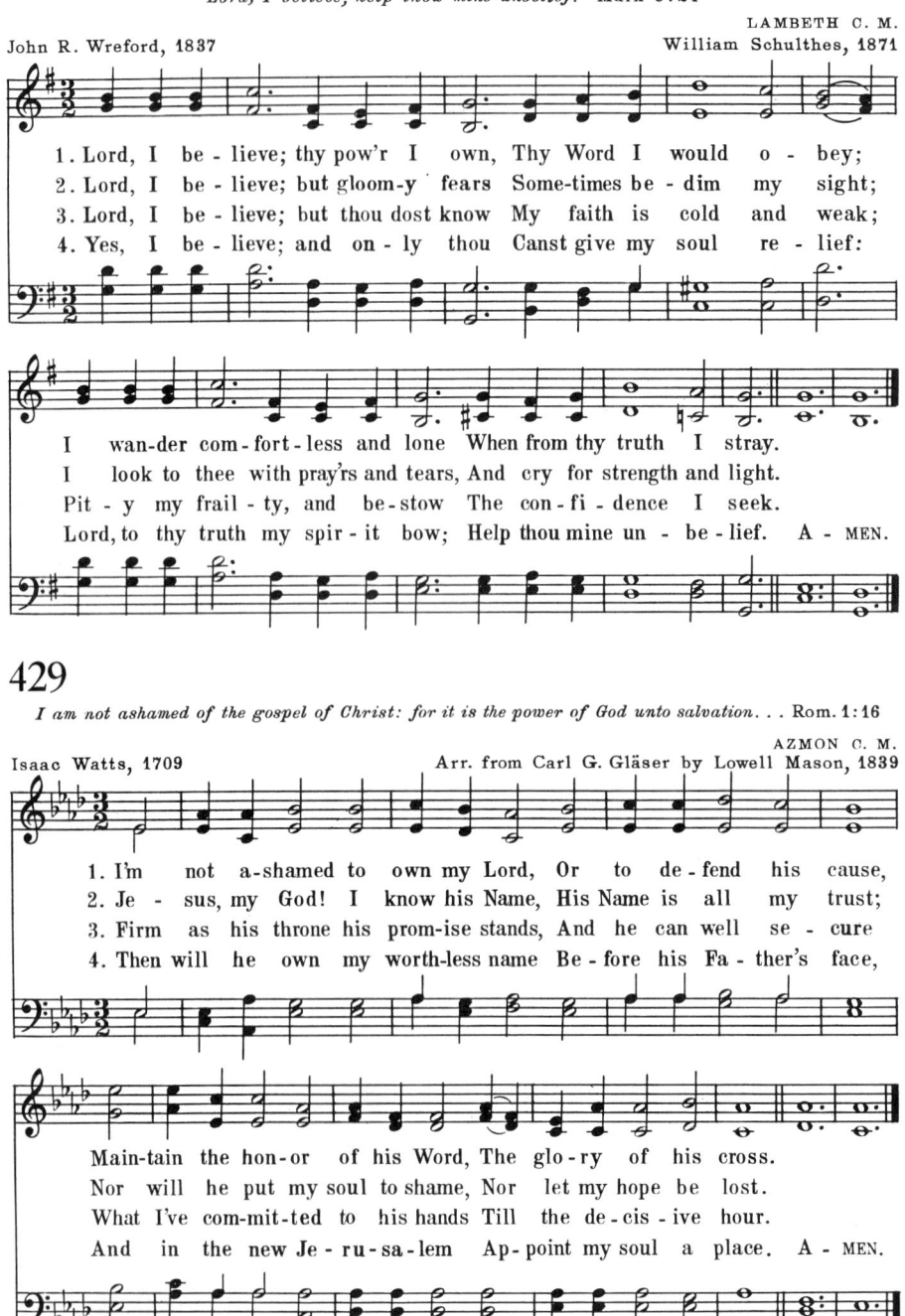

John R. Wreford, 1837
LAMBETH C. M.
William Schulthes, 1871

1. Lord, I be-lieve; thy pow'r I own, Thy Word I would o-bey;
   I wan-der com-fort-less and lone When from thy truth I stray.
2. Lord, I be-lieve; but gloom-y fears Some-times be-dim my sight;
   I look to thee with pray'rs and tears, And cry for strength and light.
3. Lord, I be-lieve; but thou dost know My faith is cold and weak;
   Pit-y my frail-ty, and be-stow The con-fi-dence I seek.
4. Yes, I be-lieve; and on-ly thou Canst give my soul re-lief:
   Lord, to thy truth my spir-it bow; Help thou mine un-be-lief. A-MEN.

## 429

*I am not ashamed of the gospel of Christ: for it is the power of God unto salvation...* Rom. 1:16

Isaac Watts, 1709
AZMON C. M.
Arr. from Carl G. Gläser by Lowell Mason, 1839

1. I'm not a-shamed to own my Lord, Or to de-fend his cause,
   Main-tain the hon-or of his Word, The glo-ry of his cross.
2. Je-sus, my God! I know his Name, His Name is all my trust;
   Nor will he put my soul to shame, Nor let my hope be lost.
3. Firm as his throne his prom-ise stands, And he can well se-cure
   What I've com-mit-ted to his hands Till the de-cis-ive hour.
4. Then will he own my worth-less name Be-fore his Fa-ther's face,
   And in the new Je-ru-sa-lem Ap-point my soul a place. A-MEN.

# FAITH IN CHRIST           430

*If we confess our sins, he is faithful and just to forgive us our sins, and to cleanse us from all unrighteousness.* I John 1:9

Horatius Bonar, 1848

MIRIAM 7. 6. 7. 6. D.
Joseph P. Holbrook, 1865

1. I lay my sins on Jesus, The spotless Lamb of God;
   He bears them all, and frees us From the accursed load:
   I bring my guilt to Jesus, To wash my crimson stains
   White in his blood most precious, Till not a spot remains.

2. I lay my wants on Jesus; All fulness dwells in him;
   He heals all my diseases, He doth my soul redeem:
   I lay my griefs on Jesus, My burdens and my cares;
   He from them all releases, He all my sorrows shares.

3. I rest my soul on Jesus, This weary soul of mine;
   His right hand me embraces, I on his breast recline.
   I love the Name of Jesus, Immanuel, Christ, the Lord;
   Like fragrance on the breezes His Name abroad is poured.

4. I long to be like Jesus, Meek, loving, lowly, mild;
   I long to be like Jesus, The Father's holy Child:
   I long to be with Jesus Amid the heav'nly throng,
   To sing with saints his praises, To learn the angels' song. A-MEN.

# 431 (FIRST TUNE)                        THE CHRISTIAN LIFE

*Him that cometh to me I will in no wise cast out.* John 6:37

Charlotte Elliott, 1836                    WOODWORTH 8. 8. 8. 6.
                                              William B. Bradbury, 1849

1. Just as I am, with-out one plea But that thy blood was shed for me,
2. Just as I am, and wait-ing not To rid my soul of one dark blot,
3. Just as I am, though tossed a-bout With ma-ny a con-flict, ma-ny a doubt,
4. Just as I am, poor, wretch-ed, blind; Sight, rich-es, heal-ing of the mind,
5. Just as I am! thou wilt re-ceive, Wilt wel-come, par-don, cleanse, re-lieve;
6. Just as I am! thy love un-known Has bro-ken ev-'ry bar-rier down;

And that thou bidd'st me come to thee, O Lamb of God, I come, I come.
To thee, whose blood can cleanse each spot, O Lamb of God, I come, I come.
Fight-ings and fears with-in, with-out, O Lamb of God, I come, I come.
Yea, all I need, in thee to find, O Lamb of God, I come, I come.
Be-cause thy prom-ise I be-lieve, O Lamb of God, I come, I come.
Now, to be thine, yea, thine a-lone, O Lamb of God, I come, I come. A-MEN.

# 431 (SECOND TUNE)

Charlotte Elliott, 1836                         GWYNETH 8. 8. 8. 6.
                                         John Price (Beulah), b. 1857

Just as I am, with-out one plea But that thy blood was shed for me,

And that thou bidd'st me come to thee, O Lamb of God, I come. A-MEN.

Music used by permission of the Oxford University Press, London.

# FAITH IN CHRIST  432

*A friend of . . . sinners.* Matt. 11:19

J. Wilbur Chapman, 1910

HYFRYDOL 8. 7. 8. 7. D.
Rowland Hugh Prichard, 1855

1. Je - sus! what a Friend for sin-ners! Je - sus! Lov - er of my soul;
2. Je - sus! what a strength in weak-ness! Let me hide my - self in him;
3. Je - sus! what a help in sor - row! While the bil - lows o'er me roll,
4. Je - sus! what a guide and keep - er! While the temp-est still is high,
5. Je - sus! I do now re - ceive him, More than all in him I find,

Friends may fail me, foes as - sail me, He, my Sav - iour, makes me whole.
Tempt - ed, tried, and some-times fail - ing, He, my strength, my vic - t'ry wins.
E - ven when my heart is break-ing, He, my com - fort, helps my soul.
Storms a - bout me, night o'er-takes me, He, my pi - lot, hears my cry.
He hath grant-ed me for - give-ness, I am his, and he is mine.

REFRAIN

Hal - le - lu - jah! what a Sav-iour! Hal - le - lu - jah! what a Friend!

Sav - ing, help - ing, keep - ing, lov - ing, He is with me to the end. A - MEN.

Copyright, 1910. Renewal, 1938, by R. Harkness. Assigned to Hope Publishing Co. All rights reserved. Used by permission.

# 433 THE CHRISTIAN LIFE

*Greater love hath no man than this, that a man lay down his life for his friends.* John 15:13

CONSTANCE 8.7.8.7. D.
James G. Small, 1866  
Sir Arthur S. Sullivan, 1875

1. I've found a Friend, O such a Friend! He loved me ere I knew him;
2. I've found a Friend, O such a Friend! He bled, he died to save me;
3. I've found a Friend, O such a Friend! All pow'r to him is giv-en,
4. I've found a Friend, O such a Friend! So kind and true and ten-der,

He drew me with the cords of love, And thus he bound me to him;
And not a-lone the gift of life, But his own self he gave me!
To guard me on my on-ward course, And bring me safe to heav-en:
So wise a Coun-sel-or and Guide, So might-y a De-fend-er!

And round my heart still close-ly twine Those ties which nought can sev-er,
Nought that I have mine own I'll call, I'll hold it for the Giv-er,
E-ter-nal glo-ry gleams a-far, To nerve my faint en-deav-or:
From him who loves me now so well What pow'r my soul can sev-er?

For I am his, and he is mine, For ev-er and for ev-er.
My heart, my strength, my life, my all Are his, and his for ev-er.
So now to watch, to work, to war; And then to rest for ev-er.
Shall life or death, shall earth or hell? No! I am his for ev-er. A-MEN.

# UNION WITH CHRIST 434

*I am the root and the offspring of David, and the bright and morning star.* Rev. 22:16

WIE SCHÖN LEUCHTET DER MORGENSTERN
8. 8. 7. 8. 8. 7. 4. 4. 4. 4. 8.

Philipp Nicolai, 1597
Tr., composite

Philipp Nicolai, 1599
Arr. Johann Sebastian Bach, c. 1730

1. How lovely shines the Morning Star! The nations see and hail afar The light in Judah shining. Thou David's Son of Jacob's race, My Bridegroom and my King of Grace, For thee my heart is pining. Lowly, Holy, Great and glorious, Thou victorious Prince of graces, Filling all the heav'nly places.

2. Now richly to my waiting heart, O thou, my God, deign to impart The grace of love undying. In thy blest body let me be, E'en as the branch is in the tree, Thy life my life supplying. Sighing, crying, For the savor Of thy favor; Resting never Till I rest in thee forever.

3. Thou, mighty Father, in thy Son Didst love me ere thou hadst begun This ancient world's foundation. Thy Son hath made a friend of me, And when in spirit him I see, I joy in tribulation. What bliss is this! He that liveth To me giveth Life forever; Nothing me from him can sever. A-MEN.

## 435 THE CHRISTIAN LIFE

*For I am determined not to know anything among you, save Jesus Christ, and him crucified.* I Cor. 2:2

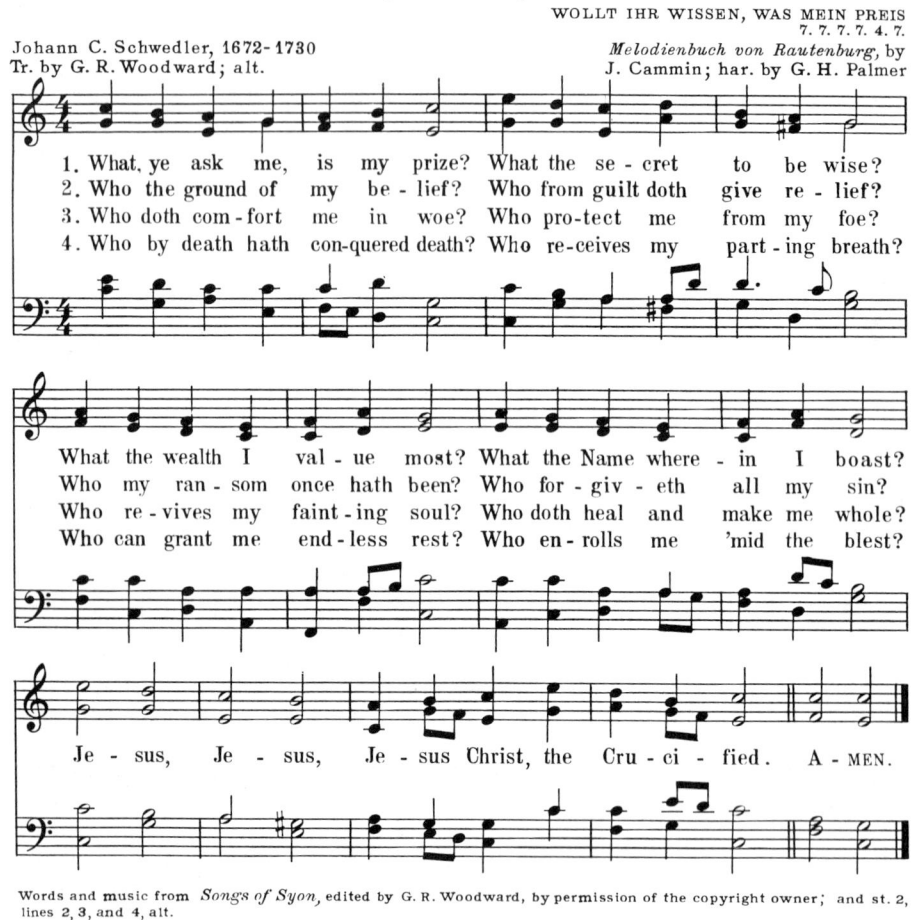

WOLLT IHR WISSEN, WAS MEIN PREIS
7. 7. 7. 7. 4. 7.

Johann C. Schwedler, 1672-1730
Tr. by G. R. Woodward; alt.

*Melodienbuch von Rautenburg*, by J. Cammin; har. by G. H. Palmer

1. What, ye ask me, is my prize? What the se-cret to be wise?
2. Who the ground of my be-lief? Who from guilt doth give re-lief?
3. Who doth com-fort me in woe? Who pro-tect me from my foe?
4. Who by death hath con-quered death? Who re-ceives my part-ing breath?

What the wealth I val-ue most? What the Name where-in I boast?
Who my ran-som once hath been? Who for-giv-eth all my sin?
Who re-vives my faint-ing soul? Who doth heal and make me whole?
Who can grant me end-less rest? Who en-rolls me 'mid the blest?

Je-sus, Je-sus, Je-sus Christ, the Cru-ci-fied. A-MEN.

Words and music from *Songs of Syon*, edited by G. R. Woodward, by permission of the copyright owner; and st. 2, lines 2, 3, and 4, alt.

## 436

*For he hath made him to be sin for us, who knew no sin; that we might be made the righteousness of God in him.* II Cor. 5:21

MANOAH C. M.
Arr. in Henry W. Greatorex's *Collection*

Thomas H. Gill, 1864

Boston, 1851

1. O mys-ter-y of love di-vine That thought and thanks o'er-pow'rs!
2. Didst thou ful-fil each right-eous deed, God's per-fect will ex-press,
3. For thee the Fa-ther's hid-den face? For thee the bit-ter cry?
4. Our load of sin and mis-er-y Didst thou, the Sin-less, bear?
5. Thou, who our ver-y place didst take, Dwell in our ver-y heart:

# UNION WITH CHRIST

Lord Je-sus, was our por-tion thine, And is thy por-tion ours?
That we th' un-faith-ful ones might plead Thy per-fect faith-ful-ness?
For us the Fa-ther's end-less grace, The song of vic-to-ry?
Thy spot-less robe of pur-i-ty Do we the sin-ners wear?
Thou, who thy por-tion ours dost make, Thy-self, thy-self im-part. A-MEN.

*For to me to live is Christ, and to die is gain.* Phil. 1:21

437

Ralph Wardlaw, 1817

HENDON 7. 7. 7. 7. with repeat
H. A. César Malan, 1827

1. Christ, of all my hopes the ground, Christ, the spring of all my joy, Still in thee may I be found, Still for thee my pow'rs em-ploy, Still for thee my pow'rs em-ploy.
2. Let thy love my heart in-flame; Keep thy fear be-fore my sight; Be thy praise my high-est aim; Be thy smile my chief de-light, Be thy smile my chief de-light.
3. Foun-tain of o'er-flow-ing grace, Free-ly from thy ful-ness give; Till I close my earth-ly race, May I prove it "Christ to live," May I prove it "Christ to live."
4. Firm-ly trust-ing in thy blood, Noth-ing shall my heart con-found; Safe-ly I shall pass the flood, Safe-ly reach Im-man-uel's ground, Safe-ly reach Im-man-uel's ground.
5. Thus, O thus, an en-trance give To the land of cloud-less sky; Hav-ing known it "Christ to live," Let me know it "gain to die," Let me know it "gain to die." A-MEN.

## THE CHRISTIAN LIFE

**438**

*Whether we live therefore, or die, we are the Lord's.* Rom. 14:8

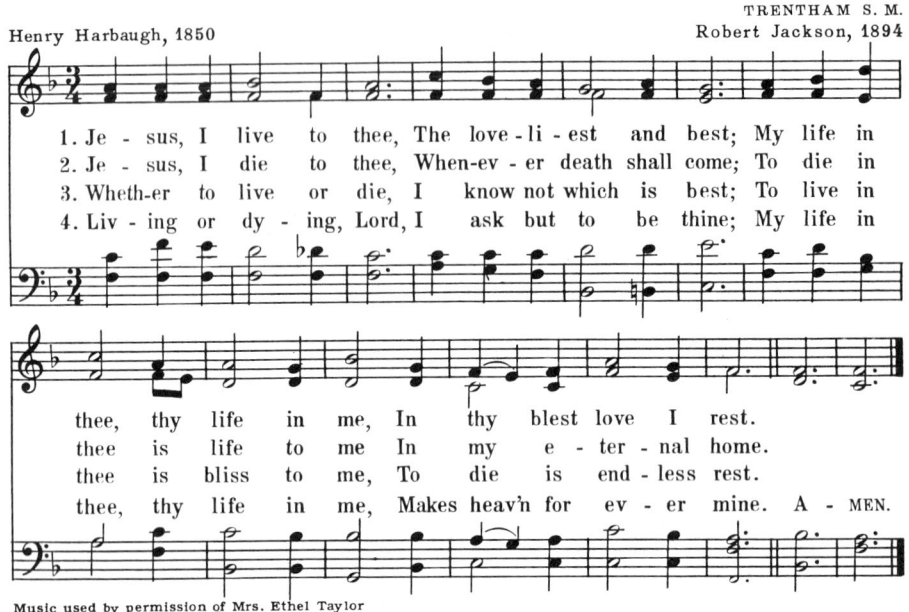

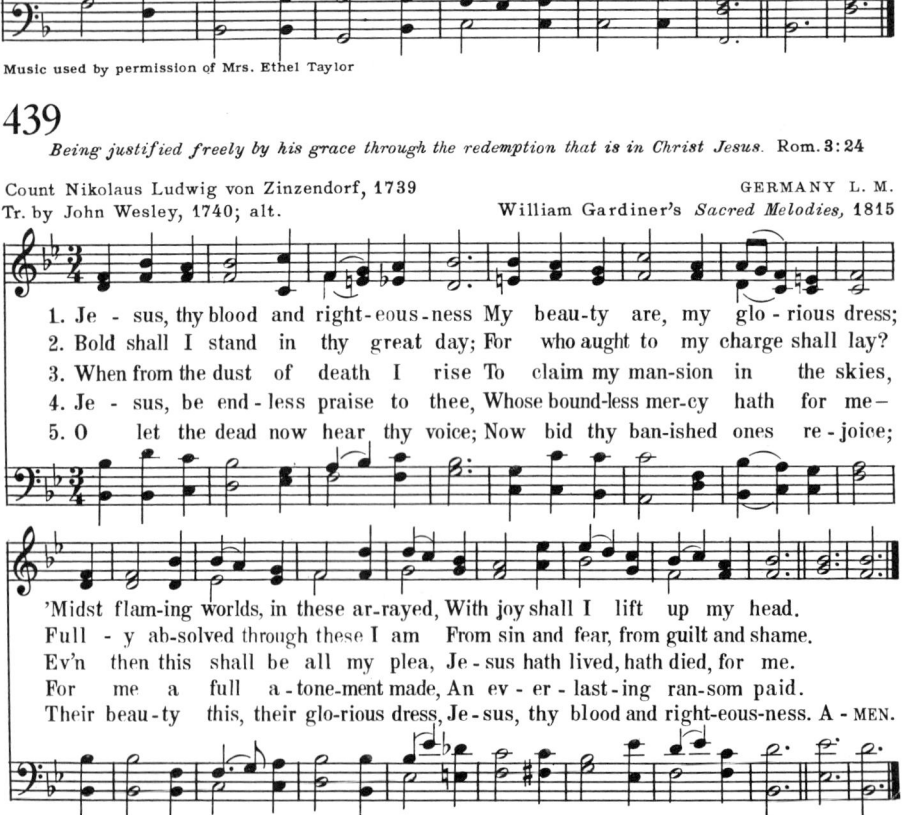

Henry Harbaugh, 1850
TRENTHAM S. M.
Robert Jackson, 1894

1. Je - sus, I live to thee, The love - li - est and best; My life in thee, thy life in me, In thy blest love I rest.
2. Je - sus, I die to thee, When-ev - er death shall come; To die in thee is life to me In my e - ter - nal home.
3. Wheth-er to live or die, I know not which is best; To live in thee is bliss to me, To die is end - less rest.
4. Liv - ing or dy - ing, Lord, I ask but to be thine; My life in thee, thy life in me, Makes heav'n for ev - er mine. A - MEN.

Music used by permission of Mrs. Ethel Taylor

**439**

*Being justified freely by his grace through the redemption that is in Christ Jesus.* Rom. 3:24

Count Nikolaus Ludwig von Zinzendorf, 1739
Tr. by John Wesley, 1740; alt.
GERMANY L. M.
William Gardiner's *Sacred Melodies*, 1815

1. Je - sus, thy blood and right-eous-ness My beau-ty are, my glo - rious dress; 'Midst flam-ing worlds, in these ar-rayed, With joy shall I lift up my head.
2. Bold shall I stand in thy great day; For who aught to my charge shall lay? Full - y ab-solved through these I am From sin and fear, from guilt and shame.
3. When from the dust of death I rise To claim my man-sion in the skies, Ev'n then this shall be all my plea, Je - sus hath lived, hath died, for me.
4. Je - sus, be end - less praise to thee, Whose bound-less mer-cy hath for me— For me a full a-tone-ment made, An ev - er - last-ing ran-som paid.
5. O let the dead now hear thy voice; Now bid thy ban-ished ones re - joice; Their beau - ty this, their glo-rious dress, Je - sus, thy blood and right-eous-ness. A - MEN.

# JUSTIFICATION 440

*If any man thirst, let him come unto me, and drink.* John 7:37

Augustus M. Toplady, 1740-1778

ST. MATTHEW C. M. D.
William Croft, 1678-1727

1. Foun-tain of nev-er-ceas-ing grace, Thy saints' ex-haust-less theme,
Great ob-ject of im-mor-tal praise, Es-sen-tial-ly su-preme;
We bless thee for the glo-rious fruits Thine in-car-na-tion gives;
The right-eous-ness which grace im-putes, And faith a-lone re-ceives.

2. In thee we have a right-eous-ness By God him-self ap-proved;
Our rock, our sure foun-da-tion this, Which nev-er can be moved.
Our ran-som by thy death was paid, For all thy peo-ple giv'n,
The law thou per-fect-ly o-beyed, That they might en-ter heav'n.

3. As all, when Ad-am sinned a-lone, In his trans-gres-sion died,
So by the right-eous-ness of one Are sin-ners jus-ti-fied;
We to thy mer-it, gra-cious Lord, With hum-blest joy sub-mit,
A-gain to Par-a-dise re-stored, In thee a-lone com-plete. A-MEN.

St. 2, alt.

## 441 THE CHRISTIAN LIFE

*Not by works of righteousness which we have done, but according to his mercy he saved us . . . Titus 3:5*

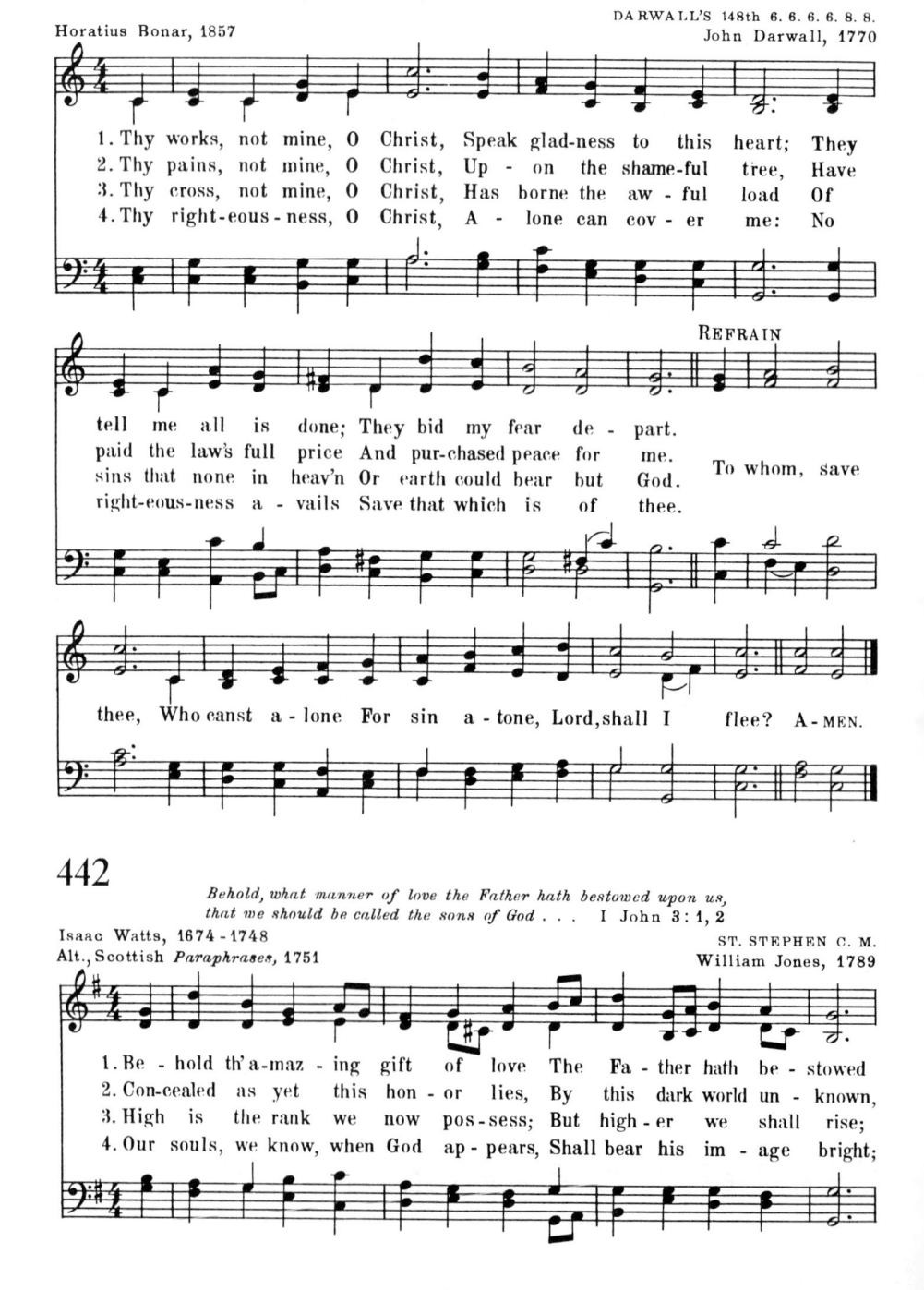

Horatius Bonar, 1857
DARWALL'S 148th 6. 6. 6. 6. 8. 8.
John Darwall, 1770

1. Thy works, not mine, O Christ, Speak gladness to this heart; They tell me all is done; They bid my fear depart.
2. Thy pains, not mine, O Christ, Upon the shameful tree, Have paid the law's full price And purchased peace for me.
3. Thy cross, not mine, O Christ, Has borne the awful load Of sins that none in heav'n Or earth could bear but God.
4. Thy righteousness, O Christ, Alone can cover me: No righteousness avails Save that which is of thee.

REFRAIN

To whom, save thee, Who canst alone For sin atone, Lord, shall I flee? A-MEN.

## 442

*Behold, what manner of love the Father hath bestowed upon us, that we should be called the sons of God . . . I John 3:1, 2*

Isaac Watts, 1674-1748
Alt., Scottish *Paraphrases*, 1751
ST. STEPHEN C. M.
William Jones, 1789

1. Behold th' amazing gift of love The Father hath bestowed
2. Concealed as yet this honor lies, By this dark world unknown,
3. High is the rank we now possess; But higher we shall rise;
4. Our souls, we know, when God appears, Shall bear his image bright;

## ADOPTION

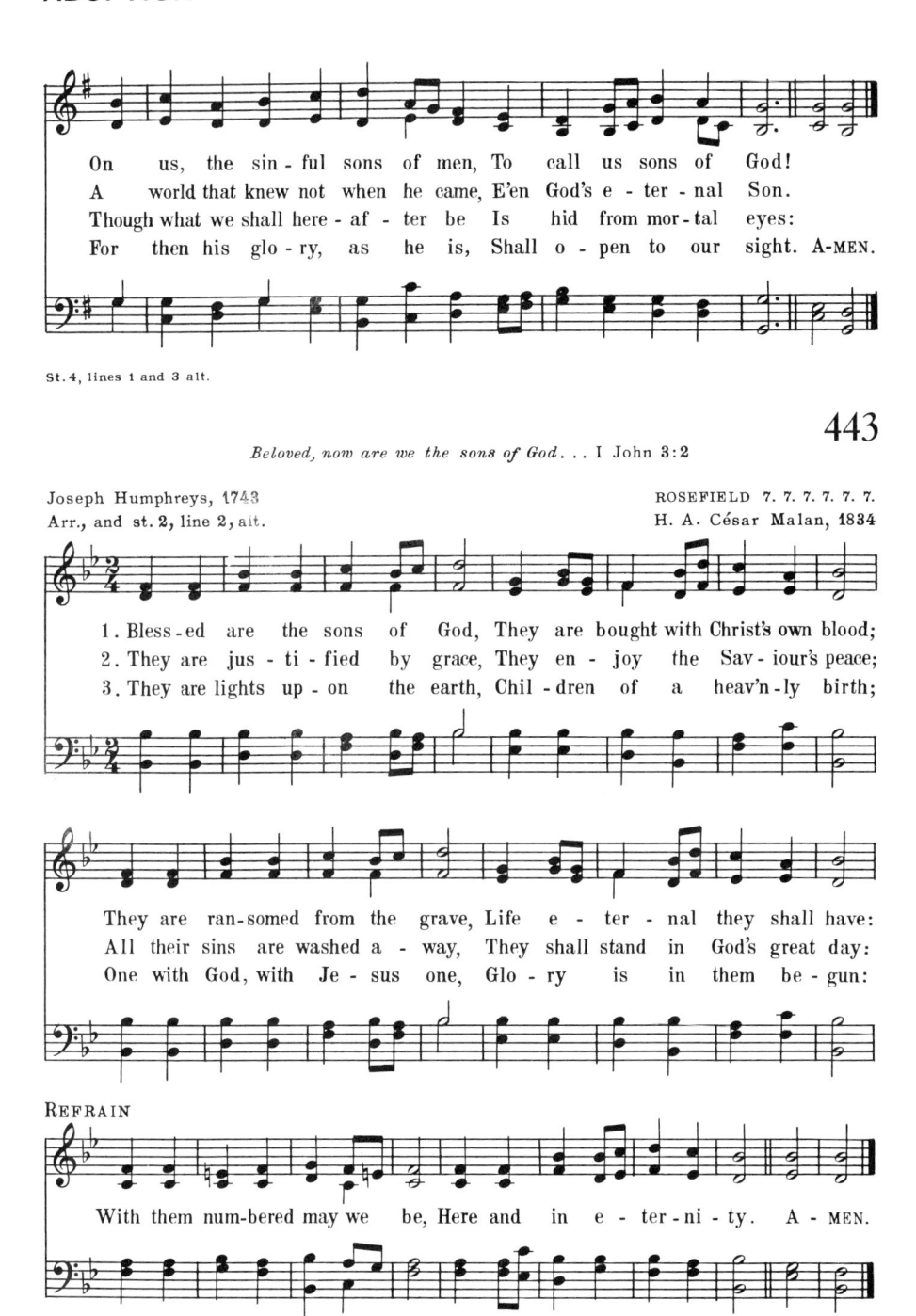

On us, the sin-ful sons of men, To call us sons of God!
A world that knew not when he came, E'en God's e-ter-nal Son.
Though what we shall here-af-ter be Is hid from mor-tal eyes:
For then his glo-ry, as he is, Shall o-pen to our sight. A-MEN.

St. 4, lines 1 and 3 alt.

*Beloved, now are we the sons of God... I John 3:2*

**443**

Joseph Humphreys, 1743  
Arr., and st. 2, line 2, alt.

ROSEFIELD 7. 7. 7. 7. 7. 7.  
H. A. César Malan, 1834

1. Bless-ed are the sons of God, They are bought with Christ's own blood;
2. They are jus-ti-fied by grace, They en-joy the Sav-iour's peace;
3. They are lights up-on the earth, Chil-dren of a heav'n-ly birth;

They are ran-somed from the grave, Life e-ter-nal they shall have:
All their sins are washed a-way, They shall stand in God's great day:
One with God, with Je-sus one, Glo-ry is in them be-gun:

REFRAIN

With them num-bered may we be, Here and in e-ter-ni-ty. A-MEN.

## 444 THE CHRISTIAN LIFE

*I have learned, in whatsoever state I am, therewith to be content.* Phil. 4:11

Anna L. Waring, 1850
MORWELLHAM 8.6.8.6.8.6.
Charles Steggall, 1826-1905

1. Fa - ther, I know that all my life Is por-tioned out for me;
2. I would not have the rest-less will That hur - ries to and fro,
3. I ask thee for the dai-ly strength, To none that ask de - nied,
4. In serv - ice which thy will ap - points There are no bonds for me;

The chang - es that are sure to come, I do not fear to see:
Seek - ing for some great thing to do, Or se - cret thing to know;
A mind to blend with out-ward life, While keep-ing at thy side,
My se - cret heart is taught the truth That makes thy chil - dren free;

I ask thee for a pres-ent mind, In - tent on pleas - ing thee.
I would be treat-ed as a child, And guid-ed where I go.
Con-tent to fill a lit-tle space, If thou be glo - ri - fied.
A life of self-re-nounc-ing love Is one of lib - er - ty. A - MEN.

## 445

*Lord, who shall abide in thy tabernacle? who shall dwell in thy holy hill?* Psalm 15:1

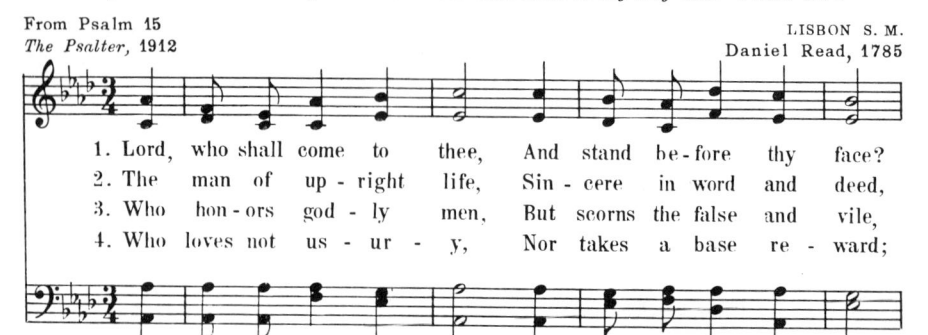

From Psalm 15
*The Psalter,* 1912
LISBON S. M.
Daniel Read, 1785

1. Lord, who shall come to thee, And stand be - fore thy face?
2. The man of up - right life, Sin - cere in word and deed,
3. Who hon - ors god - ly men, But scorns the false and vile,
4. Who loves not us - ur - y, Nor takes a base re - ward;

## OBEDIENCE

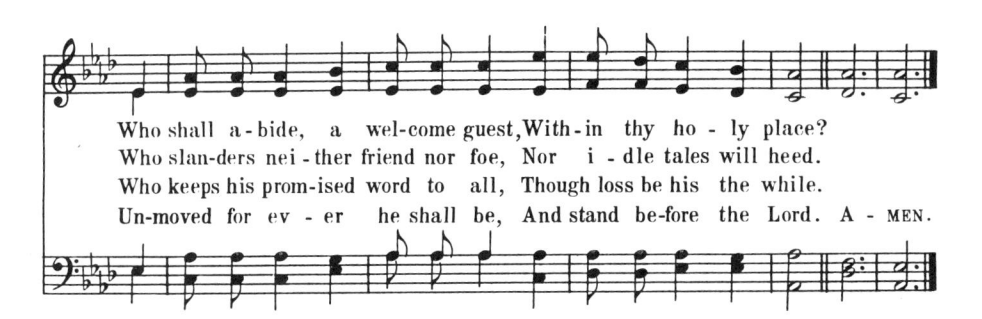

Who shall a-bide, a wel-come guest, With-in thy ho - ly place?
Who slan-ders nei - ther friend nor foe, Nor i - dle tales will heed.
Who keeps his prom-ised word to all, Though loss be his the while.
Un-moved for ev - er he shall be, And stand be-fore the Lord. A - MEN.

*Blessed is the man that walketh not in the counsel of the ungodly ... Psalm 1:1*

446

From PSALM 1
*The Psalter,* 1912

IRISH C. M.
*Hymns and Sacred Poems,* Dublin, 1749

1. That man is blest who, fear - ing God, From sin re - strains his feet, Who will not stand with wick - ed men, Who shuns the scorn - ers' seat.
2. Yea, blest is he who makes God's law His por - tion and de - light, And med - i - tates up - on that law With glad - ness day and night.
3. That man is nour - ished like a tree Set by the riv - ers' side; Its leaf is green, its fruit is sure, And thus his works a - bide.
4. The wick - ed like the driv - en chaff Are swept from off the land; They shall not gath - er with the just, Nor in the judg-ment stand.
5. The Lord will guard the right - eous well, Their way to him is known; The way of sin - ners, far from God, Shall sure - ly be o'er - thrown. A - MEN.

St. 3, line 2, alt.

## 447 THE CHRISTIAN LIFE

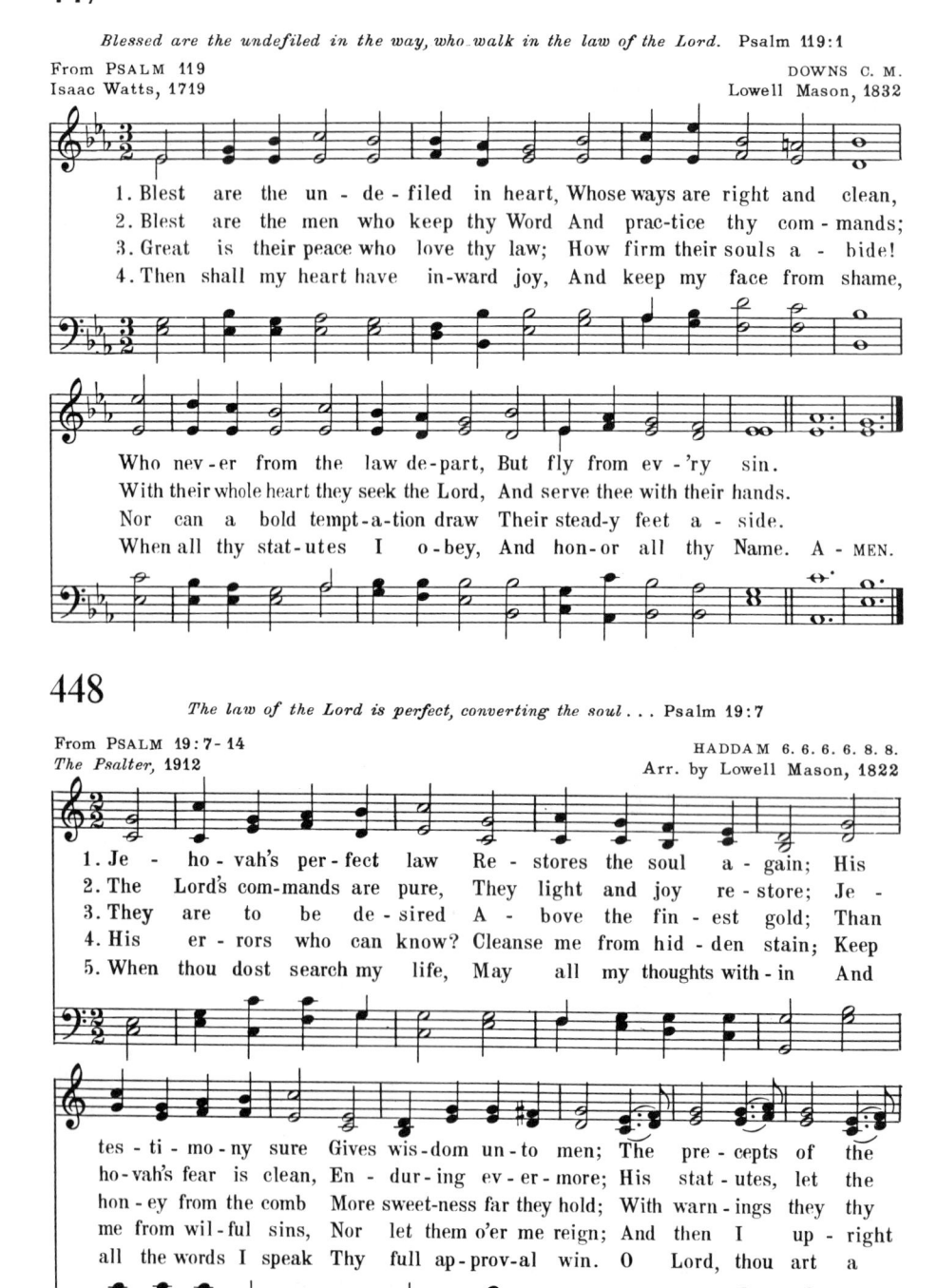

*Blessed are the undefiled in the way, who walk in the law of the Lord.* Psalm 119:1

From PSALM 119
Isaac Watts, 1719

DOWNS C. M.
Lowell Mason, 1832

1. Blest are the un-de-filed in heart, Whose ways are right and clean,
Who nev-er from the law de-part, But fly from ev-'ry sin.
2. Blest are the men who keep thy Word And prac-tice thy com-mands;
With their whole heart they seek the Lord, And serve thee with their hands.
3. Great is their peace who love thy law; How firm their souls a-bide!
Nor can a bold tempt-a-tion draw Their stead-y feet a-side.
4. Then shall my heart have in-ward joy, And keep my face from shame,
When all thy stat-utes I o-bey, And hon-or all thy Name. A-MEN.

## 448

*The law of the Lord is perfect, converting the soul...* Psalm 19:7

From PSALM 19:7-14
The Psalter, 1912

HADDAM 6. 6. 6. 6. 8. 8.
Arr. by Lowell Mason, 1822

1. Je-ho-vah's per-fect law Re-stores the soul a-gain; His tes-ti-mo-ny sure Gives wis-dom un-to men; The pre-cepts of the
2. The Lord's com-mands are pure, They light and joy re-store; Je-ho-vah's fear is clean, En-dur-ing ev-er-more; His stat-utes, let the
3. They are to be de-sired A-bove the fin-est gold; Than hon-ey from the comb More sweet-ness far they hold; With warn-ings they thy
4. His er-rors who can know? Cleanse me from hid-den stain; Keep me from wil-ful sins, Nor let them o'er me reign; And then I up-right
5. When thou dost search my life, May all my thoughts with-in And all the words I speak Thy full ap-prov-al win. O Lord, thou art a

# THE LAW OF GOD

Lord are right, And fill the heart with great de-light.
world con-fess, Are whol-ly truth and right-eous-ness.
serv-ant guard, In keep-ing them is great re-ward.
shall ap-pear And be from great trans-gress-ions clear.
rock to me, And my Re-deem-er thou shalt be. A-MEN.

*The statutes of the Lord are right, rejoicing the heart: the commandment of the Lord is pure, enlightening the eyes.* Psalm 19:8

449

Matthias Loy, 1863

ERHALT UNS, HERR L. M.
*Geistliche Lieder,* Wittenberg, 1543

1. The law of God is good and wise And sets his will be-fore our eyes, Shows us the way of right-eous-ness, And dooms to death when we trans-gress.
2. Its light of ho-li-ness im-parts The knowl-edge of our sin-ful hearts That we may see our lost es-tate And seek de-liv-'rance ere too late.
3. To those who help in Christ have found And would in works of love a-bound It shows what deeds are his de-light And should be done as good and right.
4. When men the of-fered help dis-dain And wil-ful-ly in sin re-main, Its ter-ror in their ear re-sounds And keeps their wick-ed-ness in bounds.
5. The law is good; but since the fall Its ho-li-ness con-demns us all; It dooms us for our sin to die And has no pow'r to jus-ti-fy.
6. To Je-sus we for ref-uge flee, Who from the curse has set us free, And hum-bly wor-ship at his throne, Saved by his grace through faith a-lone. A-MEN.

# 450 THE CHRISTIAN LIFE

*O how love I thy law! it is my meditation all the day.* Psalm 119:97

From PSALM 19:7-11 and PSALM 119:97
*The Psalter,* 1912

KINSMAN C. M. with refrain
James McGranahan, 1840-1907

1. Most perfect is the law of God, Re-stor-ing those that stray;
2. The pre-cepts of the Lord are right; With joy they fill the heart;
3. The fear of God is un-de-filed And ev-er shall en-dure;
4. They warn from ways of wick-ed-ness Dis-pleas-ing to the Lord,

His tes-ti-mo-ny is most sure, Pro-claim-ing wis-dom's way.
The Lord's com-mand-ments all are pure, And clear-est light im-part.
The stat-utes of the Lord are truth And right-eous-ness most pure.
And in the keep-ing of his Word There is a great re-ward.

REFRAIN

O how love I thy law! O how love I thy law! It is my med-i-ta-tion all... the day... O how love I thy law! O how

# THE LAW OF GOD

love I thy law! It is my med-i-ta-tion all the day. A-MEN.

### 451

*Teach me, O Lord, the way of thy statutes; and I shall keep it unto the end.* Psalm 119:33

From PSALM 119:33-40  
*The Psalter,* 1912

BISHOP L. M.  
Joseph P. Holbrook, 1822-1888

1. Teach me, O Lord, thy way of truth, And from it I will not de-part; That I may sted-fast-ly o-bey, Give me an un-der-stand-ing heart.
2. In thy com-mand-ments make me walk, For in thy law my joy shall be; Give me a heart that loves thy will, From dis-con-tent and en-vy free.
3. Turn thou mine eyes from van-i-ty, And cause me in thy ways to tread; O let thy serv-ant prove thy Word And thus to god-ly fear be led.
4. Turn thou a-way re-proach and fear; Thy right-eous judg-ments I con-fess; To know thy pre-cepts I de-sire; Re-vive me in thy right-eous-ness. A-MEN.

# 452 THE CHRISTIAN LIFE

*Now is our salvation nearer than when we believed.* Rom. 13:11

Godfrey Thring, 1862; text of 1882

HERMAS 6. 5. 6. 5. D.
Frances R. Havergal, 1871

1. Sav - iour, bless - ed Sav - iour, Lis - ten while we sing;
   Hearts and voic - es rais - ing Prais - es to our King:
   All we have we of - fer, All we hope to be,
   Bo - dy, soul, and spir - it, All we yield to thee.

2. Near - er, ev - er near - er, Christ, we draw to thee,
   Deep in ad - o - ra - tion Bend - ing low the knee:
   Thou for our re - demp - tion Cam'st on earth to die;
   Thou, that we might fol - low, Hast gone up on high.

3. Great, and ev - er great - er, Are thy mer - cies here;
   True and ev - er - last - ing Are the glo - ries there,
   Where no pain nor sor - row, Fear nor care, is known,
   Where the an - gel le - gions Cir - cle round thy throne.

4. High - er then, and high - er, Bear the ran - somed soul,
   Earth - ly toils for - got - ten, Sav - iour, to its goal;
   Where, in joys un - thought of, Saints with an - gels sing,
   Nev - er wea - ry, rais - ing Prais - es to their King. A - MEN.

St. 3, line 6, alt.

# SANCTIFICATION 453

*Jesus...having loved his own which were in the world, he loved them unto the end.* John 13:1

Samuel Trevor Francis, 1834-1925

EBENEZER 8.7.8.7. D.
Thomas John Williams, 1890

1. O the deep, deep love of Jesus! Vast, un-meas-ured, bound-less, free;
   Roll-ing as a might-y o-cean In its full-ness o-ver me.
   Un-der-neath me, all a-round me, Is the cur-rent of thy love;
   Lead-ing on-ward, lead-ing home-ward, To thy glo-rious rest a-bove.

2. O the deep, deep love of Jesus! Spread his praise from shore to shore;
   How he lov-eth, ev-er lov-eth, Chang-eth nev-er, nev-er-more;
   How he watch-es o'er his loved ones, Died to call them all his own;
   How for them he in-ter-ced-eth, Watch-eth o'er them from the throne.

3. O the deep, deep love of Jesus! Love of ev-'ry love the best:
   'Tis an o-cean vast of bless-ing, 'Tis a ha-ven sweet of rest.
   O the deep, deep love of Jesus! 'Tis a heav'n of heav'ns to me;
   And it lifts me up to glo-ry, For it lifts me up to thee. A-MEN.

Words used by permission of Pickering & Inglis, Ltd.
Music copyright by Gwenlyn Evans, Ltd. Used by permission.

## 454 THE CHRISTIAN LIFE

*Let us run with patience the race that is set before us, looking unto Jesus the author and finisher of our faith... Heb. 12:1, 2*

OLIVET 6. 6. 4. 6. 6. 4.
Ray Palmer, 1830
Lowell Mason, 1832

1. My faith looks up to thee, Thou Lamb of Cal-va-ry,
2. May thy rich grace im-part Strength to my faint-ing heart,
3. While life's dark maze I tread, And griefs a-round me spread,
4. When ends life's tran-sient dream, When death's cold, sul-len stream

Sav-iour Di-vine: Now hear me while I pray, Take all my
My zeal in-spire; As thou hast died for me, O may my
Be thou my guide; Bid dark-ness turn to day, Wipe sor-row's
Shall o'er me roll, Blest Sav-iour, then, in love, Fear and dis-

guilt a-way, O let me from this day Be whol-ly thine.
love to thee Pure, warm, and change-less be, A liv-ing fire.
tears a-way, Nor let me ev-er stray From thee a-side.
trust re-move; O bear me safe a-bove, A ran-somed soul. A-MEN.

## 455

*Search me, O God, and know my heart... Psalm 139:23*

BEATITUDO C. M.
George P. Morris, 1838
John B. Dykes, 1875

1. Search-er of hearts, from mine e-rase All thoughts that should not be,
2. Hear-er of prayer, O guide a-right Each word and deed of mine;
3. Giv-er of all— for ev-'ry good In the Re-deem-er came—
4. Fa-ther, and Son, and Ho-ly Ghost, Thou glo-rious Three in One,

## SANCTIFICATION

And in its deep re-cess-es trace My grat-i-tude to thee.
Life's bat-tle teach me how to fight, And be the vic-t'ry thine.
For rai-ment, shel-ter, and for food, I thank thee in his Name.
Thou know-est best what I need most, And let thy will be done. A-MEN.

### 456

*Teach me thy way, O Lord; I will walk in thy truth: unite my heart to fear thy name.* Psalm 86:11

William T. Matson, 1866

PENITENCE L. M.
*St. Albans Tune Book,* 1875

1. Teach me, O Lord, thy ho-ly way, And give me
2. Guide me, O Sav-iour, with thy hand, And so con-
3. Help me, O Sav-iour, here to trace The sa-cred
4. Guard me, O Lord, that I may ne'er For-sake the
5. Bless me in ev-'ry task, O Lord, Be-gun, con-

an o-be-dient mind; That in thy serv-ice I may
trol my thoughts and deeds, That I may tread the path which
foot-steps thou hast trod; And, meek-ly walk-ing with my
right, or do the wrong: A-gainst temp-ta-tion make me
tin-ued, done for thee: Ful-fil thy per-fect work in

find My soul's de-light from day to day.
leads Right on-ward to the bless-ed land.
God, To grow in good-ness, truth, and grace.
strong, And round me spread thy shel-t'ring care.
me; And thine a-bound-ing grace af-ford. A-MEN.

## THE CHRISTIAN LIFE

### 457

*Remember thou me for thy goodness' sake, O Lord.* Psalm 25:7

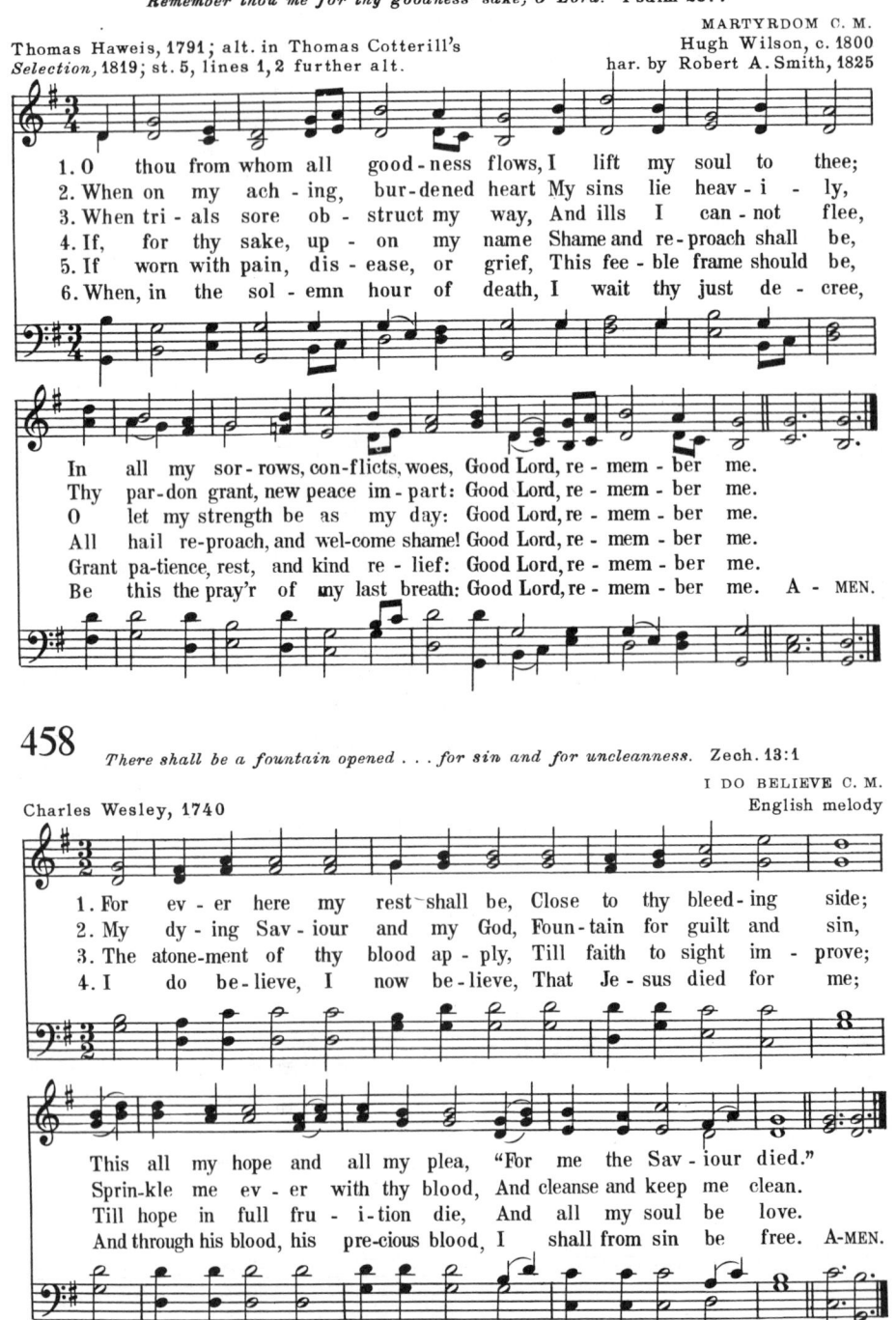

Thomas Haweis, 1791; alt. in Thomas Cotterill's
Selection, 1819; st. 5, lines 1, 2 further alt.

MARTYRDOM C. M.
Hugh Wilson, c. 1800
har. by Robert A. Smith, 1825

1. O thou from whom all good-ness flows, I lift my soul to thee;
2. When on my ach-ing, bur-dened heart My sins lie heav-i-ly,
3. When tri-als sore ob-struct my way, And ills I can-not flee,
4. If, for thy sake, up-on my name Shame and re-proach shall be,
5. If worn with pain, dis-ease, or grief, This fee-ble frame should be,
6. When, in the sol-emn hour of death, I wait thy just de-cree,

In all my sor-rows, con-flicts, woes, Good Lord, re-mem-ber me.
Thy par-don grant, new peace im-part: Good Lord, re-mem-ber me.
O let my strength be as my day: Good Lord, re-mem-ber me.
All hail re-proach, and wel-come shame! Good Lord, re-mem-ber me.
Grant pa-tience, rest, and kind re-lief: Good Lord, re-mem-ber me.
Be this the pray'r of my last breath: Good Lord, re-mem-ber me. A-MEN.

### 458

*There shall be a fountain opened . . . for sin and for uncleanness.* Zech. 13:1

Charles Wesley, 1740

I DO BELIEVE C. M.
English melody

1. For ev-er here my rest shall be, Close to thy bleed-ing side;
2. My dy-ing Sav-iour and my God, Foun-tain for guilt and sin,
3. The atone-ment of thy blood ap-ply, Till faith to sight im-prove;
4. I do be-lieve, I now be-lieve, That Je-sus died for me;

This all my hope and all my plea, "For me the Sav-iour died."
Sprin-kle me ev-er with thy blood, And cleanse and keep me clean.
Till hope in full fru-i-tion die, And all my soul be love.
And through his blood, his pre-cious blood, I shall from sin be free. A-MEN.

# SANCTIFICATION 459

*For thy name's sake lead me, and guide me.* Psalm 31:3

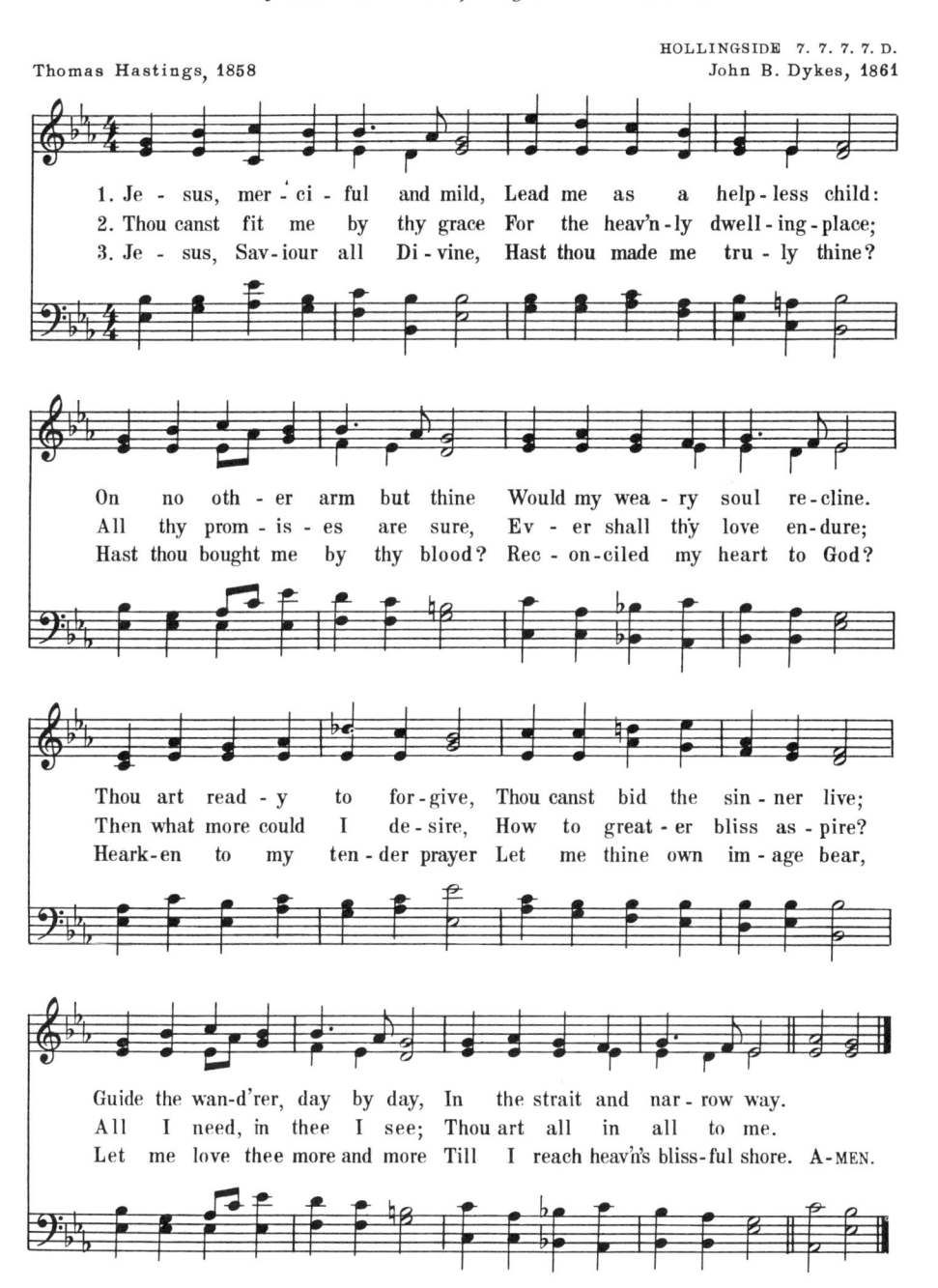

Thomas Hastings, 1858

HOLLINGSIDE 7. 7. 7. 7. D.
John B. Dykes, 1861

1. Je - sus, mer - ci - ful and mild, Lead me as a help - less child:
On no oth - er arm but thine Would my wea - ry soul re - cline.
Thou art read - y to for - give, Thou canst bid the sin - ner live;
Guide the wan - d'rer, day by day, In the strait and nar - row way.

2. Thou canst fit me by thy grace For the heav'n - ly dwell - ing - place;
All thy prom - is - es are sure, Ev - er shall thy love en - dure;
Then what more could I de - sire, How to great - er bliss as - pire?
All I need, in thee I see; Thou art all in all to me.

3. Je - sus, Sav - iour all Di - vine, Hast thou made me tru - ly thine?
Hast thou bought me by thy blood? Rec - on - ciled my heart to God?
Heark - en to my ten - der prayer Let me thine own im - age bear,
Let me love thee more and more Till I reach heav'n's bliss - ful shore. A-MEN.

# 460 (FIRST TUNE)  THE CHRISTIAN LIFE

*He that loveth me shall be loved of my Father, and I will love him, and will manifest myself to him.* John 14:21

Charles Wesley, 1747
St. 2, lines 4, 5, alt.

LOVE DIVINE (LE JEUNE)
8. 7. 8. 7. D.
George F. LeJeune, 1887

1. Love Divine, all loves excelling, Joy of heav'n, to earth come down:
Fix in us thy humble dwelling, All thy faithful mercies crown:
Jesus, thou art all compassion, Pure, unbounded love thou art;
Visit us with thy salvation, Enter ev'ry trembling heart.

2. Breathe, O breathe thy loving Spirit Into ev'ry troubled breast;
Let us all in thee inherit, Let us find the promised rest:
Take away the love of sinning; Alpha and Omega be;
End of faith, as its Beginning, Set our hearts at liberty.

3. Come, Almighty to deliver, Let us all thy life receive;
Suddenly return, and never, Nevermore thy temples leave.
Thee we would be always blessing, Serve thee as thy hosts above,
Pray, and praise thee, without ceasing, Glory in thy perfect love.

4. Finish, then, thy new creation; Pure and spotless let us be:
Let us see thy great salvation Perfectly restored in thee;
Changed from glory into glory, Till in heav'n we take our place,
Till we cast our crowns before thee, Lost in wonder, love, and praise. A-MEN.

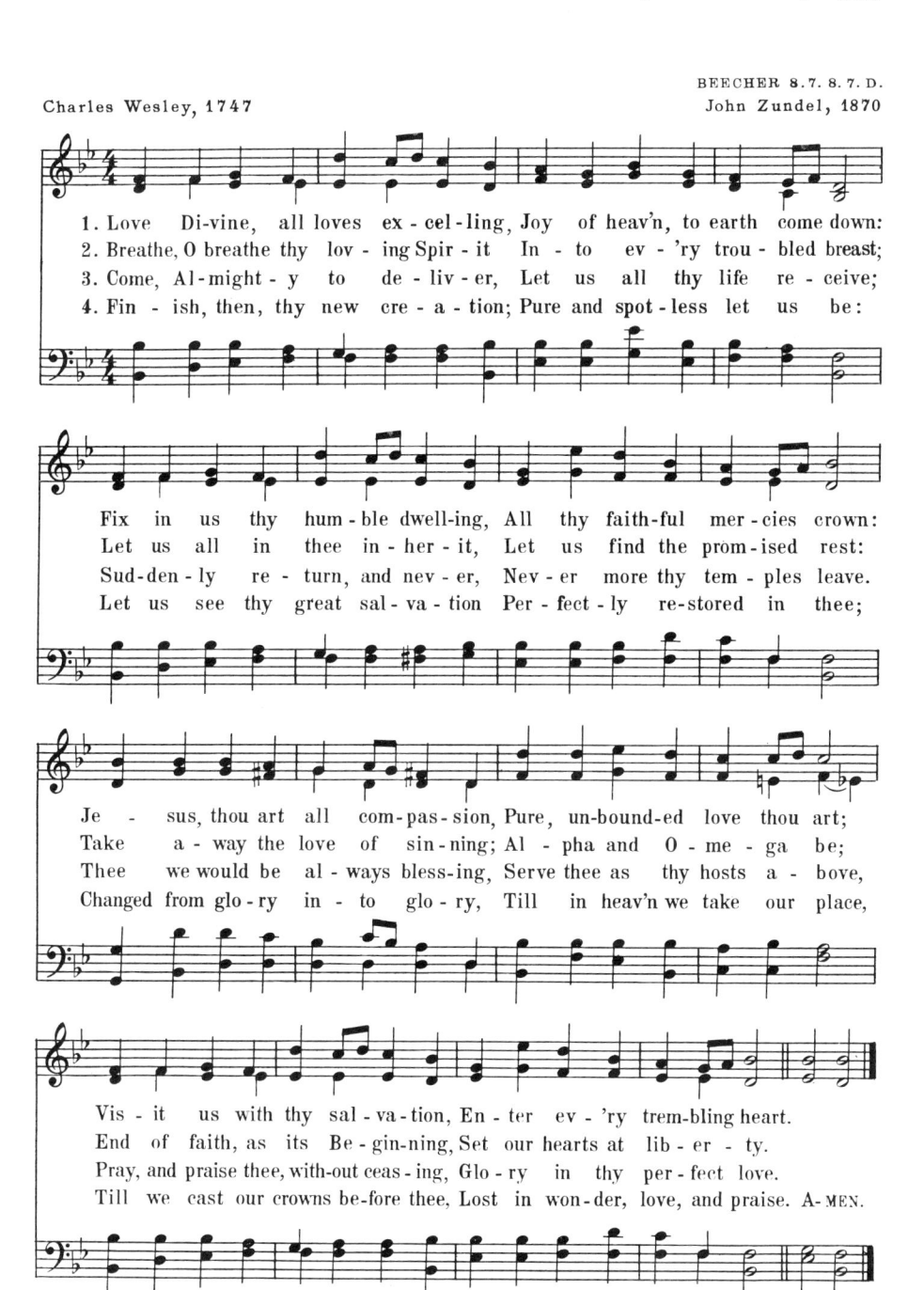

# SANCTIFICATION (SECOND TUNE) 460

BEECHER 8.7.8.7. D.
Charles Wesley, 1747
John Zundel, 1870

1. Love Divine, all loves excelling, Joy of heav'n, to earth come down:
Fix in us thy humble dwelling, All thy faithful mercies crown:
Jesus, thou art all compassion, Pure, unbounded love thou art;
Visit us with thy salvation, Enter ev'ry trembling heart.

2. Breathe, O breathe thy loving Spirit Into ev'ry troubled breast;
Let us all in thee inherit, Let us find the promised rest:
Take away the love of sinning; Alpha and Omega be;
End of faith, as its Beginning, Set our hearts at liberty.

3. Come, Almighty to deliver, Let us all thy life receive;
Suddenly return, and never, Nevermore thy temples leave.
Thee we would be always blessing, Serve thee as thy hosts above,
Pray, and praise thee, without ceasing, Glory in thy perfect love.

4. Finish, then, thy new creation; Pure and spotless let us be:
Let us see thy great salvation Perfectly restored in thee;
Changed from glory into glory, Till in heav'n we take our place,
Till we cast our crowns before thee, Lost in wonder, love, and praise. A-MEN.

## 461 THE CHRISTIAN LIFE

*Out of the depths have I cried unto thee, O Lord.* Psalm 130:1

ALLEIN GOTT IN DER HÖH' 8.7.8.7.8.8.7.
*Geistliche Lieder,* Leipzig, 1539.
Martin Luther, 1523; tr.,cento
Arr. Felix Mendelssohn-Bartholdy, 1809-1847

1. From depths of woe I raise to thee The voice of lam-en-ta-tion; Lord, turn a gra-cious ear to me And hear my sup-pli-ca-tion: If thou in-iq-ui-ties dost mark, Our se-cret sins and mis-deeds dark, O who shall stand be-fore thee?
2. To wash a-way the crim-son stain, Grace, grace a-lone a-vail-eth; Our works, a-las! are all in vain; In much the best life fail-eth: No man can glo-ry in thy sight, All must a-like con-fess thy might, And live a-lone by mer-cy.
3. There-fore my trust is in the Lord, And not in mine own mer-it; On him my soul shall rest, his Word Up-holds my faint-ing spir-it: His prom-ised mer-cy is my fort, My com-fort and my sweet sup-port; I wait for it with pa-tience.
4. What though I wait the live-long night, And till the dawn ap-pear-eth, My heart still trust-eth in his might; It doubt-eth not nor fear-eth: Do thus, O ye of Is-rael's seed, Ye of the Spir-it born in-deed; And wait till God ap-pear-eth.
5. Though great our sins and sore our woes His grace much more a-bound-eth; His help-ing love no lim-it knows, Our ut-most need it sound-eth. Our Shep-herd good and true is he, Who will at last his Is-rael free From all their sin and sor-row. A-MEN.

St. 1, lines 5-7, alt.

# THE FORGIVENESS OF SINS 462

*Blessed is he whose transgression is forgiven... Psalm 32:1*

From PSALM 32
*The Psalter,* 1912

PRYSGOL 7. 6. 7. 6. D.
William Owen, 1814-1893

1. How blest is he whose tres-pass Has free-ly been for-giv'n,
2. While I kept guilt-y si-lence My strength was spent with grief,
3. So let the god-ly seek thee In times when thou art near;
4. I gra-cious-ly will teach thee The way that thou shalt go,
5. The sor-rows of the wick-ed In num-ber shall a-bound,

Whose sin is whol-ly cov-ered Be-fore the sight of heav'n.
Thy hand was heav-y on me, My soul found no re-lief;
No whelm-ing floods shall reach them, Nor cause their hearts to fear.
And with Mine eye up-on thee My coun-sel make thee know.
But those that trust Je-ho-vah, His mer-cy shall sur-round.

Blest he to whom Je-ho-vah Will not im-pute his sin,
But when I owned my tres-pass, My sin hid not from thee,
In thee, O Lord, I hide me, Thou sav-est me from ill,
But be ye not un-rul-y, Or slow to un-der-stand,
Then in the Lord be joy-ful, In song lift up your voice;

Who has a guile-less spir-it, Whose heart is true with-in.
When I con-fessed trans-gres-sion, Then thou for-gav-est me.
And songs of thy sal-va-tion My heart with rap-ture thrill.
Be not per-verse, but will-ing To heed My wise com-mand.
Be glad in God, ye right-eous, Re-joice, ye saints, re-joice. A-MEN.

## 463 THE CHRISTIAN LIFE

*Out of the depths have I cried unto thee, O Lord.* Psalm 130:1

From PSALM 130
*The Psalter,* 1912

SANDON 10. 4. 10. 4. 10. 10.
Charles H. Purday, 1799-1885

1. From out the depths I cry, O Lord, to thee; Lord, hear my call.
   I love thee, Lord, for thou dost heed my plea,
   For - giv - ing all. If thou dost mark our sins, who then shall stand?
   But grace and mer - cy dwell at thy right hand.

2. I wait for God, the Lord, and on his Word My hope re - lies;
   My soul still waits and looks un - to the Lord
   Till light a - rise. I look for him to drive a - way my night,
   Yea, more than watch - men look for morn - ing light.

3. Hope in the Lord, ye wait - ing saints, and he Will well pro - vide;
   For mer - cy and re - demp - tion full and free
   With him a - bide. From sin and e - vil, might - y though they seem,
   His arm al - might - y will his saints re - deem. A - MEN.

St. 1, line 5, alt.

# THE FORGIVENESS OF SINS 464

*For thy name's sake, O Lord, pardon mine iniquity; for it is great.* Psalm 25:11

John S. B. Monsell, 1863  
MONSELL 7.6.7.6.D.  
John S. B. Monsell, 1863

1. My sins, my sins, my Sav-iour! They take such hold on me,
I am not a-ble to look up, Save on-ly, Christ, to thee;
In thee is all for-give-ness, In thee a-bun-dant grace,
My shad-ow and my sun-shine The bright-ness of thy face.

2. My sins, my sins, my Sav-iour! Their guilt I nev-er knew
Till with thee in the des-ert I near thy pas-sion drew;
Till with thee in the gar-den I heard thy plead-ing pray'r,
And saw the sweat-drops blood-y That told thy sor-row there.

3. There-fore my songs, my Sav-iour, E'en in this time of woe,
Shall tell of all thy good-ness To suf-f'ring man be-low;
Thy good-ness and thy fa-vor, Whose pres-ence from a-bove
Re-joice those hearts, my Sav-iour, That live in thee and love. A-MEN.

# 465 THE CHRISTIAN LIFE

*Though your sins be as scarlet, they shall be as white as snow; though they be red like crimson, they shall be as wool.* Isaiah 1:18

COMPASSION 7.7.7.7.7.5.7.7.7.7.
William H. Doane, 1832-1915
Alt. by Henry J. Van Andel

Fanny J. Crosby, 1820-1915

1. "Though your sins be as scar-let, They shall be as white as snow;
2. Hear the voice that en-treats you, O re-turn ye un-to God!
3. He'll for-give your trans-gres-sions, And re-mem-ber them no more;

Though your sins be as scar-let, They shall be as white as snow.
Hear the voice that en-treats you, O re-turn ye un-to God!
He'll for-give your trans-gres-sions, And re-mem-ber them no more.

Though they be red . . . like crim-son, They shall be as wool.
He is of great . . . com-pas-sion, And of won-drous love.
"Look un-to me, . . . ye peo-ple," Saith the Lord your God.

Though your sins be as scar-let, Though your sins be as scar-let,
Hear the voice that en-treats you, Hear the voice that en-treats you,
He'll for-give your trans-gres-sions, He'll for-give your trans-gres-sions,

# THE FORGIVENESS OF SINS

They shall be as white as snow, They shall be as white as snow."
O re-turn ye un-to God! O re-turn ye un-to God!
And re-mem-ber them no more, And re-mem-ber them no more. A-MEN.

Music used by permission of the Publication Committee of the Christian Reformed Church.

466

*Hear thou from heaven, and forgive the sin of thy servants... II Chron. 6:27*

ETERNITY 7. 7. 7. 5.

Eliza F. Morris, 1857     Samuel S. Wesley, 1810-1876

1. God of pit-y, God of grace, When we hum-bly seek thy face,
2. When we in thy tem-ple meet, Spread our wants be-fore thy feet,
3. When thy love our hearts shall fill, And we long to do thy will,
4. Should we wan-der from thy fold, And our love to thee grow cold,

Bend from heav'n, thy dwell-ing-place; Hear, for-give, and save.
Plead-ing at thy mer-cy-seat, Look from heav'n and save.
Turn-ing to thy ho-ly hill, Lord, ac-cept and save.
With a pit-ying eye be-hold; Lord, for-give and save. A-MEN.

5. Should the hand of sorrow press,
   Earthly care and want distress,
   May our souls thy peace possess;
   Jesus, hear and save.

6. And, whate'er our cry may be,
   When we lift our hearts to thee,
   From our burden set us free;
   Hear, forgive, and save.

## 467 THE CHRISTIAN LIFE: FORGIVENESS OF SINS

*Come unto me, all ye that labour and are heavy laden... Matt. 11:28*

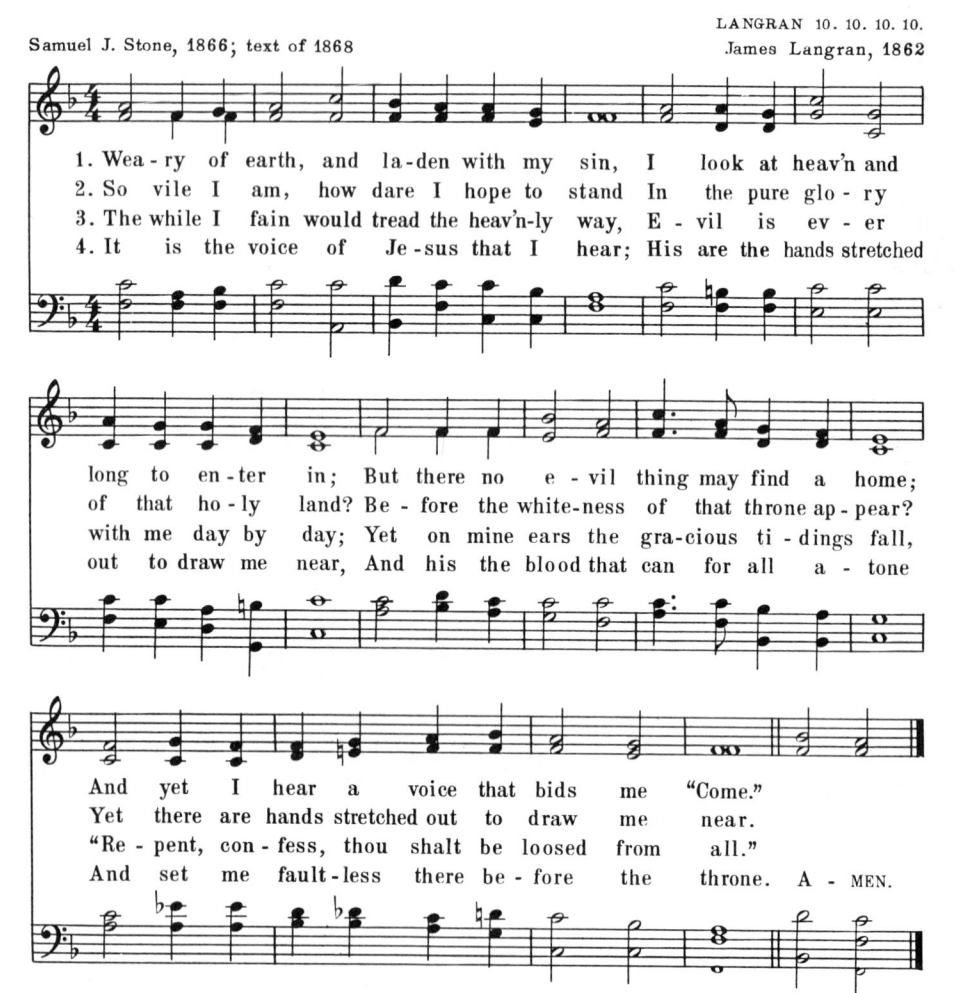

Samuel J. Stone, 1866; text of 1868  
LANGRAN 10. 10. 10. 10.  
James Langran, 1862

1. Wea-ry of earth, and la-den with my sin, I look at heav'n and long to en-ter in; But there no e-vil thing may find a home; And yet I hear a voice that bids me "Come."

2. So vile I am, how dare I hope to stand In the pure glo-ry of that ho-ly land? Be-fore the white-ness of that throne ap-pear? Yet there are hands stretched out to draw me near.

3. The while I fain would tread the heav'n-ly way, E-vil is ev-er with me day by day; Yet on mine ears the gra-cious ti-dings fall, "Re-pent, con-fess, thou shalt be loosed from all."

4. It is the voice of Je-sus that I hear; His are the hands stretched out to draw me near, And his the blood that can for all a-tone And set me fault-less there be-fore the throne. A-MEN.

5. O great Absolver, grant my soul may wear
The lowliest garb of penitence and prayer,
That in the Father's courts my glorious dress
May be the garment of thy righteousness.

6. Yea, thou wilt answer for me, righteous Lord;
Thine all the merits, mine the great reward;
Thine the sharp thorns, and mine the golden crown;
Mine the life won, and thine the life laid down.

# THE CHRISTIAN LIFE: CONFLICT WITH SIN  468

*Sanctify them through thy truth: thy word is truth.* John 17:17

Thomas Hughes, 1859

MIRFIELD C. M.
Arthur Cottman, 1872

1. O God of truth, whose liv-ing Word Up-holds what-e'er hath breath, Look down on thy cre-a-tion, Lord, En-slaved by sin and death.
2. Set up thy stan-dard, Lord, that we Who claim a heav'n-ly birth, May march with thee to smite the lies That vex thy groan-ing earth.
3. Ah! would we join that blest ar-ray, And fol-low in the might Of him, the Faith-ful and the True, In rai-ment clean and white!
4. Then, God of truth for whom we long, Thou who wilt hear our pray'r, Do thine own bat-tle in our hearts, And slay the false-hood there. A-MEN.

469

*Lord, how are they increased that trouble me!* Psalm 3:1

From PSALM 3
The Psalter, 1912

EDEN C. M.
William Henry Havergal, 1793-1870

1. O Lord, how are my foes in-creased! A-gainst me ma-ny rise; How ma-ny say, "In vain for help He on his God re-lies."
2. Thou art my shield and glo-ry, Lord, My Sav-iour, O Most High. The Lord from out his ho-ly hill Gives an-swer when I cry.
3. I laid me down and slept, I waked, Be-cause the Lord sus-tains; Though ma-ny thou-sands com-pass me, Un-moved my soul re-mains.
4. A-rise, O Lord; save me, my God; For thou hast owned my cause, And oft hast beat-en down my foes, Who scorn thy right-eous laws.
5. Sal-va-tion to the Lord be-longs; In him his saints are blest; O let thy bless-ing ev-er-more Up-on thy peo-ple rest. A-MEN.

## 470 THE CHRISTIAN LIFE

*Fear not, little flock; for it is your Father's good pleasure to give you the kingdom.* Luke 12:32

Ascribed to Johann Michael Altenburg, 1584-1640
Tr. by Catherine Winkworth, 1855

JEHOVAH NISSI 8. 8. 6. D.
Edward Patrick Crawford, 1846-1912

1. Fear not, O little flock, the foe Who madly seeks your overthrow;
Dread not his rage and pow'r: What though your courage sometimes faints,
His seeming triumph o'er God's saints Lasts but a little hour.

2. Be of good cheer; your cause belongs To him who can avenge your wrongs;
Leave it to him, our Lord: Though hidden yet from all our eyes,
He sees the Gideon who shall rise To save us and his Word.

3. As true as God's own Word is true, Nor earth nor hell with all their crew
Against us shall prevail. A jest and byword are they grown;
God is with us, we are his own; Our vict'ry cannot fail.

4. Amen, Lord Jesus, grant our pray'r; Great Captain, now thine arm make bare,
Fight for us once again; So shall thy saints and martyrs raise
A mighty chorus to thy praise, World without end. A - men. A-MEN.

## 471

*Watch unto prayer.* I Peter 4:7

Charlotte Elliott, 1839
St. 1, line 2, alt.

VIGILATE 7. 7. 7. 3.
William H. Monk, 1868

1. Christian, seek not yet repose, Cast thy dreams of ease away;
2. Principalities and pow'rs, Must'ring their unseen array,
3. Gird thy heav'nly armor on, Wear it ever, night and day;
4. Hear the victors who o'er-came; Still they mark each warrior's way;
5. Hear, above all, hear thy Lord, Him thou lovest to obey;
6. Watch, as if on that alone Hung the issue of the day;

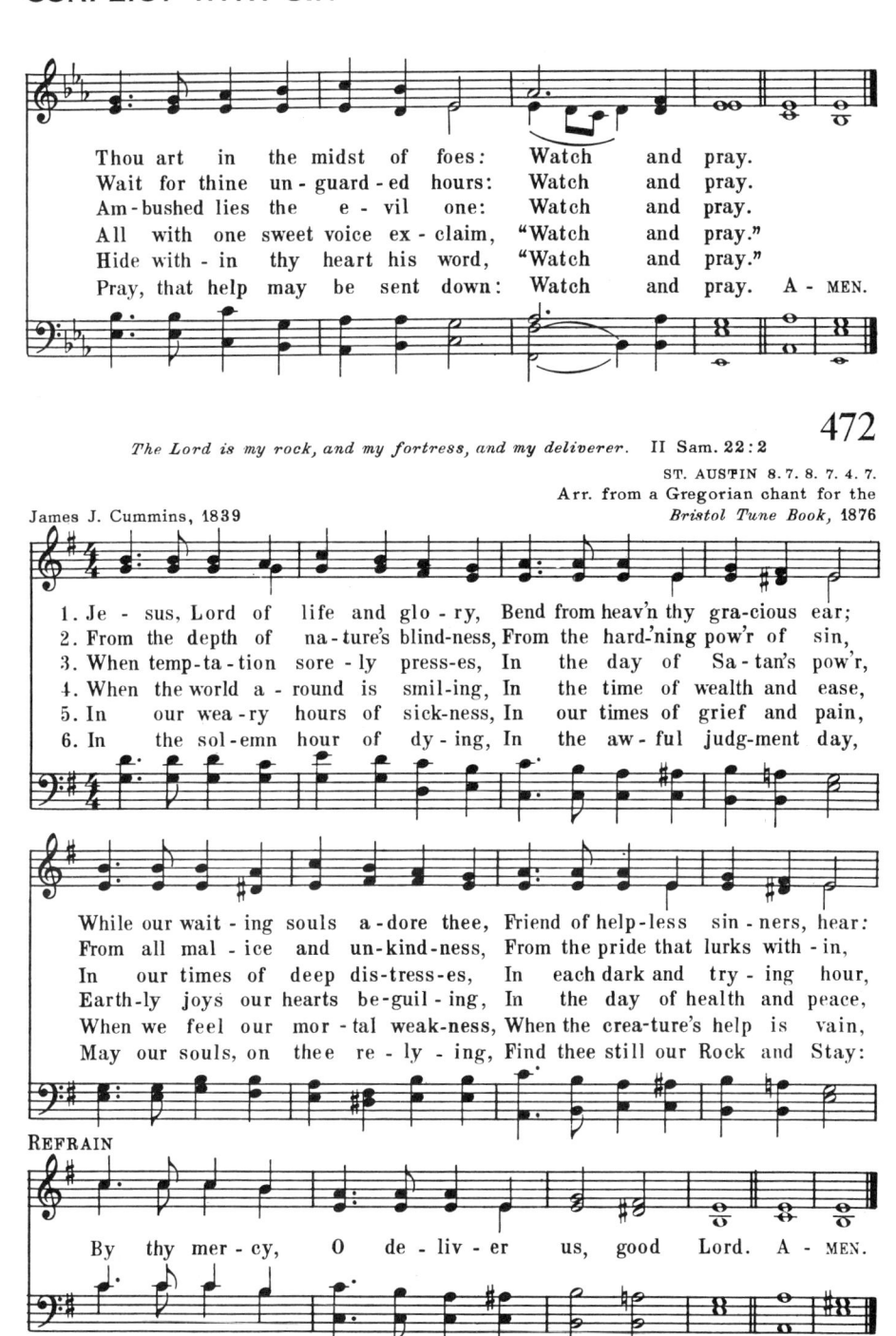

# CONFLICT WITH SIN

Thou art in the midst of foes: Watch and pray.
Wait for thine un-guard-ed hours: Watch and pray.
Am-bushed lies the e-vil one: Watch and pray.
All with one sweet voice ex-claim, "Watch and pray."
Hide with-in thy heart his word, "Watch and pray."
Pray, that help may be sent down: Watch and pray. A-MEN.

*The Lord is my rock, and my fortress, and my deliverer.* II Sam. 22:2

472

James J. Cummins, 1839

ST. AUSTIN 8.7.8.7.4.7.
Arr. from a Gregorian chant for the
*Bristol Tune Book*, 1876

1. Je-sus, Lord of life and glo-ry, Bend from heav'n thy gra-cious ear;
2. From the depth of na-ture's blind-ness, From the hard'-ning pow'r of sin,
3. When temp-ta-tion sore-ly press-es, In the day of Sa-tan's pow'r,
4. When the world a-round is smil-ing, In the time of wealth and ease,
5. In our wea-ry hours of sick-ness, In our times of grief and pain,
6. In the sol-emn hour of dy-ing, In the aw-ful judg-ment day,

While our wait-ing souls a-dore thee, Friend of help-less sin-ners, hear:
From all mal-ice and un-kind-ness, From the pride that lurks with-in,
In our times of deep dis-tress-es, In each dark and try-ing hour,
Earth-ly joys our hearts be-guil-ing, In the day of health and peace,
When we feel our mor-tal weak-ness, When the crea-ture's help is vain,
May our souls, on thee re-ly-ing, Find thee still our Rock and Stay:

REFRAIN

By thy mer-cy, O de-liv-er us, good Lord. A-MEN.

## 473 THE CHRISTIAN LIFE

*Help us, O God of our salvation, for the glory of thy name... Psalm 79:9*

Philip Pusey, 1840; based on
Matthäus A. von Löwenstern, 1644

CLOISTERS 11. 11. 11. 5.
Sir Joseph Barnby, 1868

1. Lord of our life, and God of our sal-va-tion, Star of our
2. See round thine ark the hun-gry bil-lows curl-ing, See how thy
3. Lord, thou canst help when earth-ly ar-mor fail-eth; Lord, thou canst
4. Peace in our hearts, our e-vil thoughts as-suag-ing, Peace in thy
5. Grant us thy help till back-ward they are driv-en; Grant them thy

night, and hope of ev-'ry na-tion, Hear and re-ceive thy
foes their ban-ners are un-furl-ing; Lord, while their darts en-
save when sin it-self as-sail-eth; Christ, o'er thy Rock nor
church, where broth-ers are en-gag-ing, Peace, when the world its
truth, that they may be for-giv-en; Grant peace on earth, or,

church's sup-pli-ca-tion, Lord God Al-might-y.
ven-omed they are hurl-ing, Thou canst pre-serve us.
death nor hell pre-vail-eth: Grant us thy peace, Lord:
bus-y war is wag-ing: Calm thy foes' rag-ing.
af-ter we have striv-en, Peace in thy heav-en. A-MEN.

## 474

*The Lord looked down from heaven upon the children of men... Psalm 14:2*

From PSALM 14:2-7
*The Psalter,* 1912

EISENACH L. M.
Johann Hermann Schein, 1628

1. From heav'n the Lord with search-ing eye Looked down the sons of men to try, To
2. From right-eous-ness they all de-part, Cor-rupt are all, and vile in heart; Yea,
3. Has knowl-edge with the wick-ed failed, That they my peo-ple have as-sailed, That
4. Thy low-ly serv-ant they de-spise, Be-cause he on the Lord re-lies; But
5. O that from Zi-on his a-bode Sal-va-tion were on us be-stowed! When

# CONFLICT WITH SIN

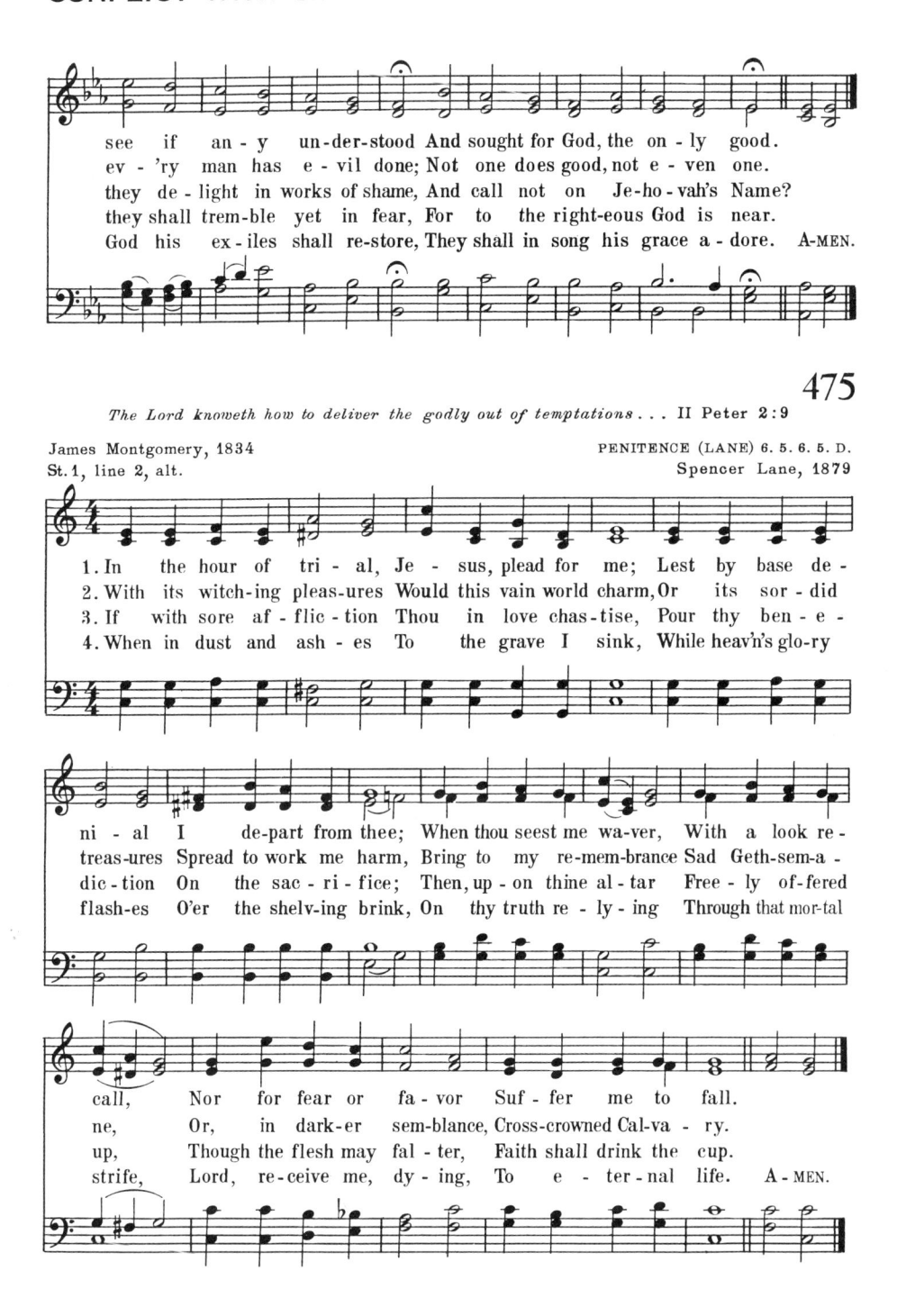

see if an-y un-der-stood And sought for God, the on-ly good.
ev-'ry man has e-vil done; Not one does good, not e-ven one.
they de-light in works of shame, And call not on Je-ho-vah's Name?
they shall trem-ble yet in fear, For to the right-eous God is near.
God his ex-iles shall re-store, They shall in song his grace a-dore. A-MEN.

## 475

*The Lord knoweth how to deliver the godly out of temptations... II Peter 2:9*

James Montgomery, 1834  
St. 1, line 2, alt.

PENITENCE (LANE) 6. 5. 6. 5. D.  
Spencer Lane, 1879

1. In the hour of tri-al, Je-sus, plead for me; Lest by base de-ni-al I de-part from thee; When thou seest me wa-ver, With a look re-call, Nor for fear or fa-vor Suf-fer me to fall.

2. With its witch-ing pleas-ures Would this vain world charm, Or its sor-did treas-ures Spread to work me harm, Bring to my re-mem-brance Sad Geth-sem-a-ne, Or, in dark-er sem-blance, Cross-crowned Cal-va-ry.

3. If with sore af-flic-tion Thou in love chas-tise, Pour thy ben-e-dic-tion On the sac-ri-fice; Then, up-on thine al-tar Free-ly of-fered up, Though the flesh may fal-ter, Faith shall drink the cup.

4. When in dust and ash-es To the grave I sink, While heav'n's glo-ry flash-es O'er the shelv-ing brink, On thy truth re-ly-ing Through that mor-tal strife, Lord, re-ceive me, dy-ing, To e-ter-nal life. A-MEN.

# 476                                       THE CHRISTIAN LIFE

*Watch and pray, that ye enter not into temptation... Matt. 26:41*

Johann B. Freystein, 1697, cento  
Tr. by Catherine Winkworth, 1863, alt.

STRAF MICH NICHT 7. 6. 7. 6. 8. 3. 6. 6.  
*Hundert Arien,* Dresden, 1694

1. Rise, my soul, to watch and pray, From thy sleep a-waken; Be not by the evil day Unawares o'er-taken. For the foe, Well we know, Oft his harvest reapeth While the Christian sleepeth.

2. Watch against the devil's snares Lest asleep he find thee; For indeed no pains he spares To deceive and blind thee. Satan's prey Oft are they Who secure are sleeping And no watch are keeping.

3. Watch! Let not the wicked world With its pow'r defeat thee. Watch lest with her pomp unfurled She betray and cheat thee. Watch and see Lest there be Faithless friends to charm thee, Who but seek to harm thee.

4. Watch against thyself, my soul, Lest with grace thou trifle; Let not self thy thoughts control Nor God's mercy stifle. Pride and sin Lurk within All thy hopes to scatter; Heed not when they flatter.

5. But while watching, also pray To the Lord unceasing. He will free thee, be thy stay, Strength and faith increasing. O Lord, bless In distress And let nothing swerve me From the will to serve thee. A-MEN.

# THE CHRISTIAN WARFARE 477

*Endure hardness, as a good soldier of Jesus Christ.* II Tim. 2:3

George Duffield, 1858

WEBB 7. 6. 7. 6. D.
George J. Webb, 1837

1. Stand up, stand up for Je - sus, Ye sol - diers of the cross;
Lift high his roy - al ban - ner, It must not suf - fer loss:
From vic - t'ry un - to vic - t'ry His ar - my he shall lead,
Till ev - 'ry foe is van - quished, And Christ is Lord in - deed.

2. Stand up, stand up for Je - sus, The trum - pet call o - bey;
Forth to the might - y con - flict In this his glo - rious day:
Ye that are men now serve him A - gainst un - num - bered foes;
Let cour - age rise with dan - ger, And strength to strength op - pose.

3. Stand up, stand up for Je - sus, Stand in his strength a - lone;
The arm of flesh will fail you, Ye dare not trust your own:
Put on the gos - pel ar - mor, Each piece put on with pray'r;
Where du - ty calls, or dan - ger, Be nev - er want - ing there.

4. Stand up, stand up for Je - sus, The strife will not be long;
This day the noise of bat - tle, The next the vic - tor's song:
To him that o - ver - com - eth A crown of life shall be;
He with the King of Glo - ry Shall reign e - ter - nal - ly. A - MEN.

## 478 THE CHRISTIAN LIFE

*Take unto you the whole armour of God.* Eph. 6:13

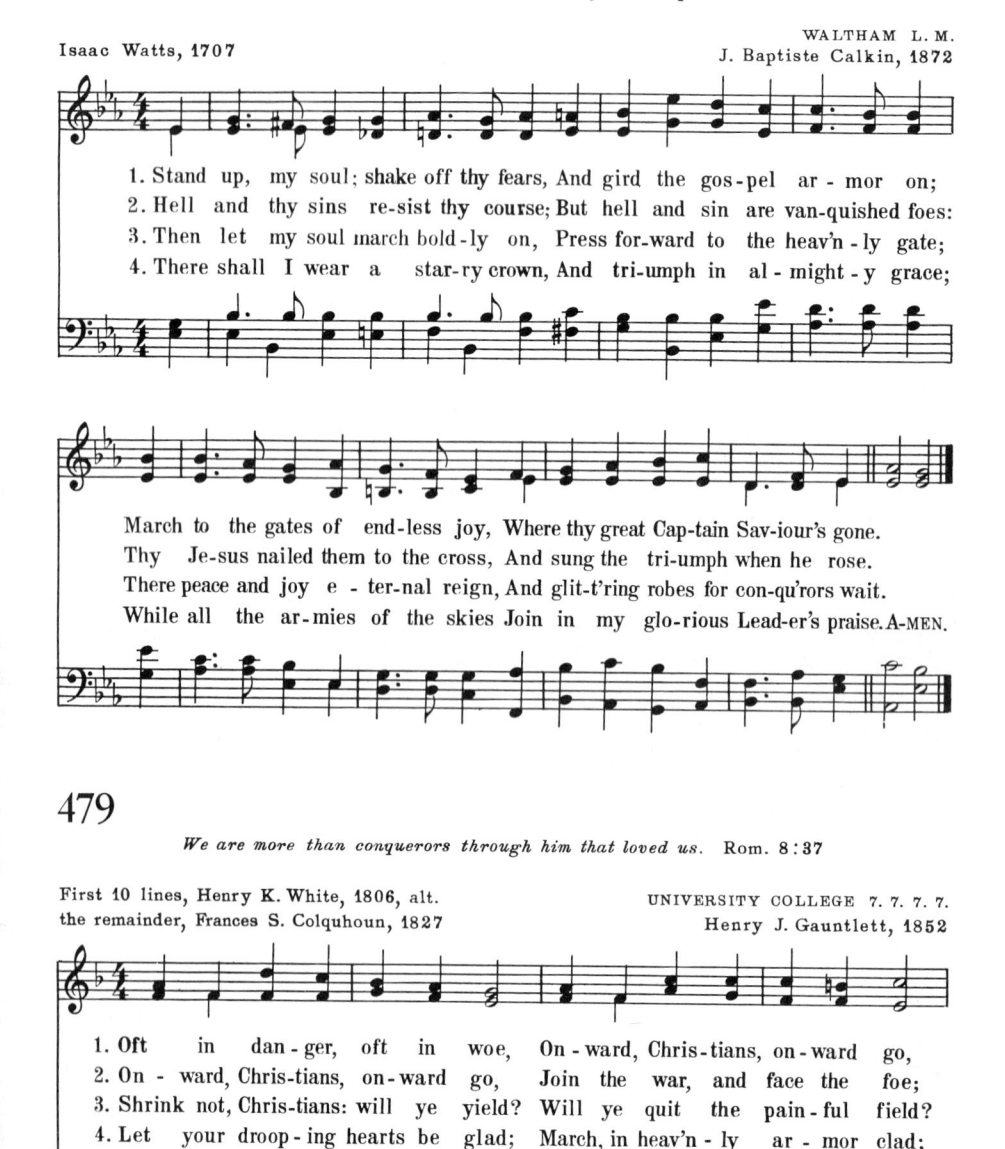

Isaac Watts, 1707

WALTHAM L. M.
J. Baptiste Calkin, 1872

1. Stand up, my soul; shake off thy fears, And gird the gos-pel ar - mor on;
   March to the gates of end-less joy, Where thy great Cap-tain Sav-iour's gone.
2. Hell and thy sins re-sist thy course; But hell and sin are van-quished foes:
   Thy Je-sus nailed them to the cross, And sung the tri-umph when he rose.
3. Then let my soul march bold-ly on, Press for-ward to the heav'n - ly gate;
   There peace and joy e - ter-nal reign, And glit-t'ring robes for con-qu'rors wait.
4. There shall I wear a star-ry crown, And tri-umph in al - might - y grace;
   While all the ar-mies of the skies Join in my glo-rious Lead-er's praise. A-MEN.

## 479

*We are more than conquerors through him that loved us.* Rom. 8:37

First 10 lines, Henry K. White, 1806, alt.
the remainder, Frances S. Colquhoun, 1827

UNIVERSITY COLLEGE 7. 7. 7. 7.
Henry J. Gauntlett, 1852

1. Oft in dan - ger, oft in woe, On - ward, Chris-tians, on - ward go,
2. On - ward, Chris-tians, on-ward go, Join the war, and face the foe;
3. Shrink not, Chris-tians: will ye yield? Will ye quit the pain-ful field?
4. Let your droop - ing hearts be glad; March, in heav'n - ly ar - mor clad;
5. Let not sor - row dim your eye, Soon shall ev - 'ry tear be dry;
6. On - ward then to bat - tle move; More than con-qu'rors ye shall prove:

# THE CHRISTIAN WARFARE

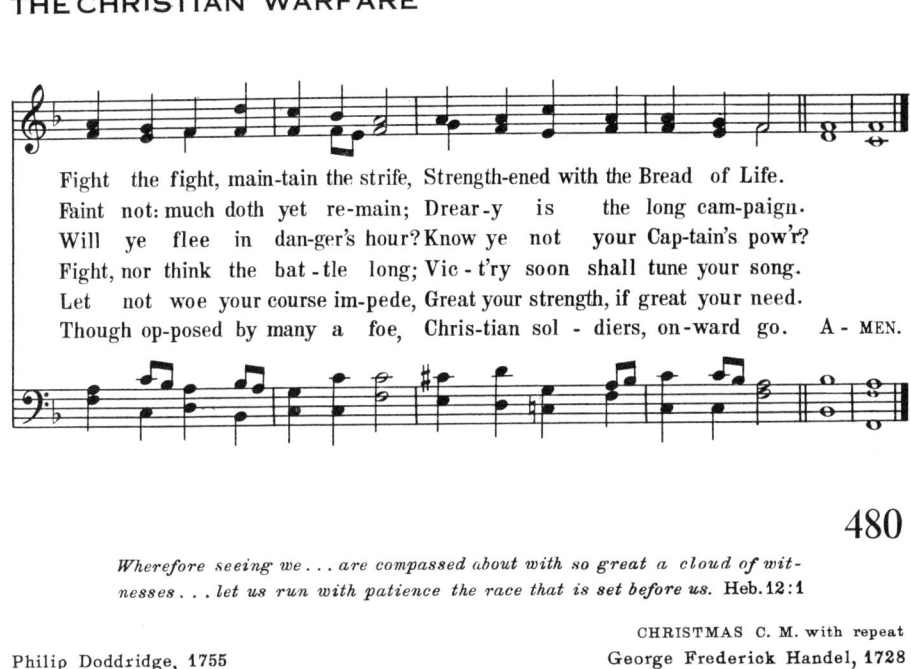

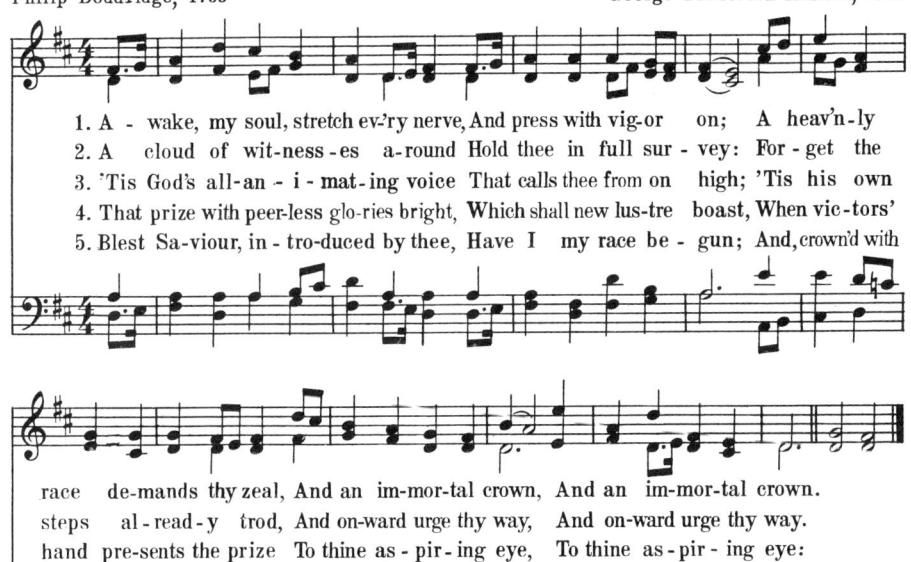

Fight the fight, main-tain the strife, Strength-ened with the Bread of Life.
Faint not: much doth yet re-main; Drear-y is the long cam-paign.
Will ye flee in dan-ger's hour? Know ye not your Cap-tain's pow'r?
Fight, nor think the bat-tle long; Vic-t'ry soon shall tune your song.
Let not woe your course im-pede, Great your strength, if great your need.
Though op-posed by many a foe, Chris-tian sol-diers, on-ward go. A-MEN.

### 480

*Wherefore seeing we ... are compassed about with so great a cloud of witnesses ... let us run with patience the race that is set before us.* Heb. 12:1

Philip Doddridge, 1755

CHRISTMAS C. M. with repeat
George Frederick Handel, 1728

1. A - wake, my soul, stretch ev-'ry nerve, And press with vig-or on; A heav'n-ly
2. A cloud of wit-ness-es a-round Hold thee in full sur-vey: For-get the
3. 'Tis God's all-an-i-mat-ing voice That calls thee from on high; 'Tis his own
4. That prize with peer-less glo-ries bright, Which shall new lus-tre boast, When vic-tors'
5. Blest Sa-viour, in-tro-duced by thee, Have I my race be-gun; And, crown'd with

race de-mands thy zeal, And an im-mor-tal crown, And an im-mor-tal crown.
steps al-read-y trod, And on-ward urge thy way, And on-ward urge thy way.
hand pre-sents the prize To thine as-pir-ing eye, To thine as-pir-ing eye:
wreaths and mon-archs' gems Shall blend in com-mon dust, Shall blend in com-mon dust.
vic-t'ry, at thy feet I'll lay my hon-ors down, I'll lay my hon-ors down. A-MEN.

# 481 THE CHRISTIAN LIFE

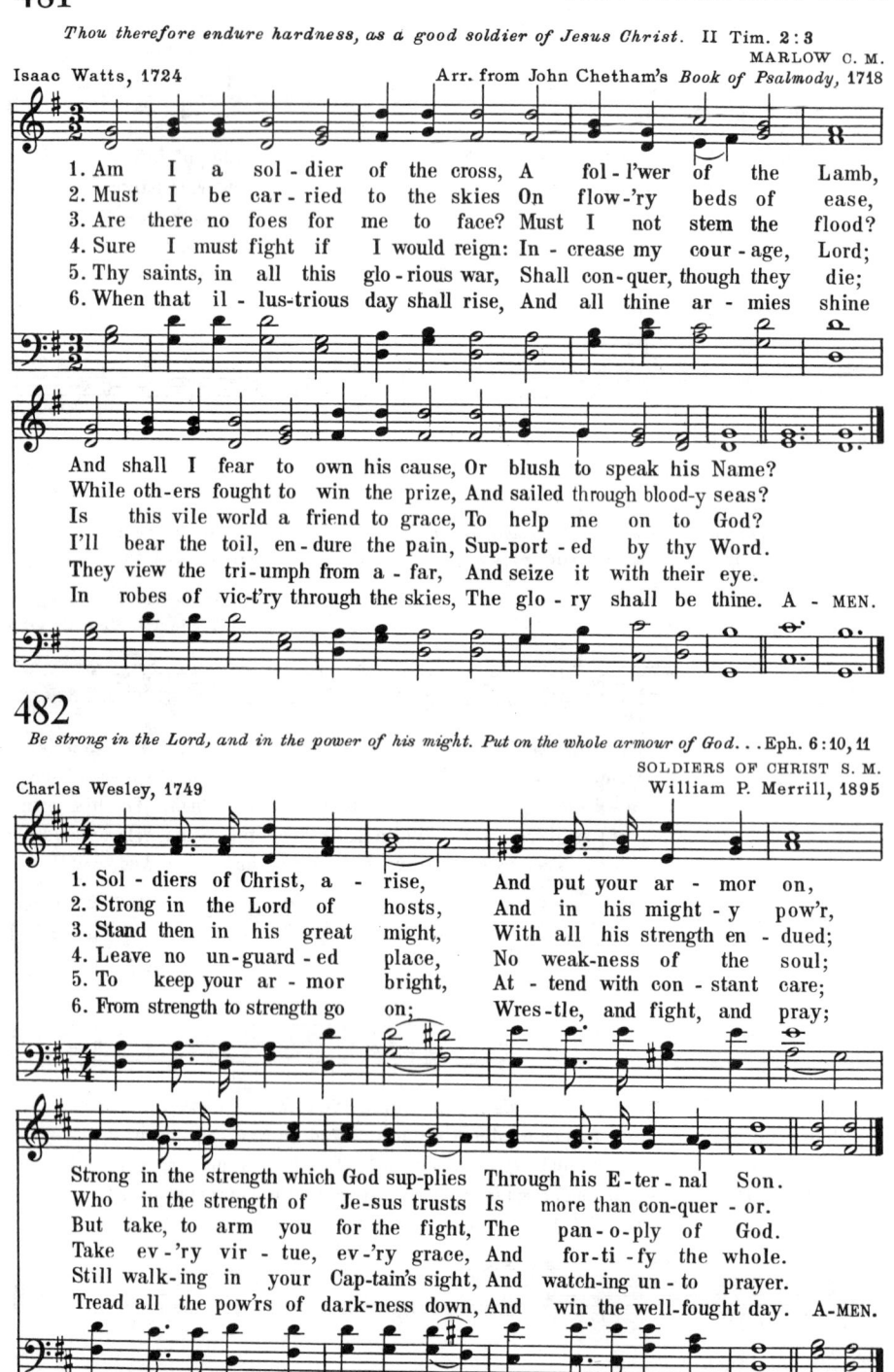

*Thou therefore endure hardness, as a good soldier of Jesus Christ.* II Tim. 2:3

MARLOW C. M.

Isaac Watts, 1724      Arr. from John Chetham's *Book of Psalmody*, 1718

1. Am I a sol-dier of the cross, A fol-l'wer of the Lamb,
2. Must I be car-ried to the skies On flow-'ry beds of ease,
3. Are there no foes for me to face? Must I not stem the flood?
4. Sure I must fight if I would reign: In-crease my cour-age, Lord;
5. Thy saints, in all this glo-rious war, Shall con-quer, though they die;
6. When that il-lus-trious day shall rise, And all thine ar-mies shine

And shall I fear to own his cause, Or blush to speak his Name?
While oth-ers fought to win the prize, And sailed through blood-y seas?
Is this vile world a friend to grace, To help me on to God?
I'll bear the toil, en-dure the pain, Sup-port-ed by thy Word.
They view the tri-umph from a-far, And seize it with their eye.
In robes of vic-t'ry through the skies, The glo-ry shall be thine. A-MEN.

# 482

*Be strong in the Lord, and in the power of his might. Put on the whole armour of God...* Eph. 6:10, 11

SOLDIERS OF CHRIST S. M.

Charles Wesley, 1749      William P. Merrill, 1895

1. Sol-diers of Christ, a-rise, And put your ar-mor on,
2. Strong in the Lord of hosts, And in his might-y pow'r,
3. Stand then in his great might, With all his strength en-dued;
4. Leave no un-guard-ed place, No weak-ness of the soul;
5. To keep your ar-mor bright, At-tend with con-stant care;
6. From strength to strength go on; Wres-tle, and fight, and pray;

Strong in the strength which God sup-plies Through his E-ter-nal Son.
Who in the strength of Je-sus trusts Is more than con-quer-or.
But take, to arm you for the fight, The pan-o-ply of God.
Take ev-'ry vir-tue, ev-'ry grace, And for-ti-fy the whole.
Still walk-ing in your Cap-tain's sight, And watch-ing un-to prayer.
Tread all the pow'rs of dark-ness down, And win the well-fought day. A-MEN.

# THE CHRISTIAN WARFARE 483

*Put on the whole armour of God, that ye may be able
to stand against the wiles of the devil.* Eph. 6:11

Tr. from an unknown Greek source
by John Mason Neale, 1862;
alt. in *The Parish Hymn Book*, 1863

ST. ANDREW OF CRETE 6.5.6.5.D.
John B. Dykes, 1868

1. Chris-tian, dost thou see them On the ho-ly ground,
2. Chris-tian, dost thou feel them, How they work with-in,
3. Chris-tian, dost thou hear them, How they speak thee fair?
4. Hear the words of Je-sus: "O my serv-ant true;

How the pow'rs of dark-ness Rage thy steps a-round?
Striv-ing, tempt-ing, lur-ing, Goad-ing in-to sin?
"Al-ways fast and vig-il? Al-ways watch and prayer?"
Thou art ver-y wea-ry,— I was wea-ry too;

*Faster*

Chris-tian, up and smite them, Count-ing gain but loss,
Chris-tian, nev-er trem-ble; Nev-er be down-cast;
Chris-tian, an-swer bold-ly, "While I breathe I pray!"
But that toil shall make thee Some day all mine own,

In the strength that com-eth By the ho-ly cross.
Gird thee for the bat-tle, Watch and pray and fast.
Peace shall fol-low bat-tle, Night shall end in day.
And the end of sor-row Shall be near my throne." A-MEN.

## 484 THE CHRISTIAN LIFE

*Fight the good fight of faith... I Tim. 6:12*

John S. B. Monsell, 1863

MOZART L. M.
Arr. from the *Kyrie* in the *Twelfth Mass*, attributed to Mozart

1. Fight the good fight With all thy might; Christ is thy
Strength, and Christ thy Right: Lay hold on life, and
it shall be Thy joy and crown e - ter - nal - ly.

2. Run the straight race Through God's good grace, Lift up thine
eyes, and seek his face; Life with its way be -
fore us lies, Christ is the Path, and Christ the Prize.

3. Cast care a - side; Up - on thy Guide Lean, and his
mer - cy will pro - vide; Lean, and the trust - ing
soul shall prove, Christ is its Life, and Christ its Love.

4. Faint not, nor fear, His arms are near; He chang - eth
not, and thou art dear; On - ly be - lieve, and
thou shalt see That Christ is all in all to thee. A - MEN.

## 485

*Ye shall receive a crown of glory that fadeth not away.* I Peter 5:4

Anon. in *Breviary* of Châlons-sur-Marne, 1736
Tr. by Isaac Williams, 1839;. recast in
*The Hymnary,* 1872

NUREMBERG 7. 7. 7. 7.
Alt. from Johann R. Ahle, 1664

1. Sol - diers who to Christ be - long, Trust ye in his Word, be strong;
2. His no crowns that pass a - way, His no palm that sees de - cay,
3. His the home for spir - its blest, Where he gives them peace - ful rest,
4. Here on earth ye can but clasp Things that per - ish in the grasp:
5. Praise we now with saints at rest Fa - ther, Son, and Spir - it blest;

# THE CHRISTIAN WARFARE

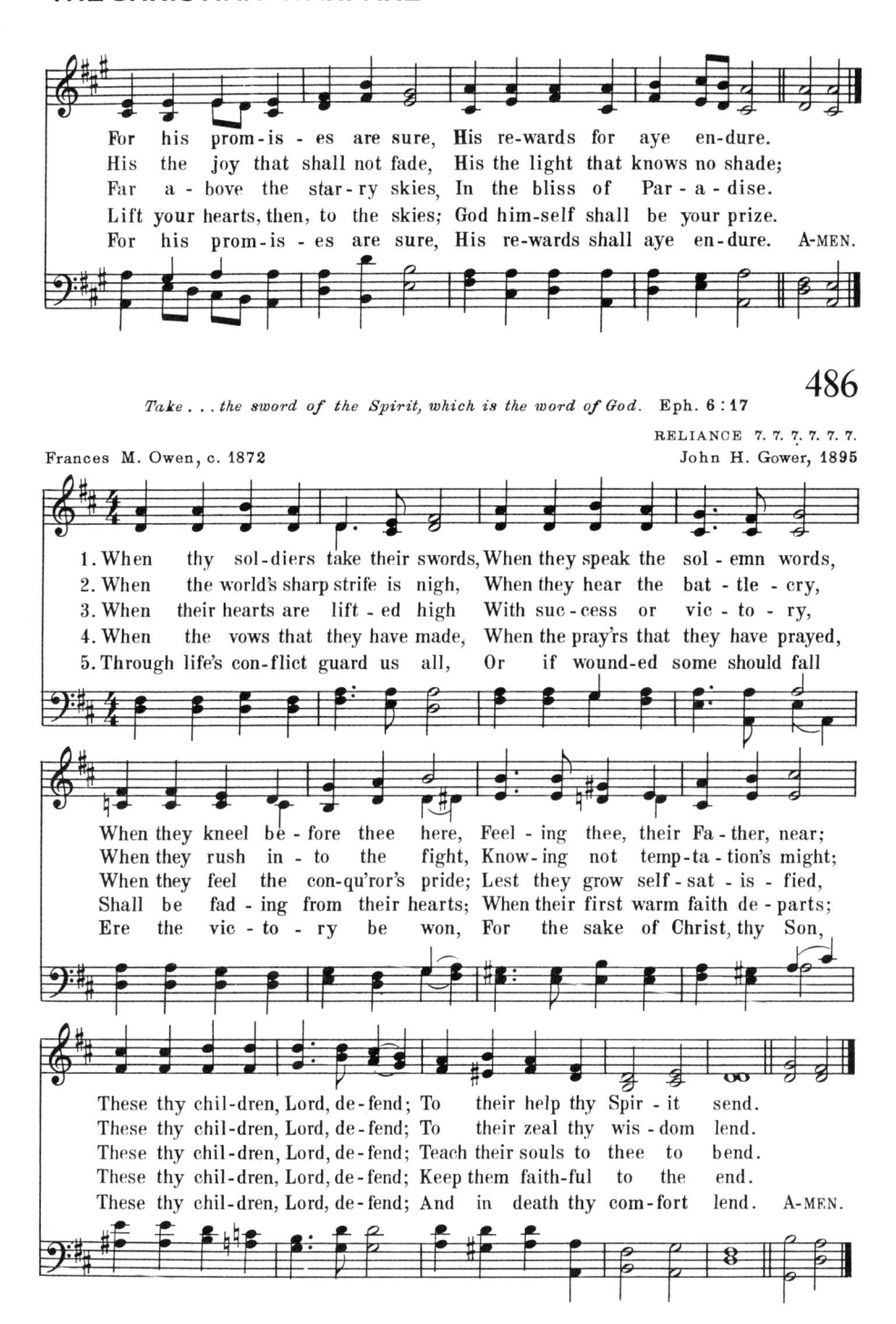

For his prom-is-es are sure, His re-wards for aye en-dure.
His the joy that shall not fade, His the light that knows no shade;
Far a-bove the star-ry skies, In the bliss of Par-a-dise.
Lift your hearts, then, to the skies; God him-self shall be your prize.
For his prom-is-es are sure, His re-wards shall aye en-dure. A-MEN.

### 486

*Take . . . the sword of the Spirit, which is the word of God.* Eph. 6:17

RELIANCE 7. 7. 7. 7. 7. 7.

Frances M. Owen, c. 1872

John H. Gower, 1895

1. When thy sol-diers take their swords, When they speak the sol-emn words,
2. When the world's sharp strife is nigh, When they hear the bat-tle-cry,
3. When their hearts are lift-ed high With suc-cess or vic-to-ry,
4. When the vows that they have made, When the pray'rs that they have prayed,
5. Through life's con-flict guard us all, Or if wound-ed some should fall

When they kneel be-fore thee here, Feel-ing thee, their Fa-ther, near;
When they rush in-to the fight, Know-ing not temp-ta-tion's might;
When they feel the con-qu'ror's pride; Lest they grow self-sat-is-fied,
Shall be fad-ing from their hearts; When their first warm faith de-parts;
Ere the vic-to-ry be won, For the sake of Christ, thy Son,

These thy chil-dren, Lord, de-fend; To their help thy Spir-it send.
These thy chil-dren, Lord, de-fend; To their zeal thy wis-dom lend.
These thy chil-dren, Lord, de-fend; Teach their souls to thee to bend.
These thy chil-dren, Lord, de-fend; Keep them faith-ful to the end.
These thy chil-dren, Lord, de-fend; And in death thy com-fort lend. A-MEN.

# 487          THE CHRISTIAN LIFE

*Earnestly contend for the faith which was once delivered unto the saints.*   Jude 3

Frederick W. Faber, 1849  
St. 2, line 4; st. 3, lines 1-4, alt.

ST. CATHERINE 8.8.8.8.8.8.  
Henri F. Hemy, 1864  
alt. by James G. Walton, 1870

1. Faith of our fa - thers! liv - ing still In spite of dun - geon, fire and sword; O how our hearts beat high with joy When-e'er we hear God's glo - rious Word: Faith of our fa - thers, ho - ly faith! We will be true to thee till death.

2. Our fa - thers, chained in pris - ons dark, Were still in heart and con - science free; And blest would be their chil - dren's fate If they, like them, should die for thee: Faith of our fa - thers, ho - ly faith! We will be true to thee till death.

3. Faith of our fa - thers! God's great pow'r Shall draw all na - tions un - to thee; And through the truth that comes from God His peo - ple shall in - deed be free: Faith of our fa - thers, ho - ly faith! We will be true to thee till death.

4. Faith of our fa - thers! we will love Both friend and foe in all our strife, And preach thee, too, as love knows how By wit - ness true and vir - tuous life: Faith of our fa - thers, ho - ly faith! We will be true to thee till death. A - MEN.

St. 1, line 4; st. 3, lines 2 and 4; st. 4, line 4: alt.

# THE CHRISTIAN WARFARE

**488**

*I am the Lord thy God . . . which leadeth thee by the way that thou shouldest go.* Isa. 48:17

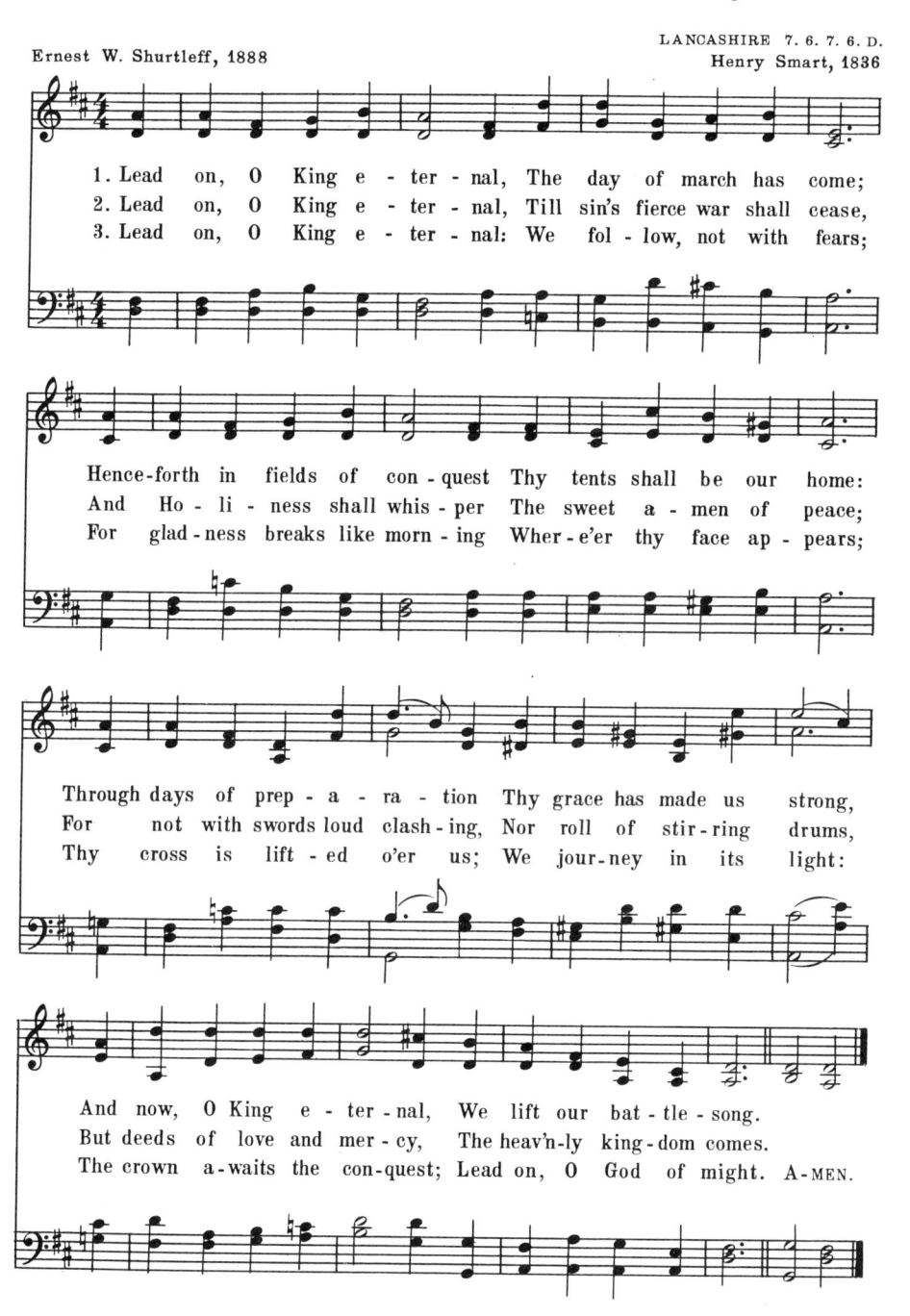

Ernest W. Shurtleff, 1888

LANCASHIRE 7. 6. 7. 6. D.
Henry Smart, 1836

1. Lead on, O King e-ter-nal, The day of march has come;
Hence-forth in fields of con-quest Thy tents shall be our home:
Through days of prep-a-ra-tion Thy grace has made us strong,
And now, O King e-ter-nal, We lift our bat-tle-song.

2. Lead on, O King e-ter-nal, Till sin's fierce war shall cease,
And Ho-li-ness shall whis-per The sweet a-men of peace;
For not with swords loud clash-ing, Nor roll of stir-ring drums,
But deeds of love and mer-cy, The heav'n-ly king-dom comes.

3. Lead on, O King e-ter-nal: We fol-low, not with fears;
For glad-ness breaks like morn-ing Wher-e'er thy face ap-pears;
Thy cross is lift-ed o'er us; We jour-ney in its light:
The crown a-waits the con-quest; Lead on, O God of might. A-MEN.

## 489 THE CHRISTIAN LIFE

*They loved not their lives unto the death.* Rev. 12:11

Reginald Heber, 1827

ALL SAINTS NEW C. M. D.
Henry S. Cutler, 1872

1. The Son of God goes forth to war, A king-ly crown to gain;
His blood-red ban-ner streams a-far: Who fol-lows in His train?
Who best can drink his cup of woe, Tri-um-phant o-ver pain,
Who pa-tient bears his cross be-low, He fol-lows in His train.

2. The mar-tyr first, whose ea-gle eye Could pierce be-yond the grave,
Who saw his Mas-ter in the sky, And called on Him to save:
Like Him, with par-don on his tongue In midst of mor-tal pain,
He prayed for them that did the wrong: Who fol-lows in his train?

3. A glo-rious band, the cho-sen few On whom the Spir-it came,
Twelve va-liant saints, their hope they knew, And mocked the cross and flame:
They met the ty-rant's brand-ished steel, The li-on's gor-y mane;
They bowed their necks the death to feel: Who fol-lows in their train?

4. A no-ble ar-my, men and boys, The ma-tron and the maid,
A-round the Sav-iour's throne re-joice, In robes of light ar-rayed:
They climbed the steep as-cent of heav'n Through per-il, toil, and pain:
O God, to us may grace be giv'n To fol-low in their train. A-MEN.

# THE CHRISTIAN WARFARE 490

*I will build my church; and the gates of hell shall not prevail against it.* Matt. 16:18

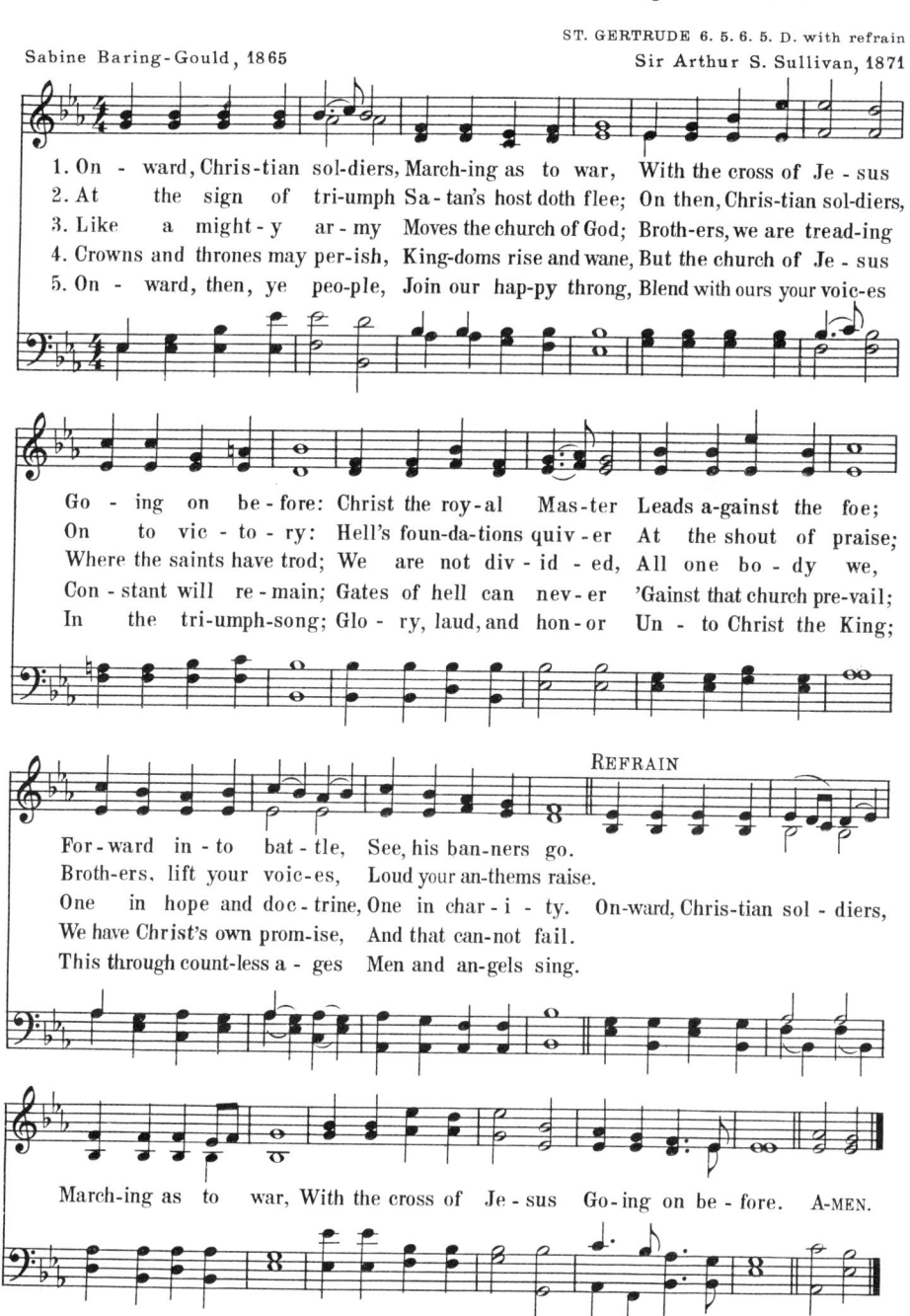

Sabine Baring-Gould, 1865

ST. GERTRUDE 6. 5. 6. 5. D. with refrain
Sir Arthur S. Sullivan, 1871

1. On-ward, Chris-tian sol-diers, March-ing as to war, With the cross of Je-sus
2. At the sign of tri-umph Sa-tan's host doth flee; On then, Chris-tian sol-diers,
3. Like a might-y ar-my Moves the church of God; Broth-ers, we are tread-ing
4. Crowns and thrones may per-ish, King-doms rise and wane, But the church of Je-sus
5. On-ward, then, ye peo-ple, Join our hap-py throng, Blend with ours your voic-es

Go-ing on be-fore: Christ the roy-al Mas-ter Leads a-gainst the foe;
On to vic-to-ry: Hell's foun-da-tions quiv-er At the shout of praise;
Where the saints have trod; We are not div-id-ed, All one bo-dy we,
Con-stant will re-main; Gates of hell can nev-er 'Gainst that church pre-vail;
In the tri-umph-song; Glo-ry, laud, and hon-or Un-to Christ the King;

REFRAIN

For-ward in-to bat-tle, See, his ban-ners go.
Broth-ers, lift your voic-es, Loud your an-thems raise.
One in hope and doc-trine, One in char-i-ty.       On-ward, Chris-tian sol-diers,
We have Christ's own prom-ise, And that can-not fail.
This through count-less a-ges Men and an-gels sing.

March-ing as to war, With the cross of Je-sus Go-ing on be-fore. A-MEN.

## 491 THE CHRISTIAN LIFE

*And he saith unto them, Follow me ... And they straightway ... followed him.* Matt. 4:19, 20

Cecil Frances Alexander, 1852
St. 2, line 1, alt.

GALILEE 8. 7. 8. 7.
William H. Jude, 1887

1. Je-sus calls us: o'er the tu-mult Of our life's wild, rest-less sea,
2. As, of old, a-pos-tles heard it By the Gal-i-le-an lake,
3. Je-sus calls us from the wor-ship Of the vain world's gold-en store,
4. In our joys and in our sor-rows, Days of toil and hours of ease,
5. Je-sus calls us: by thy mer-cies, Sav-iour, may we hear thy call,

Day by day his sweet voice sound-eth, Say-ing, "Chris-tian, fol-low me."
Turned from home and toil and kin-dred, Leav-ing all for his dear sake.
From each i-dol that would keep us, Say-ing, "Chris-tian, love me more."
Still he calls, in cares and pleas-ures, "Chris-tian, love me more than these."
Give our hearts to thine o-be-dience, Serve and love thee best of all. A-MEN.

## 492

*Yield your members servants to righteousness unto holiness.* Rom. 6:19

Frances R. Havergal, 1874

ST. BEES 7. 7. 7. 7.
John B. Dykes, 1862

1. Take my life, and let it be Con-se-cra-ted, Lord, to thee.
2. Take my hands, and let them move At the im-pulse of thy love.
3. Take my voice, and let me sing, Al-ways, on-ly, for my King.
4. Take my sil-ver and my gold; Not a mite would I with-hold.
5. Take my will, and make it thine; It shall be no long-er mine.
6. Take my love; my Lord, I pour At thy feet its treas-ure-store.

Take my mo-ments and my days; Let them flow in cease-less praise.
Take my feet, and let them be Swift and beau-ti-ful for thee.
Take my lips, and let them be Filled with mes-sag-es from thee.
Take my in-tel-lect, and use Ev-'ry pow'r as thou shalt choose.
Take my heart, it is thine own; It shall be thy roy-al throne.
Take my-self, and I will be Ev-er, on-ly, all for thee. A-MEN.

# CHRISTIAN SERVICE 493

*Who is on the Lord's side?* Ex. 32:26

Frances R. Havergal, 1877

ARMAGEDDON 6. 5. 6. 5. 6. 5. D.
German melody arr. by Sir John Goss, 1871

1. Who is on the Lord's side? Who will serve the King?
2. Not for weight of glo - ry, Not for crown and palm,
3. Je - sus, thou hast bought us, Not with gold or gem,
4. Fierce may be the con - flict, Strong may be the foe,

Who will be his help - ers, Oth - er lives to bring? Who will leave the
En - ter we the ar - my, Raise the war - rior psalm; But for Love that
But with thine own life - blood, For thy di - a - dem: With thy bless - ing
But the King's own ar - my None can o - ver - throw: Round his stan - dard

world's side? Who will face the foe? Who is on the Lord's side? Who for
claim - eth Lives for whom he died: He whom Je - sus nam - eth Must be
fill - ing Each who comes to thee, Thou hast made us will - ing, Thou hast
rang - ing, Vic - t'ry is se - cure; For his truth un - chang - ing Makes the

him will go? By thy call of mer - cy, By thy grace Di - vine,
on his side. By thy love con - strain - ing, By thy grace Di - vine,
made us free. By thy grand re - demp - tion, By thy grace Di - vine,
tri - umph sure. Joy - ful - ly en - list - ing By thy grace Di - vine,

We are on the Lord's side, Sav - iour, we are thine. A - MEN.

## 494 THE CHRISTIAN LIFE

*Whose I am, and whom I serve.* Acts 27:23

Frances R. Havergal, 1865
WELLS 7. 7. 7. 7. 7. 7.
Adapted from Dimitri Bortnianski, 1752-1825

1. Jesus, Master, whose I am, Purchased thine alone to be
2. Jesus, Master, I am thine: Keep me faithful, keep me near;
3. Jesus, Master, whom I serve, Though so feebly and so ill,
4. Lord, thou needest not, I know, Service such as I can bring;

By thy blood, O spotless Lamb, Shed so willingly for me,
Let thy presence in me shine All my homeward way to cheer.
Strengthen hand and heart and nerve All thy bidding to fulfil.
Yet I long to prove and show Full allegiance to my King.

Let my heart be all thine own, Let me live to thee alone.
Jesus, at thy feet I fall, O be thou my all in all.
Open thou mine eyes to see All the work thou hast for me.
Thou an honor art to me: Let me be a praise to thee. A-MEN.

## 495

*I will bless the Lord at all times: his praise shall continually be in my mouth.* Psalm 34:1

Horatius Bonar, 1866
LAMBETH C. M.
William Schulthes, 1871

1. Fill thou my life, O Lord my God, In ev'ry part with praise,
2. Not for the lip of praise alone, Nor e'en the praising heart,
3. Praise in the common things of life, Its goings out and in,
4. Fill ev'ry part of me with praise; Let all my being speak
5. So shalt thou, Lord, from me, e'en me, Receive the glory due,
6. So shall no part of day or night From sacredness be free:

## CHRISTIAN SERVICE

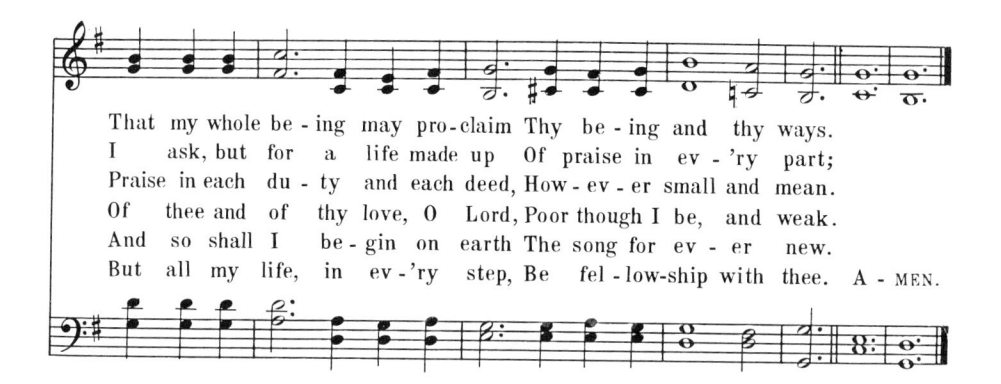

That my whole be-ing may pro-claim Thy be-ing and thy ways.
I ask, but for a life made up Of praise in ev-'ry part;
Praise in each du-ty and each deed, How-ev-er small and mean.
Of thee and of thy love, O Lord, Poor though I be, and weak.
And so shall I be-gin on earth The song for ev-er new.
But all my life, in ev-'ry step, Be fel-low-ship with thee. A-MEN.

496

*Let us not be weary in well doing: for in due season we shall reap, if we faint not.* Gal. 6:9

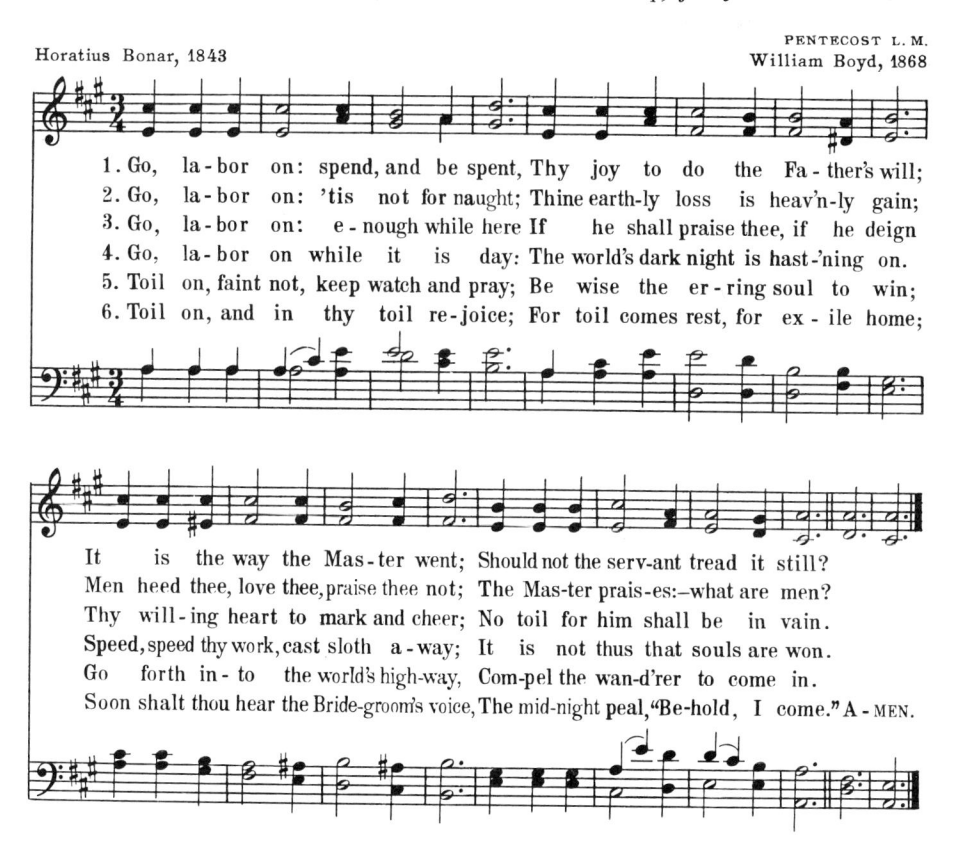

Horatius Bonar, 1843

PENTECOST L. M.
William Boyd, 1868

1. Go, la-bor on: spend, and be spent, Thy joy to do the Fa-ther's will;
2. Go, la-bor on: 'tis not for naught; Thine earth-ly loss is heav'n-ly gain;
3. Go, la-bor on: e-nough while here If he shall praise thee, if he deign
4. Go, la-bor on while it is day: The world's dark night is hast-'ning on.
5. Toil on, faint not, keep watch and pray; Be wise the er-ring soul to win;
6. Toil on, and in thy toil re-joice; For toil comes rest, for ex-ile home;

It is the way the Mas-ter went; Should not the serv-ant tread it still?
Men heed thee, love thee, praise thee not; The Mas-ter prais-es:—what are men?
Thy will-ing heart to mark and cheer; No toil for him shall be in vain.
Speed, speed thy work, cast sloth a-way; It is not thus that souls are won.
Go forth in-to the world's high-way, Com-pel the wan-d'rer to come in.
Soon shalt thou hear the Bride-groom's voice, The mid-night peal, "Be-hold, I come." A-MEN.

Music used by permission of Novello & Company, Ltd.

## 497

THE CHRISTIAN LIFE

*When thou passest through the waters, I will be with thee.* Isa. 43:2

Edward Hopper, 1871

PILOT 7. 7. 7. 7. 7. 7.
John E. Gould, 1871

1. Jesus, Saviour, pilot me Over life's tempestuous sea;
   Unknown waves before me roll, Hiding rock and treach'rous shoal;
   Chart and compass came from thee: Jesus, Saviour, pilot me.
2. As a mother stills her child, Thou canst hush the ocean wild;
   Bois-t'rous waves obey thy will When thou sayest to them, "Be still."
   Won-drous Sovereign of the sea, Jesus, Saviour, pilot me.
3. When at last I near the shore, And the fearful breakers roar
   'Twixt me and the peaceful rest, Then, while leaning on thy breast,
   May I hear thee say to me, "Fear not, I will pilot thee." A-MEN.

## 498

*Behold, I am with thee, and will keep thee in all places whither thou goest.* Gen. 28:15

Philip Doddridge, 1737
John Logan, 1781
St. 5 added in *Scottish Paraphrases,* 1781

GREEN HILL C. M.
Albert L. Peace, 1885

1. O God of Bethel, by whose hand Thy people still are fed,
2. Our vows, our pray'rs, we now present Before thy Throne of grace;
3. Through each perplexing path of life Our wand'ring footsteps guide;
4. O spread thy cov'ring wings around Till all our wand'rings cease,
5. Such blessings from thy gracious hand Our humble pray'rs implore;

# PILGRIMAGE AND GUIDANCE

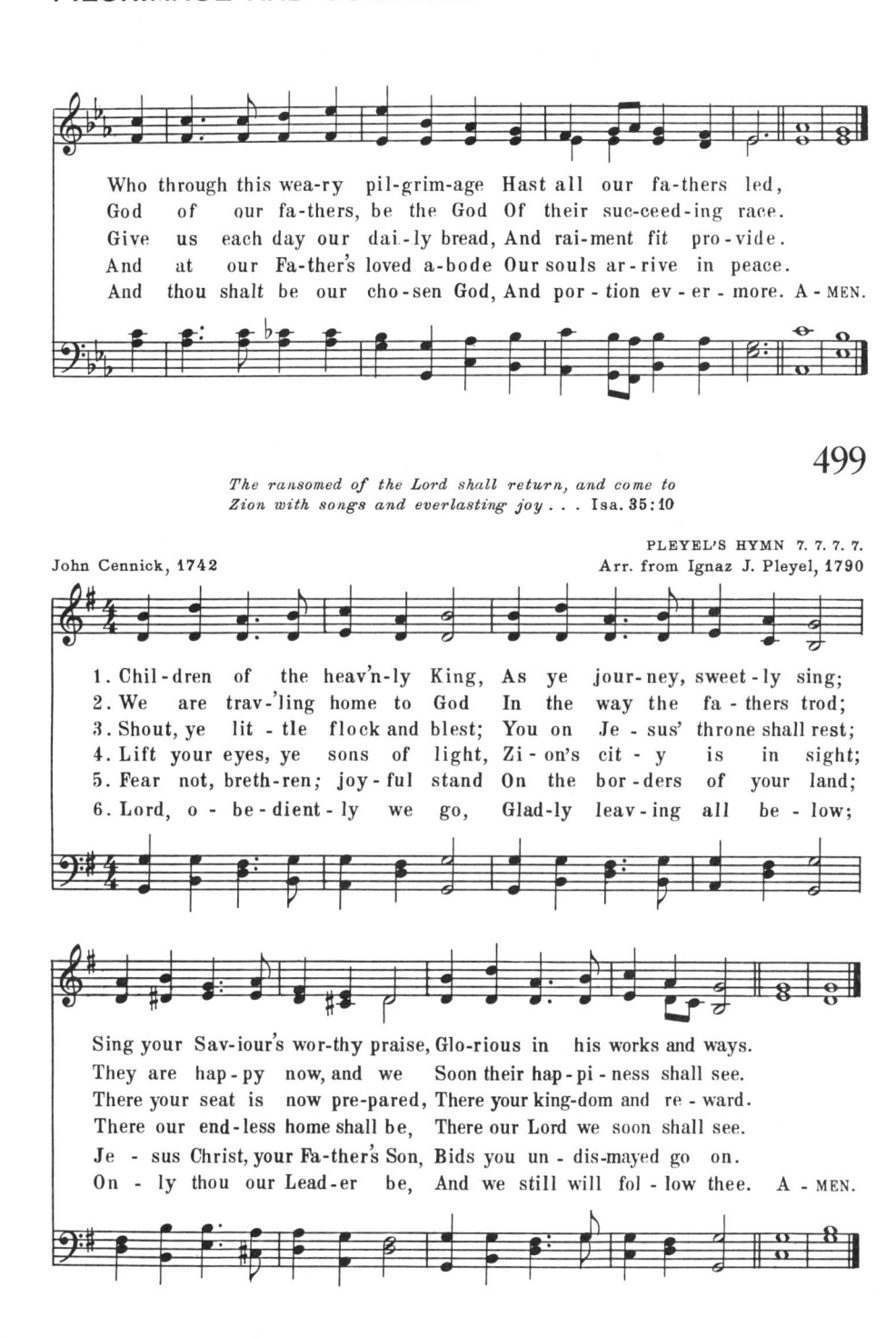

Who through this wea-ry pil-grim-age Hast all our fa-thers led,
God of our fa-thers, be the God Of their suc-ceed-ing race.
Give us each day our dai-ly bread, And rai-ment fit pro-vide.
And at our Fa-ther's loved a-bode Our souls ar-rive in peace.
And thou shalt be our cho-sen God, And por-tion ev-er-more. A-MEN.

499

*The ransomed of the Lord shall return, and come to Zion with songs and everlasting joy . . . Isa. 35:10*

John Cennick, 1742

PLEYEL'S HYMN 7. 7. 7. 7.
Arr. from Ignaz J. Pleyel, 1790

1. Chil-dren of the heav'n-ly King, As ye jour-ney, sweet-ly sing;
2. We are trav-'ling home to God In the way the fa-thers trod;
3. Shout, ye lit-tle flock and blest; You on Je-sus' throne shall rest;
4. Lift your eyes, ye sons of light, Zi-on's cit-y is in sight;
5. Fear not, breth-ren; joy-ful stand On the bor-ders of your land;
6. Lord, o-be-dient-ly we go, Glad-ly leav-ing all be-low;

Sing your Sav-iour's wor-thy praise, Glo-rious in his works and ways.
They are hap-py now, and we Soon their hap-pi-ness shall see.
There your seat is now pre-pared, There your king-dom and re-ward.
There our end-less home shall be, There our Lord we soon shall see.
Je-sus Christ, your Fa-ther's Son, Bids you un-dis-mayed go on.
On-ly thou our Lead-er be, And we still will fol-low thee. A-MEN.

# 500  THE CHRISTIAN LIFE

*Thou hast holden me by my right hand. Thou shalt guide me...* Psalm 73:23-24

Joseph H. Gilmore, 1862  
Lines 3, 4 of refrain added

HE LEADETH ME L.M.D.  
William B. Bradbury, 1864

1. He lead-eth me: O bless-ed thought! O words with heav'n-ly com-fort fraught! What-e'er I do, wher-e'er I be, Still 'tis God's hand that lead-eth me.
2. Some-times 'mid scenes of deep-est gloom, Some-times where E-den's bow-ers bloom, By wa-ters calm, o'er trou-bled sea, Still 'tis his hand that lead-eth me.
3. Lord, I would clasp thy hand in mine, Nor ev-er mur-mur nor re-pine; Con-tent, what-ev-er lot I see, Since 'tis my God that lead-eth me.
4. And when my task on earth is done, When, by thy grace, the vic-t'ry's won, E'en death's cold wave I will not flee, Since God through Jor-dan lead-eth me.

REFRAIN

He lead-eth me, he lead-eth me; By his own hand he lead-eth me: His faith-ful fol-l'wer I would be, For by his hand he lead-eth me. A-MEN.

## PILGRIMAGE AND GUIDANCE 501

*He will be our guide even unto death.* Psalm 48:14

William Williams (Welsh), 1745
St. 1 tr. by Peter Williams, 1771
St. 2-3 tr. by William Williams, c. 1772

CWM RHONDDA 8.7.8.7.8.7. with repeat
John Hughes, 1907

*In moderate time*

1. Guide me, O thou great Je - ho - vah, Pil - grim through this bar - ren land; I am weak, but thou art might - y; Hold me with thy pow'r - ful hand; Bread of heav - en, Bread of heav - en, Feed me till I want no more, Feed me till I want no more.

2. O - pen now the crys - tal foun - tain, Whence the heal - ing stream doth flow; Let the fire and cloud - y pil - lar Lead me all my jour - ney through; Strong De - liv - erer, strong De - liv - erer, Be thou still my Strength and Shield, Be thou still my Strength and Shield.

3. When I tread the verge of Jor - dan, Bid my anx - ious fears sub - side; Death of death, and hell's De - struc - tion, Land me safe on Ca - naan's side; Songs of prais - es, songs of prais - es I will ev - er give to thee, I will ev - er give to thee. A-MEN.

Music copyrighted. Used by permission of Mrs. John Hughes.

# THE CHRISTIAN LIFE

**502**

*Who shall ascend into the hill of the Lord?... He that hath clean hands and a pure heart... Psalm 24:3, 4*

Edward H. Plumptre, 1865
MARION S.M. with refrain
Arthur H. Messiter, 1885

1. Rejoice, ye pure in heart, Rejoice, give thanks, and sing:
2. Bright youth and snow-crowned age, Strong men and maidens meek,
3. With all the angel choirs, With all the saints on earth,
4. Yes, on through life's long path, Still chanting as ye go;
5. At last the march shall end, The wearied ones shall rest,
6. Then on, ye pure in heart, Rejoice, give thanks, and sing;

Your festal banner wave on high, The cross of Christ your King.
Raise high your free, exulting song, God's wondrous praises speak.
Pour out the strains of joy and bliss, True rapture, noblest mirth!
From youth to age, by night and day, In gladness and in woe.
The pilgrims find their Father's house, Jerusalem the blest.
Your glorious banner wave on high, The cross of Christ your King.

**REFRAIN**

Rejoice, rejoice, Rejoice, give thanks, and sing. A-MEN.

---

**503**

*In all things approving ourselves as the ministers of God... by evil report and good report... II Cor. 6:4, 8*

Horatius Bonar, 1866
HANFORD 8.8.8.4.
Sir Arthur S. Sullivan, 1874

1. Through good report and evil, Lord, Still guided by thy faithful Word,
2. With enemies on ev'ry side, We lean on thee, the Crucified;
3. O Master, point thou out the way, Nor suffer thou our steps to stray;
4. Thou hast passed on before our face; Thy footsteps on the way we trace:
5. Whom have we in the heav'n above, Whom on this earth, save thee, to love?

## PILGRIMAGE AND GUIDANCE

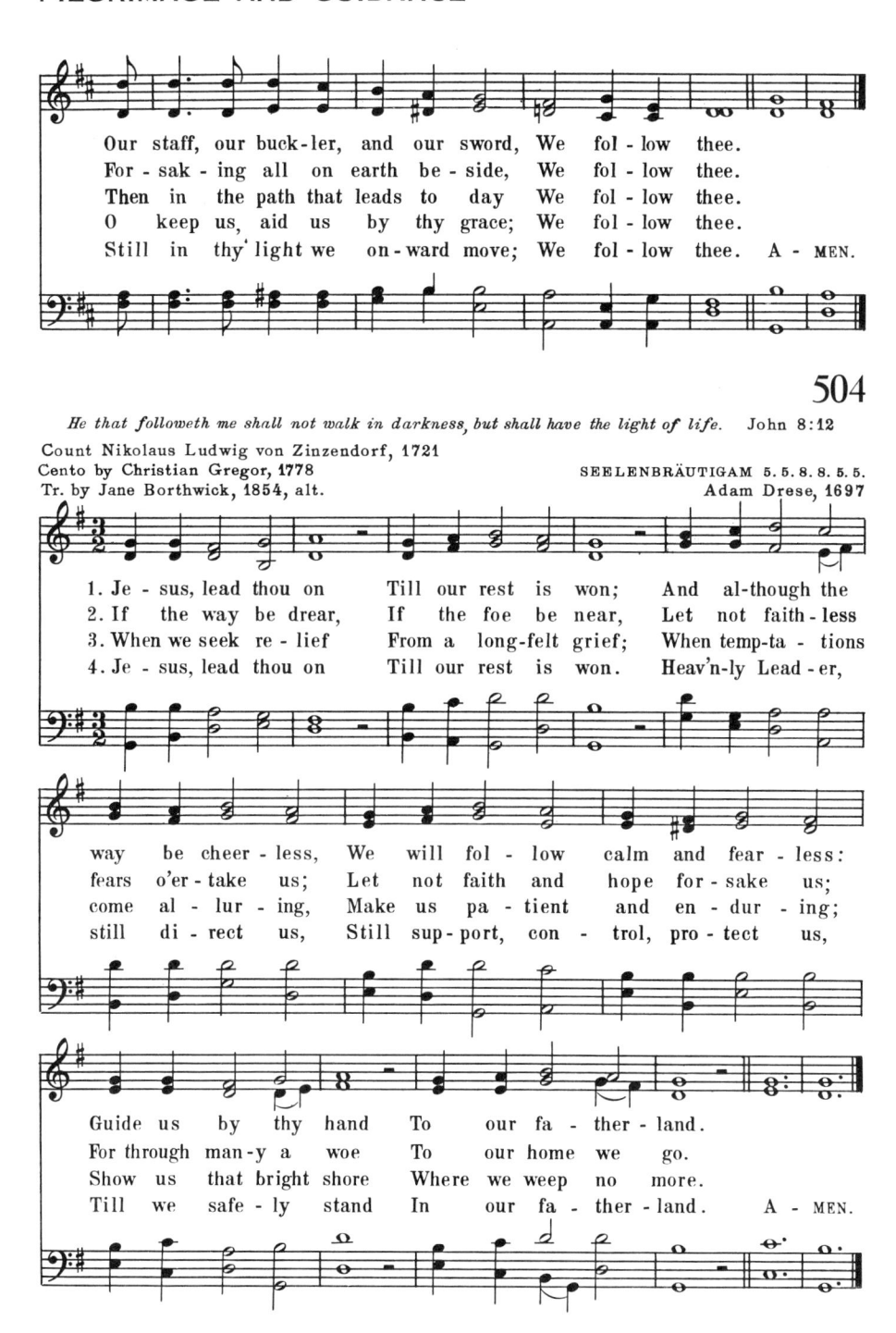

Our staff, our buck-ler, and our sword, We fol-low thee.
For-sak-ing all on earth be-side, We fol-low thee.
Then in the path that leads to day We fol-low thee.
O keep us, aid us by thy grace; We fol-low thee.
Still in thy light we on-ward move; We fol-low thee. A-MEN.

**504**

*He that followeth me shall not walk in darkness, but shall have the light of life.* John 8:12

Count Nikolaus Ludwig von Zinzendorf, 1721
Cento by Christian Gregor, 1778
Tr. by Jane Borthwick, 1854, alt.

SEELENBRÄUTIGAM 5.5.8.8.5.5.
Adam Drese, 1697

1. Je-sus, lead thou on    Till our rest is won;    And al-though the
2. If the way be drear,    If the foe be near,    Let not faith-less
3. When we seek re-lief    From a long-felt grief;    When temp-ta-tions
4. Je-sus, lead thou on    Till our rest is won.    Heav'n-ly Lead-er,

way be cheer-less,    We will fol-low    calm and fear-less:
fears o'er-take us;    Let not faith and    hope for-sake us;
come al-lur-ing,    Make us pa-tient    and en-dur-ing;
still di-rect us,    Still sup-port, con-trol, pro-tect us,

Guide us by thy hand    To our fa-ther-land.
For through man-y a woe    To our home we go.
Show us that bright shore    Where we weep no more.
Till we safe-ly stand    In our fa-ther-land. A-MEN.

# 505 THE CHRISTIAN LIFE: PILGRIMAGE

*He goeth before them, and the sheep follow him . . . John 10:4*

Fanny J. Crosby, 1820-1915

ALL THE WAY 8. 7. 8. 7. D.
Robert Lowry, 1826-1899

1. All the way my Sav-iour leads me—What have I to ask be-side?
2. All the way my Sav-iour leads me, Cheers each wind-ing path I tread,
3. All the way my Sav-iour leads me— O the ful-ness of his love!

Can I doubt his ten-der mer-cy Who through life has been my Guide?
Gives me grace for ev-'ry tri-al, Feeds me with the liv-ing Bread.
Per-fect rest to me is prom-ised In my Fa-ther's house a-bove:

Heav'n-ly peace, di-vin-est com-fort, Here by faith in him to dwell—
Though my wea-ry steps may fal-ter, And my soul a-thirst may be,
When my spir-it, clothed, im-mor-tal, Wings its flight to realms of day,

For I know, what-e'er be-fall me, Je-sus do-eth all things well.
Gush-ing from the rock be-fore me, Lo, a spring of joy I see!
This my song through end-less a-ges: Je-sus led me all the way! A-MEN.

# THE CHRISTIAN LIFE: TRIBULATION  506

*I am continually with thee: thou hast holden me by my right hand. Thou shalt guide me with thy counsel, and afterward receive me to glory.* Psalm 73:23-24

Paul Gerhardt, 1653, cento
Tr., composite, based on John Kelly, 1867

WARUM SOLLT' ICH MICH DENN GRÄMEN
8. 3. 3. 6. 8. 3. 3. 6.
Johann G. Ebeling, 1666

1. Why should cross and tri-al grieve me? Christ is near With his cheer; That God's Son For my own To my faith hath giv-en?
2. God oft gives me days of glad-ness; Shall I grieve If he give Sea-sons, too, of sad-ness? God is good and tem-pers ev-er All my ill, And he will Whol-ly leave me nev-er.
3. Death can-not de-stroy for ev-er; From our fears, Cares, and tears It will us de-liv-er. It will close life's mourn-ful sto-ry, Make a way That we may En-ter heav'n-ly glo-ry.
4. Lord, my Shep-herd, take me to thee. Thou art mine; I was thine, E-ven ere I knew thee. I am thine, for thou hast bought me; Lost I stood, But thy blood Free sal-va-tion brought me.
5. Thou art mine; I love and own thee. Light of Joy, Ne'er shall I Nev-er will he leave me. Who can rob me of the heav-en From my heart de-throne thee. Sav-iour, let me soon be-hold thee Face to face,—May thy grace Ev-er-more en-fold me! A-MEN.

## 507 THE CHRISTIAN LIFE

*If any man will come after me, let him deny himself, and take up his cross, and follow me.* Matt. 16:24

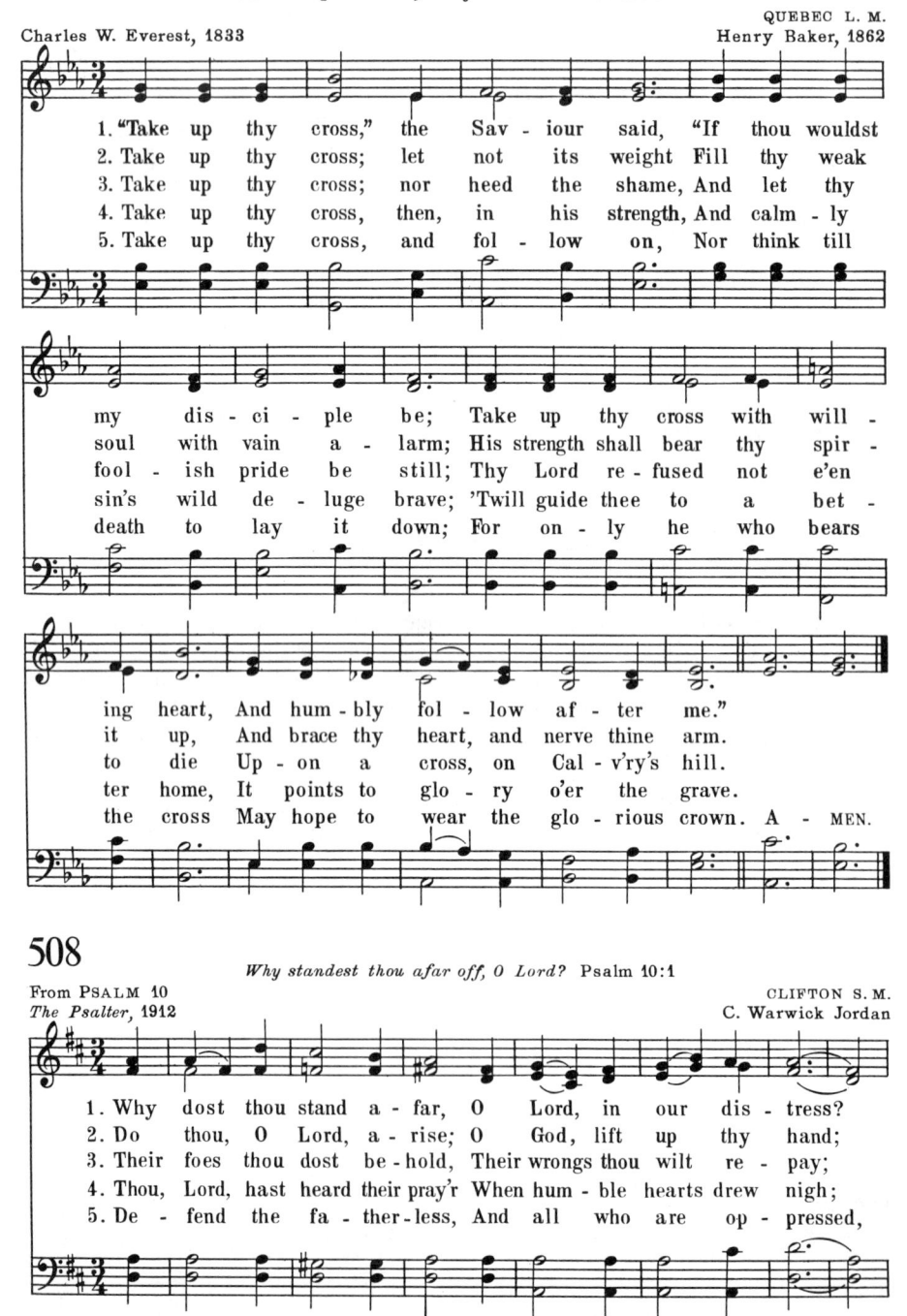

Charles W. Everest, 1833

QUEBEC L. M.
Henry Baker, 1862

1. "Take up thy cross," the Saviour said, "If thou wouldst my disciple be; Take up thy cross with willing heart, And humbly follow after me."
2. Take up thy cross; let not its weight Fill thy weak soul with vain alarm; His strength shall bear thy spirit up, And brace thy heart, and nerve thine arm.
3. Take up thy cross; nor heed the shame, And let thy foolish pride be still; Thy Lord refused not e'en to die Upon a cross, on Cal'vry's hill.
4. Take up thy cross, then, in his strength, And calmly sin's wild deluge brave; 'Twill guide thee to a better home, It points to glory o'er the grave.
5. Take up thy cross, and follow on, Nor think till death to lay it down; For only he who bears the cross May hope to wear the glorious crown. A-MEN.

## 508

*Why standest thou afar off, O Lord?* Psalm 10:1

From PSALM 10
The Psalter, 1912

CLIFTON S. M.
C. Warwick Jordan

1. Why dost thou stand afar, O Lord, in our distress?
2. Do thou, O Lord, arise; O God, lift up thy hand;
3. Their foes thou dost behold, Their wrongs thou wilt repay;
4. Thou, Lord, hast heard their pray'r When humble hearts drew nigh;
5. Defend the fatherless, And all who are oppressed,

# TRIBULATION AND SUFFERING

And why dost thou con-ceal thy-self When trou-blous times op-press?
For - get thou not the suf-f'ring poor, The hum-ble in the land.
The poor com-mit them-selves to thee, Thou art the or-phans' stay.
Thou al - so wilt re-vive their strength And ev - er hear their cry.
That they by hu-man pride and pow'r May be no more dis-tressed. A - MEN.

*I cried unto the Lord with my voice; with my voice unto the Lord did I make my supplication.* Psalm 142:1

509

From PSALM 142
*The Psalter,* 1912

ROCKINGHAM OLD L. M.
Arr. by Edward Miller, 1790

1. To God my ear - nest voice I raise, To God my
voice im - plor - ing prays; Be - fore his face my
grief I show And tell my trou - ble and my woe.

2. When gloom and sor - row com - pass me, The path I
take is known to thee, And all the toils that
foes do lay To snare thy serv - ant in his way.

3. O Lord, my Sav - iour, now to thee, With - out a
hope be - sides, I flee, To thee, my shel - ter
from the strife, My por - tion in the land of life.

4. Be thou my help when trou - bles throng, For I am
weak and foes are strong; My cap - tive soul from
pris - on bring, And thank - ful prais - es I will sing. A - MEN.

# 510 THE CHRISTIAN LIFE

*Hear me, O Lord; for thy lovingkindness is good... Psalm 69:16*

From PSALM 69:16-17, 29-30, 32-36  
The Psalter, 1912

ELLERS 10. 10. 10. 10.  
Edward J. Hopkins, 1869

1. Thy lov-ing-kind-ness, Lord, is good and free:
In ten-der mer-cy turn thou un-to me;
Hide not thy face from me in my dis-tress,
In mer-cy hear my pray'r, thy serv-ant bless.

2. Need-y and sor-row-ful, to thee I cry;
Let thy sal-va-tion set my soul on high;
Then I will sing and praise thy ho-ly Name,
My thank-ful song thy mer-cy shall pro-claim.

3. With joy the meek shall see my soul re-stored;
Your heart shall live, ye saints that seek the Lord;
He helps the need-y and re-gards their cries,
Those in dis-tress the Lord will not de-spise.

4. Let heav'n a-bove his grace and glo-ry tell,
Let earth and sea and all that in them dwell;
Sal-va-tion to his peo-ple God will give,
And they that love his Name with him shall live. A-MEN.

# TRIBULATION AND SUFFERING 511

*O Lord, rebuke me not in thine anger, neither chasten me in thy hot displeasure.* Psalm 6:1

From PSALM 6
Edward A. Collier, 1911

PLEADING 7.7.6. D.
Louis Bourgeois, 1551
Harmony adapted from Dutch *Koraalboek*
of B. De Vries by Henry A. Bruinsma

1. No longer, Lord, despise me, Nor in thy wrath chastise me, Thy mercy I implore. How long thine anger cherish? Consumed thereby I perish; My soul is troubled sore.
2. To me, O Lord, returning, Save thou, with pity yearning. Shall death thy mem'ry keep? Or shall the grave confess thee? Or I give thanks and bless thee, While day and night I weep?
3. The Lord will ever hear me, And when I pray be near me, To put my foes to shame; Turned back, no more to grieve me, They suddenly shall leave me. All glory to his Name! A-MEN.

Words and music used by permission of the Publication Committee of the Christian Reformed Church.

## 512 THE CHRISTIAN LIFE

*O give thanks unto the Lord; for he is good: because his mercy endureth for ever. Psalm 118:1*

From PSALM 118:1-9, 17-25　　　　　　　　　　　　RENDEZ A DIEU 9.8.9.8.D.
Anon.　　　　　　　　　　　　　　　　　　　　　Louis Bourgeois, 1551

1. Give thanks un-to the Lord, Je-ho-vah, For he is good, O praise his Name! Let Is-rael say: The Lord be prais-ed, His mer-cy ev-er is the same. Let Aa-ron's house now praise Je-ho-vah; The Lord is good, O praise his Name; Let all that fear

2. In a large place the Lord hath set me, In my dis-tress he heard my cry; I will not fear; the Lord is with me, What can man do, when God is nigh? The Lord is chief a-mong my help-ers; And I shall see my foes o'er-thrown: Far bet-ter than

3. I shall not die, but live, de-clar-ing The works of God, who tried me sore, And chast-ened me; but in his mer-cy Not un-to death hath giv'n me o'er. The gates of right-eous-ness set o - pen, The gate of God! I'll en-ter in To praise thee, Lord,

4. The stone—O Lord, it is thy do-ing— The stone, the build-ers did de-spise, Is made the head-stone of the cor-ner, And it is mar-v'lous in our eyes. This is the day, of days most glo - rious, The Lord hath made; we'll joy and sing: Send now pros-per-

# DELIVERANCE

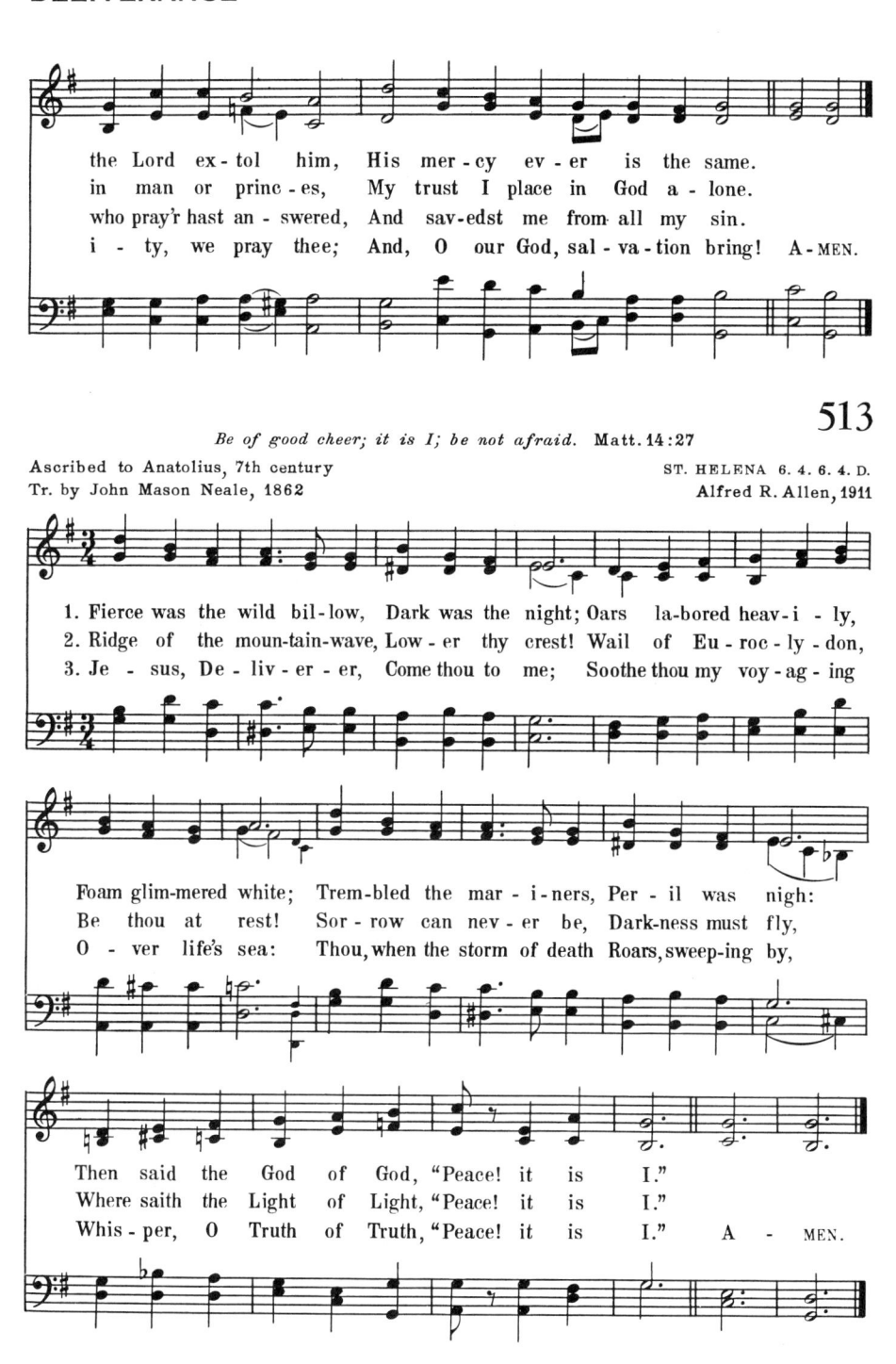

the Lord ex-tol him, His mer-cy ev-er is the same.
in man or princ-es, My trust I place in God a-lone.
who pray'r hast an-swered, And sav-edst me from all my sin.
i-ty, we pray thee; And, O our God, sal-va-tion bring! A-MEN.

**513**

*Be of good cheer; it is I; be not afraid.* Matt. 14:27

Ascribed to Anatolius, 7th century  
Tr. by John Mason Neale, 1862

ST. HELENA 6. 4. 6. 4. D.  
Alfred R. Allen, 1911

1. Fierce was the wild bil-low, Dark was the night; Oars la-bored heav-i-ly,
2. Ridge of the moun-tain-wave, Low-er thy crest! Wail of Eu-roc-ly-don,
3. Je-sus, De-liv-er-er, Come thou to me; Soothe thou my voy-ag-ing

Foam glim-mered white; Trem-bled the mar-i-ners, Per-il was nigh:
Be thou at rest! Sor-row can nev-er be, Dark-ness must fly,
O-ver life's sea: Thou, when the storm of death Roars, sweep-ing by,

Then said the God of God, "Peace! it is I."
Where saith the Light of Light, "Peace! it is I."
Whis-per, O Truth of Truth, "Peace! it is I." A-MEN.

## 514                                          THE CHRISTIAN LIFE

*If it had not been the Lord who was on our side...*
*then they had swallowed us up quick... Psalm 124:1, 3*

From PSALM 124                                                     OLD 124th 10. 10. 10. 10. 10.
*The Psalter*, 1912                                                       Louis Bourgeois, 1551

1. Now Is-ra-el may say, and that in truth, If that the Lord had not our right main-tained, If that the Lord had not with us re-mained, When cru-el men a-gainst us rose to strive, We sure-ly had been swal-lowed up a-live.

2. Yea, when their wrath a-gainst us fierce-ly rose, The swell-ing tide had o'er us spread its wave, The rag-ing stream had then be-come our grave, The surg-ing flood, in proud-ly swell-ing roll, Most sure-ly then had o-ver-whelmed our soul.

3. Blest be the Lord who made us not their prey: As from the snare a bird es-cap-eth free, Their net is rent and so es-caped are we: Our on-ly help is in Je-ho-vah's Name, Who made the earth and all the heav'n-ly frame. A-MEN.

# DELIVERANCE  515

*If we have forgotten the name of our God ... shall not God search this out?* Psalm 44:20, 21

From PSALM 44:20-26  
The Psalter, 1912

MAGNUS 11. 11. 11. 11. with refrain  
John B. Herbert, 1852-1927

1. If we have for-got-ten the Name of our God, Or un-to an
2. We all the day long for thy sake are con-sumed, De-feat-ed and
3. O why art thou hid-ing the light of thy face, For-get-ting our

i-dol our hands spread a-broad, Shall not the Al-might-y un-
help-less, to death we are doomed; Then why dost thou tar-ry? Je-
bur-den of grief and dis-grace? Our soul is bowed down, yea, we

cov-er this sin? He knows all our hearts and the se-crets with-in.
ho-vah, a-wake; Nor spurn us for ev-er; a-rise for our sake.
cleave to the dust; Rise, help, and re-deem us, thy mer-cy we trust.

REFRAIN

Rise, help, and re-deem us, Thy mer-cy we trust;

Rise, help, and re-deem us, Thy mer-cy we trust. A-MEN.

# 516 THE CHRISTIAN LIFE

*O Israel, return unto the Lord thy God ... Hosea 14:1*

John Morison, 1781　　　　　　　　　　　　　　　　　　　　　　　　　SOHO C. M.
in Scottish *Translations and Paraphrases*　　　　　　　　　　　Sir Joseph Barnby, 1881

1. Come, let us to the Lord our God With con-trite hearts re - turn;
2. His voice com-mands the tem-pest forth, And stills the storm-y wave;
3. Long hath the night of sor-row reigned; The dawn shall bring us light:
4. Our hearts, if God we seek to know, Shall know him, and re - joice;
5. As dew up - on the ten-der herb, Dif - fus - ing fra-grance round,
6. So shall his pres-ence bless our souls, And shed a joy - ful light;

Our God is gra-cious, nor will leave The des - o - late to mourn.
And, though his arm be strong to smite, 'Tis al - so strong to save.
God shall ap-pear, and we shall rise With glad-ness in his sight.
His com-ing like the morn shall be, Like morn-ing songs his voice.
As show'rs that ush - er in the spring, And cheer the thirst-y ground;
That hal-lowed morn shall chase a - way The sor-rows of the night. A-MEN.

# 517

*For we have not an high priest which cannot be touched with the feeling of our infirmities ... Heb. 4:15*

Jane Crewdson, 1809-1863　　　　　　　　　　　　　　　　　HOLY TRINITY C. M.
　　　　　　　　　　　　　　　　　　　　　　　　　　　Sir Joseph Barnby, 1861

*Slowly*

1. There is no sor - row, Lord, too light To bring in pray'r to thee;
2. Thou, who hast trod the thorn-y road, Wilt share each small dis - tress;
3. There is no se - cret sigh we breathe, But meets thine ear di - vine;
4. Life's ills with - out, sin's strife with - in, The heart would o - ver - flow,

There is no anx - ious care too slight To wake thy sym - pa - thy.
The love, which bore the great - er load, Will not re - fuse the less.
And ev - 'ry cross grows light be-neath The shad - ow, Lord, of thine.
But for that love which died for sin, That love which wept with woe. A-MEN.

# CONSOLATION 518

*Let us therefore come boldly unto the throne of grace, that we may obtain mercy, and find grace to help in time of need. Heb. 4:16*

St. 1-2, Thomas Moore, 1816, alt.
St. 3, Thomas Hastings, 1832

ALMA 11. 10. 11. 10.
Arr. from Samuel Webbe, 1792

1. Come, ye dis-con-so-late, wher-e'er ye lan-guish,
2. Joy of the com-fort-less, light of the stray-ing,
3. Here see the Bread of Life; see wa-ters flow-ing

Come to the mer-cy-seat, fer-vent-ly kneel:
Hope of the pen-i-tent, fade-less and pure!
Forth from the throne of God, pure from a-bove:

Here bring your wound-ed hearts, here tell your an-guish;
Here speaks the Com-fort-er, in mer-cy say-ing,
Come to the feast pre-pared; come, ev-er know-ing

Earth has no sor-rows that heav'n can-not heal.
"Earth has no sor-rows that heav'n can-not cure."
Earth has no sor-rows but heav'n can re-move. A-MEN.

## 519 THE CHRISTIAN LIFE

*The Lord is merciful and gracious, slow to anger, and plenteous in mercy.* Psalm 103:8

Thomas T. Lynch, 1850

RIPON C. M. D.
W. Gawler's *Hymns and Psalms*, 1789

1. The Lord is rich and mer-ci-ful, The Lord is ver-y kind;
O come to him, come now to him, With a be-liev-ing mind:
His com-forts, they shall strength-en thee, Like flow-ing wa-ters cool;
And he shall for thy spir-it be A foun-tain ev-er full.

2. The Lord is glo-ri-ous and strong, Our God is ver-y high;
O trust in him, trust now in him, And have se-cur-i-ty:
He shall be to thee like the sea, And thou shalt sure-ly feel
His wind, that blow-eth health-i-ly Thy sick-ness-es to heal.

3. The Lord is won-der-ful and wise, As all the a-ges tell;
O learn of him, learn now of him, Then with thee it is well;
And with his light thou shalt be blest, There-in to work and live;
And he shall be to thee a rest When eve-ning hours ar-rive. A-MEN.

# GOD'S REFRESHING GRACE 520

*Unto you that fear my name shall the Sun of righteousness arise with healing in his wings... Mal. 4:2*

William Cowper, 1779
BENTLEY 7. 6. 7. 6. D.
John Hullah, 1867

1. Sometimes a light surprises The Christian while he sings;
It is the Lord, who rises With healing in his wings:
When comforts are declining, He grants the soul again
A season of clear shining, To cheer it after rain.

2. In holy contemplation We sweetly then pursue
The theme of God's salvation, And find it ever new;
Set free from present sorrow, We cheerfully can say,
Let the unknown tomorrow Bring with it what it may.

3. It can bring with it nothing But he will bear us through;
Who gives the lilies clothing Will clothe his people too:
Beneath the spreading heavens No creature but is fed;
And he who feeds the ravens Will give his children bread.

4. Though vine nor fig-tree neither Their wonted fruit shall bear,
Though all the field should wither, Nor flocks nor herds be there;
Yet God the same abiding, His praise shall tune my voice,
For, while in him confiding, I cannot but rejoice. A-MEN.

## 521 THE CHRISTIAN LIFE

*The preaching of the cross ... unto us which are saved ... is the power of God.* I Cor. 1:18

Katherine Hankey, 1866; refrain added
EVANGEL 7. 6. 7. 6. D. with refrain
William H. Doane, 1869

1. Tell me the old, old story Of unseen things above,
Of Jesus and his glory, Of Jesus and his love:
Tell me the story simply, As to a little child,
For I am weak and weary, And helpless and defiled.

2. Tell me the story softly, With earnest tones and grave;
Remember, I'm the sinner Whom Jesus came to save:
Tell me the story always, If you would really be,
In any time of trouble, A comforter to me.

3. Tell me the same old story, When you have cause to fear
That this world's empty glory Is costing me too dear:
Yes, and when that world's glory Is dawning on my soul,
Tell me the old, old story, "Christ Jesus makes thee whole."

# GOD'S REFRESHING GRACE

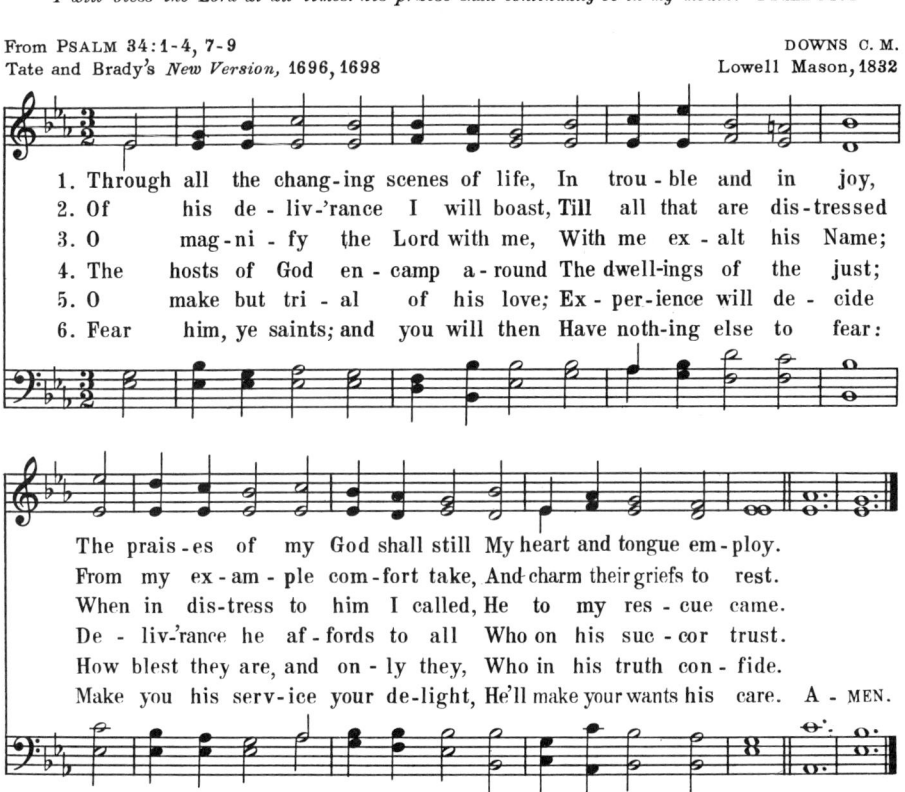

**REFRAIN**

Tell me the old, old story, Tell me the old, old story,
Tell me the old, old story Of Jesus and his love. A-MEN.

**522**

*I will bless the Lord at all times: his praise shall continually be in my mouth.* Psalm **34:1**

From PSALM 34:1-4, 7-9  
Tate and Brady's *New Version*, 1696, 1698

DOWNS C. M.  
Lowell Mason, 1832

1. Through all the chang-ing scenes of life, In trou-ble and in joy,
2. Of his de-liv-'rance I will boast, Till all that are dis-tressed
3. O mag-ni-fy the Lord with me, With me ex-alt his Name;
4. The hosts of God en-camp a-round The dwell-ings of the just;
5. O make but tri-al of his love; Ex-per-ience will de-cide
6. Fear him, ye saints; and you will then Have noth-ing else to fear:

The prais-es of my God shall still My heart and tongue em-ploy.
From my ex-am-ple com-fort take, And charm their griefs to rest.
When in dis-tress to him I called, He to my res-cue came.
De-liv-'rance he af-fords to all Who on his suc-cor trust.
How blest they are, and on-ly they, Who in his truth con-fide.
Make you his serv-ice your de-light, He'll make your wants his care. A-MEN.

## 523 THE CHRISTIAN LIFE

*I waited patiently for the Lord; and he inclined unto me, and heard my cry.* Psalm 40:1

PSALM 40:1-5　　　　　　　　　　　　　　　　　　　　　　DUNSTAN 8.8.8.6.8.6.
The Psalter, 1912　　　　　　　　　　　　　　　　　　　Sir Joseph Barnby, 1838-1896

1. I wait-ed for the Lord most high, And he in-clined to hear my cry;
2. A new and joy-ful song of praise He taught my thank-ful heart to raise;
3. O Lord my God, how man-i-fold Thy won-drous works which I be-hold,

He took me from de-struc-tion's pit And from the mir-y clay;
And man-y, see-ing me re-stored, Shall fear the Lord and trust;
And all thy lov-ing, gra-cious thought Thou hast be-stowed on man;

Up-on a rock he set my feet, And sted-fast made my way.
And blest are they that trust the Lord, The hum-ble and the just.
To count thy mer-cies I have sought, But bound-less is their span. A-MEN.

## 524

*I will love thee, O Lord, my strength.* Psalm 18:1

From PSALM 18:1-2, 6, 9-10, 30　　　　　　　　　　　　　　　ST. MAGNUS C. M.
Thomas Sternhold, 1561　　　　　　　　　　　　　　Jeremiah Clark, 1670-1707

1. O God, my Strength and For-ti-tude, Of force I must love thee;
2. My God, my Rock, in whom I trust, The work-er of my wealth,
3. I, when be-set with pain and grief, Did pray to God for grace;
4. The Lord de-scend-ed from a-bove And bowed the heav-ens high,
5. On cher-ub and on cher-u-bim Full roy-al-ly he rode,
6. Un-spot-ted are the ways of God, His word is pure-ly tried;

# GOD'S REFRESHING GRACE

Thou art my Cas-tle and De-fence In my ne-cess-i-ty;
My Ref-uge, Buck-ler, and my Shield, The horn of all my health.
And he forth-with did hear my plaint Out of his ho-ly place.
And un-der-neath' his feet he cast The dark-ness of the sky.
And on the wings of all the winds Came fly-ing all a-broad.
He is a sure de-fence to such As in his faith a-bide. A-MEN.

*The darkness and the light are both alike to thee.* Psalm 139:12

525

Count Nikolaus Ludwig von Zinzendorf, 1721
Tr. by John Wesley, 1738; st. 3, line 4, alt.

BERA L. M.
John E. Gould, 1849

1. O thou to whose all-search-ing sight The dark-ness shin-eth as the light, Search, prove my heart; it pants for thee; O burst these bands and set it free.
2. Wash out its stains, re-fine its dross; Nail my af-fec-tions to the cross; Hal-low each thought; let all with-in Be clean, as thou, my Lord, art clean.
3. If in this dark-some wild I stray, Be thou my Light, be thou my Way; No foes, no vi-o-lence I fear, No harm, while thou, my God, art near.
4. Sav-iour, wher-e'er thy steps I see, Daunt-less, un-tired, I fol-low thee: O let thy hand sup-port me still, And lead me to thy ho-ly hill.
5. If rough and thorn-y be my way, My strength pro-por-tion to my day; Till toil and grief and pain shall cease, Where all is calm and joy and peace. A-MEN.

# 526                           THE CHRISTIAN LIFE

*I will extol thee, O Lord; for thou hast lifted me up*... Psalm 30:1

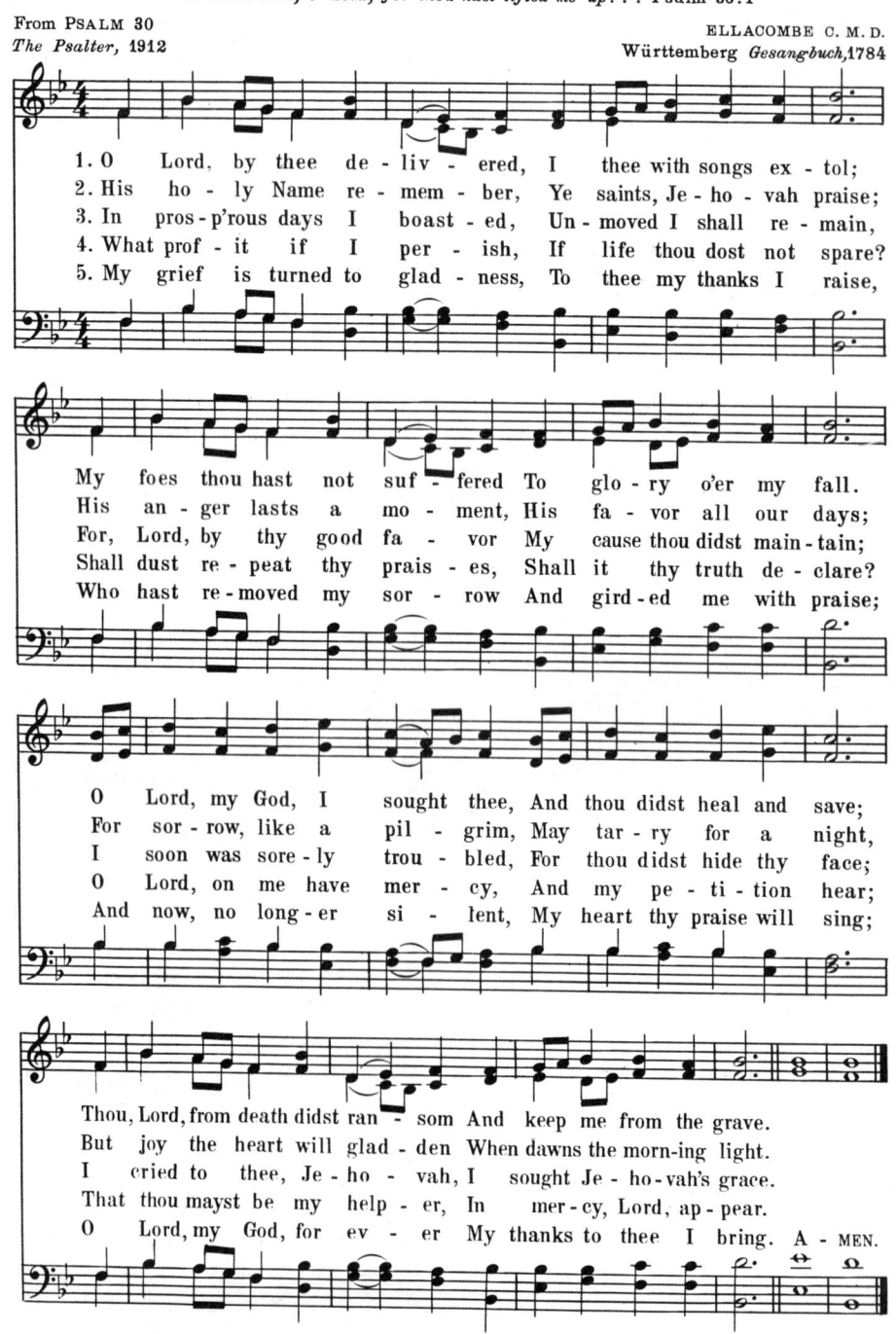

From PSALM 30                                     ELLACOMBE C. M. D.
*The Psalter*, 1912                              Württemberg *Gesangbuch*, 1784

1. O Lord, by thee delivered, I thee with songs extol;
   My foes thou hast not suffered To glory o'er my fall.
   O Lord, my God, I sought thee, And thou didst heal and save;
   Thou, Lord, from death didst ransom And keep me from the grave.

2. His holy Name remember, Ye saints, Jehovah praise;
   His anger lasts a moment, His favor all our days;
   For sorrow, like a pilgrim, May tarry for a night,
   But joy the heart will gladden When dawns the morning light.

3. In pros-p'rous days I boasted, Unmoved I shall remain,
   For, Lord, by thy good favor My cause thou didst maintain;
   I soon was sorely troubled, For thou didst hide thy face;
   I cried to thee, Jehovah, I sought Jehovah's grace.

4. What profit if I perish, If life thou dost not spare?
   Shall dust repeat thy praises, Shall it thy truth declare?
   O Lord, on me have mercy, And my petition hear;
   That thou mayst be my helper, In mercy, Lord, appear.

5. My grief is turned to gladness, To thee my thanks I raise,
   Who hast removed my sorrow And girded me with praise;
   And now, no longer silent, My heart thy praise will sing;
   O Lord, my God, forever My thanks to thee I bring. A-MEN.

# GOD'S REFRESHING GRACE 527

*I will cause the shower to come down in his season;
there shall be showers of blessing.* Ezekiel 34:26

Elizabeth Codner, 1860

RHEIDOL 8. 7. 8. 7. 3. 8. 7.
John Roberts, 1822-1877

1. Lord, I hear of show'rs of bless-ing Thou art scat-t'ring, full and free,— Show'rs, the thirst-y land re-fresh-ing; Let some drops de-scend on me, E-ven me, e-ven me; Let some drops de-scend on me.

2. Pass me not, O gra-cious Fa-ther, Sin-ful though my heart may be! Thou might'st leave me, but the rath-er Let thy mer-cy light on me, E-ven me, e-ven me; Let thy mer-cy light on me.

3. Pass me not, O ten-der Sav-iour! Let me love and cling to thee; I am long-ing for thy fa-vor; When thou com-est, call for me, E-ven me, e-ven me; When thou com-est, call for me.

4. Pass me not, O might-y Spir-it! Thou canst make the blind to see; Wit-ness-er of Je-sus' mer-it, Speak the word of pow'r to me, E-ven me, e-ven me; Speak the word of pow'r to me. A-MEN.

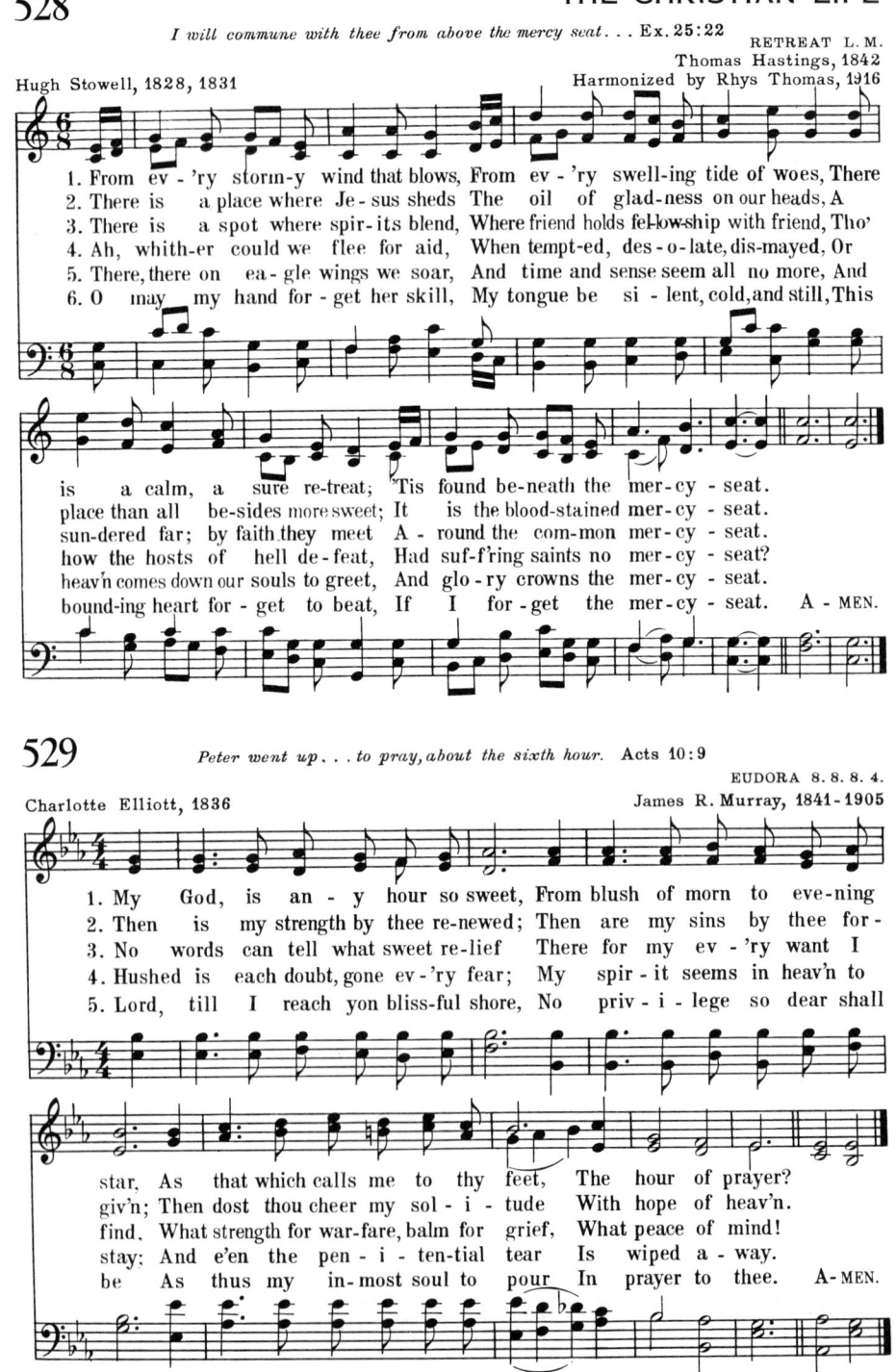

## THE CHRISTIAN LIFE

**528**

*I will commune with thee from above the mercy seat... Ex. 25:22*

Hugh Stowell, 1828, 1831

RETREAT L. M.
Thomas Hastings, 1842
Harmonized by Rhys Thomas, 1916

1. From ev-'ry storm-y wind that blows, From ev-'ry swell-ing tide of woes, There is a calm, a sure re-treat; 'Tis found be-neath the mer-cy-seat.
2. There is a place where Je-sus sheds The oil of glad-ness on our heads, A place than all be-sides more sweet; It is the blood-stained mer-cy-seat.
3. There is a spot where spir-its blend, Where friend holds fel-low-ship with friend, Tho' sun-dered far; by faith they meet A-round the com-mon mer-cy-seat.
4. Ah, whith-er could we flee for aid, When tempt-ed, des-o-late, dis-mayed, Or how the hosts of hell de-feat, Had suf-f'ring saints no mer-cy-seat?
5. There, there on ea-gle wings we soar, And time and sense seem all no more, And heav'n comes down our souls to greet, And glo-ry crowns the mer-cy-seat.
6. O may my hand for-get her skill, My tongue be si-lent, cold, and still, This bound-ing heart for-get to beat, If I for-get the mer-cy-seat. A-MEN.

**529**

*Peter went up... to pray, about the sixth hour. Acts 10:9*

Charlotte Elliott, 1836

EUDORA 8.8.8.4.
James R. Murray, 1841-1905

1. My God, is an-y hour so sweet, From blush of morn to eve-ning star, As that which calls me to thy feet, The hour of prayer?
2. Then is my strength by thee re-newed; Then are my sins by thee for-giv'n; Then dost thou cheer my sol-i-tude With hope of heav'n.
3. No words can tell what sweet re-lief There for my ev-'ry want I find. What strength for war-fare, balm for grief, What peace of mind!
4. Hushed is each doubt, gone ev-'ry fear; My spir-it seems in heav'n to stay; And e'en the pen-i-ten-tial tear Is wiped a-way.
5. Lord, till I reach yon bliss-ful shore, No priv-i-lege so dear shall be As thus my in-most soul to pour In prayer to thee. A-MEN.

## PRAYER

**530**

*Let us... come boldly unto the throne of grace, that we may obtain mercy, and find grace to help in time of need.* Heb. 4:16

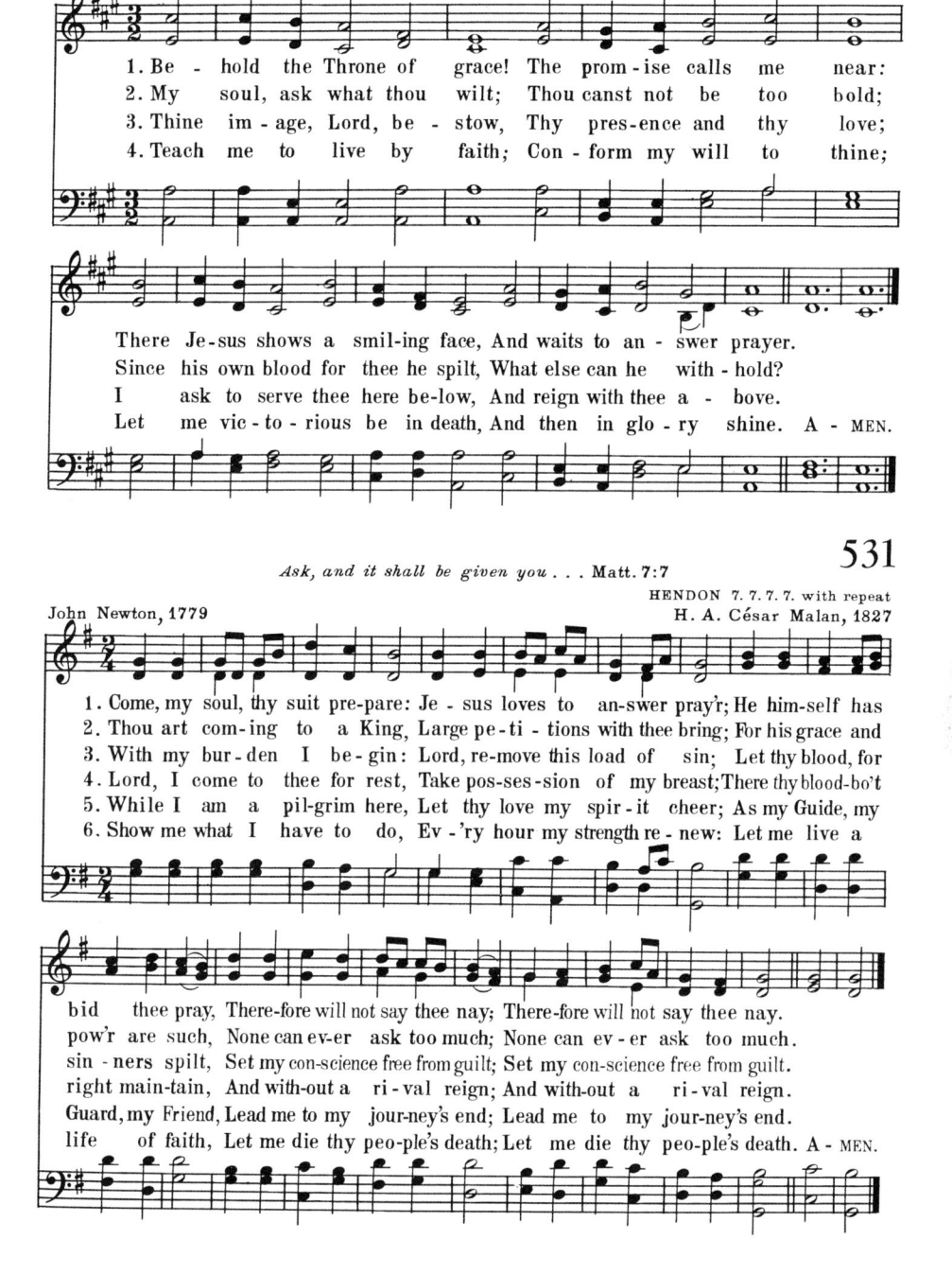

John Newton, 1779  
STATE STREET S. M.  
Jonathan C. Woodman, 1844

1. Be - hold the Throne of grace! The prom - ise calls me near:
2. My soul, ask what thou wilt; Thou canst not be too bold;
3. Thine im - age, Lord, be - stow, Thy pres - ence and thy love;
4. Teach me to live by faith; Con - form my will to thine;

There Je - sus shows a smil - ing face, And waits to an - swer prayer.
Since his own blood for thee he spilt, What else can he with - hold?
I ask to serve thee here be - low, And reign with thee a - bove.
Let me vic - to - rious be in death, And then in glo - ry shine. A - MEN.

**531**

*Ask, and it shall be given you... Matt. 7:7*

John Newton, 1779  
HENDON 7.7.7.7. with repeat  
H. A. César Malan, 1827

1. Come, my soul, thy suit pre - pare: Je - sus loves to an - swer pray'r; He him - self has
2. Thou art com - ing to a King, Large pe - ti - tions with thee bring; For his grace and
3. With my bur - den I be - gin: Lord, re - move this load of sin; Let thy blood, for
4. Lord, I come to thee for rest, Take pos - ses - sion of my breast; There thy blood-bo't
5. While I am a pil - grim here, Let thy love my spir - it cheer; As my Guide, my
6. Show me what I have to do, Ev - 'ry hour my strength re - new: Let me live a

bid thee pray, There-fore will not say thee nay; There-fore will not say thee nay.
pow'r are such, None can ev - er ask too much; None can ev - er ask too much.
sin - ners spilt, Set my con - science free from guilt; Set my con - science free from guilt.
right main-tain, And with - out a ri - val reign; And with - out a ri - val reign.
Guard, my Friend, Lead me to my jour-ney's end; Lead me to my jour-ney's end.
life of faith, Let me die thy peo - ple's death; Let me die thy peo - ple's death. A - MEN.

# 532 THE CHRISTIAN LIFE

*Hear thou in heaven thy dwelling place: and when thou hearest, forgive.* I Kings 8:30

INTERCESSION NEW 7. 5. 7. 5. 7. 5. 7. 5. 8. 8.
William H. Callcott, 1867;
the last two lines from Mendelssohn, 1846

Horatius Bonar, 1866

1. When the wea - ry, seek - ing rest, To thy good - ness flee;
2. When the strang - er asks a home, All his toils to end;
3. When the world - ling, sick at heart, Lifts his soul a - bove;

When the heav - y - la - den cast All their load on thee; When the troub - led,
When the hun - gry crav - eth food, And the poor a friend; When the wid - ow
When the prod - i - gal looks back To his Fa - ther's love; When the proud man,

seek - ing peace, On thy Name shall call; When the sin - ner, seek - ing life,
weeps to thee, Sad and lone and low; When the or - phan brings to thee
in his pride, Stoops to seek thy face; When the bur - dened brings his guilt

At thy feet shall fall: Hear then in love, O Lord, the cry
All his or - phan woe: Hear then in love, O Lord, the cry
To thy Throne of grace: Hear then in love, O Lord, the cry

In heav'n, thy dwell - ing - place on high. A - MEN.

PRAYER

533

*In nothing be anxious; but in everything by prayer and supplication with thanksgiving let your requests be made known unto God.* Phil. 4:6 (A. S. V.)

Joseph Scriven, c. 1855

WHAT A FRIEND 8. 7. 8. 7. D.
C. C. Converse, 1868

1. What a Friend we have in Je - sus, All our sins and griefs to bear!
2. Have we tri - als and temp-ta - tions? Is there trou - ble an - y - where?
3. Are we weak and heav - y la - den, Cum-bered with a load of care?

What a priv - i - lege to car - ry Ev - 'ry - thing to God in prayer!
We should nev - er be dis - cour - aged: Take it to the Lord in prayer!
Pre - cious Sav - iour, still our Ref - uge— Take it to the Lord in prayer!

O what peace we of - ten for - feit, O what need-less pain we bear,
Can we find a friend so faith - ful, Who will all our sor - rows share?
Do thy friends de - spise, for - sake thee? Take it to the Lord in prayer!

All be-cause we do not car - ry Ev - 'ry-thing to God in prayer.
Je - sus knows our ev - 'ry weak-ness— Take it to the Lord in prayer!
In his arms he'll take and shield thee, Thou wilt find a so - lace there. A - MEN.

## 534 THE CHRISTIAN LIFE: PRAYER

*Now Peter and John went up together into the temple at the hour of prayer...* Acts 3:1

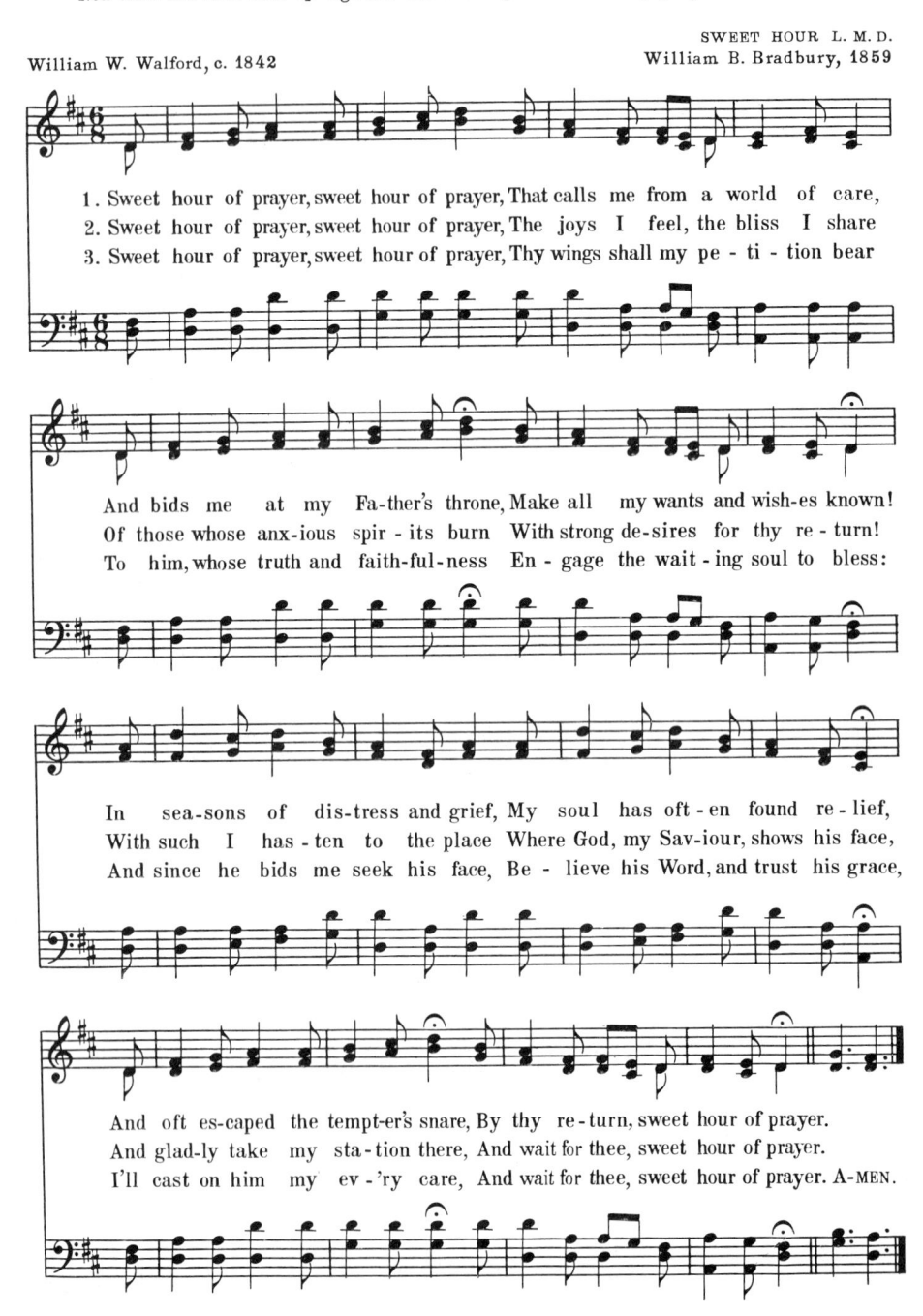

SWEET HOUR L. M. D.
William W. Walford, c. 1842
William B. Bradbury, 1859

1. Sweet hour of prayer, sweet hour of prayer, That calls me from a world of care,
And bids me at my Father's throne, Make all my wants and wishes known!
In seasons of distress and grief, My soul has often found relief,
And oft escaped the tempter's snare, By thy return, sweet hour of prayer.

2. Sweet hour of prayer, sweet hour of prayer, The joys I feel, the bliss I share
Of those whose anxious spirits burn With strong desires for thy return!
With such I hasten to the place Where God, my Saviour, shows his face,
And gladly take my station there, And wait for thee, sweet hour of prayer.

3. Sweet hour of prayer, sweet hour of prayer, Thy wings shall my petition bear
To him, whose truth and faithfulness Engage the waiting soul to bless:
And since he bids me seek his face, Believe his Word, and trust his grace,
I'll cast on him my ev'ry care, And wait for thee, sweet hour of prayer. A-MEN.

# THE CHRISTIAN LIFE: THANKFULNESS  535

*It is a good thing to give thanks unto the Lord... Psalm 92:1*

From PSALM 92:1-9, 12-15  
The Psalter, 1912

ST. PETERSBURG 8. 8. 8. 8. 8. 8.  
Dimitri Bortniansky, 1752-1825

1. How good it is to thank the Lord, And praise to thee, Most High, ac-cord, To show thy love with morn-ing light, And tell thy faith-ful-ness each night; Yea, good it is thy praise to sing, And all our sweet-est mu-sic bring.

2. O Lord, with joy my heart ex-pands Be-fore the won-ders of thy hands; Great works, Je-ho-vah, thou hast wrought, Ex-ceed-ing deep thine ev-'ry thought; A fool-ish man knows not their worth, Nor he whose mind is of the earth.

3. When as the grass the wick-ed grow, When sin-ners flour-ish here be-low, Then is there end-less ru-in nigh, But thou, O Lord, art throned on high; Thy foes shall fall be-fore thy might, The wick-ed shall be put to flight.

4. The right-eous man shall flour-ish well, And in the house of God shall dwell; He shall be like a good-ly tree, And all his life shall fruit-ful be; For right-eous is the Lord and just, He is my Rock, in him I trust. A-MEN.

## 536 THE CHRISTIAN LIFE

*For the love of Christ constraineth us ... that they which live should not henceforth live unto themselves, but unto him who died for them, and rose again.* II Cor. 5:14, 15

Frances R. Havergal, 1858
Recast in *Church Hymns*, 1871

DEVOTION 6.6.6.D.
John H. Gower, 1895

1. Thy life was given for me, Thy blood, O Lord, was shed,
2. Long years were spent for me In wea-ri-ness and woe,
3. Thou, Lord, hast borne for me More than my tongue can tell
4. And thou hast brought to me Down from thy home a-bove
5. O let my life be given My years for thee be spent;

That I might ran-somed be, And quick-ened from the dead:
That through e-ter-ni-ty Thy glo-ry I might know:
Of bit-t'rest ag-o-ny, To res-cue me from hell;
Sal-va-tion full and free, Thy par-don and thy love:
World-fet-ters all be riven And joy with suf-f'ring blent:

*rit.*

Thy life was given for me; What have I given for thee?
Long years were spent for me; Have I spent one for thee?
Thou suf-feredst all for me; What have I borne for thee?
Great gifts thou brought-est me; What have I brought to thee?
Thou gav'st thy-self for me, I give my-self to thee. A-MEN.

## 537

*What shall I render unto the Lord for all his benefits toward me?* Psalm 116:12

From PSALM 116:12-19
Isaac Watts, 1719

DOWNS C. M.
Lowell Mason, 1832

1. What shall I ren-der to my God For all his kind-ness shown?
2. How much is mer-cy thy de-light, Thou ev-er-bless-ed God!
3. How hap-py all thy serv-ants are! How great thy grace to me!
4. Now I am thine, for ev-er thine, Nor shall my pur-pose move;
5. Here in thy courts I leave my vow, And thy rich grace re-cord;

## THANKFULNESS

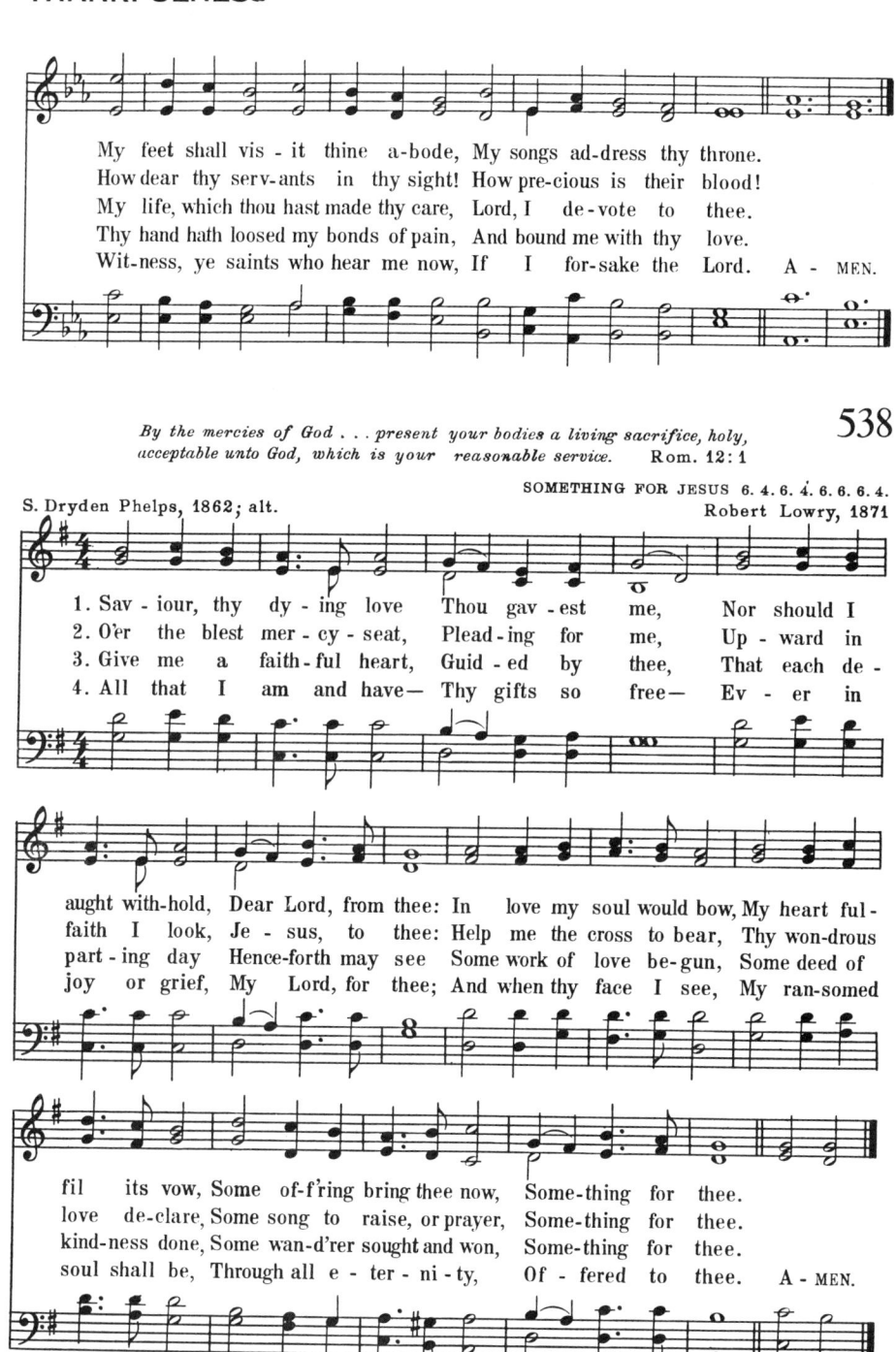

My feet shall vis-it thine a-bode, My songs ad-dress thy throne.
How dear thy serv-ants in thy sight! How pre-cious is their blood!
My life, which thou hast made thy care, Lord, I de-vote to thee.
Thy hand hath loosed my bonds of pain, And bound me with thy love.
Wit-ness, ye saints who hear me now, If I for-sake the Lord. A - MEN.

*By the mercies of God ... present your bodies a living sacrifice, holy, acceptable unto God, which is your reasonable service.* Rom. 12:1

**538**

SOMETHING FOR JESUS 6. 4. 6. 4. 6. 6. 6. 4.

S. Dryden Phelps, 1862; alt.                         Robert Lowry, 1871

1. Sav-iour, thy dy-ing love Thou gav-est me, Nor should I
2. O'er the blest mer-cy-seat, Plead-ing for me, Up-ward in
3. Give me a faith-ful heart, Guid-ed by thee, That each de-
4. All that I am and have— Thy gifts so free— Ev-er in

aught with-hold, Dear Lord, from thee: In love my soul would bow, My heart ful-
faith I look, Je-sus, to thee: Help me the cross to bear, Thy won-drous
part-ing day Hence-forth may see Some work of love be-gun, Some deed of
joy or grief, My Lord, for thee; And when thy face I see, My ran-somed

fil its vow, Some of-f'ring bring thee now, Some-thing for thee.
love de-clare, Some song to raise, or prayer, Some-thing for thee.
kind-ness done, Some wan-d'rer sought and won, Some-thing for thee.
soul shall be, Through all e-ter-ni-ty, Of-fered to thee. A - MEN.

**539**                                              THE CHRISTIAN LIFE

*Judge me, O God, and plead my cause.* Psalm 43:1

From PSALM 43                                         BLAENHAFREN 8.7.8.7.D.
*The Psalter*, 1912                                        Traditional Welsh melody

1. Judge me, God of my sal-va-tion, Plead my cause, for thee I trust: Hear my ear-nest sup-pli-ca-tion, Save me from my foes un-just. O my soul, why art thou griev-ing? What dis-qui-ets and dis-mays? Hope in

2. For my Strength, my God, thou art: Why am I cast off by thee In the sor-row of my heart, While the foe op-press-es me? Light and truth, my way at-tend-ing, Send thou forth to be my guide, Till thy

3. At thy sa-cred al-tar bend-ing, God, my God, my bound-less joy, Harp and voice, in wor-ship blend-ing, For thy praise will I em-ploy. O my soul, why art thou griev-ing? What dis-qui-ets and dis-mays? Hope in

# HOPE

God; his help re - ceiv-ing, I shall yet my Sav-iour praise.
ho - ly mount as - cend-ing, I with - in thy house a - bide.
God; his help re - ceiv-ing, I shall yet my Sav-iour praise. A-MEN.

St. 2, lines 1 and 3, alt.

**540**

*Unto thee lift I up mine eyes, O thou that dwellest in the heavens.* Psalm 123:1

PSALM 123  PATER OMNIUM 8.8.8.8.8.8.
*The Psalter,* 1912  Henry J. E. Holmes, 1875

1. To thee, O Lord, I lift mine eyes, O thou en-throned a - bove the skies;
2. O Lord, our God, thy mer - cy show, For man's con-tempt and scorn we know;

As serv-ants watch their mas-ter's hand, Or maid-ens by their mis-tress stand,
Re-proach and shame thy saints en - dure From wick-ed men who dwell se - cure;

So to the Lord our eyes we raise, Un-til his mer - cy he dis-plays.
Man's proud con-tempt and scorn we know; O Lord, our God, thy mer-cy show. A - MEN.

# 541　THE CHRISTIAN LIFE: HOPE

*How long wilt thou forget me, O Lord?* Psalm 13:1

From PSALM 13
*The Psalter*, 1912

ANGEL'S STORY 7. 6. 7. 6. D.
Arthur H. Mann, 1883

1. How long wilt thou for-get me, O Lord, thou God of grace?
How long shall fears be-set me, While dark-ness hides thy face?
How long shall griefs dis-tress me And turn my day to night?
How long shall foes op-press me And tri-umph in their might?

2. O Lord my God, be-hold me, And hear my ear-nest cries;
Lest sleep of death en-fold me, En-light-en thou mine eyes;
Lest now my foe in-sult-ing Should boast of his suc-cess,
And en-e-mies ex-ult-ing Re-joice in my dis-tress.

3. But I with ex-pec-ta-tion Have on thy grace re-lied;
My heart in thy sal-va-tion Shall still with joy con-fide;
And I with voice of sing-ing Will praise the Lord a-bove,
Who, rich-est boun-ties bring-ing, Has dealt with me in love. A-MEN.

# THE CHRISTIAN LIFE: LOVE FOR CHRIST 542

*The love of Christ, which passeth knowledge... Eph. 3:19*

Anon., Latin, 11th century  
Tr. by Edward Caswall, 1849

ST. AGNES C. M.  
John B. Dykes, 1866

1. Je-sus, the ver-y thought of thee With sweet-ness fills my breast;
2. Nor voice can sing, nor heart can frame, Nor can the mem-'ry find,
3. O Hope of ev-'ry con-trite heart, O Joy of all the meek,
4. But what to those who find? Ah, this Nor tongue nor pen can show:
5. Je-sus, our on-ly Joy be thou, As thou our Prize wilt be;

But sweet-er far thy face to see, And in thy pres-ence rest.
A sweet-er sound than thy blest Name, O Sav-iour of man-kind.
To those who fall, how kind thou art! How good to those who seek!
The love of Je-sus, what it is None but his loved ones know.
Je-sus, be thou our Glo-ry now, And through e-ter-ni-ty. A-MEN.

## 543

*Delight thyself also in the Lord... Psalm 37:4*

John Ryland, 1777

BELMONT C. M.  
Arr. from William Gardiner, 1812

1. O Lord, I would de-light in thee, And on thy care de-pend;
2. When all cre-at-ed streams are dried, Thy ful-ness is the same;
3. No good in crea-tures can be found, But may be found in thee;
4. O that I had a strong-er faith, To look with-in the veil!
5. He that has made my heav'n se-cure, Will here all good pro-vide;
6. O Lord, I cast my care on thee; I tri-umph and a-dore:

To thee in ev-'ry trou-ble flee, My best, my on-ly Friend.
May I with this be sat-is-fied, And glo-ry in thy Name.
I must have all things and a-bound, While God is God to me.
To cred-it what my Sav-iour saith, Whose Word can nev-er fail!
While Christ is rich, can I be poor? What can I want be-side?
Hence-forth my great con-cern shall be To love and please thee more. A-MEN.

## 544 THE CHRISTIAN LIFE

*Thy name is as ointment poured forth...* Song of Solomon 1:3

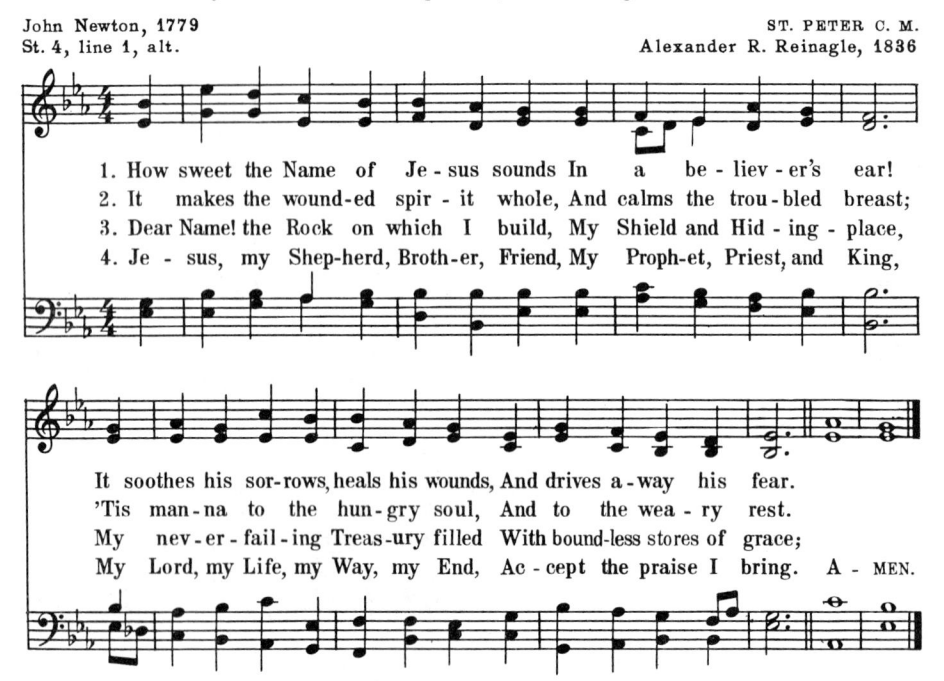

John Newton, 1779
St. 4, line 1, alt.

ST. PETER C. M.
Alexander R. Reinagle, 1836

1. How sweet the Name of Jesus sounds In a believer's ear!
It soothes his sorrows, heals his wounds, And drives away his fear.

2. It makes the wounded spirit whole, And calms the troubled breast;
'Tis manna to the hungry soul, And to the weary rest.

3. Dear Name! the Rock on which I build, My Shield and Hiding-place,
My never-failing Treasury filled With boundless stores of grace;

4. Jesus, my Shepherd, Brother, Friend, My Prophet, Priest, and King,
My Lord, my Life, my Way, my End, Accept the praise I bring. A-MEN.

5. Weak is the effort of my heart,
And cold my warmest thought;
But when I see thee as thou art,
I'll praise thee as I ought.

6. Till then I would thy love proclaim
With every fleeting breath;
And may the music of thy Name
Refresh my soul in death.

## 545

*Whom having not seen, ye love...* I Peter 1:8

Ray Palmer, 1858

SAWLEY C. M.
James Walch, 1860

1. Jesus, these eyes have never seen That radiant form of thine;
2. I see thee not, I hear thee not, Yet art thou oft with me;
3. Yet though I have not seen, and still Must rest in faith alone;
4. When death these mortal eyes shall seal, And still this throbbing heart,

# LOVE FOR CHRIST

The veil of sense hangs dark be-tween Thy bless-ed face and mine.
And earth hath ne'er so dear a spot As where I meet with thee.
I love thee, dear-est Lord, and will, Un-seen, but not un-known.
The rend-ing veil shall thee re-veal, All glo-rious as thou art. A-MEN.

*Wherefore God also hath highly exalted him, and given him a name which is above every name.* Phil. 2:9

**546**

James G. Deck, 1842
each st. alt.

STOBEL 6. 6. 4. 6. 6. 6. 4.
J. D. Müller's *Choral Buch,* 1754;
arr. by William H. Havergal, 1860

1. Je-sus, thy Name I love All oth-er names a-bove,
2. Thou, bless-ed Son of God, Hast bought me with thy blood,
3. When un-to thee I flee, Thou wilt my ref-uge be,
4. Soon thou wilt come a-gain; I shall be hap-py then,

Je-sus, my Lord: O thou art all to me; Noth-ing to please I see,
Je-sus, my Lord: O how great is thy love, All oth-er loves a-bove,
Je-sus, my Lord: What need I now to fear, What earth-ly grief or care,
Je-sus, my Lord: Then thine own face I'll see, Then I shall like thee be,

Noth-ing a-part from thee, Je-sus, my Lord.
Love that I dai-ly prove, Je-sus, my Lord.
Since thou art ev-er near? Je-sus, my Lord.
Then ev-er-more with thee, Je-sus, my Lord. A-MEN.

## 547 THE CHRISTIAN LIFE

*We love him, because he first loved us.* I John 4:19

William R. Featherstone, 1864
CARITAS 11. 11. 11. 11.
Adoniram J. Gordon, 1894

1. My Jesus, I love thee, I know thou art mine;
   For thee all the follies of sin I resign.
   My gracious Redeemer, my Saviour art thou;
   If ever I loved thee, my Jesus, 'tis now.

2. I love thee because thou hast first loved me,
   And purchased my pardon on Calvary's tree.
   I love thee for wearing the thorns on thy brow;
   If ever I loved thee, my Jesus, 'tis now.

3. I'll love thee in life, I will love thee in death;
   And praise thee as long as thou lendest me breath;
   And say, when the death-dew lies cold on my brow:
   If ever I loved thee, my Jesus, 'tis now.

4. In mansions of glory and endless delight,
   I'll ever adore thee in heaven so bright;
   I'll sing with the glittering crown on my brow:
   If ever I loved thee, my Jesus, 'tis now. A-MEN.

# LOVE FOR CHRIST
## 548

*Lord, thou knowest all things; thou knowest that I love thee.* John 21:17

Elizabeth Payson Prentiss, 1869

MORE LOVE TO THEE 6.4.6.4.6.6.4.4.
William H. Doane, 1868

1. More love to thee, O Christ, More love to thee!
2. Once earth-ly joy I craved, Sought peace and rest;
3. Let sor-row do its work, Send grief and pain;
4. Then shall my lat-est breath Whis-per thy praise;

Hear thou the prayer I make On bend-ed knee;
Now thee a-lone I seek; Give what is best:
Sweet are thy mes-sen-gers, Sweet their re-frain,
This be the part-ing cry My heart shall raise,

This is my ear-nest plea, More love, O Christ, to thee,
This all my prayer shall be, More love, O Christ, to thee,
When they can sing with me, More love, O Christ, to thee,
This still its prayer shall be, More love, O Christ, to thee,

More love to thee, More love to thee!
More love to thee, More love to thee!
More love to thee, More love to thee!
More love to thee, More love to thee! A-MEN.

**549** (FIRST TUNE)                      THE CHRISTIAN LIFE

*These things have I spoken unto you, that my joy might remain in you, and that your joy might be full.*    John 15:11

Attributed to Bernard of Clairvaux, c. 1150                  QUEBEC L. M.
Arr. and tr. by Ray Palmer, 1858                           Henry Baker, 1862

1. Jesus, thou Joy of loving hearts, Thou Fount of life, thou Light of men,
From the best bliss that earth imparts We turn unfilled to thee again.

2. Thy truth unchanged hath ever stood; Thou sav-est those that on thee call;
To them that seek thee thou art good, To them that find thee All in all.

3. We taste thee, O thou living Bread, And long to feast upon thee still;
We drink of thee, the Fountain-head, And thirst our souls from thee to fill.

4. Our restless spirits yearn for thee, Wher-e'er our changeful lot is cast;
Glad when thy gracious smile we see, Blest when our faith can hold thee fast.

5. O Jesus, ever with us stay, Make all our moments calm and bright;
Chase the dark night of sin away, Shed o'er the world thy holy light. A-MEN.

**549** (SECOND TUNE)

Attributed to Bernard of Clairvaux, c. 1150               BACA L. M. with repeat
Arr. and tr. by Ray Palmer, 1858                    William B. Bradbury, 1816-1868

Jesus, thou Joy of loving hearts, Thou Fount of life, thou Light of men, From the best bliss that earth imparts We turn unfilled to thee again, We turn unfilled to thee again. A-MEN.

# COMMUNION WITH CHRIST 550

*Unto you therefore which believe he is precious... I Peter 2:7*

Johann Franck, 1655
Tr. by Catherine Winkworth, 1863

LINDEMAN 6. 6. 5. 6. 6. 5. 3. 4. 8. 6.
Ludvig M. Lindeman, 1812-1887

1. Jesus, priceless treasure, Fount of purest pleasure, Truest friend to me: Ah, how long in anguish Shall my spirit languish, Yearning, Lord, for thee? Thine I am, O spotless Lamb! I will suffer naught to hide thee, Naught I ask beside thee.

2. In thine arms I rest me; Foes who would molest me Cannot reach me here. Though the earth be shaking, Ev'ry heart be quaking, Jesus calms my fear. Light-nings flash and thunders crash; Yet, though sin and hell assail me, Jesus will not fail me.

3. Satan, I defy thee; Death, I now decry thee; Fear, I bid thee cease. World, thou shalt not harm me Nor thy threats alarm me While I sing of peace. God's great pow'r guards ev'ry hour; Earth and all its depths adore him, Silent bow before him.

4. Hence with earthly treasure! Thou art all my pleasure, Jesus, all my choice. Hence, thou empty glory! Naught to me thy story, Told with tempting voice. Pain or loss or shame or cross Shall not from my Saviour move me, Since he deigns to love me.

5. Hence, all fear and sadness! For the Lord of gladness, Jesus, enters in. Those who love the Father, Though the storms may gather, Still have peace within. Yea, what-e'er I here must bear, Thou art still my purest pleasure, Jesus, priceless treasure. A-MEN.

## 551 THE CHRISTIAN LIFE

*The Lord is my defense; and my God is the rock of my refuge.* Psalm 94:22

William O. Cushing, 1823-1903

HIDING IN THEE 11. 11. 11. 11. with refrain
Ira D. Sankey, 1840-1908

1. O safe to the Rock that is high-er than I My soul in its con-flicts and sor-rows would fly; So sin-ful, so wea-ry, thine, thine would I be;
2. In the calm of the noon-tide, in sor-row's lone hour, In times when temp-ta - tion casts o'er me its power, In the tem-pests of life, on its wide, heav-ing sea,
3. How oft in the con-flict, when pressed by the foe, I have fled to my ref - uge and breathed out my woe! How oft-en when tri-als like sea-bil-lows roll,

REFRAIN

Thou blest Rock of Ag - es, I'm hid - ing in thee.
Thou blest Rock of Ag - es, I'm hid - ing in thee. Hid - ing in thee,
Have I hid - den in thee, O thou Rock of my soul!

hid - ing in thee—Thou blest Rock of Ag - es, I'm hid - ing in thee. A - MEN.

# COMMUNION WITH CHRIST 552

*If any man serve me, let him follow me; and where I am, there shall also my servant be . . .* John 12:26

John E. Bode, 1868

ANGEL'S STORY 7. 6. 7. 6. D.
Arthur H. Mann, 1883

1. O Jesus, I have promised To serve thee to the end;
Be thou forever near me, My Master and my Friend:
I shall not fear the battle If thou art by my side,
Nor wander from the pathway If thou wilt be my Guide.

2. O let me feel thee near me, The world is ever near;
I see the sights that dazzle, The tempting sounds I hear:
My foes are ever near me, Around me and within;
But, Jesus, draw thou nearer, And shield my soul from sin.

3. O Jesus, thou hast promised To all who follow thee
That where thou art in glory There shall thy servant be;
And, Jesus, I have promised To serve thee to the end;
O give me grace to follow, My Master and my Friend. A-MEN.

## 553 THE CHRISTIAN LIFE: COMMUNION WITH CHRIST

*Thou art my hiding place; thou shalt preserve me from trouble* . . . Psalm 32:7

Thomas Raffles, 1833

ST. LEONARD C. M. D.
Henry Hiles, 1867

1. Thou art my hid-ing-place, O Lord, In thee I put my trust;
   En-cour-aged by thy ho-ly Word, A fee-ble child of dust:
   I have no ar-gu-ment be-side, I urge no oth-er plea;
   And 'tis e-nough my Sav-iour died, My Sav-iour died for me.

2. When storms of fierce temp-ta-tion beat, And fur-ious foes as-sail,
   My ref-uge is the mer-cy-seat, My hope with-in the veil.
   From strife of tongues and bit-ter words My spir-it flies to thee:
   Joy to my heart the thought af-fords, My Sav-iour died for me.

3. 'Mid tri-als heav-y to be borne, When mor-tal strength is vain,
   A heart with grief and an-guish torn, A bod-y racked with pain,
   Ah! what could give the suf-f'rer rest, Bid ev-'ry mur-mur flee,
   But this, the wit-ness in my breast That Je-sus died for me?

4. And when thine aw-ful voice com-mands This bod-y to de-cay,
   And life, in its last lin-g'ring sands, Is eb-bing fast a-way,
   Then, though it be in ac-cents weak, And faint and trem-bling-ly,
   O give me strength in death to speak, "My Sav-iour died for me." A-MEN.

# THE CHRISTIAN LIFE: LOVE FOR GOD 554

*As the hart panteth after the water brooks, so panteth my soul after thee, O God.* Psalm 42:1

From PSALM 42
Tate and Brady's *New Version*, 1696, 1698

SPOHR C. M.
Arr. from Louis Spohr, 1835

1. As pants the hart for cool-ing streams When heat-ed in the chase,
2. For thee, my God, the liv-ing God, My thirst-y soul doth pine;
3. Why rest-less, why cast down, my soul? Trust God; and he'll em-ploy
4. Why rest-less, why cast down, my soul? Hope still; and thou shalt sing

So longs my soul, O God, for thee, And thy re-fresh-ing grace.
O when shall I be-hold thy face, Thou Maj-es-ty Di-vine!
His aid for thee, and change these sighs To thank-ful hymns of joy.
The praise of him who is thy God, Thy health's e-ter-nal spring. A-MEN.

## 555

*Whatsoever ye do, do all to the glory of God.* I Cor. 10:31

George Herbert, 1633

RHIW S. M.
From *A Students' Hymnal*,
University of Wales, 1923

1. Teach me, my God and King, In all things thee to see,
2. A man that looks on glass, On it may stay his eye,
3. All may of thee par-take: Noth-ing can be so mean
4. This is the fa-mous stone That turn-eth all to gold;

And what I do in an-y-thing, To do it as for thee.
Or, if he pleas-eth, through it pass, And then the heav'n es-py.
Which with this mo-tive, "For thy sake," Will not grow bright and clean.
For that which God doth touch and own Can-not for less be told. A-MEN.

Music from *A Students' Hymnal*, by permission of the Oxford University Press, London.
St. 3, line 3, alt.

## 556 THE CHRISTIAN LIFE

*O God, thou art my God; early will I seek thee... Psalm 63:1*

From PSALM 63:1-8 and 73:25  
James Montgomery, 1822

SARRATT L. M.  
Geoffrey C. E. Ryley, 1866-1947

1. O God, thou art my God a-lone; Ear-ly to thee my soul shall cry;  
A pil-grim in a land un-known, A thirst-y land whose springs are dry.

2. O that it were as it hath been! When, pray-ing in the ho-ly place,  
Thy pow'r and glo-ry I have seen, And marked the foot-steps of thy grace.

3. Yet, through this rough and thorn-y maze, I fol-low hard on thee, my God:  
Thy hand, un-seen, up-holds my ways; I safe-ly tread where thou hast trod.

4. Thee, in the watch-es of the night, When I re-mem-ber on my bed,  
Thy pres-ence makes the dark-ness light, Thy guard-ian wings are round my head.

5. Bet-ter than life it-self thy love, Dear-er than all be-side to me:  
For whom have I in heav'n a-bove, Or what on earth, com-pared to thee?

6. Praise with my heart, my mind, my voice, For all thy mer-cy I will give;  
My soul shall still in God re-joice; My tongue shall bless thee while I live. A-MEN.

## 557

*I am continually with thee: thou hast holden me by my right hand. Psalm 73:23*

From PSALM 73:23-28  
The Psalter, 1912

ST. FLAVIAN C. M.  
Day's *Psalter*, 1562

1. In sweet com-mun-ion, Lord, with thee I con-stant-ly a-bide;  
My hand thou hold-est in thine own To keep me near thy side.

2. Thy coun-sel through my earth-ly way Shall guide me and con-trol,  
And then to glo-ry af-ter-ward Thou wilt re-ceive my soul.

3. Whom have I, Lord, in heav'n but thee, To whom my thoughts as-pire?  
And, hav-ing thee, on earth is nought That I can yet de-sire.

4. Though flesh and heart should faint and fail, The Lord will ev-er be  
The strength and por-tion of my heart, My God e-tern-al-ly.

5. To live a-part from God is death, 'Tis good his face to seek;  
My ref-uge is the liv-ing God, His praise I long to speak. A-MEN.

# TRUST IN GOD 558

*God . . . is my high tower, and my refuge, my saviour . . .* II Sam. 22:3

St. 1, Joachim Magdeburg, 1572; st. 2-3, anon., 1597
Tr. by Benjamin H. Kennedy, 1863; alt. by
W. Walsham How, 1864

CONSTANCE 8. 7. 8. 7. D.
Sir Arthur S. Sullivan, 1875

1. Who trusts in God, a strong a-bode In heav'n and earth pos-sess-es;
2. Though Sa-tan's wrath be-set our path, And world-ly scorn as-sail us,
3. In all the strife of mor-tal life Our feet shall stand se-cure-ly;

Who looks in love to Christ a-bove, No fear his heart op-press-es.
While thou art near we will not fear, Thy strength shall nev-er fail us:
Temp-ta-tion's hour shall lose its pow'r, For thou shalt guard us sure-ly.

In thee a-lone, dear Lord, we own Sweet hope and con-so-la-tion;
Thy rod and staff shall keep us safe, And guide our steps for ev-er;
O God, re-new, with heav'n-ly dew, Our bod-y, soul, and spir-it,

Our shield from foes, our balm for woes, Our great and sure sal-va-tion.
Nor shades of death, nor hell be-neath, Our souls from thee shall sev-er.
Un-til we stand at thy right hand, Through Je-sus' sav-ing mer-it. A-MEN.

## 559 THE CHRISTIAN LIFE

*Cast thy burden upon the Lord, and he shall sustain thee ... Psalm 55:22*

MERCY 7. 7. 7. 7.
Anon. in Rowland Hill's *Psalms and Hymns*, 1783
Arr. from Louis M. Gottschalk, 1867

1. Cast thy bur-den on the Lord, On-ly lean up-on his word;
2. He sus-tains thee by his hand, He en-a-bles thee to stand;
3. Hu-man coun-sels come to naught; That shall stand which God hath wrought;
4. Heav'n and earth may pass a-way, God's free grace shall not de-cay;
5. Je-sus, Guard-ian of thy flock, Be thy-self our con-stant rock;

Thou wilt soon have cause to bless His e-ter-nal faith-ful-ness.
Those whom Je-sus once hath loved From his grace are nev-er moved.
His com-pas-sion, love, and pow'r Are the same for ev-er-more.
He hath prom-ised to ful-fil All the pleas-ure of his will.
Make us, by thy pow'r-ful hand, Strong as Zi-on's moun-tain stand. A-MEN.

## 560

*Commit thy way unto the Lord; trust also in him; and he shall bring it to pass. Psalm 37:5*

Paul Gerhardt, 1656
Tr. by John Wesley, 1739
ST. GEORGE S. M.
Henry J. Gauntlett, 1848

1. Com-mit thou all thy griefs And ways in-to his hands;
2. Who points the clouds their course, Whom winds and seas o-bey,
3. Give to the winds thy fears; Hope, and be un-dis-mayed;
4. What though thou rul-est not? Yet heav'n and earth and hell
5. Leave to his sov-ereign sway To choose and to com-mand;

To his sure truth and ten-der care, Who earth and heav'n com-mands.
He shall di-rect thy wan-d'ring feet, He shall pre-pare thy way.
God hears thy sighs, and counts thy tears, God shall lift up thy head.
Pro-claim, God sit-teth on the throne, And rul-eth all things well.
So shalt thou won-d'ring own, his way How wise, how strong his hand! A-MEN.

# TRUST IN GOD

## 561

*My yoke is easy, and my burden is light.* Matt. 11:30

Philip Doddridge, 1755

DENNIS S. M.
Arr. from Hans G. Nägeli by Lowell Mason, 1845

1. How gen-tle God's com-mands, How kind his pre-cepts are!
2. While Prov-i-dence sup-ports, Let saints se-cure-ly dwell;
3. Why should this anx-ious load Press down your wea-ry mind?
4. His good-ness stands ap-proved, Down to the pres-ent day;

Come, cast your bur-dens on the Lord, And trust his con-stant care.
That hand, which bears all na-ture up, Shall guide his chil-dren well.
Haste to your heav'n-ly Fa-ther's throne, And sweet re-fresh-ment find.
I'll drop my bur-den at his feet, And bear a song a-way. A-MEN.

## 562

*It is the Lord: let him do what seemeth him good.* I Sam. 3:18

Anne Steele, 1760; alt. by
Augustus M. Toplady, 1776

NAOMI C. M.
Arr. from Hans G. Nägeli by Lowell Mason, 1836

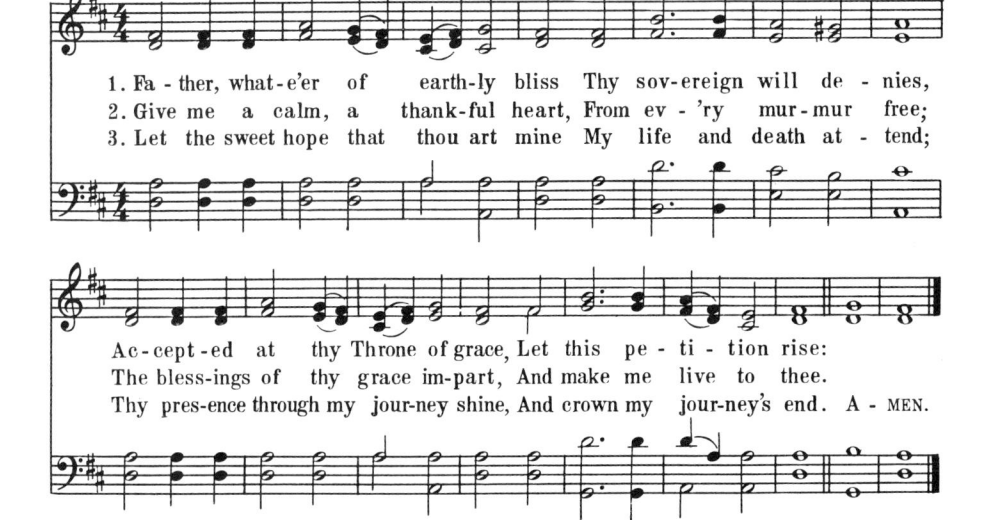

1. Fa-ther, what-e'er of earth-ly bliss Thy sov-ereign will de-nies,
2. Give me a calm, a thank-ful heart, From ev-'ry mur-mur free;
3. Let the sweet hope that thou art mine My life and death at-tend;

Ac-cept-ed at thy Throne of grace, Let this pe-ti-tion rise:
The bless-ings of thy grace im-part, And make me live to thee.
Thy pres-ence through my jour-ney shine, And crown my jour-ney's end. A-MEN.

## 563 THE CHRISTIAN LIFE

*Oh how great is thy goodness, which thou hast laid up for them that fear thee ... Psalm 31:19*

From PSALM 31:19-24  
The Psalter, 1912

MERIBAH 8.8.6.D.  
Lowell Mason, 1839

1. How great the good-ness kept in store For those who fear thee and a-dore
   In meek hu-mil-i-ty. How great the deeds with mer-cy fraught
   Which o-pen-ly thy hand has wrought For those who trust in thee.

2. Se-cured by thine un-fail-ing grace, In thee they find a hid-ing-place
   When foes their plots de-vise; A sure re-treat thou wilt pre-pare,
   And keep them safe-ly shel-tered there, When strife of tongues shall rise.

3. Blest be the Lord, for he has showed, While giv-ing me a safe a-bode,
   His love be-yond com-pare; Al-though his face he seemed to hide,
   He ev-er heard me when I cried, And made my wants his care.

4. Ye saints, Je-ho-vah love and serve, For he the faith-ful will pre-serve,
   And shield from men of pride; Be strong, and let your hearts be brave,
   All ye that wait for him to save, In God the Lord con-fide. A-MEN.

## 564

*What time I am afraid, I will trust in thee. Psalm 56:3*

From PSALM 56:3-4, 11-13  
The Psalter, 1912

HOLY GUIDE 6.6.6.6.  
Uzziah C. Burnap, 1895

1. What time I am a-fraid I put my trust in thee;
2. In God I put my trust, I nei-ther doubt nor fear,
3. In God, the Lord, I rest, His Word of grace I praise,
4. Up-on me are thy vows, O God, in whom I live;
5. For thou hast saved from death, From fall-ing kept me free,

# TRUST IN GOD

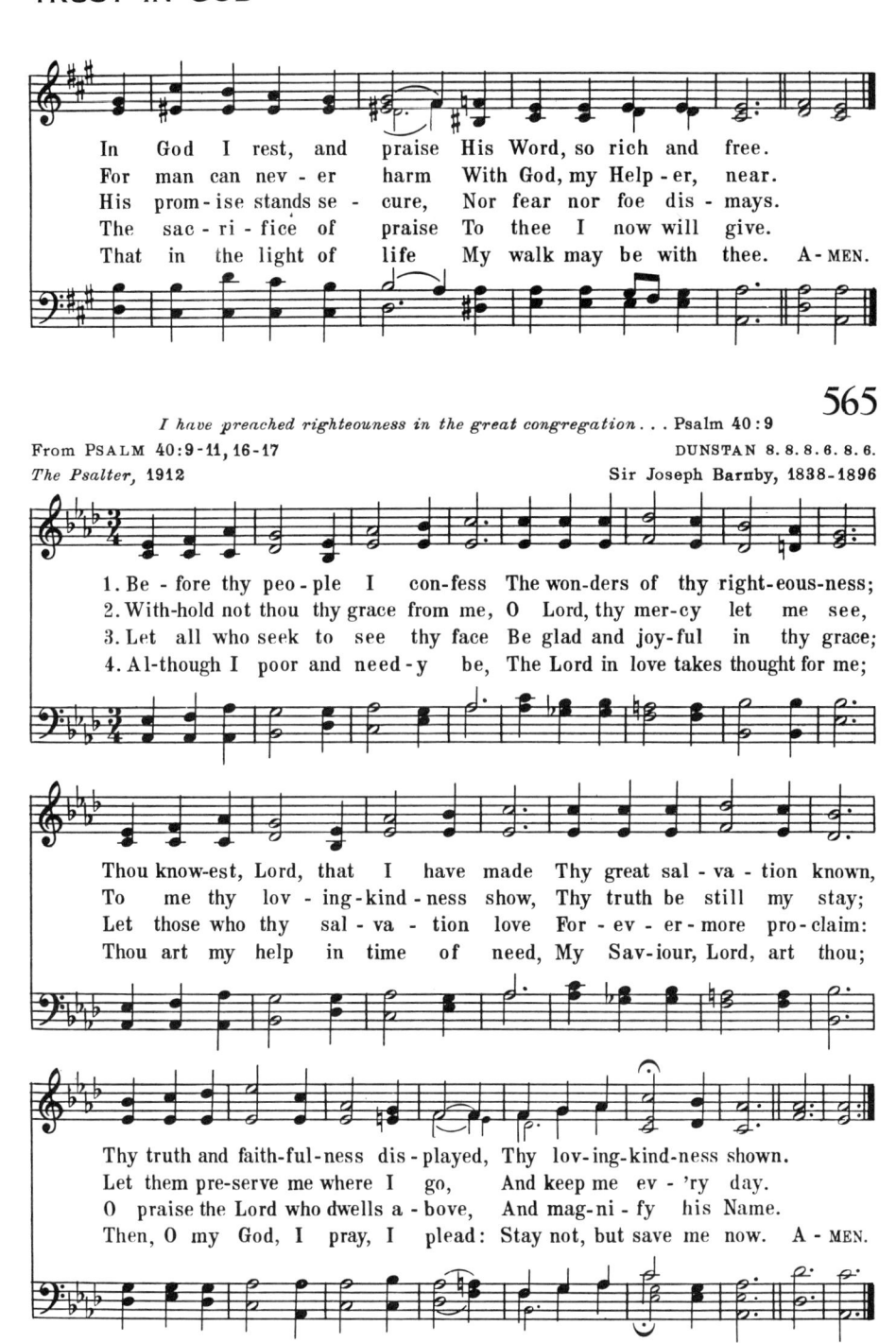

In God I rest, and praise His Word, so rich and free.
For man can nev-er harm With God, my Help-er, near.
His prom-ise stands se-cure, Nor fear nor foe dis-mays.
The sac-ri-fice of praise To thee I now will give.
That in the light of life My walk may be with thee. A-MEN.

*I have preached righteouness in the great congregation... Psalm 40:9*

565

From PSALM 40:9-11, 16-17
*The Psalter,* 1912

DUNSTAN 8.8.8.6.8.6.
Sir Joseph Barnby, 1838-1896

1. Be-fore thy peo-ple I con-fess The won-ders of thy right-eous-ness;
2. With-hold not thou thy grace from me, O Lord, thy mer-cy let me see,
3. Let all who seek to see thy face Be glad and joy-ful in thy grace;
4. Al-though I poor and need-y be, The Lord in love takes thought for me;

Thou know-est, Lord, that I have made Thy great sal-va-tion known,
To me thy lov-ing-kind-ness show, Thy truth be still my stay;
Let those who thy sal-va-tion love For-ev-er-more pro-claim:
Thou art my help in time of need, My Sav-iour, Lord, art thou;

Thy truth and faith-ful-ness dis-played, Thy lov-ing-kind-ness shown.
Let them pre-serve me where I go, And keep me ev-'ry day.
O praise the Lord who dwells a-bove, And mag-ni-fy his Name.
Then, O my God, I pray, I plead: Stay not, but save me now. A-MEN.

# 566 THE CHRISTIAN LIFE

*He . . . shall abide under the shadow of the Almighty.* Psalm 91:1

From PSALM 91  
James Montgomery, 1822

AUTUMN 8. 7. 8. 7. D.  
François H. Barthélémon, 1741-1808

1. Call Jehovah thy Salvation, Rest beneath th' Almighty's shade,
2. From the sword at noonday wasting, From the noisome pestilence,
3. Since, with pure and firm affection Thou on God hast set thy love,

In his secret habitation Dwell, and never be dismayed:
In the depth of midnight blasting, God shall be thy sure Defence:
With the wings of his protection He will shield thee from above:

There no tumult shall alarm thee, Thou shalt dread no hidden snare:
He shall charge his angel legions Watch and ward o'er thee to keep;
Thou shalt call on him in trouble, He will hearken, he will save;

Guile nor violence can harm thee, In eternal safeguard there.
Though thou walk through hostile regions, Though in desert wilds thou sleep.
Here for grief reward thee double, Crown with life beyond the grave. A-MEN.

See also HYFRYDOL, No. 145

# TRUST IN GOD 567

*He shall never suffer the righteous to be moved.* Psalm 55:22

Georg Neumark, 1641  
Tr. by Catherine Winkworth, 1855, 1863

NEUMARK 9.8.9.8.8.8.  
Georg Neumark, 1657

1. If thou but suf-fer God to guide thee, And hope in him through all thy ways, He'll give thee strength, what-e'er be-tide thee, And bear thee through the e-vil days: Who trusts in God's un-chang-ing love Builds on the rock that naught can move.

2. What can these anx-ious cares a-vail thee, These nev-er-ceas-ing moans and sighs? What can it help, if thou be-wail thee O'er each dark mo-ment as it flies? Our cross and tri-als do but press The heav-ier for our bit-ter-ness.

3. On-ly be still, and wait his lei-sure In cheer-ful hope, with heart con-tent To take what-e'er thy Fa-ther's pleas-ure And all-de-serv-ing love hath sent; Nor doubt our in-most wants are known To him who chose us for his own.

4. All are a-like be-fore the High-est; 'Tis eas-y to our God, we know, To raise thee up though low thou li-est, To make the rich man poor and low; True won-ders still by him are wrought Who set-teth up and brings to naught.

5. Sing, pray, and keep his ways un-swerv-ing, So do thine own part faith-ful-ly, And trust his Word,—though un-de-serv-ing, Thou yet shalt find it true for thee; God nev-er yet for-sook at need The soul that trust-ed him in-deed. A-MEN.

## 568 THE CHRISTIAN LIFE

*The Lord is my light and my salvation; whom shall I fear?* Psalm 27:1

From PSALM 27
James Montgomery, 1822

MEIN LEBEN 7. 6. 7. 6.
Arr. from Melchior Vulpius, 1609

1. God is my strong Sal-va-tion; What foe have I to fear?
In dark-ness and temp-ta-tion My Light, my Help is near.

2. Though hosts en-camp a-round me, Firm to the fight I stand;
What ter-ror can con-found me, With God at my right hand?

3. Place on the Lord re-li-ance, My soul, with cour-age wait;
His truth be thine af-fi-ance, When faint and des-o-late.

4. His might thy heart shall strength-en, His love thy joy in-crease;
Mer-cy thy days shall length-en; The Lord will give thee peace. A-MEN.

## 569

*Trust in the Lord, and do good . . .* Psalm 37:3

From PSALM 37:3-7
The Psalter, 1912

MEDITATION C. M.
John H. Gower, 1890

1. For ev-er trust-ing in the Lord, Take heed to do his will;
So shalt thou dwell with-in the land, And he thy needs shall fill.

2. De-light thee in the Lord, and he Will grant thy heart's re-quest;
To him com-mit thy way in faith, And thus thou shalt be blessed.

3. And he shall make thy right-eous-ness Shine bright-ly as the light,
And as the burn-ing noon-day sun Thy judg-ment shall be bright.

4. Rest in the Lord with qui-et trust, Wait pa-tient-ly for him;
Though wick-ed-ness tri-um-phant seem, Let not thy faith grow dim. A-MEN.

# TRUST IN GOD

## 570

*Out of the depths have I cried unto thee, O Lord.* Psalm 130:1

From PSALM 130
*The Psalter,* 1912

BULLINGER 8. 5. 8. 3.
Ethelbert W. Bullinger, 1874

1. From the depths my prayer as-cend-eth Un-to God on high;
2. None can stand un-scathed and blame-less In thy judg-ment just,
3. Lord, my hope is in thy prom-ise, And I wait for thee
4. With the Lord is ten-der mer-cy, And re-deem-ing love;

Hear, O Lord, my sup-pli-ca-tion And my cry.
But the con-trite in thy mer-cy Hum-bly trust.
More than they who watch for morn-ing, Light to see.
Is-rael, look for full sal-va-tion From a-bove. A-MEN.

## 571

*Truly my soul waiteth upon God: from him cometh my salvation.* Psalm 62:1

From PSALM 62
*The Psalter,* 1912

HOWARD C. M.
Wilson's *Selection of Psalm Tunes,* 1825

1. My soul in si-lence waits for God, My Sav-iour he has proved;
2. My hon-or is se-cure with God, My Sav-iour he is known;
3. On him, ye peo-ple, ev-er-more Re-ly with con-fid-ence;
4. For God has spok-en o'er and o'er, And un-to me has shown,
5. Yea, lov-ing-kind-ness ev-er-more Be-longs to thee, O Lord;

He on-ly is my Rock and Tow'r; I nev-er shall be moved.
My Ref-uge and my Rock of strength Are found in God a-lone.
Be-fore him pour ye out your heart, For God is our de-fense.
That sav-ing pow'r and last-ing strength Be-long to him a-lone.
And thou ac-cord-ing to his work Dost ev-'ry man re-ward. A-MEN.

# 572 THE CHRISTIAN LIFE

*Not as I will, but as thou wilt.* **Matt. 26:39**

Benjamin Schmolck, c. 1704
Tr. by Jane Borthwick, 1854

JEWETT 6.6.6.6.D.
Carl Maria von Weber, 1820
Arr. by Joseph P. Holbrook, 1862

1. My Je-sus, as thou wilt! O may thy will be mine;
2. My Je-sus, as thou wilt! If need-y here and poor,
3. My Je-sus, as thou wilt! Though seen through man-y a tear,
4. My Je-sus, as thou wilt! All shall be well for me;

In-to thy hand of love I would my all re-sign.
Give me thy peo-ple's bread, Their por-tion rich and sure.
Let not my star of hope Grow dim or dis-ap-pear.
Each chang-ing fu-ture scene I glad-ly trust with thee.

Through sor-row, or through joy, Con-duct me as thine own;
The man-na of thy Word Let my soul feed up-on;
Since thou on earth hast wept, And sor-rowed oft a-lone,
Straight to my home a-bove I trav-el calm-ly on,

And help me still to say, My Lord, thy will be done.
And if all else should fail, My Lord, thy will be done.
If I must weep with thee, My Lord, thy will be done.
And sing, in life or death, "My Lord, thy will be done." A-MEN.

## SUBMISSION 573

*Yield yourselves unto God... Rom. 6:13*

Horatius Bonar, 1857

INVITATION 6.6.6.6.D.
Frederick C. Maker, 1881

1. Thy way, not mine, O Lord, How-ev-er dark it be!
Lead me by thine own hand, Choose out the path for me;
Smooth let it be or rough, It will be still the best;
Wind-ing or straight, it leads Right on-ward to thy rest.

2. The king-dom that I seek Is thine; so let the way
That leads to it be thine, Else I must sure-ly stray.
I dare not choose my lot; I would not if I might:
Choose thou for me, my God, So shall I walk a-right.

3. Take thou my cup, and it With joy or sor-row fill
As best to thee may seem; Choose thou my good and ill.
Not mine, not mine the choice In things or great or small;
Be thou my Guide, my Strength, My Wis-dom, and my All. A-MEN.

# 574 THE CHRISTIAN LIFE

*Hath not the potter power over the clay . . . ? Rom. 9:21*

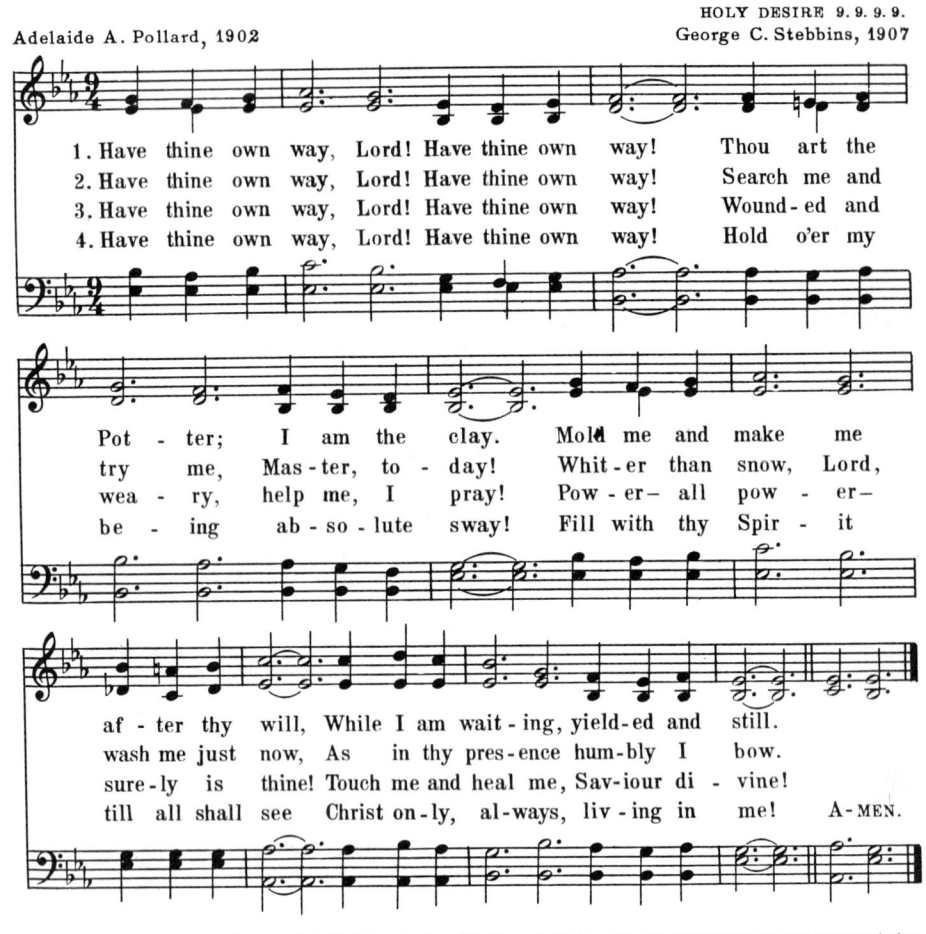

HOLY DESIRE 9.9.9.9.

Adelaide A. Pollard, 1902  
George C. Stebbins, 1907

1. Have thine own way, Lord! Have thine own way! Thou art the Pot-ter; I am the clay. Mold me and make me af-ter thy will, While I am wait-ing, yield-ed and still.
2. Have thine own way, Lord! Have thine own way! Search me and try me, Mas-ter, to-day! Whit-er than snow, Lord, wash me just now, As in thy pres-ence hum-bly I bow.
3. Have thine own way, Lord! Have thine own way! Wound-ed and wea-ry, help me, I pray! Pow-er— all pow-er— sure-ly is thine! Touch me and heal me, Sav-iour di-vine!
4. Have thine own way, Lord! Have thine own way! Hold o'er my be-ing ab-so-lute sway! Fill with thy Spir-it till all shall see Christ on-ly, al-ways, liv-ing in me! A-MEN.

Copyright, 1907. Renewal, 1935, by G. C. Stebbins. Assigned to Hope Publishing Co. All rights reserved. Used by permission.

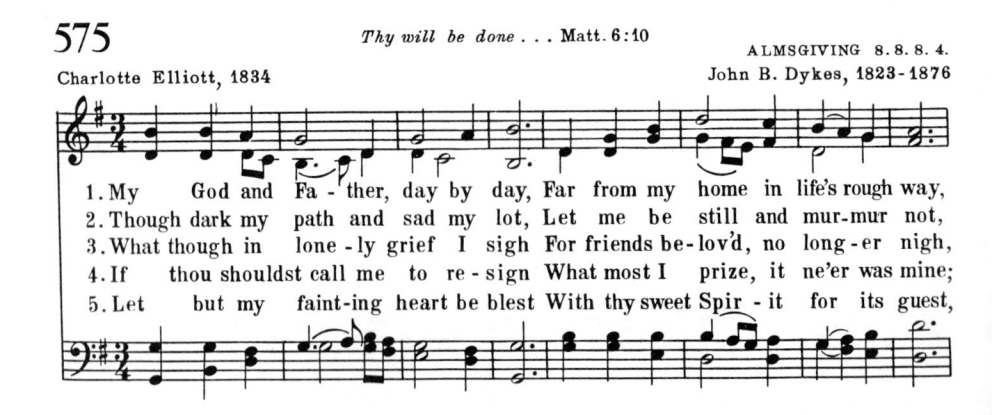

# 575

*Thy will be done . . . Matt. 6:10*

ALMSGIVING 8.8.8.4.

Charlotte Elliott, 1834  
John B. Dykes, 1823-1876

1. My God and Fa-ther, day by day, Far from my home in life's rough way,
2. Though dark my path and sad my lot, Let me be still and mur-mur not,
3. What though in lone-ly grief I sigh For friends be-lov'd, no long-er nigh,
4. If thou shouldst call me to re-sign What most I prize, it ne'er was mine;
5. Let but my faint-ing heart be blest With thy sweet Spir-it for its guest,

## SUBMISSION

O teach me from my heart to say, "Thy will be done."
Or breathe the prayer di-vine-ly taught, "Thy will be done."
Sub-mis-sive still would I re - ply, "Thy will be done."
I on - ly yield thee what was thine, "Thy will be done."
My God, to thee I leave the rest: "Thy will be done." A - MEN.

St. 1, line 1, alt.

576

*A servant of God and of the Lord Jesus Christ . . . James 1:1*

Thomas H. Gill, 1863

FERGUSON S. M.
George Kingsley, 1843

1. Dear Lord and Mas - ter mine, Thy hap - py serv - ant see;
2. I love thy yoke to wear, To feel thy gra - cious bands;
3. No bar would I re - move, No bond would I un - bind;
4. I would not walk a - lone, But still with thee, my God;

My Con-queror, with what joy di - vine Thy cap-tive clings to thee!
Sweet-ly re - strain-ed by thy care And hap - py in thy hands.
With-in the lim - its of thy love Full lib - er - ty I find.
At ev -'ry step my blind-ness own, And ask of thee the road. A - MEN.

5. Dear Lord and Master mine,
   Still keep thy servant true;
   My Guardian and my Guide divine,
   Bring, bring thy pilgrim through.

6. My Conqueror and my King,
   Still keep me in thy train;
   And with thee thy glad captive bring
   When thou return'st to reign.

## 577 THE CHRISTIAN LIFE

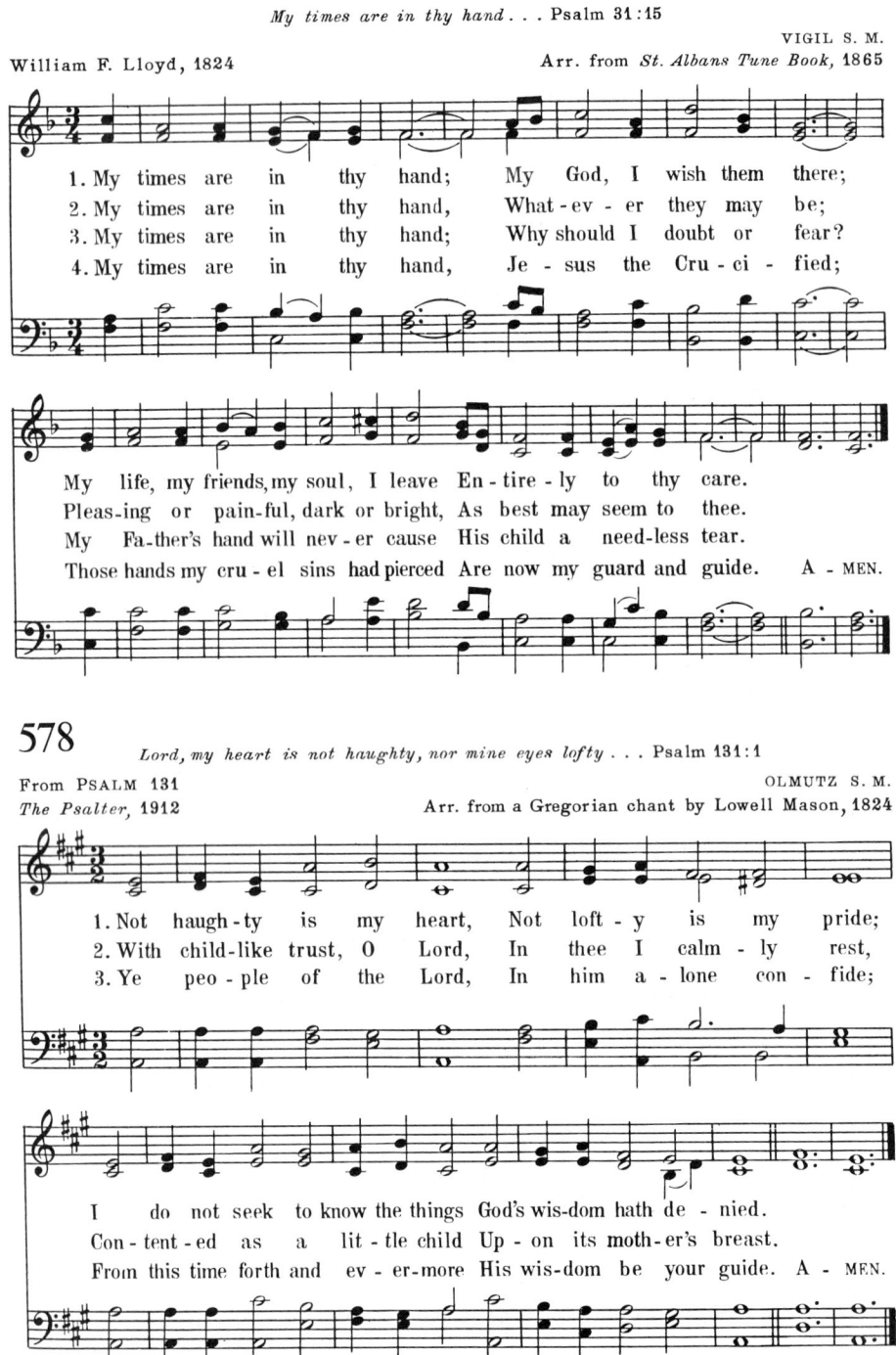

*My times are in thy hand* . . . Psalm 31:15

William F. Lloyd, 1824

VIGIL S. M.
Arr. from *St. Albans Tune Book*, 1865

1. My times are in thy hand; My God, I wish them there;
   My life, my friends, my soul, I leave En-tire-ly to thy care.
2. My times are in thy hand, What-ev-er they may be;
   Pleas-ing or pain-ful, dark or bright, As best may seem to thee.
3. My times are in thy hand; Why should I doubt or fear?
   My Fa-ther's hand will nev-er cause His child a need-less tear.
4. My times are in thy hand, Je-sus the Cru-ci-fied;
   Those hands my cru-el sins had pierced Are now my guard and guide. A-MEN.

## 578

*Lord, my heart is not haughty, nor mine eyes lofty* . . . Psalm 131:1

From PSALM 131
*The Psalter*, 1912

OLMUTZ S. M.
Arr. from a Gregorian chant by Lowell Mason, 1824

1. Not haugh-ty is my heart, Not loft-y is my pride;
   I do not seek to know the things God's wis-dom hath de-nied.
2. With child-like trust, O Lord, In thee I calm-ly rest,
   Con-tent-ed as a lit-tle child Up-on its moth-er's breast.
3. Ye peo-ple of the Lord, In him a-lone con-fide;
   From this time forth and ev-er-more His wis-dom be your guide. A-MEN.

# SUBMISSION 579

*Be patient therefore, brethren, unto the coming of the Lord.* James 5:7

Katharina von Schlegel, b. 1697
Tr. by Jane Borthwick, 1855

UNDE ET MEMORES 10. 10. 10. 10. 10. 10.
William H. Monk, 1875

1. Be still, my soul: the Lord is on thy side; Bear patiently the cross of grief or pain; Leave to thy God to order and provide; In ev-'ry change he faithful will remain. Be still, my soul: thy best, thy heav'n-ly Friend Through thorn-y ways leads to a joy-ful end.

2. Be still, my soul: thy God doth undertake To guide the future as he has the past. Thy hope, thy confidence let nothing shake; All now mysterious shall be bright at last. Be still, my soul: the waves and winds still know His voice who ruled them while he dwelt below.

3. Be still, my soul: when dearest friends depart, And all is darkened in the vale of tears, Then shalt thou better know his love, his heart, Who comes to soothe thy sorrow and thy fears. Be still, my soul: thy Jesus can repay From his own fullness all he takes away.

4. Be still, my soul: the hour is hast'ning on When we shall be forever with the Lord, When disappointment, grief, and fear are gone, Sorrow forgot, love's purest joys restored. Be still, my soul: when change and tears are past, All safe and blessed we shall meet at last. A-MEN.

## 580 THE CHRISTIAN LIFE

*The peace of God, which passeth all understanding, shall keep your hearts and minds through Christ Jesus.* Phil. 4:7

Horatio G. Spafford, 1828-1888
IT IS WELL 11.8.11.9. with refrain
Philip P. Bliss, 1876

1. When peace, like a riv-er, at-tend-eth my way,
2. Though Sa-tan should buf-fet, though tri-als should come,
3. My sin— O the bliss of this glo-ri-ous thought!—
4. O Lord, haste the day when the faith shall be sight,

When sor-rows like sea-bil-lows roll; What-ev-er my
Let this blest as-sur-ance con-trol, That Christ has re-
My sin, not in part, but the whole, Is nailed to the
The clouds be rolled back as a scroll, The trump shall re-

lot, thou hast taught me to say, It is well, it is
gard-ed my help-less es-tate, And has shed his own
cross and I bear it no more; Praise the Lord, praise the
sound and the Lord shall de-scend; "E-ven so"— it is

REFRAIN

well with my soul.
blood for my soul. It is well with my
Lord, O my soul!
well with my soul. It is well

soul; It is well, it is well with my soul. A-MEN.
with my soul;

# ASSURANCE

## 581

*Preserve me, O God: for in thee do I put my trust.* Psalm 16:1

From PSALM 16:1-2, 5-8, 11  
*The Psalter*, 1912

LEOMINSTER S.M.D.  
George William Martin, 1862  
Har. by Sir Arthur S. Sullivan, 1874

1. To thee, O Lord, I fly And on thy help de-pend;
   Thou art my Lord and King Most High; Do thou my soul de-fend.
   A her-it-age for me Je-ho-vah will re-main;
   My por-tion rich and full is he, My right he will main-tain.

2. The lot to me that fell Is beau-ti-ful and fair;
   The her-it-age in which I dwell Is good be-yond com-pare.
   I praise the Lord a-bove Whose coun-sel guides a-right;
   My heart in-structs me in his love In sea-sons of the night.

3. I keep be-fore me still The Lord whom I have proved;
   At my right hand he guards from ill, And I shall not be moved.
   Life's path-way thou wilt show, To thy right hand wilt guide,
   Where streams of pleas-ure ev-er flow, And bound-less joys a-bide. A-MEN.

## 582 THE CHRISTIAN LIFE

*For other foundation can no man lay than that is laid, which is Jesus Christ.* I Cor. 3:11

Edward Mote, c. 1834; st. 1, arr.
ST. PETERSBURG 8.8.8.8.8.8.
Dimitri Bortniansky, 1752-1825

1. My hope is built on nothing less Than Jesus' blood and righteousness;
   I dare not trust the sweetest frame, But wholly lean on Jesus' Name.
2. When darkness veils his lovely face, I rest upon unchanging grace;
   In ev'ry rough and stormy gale My anchor holds within the veil.
3. His oath, his covenant, his blood Support me in the whelming flood;
   When all around my soul gives way, He then is all my Hope and Stay.
4. When I shall launch in worlds unseen, O may I then be found in him;
   Dressed in his righteousness alone, Faultless to stand before the throne.

REFRAIN

On Christ, the solid Rock, I stand; All other ground is sinking sand. A-MEN.

## 583

*Unto thee, O Lord, do I lift up my soul.* Psalm 25:1

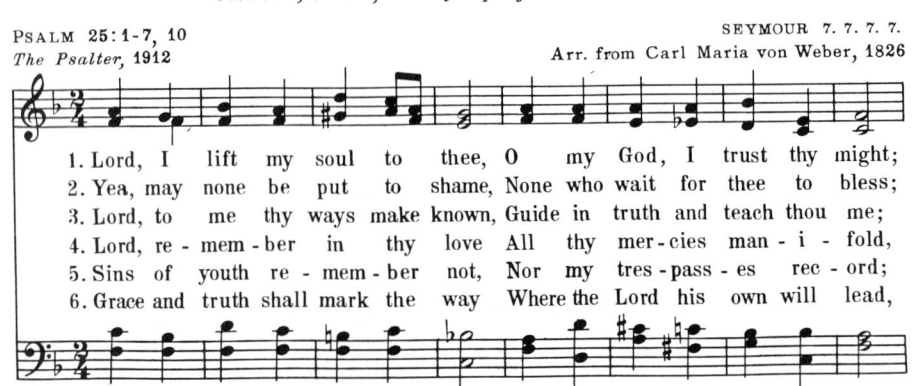

PSALM 25:1-7, 10
The Psalter, 1912
SEYMOUR 7.7.7.7.
Arr. from Carl Maria von Weber, 1826

1. Lord, I lift my soul to thee, O my God, I trust thy might;
2. Yea, may none be put to shame, None who wait for thee to bless;
3. Lord, to me thy ways make known, Guide in truth and teach thou me;
4. Lord, remember in thy love All thy mercies manifold,
5. Sins of youth remember not, Nor my trespasses record;
6. Grace and truth shall mark the way Where the Lord his own will lead,

## ASSURANCE

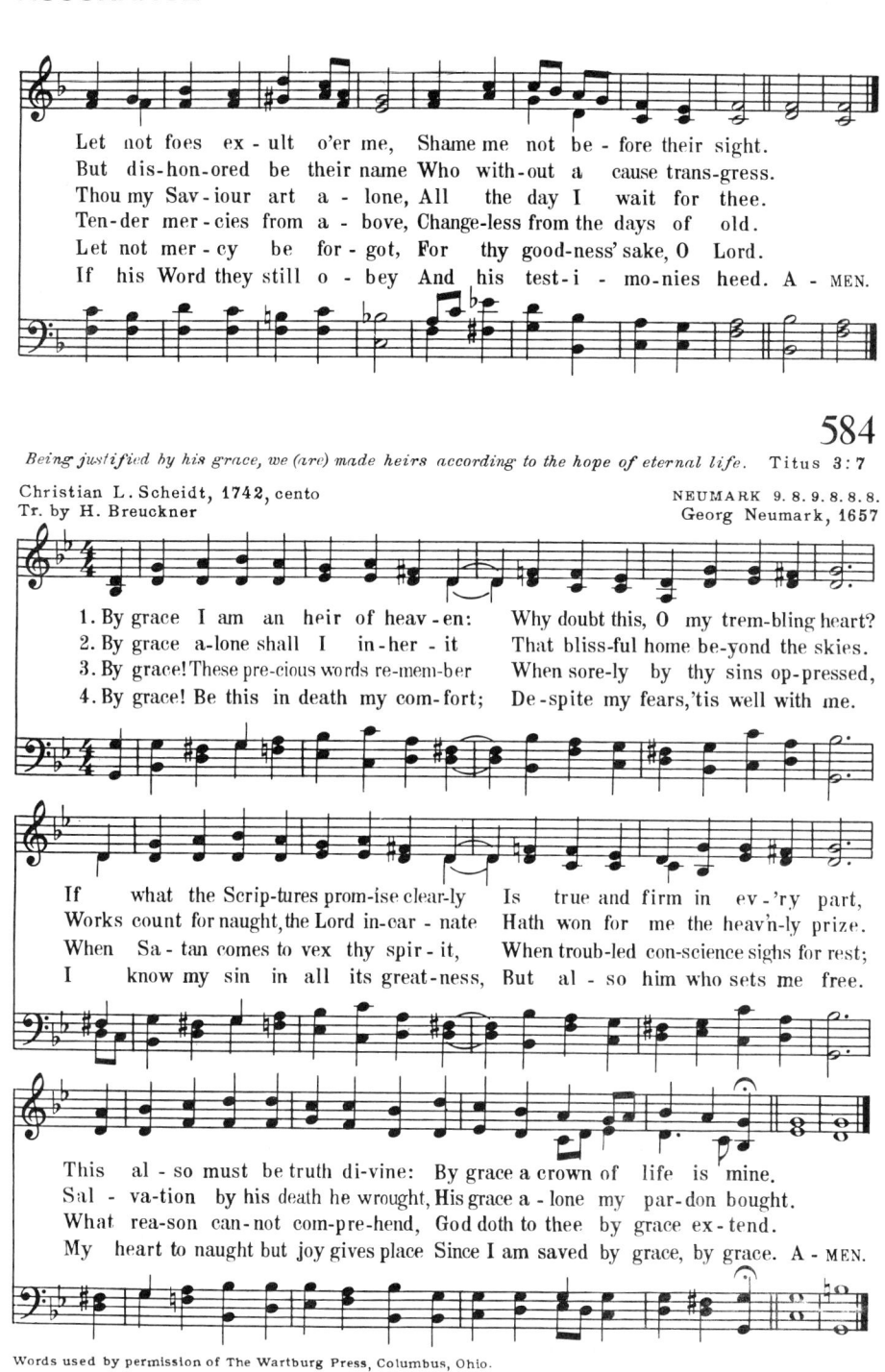

Let not foes ex-ult o'er me, Shame me not be-fore their sight.
But dis-hon-ored be their name Who with-out a cause trans-gress.
Thou my Sav-iour art a-lone, All the day I wait for thee.
Ten-der mer-cies from a-bove, Change-less from the days of old.
Let not mer-cy be for-got, For thy good-ness' sake, O Lord.
If his Word they still o-bey And his test-i-mo-nies heed. A-MEN.

### 584

*Being justified by his grace, we (are) made heirs according to the hope of eternal life.* Titus 3:7

Christian L. Scheidt, 1742, cento
Tr. by H. Brueckner

NEUMARK 9.8.9.8.8.8.
Georg Neumark, 1657

1. By grace I am an heir of heav-en: Why doubt this, O my trem-bling heart?
2. By grace a-lone shall I in-her-it That bliss-ful home be-yond the skies.
3. By grace! These pre-cious words re-mem-ber When sore-ly by thy sins op-pressed,
4. By grace! Be this in death my com-fort; De-spite my fears, 'tis well with me.

If what the Scrip-tures prom-ise clear-ly Is true and firm in ev-'ry part,
Works count for naught, the Lord in-car-nate Hath won for me the heav'n-ly prize.
When Sa-tan comes to vex thy spir-it, When troub-led con-science sighs for rest;
I know my sin in all its great-ness, But al-so him who sets me free.

This al-so must be truth di-vine: By grace a crown of life is mine.
Sal-va-tion by his death he wrought, His grace a-lone my par-don bought.
What rea-son can-not com-pre-hend, God doth to thee by grace ex-tend.
My heart to naught but joy gives place Since I am saved by grace, by grace. A-MEN.

Words used by permission of The Wartburg Press, Columbus, Ohio.

## 585 THE CHRISTIAN LIFE: ASSURANCE

*They that trust in the Lord shall be as mount Zion, which cannot be removed... Psalm 125:1*

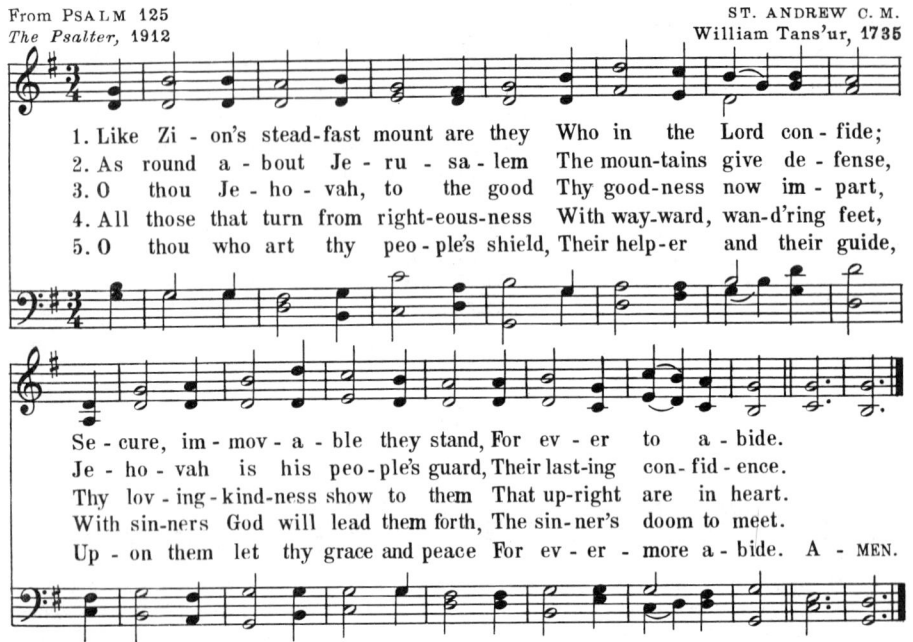

From PSALM 125  
The Psalter, 1912

ST. ANDREW C. M.  
William Tans'ur, 1735

1. Like Zi-on's stead-fast mount are they Who in the Lord con-fide;
2. As round a-bout Je-ru-sa-lem The moun-tains give de-fense,
3. O thou Je-ho-vah, to the good Thy good-ness now im-part,
4. All those that turn from right-eous-ness With way-ward, wand'ring feet,
5. O thou who art thy peo-ple's shield, Their help-er and their guide,

Se-cure, im-mov-a-ble they stand, For ev-er to a-bide.
Je-ho-vah is his peo-ple's guard, Their last-ing con-fid-ence.
Thy lov-ing-kind-ness show to them That up-right are in heart.
With sin-ners God will lead them forth, The sin-ner's doom to meet.
Up-on them let thy grace and peace For ev-er-more a-bide. A-MEN.

## 586

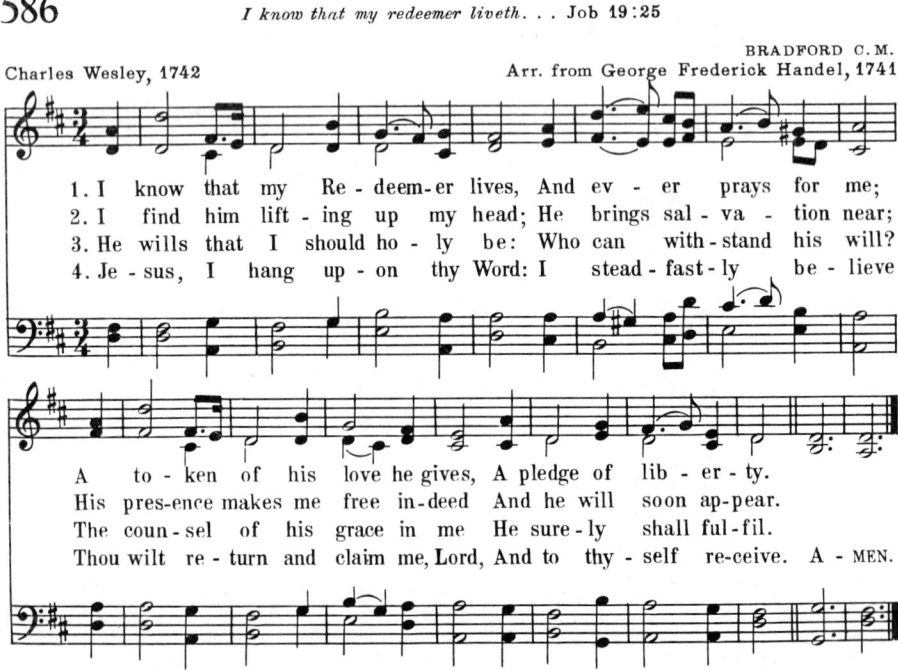

*I know that my redeemer liveth... Job 19:25*

Charles Wesley, 1742

BRADFORD C. M.  
Arr. from George Frederick Handel, 1741

1. I know that my Re-deem-er lives, And ev-er prays for me;
2. I find him lift-ing up my head; He brings sal-va-tion near;
3. He wills that I should ho-ly be: Who can with-stand his will?
4. Je-sus, I hang up-on thy Word: I stead-fast-ly be-lieve

A to-ken of his love he gives, A pledge of lib-er-ty.
His pres-ence makes me free in-deed And he will soon ap-pear.
The coun-sel of his grace in me He sure-ly shall ful-fil.
Thou wilt re-turn and claim me, Lord, And to thy-self re-ceive. A-MEN.

# THE CHRISTIAN LIFE: PEACE AND JOY 587

*Behold, I will extend peace ... like a river.* Isa. 66:12

Frances R. Havergal, 1878
LIKE A RIVER 6.5.6.5. D. and refrain
James Mountain, 1844-1933

1. Like a river glorious Is God's perfect peace, O-ver all victorious In its bright in-crease; Perfect, yet it floweth Fuller ev'ry day,— Perfect, yet it groweth Deeper all the way.
2. Hidden in the hollow Of his blessed hand, Never foe can follow, Never traitor stand; Not a surge of worry, Not a shade of care, Not a blast of hurry, Touch the spirit there.
3. Ev-'ry joy or trial Falleth from above, Traced upon our dial By the Sun of Love. We may trust him fully All for us to do; They who trust him wholly Find him wholly true.

REFRAIN

Stayed upon Jehovah, Hearts are fully blest, Finding, as he promised, Perfect peace and rest. A-MEN.

Music used by permission of Marshall, Morgan & Scott, Ltd.

THE CHRISTIAN LIFE

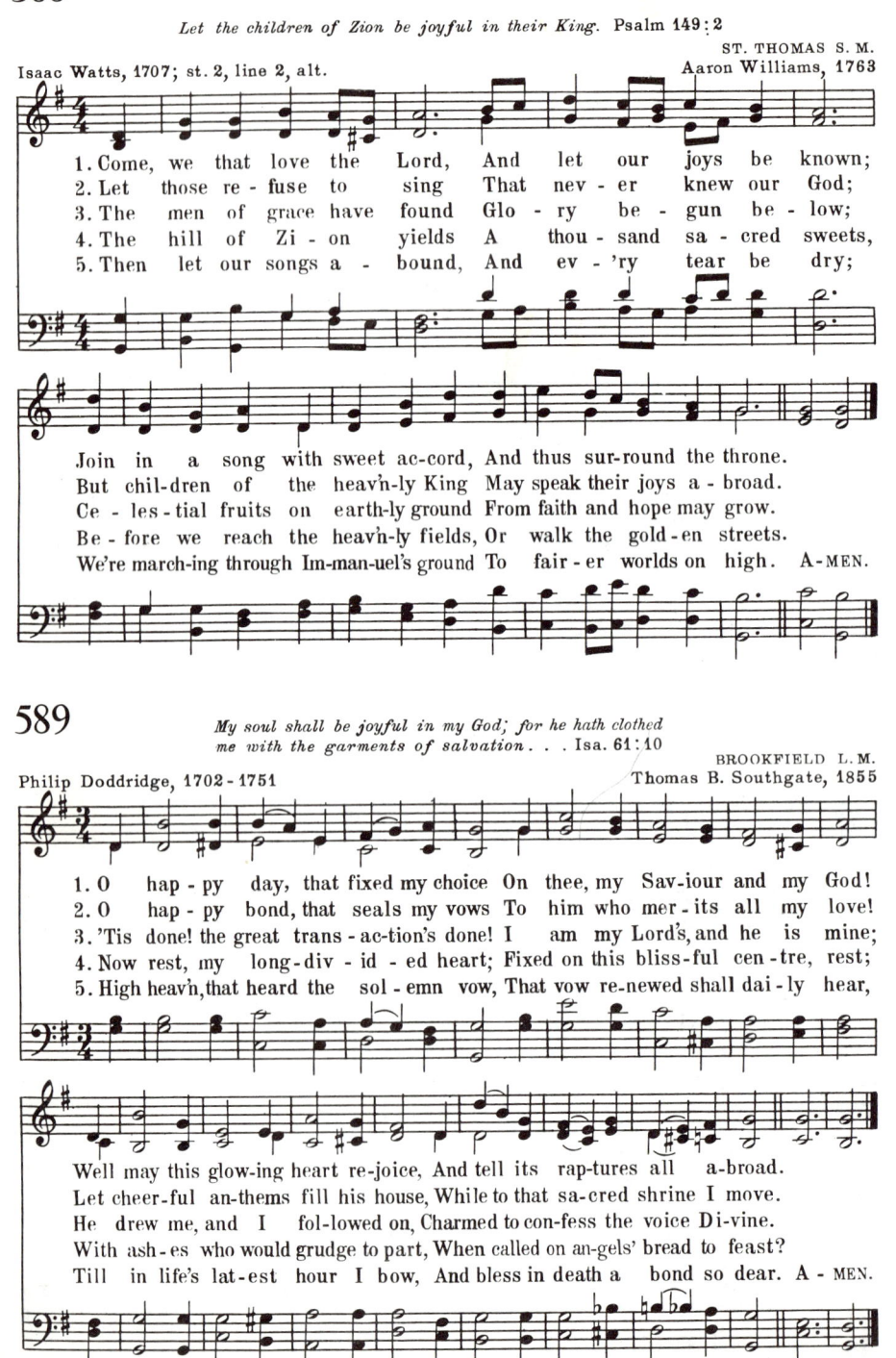

## 588

*Let the children of Zion be joyful in their King.* Psalm 149:2

Isaac Watts, 1707; st. 2, line 2, alt.

ST. THOMAS S. M.
Aaron Williams, 1763

1. Come, we that love the Lord, And let our joys be known;
2. Let those re-fuse to sing That nev-er knew our God;
3. The men of grace have found Glo-ry be-gun be-low;
4. The hill of Zi-on yields A thou-sand sa-cred sweets,
5. Then let our songs a-bound, And ev-'ry tear be dry;

Join in a song with sweet ac-cord, And thus sur-round the throne.
But chil-dren of the heav'n-ly King May speak their joys a-broad.
Ce-les-tial fruits on earth-ly ground From faith and hope may grow.
Be-fore we reach the heav'n-ly fields, Or walk the gold-en streets.
We're march-ing through Im-man-uel's ground To fair-er worlds on high. A-MEN.

## 589

*My soul shall be joyful in my God; for he hath clothed me with the garments of salvation...* Isa. 61:10

Philip Doddridge, 1702-1751

BROOKFIELD L. M.
Thomas B. Southgate, 1855

1. O hap-py day, that fixed my choice On thee, my Sav-iour and my God!
2. O hap-py bond, that seals my vows To him who mer-its all my love!
3. 'Tis done! the great trans-ac-tion's done! I am my Lord's, and he is mine;
4. Now rest, my long-div-id-ed heart; Fixed on this bliss-ful cen-tre, rest;
5. High heav'n, that heard the sol-emn vow, That vow re-newed shall dai-ly hear,

Well may this glow-ing heart re-joice, And tell its rap-tures all a-broad.
Let cheer-ful an-thems fill his house, While to that sa-cred shrine I move.
He drew me, and I fol-lowed on, Charmed to con-fess the voice Di-vine.
With ash-es who would grudge to part, When called on an-gels' bread to feast?
Till in life's lat-est hour I bow, And bless in death a bond so dear. A-MEN.

# PEACE AND JOY 590

*Thou wilt keep him in perfect peace, whose mind is stayed on thee . . Isa. 26:3*

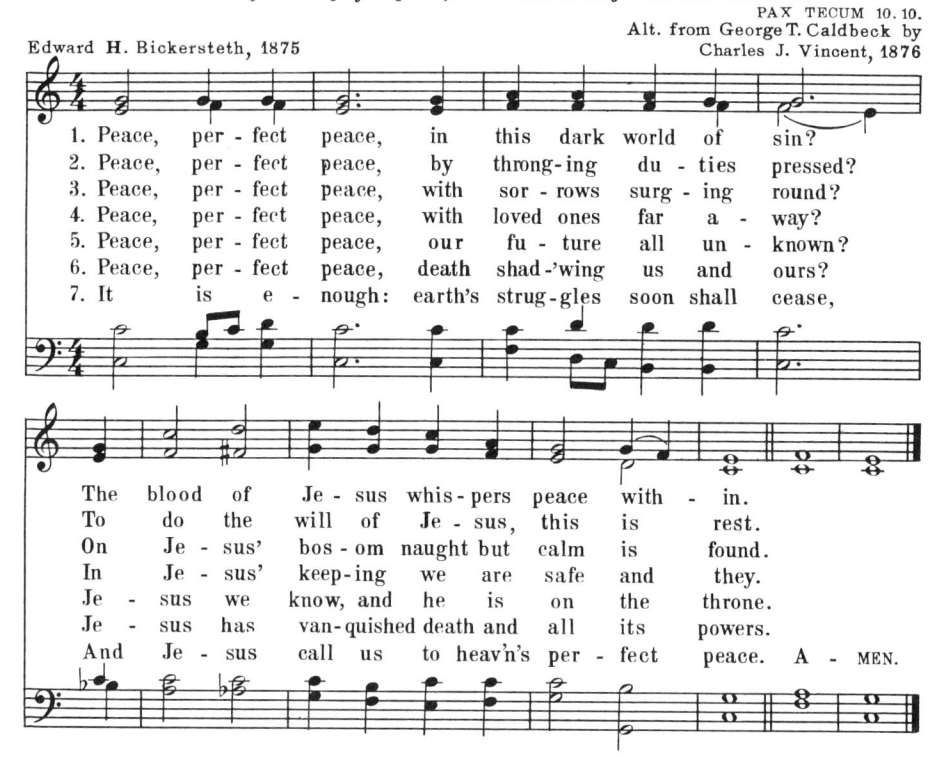

Edward H. Bickersteth, 1875

PAX TECUM 10.10.
Alt. from George T. Caldbeck by
Charles J. Vincent, 1876

1. Peace, per-fect peace, in this dark world of sin?
2. Peace, per-fect peace, by throng-ing du-ties pressed?
3. Peace, per-fect peace, with sor-rows surg-ing round?
4. Peace, per-fect peace, with loved ones far a-way?
5. Peace, per-fect peace, our fu-ture all un-known?
6. Peace, per-fect peace, death shad-'wing us and ours?
7. It is e-nough: earth's strug-gles soon shall cease,

The blood of Je-sus whis-pers peace with-in.
To do the will of Je-sus, this is rest.
On Je-sus' bos-om naught but calm is found.
In Je-sus' keep-ing we are safe and they.
Je-sus we know, and he is on the throne.
Je-sus has van-quished death and all its powers.
And Je-sus call us to heav'n's per-fect peace. A-MEN.

# 591

*In that day there shall be a fountain opened to the house of David. . . Zech. 13:1*

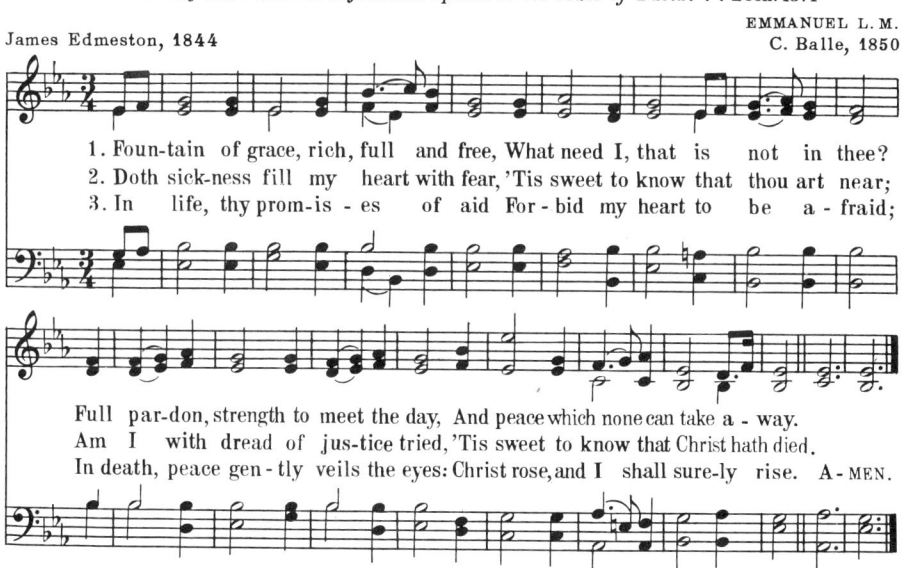

James Edmeston, 1844

EMMANUEL L. M.
C. Balle, 1850

1. Foun-tain of grace, rich, full and free, What need I, that is not in thee?
2. Doth sick-ness fill my heart with fear, 'Tis sweet to know that thou art near;
3. In life, thy prom-is-es of aid For-bid my heart to be a-fraid;

Full par-don, strength to meet the day, And peace which none can take a-way.
Am I with dread of jus-tice tried, 'Tis sweet to know that Christ hath died.
In death, peace gen-tly veils the eyes: Christ rose, and I shall sure-ly rise. A-MEN.

## 592 THE CHRISTIAN LIFE: PEACE AND JOY

*When he had found one pearl of great price, (he) went and sold all that he had, and bought it.* Matt. 13:46

John Mason, 1683; alt.
JERUSALEM C. M. D.
Charles H. Purday, 1799-1885

1. I've found the pearl of great-est price! My heart doth sing for joy; And sing I must, for Christ is mine!
2. Christ is my Proph-et, Priest, and King; My Proph-et full of light, My great High Priest be-fore the Throne,
3. For he in-deed is Lord of lords, And he the King of kings; He is the Sun of Right-eous-ness,
4. Christ is my peace; He died for me, For me he shed his blood; And as my won-drous Sac-ri-fice,
5. Christ Je-sus is my all in all, My com-fort and my love; My life be-low, and he shall be

REFRAIN

Christ shall my song em-ploy.
My King of heav'n-ly might.
With heal-ing in his wings.
Of-fered him-self to God.
My joy and crown a-bove.

I've found the pearl of great-est price! My heart doth sing for joy; And sing I must, for Christ is mine! Christ shall my song em-ploy. A-MEN.

# THE CHRISTIAN LIFE: PERSEVERANCE 593

*There is no man that hath left house, or brethren... for my sake, and the gospel's, but he shall receive an hundredfold now... with persecutions; and in the world to come eternal life.* Mark 10:29-30

Henry F. Lyte, 1824; text of 1833

CRUCIFER 8. 7. 8. 7. D.
Henry Smart, 1867

1. Je - sus, I my cross have tak-en, All to leave, and fol - low thee;
2. Man may trou - ble and dis-tress me, 'Twill but drive me to thy breast;
3. Take, my soul, thy full sal - va-tion, Rise o'er sin and fear and care;
4. Haste then on from grace to glo - ry, Armed by faith, and winged by prayer;

Des - ti - tute, de-spised, for - sa - ken, Thou from hence my all shalt be:
Life with tri - als hard may press me, Heav'n will bring me sweet-er rest:
Joy to find in ev - 'ry sta-tion Some-thing still to do or bear;
Heav'n's e - ter - nal day's be - fore thee, God's own hand shall guide thee there.

Per - ish ev - 'ry fond am - bi - tion, All I've sought, or hoped, or known;
O 'tis not in grief to harm me While thy love is left to me;
Think what Spir - it dwells with - in thee, What a Fa - ther's smile is thine,
Soon shall close thy earth - ly mis - sion; Swift shall pass thy pil - grim days;

Yet how rich is my con - di - tion, God and heav'n are still my own.
O 'twere not in joy to charm me, Were that joy un - mixed with thee.
What a Sav - iour died to win thee: Child of heav'n, shouldst thou re - pine?
Hope soon change to glad fru - i - tion, Faith to sight, and prayer to praise. A - MEN.

See also DISCIPLE, No. 691

## 594 — THE CHRISTIAN LIFE

*Yea, I have loved thee with an everlasting love: therefore with lovingkindness have I drawn thee.* Jer. 31:3

George Matheson, 1882
ST. MARGARET 8.8.8.8.6.
Albert L. Peace, 1885

1. O Love that wilt not let me go, I rest my wea-ry soul in thee; I give thee back the life I owe, That in thine o-cean depths its flow May rich-er, full-er be.
2. O Light that fol-lowest all my way, I yield my flick-'ring torch to thee; My heart re-stores its bor-rowed ray, That in thy sun-shine's blaze its day May bright-er, fair-er be.
3. O Joy that seek-est me through pain, I can-not close my heart to thee; I trace the rain-bow through the rain, And feel the prom-ise is not vain That morn shall tear-less be.
4. O Cross that lift-est up my head, I dare not ask to fly from thee; I lay in dust life's glo-ry dead, And from the ground there blos-soms red Life that shall end-less be. A-MEN.

## 595

*My soul trusteth in thee: yea, in the shadow of thy wings will I make my refuge, until these calamities be overpast.* Psalm 57:1

Augustus M. Toplady, 1772
ST. ETHELWALD S. M.
William H. Monk, 1861

1. Your harps, ye trem-bling saints, Down from the wil-lows take;
2. Though in a for-eign land, We are not far from home;
3. His grace will to the end Strong-er and bright-er shine;
4. When we in dark-ness walk, Nor feel the heav'n-ly flame,
5. Soon shall our doubts and fears Sub-side at his con-trol;
6. Blest is the man, O God, That stays him-self on thee:

# PERSEVERANCE

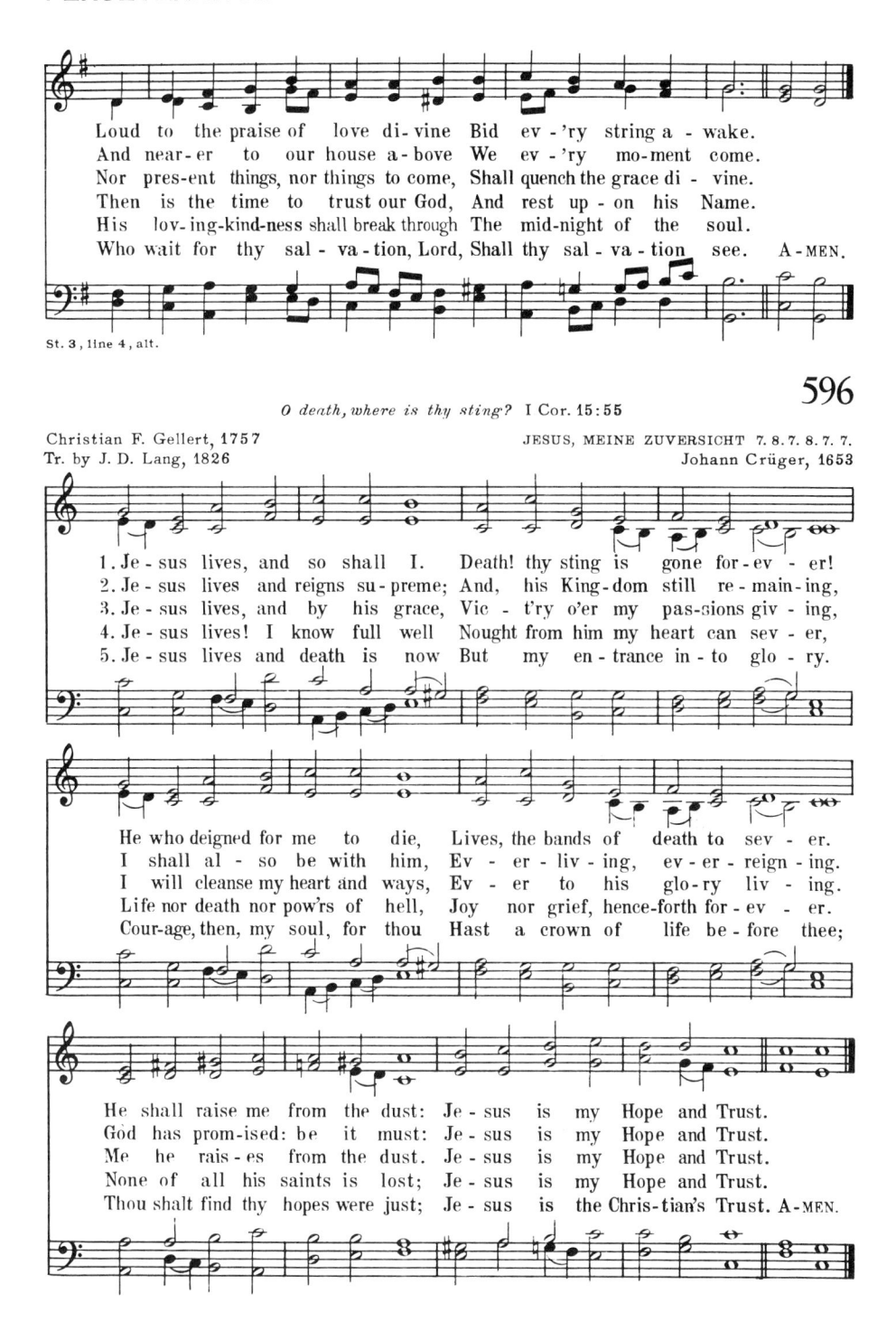

Loud to the praise of love di-vine Bid ev-'ry string a-wake.
And near-er to our house a-bove We ev-'ry mo-ment come.
Nor pres-ent things, nor things to come, Shall quench the grace di-vine.
Then is the time to trust our God, And rest up-on his Name.
His lov-ing-kind-ness shall break through The mid-night of the soul.
Who wait for thy sal-va-tion, Lord, Shall thy sal-va-tion see. A-MEN.

St. 3, line 4, alt.

*O death, where is thy sting?* I Cor. 15:55

**596**

Christian F. Gellert, 1757
Tr. by J. D. Lang, 1826

JESUS, MEINE ZUVERSICHT 7.8.7.8.7.7.
Johann Crüger, 1653

1. Je-sus lives, and so shall I. Death! thy sting is gone for-ev-er!
2. Je-sus lives and reigns su-preme; And, his King-dom still re-main-ing,
3. Je-sus lives, and by his grace, Vic-t'ry o'er my pas-sions giv-ing,
4. Je-sus lives! I know full well Nought from him my heart can sev-er,
5. Je-sus lives and death is now But my en-trance in-to glo-ry.

He who deigned for me to die, Lives, the bands of death to sev-er.
I shall al-so be with him, Ev-er-liv-ing, ev-er-reign-ing.
I will cleanse my heart and ways, Ev-er to his glo-ry liv-ing.
Life nor death nor pow'rs of hell, Joy nor grief, hence-forth for-ev-er.
Cour-age, then, my soul, for thou Hast a crown of life be-fore thee;

He shall raise me from the dust: Je-sus is my Hope and Trust.
God has prom-ised: be it must: Je-sus is my Hope and Trust.
Me he rais-es from the dust. Je-sus is my Hope and Trust.
None of all his saints is lost; Je-sus is my Hope and Trust.
Thou shalt find thy hopes were just; Je-sus is the Chris-tian's Trust. A-MEN.

## 597 THE RESURRECTION AND THE LIFE EVERLASTING

*Ye shall go over, and possess that good land. Deut. 4:22*

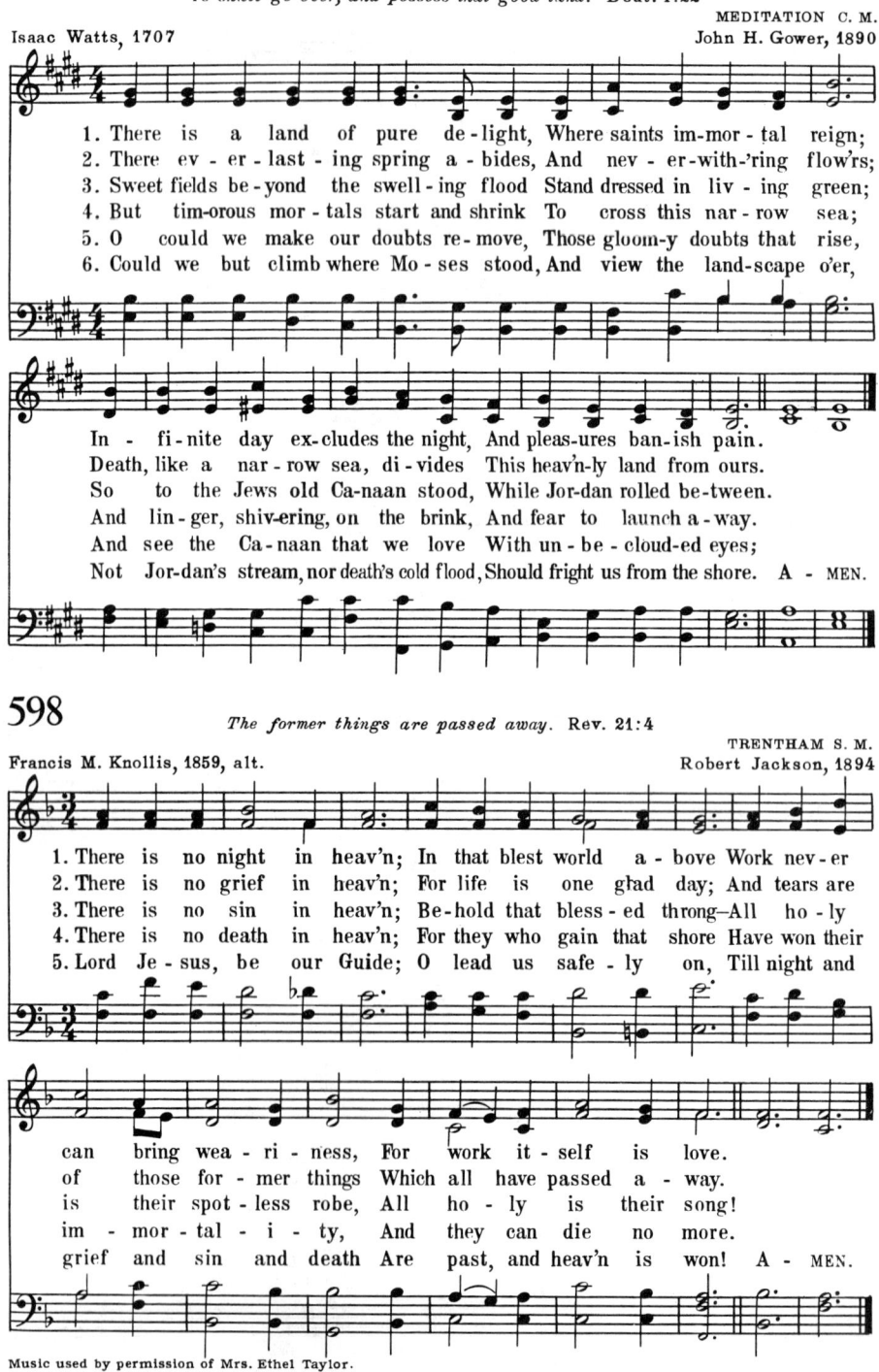

Isaac Watts, 1707
MEDITATION C. M.
John H. Gower, 1890

1. There is a land of pure de-light, Where saints im-mor-tal reign;
2. There ev-er-last-ing spring a-bides, And nev-er-with-'ring flow'rs;
3. Sweet fields be-yond the swell-ing flood Stand dressed in liv-ing green;
4. But tim-orous mor-tals start and shrink To cross this nar-row sea;
5. O could we make our doubts re-move, Those gloom-y doubts that rise,
6. Could we but climb where Mo-ses stood, And view the land-scape o'er,

In-fi-nite day ex-cludes the night, And pleas-ures ban-ish pain.
Death, like a nar-row sea, di-vides This heav'n-ly land from ours.
So to the Jews old Ca-naan stood, While Jor-dan rolled be-tween.
And lin-ger, shiv-ering, on the brink, And fear to launch a-way.
And see the Ca-naan that we love With un-be-cloud-ed eyes;
Not Jor-dan's stream, nor death's cold flood, Should fright us from the shore. A-MEN.

## 598

*The former things are passed away. Rev. 21:4*

Francis M. Knollis, 1859, alt.
TRENTHAM S. M.
Robert Jackson, 1894

1. There is no night in heav'n; In that blest world a-bove Work nev-er
2. There is no grief in heav'n; For life is one glad day; And tears are
3. There is no sin in heav'n; Be-hold that bless-ed throng—All ho-ly
4. There is no death in heav'n; For they who gain that shore Have won their
5. Lord Je-sus, be our Guide; O lead us safe-ly on, Till night and

can bring wea-ri-ness, For work it-self is love.
of those for-mer things Which all have passed a-way.
is their spot-less robe, All ho-ly is their song!
im-mor-tal-i-ty, And they can die no more.
grief and sin and death Are past, and heav'n is won! A-MEN.

Music used by permission of Mrs. Ethel Taylor.

# THE RESURRECTION AND THE LIFE EVERLASTING    599

*They shall see his face... Rev. 22:4*

Anne R. Cousin, 1857,
based upon Samuel Rutherford, 1600-1661

RUTHERFORD 7. 6. 7. 6. 7. 6. 7. 5.
Arr. from Chrétien Urhan, 1834,
by Edward F. Rimbault, 1867

1. The sands of time are sink-ing, The dawn of heav-en breaks,
2. The King there in his beau-ty With-out a veil is seen;
3. O Christ, he is the foun-tain, The deep sweet well of love!
4. The bride eyes not her gar-ment, But her dear bride-groom's face;

The sum-mer morn I've sighed for, The fair sweet morn a-wakes;
It were a well-spent jour-ney Though sev'n deaths lay be-tween:
The streams on earth I've tast-ed More deep I'll drink a-bove:
I will not gaze at glo-ry, But on my King of grace;

Dark, dark hath been the mid-night, But day-spring is at hand,
The Lamb with his fair ar-my Doth on Mount Zi-on stand,
There to an o-cean ful-ness His mer-cy doth ex-pand,
Not at the crown he gift-eth, But on his pier-ced hand:

And glo-ry, glo-ry dwell-eth In Em-man-uel's land.
And glo-ry, glo-ry dwell-eth In Em-man-uel's land.
And glo-ry, glo-ry dwell-eth In Em-man-uel's land.
The Lamb is all the glo-ry Of Em-man-uel's land. A-MEN.

## 600 THE RESURRECTION AND THE LIFE EVERLASTING

*Therefore, brethren, we are debtors... Rom. 8:12*

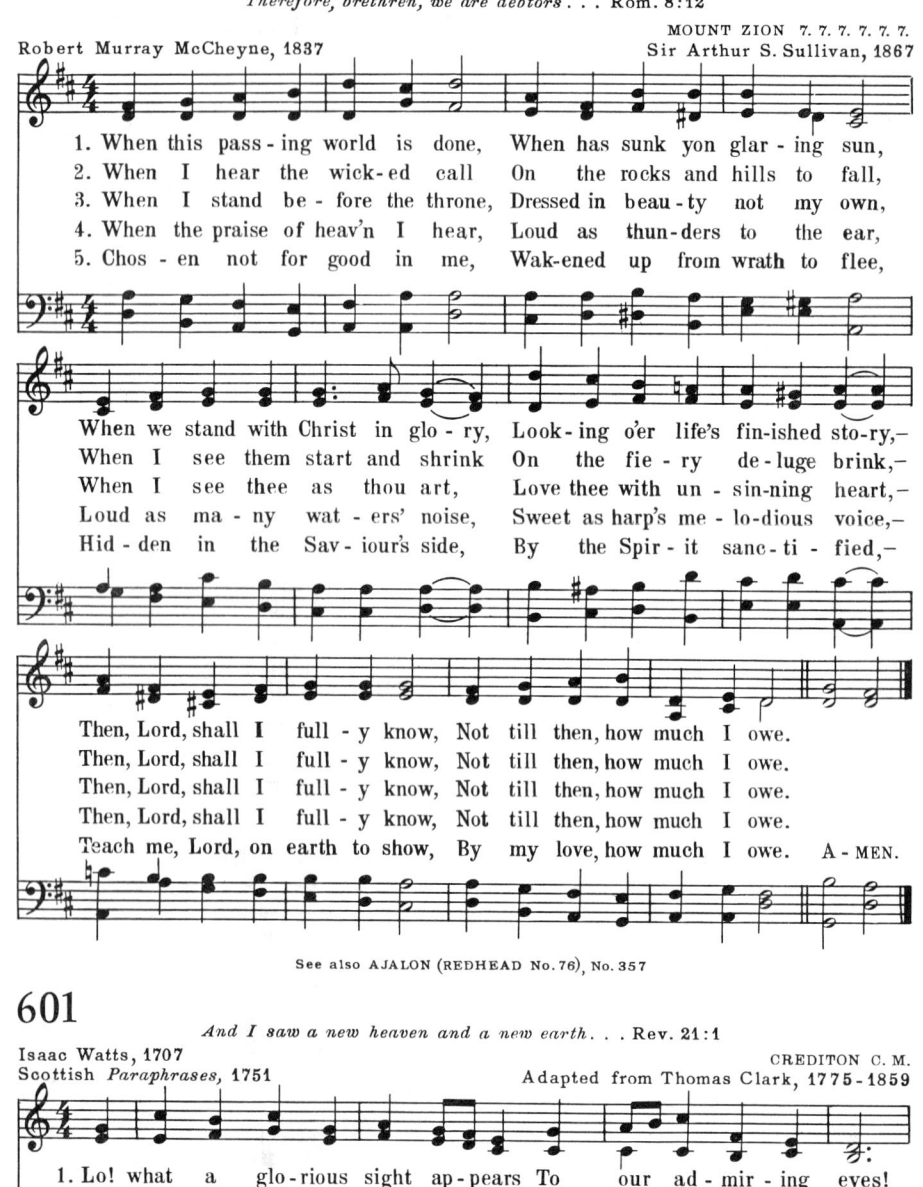

Robert Murray McCheyne, 1837
MOUNT ZION 7. 7. 7. 7. 7. 7.
Sir Arthur S. Sullivan, 1867

1. When this pass-ing world is done, When has sunk yon glar-ing sun,
2. When I hear the wick-ed call On the rocks and hills to fall,
3. When I stand be-fore the throne, Dressed in beau-ty not my own,
4. When the praise of heav'n I hear, Loud as thun-ders to the ear,
5. Chos-en not for good in me, Wak-ened up from wrath to flee,

When we stand with Christ in glo-ry, Look-ing o'er life's fin-ished sto-ry,—
When I see them start and shrink On the fie-ry de-luge brink,—
When I see thee as thou art, Love thee with un-sin-ning heart,—
Loud as ma-ny wat-ers' noise, Sweet as harp's me-lo-dious voice,—
Hid-den in the Sav-iour's side, By the Spir-it sanc-ti-fied,—

Then, Lord, shall I full-y know, Not till then, how much I owe.
Then, Lord, shall I full-y know, Not till then, how much I owe.
Then, Lord, shall I full-y know, Not till then, how much I owe.
Then, Lord, shall I full-y know, Not till then, how much I owe.
Teach me, Lord, on earth to show, By my love, how much I owe. A-MEN.

See also AJALON (REDHEAD No. 76), No. 357

## 601

*And I saw a new heaven and a new earth... Rev. 21:1*

Isaac Watts, 1707
Scottish *Paraphrases*, 1751
CREDITON C. M.
Adapted from Thomas Clark, 1775-1859

1. Lo! what a glo-rious sight ap-pears To our ad-mir-ing eyes!
2. The God of glo-ry down to men Re-moves his blest a-bode;
3. His gra-cious hand shall wipe the tear From ev-'ry weep-ing eye;
4. How long, dear Sav-iour, O how long Shall this bright hour de-lay?
5. O may we stand be-fore the Lamb, When earth and seas are fled,

# THE RESURRECTION AND THE LIFE EVERLASTING

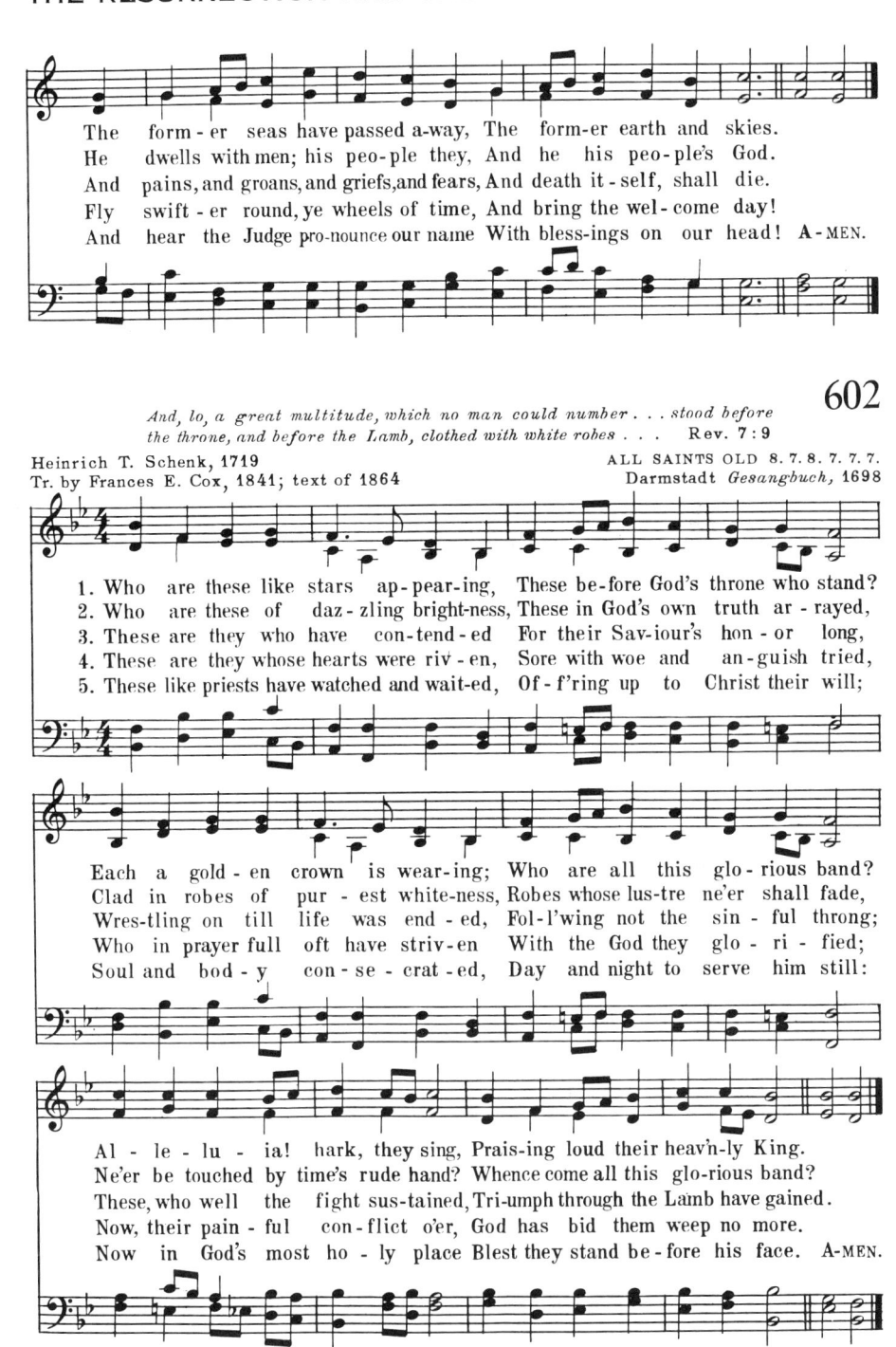

The former seas have passed a-way, The form-er earth and skies.
He dwells with men; his peo-ple they, And he his peo-ple's God.
And pains, and groans, and griefs, and fears, And death it-self, shall die.
Fly swift-er round, ye wheels of time, And bring the wel-come day!
And hear the Judge pro-nounce our name With bless-ings on our head! A-MEN.

---

*And, lo, a great multitude, which no man could number . . . stood before the throne, and before the Lamb, clothed with white robes . . .* Rev. 7:9

**602**

Heinrich T. Schenk, 1719
Tr. by Frances E. Cox, 1841; text of 1864

ALL SAINTS OLD 8.7.8.7.7.7.
Darmstadt *Gesangbuch*, 1698

1. Who are these like stars ap-pear-ing, These be-fore God's throne who stand?
2. Who are these of daz-zling bright-ness, These in God's own truth ar-rayed,
3. These are they who have con-tend-ed For their Sav-iour's hon-or long,
4. These are they whose hearts were riv-en, Sore with woe and an-guish tried,
5. These like priests have watched and wait-ed, Of-f'ring up to Christ their will;

Each a gold-en crown is wear-ing; Who are all this glo-rious band?
Clad in robes of pur-est white-ness, Robes whose lus-tre ne'er shall fade,
Wres-tling on till life was end-ed, Fol-l'wing not the sin-ful throng;
Who in prayer full oft have striv-en With the God they glo-ri-fied;
Soul and bod-y con-se-crat-ed, Day and night to serve him still:

Al-le-lu-ia! hark, they sing, Prais-ing loud their heav'n-ly King.
Ne'er be touched by time's rude hand? Whence come all this glo-rious band?
These, who well the fight sus-tained, Tri-umph through the Lamb have gained.
Now, their pain-ful con-flict o'er, God has bid them weep no more.
Now in God's most ho-ly place Blest they stand be-fore his face. A-MEN.

For a higher setting of this tune, see No. 127.

# 603 THE RESURRECTION AND THE LIFE EVERLASTING

*He... shewed me that great city, the holy Jerusalem, descending out of heaven from God.* Rev. 21:10

"F. B. P." in MS. of 16th or 17th century
St.1, line 1 from W. Prid, 1585
Alt. by David Dickson, 1583-1663

MATERNA C. M. D.
Samuel A. Ward, 1882

1. O Mother dear, Jerusalem, When shall I come to thee?
   When shall my sorrows have an end? Thy joys when shall I see?
   O happy harbor of the saints! O sweet and pleasant soil!
   In thee no sorrow may be found, No grief, no care, no toil.

2. Thy walls are made of precious stones, Thy bulwarks diamonds square;
   Thy gates are of right orient pearl, Exceeding rich and rare.
   Thy turrets and thy pinnacles With garnets rare do shine;
   Thy very streets are paved with gold, Surpassing clear and fine.

3. Thy gardens and thy gallant walks Continually are green,
   There grow such sweet and pleasant flow'rs As nowhere else are seen.
   Quite through the streets, with silver sound, The flood of life doth flow;
   Upon whose banks on ev'ry side The wood of life doth grow.

4. There trees for evermore bear fruit, And evermore do spring;
   There evermore the angels sit, And evermore do sing.
   Jerusalem, my happy home, Would God I were in thee!
   Would God my woes were at an end, Thy joys that I might see! A-MEN.

St. 2, line 6, alt.

# THE RESURRECTION AND THE LIFE EVERLASTING  604

*And the city was pure gold, like unto clear glass.* Rev. 21:18

Bernard of Cluny, 12th century
Tr. by John Mason Neale, 1851; alt.

EWING 7. 6. 7. 6. D.
Alexander Ewing, 1853

1. Je-ru-sa-lem the gold-en, With milk and hon-ey blest,
Beneath thy con-tem-pla-tion Sink heart and voice op-pressed.
I know not, O I know not, What joys a-wait us there;
What ra-dian-cy of glo-ry, What bliss be-yond com-pare.

2. They stand, those halls of Zi-on, All ju-bi-lant with song,
And bright with man-y an an-gel, And all the mar-tyr throng.
The Prince is ev-er in them, The day-light is se-rene;
The pas-tures of the bless-ed Are decked in glo-rious sheen.

3. There is the throne of Da-vid; And there, from care re-leased,
The song of them that tri-umph, The shout of them that feast;
And they who with their Lead-er Have con-quered in the fight,
For ev-er and for ev-er Are clad in robes of white.

4. O sweet and bless-ed coun-try, The home of God's e-lect!
O sweet and bless-ed coun-try That ea-ger hearts ex-pect!
Je-sus, in mer-cy bring us To that dear land of rest;
Who art, with God the Fa-ther And Spir-it, ev-er blest. A-MEN.

## 605 THE RESURRECTION AND THE LIFE EVERLASTING

*They were strangers and pilgrims on the earth.* Heb. 11:13

Thomas R. Taylor, 1836

ST. EDMUND 6. 4. 6. 4. 6. 6. 6. 4.
Sir Arthur S. Sullivan, 1872

1. I'm but a stran-ger here, Heav'n is my home;
2. What though the temp-est rage, Heav'n is my home;
3. There, at my Sav-iour's side, Heav'n is my home;
4. There-fore I mur-mur not, Heav'n is my home;

Earth is a des-ert drear, Heav'n is my home:
Short is my pil-grim-age, Heav'n is my home:
I shall be glo-ri-fied, Heav'n is my home.
What-e'er my earth-ly lot, Heav'n is my home:

Dan-ger and sor-row stand Round me on ev-'ry hand;
And time's wild win-try blast Soon shall be o-ver-past;
There are the good and blest, Those I love most and best;
And I shall sure-ly stand There at my Lord's right hand;

Heav'n is my fa-ther-land, Heav'n is my home.
I shall reach home at last, Heav'n is my home.
And there I too shall rest, Heav'n is my home.
Heav'n is my fa-ther-land, Heav'n is my home. A-MEN.

# THE RESURRECTION AND THE LIFE EVERLASTING 606

*What are these which are arrayed in white robes?* Rev. 7:13

Isaac Watts, 1707
Scottish *Paraphrases*, 1781

BETHLEHEM C. M. D.
Gottfried W. Fink, 1842

1. How bright these glo-rious spir-its shine! Whence all their white ar-ray?
2. Now, with tri-um-phal palms, they stand Be-fore the throne on high,
3. Hun-ger and thirst are felt no more, Nor suns with scorch-ing ray;
4. 'Mong pas-tures green he'll lead his flock Where liv-ing streams ap-pear;

How came they to the bliss-ful seats Of ev-er-last-ing day?
And serve the God they love, a-midst The glo-ries of the sky.
God is their Sun, whose cheer-ing beams Dif-fuse e-ter-nal day.
And God the Lord from ev-'ry eye Shall wipe off ev-'ry tear.

Lo! these are they from suf-f'rings great Who came to realms of light,
His pres-ence fills each heart with joy, Tunes ev-'ry mouth to sing:
The Lamb which dwells a-midst the throne Shall o'er them still pre-side,
To him who sits up-on the throne, The God whom we a-dore,

And in the blood of Christ have washed Those robes which shine so bright.
By day, by night, the sa-cred courts With glad ho-san-nas ring.
Feed them with nour-ish-ment di-vine, And all their foot-steps guide.
And to the Lamb that once was slain, Be glo-ry ev-er-more! A-MEN.

## 607 THE RESURRECTION AND THE LIFE EVERLASTING

*Lo, a great multitude, which no man could number... stood before the throne... Rev. 7:9*

Christopher Wordsworth, 1862
SANCTUARY 8. 7. 8. 7. D.
John B. Dykes, 1871

1. Hark! the sound of ho-ly voic-es, chant-ing at the crys-tal sea,
2. They have come from trib-u-la-tion, and have washed their robes in blood,
3. March-ing with thy cross their ban-ner, they have tri-umphed, fol-low-ing
4. God of God, the One-be-got-ten, Light of light, Em-man-u-el,

Al - le - lu - ia! Al - le - lu - ia! Al - le - lu - ia! Lord, to thee:
Washed them in the blood of Je - sus; tried they were, and firm they stood;
Thee, the Cap-tain of sal - va - tion, thee, their Sav-iour and their King;
In whose bod-y joined to-geth-er all the saints for ev - er dwell;

Mul - ti - tude, which none can num - ber, like the stars in glo - ry stand
Mocked, im-pris-oned, stoned, tor-ment-ed, sawn as - un - der, slain with sword,
Glad - ly, Lord, with thee they suf-fered; glad-ly, Lord, with thee they died;
Pour up - on us of thy ful - ness that we may for ev - er - more

Clothed in white ap - par - el, hold-ing palms of vic - t'ry in their hand.
They have con-quered death and Sa - tan by the might of Christ the Lord.
And by death to life im - mor-tal they were born and glo - ri - fied.
God the Fa - ther, God the Son, and God the Ho - ly Ghost a - dore. A - MEN.

# THE RESURRECTION AND THE LIFE EVERLASTING 608

*And he took them up in his arms, put his hands upon them, and blessed them.* Mark 10:16

SAFE IN THE ARMS OF JESUS 7. 6. 7. 6. D. with refrain

Fanny J. Crosby, 1870 — William H. Doane, 1870

1. Safe in the arms of Je - sus, Safe on his gen - tle breast,
   There by his love o'er - sha - ded, Sweet-ly my soul shall rest. Hark! 'tis the voice of an - gels, Borne in a song to me, O - ver the fields of glo - ry, O - ver the jas-per sea.

2. Safe in the arms of Je - sus, Safe from cor - rod - ing care,
   Safe from the world's temp-ta-tions, Sin can-not harm me there. Free from the blight of sor - row, Free from my doubts and fears, On - ly a few more tri - als, On - ly a few more tears.

3. Je - sus, my heart's dear Ref - uge, Je - sus has died for me;
   Firm on the Rock of A - ges Ev - er my trust shall be. Here let me wait with pa - tience, Wait till the night is o'er, Wait till I see the morn-ing Break on the gold - en shore.

REFRAIN

Safe in the arms of Je - sus, Safe on his gen-tle breast, There by his love o'er - sha - ded, Sweet-ly my soul shall rest. A-MEN.

# 609 THE RESURRECTION AND THE LIFE EVERLASTING

*My days are like a shadow that declineth...Psalm 102:11*

Horatius Bonar, 1844

LEOMINSTER S. M. D.
George William Martin, 1862
Har. by Sir Arthur S. Sullivan, 1874

1. A few more years shall roll, A few more sea-sons come, And we shall be with those that rest A-sleep with-in the tomb: Then, O my Lord, pre-pare My soul for that great day;

2. A few more storms shall beat On this wild rock-y shore, And we shall be where tem-pests cease, And sur-ges swell no more, Then, O my Lord, pre-pare My soul for that calm day;

3. A few more Sab-baths here Shall cheer us on our way, And we shall reach the end-less rest, Th' e-ter-nal Sab-bath-day: Then, O my Lord, pre-pare My soul for that sweet day;

4. 'Tis but a lit-tle while, And he shall come a-gain Who died that we might live, who lives That we with him may reign: Then, O my Lord, pre-pare My soul for that glad day;

REFRAIN

O wash me in thy pre-cious blood, And take my sins a-way. A-MEN.

*The following hymns are also appropriate:*

Around the throne of God in heaven..........648
For all the saints who from their labors rest....281
I will sing you a song of that beautiful land...729
In the land of fadeless day..................730
Jesus lives, and so shall I...................596

Lo, God to heaven ascendeth................210
Some day the silver cord will break..........726
The God of Abraham praise.................. 32
The golden gates are lifted up...............214
There is a city bright .....................662

# OCCASIONAL HYMNS

## THE OPENING AND CLOSING OF THE YEAR

### 610

*Blessed be the Lord, who daily loadeth us with benefits, even the God of our salvation.* Psalm 68:19

James D. Burns, 1861

CRUCIFER 8. 7. 8. 7. D.
Henry Smart, 1867

1. At thy feet, our God and Fa-ther, Who hast blessed us all our days,
We with grate-ful hearts would gath-er, To be-gin the year with praise:
Praise for light so bright-ly shin-ing On our steps from heav'n a-bove;
Praise for mer-cies dai-ly twi-ning Round us gold-en cords of love.

2. Je-sus, for thy love most ten-der, On the cross for sin-ners shown,
We would praise thee, and sur-ren-der All our hearts to be thine own:
With so blest a Friend pro-vid-ed, We up-on our way would go,
Sure of be-ing safe-ly guid-ed, Guard-ed well from ev-'ry foe.

3. Ev-'ry day will be the bright-er When thy gra-cious face we see;
Ev-'ry bur-den will be light-er When we know it comes from thee.
Spread thy love's broad ban-ner o'er us, Give us strength to serve and wait,
Till the glo-ry breaks be-fore us Through the cit-y's o-pen gate. A-MEN.

## 611 THE OPENING AND CLOSING OF THE YEAR

*Thou shalt guide me with thy counsel, and afterward receive me to glory.* Psalm 73:24

Henry Downton, 1841
ST. AUSTELL 7. 7. 7. 7.
Arthur H. Brown, 1876

1. For thy mer-cy and thy grace, Faith-ful through an-oth-er year,
   Hear our song of thank-ful-ness; Fa-ther, and Re-deem-er, hear.
2. Lo! our sins on thee we cast, Thee, our per-fect Sac-ri-fice;
   And, for-get-ting all the past, Press towards our glo-rious prize.
3. Dark the fu-ture; let thy light Guide us, Bright and Morn-ing Star:
   Fierce our foes, and hard the fight; Arm us, Sav-iour, for the war.
4. In our weak-ness and dis-tress, Rock of strength, be thou our stay;
   In the path-less wil-der-ness Be our true and liv-ing Way.
5. Keep us faith-ful, keep us pure, Keep us ev-er-more thine own;
   Help, O help us to en-dure; Fit us for the prom-ised crown.
6. So with-in thy pal-ace gate We shall praise, on gold-en strings,
   Thee, the on-ly Po-ten-tate, Lord of lords, and King of kings. A-MEN.

## 612

*The hand of our God is upon all them for good that seek him.* Ezra 8:22

Philip Doddridge, 1755
St. 5, line 4, alt.
WAREHAM L. M.
William Knapp, 1738

1. Great God, we sing that might-y hand By which sup-port-ed still we stand;
   The ope-ning year thy mer-cy shows; That mer-cy crowns it till it close.
2. By day, by night, at home, a-broad, Still are we guard-ed by our God;
   By his in-ces-sant boun-ty fed, By his un-er-ring coun-sel led.
3. With grate-ful hearts the past we own; The fu-ture, all to us un-known,
   We to thy guard-ian care com-mit, And peace-ful leave be-fore thy feet.
4. In scenes ex-alt-ed or de-pressed, Thou art our Joy, and thou our Rest;
   Thy good-ness all our hopes shall raise, A-dored through all our chang-ing days.
5. When death shall in-ter-rupt these songs, And seal in si-lence mor-tal tongues,
   Our Help-er God, in whom we trust, Shall keep our souls and guard our dust. A-MEN.

# THE OPENING AND CLOSING OF THE YEAR 613

*So teach us to number our days, that we may apply our hearts unto wisdom.* Psalm 90:12

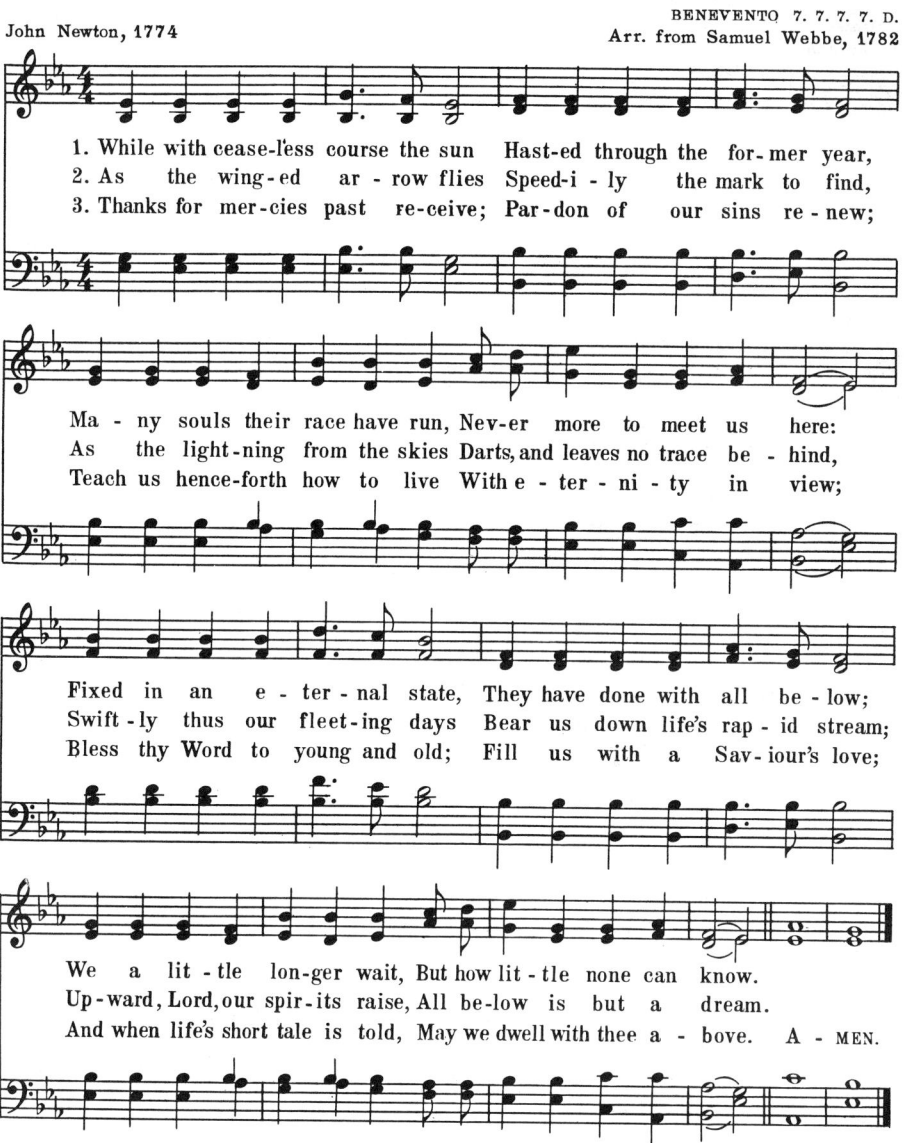

John Newton, 1774

BENEVENTO 7. 7. 7. 7. D.
Arr. from Samuel Webbe, 1782

1. While with cease-less course the sun Hast-ed through the for-mer year,
Ma-ny souls their race have run, Nev-er more to meet us here:
Fixed in an e-ter-nal state, They have done with all be-low;
We a lit-tle lon-ger wait, But how lit-tle none can know.

2. As the wing-ed ar-row flies Speed-i-ly the mark to find,
As the light-ning from the skies Darts, and leaves no trace be-hind,
Swift-ly thus our fleet-ing days Bear us down life's rap-id stream;
Up-ward, Lord, our spir-its raise, All be-low is but a dream.

3. Thanks for mer-cies past re-ceive; Par-don of our sins re-new;
Teach us hence-forth how to live With e-ter-ni-ty in view;
Bless thy Word to young and old; Fill us with a Sav-iour's love;
And when life's short tale is told, May we dwell with thee a-bove. A-MEN.

*The following hymns are also appropriate:*

A few more years shall roll.................609
Great God, how infinite art thou.............. 22
My Jesus, as thou wilt....................572

My times are in thy hand..................577
Our God, our Help in ages past.............. 26
Sometimes a light surprises................520

## 614 HARVEST AND THANKSGIVING

*He . . . gave us rain from heaven, and fruitful seasons, filling our hearts with food and gladness.* Acts 14:17

Matthias Claudius, 1782
Tr. by Jane M. Campbell, 1861

WIR PFLÜGEN 7. 6. 7. 6. D. with refrain
Johann A. P. Schulz, 1800

1. We plough the fields, and scat-ter The good seed on the land, But it is fed and wa-tered By God's al-might-y hand; He sends the snow in win-ter, The warmth to swell the grain, The breez-es and the sun-shine, And soft re-fresh-ing rain.

2. He on-ly is the Ma-ker Of all things near and far; He paints the way-side flow-er, He lights the eve-ning star; The winds and waves o-bey him, By him the birds are fed; Much more to us, his chil-dren, He gives our dai-ly bread.

3. We thank thee, then, O Fa-ther, For all things bright and good, The seed-time and the har-vest, Our life, our health, our food: No gifts have we to of-fer For all thy love im-parts, But that which thou de-sir-est, Our hum-ble, thank-ful hearts.

REFRAIN

All good gifts a-round us Are sent from heav'n a-bove; Then thank the Lord, O thank the Lord For all his love. A-MEN.

# HARVEST AND THANKSGIVING  615

*The harvest is the end of the world; and the reapers are the angels.* Matt. 13:39

Henry Alford, 1844, text of 1867
ST. GEORGE'S, WINDSOR 7.7.7.7. D.
Sir George J. Elvey, 1859

1. Come, ye thank-ful peo-ple, come, Raise the song of har-vest-home:
   All is safe-ly gath-ered in, Ere the win-ter storms be-gin;
   God, our Mak-er, doth pro-vide For our wants to be sup-plied:
   Come to God's own tem-ple, come, Raise the song of har-vest-home.

2. All the world is God's own field, Fruit un-to his praise to yield;
   Wheat and tares to-geth-er sown, Un-to joy or sor-row grown:
   First the blade, and then the ear, Then the full corn shall ap-pear:
   Lord of har-vest, grant that we Whole-some grain and pure may be.

3. For the Lord our God shall come, And shall take his har-vest home;
   From his field shall in that day All of-fenc-es purge a-way;
   Give his an-gels charge at last In the fire the tares to cast,
   But the fruit-ful ears to store In his gar-ner ev-er-more.

4. E-ven so, Lord, quick-ly come To thy fi-nal har-vest-home;
   Gath-er thou thy peo-ple in, Free from sor-row, free from sin;
   There for ev-er pur-i-fied, In thy pres-ence to a-bide:
   Come, with all thine an-gels, come, Raise the glo-rious har-vest-home. A-MEN.

*The following hymns are also appropriate:*

Christ, by heavenly hosts adored............623
Give thanks unto the Lord, Jehovah.........512
"Great is thy faithfulness".................. 27
Let us, with a gladsome mind................ 30
My soul, bless the Lord....................110

Now thank we all our God ................... 86
O people blest, whose sons in youth.........289
Praise to God, immortal praise..............112
Thy might sets fast the mountains...........111
We gather together to ask the Lord's blessing..286

We praise thee, O God, our Redeemer, Creator. 83

# 616 NATIONAL

*The Lord of hosts is with us; the God of Jacob is our refuge.* Psalm 46:7

Daniel C. Roberts, 1876
NATIONAL HYMN. 10. 10. 10. 10.
George William Warren, 1892

Organ, as trumpets, before each stanza.

1. God of our fa-thers, whose al-might-y hand
2. Thy love di-vine hath led us in the past;
3. From war's a-larms, from dead-ly pes-ti-lence,
4. Re-fresh thy peo-ple on their toil-some way,

Leads forth in beau-ty all the star-ry band
In this free land by thee our lot is cast;
Be thy strong arm our ev-er sure de-fence;
Lead us from night to nev-er-end-ing day;

Of shin-ing worlds in splen-dor through the skies,
Be thou our Rul-er, Guard-ian, Guide, and Stay;
Thy true re-lig-ion in our hearts in-crease,
Fill all our lives with love and grace di-vine,

Our grate-ful songs be-fore thy throne a-rise.
Thy Word our law, thy paths our cho-sen way.
Thy boun-teous good-ness nour-ish us in peace.
And glo-ry, laud, and praise be ev-er thine. A-MEN.

# NATIONAL

**617**

*Come, behold the works of the Lord . . . He maketh wars to cease unto the end of the earth.* Psalm **46:8-9**

Arr. from Henry F. Chorley, 1842
and John Ellerton, 1870

RUSSIAN HYMN 11. 10. 11. 9.
Alexis Lwoff, 1833

1. God the All-ter-ri-ble! King, who or-dain-est
2. God the Om-nip-o-tent! Might-y A-veng-er,
3. God the All-mer-ci-ful! earth hath for-sak-en
4. God the All-right-eous One! man hath de-fied thee;
5. God the All-wise! by the fire of thy chast-'ning,

Great winds thy clar-i-ons, light-nings thy sword,
Watch-ing in-vis-i-ble, judg-ing un-heard,
Thy ways of bless-ed-ness, slight-ed thy Word;
Yet to e-ter-ni-ty stand-eth thy Word;
Earth shall to free-dom and truth be re-stored;

Show forth thy pit-y on high where thou reign-est;
Save us in mer-cy, O save us from dan-ger;
Bid not thy wrath in its ter-rors a-wak-en;
False-hood and wrong shall not tar-ry be-side thee;
Through the thick dark-ness thy king-dom is hast-'ning;

Give to us peace in our time, O Lord.
Give to us peace in our time, O Lord.
Give to us peace in our time, O Lord.
Give to us peace in our time, O Lord.
Thou wilt give peace in thy time, O Lord. A-MEN.

## 618 NATIONAL

*Thou hast a mighty arm: strong is thy hand, and high is thy right hand.* Psalm 89:13

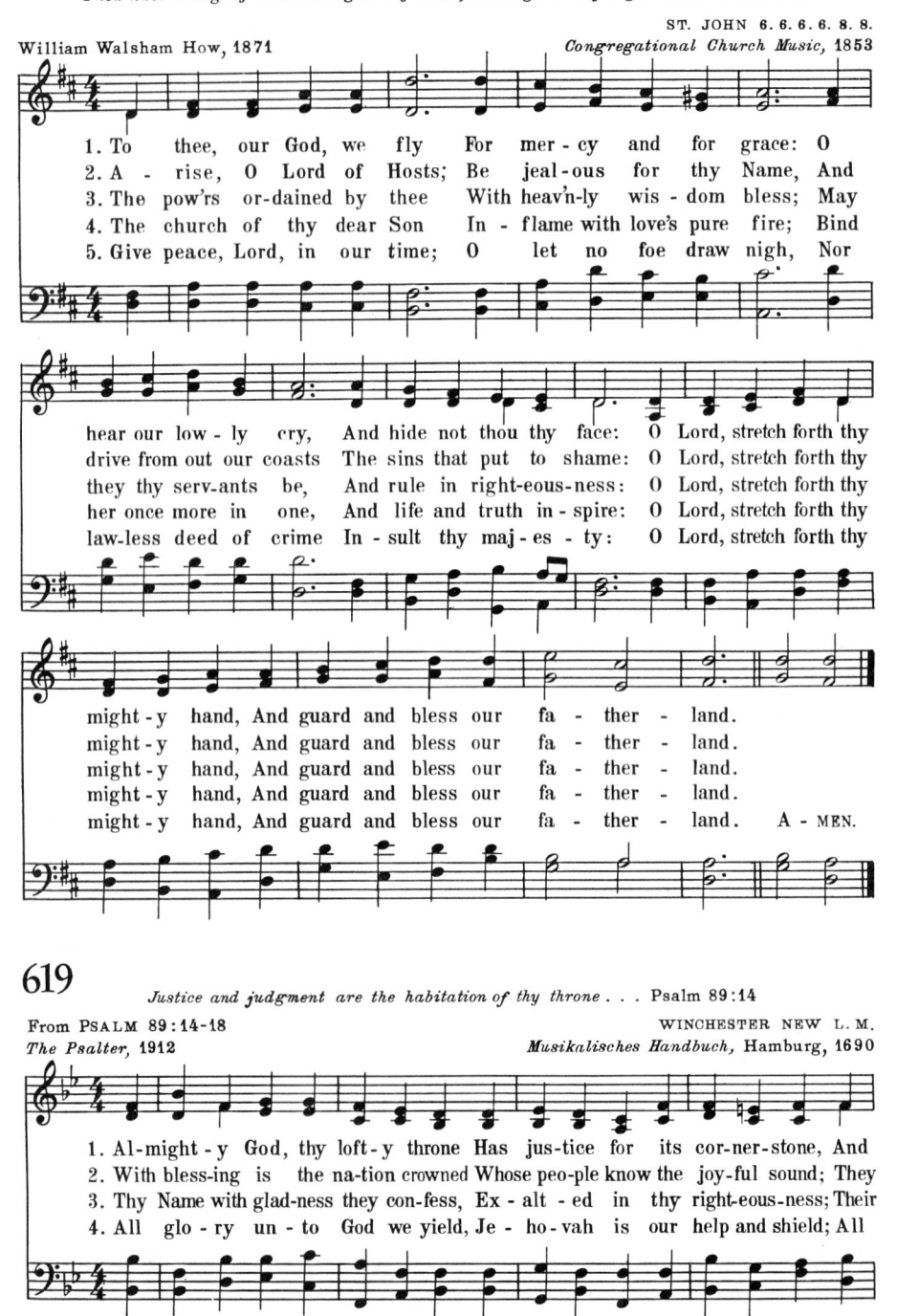

William Walsham How, 1871
ST. JOHN 6.6.6.6.8.8.
*Congregational Church Music,* 1853

1. To thee, our God, we fly For mer-cy and for grace: O hear our low-ly cry, And hide not thou thy face: O Lord, stretch forth thy might-y hand, And guard and bless our fa - ther - land.
2. A - rise, O Lord of Hosts; Be jeal-ous for thy Name, And drive from out our coasts The sins that put to shame: O Lord, stretch forth thy might-y hand, And guard and bless our fa - ther - land.
3. The pow'rs or-dained by thee With heav'n-ly wis - dom bless; May they thy serv-ants be, And rule in right-eous-ness: O Lord, stretch forth thy might-y hand, And guard and bless our fa - ther - land.
4. The church of thy dear Son In - flame with love's pure fire; Bind her once more in one, And life and truth in - spire: O Lord, stretch forth thy might-y hand, And guard and bless our fa - ther - land.
5. Give peace, Lord, in our time; O let no foe draw nigh, Nor law-less deed of crime In - sult thy maj - es - ty: O Lord, stretch forth thy might-y hand, And guard and bless our fa - ther - land. A - MEN.

## 619

*Justice and judgment are the habitation of thy throne* . . . Psalm 89:14

From PSALM 89:14-18
The Psalter, 1912
WINCHESTER NEW L. M.
*Musikalisches Handbuch,* Hamburg, 1690

1. Al-might-y God, thy loft-y throne Has jus-tice for its cor-ner-stone, And
2. With bless-ing is the na-tion crowned Whose peo-ple know the joy-ful sound; They
3. Thy Name with glad-ness they con-fess, Ex - alt - ed in thy right-eous-ness; Their
4. All glo - ry un - to God we yield, Je - ho-vah is our help and shield; All

NATIONAL

shin-ing bright be-fore thy face  Are truth and love and bound-less grace.
in the light, O Lord, shall live,  The light thy face and fa-vor give.
fame and might to thee be-long,  For in thy fa-vor they are strong.
praise and hon-or we will bring  To Is-rael's Ho-ly One, our King. A-MEN.

*He shall judge the poor of the people, he shall save the children of the needy, and shall break in pieces the oppressor.* Psalm 72:4

620

Henry Scott Holland, 1902

RHUDDLAN 8.7.8.7.8.7.
Welsh traditional melody

1. Judge E-ter-nal, throned in splen-dor, Lord of lords and King of kings,
2. Still the wea-ry folk are pin-ing For the hour that brings re-lease;
3. Crown, O God, thine own en-deav-or; Cleave our dark-ness with thy sword;

With thy liv-ing fire of judg-ment  Purge this land of bit-ter things;
And the cit-y's crowd-ed clan-gor  Cries a-loud for sin to cease;
Feed the faint and hun-gry hea-then  With the rich-ness of thy Word;

So-lace all its wide do-min-ion  With the heal-ing of thy wings.
And the home-steads and the wood-lands  Plead in si-lence for their peace.
Cleanse the bo-dy of this na-tion  Through the gos-pel of the Lord. A-MEN.

St. 3, lines 5 and 6, alt.

Words used by permission of the Oxford University Press, London.

## 621 NATIONAL

*His mercy is on them that fear him from generation to generation.* Luke 1:50

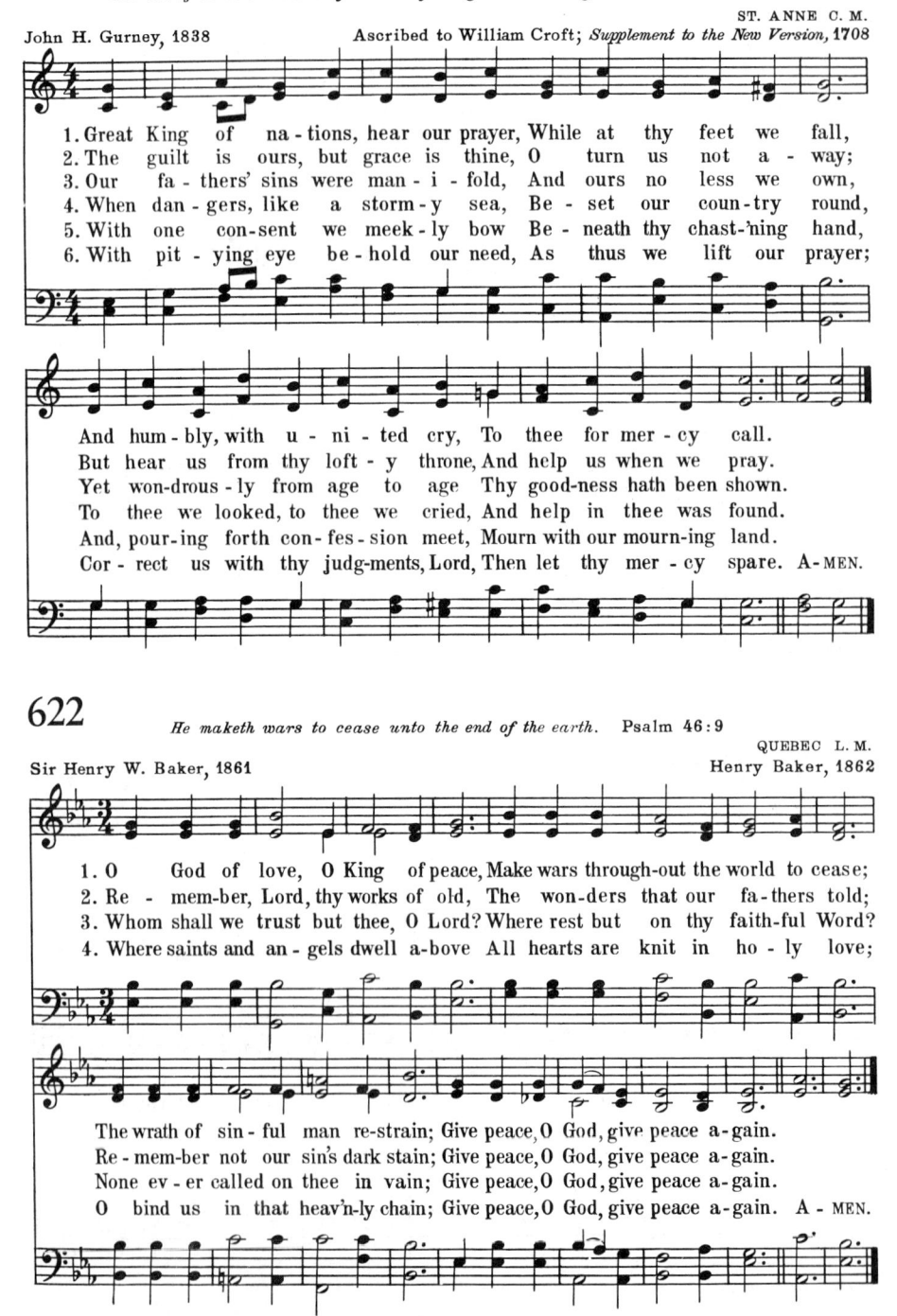

John H. Gurney, 1838

ST. ANNE C. M.
Ascribed to William Croft; *Supplement to the New Version,* 1708

1. Great King of na - tions, hear our prayer, While at thy feet we fall,
2. The guilt is ours, but grace is thine, O turn us not a - way;
3. Our fa - thers' sins were man - i - fold, And ours no less we own,
4. When dan - gers, like a storm - y sea, Be - set our coun - try round,
5. With one con - sent we meek - ly bow Be - neath thy chast - 'ning hand,
6. With pit - ying eye be - hold our need, As thus we lift our prayer;

And hum - bly, with u - ni - ted cry, To thee for mer - cy call.
But hear us from thy loft - y throne, And help us when we pray.
Yet won - drous - ly from age to age Thy good - ness hath been shown.
To thee we looked, to thee we cried, And help in thee was found.
And, pour - ing forth con - fes - sion meet, Mourn with our mourn - ing land.
Cor - rect us with thy judg - ments, Lord, Then let thy mer - cy spare. A - MEN.

## 622

*He maketh wars to cease unto the end of the earth.* Psalm 46:9

Sir Henry W. Baker, 1861

QUEBEC L. M.
Henry Baker, 1862

1. O God of love, O King of peace, Make wars through-out the world to cease;
2. Re - mem - ber, Lord, thy works of old, The won - ders that our fa - thers told;
3. Whom shall we trust but thee, O Lord? Where rest but on thy faith - ful Word?
4. Where saints and an - gels dwell a - bove All hearts are knit in ho - ly love;

The wrath of sin - ful man re - strain; Give peace, O God, give peace a - gain.
Re - mem - ber not our sin's dark stain; Give peace, O God, give peace a - gain.
None ev - er called on thee in vain; Give peace, O God, give peace a - gain.
O bind us in that heav'n - ly chain; Give peace, O God, give peace a - gain. A - MEN.

# NATIONAL 623

*For there is no power but of God: the powers that be are ordained of God.* Rom. 13:1

SALZBURG 7. 7. 7. 7. D.
Jakob Hintze, 1678;
Henry Harbaugh, 1860, cento, alt.
Har. by Johann Sebastian Bach, 1685-1750

1. Christ, by heav'n-ly hosts a-dored, Gra-cious, might-y, sov-'reign Lord,
God of na-tions, King of kings, Head of all cre-at-ed things,
By the Church with joy con-fessed, God o'er all, for ev-er blessed,
Plead-ing at thy throne we stand, Save thy peo-ple, bless our land.

2. On our fields of grass and grain Send, O Lord, the kind-ly rain;
O'er our wide and good-ly land Crown the la-bors of each hand.
Let thy kind pro-tec-tion be O'er our com-merce on the sea.
O-pen, Lord, thy boun-teous hand; Bless thy peo-ple, bless our land.

3. Let our rul-ers ev-er be Men that love and hon-or thee;
Let the pow'rs by thee or-dained Be in right-eous-ness main-tained.
In the peo-ple's hearts in-crease Love of pi-e-ty and peace.
Thus u-nit-ed, may we stand One wide, free, and hap-py land. A-MEN.

St. 3, line 8, alt.

## 624 MARRIAGE AND THE HOME

*But as for me and my house, we will serve the Lord.* Joshua 24:15

Carl J. P. Spitta, 1833
Tr., by Sarah B. Findlater, 1858; alt.

CROFTON 11. 10. 11. 10.
Edward, Lord Crofton, 1893

1. O happy home, where thou art loved the dearest,
Thou loving Friend and Saviour of our race,
And where among the guests there never cometh
One who can hold such high and honored place!

2. O happy home, where two in heart united
In holy faith and blessed hope are one,
Whom death a little while alone divideth,
And cannot end the union here begun!

3. O happy home, whose little ones are given
Early to thee in humble faith and prayer,
To thee, their Friend, who from the heights of heaven
Guides them, and guards with more than mother's care!

4. O happy home, where each one serves thee, lowly,
Whatever his appointed work may be,
Till every common task seems great and holy,
When it is done, O Lord, as unto thee!

5. O happy home, where thou art not forgotten
When joy is overflowing, full and free,
O happy home, where every wounded spirit
Is brought, Physician, Comforter, to thee,—

6. Until at last, when earth's day's-work is ended,
All meet thee in the blessed home above,
From whence thou camest, where thou hast ascended,
Thine everlasting home of peace and love. A-MEN.

# MARRIAGE AND THE HOME 625

*Husbands, love your wives, even as Christ also loved the church, and gave himself for it.* Eph. 5:25

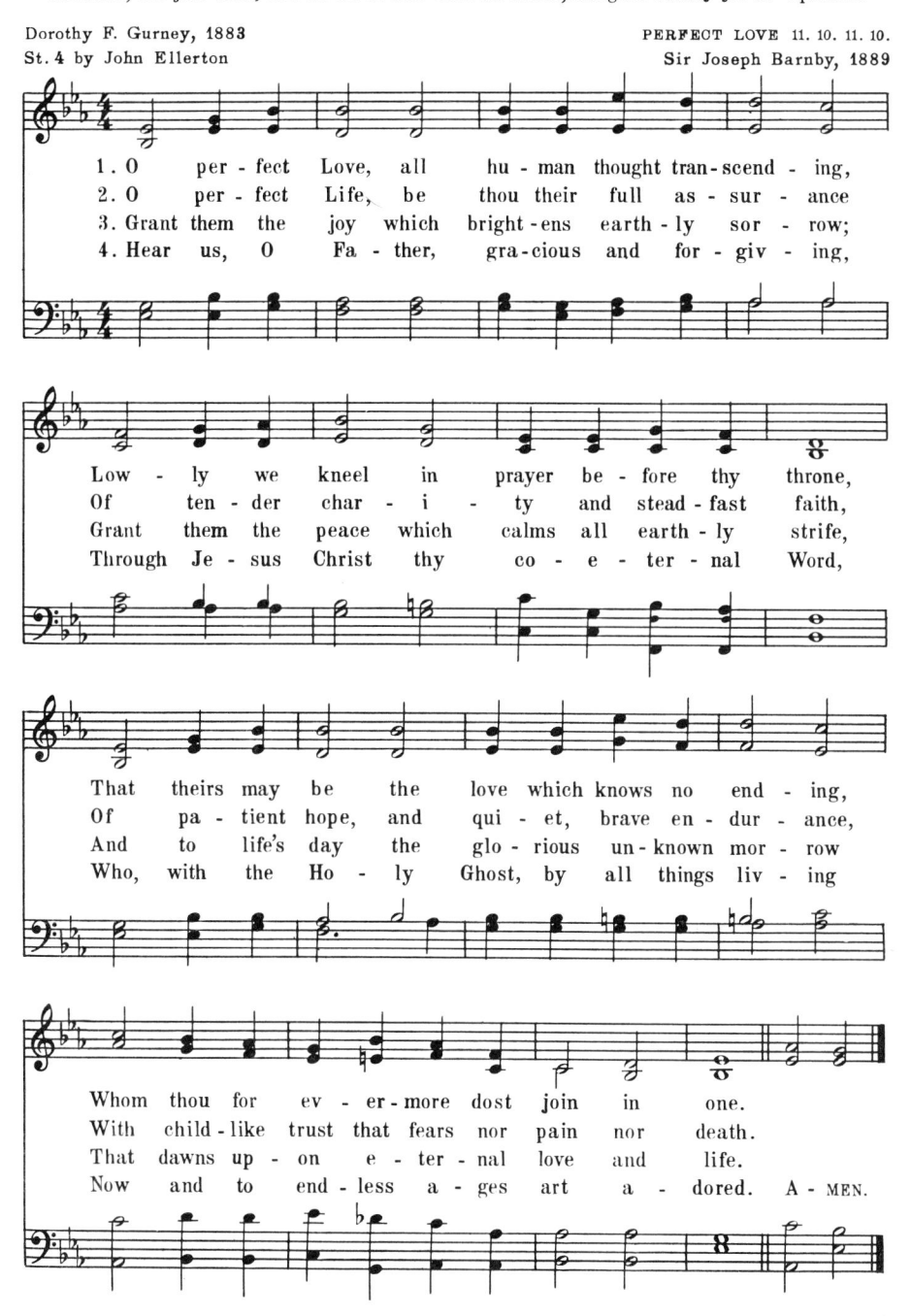

Dorothy F. Gurney, 1883　　　　　　　　　　　　　　　　　PERFECT LOVE 11. 10. 11. 10.
St. 4 by John Ellerton　　　　　　　　　　　　　　　　　Sir Joseph Barnby, 1889

1. O perfect Love, all human thought transcending,
   Lowly we kneel in prayer before thy throne,
   That theirs may be the love which knows no ending,
   Whom thou for evermore dost join in one.

2. O perfect Life, be thou their full assurance
   Of tender charity and steadfast faith,
   Of patient hope, and quiet, brave endurance,
   With childlike trust that fears nor pain nor death.

3. Grant them the joy which brightens earthly sorrow;
   Grant them the peace which calms all earthly strife,
   And to life's day the glorious unknown morrow
   That dawns upon eternal love and life.

4. Hear us, O Father, gracious and forgiving,
   Through Jesus Christ thy co-eternal Word,
   Who, with the Holy Ghost, by all things living
   Now and to endless ages art adored. A-MEN.

## 626 MARRIAGE AND THE HOME

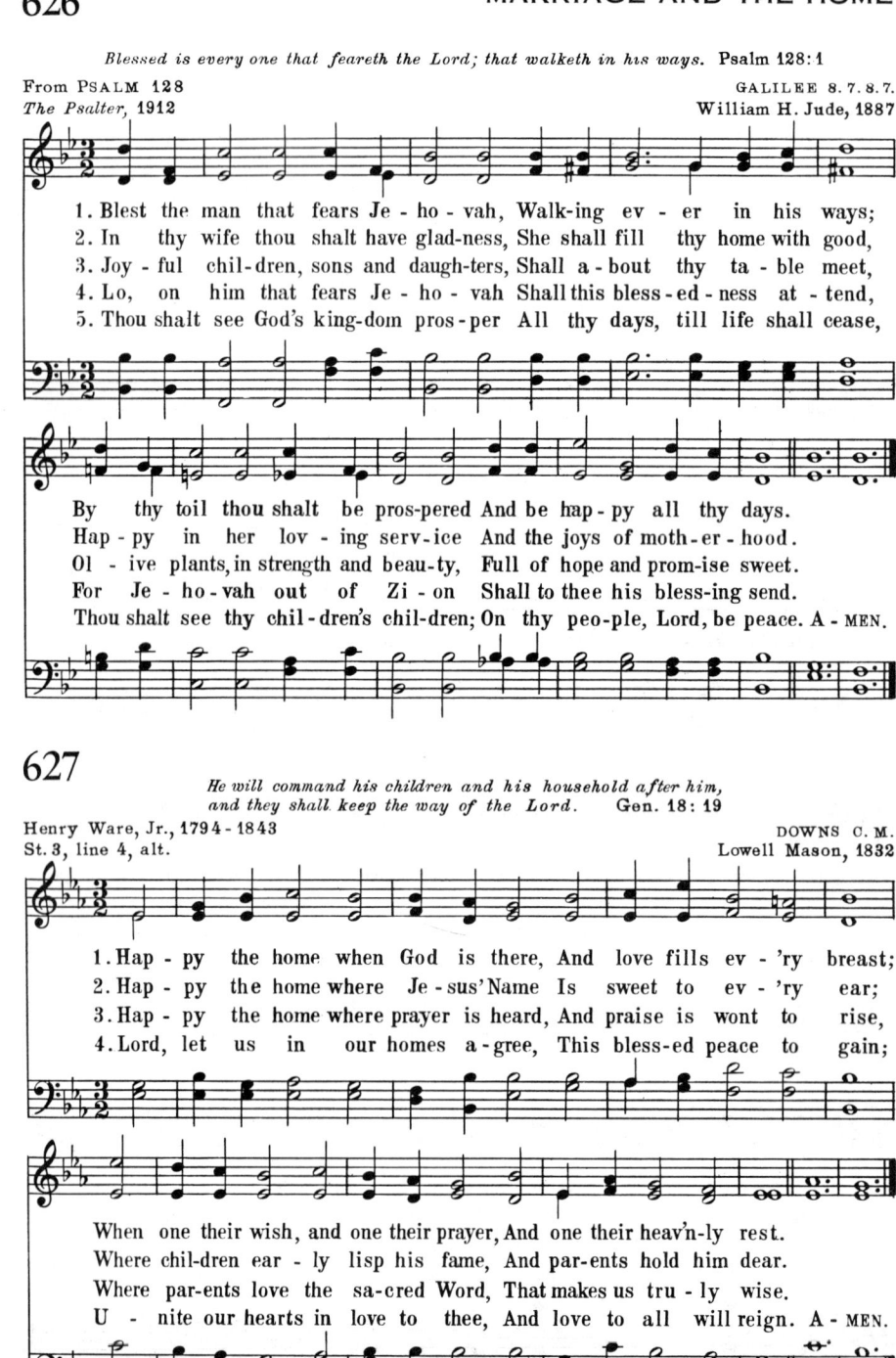

*Blessed is every one that feareth the Lord; that walketh in his ways.* Psalm 128:1

From PSALM 128  
The Psalter, 1912

GALILEE 8.7.8.7.  
William H. Jude, 1887

1. Blest the man that fears Je-ho-vah, Walk-ing ev-er in his ways;
2. In thy wife thou shalt have glad-ness, She shall fill thy home with good,
3. Joy-ful chil-dren, sons and daugh-ters, Shall a-bout thy ta-ble meet,
4. Lo, on him that fears Je-ho-vah Shall this bless-ed-ness at-tend,
5. Thou shalt see God's king-dom pros-per All thy days, till life shall cease,

By thy toil thou shalt be pros-pered And be hap-py all thy days.
Hap-py in her lov-ing serv-ice And the joys of moth-er-hood.
Ol-ive plants, in strength and beau-ty, Full of hope and prom-ise sweet.
For Je-ho-vah out of Zi-on Shall to thee his bless-ing send.
Thou shalt see thy chil-dren's chil-dren; On thy peo-ple, Lord, be peace. A-MEN.

## 627

*He will command his children and his household after him, and they shall keep the way of the Lord.* Gen. 18:19

Henry Ware, Jr., 1794-1843  
St. 3, line 4, alt.

DOWNS C. M.  
Lowell Mason, 1832

1. Hap-py the home when God is there, And love fills ev-'ry breast;
2. Hap-py the home where Je-sus' Name Is sweet to ev-'ry ear;
3. Hap-py the home where prayer is heard, And praise is wont to rise,
4. Lord, let us in our homes a-gree, This bless-ed peace to gain;

When one their wish, and one their prayer, And one their heav'n-ly rest.
Where chil-dren ear-ly lisp his fame, And par-ents hold him dear.
Where par-ents love the sa-cred Word, That makes us tru-ly wise.
U-nite our hearts in love to thee, And love to all will reign. A-MEN.

# MARRIAGE AND THE HOME

**628**

*Except the Lord build the house, they labour in vain that build it... Psalm 127:1*

John Ellerton, 1876

SAVOY CHAPEL 7. 6. 7. 6. D.
J. Baptiste Calkin, 1887

1. O Father all creating, Whose wisdom, love, and power
First bound two lives together In Eden's primal hour,
To-day to these thy children Thine earliest gifts renew,
A home by thee made happy, A love by thee kept true.

2. O Saviour, guest most bounteous Of old in Galilee,
Vouchsafe to-day thy presence With these who call on thee;
Their store of earthly gladness Transform to heav'nly wine,
And teach them in the tasting To know the gift is thine.

3. O Spirit of the Father, Breathe on them from above,
So mighty in thy pureness, So tender in thy love,
That, guarded by thy presence, From sin and strife kept free,
Their lives may own thy guidance, Their hearts be ruled by thee.

4. Except thou build it, Father, The house is built in vain;
Except thou, Saviour, bless it, The joy will turn to pain;
But nought can break the union Of hearts in thee made one;
And love thy Spirit hallows Is endless love begun. A-MEN.

## 629 HYMNS FOR SPECIAL PURPOSES

*Thou rulest the raging of the sea: when the waves thereof arise, thou stillest them.* Psalm 89:9

William Whiting, 1860; text of 1869
MELITA 8.8.8.8.8.8.
John B. Dykes, 1861

1. E-ter-nal Fa-ther, strong to save, Whose arm doth bind the rest-less wave,
2. O Sav-iour, whose al-might-y word The winds and waves sub-mis-sive heard,
3. O Sa-cred Spir-it, who didst brood Up-on the cha-os dark and rude,
4. O Trin-i-ty of love and pow'r, Our breth-ren shield in dan-ger's hour;

Who bidd'st the might-y o-cean deep Its own ap-point-ed lim-its keep:
Who walk-edst on the foam-ing deep And calm a-mid its rage didst sleep:
Who badd'st its an-gry tu-mult cease, And gav-est light and life and peace:
From rock and temp-est, fire and foe, Pro-tect them where-so-e'er they go;

O hear us when we cry to thee For those in per-il on the sea.
O hear us when we cry to thee For those in per-il on the sea.
O hear us when we cry to thee For those in per-il on the sea.
And ev-er let there rise to thee Glad hymns of praise from land and sea. A-MEN.

## 630

*We... do not cease to pray for you... that you might walk worthy of the Lord unto all pleasing...* Col. 1:9-10

Isabel Stevenson, 1889
CAIRNBROOK 8.5.8.3.
Ebenezer Prout, 1835-1909

1. Ho-ly Fa-ther, in thy mer-cy Hear our anx-ious prayer;
2. Je-sus, Sav-iour, let thy pres-ence Be their light and guide;
3. When in sor-row, when in dan-ger, When in lone-li-ness,
4. May the joy of thy sal-va-tion Be their strength and stay;
5. Ho-ly Spir-it, let thy teach-ing Sanc-ti-fy their life;
6. Fa-ther, Son, and Ho-ly Spir-it, God, the One in Three,

# HYMNS FOR SPECIAL PURPOSES

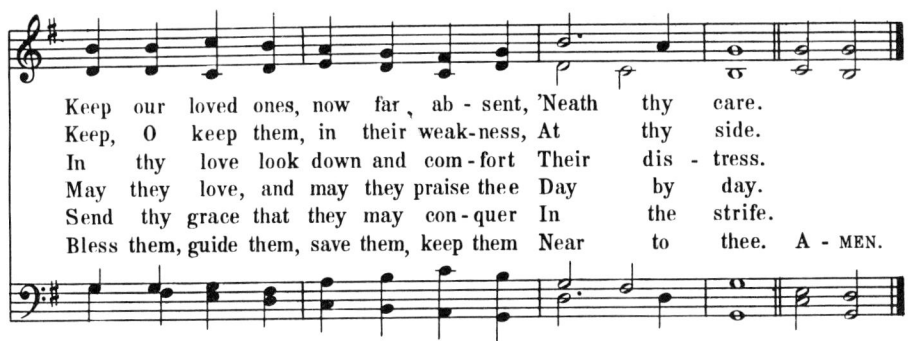

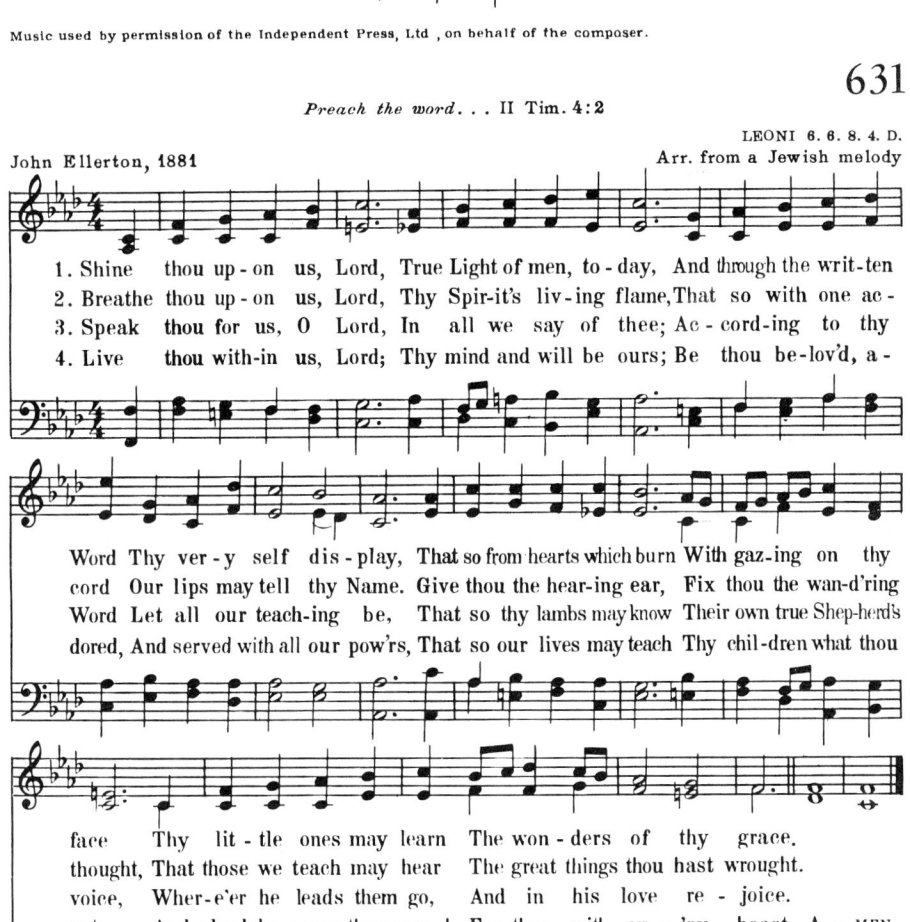

Keep our loved ones, now far absent, 'Neath thy care.
Keep, O keep them, in their weakness, At thy side.
In thy love look down and comfort Their distress.
May they love, and may they praise thee Day by day.
Send thy grace that they may conquer In the strife.
Bless them, guide them, save them, keep them Near to thee. A-MEN.

Music used by permission of the Independent Press, Ltd., on behalf of the composer.

## 631

*Preach the word... II Tim. 4:2*

John Ellerton, 1881

LEONI 6. 6. 8. 4. D.
Arr. from a Jewish melody

1. Shine thou upon us, Lord, True Light of men, today, And through the written Word Thy very self display, That so from hearts which burn With gazing on thy face Thy little ones may learn The wonders of thy grace.
2. Breathe thou upon us, Lord, Thy Spirit's living flame, That so with one accord Our lips may tell thy Name. Give thou the hearing ear, Fix thou the wand'ring thought, That those we teach may hear The great things thou hast wrought.
3. Speak thou for us, O Lord, In all we say of thee; According to thy Word Let all our teaching be, That so thy lambs may know Their own true Shepherd's voice, Wher-e'er he leads them go, And in his love rejoice.
4. Live thou within us, Lord; Thy mind and will be ours; Be thou beloved, adored, And served with all our pow'rs, That so our lives may teach Thy children what thou art, And plead, by more than speech, For thee with ev'ry heart. A-MEN.

## 632 HYMNS FOR SPECIAL PURPOSES

*And now, brethren, I commend you to God, and to the word of his grace, which is able to build you up . . . Acts 20:32*

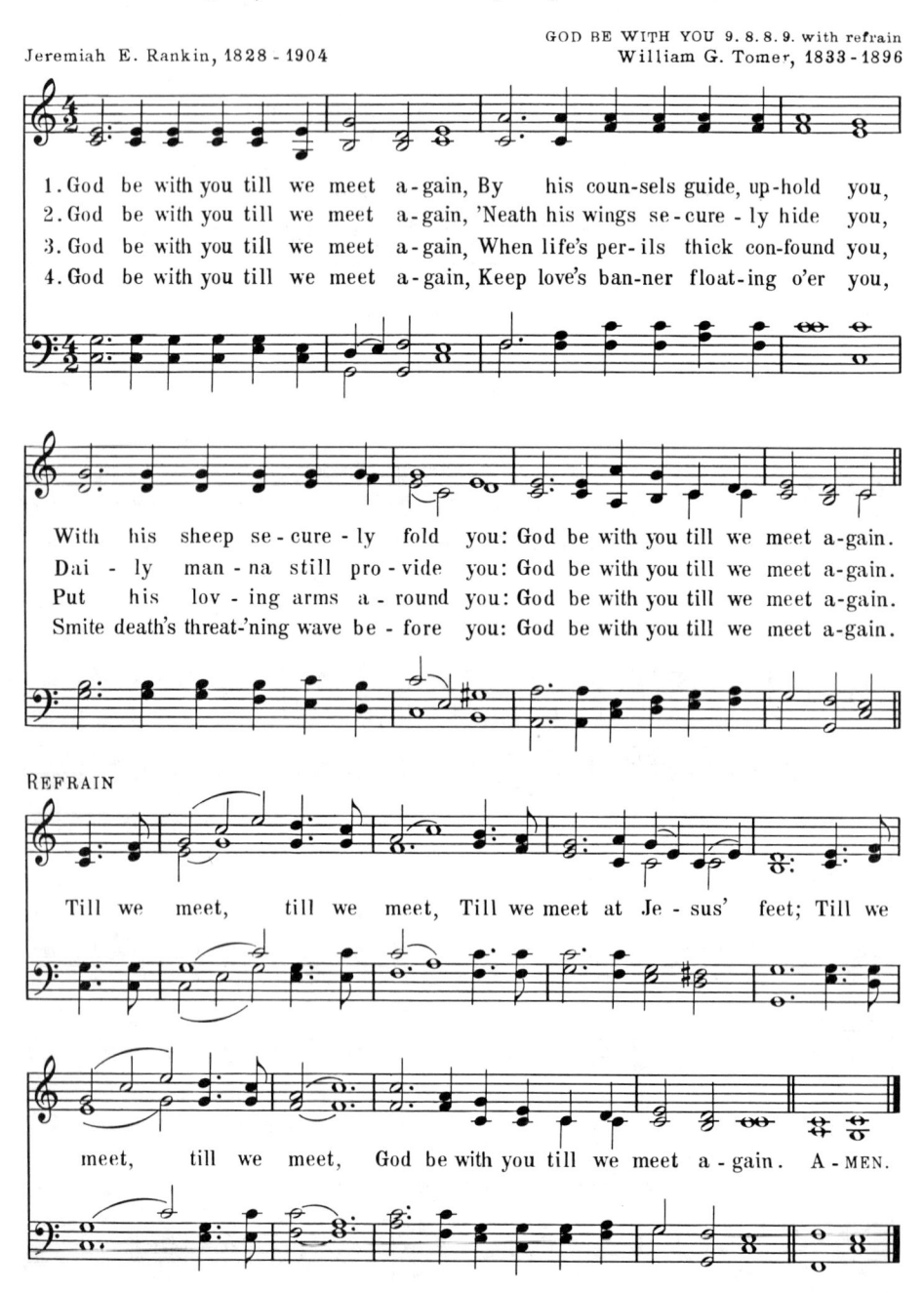

Jeremiah E. Rankin, 1828-1904
GOD BE WITH YOU 9.8.8.9. with refrain
William G. Tomer, 1833-1896

1. God be with you till we meet a-gain, By his coun-sels guide, up-hold you,
2. God be with you till we meet a-gain, 'Neath his wings se-cure-ly hide you,
3. God be with you till we meet a-gain, When life's per-ils thick con-found you,
4. God be with you till we meet a-gain, Keep love's ban-ner float-ing o'er you,

With his sheep se-cure-ly fold you: God be with you till we meet a-gain.
Dai - ly man - na still pro-vide you: God be with you till we meet a-gain.
Put his lov - ing arms a - round you: God be with you till we meet a-gain.
Smite death's threat-'ning wave be - fore you: God be with you till we meet a-gain.

REFRAIN

Till we meet, till we meet, Till we meet at Je - sus' feet; Till we meet, till we meet, God be with you till we meet a - gain. A - MEN.

# CHILDREN'S HYMNS 633

*I live by the faith of the Son of God, who loved me, and gave himself for me. Gal. 2:20*

Anna B. Warner, 1859

JESUS LOVES ME 7. 7. 7. 7. with refrain
William B. Bradbury, 1861

1. Je - sus loves me, this I know, For the Bi - ble tells me so;
2. Je - sus loves me, he who died Heav - en's gate to o - pen wide;
3. Je - sus loves me, loves me still, Though I'm ver - y weak and ill;
4. Je - sus loves me, he will stay Close be-side me all the way:

Lit - tle ones to him be - long, They are weak but he is strong.
He will wash a - way my sin, Let his lit - tle child come in.
From his shin - ing throne on high Comes to watch me where I lie.
If I love him, when I die He will take me home on high.

REFRAIN

Yes, Je - sus loves me! Yes, Je - sus loves me!
Yes, Je - sus loves me! The Bi - ble tells me so. A - MEN.

# 634 CHILDREN'S HYMNS

*Sing praises to God, sing praises... Psalm 47:6*

William P. Mackay, 1863, 1867
St. 1 added and refrain altered
by Henry J. Kuiper, 1929

THINE THE GLORY 6. 5. 7. 5. with refrain
John J. Husband, 1760-1825

1. We praise thee, O God! For the days of our youth,
   For the bright lamp that shin-eth— The Word of thy truth.
2. We praise thee, O God! For the Son of thy love,
   For Jesus who died and Is now gone a-bove.
3. We praise thee, O God! For thy Spir-it of light,
   Who has shown us our Sav-iour And scat-tered our night.
4. All glo-ry and praise To the Lamb that was slain,
   Who has borne all our sins and Has cleansed ev-'ry stain!

CHORUS

Hal-le-lu-jah! thine the glo-ry, Hal-le-lu-jah! we sing;
Hal-le-lu-jah! thine the glo-ry, Our praise now we bring. A-MEN.

First stanza and alteration of refrain copyright 1929 by Wm. B. Eerdmans. Used by permission.

# CHILDREN'S HYMNS

## 635

*Are not five sparrows sold for two farthings, and not one of them is forgotten before God?... Ye are of more value than many sparrows.* Luke 12:6, 7

Maria Straub, 1838-1898

PROVIDENCE C. M. with refrain
S. W. Straub, 1842-1899

1. God sees the lit-tle spar-row fall, It meets his ten-der view;
2. He paints the lil-y of the field, Per-fumes each lil-y bell;
3. God made the lit-tle birds and flow'rs, And all things large and small;

If God so loves the lit-tle birds, I know he loves me too.
If he so loves the lit-tle flow'rs, I know he loves me well.
He'll not for-get his lit-tle ones, I know he loves them all.

REFRAIN

He loves me too, he loves me too, I know he loves me too;

Be-cause he loves the lit-tle things, I know he loves me too. A-MEN.

## 636 CHILDREN'S HYMNS

*Thou hast made heaven, the heaven of heavens, with all their host, the earth, and all things that are therein, the seas, and all that is therein, and thou preservest them all...* Neh. 9:6

ALL THINGS BRIGHT AND BEAUTIFUL
7. 6. 7. 6. with refrain

Cecil Frances Alexander, 1823-1895, alt.
Adapted from a Danish folk song

1. Each lit-tle flow'r that o-pens, Each lit-tle bird that sings,
2. The pur-ple-head-ed moun-tain, The riv-er run-ning by,
3. The cold wind in the win-ter, The pleas-ant sum-mer sun,
4. The tall trees in the green-wood, The mea-dows where we play,
5. He gave us eyes to see them, And lips that we might tell

God made their glow-ing col-ors, He made their ti-ny wings.
The sun-set and the morn-ing That bright-ens up the sky.
The ripe fruits in the gar-den— He made them ev-'ry one.
The flow-ers by the wa-ter We gath-er ev-'ry day.
How great is God Al-migh-ty, Who do-eth all things well.

REFRAIN

Yes, all things bright and beau-ti-ful, All crea-tures great and small,

And all things wise and won-der-ful, The Lord God made them all. A-MEN.

St. 4, line 3, st. 4, line 4, alt.

Music from *Songs for Little People* by Danielson and Conant. Copyright, 1905, renewed 1933, by The Pilgrim Press. Used by permission.

# CHILDREN'S HYMNS

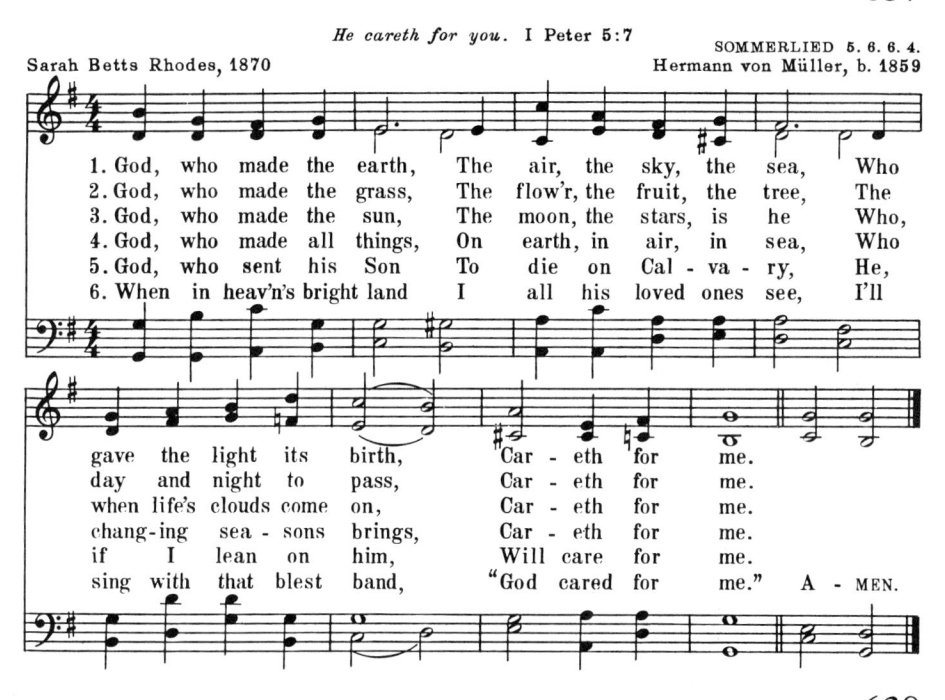

## 637

*He careth for you.* I Peter 5:7

Sarah Betts Rhodes, 1870

SOMMERLIED 5. 6. 6. 4.
Hermann von Müller, b. 1859

1. God, who made the earth, The air, the sky, the sea, Who gave the light its birth, Car-eth for me.
2. God, who made the grass, The flow'r, the fruit, the tree, The day and night to pass, Car-eth for me.
3. God, who made the sun, The moon, the stars, is he Who, when life's clouds come on, Car-eth for me.
4. God, who made all things, On earth, in air, in sea, Who chang-ing sea-sons brings, Car-eth for me.
5. God, who sent his Son To die on Cal-va-ry, He, if I lean on him, Will care for me.
6. When in heav'n's bright land I all his loved ones see, I'll sing with that blest band, "God cared for me." A-MEN.

## 638

*As many as are led by the Spirit of God, they are the sons of God.* Rom. 8:14

William H. Parker, 1845-1929

ERNSTEIN 6. 5. 6. 5.
J. Frederick Swift, 1879

1. Ho-ly Spir-it, hear us; Help us while we sing; Breathe in-to the mu-sic Of the praise we bring.
2. Ho-ly Spir-it, prompt us When we kneel to pray; Near-er come and teach us What we ought to say.
3. Ho-ly Spir-it, shine thou On the book we read; Gild its ho-ly pag-es With the light we need.
4. Ho-ly Spir-it, give us Each a low-ly mind; Make us more like Je-sus, Gen-tle, pure, and kind.
5. Ho-ly Spir-it, keep us Safe from sins which lie Hid-den by some pleas-ure From our youth-ful eye.
6. Ho-ly Spir-it, help us Dai-ly by thy might, What is wrong to con-quer, And to choose the right. A-MEN.

Copyright to words owned by the National Sunday School Union. Used by permission.
Music copyright. Used by permission of the Methodist Youth Department.

## 639 CHILDREN'S HYMNS

*Ye shall find the babe wrapped in swaddling clothes, lying in a manger.* Luke 2:12

Cecil Frances Alexander, 1848

IRBY 8.7.8.7.8.8.
Henry J. Gauntlett, 1849

1. Once in royal David's city Stood a lowly cattle-shed, Where a mother laid her Baby In a manger for his bed: Mary was that mother mild, Jesus Christ her little Child.
2. He came down to earth from heaven Who is God and Lord of all, And his shelter was a stable, And his cradle was a stall: With the poor, and mean, and lowly, Lived on earth our Saviour Holy.
3. And, through all his wondrous childhood He would honor and obey, Love and watch the lowly maiden In whose gentle arms he lay: Christian children all must be Mild, obedient, good as he.
4. And our eyes at last shall see him, Through his own redeeming love; For that Child so dear and gentle Is our Lord in heav'n above, And he leads his children on To the place where he is gone.
5. Not in that poor lowly stable, With the oxen standing by, We shall see him, but in heaven, Set at God's right hand on high; When like stars his children crowned All in white shall wait around. A-MEN.

# CHILDREN'S HYMNS 640

*And she brought forth her firstborn son, and wrapped him in swaddling clothes, and laid him in a manger . . .* Luke 2:7

TEMPUS ADEST FLORIDUM 7. 6. 7. 6. D.
Spring carol, c. 14th Century

Joseph S. Cook, 1919
Arr. by Sir Ernest MacMillan, 1930

1. Gen-tle Ma-ry laid her Child Low-ly in a man-ger;
There he lay, the Un-de-filed, To the world a stran-ger.
Such a Babe in such a place, Can he be the Sav-iour?
Ask the saved of all the race Who have found his fa-vor.

2. An-gels sang a-bout his birth, Wise men sought and found him;
Heav-en's star shone bright-ly forth Glo-ry all a-round him.
Shep-herds saw the won-drous sight, Heard the an-gels sing-ing;
All the plains were lit that night, All the hills were ring-ing.

3. Gen-tle Ma-ry laid her Child Low-ly in a man-ger;
He is still the Un-de-filed, But no more a stran-ger.
Son of God of hum-ble birth, Beau-ti-ful the sto-ry;
Praise his Name in all the earth, Hail! the King of Glo-ry! A-MEN.

Music used by permission of Sir Ernest MacMillan.

# 641 CHILDREN'S HYMNS

*And she...laid him in a manger; because there was no room for them in the inn.* Luke 2:7

Anon., c. 1884, 1892

MUELLER 11. 11. 11. 11.
James R. Murray, 1887

1. A-way in a man-ger, No crib for a bed, The lit-tle Lord Je-sus Laid down his sweet head; The stars in the sky Looked down where he lay, The lit-tle Lord Je-sus, A-sleep on the hay.
2. The cat-tle are low-ing, The Ba-by a-wakes, But lit-tle Lord Je-sus No cry-ing he makes; I love thee, Lord Je-sus! Look down from the sky, And stay by my cra-dle, Till morn-ing is nigh.
3. Be near me, Lord Je-sus, I ask thee to stay Close by me for ev-er, And love me, I pray; Bless all the dear chil-dren In thy ten-der care, And fit us for heav-en, To live with thee there. A-MEN.

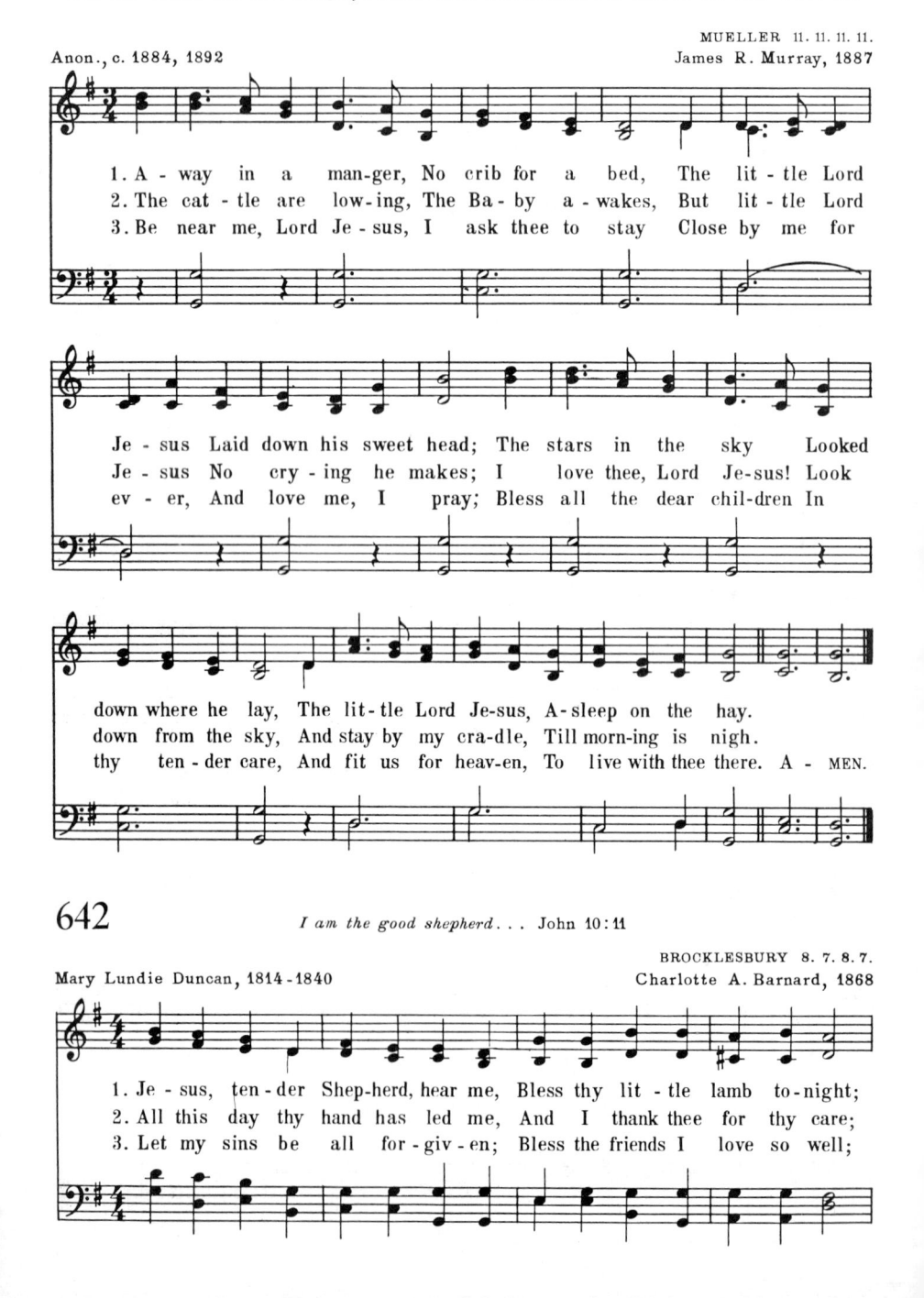

# 642

*I am the good shepherd...* John 10:11

Mary Lundie Duncan, 1814-1840

BROCKLESBURY 8. 7. 8. 7.
Charlotte A. Barnard, 1868

1. Je-sus, ten-der Shep-herd, hear me, Bless thy lit-tle lamb to-night;
2. All this day thy hand has led me, And I thank thee for thy care;
3. Let my sins be all for-giv-en; Bless the friends I love so well;

# CHILDREN'S HYMNS

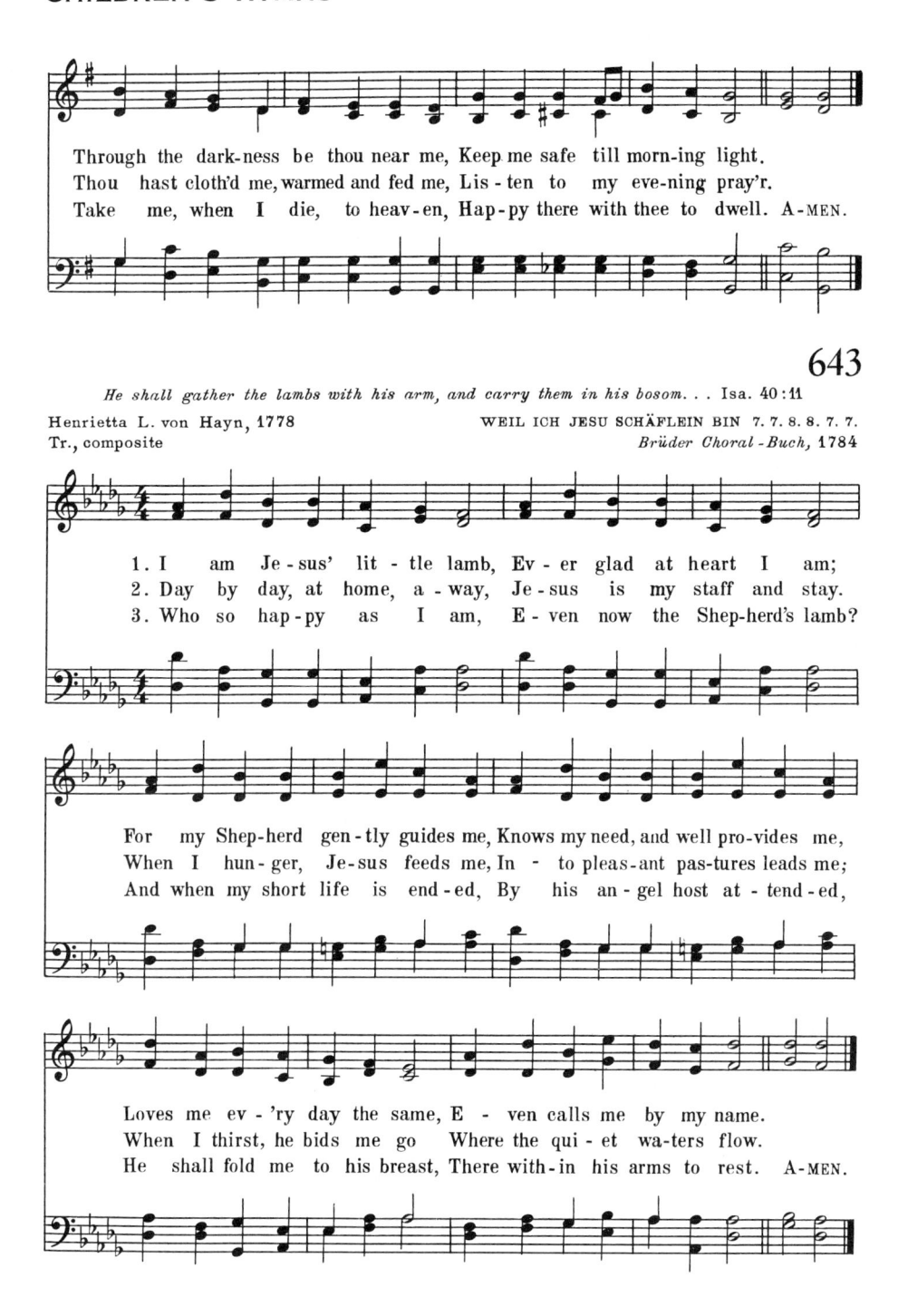

Through the darkness be thou near me, Keep me safe till morning light.
Thou hast cloth'd me, warmed and fed me, Listen to my evening pray'r.
Take me, when I die, to heaven, Happy there with thee to dwell. A-MEN.

## 643

*He shall gather the lambs with his arm, and carry them in his bosom... Isa. 40:11*

Henrietta L. von Hayn, 1778
Tr., composite

WEIL ICH JESU SCHÄFLEIN BIN 7.7.8.8.7.7.
*Brüder Choral-Buch, 1784*

1. I am Jesus' little lamb, Ever glad at heart I am;
2. Day by day, at home, away, Jesus is my staff and stay.
3. Who so happy as I am, Even now the Shepherd's lamb?

For my Shepherd gently guides me, Knows my need, and well provides me,
When I hunger, Jesus feeds me, Into pleasant pastures leads me;
And when my short life is ended, By his angel host attended,

Loves me ev-'ry day the same, Even calls me by my name.
When I thirst, he bids me go Where the quiet waters flow.
He shall fold me to his breast, There within his arms to rest. A-MEN.

# 644 CHILDREN'S HYMNS

*I am the good shepherd, and know my sheep... John 10:14*

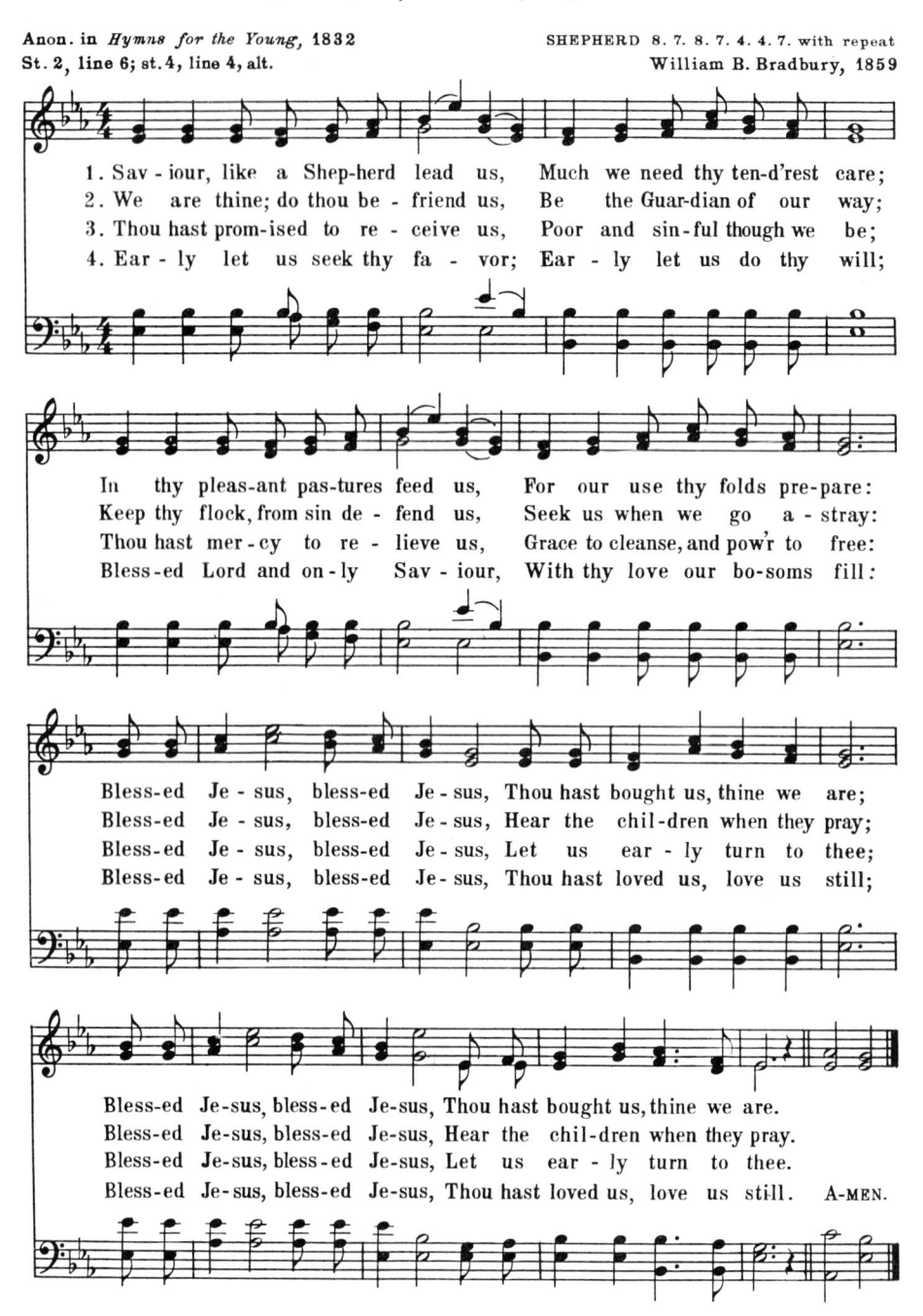

Anon. in *Hymns for the Young*, 1832
St. 2, line 6; st. 4, line 4, alt.

SHEPHERD 8. 7. 8. 7. 4. 4. 7. with repeat
William B. Bradbury, 1859

1. Saviour, like a Shepherd lead us, Much we need thy ten-d'rest care;
In thy pleasant pastures feed us, For our use thy folds prepare:
Blessed Jesus, blessed Jesus, Thou hast bought us, thine we are;
Blessed Jesus, blessed Jesus, Thou hast bought us, thine we are.

2. We are thine; do thou befriend us, Be the Guardian of our way;
Keep thy flock, from sin defend us, Seek us when we go astray:
Blessed Jesus, blessed Jesus, Hear the children when they pray;
Blessed Jesus, blessed Jesus, Hear the children when they pray.

3. Thou hast promised to receive us, Poor and sinful though we be;
Thou hast mercy to relieve us, Grace to cleanse, and pow'r to free:
Blessed Jesus, blessed Jesus, Let us early turn to thee;
Blessed Jesus, blessed Jesus, Let us early turn to thee.

4. Early let us seek thy favor; Early let us do thy will;
Blessed Lord and only Saviour, With thy love our bosoms fill:
Blessed Jesus, blessed Jesus, Thou hast loved us, love us still;
Blessed Jesus, blessed Jesus, Thou hast loved us, love us still. A-MEN.

# CHILDREN'S HYMNS 645

*Giving thanks always for all things unto... the Father.* Eph. 5:20

THANKSGIVING 7. 7. 7. 7. 7. 7. with refrain

Ascribed to Mary Mapes Dodge  
W. K. Basswood

1. Can a lit-tle child like me Thank the Fa-ther fit-ting-ly?
2. For the fruit up-on the tree, For the birds that sing of thee,
3. For the sun-shine warm and bright, For the day and for the night,
4. For our com-rades and our plays, And our hap-py ho-li-days,

Yes, O yes! be good and true, Pa-tient, kind in all you do;
For the earth in beau-ty dressed, Fa-ther, moth-er, and the rest,
For the les-sons of our youth—Hon-or, grat-i-tude and truth,
For the joy-ful work and true That a lit-tle child may do,

Love the Lord, and do your part; Learn to say with all your heart,
For thy pre-cious, lov-ing care, For thy boun-ty ev-'ry-where,
For the love that met us here, For the home and for the cheer,
For our lives but just be-gun, For the great gift of thy Son,

**Refrain**

Fa-ther, we thank thee! Fa-ther, we thank thee!
Fa-ther in heav'n, we thank thee! A-MEN.

# 646      CHILDREN'S HYMNS

*Hosanna to the Son of David... Matt. 21:9*

John King, 1830

TOURS 7. 6. 7. 6. D.
Berthold Tours, 1872

1. When his salvation bringing, To Zion Jesus came,
The children all stood singing Hosanna to his Name:
Nor did their zeal offend him, But as he rode along,
He let them still attend him, And smiled to hear their song.

2. And since the Lord retaineth His love for children still,
Though now as King he reigneth On Zion's heavn'ly hill,
We'll flock around his banner Who sits upon his throne,
And cry aloud, "Hosanna To David's royal Son!"

3. For should we fail proclaiming Our great Redeemer's praise,
The stones, our silence shaming, Would their Hosannas raise.
But shall we only render The tribute of our words?
No; while our hearts are tender, They too shall be the Lord's. A-MEN.

# CHILDREN'S HYMNS 647

*The Son of God, who loved me, and gave himself for me.* Gal. 2:20

Ascribed to Emily Sullivan Oakey, 1829-1883

GLADNESS 10. 10. 10. 10. with refrain
Philip P. Bliss, 1838-1876

1. I am so glad that our Father in heav'n Tells of his love in the book he has giv'n: Wonderful things in the Bible I see;
2. Though I forget him, and wander away, Still he doth love me wherever I stray; Back to his dear loving arms do I flee,
3. O if there's only one song I can sing, When in his beauty I see the great King, This shall my song in eternity be,

REFRAIN

This is the dearest, that Jesus loves me.
When I remember that Jesus loves me. I am so glad that
"O what a wonder that Jesus loves me."

Jesus loves me, Jesus loves me, Jesus loves me; I am so glad that Jesus loves me, Jesus loves even me. A-MEN.

## 648 CHILDREN'S HYMNS

*For the promise is unto you, and to your children... Acts 2:39*

Anne H. Shepherd, 1836
St. 4, line 3 and refrain, alt.

CHILDREN'S PRAISES C. M. with refrain
Henry E. Matthews, c. 1853

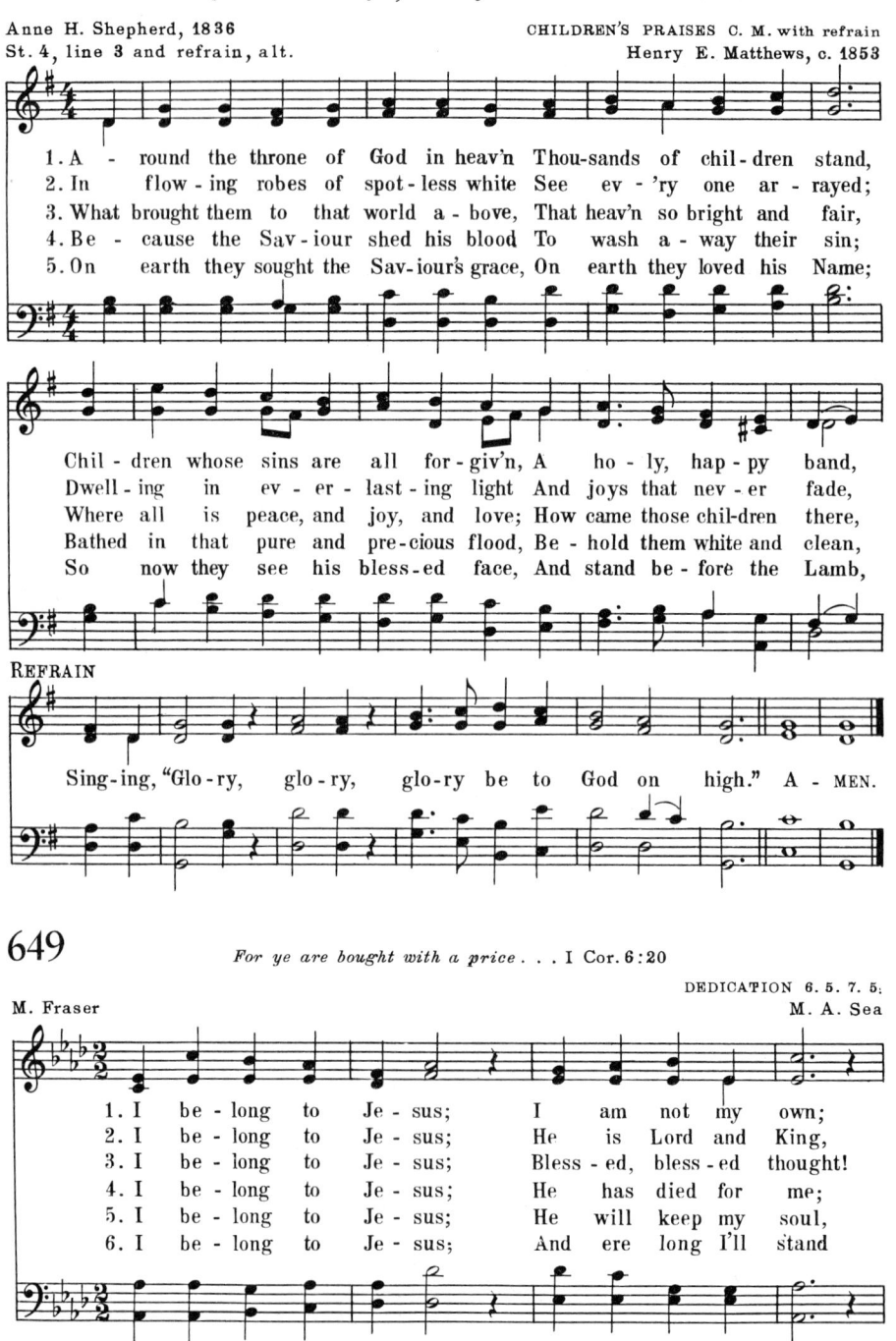

1. A - round the throne of God in heav'n Thou-sands of chil-dren stand,
2. In flow - ing robes of spot - less white See ev - 'ry one ar - rayed;
3. What brought them to that world a - bove, That heav'n so bright and fair,
4. Be - cause the Sav - iour shed his blood To wash a - way their sin;
5. On earth they sought the Sav-iour's grace, On earth they loved his Name;

Chil - dren whose sins are all for - giv'n, A ho - ly, hap - py band,
Dwell - ing in ev - er - last - ing light And joys that nev - er fade,
Where all is peace, and joy, and love; How came those chil-dren there,
Bathed in that pure and pre - cious flood, Be - hold them white and clean,
So now they see his bless - ed face, And stand be - fore the Lamb,

REFRAIN

Sing-ing, "Glo-ry, glo-ry, glo-ry be to God on high." A - MEN.

## 649

*For ye are bought with a price... I Cor. 6:20*

M. Fraser

DEDICATION 6. 5. 7. 5.
M. A. Sea

1. I be - long to Je - sus; I am not my own;
2. I be - long to Je - sus; He is Lord and King,
3. I be - long to Je - sus; Bless - ed, bless - ed thought!
4. I be - long to Je - sus; He has died for me;
5. I be - long to Je - sus; He will keep my soul,
6. I be - long to Je - sus; And ere long I'll stand

# CHILDREN'S HYMNS

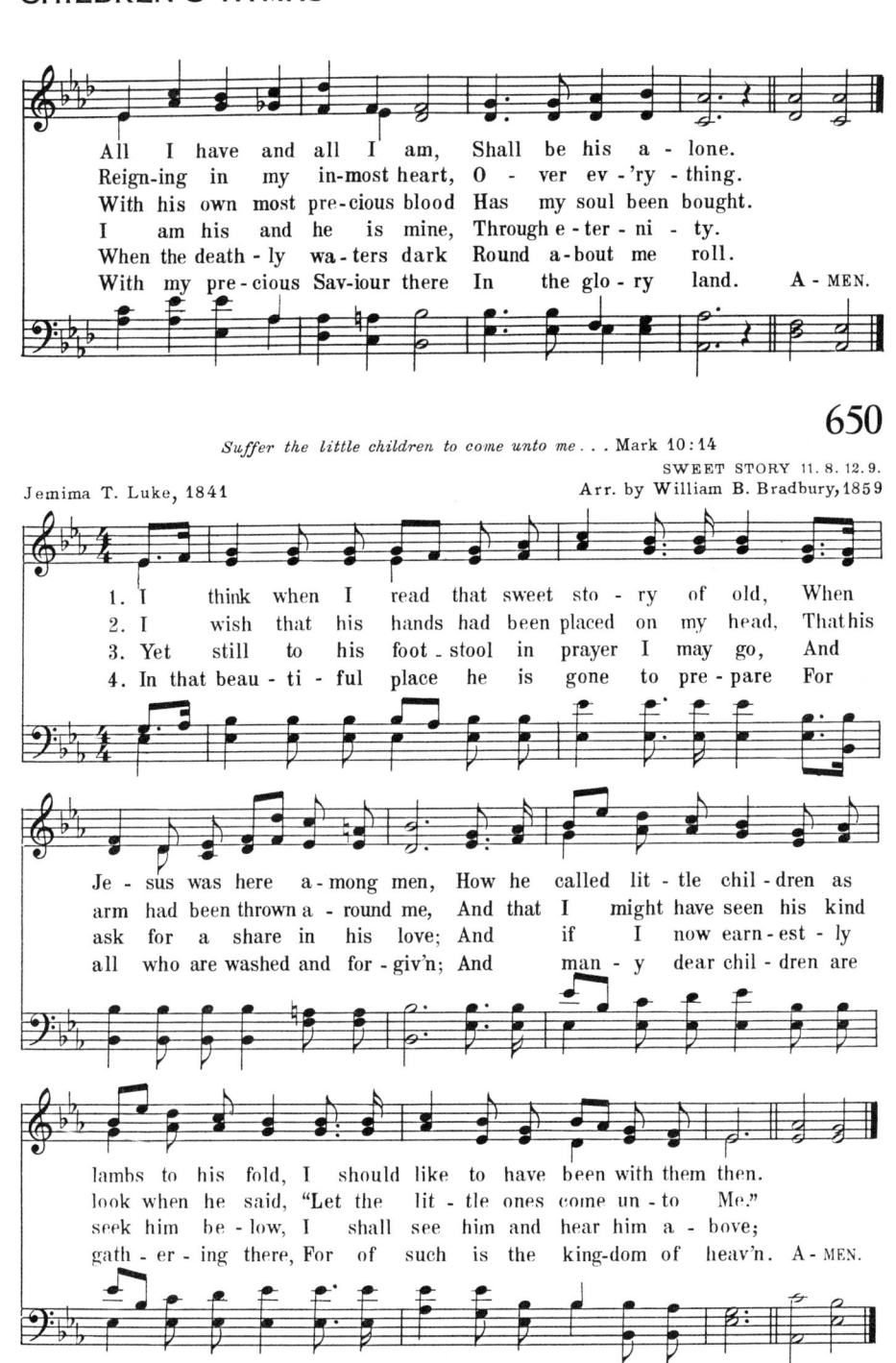

All I have and all I am, Shall be his a - lone.
Reign-ing in my in-most heart, O - ver ev - 'ry - thing.
With his own most pre-cious blood Has my soul been bought.
I am his and he is mine, Through e - ter - ni - ty.
When the death-ly wa-ters dark Round a-bout me roll.
With my pre-cious Sav-iour there In the glo - ry land. A - MEN.

## 650

*Suffer the little children to come unto me... Mark 10:14*

SWEET STORY 11. 8. 12. 9.

Jemima T. Luke, 1841

Arr. by William B. Bradbury, 1859

1. I think when I read that sweet sto - ry of old, When Je - sus was here a - mong men, How he called lit - tle chil - dren as lambs to his fold, I should like to have been with them then.
2. I wish that his hands had been placed on my head, That his arm had been thrown a - round me, And that I might have seen his kind look when he said, "Let the lit - tle ones come un - to Me."
3. Yet still to his foot-stool in prayer I may go, And ask for a share in his love; And if I now earn-est-ly seek him be - low, I shall see him and hear him a - bove;
4. In that beau - ti - ful place he is gone to pre - pare For all who are washed and for - giv'n; And man - y dear chil - dren are gath - er - ing there, For of such is the king-dom of heav'n. A - MEN.

# 651 CHILDREN'S HYMNS

*And they shall be mine ... when I make up my jewels.* Mal. 3:17

William O. Cushing, 1823-1903

JEWELS 8. 6. 8. 5. with refrain
George Frederick Root, 1820-1895

1. When he cometh, when he cometh To make up his jewels, All his jewels, precious jewels, His loved and his own.
2. He will gather, he will gather The gems for his kingdom, All the pure ones, all the bright ones, His loved and his own.
3. Little children, little children Who love their Redeemer, Are the jewels, precious jewels, His loved and his own.

REFRAIN

Like the stars of the morning, His bright crown adorning, They shall shine in their beauty, Bright gems for his crown. A-MEN.

# CHILDREN'S HYMNS
## 652

*God ... hath highly exalted him, and given him a name which is above every name.* Phil. 2:9

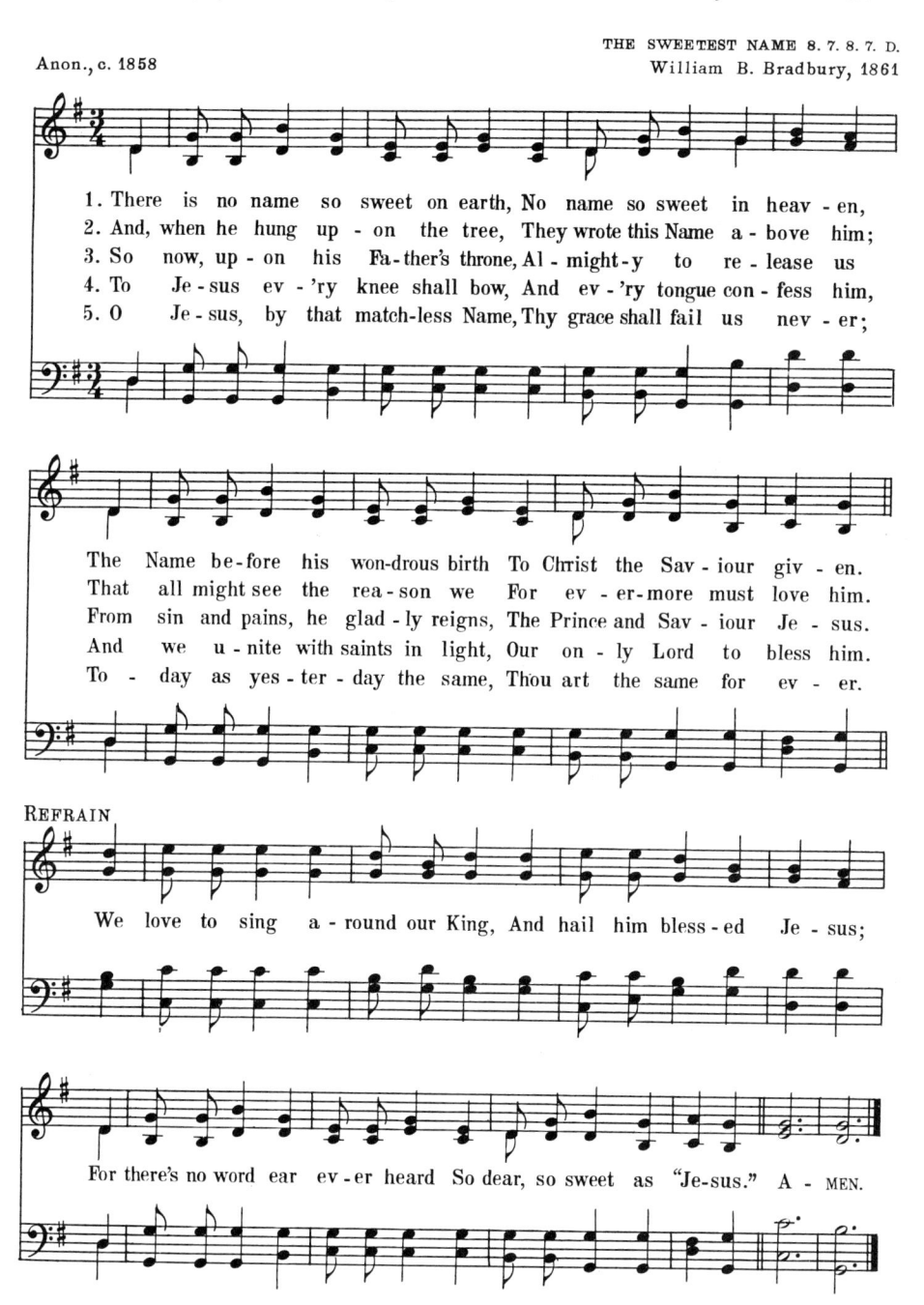

Anon., c. 1858  
THE SWEETEST NAME 8. 7. 8. 7. D.  
William B. Bradbury, 1861

1. There is no name so sweet on earth, No name so sweet in heav-en,
2. And, when he hung up-on the tree, They wrote this Name a-bove him;
3. So now, up-on his Fa-ther's throne, Al-might-y to re-lease us
4. To Je-sus ev-'ry knee shall bow, And ev-'ry tongue con-fess him,
5. O Je-sus, by that match-less Name, Thy grace shall fail us nev-er;

The Name be-fore his won-drous birth To Christ the Sav-iour giv-en.
That all might see the rea-son we For ev-er-more must love him.
From sin and pains, he glad-ly reigns, The Prince and Sav-iour Je-sus.
And we u-nite with saints in light, Our on-ly Lord to bless him.
To-day as yes-ter-day the same, Thou art the same for ev-er.

REFRAIN

We love to sing a-round our King, And hail him bless-ed Je-sus;

For there's no word ear ev-er heard So dear, so sweet as "Je-sus." A-MEN.

## 653

**CHILDREN'S HYMNS**

*Let your light so shine before men, that they may see your good works, and glorify your Father which is in heaven.* Matt. 5:16

JESUS BIDS US SHINE 5. 5. 6. 5. 6. 4. 6. 4.

Susan Warner, 1819-1885  
Edwin O. Excell, 1851-1921

1. Je-sus bids us shine With a pure, clear light, Like a lit-tle can-dle Burn-ing in the night. In this world of dark-ness So let us shine — You in your small cor-ner, And I in mine.
2. Je-sus bids us shine, First of all for him; Well he sees and knows it, If our light grows dim. He looks down from heav-en To see us shine — You in your small cor-ner, And I in mine.
3. Je-sus bids us shine, Then, for all a-round; Man-y kinds of dark-ness In the world are found — Sin and want and sor-row; So we must shine — You in your small cor-ner, And I in mine. A-MEN.

## 654

*We love him, because he first loved us.* I John 4:19

POSEN 7. 7. 7. 7.

Jane E. Leeson, 1842  
Arr. from Georg C. Strattner by J. A. Freylinghausen, 1705

1. Sav-iour, teach me, day by day, Love's sweet les-son,— to o-bey;
2. With a child's glad heart of love, At thy bid-ding may I move;
3. Teach me thus thy steps to trace, Strong to fol-low in thy grace;
4. Love in lov-ing finds em-ploy, In o-be-dience all her joy;

# CHILDREN'S HYMNS

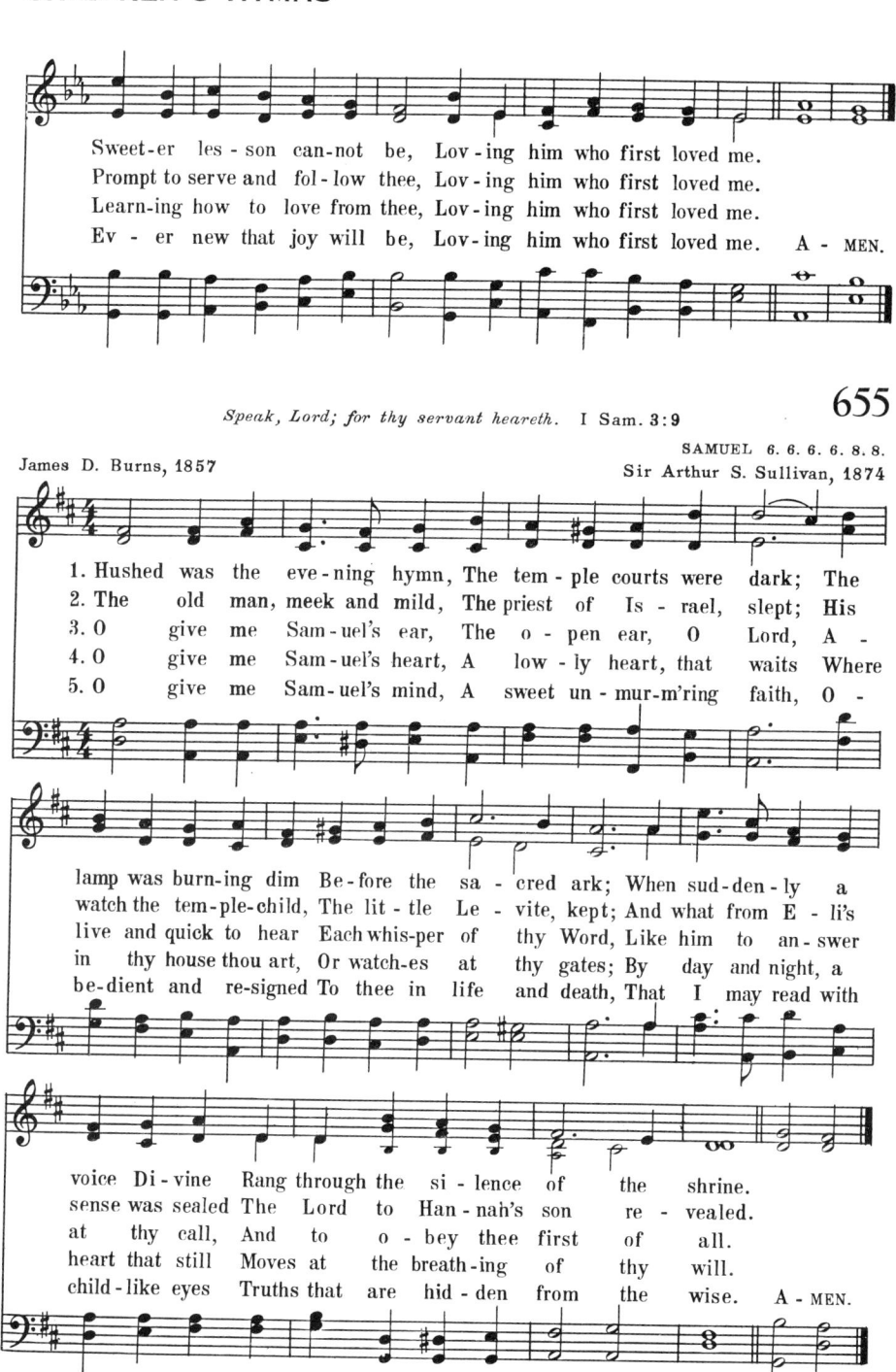

Sweet-er les-son can-not be, Lov-ing him who first loved me.
Prompt to serve and fol-low thee, Lov-ing him who first loved me.
Learn-ing how to love from thee, Lov-ing him who first loved me.
Ev - er new that joy will be, Lov-ing him who first loved me. A - MEN.

## 655

*Speak, Lord; for thy servant heareth.* I Sam. 3:9

SAMUEL 6. 6. 6. 6. 8. 8.
James D. Burns, 1857　　　　　　　　　　　　　　Sir Arthur S. Sullivan, 1874

1. Hushed was the eve-ning hymn, The tem-ple courts were dark; The lamp was burn-ing dim Be-fore the sa-cred ark; When sud-den-ly a voice Di-vine Rang through the si-lence of the shrine.
2. The old man, meek and mild, The priest of Is-rael, slept; His watch the tem-ple-child, The lit-tle Le-vite, kept; And what from E-li's sense was sealed The Lord to Han-nah's son re-vealed.
3. O give me Sam-uel's ear, The o-pen ear, O Lord, A-live and quick to hear Each whis-per of thy Word, Like him to an-swer at thy call, And to o-bey thee first of all.
4. O give me Sam-uel's heart, A low-ly heart, that waits Where in thy house thou art, Or watch-es at thy gates; By day and night, a heart that still Moves at the breath-ing of thy will.
5. O give me Sam-uel's mind, A sweet un-mur-m'ring faith, O-be-dient and re-signed To thee in life and death, That I may read with child-like eyes Truths that are hid-den from the wise. A - MEN.

# 656 CHILDREN'S HYMNS

*Come, ye children, hearken unto me: I will teach you the fear of the Lord.* Psalm 34:11

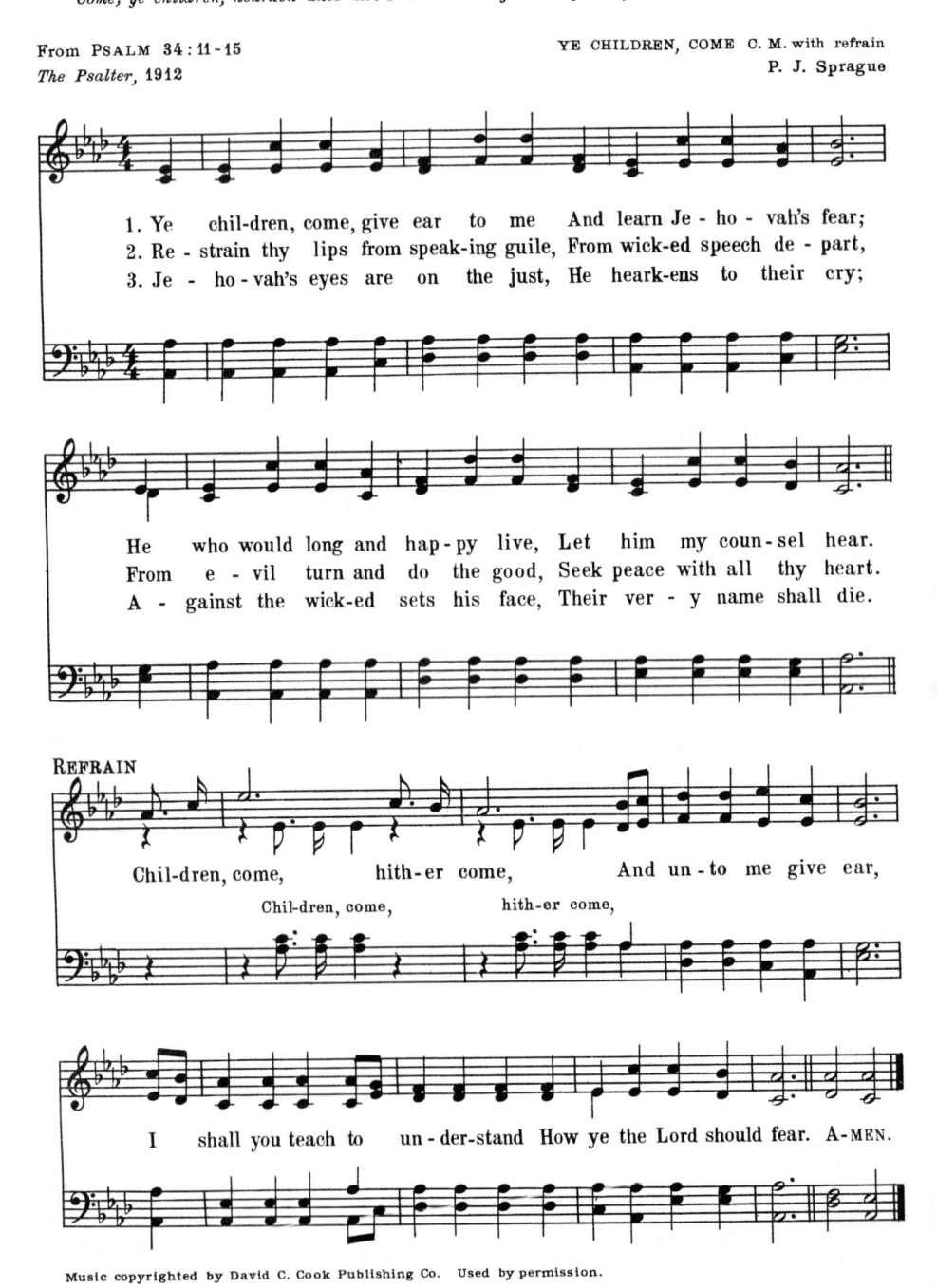

From PSALM 34:11-15
The Psalter, 1912

YE CHILDREN, COME C. M. with refrain
P. J. Sprague

1. Ye children, come, give ear to me And learn Jehovah's fear;
2. Restrain thy lips from speaking guile, From wicked speech depart,
3. Jehovah's eyes are on the just, He hearkens to their cry;

He who would long and happy live, Let him my counsel hear.
From evil turn and do the good, Seek peace with all thy heart.
Against the wicked sets his face, Their very name shall die.

REFRAIN

Children, come, hither come, And unto me give ear,
Children, come, hither come,
I shall you teach to understand How ye the Lord should fear. A-MEN.

Music copyrighted by David C. Cook Publishing Co. Used by permission.

# CHILDREN'S HYMNS 657

*To obey is better than sacrifice... I Sam. 15:22*

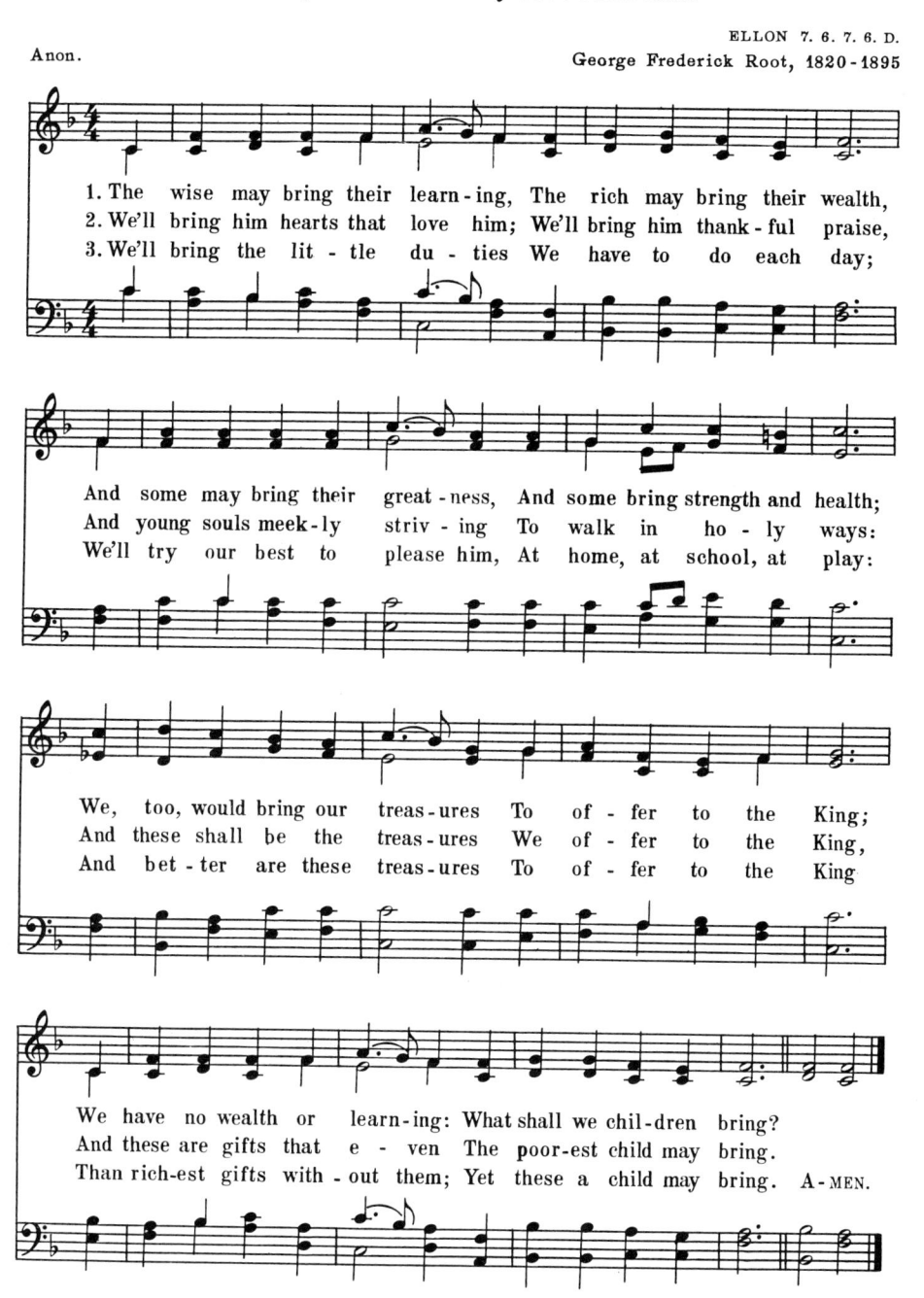

Anon.

ELLON 7. 6. 7. 6. D.
George Frederick Root, 1820-1895

1. The wise may bring their learn-ing, The rich may bring their wealth,
2. We'll bring him hearts that love him; We'll bring him thank-ful praise,
3. We'll bring the lit-tle du-ties We have to do each day;

And some may bring their great-ness, And some bring strength and health;
And young souls meek-ly striv-ing To walk in ho-ly ways:
We'll try our best to please him, At home, at school, at play:

We, too, would bring our treas-ures To of-fer to the King;
And these shall be the treas-ures We of-fer to the King,
And bet-ter are these treas-ures To of-fer to the King

We have no wealth or learn-ing: What shall we chil-dren bring?
And these are gifts that e-ven The poor-est child may bring.
Than rich-est gifts with-out them; Yet these a child may bring. A-MEN.

## 658 CHILDREN'S HYMNS

*The Lord is faithful, who shall stablish you, and keep you from evil.* II Thess. 3:3

Horatio R. Palmer, 1868

YIELD NOT 11. 11. 11. 12. with refrain
Horatio R. Palmer, 1868

1. Yield not to temp-ta-tion, for yield-ing is sin;
2. Shun e-vil com-pan-ions; bad lang-uage dis-dain;
3. To him that o'er-com-eth God giv-eth a crown;

Each vic-t'ry will help you some oth-er to win;
God's Name hold in rev-'rence, nor take it in vain;
Through faith we shall con-quer, though oft-en cast down;

Fight man-ful-ly on-ward; dark pas-sions sub-due;
Be thought-ful and earn-est, kind-heart-ed and true;
He who is the Sav-iour our strength will re-new;

Look ev-er to Je-sus, he will car-ry you through.
Look ev-er to Je-sus, he will car-ry you through.
Look ev-er to Je-sus, he will car-ry you through.

# CHILDREN'S HYMNS

**REFRAIN**

Ask the Saviour to help you, Comfort, strengthen, you;
He is willing to aid you, He will carry you through. A-MEN.

*Thou shalt love the Lord thy God with all thy heart...*
*Thou shalt love thy neighbor as thyself* Matt. 22:37, 39

**659**

ONSLOW L. M.
Daniel Batchellor, 1885
Arr. by E. R. B., 1904

Rebecca J. Weston, 1885

1. Father, we thank thee for the night, And for the pleasant morning light;
   For rest and food and loving care, And all that makes the day so fair.
2. Help us to do the things we should, To be to others kind and good;
   In all we do, in work or play, To grow more loving ev'ry day. A-MEN.

## 660     CHILDREN'S HYMNS

*Daniel . . . regardeth not thee, O king, nor the decree that thou hast signed . . .*
*Then . . . they brought Daniel, and cast him into the den of lions . . .* — Dan. 6:13, 16

Philip P. Bliss, 1873
DANIEL 7. 5. 7. 6. with refrain
Philip P. Bliss, 1873

1. Stand-ing by a pur-pose true, Heed-ing God's com-mand,
Hon-or them, the faith-ful few! All hail to Dan-iel's band!

2. Ma-ny might-y men are lost, Dar-ing not to stand,
Who for God had been a host By join-ing Dan-iel's band.

3. Ma-ny gi-ants, great and tall, Stalk-ing through the land,
Head-long to the earth would fall, If met by Dan-iel's band.

4. Hold the gos-pel ban-ner high; On to vic-t'ry grand;
Sa-tan and his host de-fy, And shout for Dan-iel's band.

REFRAIN

Dare to be a Dan-iel! Dare to stand a-lone!
Dare to have a pur-pose firm! Dare to make it known! A-MEN.

# CHILDREN'S HYMNS 661

*God also hath highly exalted him, and given him a name which is above every name: that at the name of Jesus every knee should bow... Phil. 2:9-10*

Harriet Burn McKeever, 1847

GOTT EIN VATER 6.5.6.5.
Friedrich Silcher, 1789-1860
Arr. by Wilhelm Tschirsch, 1818-1892

1. Je - sus, high in glo - ry, Lend a lis - t'ning ear;
2. Though thou art so ho - ly, Heav'n's al - might - y King,
3. We are lit - tle chil - dren, Weak and apt to stray,
4. Save us, Lord, from sin - ning; Watch us day by day;
5. Then, when thou shalt call us To our heav'n - ly home,

When we bow be - fore thee, Chil - dren's prais - es hear.
Thou wilt stoop to lis - ten When thy praise we sing.
Sav - iour, guide and keep us In the heav'n - ly way.
Help us now to love thee; Take our sins a - way.
We will glad - ly an - swer, "Sav - iour, Lord, we come." A - MEN.

# 662

*And I... saw the holy city, new Jerusalem... And there shall in no wise enter into it any thing that defileth... Rev. 21:2, 27*

Mary Anne S. Deck, 1813-1902

CITY BRIGHT 6.6.5.5.6.
James S. Tyler, 1876

1. There is a cit - y bright; Closed are its gates to sin; Naught that de -
2. Sav - iour, I come to thee; O Lamb of God, I pray, Cleanse me and
3. Lord, make me, from this hour, Thy lov - ing child to be, Kept by thy
4. Till in the snow-white dress Of thy re-deemed I stand, Fault - less and

fi - leth, Naught that de - fi - leth Can ev - er en - ter in.
save me, Cleanse me and save me, Wash all my sins a - way.
pow - er, Kept by thy pow - er From all that griev - eth thee,—
stain-less, Fault - less and stain-less, Safe in that hap - py land. A - MEN.

# HYMNS FOR INFORMAL OCCASIONS

**663**  The Lord Is My Shepherd

*The Lord is my shepherd; I shall not want.* Psalm 23:1

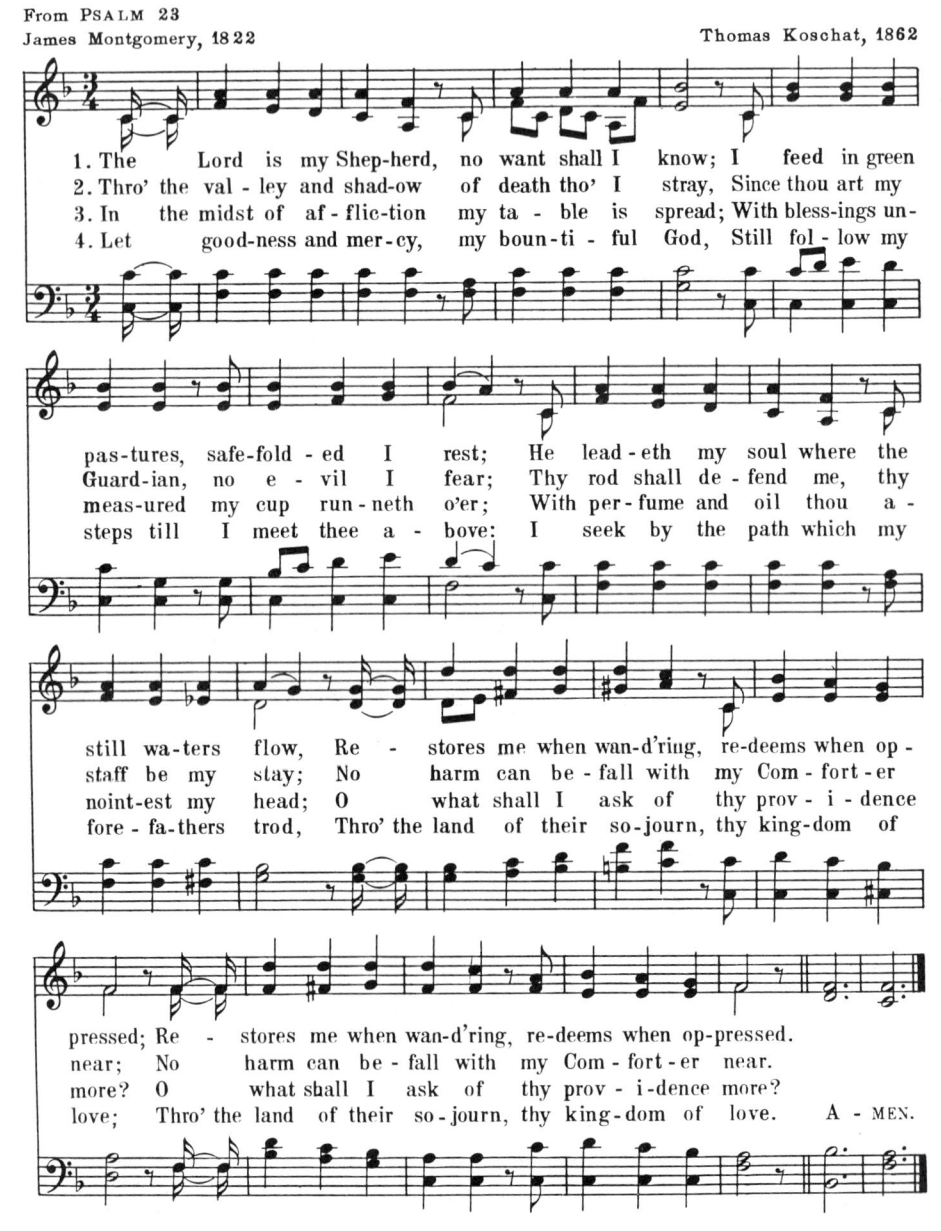

From PSALM 23
James Montgomery, 1822

Thomas Koschat, 1862

1. The Lord is my Shep-herd, no want shall I know; I feed in green pas-tures, safe-fold-ed I rest; He lead-eth my soul where the still wa-ters flow, Re - stores me when wan-d'ring, re-deems when op-pressed; Re - stores me when wan-d'ring, re-deems when op-pressed.

2. Thro' the val-ley and shad-ow of death tho' I stray, Since thou art my Guard-ian, no e - vil I fear; Thy rod shall de-fend me, thy staff be my stay; No harm can be-fall with my Com-fort-er near; No harm can be-fall with my Com-fort-er near.

3. In the midst of af - flic-tion my ta - ble is spread; With bless-ings un-meas-ured my cup run-neth o'er; With per-fume and oil thou a-noint-est my head; O what shall I ask of thy prov - i-dence more? O what shall I ask of thy prov - i-dence more?

4. Let good-ness and mer-cy, my boun-ti - ful God, Still fol - low my steps till I meet thee a - bove: I seek by the path which my fore - fa-thers trod, Thro' the land of their so-journ, thy king-dom of love; Thro' the land of their so - journ, thy king-dom of love. A - MEN.

## Jesus Is All the World to Me 664

*Ye are my friends, if ye do whatsoever I command you.* John 15:14

Will L. Thompson, 1847-1909  Will L. Thompson, 1847-1909

1. Je-sus is all the world to me, My life, my joy, my all;
2. Je-sus is all the world to me, My Friend in tri-als sore;
3. Je-sus is all the world to me, And true to him I'll be;
4. Je-sus is all the world to me, I want no bet-ter friend;

He is my strength from day to day, With-out him I would fall.
I go to him for bless-ings, and He gives them o'er and o'er.
Oh, how could I this Friend de-ny, When he's so true to me?
I trust him now, I'll trust him when Life's fleet-ing days shall end.

When I am sad, to him I go, No oth-er one can
He sends the sun-shine and the rain, He sends the har-vest's
Fol-low-ing him I know I'm right, He watch-es o'er me
Beau-ti-ful life with such a Friend; Beau-ti-ful life that

cheer me so; When I am sad he makes me glad, He's my Friend.
gold-en grain; Sun-shine and rain, har-vest of grain, He's my Friend.
day and night; Fol-low-ing him, by day and night, He's my Friend.
has no end; E-ter-nal life, e-ter-nal joy, He's my Friend. A-MEN.

Copyright, 1904. Renewal, 1932, by W. L. Thompson, Jr. Assigned to Hope Publishing Co. All rights reserved. Used by permission.

HYMNS FOR INFORMAL OCCASIONS

# 665 Conquering Now and Still to Conquer

*And he went forth conquering, and to conquer.* Rev. 6:2

Fanny J. Crosby, 1820-1915     John R. Sweney, 1837-1899

1. Con-quer-ing now and still to con-quer, Rid-eth a King in his might,
Lead-ing the host of all the faith-ful In - to the midst of the fight;
See them with cour-age ad-vanc-ing, Clad in their bril-liant ar - ray,
Shout-ing the name of their Lead-er, Hear them ex - ult - ing - ly say:

2. Con-quer-ing now and still to con-quer, Who is this won-der-ful King?
Whence are the ar-mies which he lead-eth, While of his glo - ry they sing?
He is our Lord and Re-deem-er, Sav-iour and Mon-arch di - vine;
They are the stars that for ev - er Bright in his King-dom will shine.

3. Con-quer-ing now and still to con-quer, Je-sus, thou Ru-ler of all,
Thrones and their scep-ters all shall per-ish, Crowns and their splen-dor shall fall,
Yet shall the ar-mies thou lead-est, Faith-ful and true to the last,
Find in thy man-sions e - ter-nal Rest, when their war-fare is past.

HYMNS FOR INFORMAL OCCASIONS

**REFRAIN**

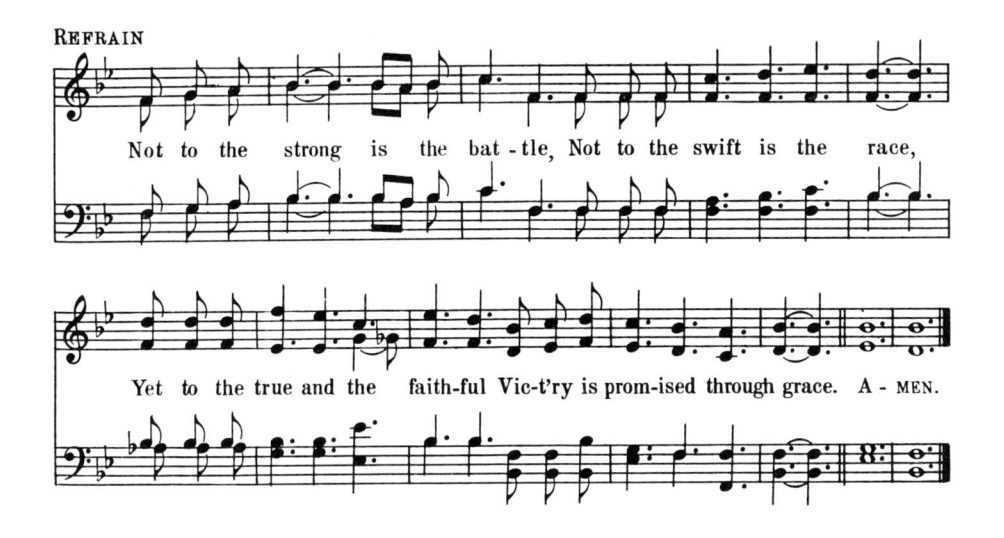

Not to the strong is the bat-tle, Not to the swift is the race,
Yet to the true and the faith-ful Vic-t'ry is prom-ised through grace. A-MEN.

## Now the Day Is Over 666

*When thou liest down, thou shalt not be afraid: yea, thou shalt lie down, and thy sleep shall be sweet.* Prov. 3:24

Sabine Baring-Gould, 1865      Sir Joseph Barnby, 1868

1. Now the day is o - ver, Night is draw-ing nigh,
2. Je - sus, give the wea - ry Calm and sweet re - pose;
3. Grant to lit - tle chil - dren Vi - sions bright of thee;
4. Com - fort ev - 'ry suf - f'rer Watch-ing late in pain;
5. Through the long night-watch - es May thine an - gels spread
6. Glo - ry to the Fa - ther, Glo - ry to the Son,

Shad - ows of the eve - ning Steal a-cross the sky.
With thy ten-d'rest bless - ing May our eye - lids close.
Guard the sail - ors, toss - ing On the deep blue sea.
Those who plan some e - vil From their sin re - strain.
Their white wings a - bove me, Watch-ing round my bed.
And to thee, blest Spir - it, Whilst all a - ges run. A-MEN.

HYMNS FOR INFORMAL OCCASIONS

# 667 To God Be the Glory

*All men glorified God for that which was done.* Acts 4:21

Fanny J. Crosby, 1875
St. 1, line 4; st. 2, line 4, alt.

William H. Doane, 1832-1916

1. To God be the glo-ry, great things he hath done! So loved he the world that he gave us his Son, Who yield-ed his life an a-tone-ment for sin, And o-pened the life-gate that we may go in.
2. O per-fect re-demp-tion, the pur-chase of blood! To ev-'ry be-liev-er the prom-ise of God; The vil-est of-fend-er who tru-ly be-lieves, That mo-ment from Je-sus for-give-ness re-ceives.
3. Great things he hath taught us, great things he hath done, And great our re-joic-ing through Je-sus the Son; But pu-rer, and high-er, and great-er will be Our won-der, our trans-port, when Je-sus we see.

REFRAIN

Praise the Lord, praise the Lord, Let the earth hear his voice! Praise the Lord, praise the Lord, Let the peo-ple re-joice! O come to the Fa-ther, thro'

HYMNS FOR INFORMAL OCCASIONS

Je-sus the Son, And give him the glo-ry,— great things he hath done! A - MEN.

## Far and Near the Fields Are Teeming 668

*Pray ye therefore the Lord of the harvest, that he will send forth labourers into his harvest.* Matt. 9:38

J. O. Thompson  J. B. O. Clemm

1. Far and near the fields are teem-ing With the waves of rip - ened grain;
2. Send them forth with morn's first beam-ing, Send them in the noon-tide's glare;
3. O thou, whom thy Lord is send-ing, Gath - er now the sheaves of gold;

Far and near their gold is gleam-ing O'er the sun - ny slope and plain.
When the sun's last rays are gleam-ing, Bid them gath - er ev - 'ry-where.
Heav'n-ward then at eve-ning wend-ing, Thou shalt come with joy un - told.

REFRAIN
Lord of har-vest, send forth reap-ers! Hear us, Lord, to thee we cry;
Send them now the sheaves to gath-er, Ere the har-vest-time pass by. A - MEN.

HYMNS FOR INFORMAL OCCASIONS

# 669 Wonderful Love

*Behold, what manner of love the Father hath bestowed upon us . . . I John 3:1*

Robert Walmsley, 1831-1905  Adam Watson, 1845-1912

1. Come, let us sing of a won-der-ful love, Ten-der and true, ten-der and true; Out of the heart of the Fa-ther a-bove, Stream-ing to me and to you: Won-der-ful love, won-der-ful love Dwells in the heart of the Fa-ther a-bove.

2. Je-sus the Sav-iour this gos-pel to tell Joy-ful-ly came, joy-ful-ly came— Came with the help-less and hope-less to dwell, Shar-ing their sor-row and shame: Seek-ing the lost, seek-ing the lost; Sav-ing, re-deem-ing at meas-ure-less cost.

3. Je-sus is seek-ing the wan-der-ers yet; Why do they roam? why do they roam? Love on-ly waits to for-give and for-get; Home, wea-ry wan-der-ers, home! Won-der-ful love, won-der-ful love Dwells in the heart of the Fa-ther a-bove.

4. Come to my heart, O thou won-der-ful Love! Come and a-bide, come and a-bide; Lift-ing my life till it ris-es a-bove En-vy and false-hood and pride: Seek-ing to be, seek-ing to be Low-ly and hum-ble, a learn-er of thee. A-MEN.

Words and music used by permission of Messrs. J. Curwen & Sons, Ltd.

## Thy God Reigneth!

**670**

*How beautiful upon the mountains are the feet of him that bringeth good tidings . . . that saith unto Zion, Thy God reigneth!* Isa. 52:7

Fred S. Shepherd                                             James McGranahan, 1840-1907

1. Trembling soul, beset by fears, "Thy God reigneth!"
2. Sinful soul, thy debt is paid; "Thy God reigneth!"
3. Seeking soul, to Jesus turn; "Thy God reigneth!"
4. Join, ye saints, the truth proclaim, "Thy God reigneth!"
5. Church of Christ, awake, awake! "Thy God reigneth!"

"Thy God reigneth!"

Look above and dry thy tears: "Thy God reigneth!"
On the Lord thy sins were laid; "Thy God reigneth!"
None that seek him will he spurn; "Thy God reigneth!"
Shout it forth with glad acclaim, "Thy God reigneth!"
Forward, then, fresh courage take: "Thy God reigneth!"

"Thy God reigneth!"

Though thy foes with pow'r assail, Naught against thee shall prevail;
On the cross of Calvary, Jesus shed his blood for thee,
Wand'ring sheep the Shepherd seeks, And when found he ever keeps,
Zion, wake! the morn is nigh, See it break from yonder sky;
Soon, descending from his throne, He shall claim thee for his own;

Trust in him—he'll never fail: "Thy God reigneth, Thy God reigneth!"
From all sin to set thee free: "Thy God reigneth, Thy God reigneth!"
For "he slumbers not nor sleeps": "Thy God reigneth, Thy God reigneth!"
Loud and clear the watchmen cry: "Thy God reigneth, Thy God reigneth!"
Sin shall then be overthrown: "Thy God reigneth, Thy God reigneth!" A-MEN.

HYMNS FOR INFORMAL OCCASIONS

# 671 Thy Word Have I Hid in My Heart

*Thy word have I hid in mine heart, that I might not sin against thee.* Psalm 119:11

Adapted by E. O. Sellers, 1908      E. O. Sellers, 1908

1. Thy Word is a lamp to my feet, A light to my path al-way,
2. For ev-er, O Lord, is thy Word Es-tab-lished and fixed on high;
3. At morn-ing, at noon, and at night I ev-er will give thee praise;
4. Through him whom thy Word hath fore-told, The Sav-iour and Morn-ing Star,

To guide and to save me from sin, And show me the heav'n-ly way.
Thy faith-ful-ness un-to all men A-bid-eth for ev-er nigh.
For thou art my por-tion, O Lord, And shall be through all my days!
Sal-va-tion and peace have been brought To those who have strayed a-far.

REFRAIN

Thy Word have I hid in my heart (in my heart) That I might not sin a-gainst thee; (a-gainst thee;) That I might not sin, that I might not sin, Thy Word have I hid in my heart. A-MEN.

Words and music copyright 1908; renewal 1936. Broadman Press, owner.

HYMNS FOR INFORMAL OCCASIONS

# He Lifted Me

## 672

*He brought me up ... out of the miry clay, and set my feet upon a rock ... Psalm 40:2*

Charlotte G. Homer  
Charles H. Gabriel, 1856-1932

1. In lov-ing-kind-ness Je-sus came My soul in mer-cy to re-claim,
2. He called me long be-fore I heard, Be-fore my sin-ful heart was stirred,
3. His brow was pierced with many a thorn, His hands by cru-el nails were torn,
4. Now on a high-er plane I dwell, And with my soul I know 'tis well;

And from the depths of sin and shame Thro grace he lift-ed me.  
But when I took him at his word, For-giv'n he lift-ed me.  
When from my guilt and grief, for-lorn, In love he lift-ed me.  
Yet how or why, I can-not tell, He should have lift-ed me.

he lift-ed me.

**REFRAIN**

From sink-ing sand he lift-ed me, With ten-der hand he lift-ed me,
From shades of night to plains of light, Oh, praise his name, he lift-ed me! A-MEN.

Copyright, 1905. Renewal, 1933. The Rodeheaver Company, owner. International copyright secured. All rights reserved. Used by permission.

HYMNS FOR INFORMAL OCCASIONS

# 673 He Was Wounded for Our Transgressions

*Who hath believed our report? and to whom is the arm of the Lord revealed?* Isa. 53:1

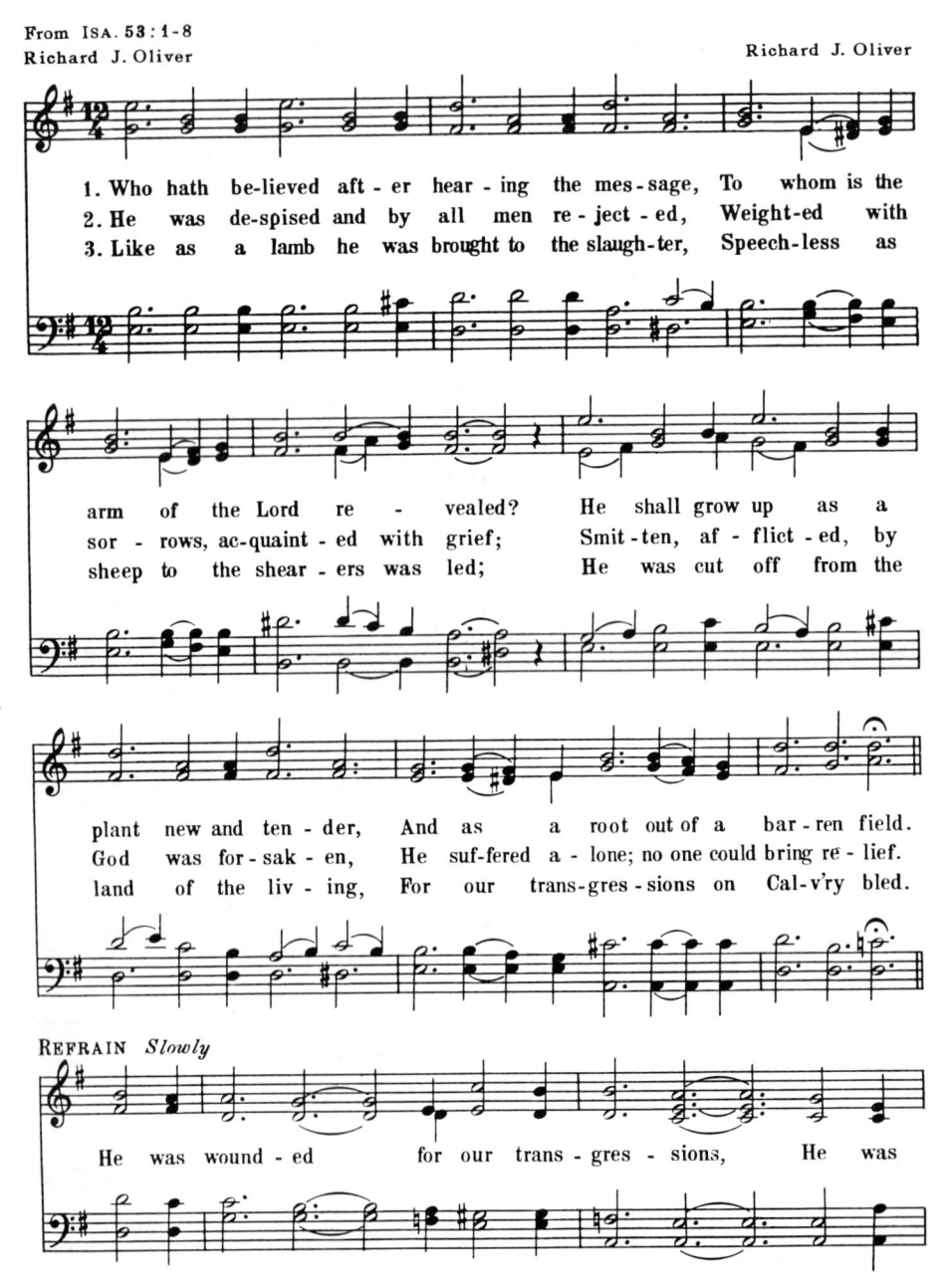

From ISA. 53:1-8
Richard J. Oliver

Richard J. Oliver

1. Who hath be-lieved aft-er hear-ing the mes-sage, To whom is the arm of the Lord re-vealed? He shall grow up as a plant new and ten-der, And as a root out of a bar-ren field.
2. He was de-spised and by all men re-ject-ed, Weight-ed with sor-rows, ac-quaint-ed with grief; Smit-ten, af-flict-ed, by God was for-sak-en, He suf-fered a-lone; no one could bring re-lief.
3. Like as a lamb he was brought to the slaugh-ter, Speech-less as sheep to the shear-ers was led; He was cut off from the land of the liv-ing, For our trans-gres-sions on Cal-v'ry bled.

REFRAIN *Slowly*

He was wound-ed for our trans-gres-sions, He was

HYMNS FOR INFORMAL OCCASIONS

bruised for our iniquities; The chastisement of our peace was upon him, And with his stripes we are healed. A-MEN.

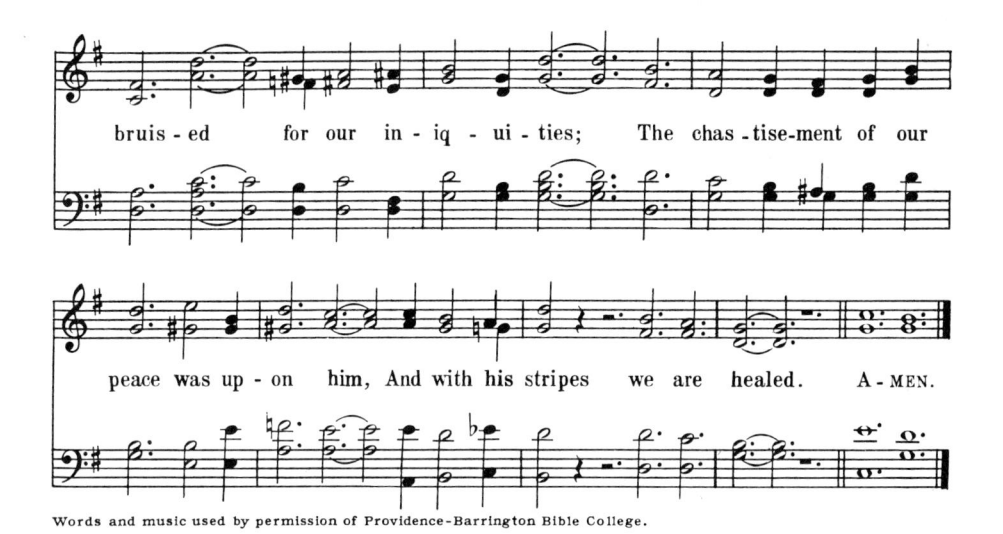

Words and music used by permission of Providence-Barrington Bible College.

## Holy Bible, Book Divine 674

*All scripture is given by inspiration of God... II Tim. 3:16*

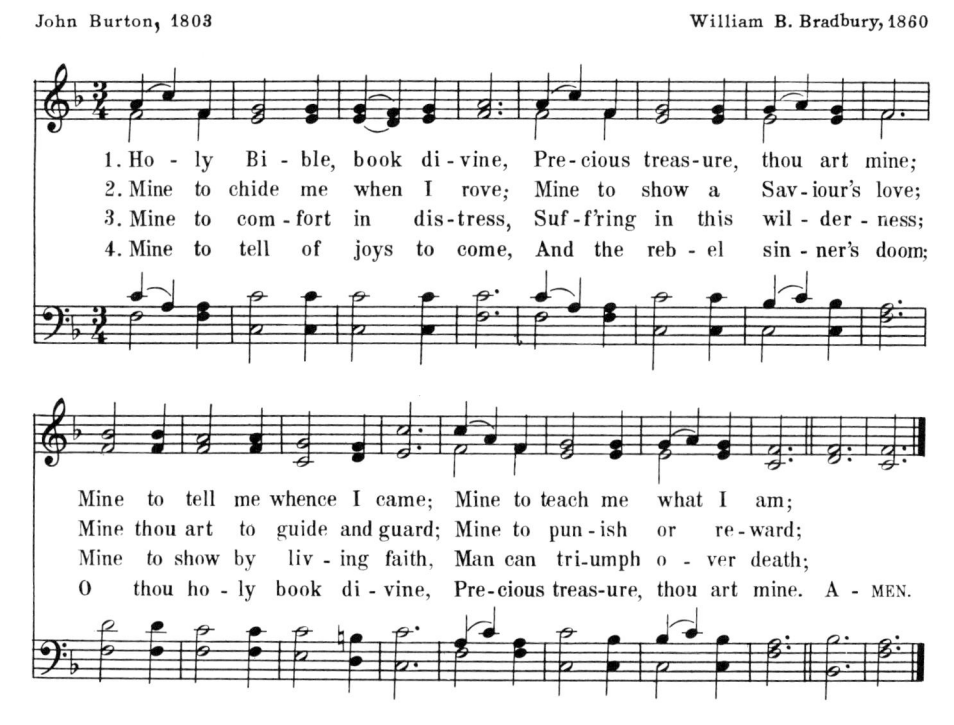

John Burton, 1803      William B. Bradbury, 1860

1. Holy Bible, book divine, Precious treasure, thou art mine;
   Mine to tell me whence I came; Mine to teach me what I am;
2. Mine to chide me when I rove; Mine to show a Saviour's love;
   Mine thou art to guide and guard; Mine to punish or reward;
3. Mine to comfort in distress, Suff'ring in this wilderness;
   Mine to show by living faith, Man can triumph o-ver death;
4. Mine to tell of joys to come, And the rebel sinner's doom;
   O thou holy book divine, Precious treasure, thou art mine. A-MEN.

HYMNS FOR INFORMAL OCCASIONS

# 675 A Wonderful Saviour

*I have covered thee in the shadow of mine hand... Isa. 51:16*

Fanny J. Crosby, 1820-1915  
William J. Kirkpatrick, 1838-1921

1. A wonderful Saviour is Jesus my Lord, A wonderful Saviour to me, He hideth my soul in the cleft of the rock, Where rivers of pleasure I see.
2. A wonderful Saviour is Jesus my Lord, He taketh my burden away, He holdeth me up, and I shall not be moved, He giveth me strength as my day.
3. With numberless blessings each moment he crowns, And filled with a fullness divine, I sing in my rapture, O glory to God For such a Redeemer as mine!
4. When clothed in his brightness, transported I rise To meet him in clouds of the sky, His perfect salvation, his wonderful love, I'll shout with the millions on high.

REFRAIN

He hideth my soul in the cleft of the rock That shadows a dry, thirsty land; He hideth my life in the depths of his love, And covers me

HYMNS FOR INFORMAL OCCASIONS

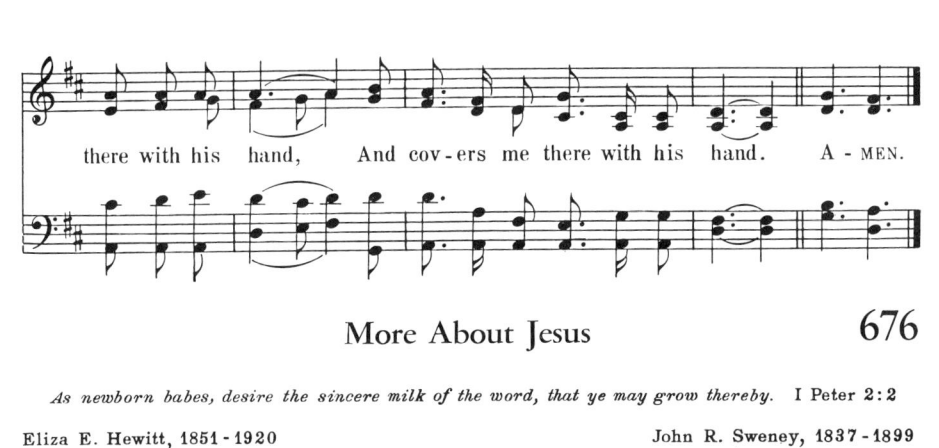

there with his hand, And cov-ers me there with his hand. A - MEN.

## More About Jesus  676

*As newborn babes, desire the sincere milk of the word, that ye may grow thereby.* I Peter 2:2

Eliza E. Hewitt, 1851-1920  
John R. Sweney, 1837-1899

1. More a-bout Je-sus would I know, More of his grace to oth-ers show;
2. More a-bout Je-sus let me learn, More of his ho-ly will dis-cern;
3. More a-bout Je-sus; in his Word, Hold-ing com-mun-ion with my Lord;
4. More a-bout Je-sus on his throne, Rich-es in glo-ry all his own;

More of his sav-ing full-ness see, More of his love who died for me.
Spir-it of God, my teach-er be, Show-ing the things of Christ to me.
Hear-ing his voice in ev-'ry line, Mak-ing each faith-ful say-ing mine.
More of his king-dom's sure in-crease; More of his com-ing, Prince of Peace.

REFRAIN

More, more a-bout Je-sus, More, more a-bout Je-sus, More of his sav-ing full-ness see, More of his love who died for me. A - MEN.

HYMNS FOR INFORMAL OCCASIONS

# 677 Nothing But the Blood

*The blood of Jesus Christ his Son cleanseth us from all sin.* I John **1:7**

Robert Lowry, 1876                                                              Robert Lowry, 1876

1. What can wash a-way my sin? Noth-ing but the blood of Je-sus;
2. For my cleans-ing this I see— Noth-ing but the blood of Je-sus;
3. Noth-ing can for sin a-tone— Noth-ing but the blood of Je-sus;
4. This is all my hope and peace— Noth-ing but the blood of Je-sus;
5. Now by this I'll o-ver-come— Noth-ing but the blood of Je-sus;

What can make me whole a-gain? Noth-ing but the blood of Je-sus.
For my par-don this my plea— Noth-ing but the blood of Je-sus.
Naught of good that I have done— Noth-ing but the blood of Je-sus.
This is all my right-eous-ness— Noth-ing but the blood of Je-sus.
Now by this I'll reach my home— Noth-ing but the blood of Je-sus.

**Refrain**

O pre-cious is the flow That makes me white as snow;
No oth-er fount I know, Noth-ing but the blood of Je-sus. A-men.

HYMNS FOR INFORMAL OCCASIONS

## Christ Shall Have Dominion    678

*He shall have dominion also from sea to sea... Psalm 72:8*

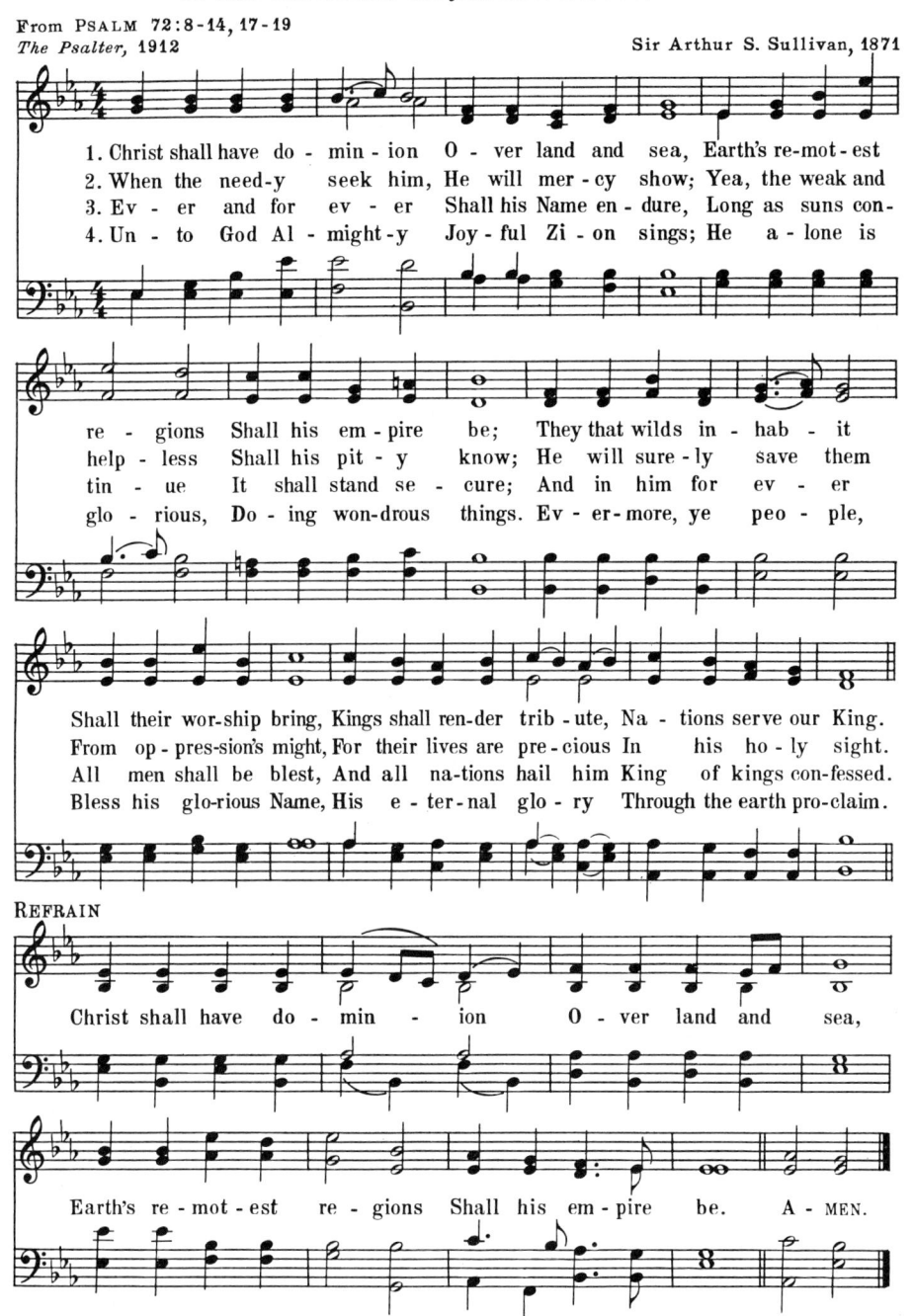

From PSALM 72:8-14, 17-19
The Psalter, 1912

Sir Arthur S. Sullivan, 1871

1. Christ shall have do-min-ion O-ver land and sea, Earth's re-mot-est re-gions Shall his em-pire be; They that wilds in-hab-it Shall their wor-ship bring, Kings shall ren-der trib-ute, Na-tions serve our King.
2. When the need-y seek him, He will mer-cy show; Yea, the weak and help-less Shall his pit-y know; He will sure-ly save them From op-pres-sion's might, For their lives are pre-cious In his ho-ly sight.
3. Ev-er and for ev-er Shall his Name en-dure, Long as suns con-tin-ue It shall stand se-cure; And in him for ev-er All men shall be blest, And all na-tions hail him King of kings con-fessed.
4. Un-to God Al-might-y Joy-ful Zi-on sings; He a-lone is glo-rious, Do-ing won-drous things. Ev-er-more, ye peo-ple, Bless his glo-rious Name, His e-ter-nal glo-ry Through the earth pro-claim.

REFRAIN

Christ shall have do-min-ion O-ver land and sea, Earth's re-mot-est re-gions Shall his em-pire be. A-MEN.

HYMNS FOR INFORMAL OCCASIONS

## 679 The Light of the World Is Jesus

*I am the light of the world: he that followeth me shall not walk in darkness, but shall have the light of life.* John 8:12

Philip P. Bliss, 1875          Philip P. Bliss, 1875

1. The whole world was lost in the dark-ness of sin; The Light of the world is Je-sus; Like sun-shine at noon-day his glo-ry shone in,
2. No dark-ness have we who in Je-sus a-bide, The Light of the world is Je-sus; We walk in the Light when we fol-low our Guide,
3. Ye dwell-ers in dark-ness with sin-blind-ed eyes, The Light of the world is Je-sus; Go, wash at his bid-ding, and light will a-rise,
4. No need of the sun-light in heav-en, we're told, The Light of the world is Je-sus; The Lamb is the Light in the Cit-y of Gold,

REFRAIN

The Light of the world is Je-sus. Come to the Light, 'tis shin-ing for thee; Sweet-ly the Light has dawned up-on me; Once I was blind, but now I can see; The Light of the world is Je-sus. A-MEN.

HYMNS FOR INFORMAL OCCASIONS

# Anywhere with Jesus 680

*Lo, I am with you alway . . . Matt. 28:20*

Jessie H. Brown, 1861-1921, and Mrs. C. M. Alexander  
Daniel B. Towner, 1850-1919

1. An-y-where with Je-sus I can safe-ly go; An-y-where he leads me in this world be-low; An-y-where with-out him dear-est joys would fade; An-y-where with Je-sus I am not a-fraid.

2. An-y-where with Je-sus I need fear no ill, Tho' temp-ta-tions gath-er round my path-way still; He him-self was tempt-ed that he might help me; An-y-where with Je-sus I may vic-tor be.

3. An-y-where with Je-sus I am not a-lone; Oth-er friends may fail me, he is still my own; Tho' his hand may lead me o-ver drear-y ways, An-y-where with Je-sus is a house of praise.

4. An-y-where with Je-sus I can go to sleep, When the dark'-ning shad-ows round a-bout me creep; Know-ing I shall wak-en, nev-er more to roam, An-y-where with Je-sus will be home, sweet home.

**REFRAIN**

An-y-where! an-y-where! Fear I can-not know; An-y-where with Je-sus I can safe-ly go. A-MEN.

HYMNS FOR INFORMAL OCCASIONS

# 681 I Will Sing of My Redeemer

*Jesus Christ; who gave himself for us, that he might redeem us . . . Titus 2:13-14*

Philip P. Bliss, 1878　　　　　　　　　　　　　　　　　James McGranahan, 1840-1907

1. I will sing of my Redeemer  And his wondrous love to me:
On the cruel cross he suffered,  From the curse to set me free.

2. I will tell the wondrous story,  How my lost estate to save,
In his boundless love and mercy,  He the ransom freely gave.

3. I will praise my dear Redeemer,  His triumphant pow'r I'll tell,
How the victory he giveth  Over sin and death and hell.

4. I will sing of my Redeemer  And his heav'nly love to me;
He from death to life has brought me,  Son of God, with him to be.

REFRAIN

Sing, O sing of my Redeemer! Sing, O sing of my Redeemer!
With his blood He purchased me, He purchased me, he purchased me;
On the cross he sealed my pardon, On the cross he sealed my pardon,

HYMNS FOR INFORMAL OCCASIONS

Paid the debt and made me free. A-MEN.
Paid the debt and made me free, and made me free, and made me free.

*See also HYFRYDOL, No. 432—*

## Trusting Jesus 682

*That we should be to the praise of his glory, who first trusted in Christ: in whom ye also trusted, after that ye heard the word of truth . . . Eph. 1:12-13*

Edgar Page Stites           Ira D. Sankey, 1840-1908

1. Sim-ply trust-ing ev-'ry day, Trust-ing through a storm-y way;
2. Bright-ly doth his Spir-it shine In-to this poor heart of mine;
3. Sing-ing if my way is clear; Pray-ing if the path be drear;
4. Trust-ing him while life shall last, Trust-ing him till earth be past;

E-ven when my faith is small, Trust-ing Je-sus, that is all.
While he leads I can-not fall; Trust-ing Je-sus, that is all.
If in dan-ger, for him call; Trust-ing Je-sus, that is all.
Till with-in the jas-per wall: Trust-ing Je-sus, that is all.

**CHORUS**

Trust-ing as the mo-ments fly, Trust-ing as the days go by;

Trust-ing him what-e'er be-fall, Trust-ing Je-sus, that is all. A-MEN.

HYMNS FOR INFORMAL OCCASIONS

# 683 Praise Him! Praise Him!

*And they sung a new song, saying, Thou art worthy...for thou...hast redeemed us to God by thy blood... Rev. 5:9*

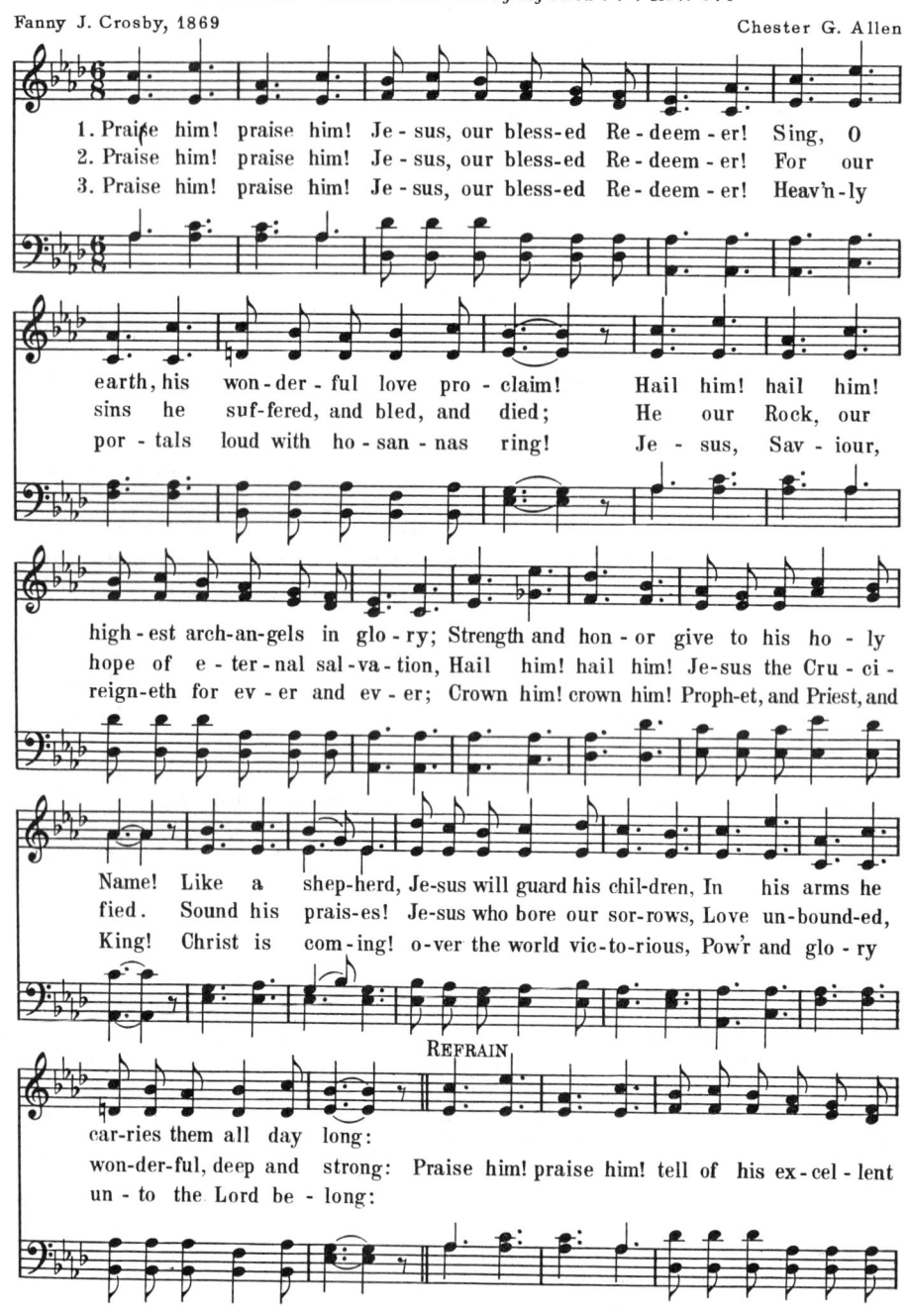

Fanny J. Crosby, 1869 — Chester G. Allen

1. Praise him! praise him! Jesus, our blessed Redeemer! Sing, O earth, his wonderful love proclaim! Hail him! hail him! highest archangels in glory; Strength and honor give to his holy Name! Like a shepherd, Jesus will guard his children, In his arms he carries them all day long:

2. Praise him! praise him! Jesus, our blessed Redeemer! For our sins he suffered, and bled, and died; He our Rock, our hope of eternal salvation, Hail him! hail him! Jesus the Crucified. Sound his praises! Jesus who bore our sorrows, Love unbounded, wonderful, deep and strong:

3. Praise him! praise him! Jesus, our blessed Redeemer! Heav'nly portals loud with hosannas ring! Jesus, Saviour, reigneth for ever and ever; Crown him! crown him! Prophet, and Priest, and King! Christ is coming! over the world victorious, Pow'r and glory unto the Lord belong:

REFRAIN: Praise him! praise him! tell of his excellent

HYMNS FOR INFORMAL OCCASIONS

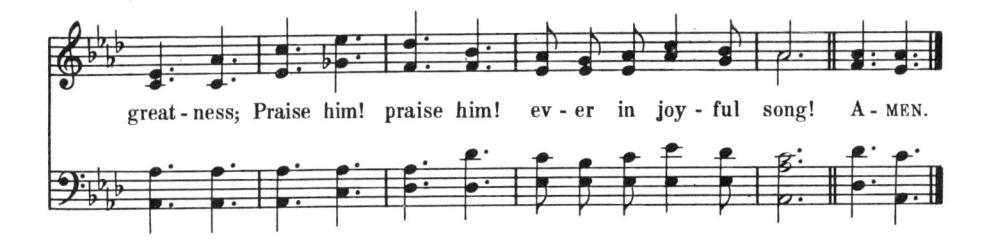

great-ness; Praise him! praise him! ev-er in joy-ful song! A-MEN.

## Bring Them In 684

*The Son of man is come to save that which was lost.* Matt. 18:11

Alexcenah Thomas  William A. Ogden, 1841-1897

1. Hark! 'tis the Shep-herd's voice I hear, Out in the des-ert dark and drear,
2. Who'll go and help this Shep-herd kind, Help him the wan-d'ring ones to find?
3. Out in the des-ert hear their cry, Out on the moun-tains wild and high;

Call-ing the sheep who've gone a-stray Far from the Shep-herd's fold a-way.
Who'll bring the lost ones to the fold, Where they'll be shel-tered from the cold?
Hark! 'tis the Mas-ter speaks to thee, "Go find my sheep wher-e'er they be."

REFRAIN

Bring them in, bring them in, Bring them in from the fields of sin;

Bring them in, bring them in, Bring the wan-d'ring ones to Je-sus. A-MEN.

HYMNS FOR INFORMAL OCCASIONS

# 685. Tell Me the Story of Jesus

*He expounded unto them in all the scriptures the things concerning himself.* Luke 24:27

Fanny J. Crosby, 1820-1915                                John R. Sweney, 1837-1899

1. Tell me the story of Jesus, Write on my heart ev-'ry word; Tell me the story most precious, Sweet-est that ev-er was heard. Tell how the an-gels, in cho-rus, Sang as they wel-comed his birth, "Glo-ry to God in the high-est! Peace and good ti-dings to earth."

2. Fast-ing a-lone in the des-ert, Tell of the days that are past, How for our sins he was tempt-ed, Yet was tri-um-phant at last. Tell of the years of his la-bor, Tell of the sor-row he bore, He was de-spised and af-flict-ed, Home-less, re-ject-ed and poor.

3. Tell of the cross where they nailed him, Writh-ing in an-guish and pain; Tell of the grave where they laid him, Tell how he liv-eth a-gain. Love in that sto-ry so ten-der, Clear-er than ev-er I see: Stay, let me weep while you whis-per, Love paid the ran-som for me.

**REFRAIN**

Tell me the sto-ry of Je-sus, Write on my heart ev-'ry word; Tell me the sto-ry most pre-cious, Sweet-est that ev-er was heard. A-MEN.

HYMNS FOR INFORMAL OCCASIONS

## Sound the Battle Cry

686

*When the enemy shall come in like a flood, the Spirit of the Lord shall lift up a standard against him.* Isa. 59:19

William F. Sherwin, 1869　　　　　　　　　　　　　William F. Sherwin, 1869

1. Sound the bat-tle cry! See! the foe is nigh! Raise the stand-ard high For the Lord: Gird your ar-mor on, Stand firm ev-'ry one; Rest your cause up-on His ho-ly Word.
2. Strong to meet the foe, March-ing on we go, While our cause we know, Must pre-vail; Shield and ban-ner bright, Gleam-ing in the light, Bat-tling for the right We ne'er can fail.
3. O thou God of all, Hear us when we call, Help us one and all By thy grace; When the bat-tle's done, And the vic-t'ry won, May we wear the crown Be-fore thy face.

REFRAIN

Rouse, then, sol-diers! Ral-ly round the ban-ner! Read-y, stead-y, Pass the word a-long; On-ward, for-ward, Shout a-loud, ho-san-na! Christ is Cap-tain Of the might-y throng! A-MEN.

HYMNS FOR INFORMAL OCCASIONS

# 687 He Is Coming Again

*Then shall they see the Son of man coming in a cloud with power and great glory.* Luke 21:27

Mabel Johnston Camp  Mabel Johnston Camp

1. Lift up your heads, Pilgrims a-weary, See day's approach Now crimson the sky; Night shadows flee, And your Beloved, Awaited with longing, At last draweth nigh.
2. Dark was the night, Sin warred against us; Heavy the load Of sorrow we bore; But now we see Signs of his coming; Our hearts glow within us, Joy's cup runneth o'er!
3. O blessed hope! O blissful promise! Filling our hearts With rapture divine; O day of days! Hail thine appearing! Thy transcendent glory Forever shall shine.
4. E-ven so come, Precious Lord Jesus; Creation waits Redemption to see; Caught up in clouds, Soon we shall meet thee; O blessed assurance, Forever with thee!

REFRAIN

He is coming again, He is coming again, The very same Jesus, Rejected of men; He is coming again, He is coming again,

HYMNS FOR INFORMAL OCCASIONS

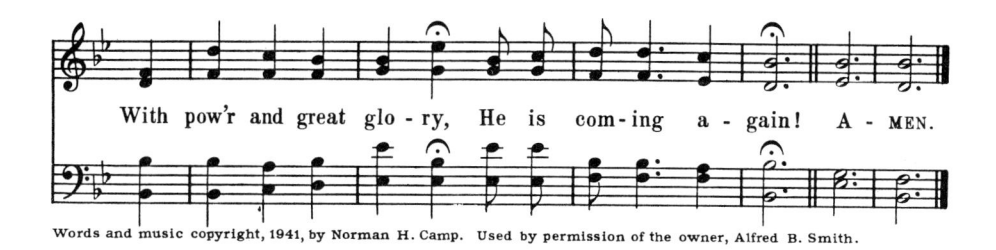

With pow'r and great glo - ry, He is com-ing a - gain! A - MEN.

Words and music copyright, 1941, by Norman H. Camp. Used by permission of the owner, Alfred B. Smith.

## Yes, For Me He Careth 688

*For he careth for you.* I Peter 5:7

Horatius Bonar, 1844 — Arr. from Emmelar

1. Yes, for me, for me he car - eth With a broth - er's ten - der care;
2. Yes, for me he stand-eth plead-ing At the mer - cy seat a - bove;

Yes, with me, with me he shar - eth Ev - 'ry bur - den, ev - 'ry fear.
Ev - er for me in - ter - ced - ing, Con-stant in un - tir - ing love.

Yes, o'er me, o'er me he watch-eth, Cease-less watch-eth, night and day;
Yes, in me, in me he dwell-eth; I in him, and he in me!

Yes, e'en me, e'en me he snatch-eth From the per - ils of the way.
And my emp-ty soul he fill - eth, Here and through e-ter - ni - ty. A - MEN.

HYMNS FOR INFORMAL OCCASIONS

# 689 One Day!

*Christ was once offered to bear the sins of many; and unto them that look for him shall he appear the second time without sin unto salvation. Heb. 9:28*

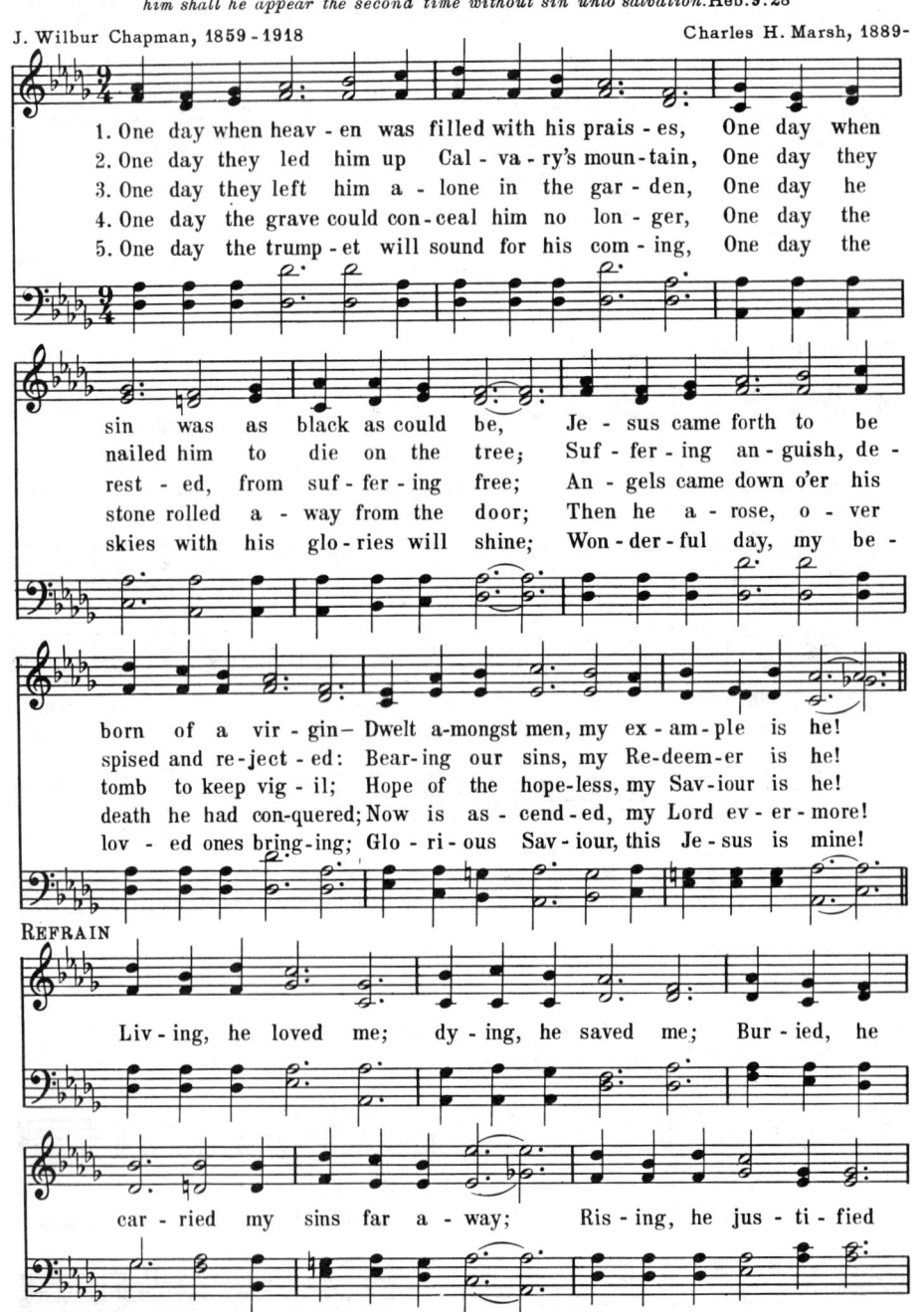

J. Wilbur Chapman, 1859-1918  
Charles H. Marsh, 1889-

1. One day when heav-en was filled with his prais-es, One day when sin was as black as could be, Je-sus came forth to be born of a vir-gin— Dwelt a-mongst men, my ex-am-ple is he!
2. One day they led him up Cal-va-ry's moun-tain, One day they nailed him to die on the tree; Suf-fer-ing an-guish, de-spised and re-ject-ed: Bear-ing our sins, my Re-deem-er is he!
3. One day they left him a-lone in the gar-den, One day he rest-ed, from suf-fer-ing free; An-gels came down o'er his tomb to keep vig-il; Hope of the hope-less, my Sav-iour is he!
4. One day the grave could con-ceal him no lon-ger, One day the stone rolled a-way from the door; Then he a-rose, o-ver death he had con-quered; Now is as-cend-ed, my Lord ev-er-more!
5. One day the trump-et will sound for his com-ing, One day the skies with his glo-ries will shine; Won-der-ful day, my be-lov-ed ones bring-ing; Glo-ri-ous Sav-iour, this Je-sus is mine!

**REFRAIN**

Liv-ing, he loved me; dy-ing, he saved me; Bur-ied, he car-ried my sins far a-way; Ris-ing, he jus-ti-fied

HYMNS FOR INFORMAL OCCASIONS

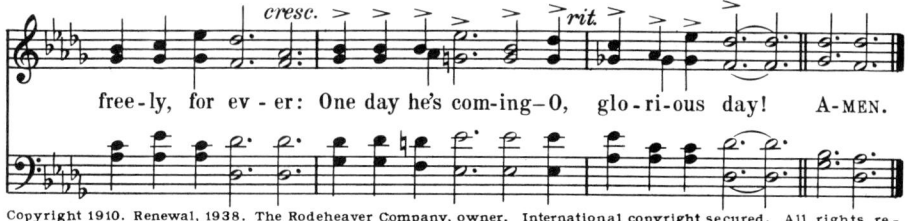

free-ly, for ev-er: One day he's com-ing—O, glo-ri-ous day! A-MEN.

Copyright 1910. Renewal, 1938. The Rodeheaver Company, owner. International copyright secured. All rights reserved. Used by permission.

## Jesus Paid It All  690

*Though your sins be as scarlet, they shall be as white as snow... Isa. 1:18*

Elvina M. Hall, 1865     John T. Grape, b. 1833

1. I hear the Sav-iour say, "Thy strength in-deed is small,
2. Lord, now in-deed I find Thy power, and thine a-lone,
3. For noth-ing good have I Where-by thy grace to claim—
4. And when, be-fore the throne, I stand in him com-plete,

Child of weak-ness, watch and pray, Find in me thine all in all."
Can change the lep-er's spots, And melt the heart of stone.
I'll wash my gar-ments white In the blood of Cal-v'ry's Lamb.
"Je-sus died my soul to save," My lips shall still re-peat.

REFRAIN

Je-sus paid it all, All to him I owe;

Sin had left a crim-son stain, He washed it white as snow. A-MEN.

HYMNS FOR INFORMAL OCCASIONS

## 691. Hark! The Voice of Jesus Crying

*The harvest truly is great, but the labourers are few... Luke 10:2*

Daniel March, 1868  
Arr. 1831 from Wolfgang Amadeus Mozart, 1756-1791

1. Hark! the voice of Jesus cry-ing, "Who will go and work to-day?
   Fields are white, and har-vests wait-ing; Who will bear the sheaves a-way?"
   Loud and long the Mas-ter call-eth, Rich re-ward he of-fers free;
   Who will an-swer, glad-ly say-ing, "Here am I; send me, send me."

2. If you can-not cross the o-cean, And the hea-then lands ex-plore,
   You can find the hea-then near-er, You can help them at your door.
   If you can-not give your thou-sands, You can give the wid-ow's mite;
   And the least you give for Je-sus Will be pre-cious in his sight.

3. If you can-not be a watch-man, Stand-ing high on Zi-on's wall,
   Point-ing out the path to heav-en, Of-f'ring life and peace to all,
   With your pray'rs and with your boun-ties You can do what God de-mands;
   You can be like faith-ful Aar-on, Hold-ing up the proph-et's hands.

4. Let none hear you i-dly say-ing, "There is noth-ing I can do,"
   While the sons of men are dy-ing, And the Mas-ter calls for you:
   Take the task he gives you glad-ly, Let his work your pleas-ure be;
   An-swer quick-ly when he call-eth, "Here am I; send me, send me." A-MEN.

St. 4, line 3, alt.

HYMNS FOR INFORMAL OCCASIONS

## Is It the Crowning Day?

**692**

*And when the chief Shepherd shall appear, ye shall receive a crown of glory that fadeth not away.* I Peter 5:4

George W. Whitcomb
Charles H. Marsh, 1889-

1. Je-sus may come to-day, Glad day! Glad day! And I would see my Friend; Dan-gers and trou-bles would end If Je-sus should come to-day.
2. I may go home to-day, Glad day! Glad day! Seem-eth I hear their song; Hail to the ra-di-ant throng! If I should go home to-day.
3. Why should I anx-ious be? Glad day! Glad day! Lights ap-pear on the shore, Storms will af-fright nev-er-more, For he is "at hand" to-day.
4. Faith-ful I'll be to-day, Glad day! Glad day! And I will free-ly tell Why I should love him so well, For he is my all to-day.

**REFRAIN**

Glad day! Glad day! Is it the crown-ing day? I'll live for to-day, nor anx-ious be, Je-sus, my Lord, I soon shall see; Glad day! Glad day! Is it the crown-ing day? A-MEN.

Copyright, 1910. Renewal 1938. The Rodeheaver Company, owner. International copyright secured. All rights reserved. Used by permission.

HYMNS FOR INFORMAL OCCASIONS

## 693 Come to the Saviour, Make No Delay

*Today if ye will hear his voice, harden not your hearts... Heb. 3:7-8*

George F. Root, 1820-1895                    George F. Root, 1820-1895

1. Come to the Sav-iour, make no de-lay; Here in his Word he's shown us the way; Here in our midst he's stand-ing to-day, Ten-der-ly say-ing, "Come!"
2. "Suf-fer the chil-dren!" O hear his voice! Let ev-'ry heart leap forth and re-joice; And let us free-ly make him our choice: Do not de-lay, but come.
3. Think once a-gain, he's with us to-day; Heed now his blest com-mand, and o-bey; Hear now his ac-cents ten-der-ly say, "Will you, my chil-dren, come?"

REFRAIN

Joy-ful, joy-ful will the meet-ing be, When from sin our hearts are pure and free; And we shall gath-er, Sav-iour, with thee, In our e-ter-nal home. A-MEN.

HYMNS FOR INFORMAL OCCASIONS

# Softly and Tenderly

694

*He calleth his own sheep by name... John 10:3*

Will L. Thompson, 1847-1909                     Will L. Thompson, 1847-1909

1. Soft-ly and ten-der-ly Je-sus is call-ing, Call-ing for you and for me;
   See, on the por-tals he's wait-ing and watch-ing, Watch-ing for you and for me.
2. Why should we tar-ry when Je-sus is plead-ing, Plead-ing for you and for me?
   Why should we lin-ger and heed not his mer-cies, Mer-cies for you and for me?
3. Time is now fleet-ing, the mo-ments are pass-ing, Pass-ing from you and from me;
   Shad-ows are gath-er-ing, death-beds are com-ing, Com-ing for you and for me.
4. Oh! for the won-der-ful love he has prom-ised, Prom-ised for you and for me;
   Though we have sinned, he has mer-cy and par-don, Par-don for you and for me.

REFRAIN

Come home, come home, Ye who are wear-y, come home; Earnest-ly, ten-der-ly, Je-sus is call-ing, Call-ing, O sin-ner, come home!  A-MEN.

HYMNS FOR INFORMAL OCCASIONS

# 695 I Am a Stranger Here

*We pray you in Christ's stead, be ye reconciled to God.* II Cor. 5:20

E. T. Cassel | Flora H. Cassel

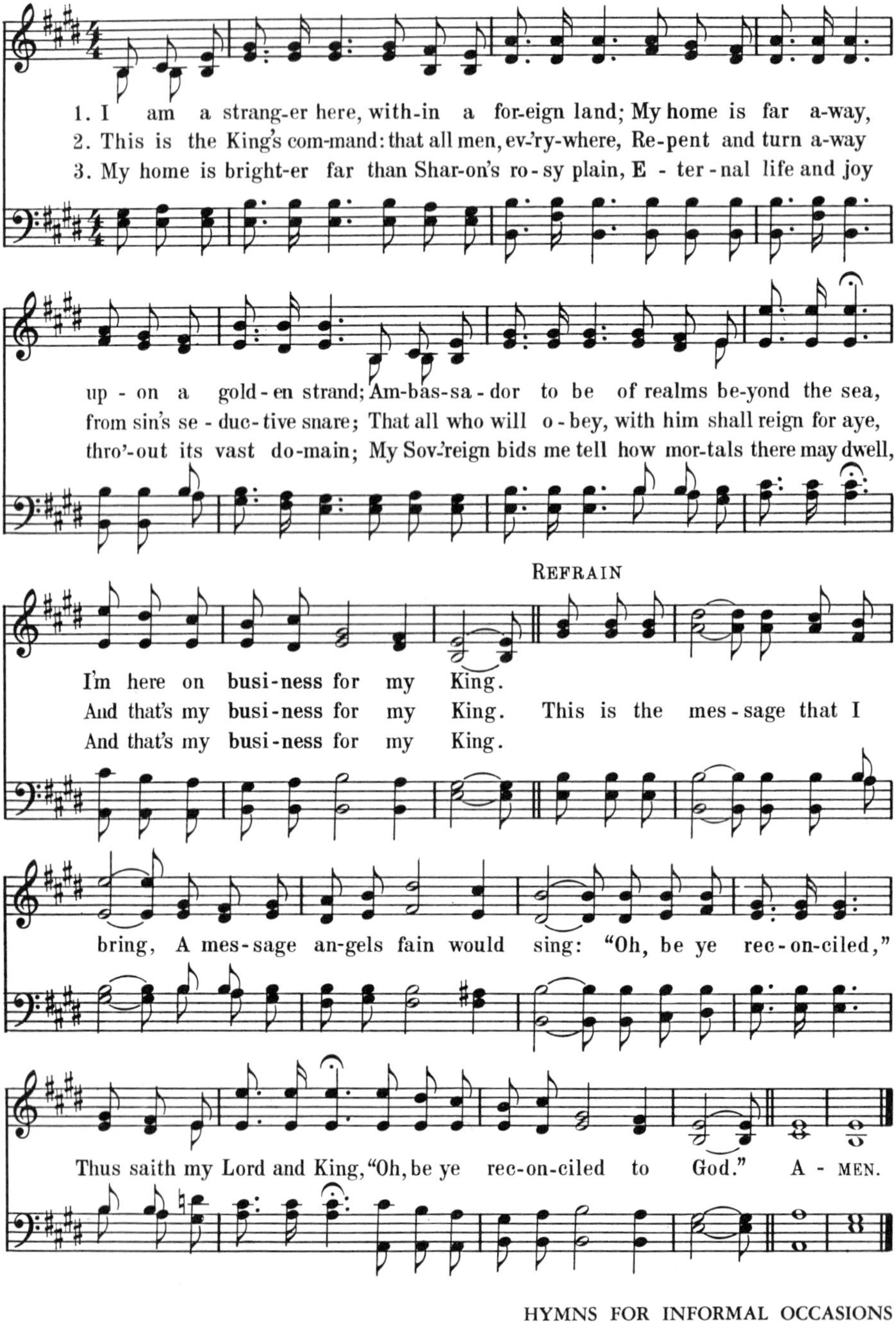

# God Will Take Care of You

**696**

*Casting all your care upon him; for he careth for you.* I Peter 5:7

Civilla D. Martin, 1905 — W. Stillman Martin, 1905

1. Be not dis-mayed what-e'er be-tide, God will take care of you;
   Be-neath his wings of love a-bide, God will take care of you.
2. Through days of toil when heart doth fail, God will take care of you;
   When dan-gers fierce your path as-sail, God will take care of you.
3. All you may need he will pro-vide, God will take care of you;
   Trust him and you will be sat-is-fied, God will take care of you.
4. No mat-ter what may be the test, God will take care of you;
   Lean, wea-ry one, up-on his breast, God will take care of you.

**REFRAIN**

God will take care of you, Through ev-'ry day, O'er all the way;
He will take care of you, God will take care of you. A-MEN.
   take care of you.

Copyright, 1905. Renewal, 1933, by W. S. Martin. Assigned to Hope Publishing Co. All rights reserved. Used by permission.

HYMNS FOR INFORMAL OCCASIONS

## 697 Jesus Is Tenderly Calling

*Come unto me, all ye that labour and are heavy laden... Matt. 11:28*

Fanny J. Crosby, 1883 — George C. Stebbins, 1883

1. Jesus is tenderly calling thee home— Calling today,
2. Jesus is calling the weary to rest— Calling today,
3. Jesus is waiting; O come to him now— Waiting today,
4. Jesus is pleading; O list to his voice: Hear him today,

calling today; Why from the sunshine of love wilt thou roam
calling today; Bring him thy burden and thou shalt be blest:
waiting today; Come with thy sins; at his feet lowly bow;
hear him today; They who believe on his name shall rejoice;

Farther and farther away?
He will not turn thee away.
Come, and no longer delay.
Quickly arise and away.

**Refrain**

Calling today, Calling today,
Calling, calling today, today,
Jesus is calling, is tenderly calling today. A-MEN.
calling today,

HYMNS FOR INFORMAL OCCASIONS

# Only a Sinner 698

*To the praise of the glory of his grace... Eph. 1:6*

James M. Gray, 1851-1935      Daniel B. Towner, 1850-1919

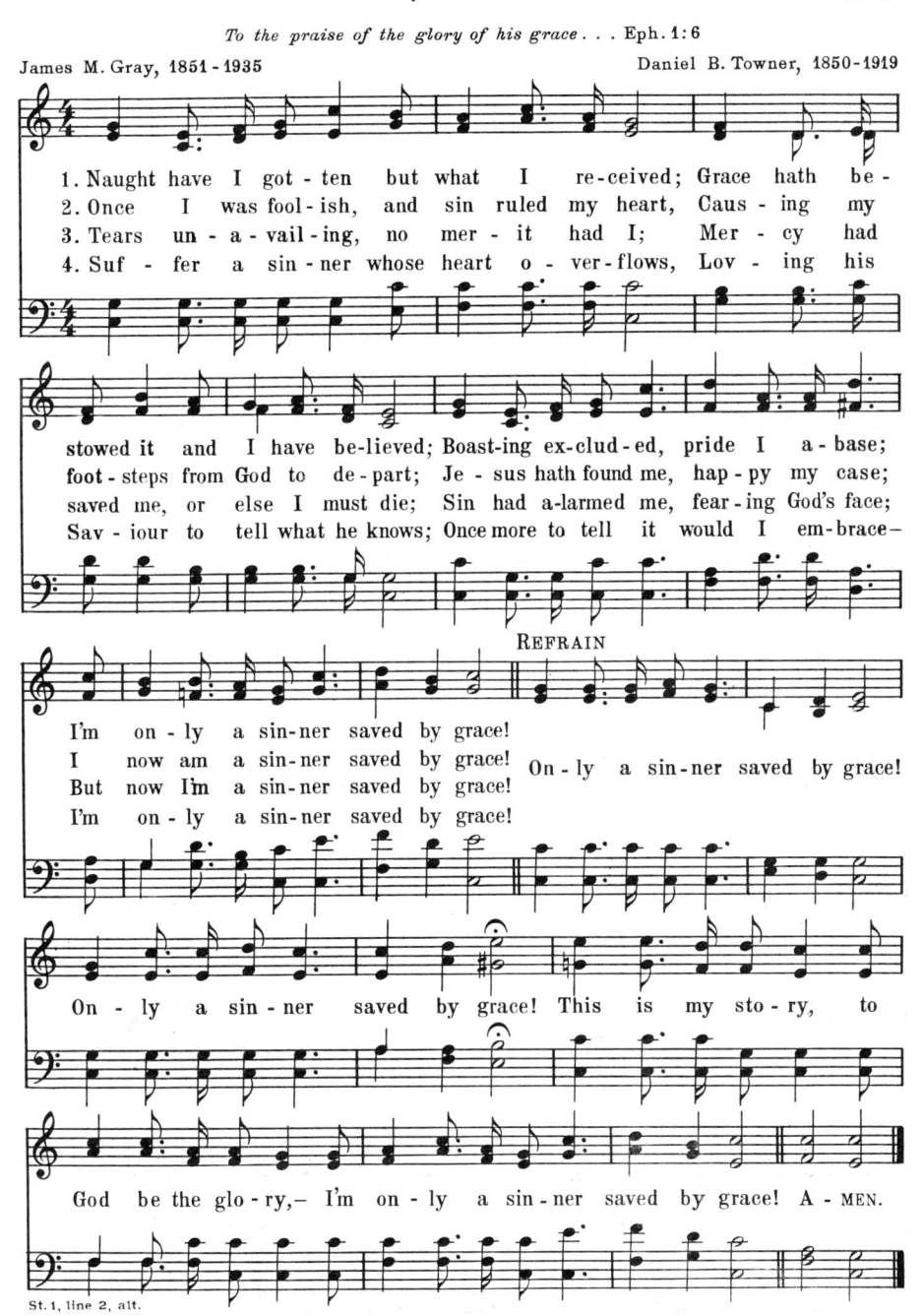

1. Naught have I got-ten but what I re-ceived; Grace hath be-stowed it and I have be-lieved; Boast-ing ex-clud-ed, pride I a-base;
2. Once I was fool-ish, and sin ruled my heart, Caus-ing my foot-steps from God to de-part; Je-sus hath found me, hap-py my case;
3. Tears un-a-vail-ing, no mer-it had I; Mer-cy had saved me, or else I must die; Sin had a-larmed me, fear-ing God's face;
4. Suf-fer a sin-ner whose heart o-ver-flows, Lov-ing his Sav-iour to tell what he knows; Once more to tell it would I em-brace—

**Refrain**

I'm on-ly a sin-ner saved by grace!
I now am a sin-ner saved by grace!   On-ly a sin-ner saved by grace!
But now I'm a sin-ner saved by grace!
I'm on-ly a sin-ner saved by grace!

On-ly a sin-ner saved by grace! This is my sto-ry, to God be the glo-ry,— I'm on-ly a sin-ner saved by grace! A-MEN.

St. 1, line 2, alt.

Copyright, 1905. Renewal, 1933, by A.P. Towner. Assigned to Hope Publishing Co. All rights reserved. Used by permission.

HYMNS FOR INFORMAL OCCASIONS

# 699 'Tis So Sweet to Trust in Jesus

*The life which I now live in the flesh I live by the faith of the Son of God, who loved me, and gave himself for me. Gal. 2:20*

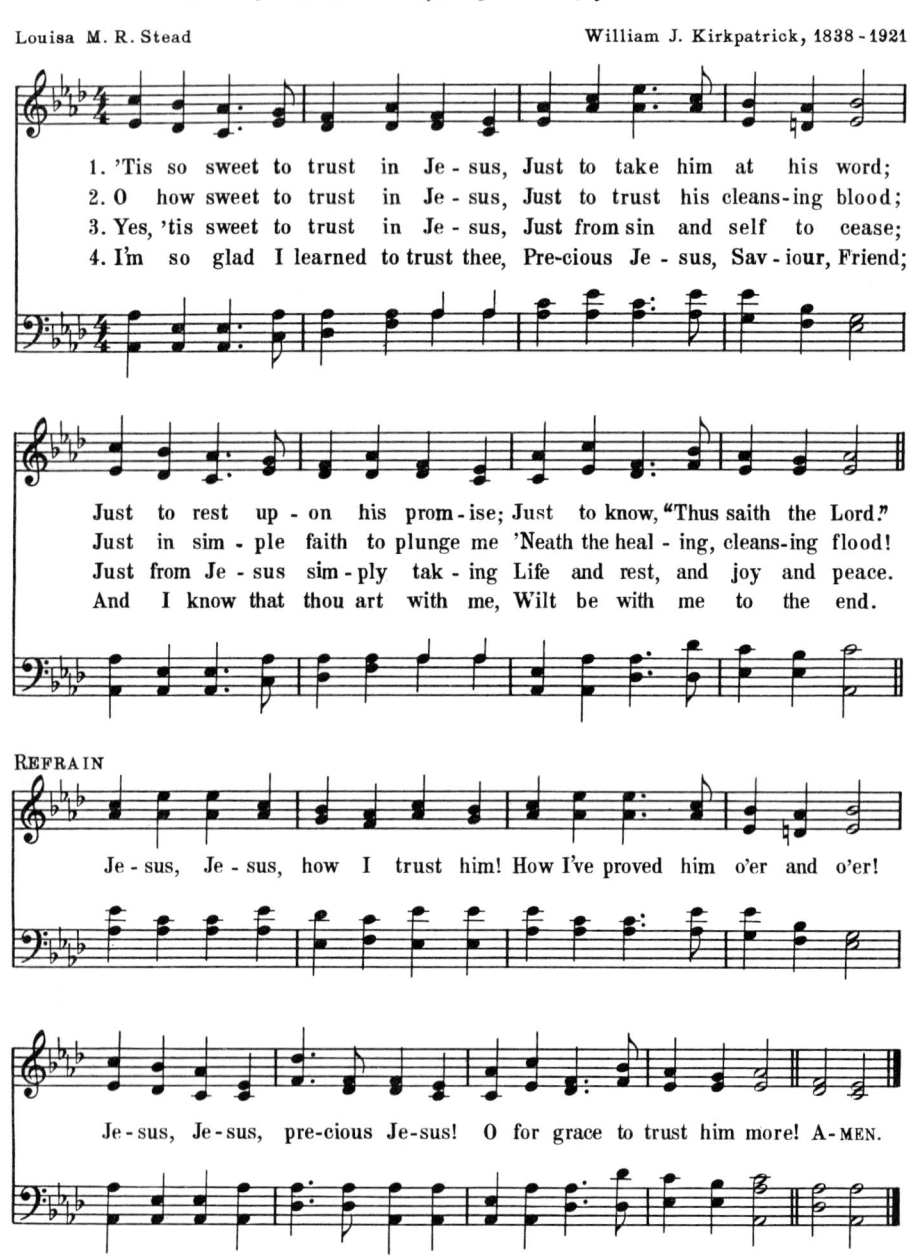

Louisa M. R. Stead  
William J. Kirkpatrick, 1838-1921

1. 'Tis so sweet to trust in Jesus, Just to take him at his word;
2. O how sweet to trust in Jesus, Just to trust his cleansing blood;
3. Yes, 'tis sweet to trust in Jesus, Just from sin and self to cease;
4. I'm so glad I learned to trust thee, Precious Jesus, Saviour, Friend;

Just to rest upon his promise; Just to know, "Thus saith the Lord."
Just in simple faith to plunge me 'Neath the healing, cleansing flood!
Just from Jesus simply taking Life and rest, and joy and peace.
And I know that thou art with me, Wilt be with me to the end.

REFRAIN

Jesus, Jesus, how I trust him! How I've proved him o'er and o'er!

Jesus, Jesus, precious Jesus! O for grace to trust him more! A-MEN.

# Trust and Obey

**700**

*Now therefore, if ye will obey my voice indeed, and keep my covenant, then ye shall be a peculiar treasure unto me above all people . . . Ex. 19:5*

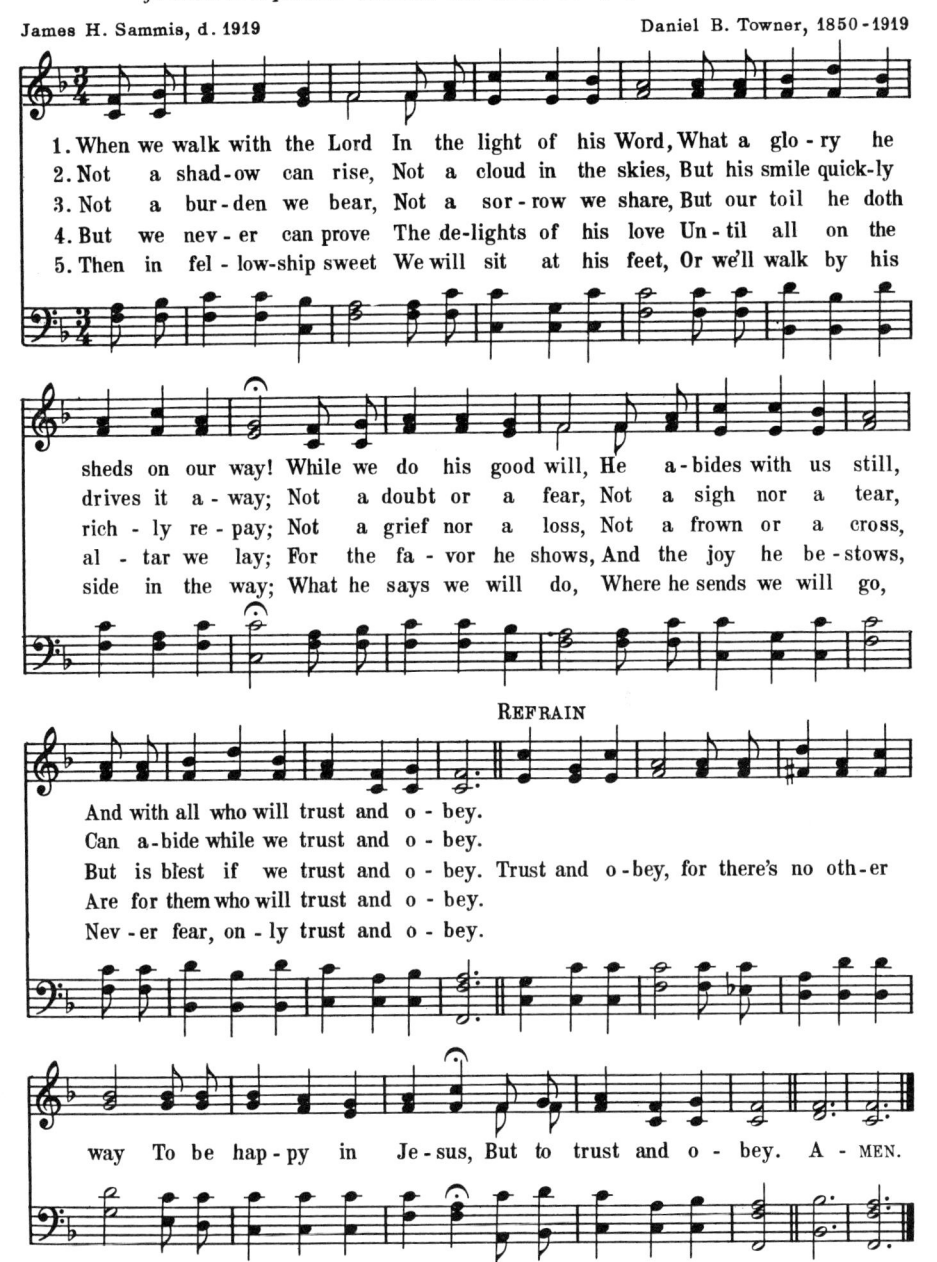

James H. Sammis, d. 1919  
Daniel B. Towner, 1850-1919

1. When we walk with the Lord In the light of his Word, What a glo-ry he sheds on our way! While we do his good will, He a-bides with us still,
2. Not a shad-ow can rise, Not a cloud in the skies, But his smile quick-ly drives it a-way; Not a doubt or a fear, Not a sigh nor a tear,
3. Not a bur-den we bear, Not a sor-row we share, But our toil he doth rich-ly re-pay; Not a grief nor a loss, Not a frown or a cross,
4. But we nev-er can prove The de-lights of his love Un-til all on the al-tar we lay; For the fa-vor he shows, And the joy he be-stows,
5. Then in fel-low-ship sweet We will sit at his feet, Or we'll walk by his side in the way; What he says we will do, Where he sends we will go,

**REFRAIN**

And with all who will trust and o-bey.
Can a-bide while we trust and o-bey.
But is blest if we trust and o-bey. Trust and o-bey, for there's no oth-er
Are for them who will trust and o-bey.
Nev-er fear, on-ly trust and o-bey.

way To be hap-py in Je-sus, But to trust and o-bey. A-MEN.

HYMNS FOR INFORMAL OCCASIONS

# 701 Master, the Tempest Is Raging

*And there arose a great storm of wind, and the waves beat into the ship . . . Mark 4:37*

Mary A. Baker  
Horatio R. Palmer, 1834-1901

1. Master, the tempest is raging! The billows are tossing high!
The sky is o'er shadowed with blackness, No shelter or help is nigh;
Carest thou not that we perish? How canst thou lie asleep,
When each moment so madly is threat'ning A grave in the angry deep?

2. Master, with anguish in spirit I bow in my grief today;
The depths of my sad heart are troubled, O waken and save, I pray;
Torrents of sin and of anguish Sweep o'er my sinking soul!
And I perish! I perish, dear Master; O hasten, and take control!

3. Master, the terror is over, The elements sweetly rest;
Earth's sun in the calm lake is mirrored, And heaven's within my breast.
Linger, O blessed Redeemer, Leave me alone no more;
And with joy I shall make the blest harbor, And rest on the blissful shore.

HYMNS FOR INFORMAL OCCASIONS

**Refrain**

The winds and the waves shall o-bey thy will: "Peace, be still!"
*Peace, be still, peace, be still!"*

Wheth-er the wrath of the storm-tossed sea, Or de-mons, or men or what-
*cres - - cen - - - - do*
ev-er it be, No wa-ter can swal-low the ship where lies the Mas-ter of

o-cean and earth and skies: They all shall sweet-ly o-bey thy will—"Peace, be still!

Peace, be still!" They all shall sweet-ly o-bey thy will—"Peace, peace, be still!" A-men.

Refrain alt.

HYMNS FOR INFORMAL OCCASIONS

## 702 Wonderful Grace of Jesus

*Christ Jesus came into the world to save sinners; of whom I am chief.* I Tim. 1:15

Haldor Lillenas, 1885-   Haldor Lillenas, 1885-

1. Won-der-ful grace of Je-sus, Great-er than all my sin;
2. Won-der-ful grace of Je-sus, Reach-ing a might-y host,
3. Won-der-ful grace of Je-sus, Reach-ing the most de-filed,

How shall my tongue de-scribe it, Where shall its praise be-gin?
By it I have been par-doned, Saved to the ut-ter-most,
By its trans-form-ing pow-er, Mak-ing him God's dear child,

Tak-ing a-way my bur-den, Set-ting my spir-it free;
Chains have been torn a-sun-der, Giv-ing me lib-er-ty;
Pur-chas-ing peace and heav-en, For all e-ter-ni-ty;

For the won-der-ful grace of Je-sus reach-es me.
For the won-der-ful grace of Je-sus reach-es me.
And the won-der-ful grace of Je-sus reach-es me.

REFRAIN

Won-der-ful the match-less grace of Je-sus, Deep-er than the

HYMNS FOR INFORMAL OCCASIONS

might-y roll-ing sea; the roll-ing sea; Won-der-ful
High-er than the moun-tain,

grace, all suf-fi-cient for
spark-ling like a foun-tain, All suf-fi-cient grace for e-ven
me, for e-ven me, Broad-er than the scope of my trans-
gres-sions, Great-er far than all my sin and shame,
O mag-ni-fy the pre-cious name of Je-sus, Praise his Name! A-MEN.

St. 2, line 2, alt.

Copyright, 1918. Renewal, 1946, by H. Lillenas. Assigned to Hope Publishing Co. All rights reserved. Used by permission.

HYMNS FOR INFORMAL OCCASIONS

# 703 Every Day Will I Bless Thee

*Daily shall he be praised.* Psalm 72:15

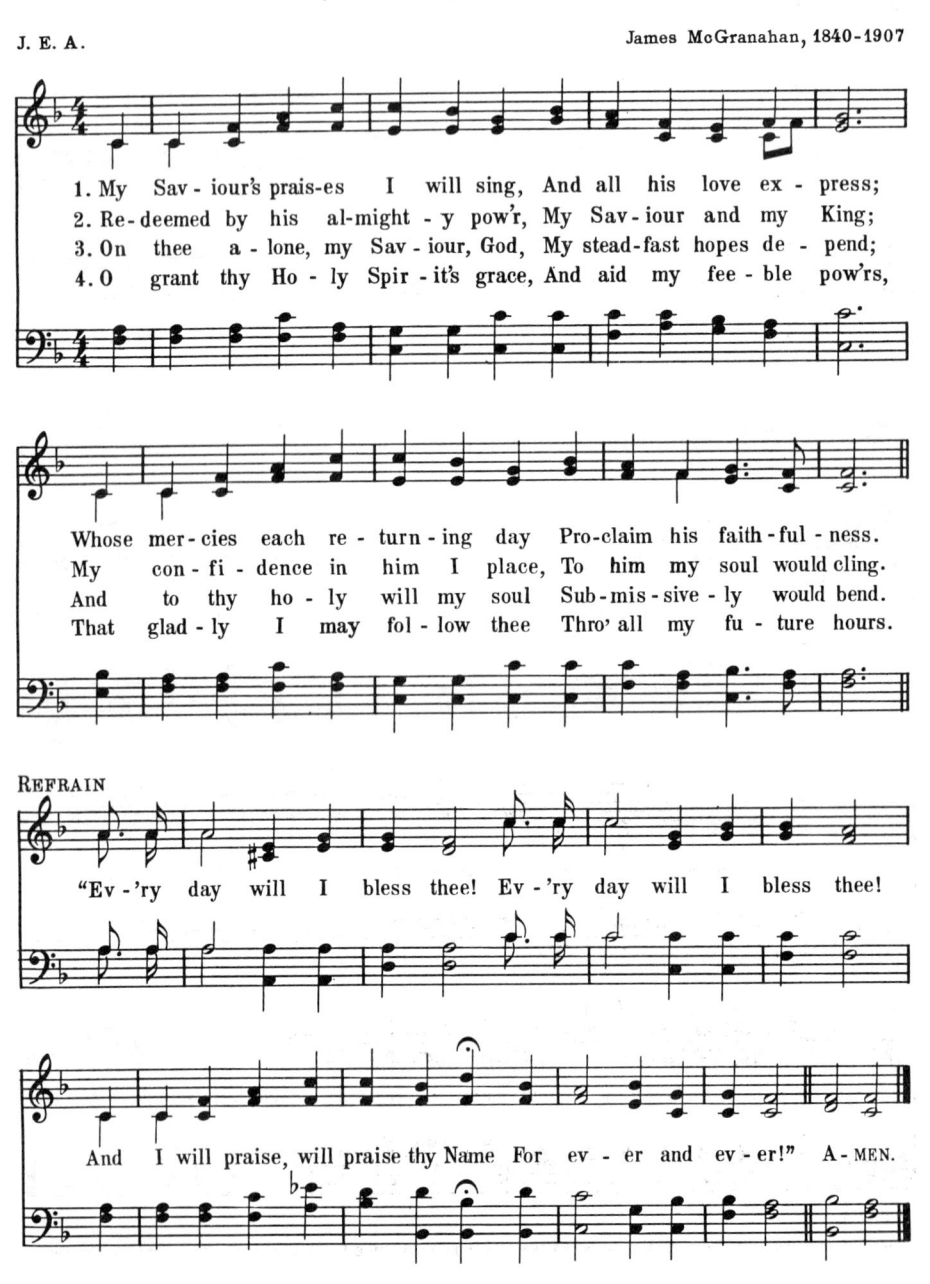

J. E. A.  
James McGranahan, 1840-1907

1. My Saviour's praises I will sing, And all his love express;
2. Redeemed by his almighty pow'r, My Saviour and my King;
3. On thee alone, my Saviour, God, My steadfast hopes depend;
4. O grant thy Holy Spirit's grace, And aid my feeble pow'rs,

Whose mercies each returning day Proclaim his faithfulness.
My confidence in him I place, To him my soul would cling.
And to thy holy will my soul Submissively would bend.
That gladly I may follow thee Thro' all my future hours.

REFRAIN

"Ev-'ry day will I bless thee! Ev-'ry day will I bless thee!
And I will praise, will praise thy Name For ever and ever!" A-MEN.

HYMNS FOR INFORMAL OCCASIONS

## Jesus, Keep Me Near The Cross

**704**

*God forbid that I should glory, save in the cross of our Lord Jesus Christ. . . Gal. 6:14*

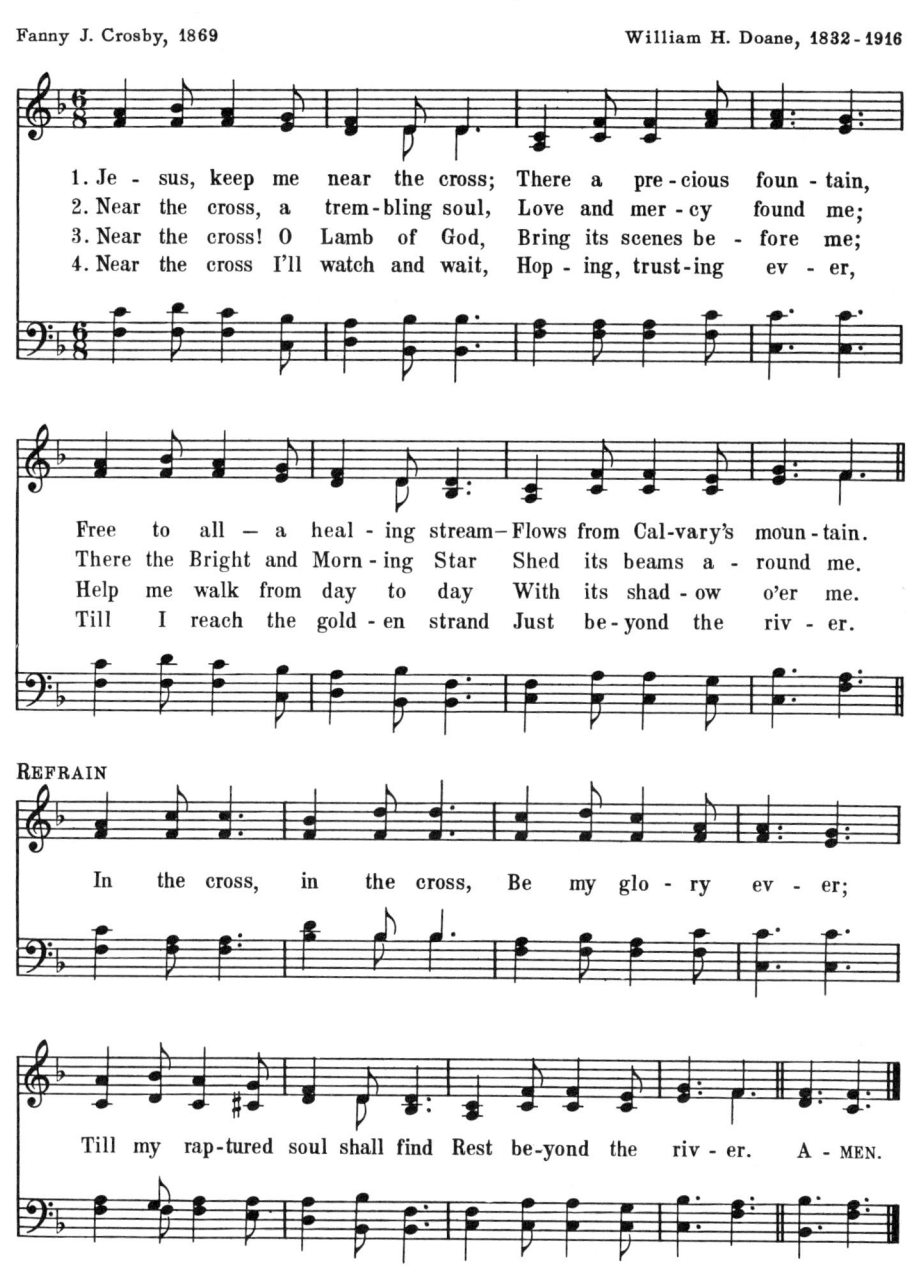

Fanny J. Crosby, 1869　　　　　　　　　　　　　William H. Doane, 1832-1916

1. Je-sus, keep me near the cross; There a pre-cious foun-tain,
2. Near the cross, a trem-bling soul, Love and mer-cy found me;
3. Near the cross! O Lamb of God, Bring its scenes be-fore me;
4. Near the cross I'll watch and wait, Hop-ing, trust-ing ev-er,

Free to all — a heal-ing stream—Flows from Cal-vary's moun-tain.
There the Bright and Morn-ing Star Shed its beams a-round me.
Help me walk from day to day With its shad-ow o'er me.
Till I reach the gold-en strand Just be-yond the riv-er.

REFRAIN

In the cross, in the cross, Be my glo-ry ev-er;

Till my rap-tured soul shall find Rest be-yond the riv-er. A-MEN.

HYMNS FOR INFORMAL OCCASIONS

## 705 Marvelous Grace of Our Loving Lord

*But where sin abounded, grace did much more abound.* Rom. 5:20

Julia H. Johnston  
Daniel B. Towner, 1850-1919

1. Mar-vel-ous grace of our lov-ing Lord, Grace that ex-ceeds our sin and our guilt, Yon-der on Cal-va-ry's mount out-poured, There where the blood of the Lamb was spilt.
2. Sin and de-spair like the sea waves cold, Threat-en the soul with in-fi-nite loss; Grace that is great-er, yes, grace un-told, Points to the Ref-uge, the might-y Cross.
3. Dark is the stain that we can-not hide, What can a-vail to wash it a-way? Look! there is flow-ing a crim-son tide; Whit-er than snow you may be to-day.

REFRAIN

Grace, grace, God's grace, Grace that will par-don and cleanse with-in; Grace, Mar-vel-ous grace, in-fi-nite grace, Mar-vel-ous grace, in-fi-nite grace, Grace that is great-er than all our sin. A-MEN.

Copyright, 1910. Renewal, 1938, by A. P. Towner. Assigned to Hope Publishing Co. All rights reserved. Used by permission.

HYMNS FOR INFORMAL OCCASIONS

## Take Time to Be Holy

706

*Yield your members servants to righteousness unto holiness.* Rom. 6:19

William D. Longstaff, 1887             George C. Stebbins, 1890

1. Take time to be ho-ly, Speak oft with thy Lord;
   A-bide in him al-ways, And feed on his Word.
   Make friends of God's chil-dren; Help those who are weak;
   For-get-ting in noth-ing His bless-ing to seek.

2. Take time to be ho-ly, The world rush-es on;
   Spend much time in se-cret With Je-sus a-lone.
   By look-ing to Je-sus, Like him thou shalt be;
   Thy friends in thy con-duct His like-ness shall see.

3. Take time to be ho-ly, Let him be thy Guide,
   And run not be-fore him, What-ev-er be-tide;
   In joy or in sor-row, Still fol-low thy Lord,
   And, look-ing to Je-sus, Still trust in his Word.

4. Take time to be ho-ly, Be calm in thy soul;
   Each thought and each mo-tive Be-neath his con-trol;
   Thus led by his Spir-it To foun-tains of love,
   Thou soon shalt be fit-ted For serv-ice a-bove. A-MEN.

HYMNS FOR INFORMAL OCCASIONS

# 707 Pass Me Not, O Gentle Saviour

*Whosoever shall call upon the name of the Lord shall be saved.* Rom. 10:13

Fanny J. Crosby, 1868  William H. Doane, 1870

1. Pass me not, O gentle Saviour, Hear my humble cry;
2. Let me at a throne of mercy Find a sweet relief;
3. Trusting only in thy merit, Would I seek thy face;
4. Thou the Spring of all my comfort, More than life to me,

While on others thou art smiling, Do not pass me by.
Kneeling there in deep contrition, Help my unbelief.
Heal my wounded, broken spirit, Save me by thy grace.
Whom have I on earth beside thee? Whom in heav'n but thee?

REFRAIN

Saviour, Saviour, hear my humble cry; While on others thou art calling, Do not pass me by. A-MEN.

HYMNS FOR INFORMAL OCCASIONS

## Moment by Moment 708

*God hath . . . appointed us . . . to obtain salvation by our Lord Jesus Christ, who died for us, that, whether we wake or sleep, we should live together with him.* I Thess 5:9-10

Daniel W. Whittle, 1840-1901  
May Whittle Moody, b. 1870

1. Dy-ing with Je-sus, by death reck-oned mine; Liv-ing with Je-sus, a new life di-vine; Look-ing to Je-sus till glo-ry doth shine, Mo-ment by mo-ment, O Lord, I am thine.

2. Nev-er a tri-al that he is not there, Nev-er a bur-den that he doth not bear, Nev-er a sor-row that he doth not share, Mo-ment by mo-ment, I'm un-der his care.

3. Nev-er a weak-ness that he doth not feel, Nev-er a sick-ness that he can-not heal; Mo-ment by mo-ment, in woe or in weal, Je-sus, my Sav-iour, a-bides with me still.

**REFRAIN**

Mo-ment by mo-ment I'm kept in his love; Mo-ment by mo-ment I've life from a-bove; Look-ing to Je-sus till glo-ry doth shine; Mo-ment by mo-ment, O Lord, I am thine. A-MEN.

HYMNS FOR INFORMAL OCCASIONS

## 709 I Will Sing the Wondrous Story

*They sing... the song of the Lamb, saying, Great and marvelous are thy works, Lord God Almighty... Rev. 15:3*

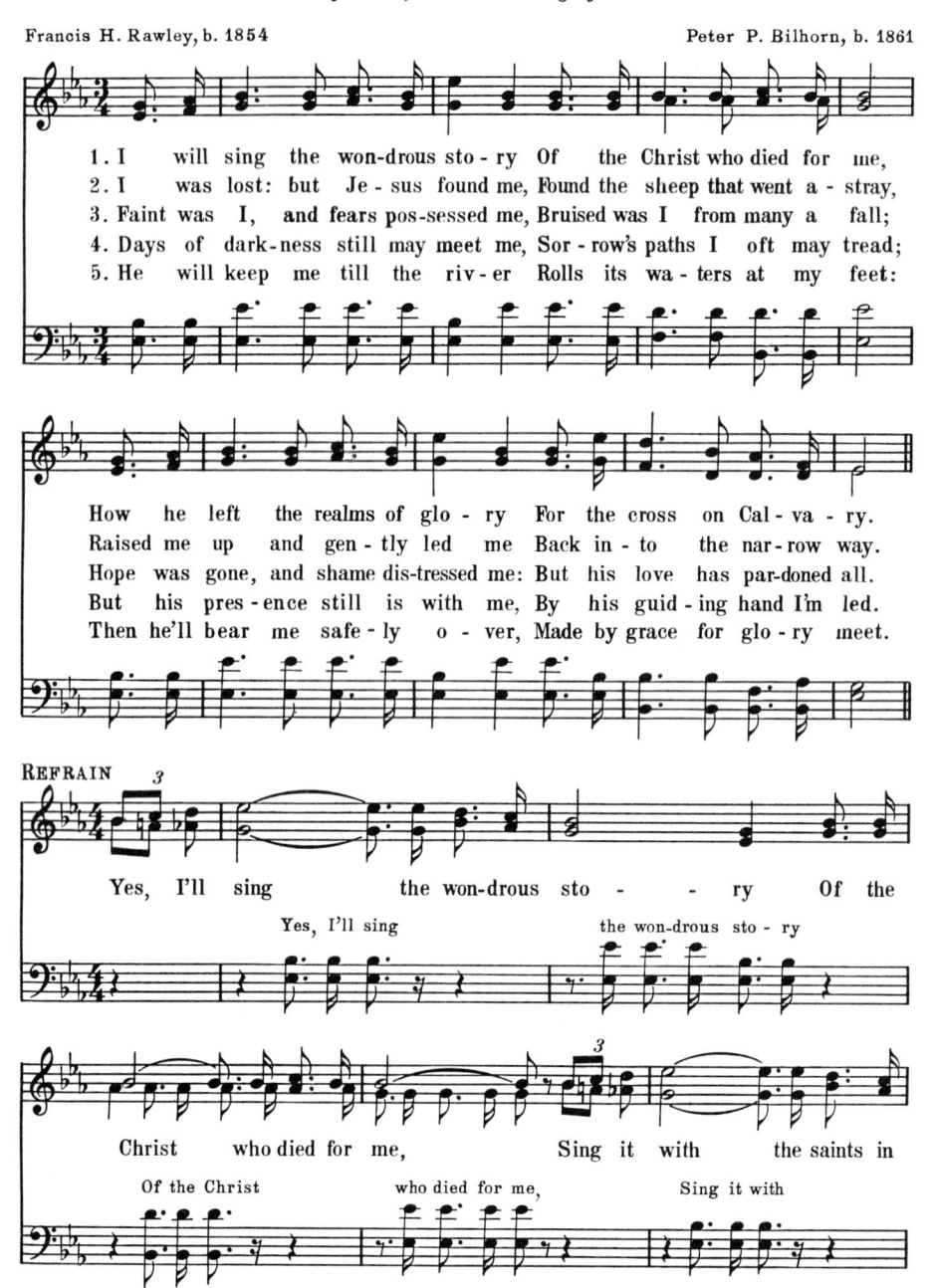

Francis H. Rawley, b. 1854 — Peter P. Bilhorn, b. 1861

1. I will sing the won-drous sto-ry Of the Christ who died for me, How he left the realms of glo-ry For the cross on Cal-va-ry.
2. I was lost: but Je-sus found me, Found the sheep that went a-stray, Raised me up and gen-tly led me Back in-to the nar-row way.
3. Faint was I, and fears pos-sessed me, Bruised was I from many a fall; Hope was gone, and shame dis-tressed me: But his love has par-doned all.
4. Days of dark-ness still may meet me, Sor-row's paths I oft may tread; But his pres-ence still is with me, By his guid-ing hand I'm led.
5. He will keep me till the riv-er Rolls its wa-ters at my feet: Then he'll bear me safe-ly o-ver, Made by grace for glo-ry meet.

**Refrain**

Yes, I'll sing the won-drous sto-ry Of the Christ who died for me, Sing it with the saints in

HYMNS FOR INFORMAL OCCASIONS

glo - ry, Gath-ered by the crys-tal sea. A-MEN.
the saints in glo-ry, Gath-ered by the crys-tal sea.

See also HYFRYDOL, No. 432

## I Need Thee Every Hour 710

*Bow down thine ear, O Lord, hear me: for I am poor and needy.* Psalm 86:1

Annie S. Hawks, 1872; refrain added by
Robert Lowry, 1872

Robert Lowry, 1872

1. I need thee ev-'ry hour, Most gra - cious Lord; No ten-der voice like thine
2. I need thee ev-'ry hour; Stay thou near by; Temp-ta-tions lose their pow'r
3. I need thee ev-'ry hour, In joy or pain; Come quick-ly, and a - bide,
4. I need thee ev-'ry hour; Teach me thy will, And thy rich prom-is - es
5. I need thee ev-'ry hour, Most Ho - ly One; O make me thine in-deed,

REFRAIN

Can peace af - ford.
When thou art nigh.
Or life is vain.    I need thee, O I need thee, Ev-'ry hour I need thee;
In me ful - fil.
Thou bless - ed Son.

O bless me now, my Sav-iour, I come to thee. A - MEN.

HYMNS FOR INFORMAL OCCASIONS

# 711 The Name of Jesus

*Wherefore God also hath highly exalted him, and given him a name which is above every name: that at the name of Jesus every knee should bow...Phil. 2:9-10*

W. C. Martin            Edmund S. Lorenz

1. The Name of Jesus is so sweet, I love its music to repeat; It makes my joys full and complete, The precious Name of Jesus.
2. I love the Name of him whose heart Knows all my griefs and bears a part; Who bids all anxious fears depart—I love the Name of Jesus.
3. No word of man can ever tell How sweet the Name I love so well; Oh, let its praises ever swell, Oh, praise the Name of Jesus.

REFRAIN

"Jesus," oh how sweet the Name! "Jesus," ev'ry day the same; "Jesus," let all saints proclaim Its worthy praise for ever. A-MEN.

HYMNS FOR INFORMAL OCCASIONS

# I Know Whom I Have Believed

**712**

*For I know whom I have believed, and am persuaded that he is able to keep that which I have committed unto him against that day.* II Tim. 1:12

Daniel W. Whittle, 1840-1901            James McGranahan, 1840-1907

1. I know not why God's won-drous grace To me he hath made known,
2. I know not how this sav-ing faith To me he did im-part,
3. I know not how the Spir-it moves, Con-vinc-ing men of sin,
4. I know not what of good or ill May be re-served for me,
5. I know not when my Lord may come, At night or noon-day fair,

Nor why, un-wor-thy, Christ in love Re-deemed me for his own.
Nor how be-liev-ing in his Word Wrought peace with-in my heart,
Re-veal-ing Je-sus through the Word, Cre-at-ing faith in him.
Of wea-ry ways or gold-en days, Be-fore his face I'll see.
Nor if I'll walk the vale with him, Or "meet him in the air."

**REFRAIN**

But "I know whom I have be-liev-ed, and am per-suad-ed that he is a-ble To keep that which I've com-mit-ted Un-to him a-gainst that day." A-MEN.

HYMNS FOR INFORMAL OCCASIONS

# 713    I Am Thine, O Lord

*My sheep hear my voice, and I know them, and they follow me.* John 10:27

Fanny J. Crosby, 1875      William H. Doane, 1832-1916

1. I am thine, O Lord, I have heard thy voice, And it told thy love to me; But I long to rise in the arms of faith, And be clos-er drawn to thee.
2. Con-se-crate me now to thy serv-ice, Lord, By the pow'r of grace di-vine; Let my soul look up with a stead-fast hope, And my will be lost in thine.
3. O the pure de-light of a sin-gle hour That be-fore thy throne I spend, When I kneel in prayer, and with thee, my God, I com-mune as friend with friend!
4. There are depths of love that I can-not know Till I cross the nar-row sea; There are heights of joy that I may not reach Till I rest in peace with thee.

REFRAIN

Draw me near-er, near-er, bless-ed Lord, To the cross where thou hast died; Draw me near-er, near-er, near-er, bless-ed Lord, To thy pre-cious, bleed-ing side. A-MEN.

HYMNS FOR INFORMAL OCCASIONS

## With Harps and With Viols 714

*And they sung as it were a new song before the throne.* Rev. 14:3

Arthur T. Pierson, 1837-1911      Philip P. Bliss, 1838-1876

1. With harps and with vi-ols, there stand a great throng
2. All these once were sin-ners, de-filed in his sight,
3. He mak-eth the reb-el a priest and a king,
4. How help-less and hope-less we sin-ners had been,
5. A-loud in his prais-es our voic-es shall ring,

In the pres-ence of Je-sus, and sing this new song:
Now ar-rayed in pure gar-ments in praise they u-nite:
He hath bought us and taught us this new song to sing:
If he nev-er had loved us till cleansed from our sin:
So that oth-ers, be-liev-ing, this new song shall sing:

REFRAIN

Un-to him who hath loved us and washed us from sin, Un-to him be the glo-ry for ev-er. A-MEN.

HYMNS FOR INFORMAL OCCASIONS

# 715 Jesus, I Come

*He hath sent me to bind up the brokenhearted, to proclaim liberty to the captives, and the opening of the prison to them that are bound. Isa. 61:1*

W. T. Sleeper, c. 1840-1920          George C. Stebbins, 1846-1945

1. Out of my bond-age, sor-row and night, Je-sus, I come, Je-sus, I come;
2. Out of my shame-ful fail-ure and loss, Je-sus, I come, Je-sus, I come;
3. Out of un-rest and ar-ro-gant pride, Je-sus, I come, Je-sus, I come;
4. Out of the fear and dread of the tomb, Je-sus, I come, Je-sus, I come;

In-to thy free-dom, glad-ness and light, Je-sus, I come to thee;
In-to the glo-rious gain of thy cross, Je-sus, I come to thee;
In-to thy bless-ed will to a-bide, Je-sus, I come to thee;
In-to the joy and light of thy home, Je-sus, I come to thee;

Out of my sick-ness in-to thy health, Out of my want and in-to thy wealth,
Out of earth's sor-rows in-to thy balm, Out of life's storms and in-to thy calm,
Out of my-self to dwell in thy love, Out of de-spair in-to rap-tures a-bove,
Out of the depths of ru-in un-told, In-to the peace of thy shel-ter-ing fold,

Out of my sin and in-to thy-self, Je-sus, I come to thee.
Out of dis-tress to ju-bi-lant psalm, Je-sus, I come to thee.
Up-ward for aye on wings like a dove, Je-sus, I come to thee.
Ev-er thy glo-rious face to be-hold, Je-sus, I come to thee. A-MEN.

**HYMNS FOR INFORMAL OCCASIONS**

## There Shall Be Showers of Blessing 716

*There shall be showers of blessing.* Ezekiel 34:26

Daniel W. Whittle, 1840-1901  
James McGranahan, 1840-1907

1. "There shall be show-ers of bless-ing," This is the prom-ise of love;
2. "There shall be show-ers of bless-ing"— Pre-cious re-viv-ing a-gain;
3. "There shall be show-ers of bless-ing": Send them up-on us, O Lord;
4. "There shall be show-ers of bless-ing": Oh, that to-day they might fall,

There shall be sea-sons re-fresh-ing, Sent from the Sav-iour a-bove.
O-ver the hills and the val-leys, Sound of a-bun-dance of rain.
Grant to us now a re-fresh-ing, Come, and now hon-or thy Word.
Now as to God we're con-fess-ing, Now as on Je-sus we call!

REFRAIN

Show - ers of bless - ing, Show-ers of bless-ing we need:
Show-ers, show-ers of bless - ing,

Mer-cy-drops round us are fall-ing, But for the show-ers we plead. A-MEN.

HYMNS FOR INFORMAL OCCASIONS

# 717 My Anchor Holds

*Which hope we have as an anchor of the soul, both sure and steadfast... Heb. 6:19*

W. C. Martin, alt.  
Daniel B. Towner, 1850-1919

1. Though the angry surges roll On my tempest-driven soul,
I am peaceful, for I know, Wildly though the winds may blow,
I've an anchor safe and sure, That can evermore endure.

2. Mighty tides about me sweep, Perils lurk within the deep,
Angry clouds o'er-shade the sky, And the tempest rises high;
Still I stand the tempest's shock, For my anchor grips the Rock.

3. I can feel the anchor fast As I meet each sudden blast,
And the cable, though unseen, Bears the heavy strain between;
Through the storm I safely ride, Till the turning of the tide.

4. Troubles almost 'whelm the soul; Griefs like billows o'er me roll;
Tempters seek to lure astray; Storms obscure the light of day:
But in Christ I can be bold, I've an anchor that shall hold.

**Refrain**

And it holds, my anchor holds; Blow your wildest, then, O gale, On my bark so small and frail: By his grace I shall not

HYMNS FOR INFORMAL OCCASIONS

fail, For my an-chor holds, my an-chor holds. A-MEN.
For my an-chor holds, it firm-ly holds,

Copyright, 1902. Renewal, 1930, by A.P. Towner. Assigned to Hope Publishing Co. All rights reserved. Used by permission.

## Leaning on the Everlasting Arms 718

*The eternal God is thy refuge, and underneath are the everlasting arms* ... Deut. 33:27

Elisha A. Hoffman, 1839-1929                                                         A. J. Showalter

1. What a fel-low-ship, what a joy di-vine, Lean-ing on the ev-er-last-ing arms;
2. Oh, how sweet to walk in this pil-grim way, Lean-ing on the ev-er-last-ing arms;
3. What have I to dread, what have I to fear, Lean-ing on the ev-er-last-ing arms?

What a bless-ed-ness, what a peace is mine, Lean-ing on the ev-er-last-ing arms.
Oh, how bright the path grows from day to day, Lean-ing on the ev-er-last-ing arms.
I have bless-ed peace with my Lord so near, Lean-ing on the ev-er-last-ing arms.

REFRAIN
Lean - ing, lean - ing, Safe and se-cure from all a-larms;
Lean - ing on Je-sus, lean-ing on Je-sus,

Lean - ing, lean - ing, Lean-ing on the ev-er-last-ing arms. A-MEN.
Lean - ing on Je-sus, lean-ing on Je-sus,

Owned by Tennessee Music and Printing Company. Used by permission.

HYMNS FOR INFORMAL OCCASIONS

# 719     A Shelter in the Time of Storm

*As the shadow of a great rock in a weary land.* Isa. 32:2

Vernon J. Charlesworth
Arr. by Ira D. Sankey, 1840-1907

Ira D. Sankey, 1840-1908

1. The Lord's our Rock, in him we hide, A shel-ter in the time of storm;
2. A shade by day, de-fense by night, A shel-ter in the time of storm;
3. The rag-ing storms may round us beat, A shel-ter in the time of storm;
4. O Rock Di-vine, O Ref-uge dear, A shel-ter in the time of storm;

Se-cure what-ev-er ill be-tide, A shel-ter in the time of storm.
No fears a-larm, no foes af-fright, A shel-ter in the time of storm.
We'll nev-er leave our safe re-treat, A shel-ter in the time of storm.
Be thou our help-er ev-er near, A shel-ter in the time of storm.

REFRAIN

Oh, Je-sus is a Rock in a wea-ry land, A wea-ry land, a wea-ry land; Oh, Je-sus is a Rock in a wea-ry land, A shel-ter in the time of storm. A-MEN.

HYMNS FOR INFORMAL OCCASIONS

## The Child of a King

**720**

*We are the children of God: and if children, then heirs; heirs of God, and joint-heirs with Christ... Rom. 8:16-17*

Hattie E. Buell                                                                       John B. Sumner

1. My Father is rich in houses and lands, He holdeth the wealth of the world in his hands! Of rubies and diamonds, of silver and gold, His coffers are full, he has riches untold.
2. My Father's own Son, the Saviour of men, Once wandered o'er earth as the poorest of them; But now he is reigning for ever on high, And will give me a home in heav'n by and by.
3. I once was an outcast stranger on earth, A sinner by choice, and an alien by birth! But I've been adopted, my name's written down, An heir to a mansion, a robe, and a crown.
4. A tent or a cottage, why should I care? They're building a palace for me over there! Though exiled from home, yet still I may sing: All glory to God, I'm the child of a King!

**REFRAIN**

I'm the child of a King, The child of a King! With Jesus, my Saviour, I'm the child of a King. A-MEN.

HYMNS FOR INFORMAL OCCASIONS

# 721. Nor Silver Nor Gold

*Ye know that ye were not redeemed with corruptible things, as silver and gold... but with the precious blood of Christ... I Peter 1:18, 19*

James M. Gray, 1851-1935  
Daniel B. Towner, 1850-1919

1. Nor silver nor gold hath obtained my redemption, Nor riches of earth could have saved my poor soul; The blood of the cross is my only foundation, The death of my Saviour now maketh me whole.
2. Nor silver nor gold hath obtained my redemption, The guilt on my conscience too heavy had grown; The blood of the cross is my only foundation, The death of my Saviour could only atone.
3. Nor silver nor gold hath obtained my redemption, The holy commandment forbade me draw near; The blood of the cross is my only foundation, The death of my Saviour removeth my fear.
4. Nor silver nor gold hath obtained my redemption, The way into heaven could not thus be bought; The blood of the cross is my only foundation, The death of my Saviour redemption hath wrought.

REFRAIN

I am redeemed, but not with silver; I am redeemed, I am redeemed, but not with silver; I am bought, but not with gold; I am bought, I am bought, but not with gold; Bought with a

HYMNS FOR INFORMAL OCCASIONS

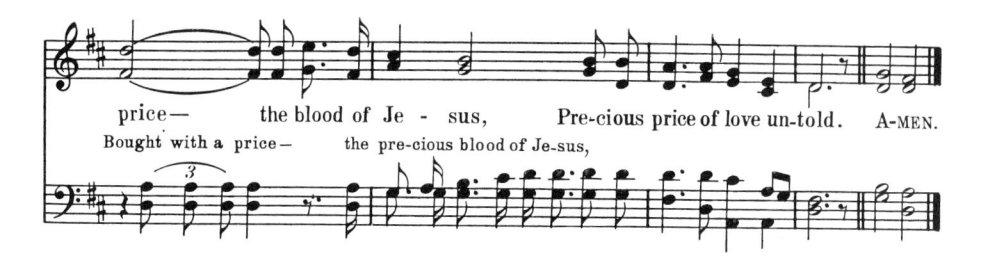

price— the blood of Je - sus, Pre-cious price of love un-told. A-MEN.
Bought with a price— the pre-cious blood of Je-sus,

## Wonderful Words of Life 722

*Lord, to whom shall we go? thou hast the words of eternal life.* John 6:68

Philip P. Bliss, 1838-1876                    Philip P. Bliss, 1838-1876

1. Sing them o-ver a-gain to me, Won-der-ful words of life;
2. Christ, the bless-ed One, gives to all, Won-der-ful words of life;
3. Sweet-ly ech-o the gos-pel call, Won-der-ful words of life;

Let me more of their beau-ty see, Won-der-ful words of life.
Sin-ner, list to the lov-ing call, Won-der-ful words of life.
Of-fer par-don and peace to all, Won-der-ful words of life.

Words of life and beau-ty, Teach me faith and du-ty:
All so free-ly giv-en, Woo-ing us to heav-en:
Je-sus, on-ly Sav-iour, Sanc-ti-fy for ev-er:

REFRAIN.
Beau-ti-ful words, won-der-ful words, Won-der-ful words of life. life. A-MEN.

HYMNS FOR INFORMAL OCCASIONS

## 723. Give Me Thy Heart

*My son, give me thy heart... Prov. 23:26*

Eliza E. Hewitt, 1851-1920
St. 2, line 4, alt.

William J. Kirkpatrick, 1838-1921

1. "Give me thy heart," says the Fa-ther a-bove, No gift so pre-cious to him as our love, Soft-ly he whis-pers wher-ev-er thou art, "Grate-ful-ly trust me, and give me thy heart."
2. "Give me thy heart," says the Sav-iour of men, Call-ing in mer-cy a-gain and a-gain; "Turn now from sin, and from e-vil de-part, Will I not suc-cor thee? give me thy heart."
3. "Give me thy heart," says the Spir-it Di-vine, "All that thou hast, to my keep-ing re-sign; Grace more a-bound-ing is mine to im-part, Make full sur-ren-der and give me thy heart."

**Refrain**

"Give me thy heart, Give me thy heart," Hear the soft whis-per, wher-ev-er thou art; From this dark world he would draw thee a-part,

HYMNS FOR INFORMAL OCCASIONS

Speak-ing so ten-der-ly, "Give me thy heart." A-MEN.

## Only Trust Him 724

*He is able also to save them to the uttermost that come unto God by him... Heb. 7:25*

John H. Stockton, 1813-1877                                    John H. Stockton, 1813-1877

1. Come, ev-'ry soul by sin op-pressed, There's mer-cy with the Lord,
2. For Je-sus shed his pre-cious blood, Rich bless-ings to be-stow;
3. Yes, Je-sus is the Truth, the Way, That leads you in-to rest;
4. Come then, and join this ho-ly band, And on to glo-ry go,

And he will sure-ly give you rest, By trust-ing in his Word.
Plunge now in-to the crim-son flood That wash-es white as snow.
Be-lieve in him with-out de-lay, And you are ful-ly blessed.
To dwell in that ce-les-tial land, Where joys im-mor-tal flow.

REFRAIN

On-ly trust him, on-ly trust him, On-ly trust him now;
He will save you, he will save you, He will save you now. A-MEN.

HYMNS FOR INFORMAL OCCASIONS

# 725 His Eye Is on the Sparrow

*Are not two sparrows sold for a farthing? and one of them shall not fall on the ground without your Father.* Matt. 10:29

Civilla D. Martin, 1868-1948      Charles H. Gabriel, 1856-1932

1. Why should I feel dis-cour-aged, Why should the shad-ows come, Why should my heart be lone-ly And long for heav'n and home, When Je-sus is my por-tion? My con-stant friend is he: His eye is on the spar-row, And I know he watch-es me; His eye is on the spar-row, And I know he watch-es me.

2. "Let not your heart be troub-led," His ten-der word I hear, And rest-ing on his good-ness, I lose my doubt and fear; Tho' by the path he lead-eth But one step I may see: His eye is on the spar-row, And I know he watch-es me; His eye is on the spar-row, And I know he watch-es me.

3. When-ev-er I am tempt-ed, When-ev-er clouds a-rise, When songs give place to sigh-ing, When hope with-in me dies, I draw the clo-ser to him, From care he sets me free; His eye is on the spar-row, And I know he cares for me; His eye is on the spar-row, And I know he cares for me. A-MEN.

Copyright, 1905. Renewal, 1933. The Rodeheaver Company, owner. International copyright secured. All rights reserved. Used by permission.

# Saved by Grace

**726**

*Or ever the silver cord be loosed . . . Ecc. 12:6*

Fanny J. Crosby 1893

George C. Stebbins, 1893
Alt. by Seymour Swets, 1934

1. Some day the sil-ver cord will break, And I no more as now shall sing;
2. Some day my earth-ly house will fall, I can-not tell how soon 'twill be;
3. Some day, when fades the gold-en sun Be-neath the ro-sy-tint-ed west,
4. Some day: till then I'll watch and wait, My lamp all trimmed and burn-ing bright,

But oh, the joy when I shall wake With-in the pal-ace of the King!
But this I know— my All in All Has now a place in heav'n for me.
My bless-ed Lord will say, "Well done!" And I shall en-ter in-to rest.
That when my Sav-iour opes the gate, My soul to him may take its flight.

**REFRAIN**

And I shall see him face to face, And tell the sto-ry— Saved by grace;

And I shall see him face to face, And tell the sto-ry— Saved by grace. A-MEN.

Arrangement of music, used by permission of the Publication Committee of the Christian Reformed Church.

HYMNS FOR INFORMAL OCCASIONS

## 727 When the Roll Is Called Up Yonder

*For the Lord himself shall descend from heaven with a shout... and with the trump of God: and the dead in Christ shall rise first.* I Thess. 4:16

James M. Black            James M. Black

1. When the trump-et of the Lord shall sound, and time shall be no more, And the morning breaks, e-ter-nal, bright and fair; When the saved of earth shall gath-er o-ver on the oth-er shore, And the roll is called up yon-der, I'll be there.

2. On that bright and cloud-less morn-ing when the dead in Christ shall rise, And the glo-ry of his res-ur-rec-tion share; When his cho-sen ones shall gath-er to their home be-yond the skies, And the roll is called up yon-der, I'll be there.

3. Let us la-bor for the Mas-ter from the dawn till set-ting sun, Let us talk of all his won-drous love and care; Then when all of life is o-ver, and our work on earth is done, And the roll is called up yon-der, I'll be there.

**REFRAIN**

When the roll is called up yon - - der, When the roll is called up yon - der, When the roll is called up
(When the roll is called up yon-der, I'll be there,     When the roll is called up)

HYMNS FOR INFORMAL OCCASIONS

yon - der, When the roll is called up yon-der, I'll be there. A - MEN.

## Work, For the Night Is Coming 728

*The night cometh, when no man can work.* John 9:4

Anna L. Coghill 1861; each st. alt.  Lowell Mason, 1864

1. Work, for the night is com - ing: Work through the morn-ing hours;
2. Work, for the night is com - ing: Work through the sun - ny noon;
3. Work, for the night is com - ing: Un - der the sun - set skies,

Work while the dew is spark - ling; Work 'mid spring - ing flowers;
Fill bright-est hours with la - bor, Rest comes sure and soon;
While their bright tints are glow - ing, Work, for day - light flies;

Work while the day grows bright - er, Un - der the glow - ing sun;
Give ev - 'ry fly - ing min - ute Some-thing to keep in store;
Work till the last beam fad - eth, Fad - eth to shine no more;

Work, for the night is com - ing, When man's work is done.
Work, for the night is com - ing, When man works no more.
Work while the night is dark-'ning, When man's work is o'er. A - MEN.

HYMNS FOR INFORMAL OCCASIONS

# 729 Home of the Soul

*And (he) shewed me that great city... Rev. 21:10*

Ellen H. Gates  
Philip Phillips, 1834-1895

1. I will sing you a song of that beau-ti-ful land, The far a-way home of the soul, Where no storms ev-er beat on the glit-ter-ing strand, While the years of e-ter-ni-ty roll, While the years of e-ter-ni-ty roll; Where no storms ev-er beat on the glit-ter-ing strand, While the years of e-ter-ni-ty roll.

2. O that home of the soul! In my vis-ions and dreams, Its bright jas-per walls I can see; Till I fan-cy but thin-ly the veil in-ter-venes Be-tween the fair cit-y and me, Be-tween the fair cit-y and me; Till I fan-cy but thin-ly the veil in-ter-venes Be-tween the fair cit-y and me.

3. That un-change-a-ble home is for you and for me, Where Je-sus of Naz-a-reth stands; The King of all king-doms for ev-er is he, And he hold-eth our crowns in his hands, And he hold-eth our crowns in his hands; The King of all king-doms for-ev-er is he, And he hold-eth our crowns in his hands.

4. O how sweet it will be in that beau-ti-ful land, So free from all sor-row and pain, With songs on our lips and with harps in our hands, To meet one an-oth-er a-gain, To meet one an-oth-er a-gain; With songs on our lips and with harps in our hands, To meet one an-oth-er a-gain. A-MEN.

HYMNS FOR INFORMAL OCCASIONS

## No Night There

**730**

*And there shall be no night there... Rev. 22:5*

John R. Clements  
Hart P. Danks

1. In the land of fade-less day Lies the cit-y four-square;
2. All the gates of pearl are made In the cit-y four-square;
3. And the gates shall nev-er close To the cit-y four-square;
4. There they need no sun-shine bright, In that cit-y four-square;

It shall nev-er pass a-way, And there is no night there.
All the streets with gold are laid, And there is no night there.
There life's crys-tal riv-er flows, And there is no night there.
For the Lamb is all the light, And there is no night there.

**Refrain**

God shall wipe a-way all tears; There's no
God shall wipe a-way all tears;

death, no pain, nor fears; And they count not
There's no death, no pain, nor fears; And they count not time

time by years; For there is no night there. A-MEN.
by years, by years, For there is no night there.

HYMNS FOR INFORMAL OCCASIONS

PSALTER SELECTIONS

# Psalter Selections

## SELECTION 1

### Psalm 1

BLESSED is the man that walketh not in the counsel of the ungodly, nor standeth in the way of sinners, nor sitteth in the seat of the scornful.

But his delight is in the law of the LORD; and in his law doth he meditate day and night.

And he shall be like a tree planted by the rivers of water, that bringeth forth his fruit in his season; his leaf also shall not wither; and whatsoever he doeth shall prosper.

The ungodly are not so: but are like the chaff which the wind driveth away.

Therefore the ungodly shall not stand in the judgment, nor sinners in the congregation of the righteous.

For the LORD knoweth the way of the righteous: but the way of the ungodly shall perish.

### Psalm 2

WHY do the heathen rage, and the people imagine a vain thing?

The kings of the earth set themselves, and the rulers take counsel together, against the LORD, and against his anointed, saying,

Let us break their bands asunder, and cast away their cords from us.

He that sitteth in the heavens shall laugh: the Lord shall have them in derision.

Then shall he speak unto them in his wrath, and vex them in his sore displeasure.

Yet have I set my king upon my holy hill of Zion.

I will declare the decree: the LORD hath said unto me, Thou art my Son; this day have I begotten thee.

Ask of me, and I shall give thee the heathen for thine inheritance, and the uttermost parts of the earth for thy possession.

Thou shalt break them with a rod of iron; thou shalt dash them in pieces like a potter's vessel.

Be wise now therefore, O ye kings: be instructed, ye judges of the earth.

Serve the LORD with fear, and rejoice with trembling.

Kiss the Son, lest he be angry, and ye perish from the way, when his wrath is kindled but a little. Blessed are all they that put their trust in him.

## SELECTION 2

### Psalm 4

HEAR me when I call, O God of my righteousness: thou hast enlarged me when I was in distress; have mercy upon me, and hear my prayer.

O ye sons of men, how long will ye turn my glory into shame? How long will ye love vanity, and seek after falsehood?

But know that the LORD hath set apart him that is godly for himself: the LORD will hear when I call unto him.

Stand in awe, and sin not: commune with your own heart upon your bed, and be still.

Offer the sacrifices of righteousness, and put your trust in the LORD.

There be many that say, Who will show us any good? LORD, lift thou up the light of thy countenance upon us.

Thou hast put gladness in my heart, more than in the time that their corn and their wine increased.

# Psalter Selections

I will both lay me down in peace, and sleep: for thou, LORD, only makest me dwell in safety.

## PSALM 5

GIVE ear to my words, O LORD, consider my meditation.

Hearken unto the voice of my cry, my King, and my God: for unto thee will I pray.

My voice shalt thou hear in the morning, O LORD; in the morning will I direct my prayer unto thee, and will look up.

For thou art not a God that hath pleasure in wickedness: neither shall evil dwell with thee.

The foolish shall not stand in thy sight: thou hatest all workers of iniquity.

Thou shalt destroy them that speak falsehood: the LORD will abhor the bloody and deceitful man.

But as for me, I will come into thy house in the multitude of thy mercy: and in thy fear will I worship toward thy holy temple.

Lead me, O LORD, in thy righteousness because of mine enemies; make thy way straight before my face.

For there is no faithfulness in their mouth; their inward part is very wickedness; their throat is an open sepulchre; they flatter with their tongue.

Destroy thou them, O God; let them fall by their own counsels; cast them out in the multitude of their transgressions; for they have rebelled against thee.

But let all those that put their trust in thee rejoice: let them ever shout for joy, because thou defendest them: let them also that love thy name be joyful in thee.

For thou, LORD, wilt bless the righteous; with favour wilt thou compass him as with a shield.

## SELECTION 3

### PSALM 8

O LORD our Lord, how excellent is thy name in all the earth! who hast set thy glory above the heavens.

Out of the mouth of babes and sucklings hast thou ordained strength because of thine enemies, that thou mightest still the enemy and the avenger.

When I consider thy heavens, the work of thy fingers, the moon and the stars, which thou hast ordained;

What is man, that thou art mindful of him? and the son of man, that thou visitest him?

For thou hast made him a little lower than the angels, and hast crowned him with glory and honour.

Thou madest him to have dominion over the works of thy hands; thou hast put all things under his feet:

All sheep and oxen, yea, and the beasts of the field;

The fowl of the air, and the fish of the sea, and whatsoever passeth through the paths of the seas.

O LORD our Lord, how excellent is thy name in all the earth!

### PSALM 9:7-11

THE LORD shall endure for ever: he hath prepared his throne for judgment.

And he shall judge the world in righteousness, he shall minister judgment to the people in uprightness.

The LORD also will be a refuge for the oppressed, a refuge in times of trouble.

And they that know thy name will put their trust in thee: for thou, LORD, hast not forsaken them that seek thee.

Sing praises to the LORD, which

# Psalter Selections

dwelleth in Zion: declare among the people his doings.

### Psalm 11

IN the LORD put I my trust: how say ye to my soul, Flee as a bird to your mountain?

For, lo, the wicked bend their bow, they make ready their arrow upon the string, that in the darkness they may shoot at the upright in heart.

If the foundations be destroyed, what can the righteous do?

The LORD is in his holy temple, the LORD's throne is in heaven: his eyes behold, his eyelids try, the children of men.

The LORD trieth the righteous: but the wicked and him that loveth violence his soul hateth.

Upon the wicked he shall rain snares, fire and brimstone, and an horrible tempest: this shall be the portion of their cup.

For the righteous LORD loveth righteousness; his countenance doth behold the upright.

## SELECTION 4

### Psalm 13

HOW long wilt thou forget me, O LORD? for ever? how long wilt thou hide thy face from me?

How long shall I take counsel in my soul, having sorrow in my heart daily? how long shall mine enemy be exalted over me?

Consider and hear me, O LORD my God: lighten mine eyes, lest I sleep the sleep of death;

Lest mine enemy say, I have prevailed against him; and those that trouble me rejoice when I am moved.

But I have trusted in thy mercy; my heart shall rejoice in thy salvation.

I will sing unto the LORD, because he hath dealt bountifully with me.

### Psalm 15

LORD, who shall abide in thy tabernacle? who shall dwell in thy holy hill?

He that walketh uprightly, and worketh righteousness, and speaketh the truth in his heart.

He that backbiteth not with his tongue, nor doeth evil to his neighbour, nor taketh up a reproach against his neighbour.

In whose eyes a vile person is contemned; but he honoureth them that fear the LORD. He that sweareth to his own hurt, and changeth not.

He that putteth not out his money to usury, nor taketh reward against the innocent. He that doeth these things shall never be moved.

### Psalm 16

PRESERVE me, O God: for in thee do I put my trust.

O my soul, thou hast said unto the LORD, Thou art my Lord: Thou art not bound to provide for my good.

As for the saints that are in the earth, and the excellent, in them is all my delight.

Their sorrows shall be multiplied that hasten after another god: their drink offerings of blood will I not offer, nor take up their names into my lips.

The LORD is the portion of mine inheritance and of my cup: thou maintainest my lot.

The lines are fallen unto me in pleasant places; yea, I have a goodly heritage.

I will bless the LORD, who hath given me counsel: my reins also instruct me in the night seasons.

# Psalter Selections

I have set the LORD always before me: because he is at my right hand, I shall not be moved.

**Therefore my heart is glad, and my glory rejoiceth: my flesh also shall rest in hope.**

For thou wilt not leave my soul in hell; neither wilt thou suffer thine Holy One to see corruption.

**Thou wilt show me the path of life: in thy presence is fulness of joy; at thy right hand there are pleasures for evermore.**

## SELECTION 5

### PSALM 17

HEAR the right, O LORD, attend unto my cry, give ear unto my prayer, from lips without deceit.

Let my sentence come forth from thy presence; let thine eyes behold the things that are equal.

Thou hast proved mine heart; thou hast visited me in the night; thou hast tried me, and shalt find nothing; I am purposed that my mouth shall not transgress.

Concerning the works of men, by the word of thy lips I have kept me from the paths of the destroyer.

Hold up my goings in thy paths, that my footsteps slip not.

**I have called upon thee, for thou wilt hear me, O God: incline thine ear unto me, and hear my speech.**

Show thy marvellous lovingkindness, O thou that savest by thy right hand them which put their trust in thee from those that rise up against them.

**Keep me as the apple of the eye, hide me under the shadow of thy wings,**

From the wicked that oppress me, from my deadly enemies, who compass me about.

**They are inclosed in their own fat: with their mouth they speak proudly.**

They have now compassed us in our steps: they have set their eyes bowing down to the earth;

Like as a lion that is greedy of his prey, and as it were a young lion lurking in secret places.

Arise, O LORD, disappoint him, cast him down: deliver my soul from the wicked, which is thy sword:

From men which are thy hand, O LORD, from men of the world, which have their portion in this life, and whose belly thou fillest with thy hid treasure: they are full of children, and leave the rest of their substance to their babes.

As for me, I will behold thy face in righteousness: I shall be satisfied, when I awake, with thy likeness.

## SELECTION 6

### PSALM 18:1-19

I WILL love thee, O LORD, my strength.

**The LORD is my rock, and my fortress, and my deliverer; my God, my strength, in whom I will trust; my buckler, and the horn of my salvation, and my high tower.**

I will call upon the LORD, who is worthy to be praised: so shall I be saved from mine enemies.

**The sorrows of death compassed me, and the floods of ungodly men made me afraid.**

The sorrows of hell compassed me about: the snares of death confronted me.

**In my distress I called upon the LORD, and cried unto my God: he heard my voice out of his temple, and my cry came before him, even into his ears.**

Then the earth shook and trembled;

# Psalter Selections

the foundations also of the hills moved and were shaken, because he was wroth.

**There went up a smoke out of his nostrils, and fire out of his mouth devoured: coals were kindled by it.**

He bowed the heavens also, and came down: and darkness was under his feet.

**And he rode upon a cherub, and did fly: yea, he did fly upon the wings of the wind.**

He made darkness his secret place; his pavilion round about him were dark waters and thick clouds of the skies.

**At the brightness that was before him his thick clouds passed, hail stones and coals of fire.**

The LORD also thundered in the heavens, and the Highest gave his voice; hail stones and coals of fire.

**Yea, he sent out his arrows, and scattered them; and he shot out lightnings, and discomfited them.**

Then the channels of waters were seen, and the foundations of the world were discovered at thy rebuke, O LORD, at the blast of the breath of thy nostrils.

**He sent from above, he took me, he drew me out of many waters.**

He delivered me from my strong enemy, and from them which hated me: for they were too strong for me.

**They confronted me in the day of my calamity: but the LORD was my stay.**

He brought me forth also into a large place; he delivered me, because he delighted in me.

## SELECTION 7

### PSALM 18:25-35

WITH the merciful thou wilt show thyself merciful; with an upright man thou wilt show thyself upright;

**With the pure thou wilt show thyself pure; and with the froward thou wilt show thyself froward.**

For thou wilt save the afflicted people; but wilt bring down high looks.

**For thou wilt light my candle: the LORD my God will enlighten my darkness.**

For by thee I have run through a troop; and by my God have I leaped over a wall.

**As for God, his way is perfect: the word of the LORD is tried: he is a buckler to all those that trust in him.**

For who is God save the LORD? or who is a rock save our God?

**It is God that girdeth me with strength, and maketh my way perfect.**

He maketh my feet like hinds' feet, and setteth me upon my high places.

**He teacheth my hands to war, so that a bow of steel is broken by mine arms.**

Thou hast also given me the shield of thy salvation: and thy right hand hath holden me up, and thy gentleness hath made me great.

### PSALM 19

THE heavens declare the glory of God; and the firmament showeth his handywork.

Day unto day uttereth speech, and night unto night showeth knowledge.

**There is no speech nor language, neither is their voice heard.**

Their line is gone out through all the earth, and their words to the end of the world. In them hath he set a tabernacle for the sun,

**Which is as a bridegroom coming out of his chamber, and rejoiceth as a strong man to run a race.**

His going forth is from the end of the heaven, and his circuit unto the ends of it:

# Psalter Selections

and there is nothing hid from the heat thereof.

The law of the LORD is perfect, converting the soul: the testimony of the LORD is sure, making wise the simple.

The statutes of the LORD are right, rejoicing the heart: the commandment of the LORD is pure, enlightening the eyes.

The fear of the LORD is clean, enduring for ever: the judgments of the LORD are true and righteous altogether.

More to be desired are they than gold, yea, than much fine gold: sweeter also than honey and the honeycomb.

Moreover by them is thy servant warned: and in keeping of them there is great reward.

Who can understand his errors? cleanse thou me from secret faults.

Keep back thy servant also from presumptuous sins; let them not have dominion over me: then shall I be upright, and I shall be innocent from the great transgression.

Let the words of my mouth, and the meditation of my heart, be acceptable in thy sight, O LORD, my strength, and my redeemer.

## SELECTION 8

### PSALM 20

THE LORD hear thee in the day of trouble; the name of the God of Jacob set thee up on high;

Send thee help from the sanctuary, and strengthen thee out of Zion;

Remember all thy offerings, and accept thy burnt sacrifice;

Grant thee according to thine own heart, and fulfil all thy counsel.

We will rejoice in thy salvation, and in the name of our God we will set up our banners: the LORD fulfil all thy petitions.

Now know I that the LORD saveth his anointed; he will hear him from his holy heaven with the saving strength of his right hand.

Some trust in chariots, and some in horses: but we will remember the name of the LORD our God.

They are brought down and fallen: but we are risen, and stand upright.

Save, LORD: let the king hear us when we call.

### PSALM 23

THE LORD is my shepherd; I shall not want.

He maketh me to lie down in green pastures: he leadeth me beside the still waters.

He restoreth my soul: he leadeth me in the paths of righteousness for his name's sake.

Yea, though I walk through the valley of the shadow of death, I will fear no evil: for thou art with me; thy rod and thy staff they comfort me.

Thou preparest a table before me in the presence of mine enemies: thou anointest my head with oil; my cup runneth over.

Surely goodness and mercy shall follow me all the days of my life; and I will dwell in the house of the LORD for ever.

### PSALM 24

THE earth is the LORD's, and the fulness thereof; the world, and they that dwell therein.

For he hath founded it upon the seas, and established it upon the floods.

Who shall ascend into the hill of the LORD? or who shall stand in his holy place?

He that hath clean hands, and a pure heart; who hath not lifted up his soul unto vanity, nor sworn deceitfully.

He shall receive the blessing from

# Psalter Selections

the LORD, and righteousness from the God of his salvation.

This is the generation of them that seek him, that seek thy face, O Jacob.

Lift up your heads, O ye gates; and be ye lift up, ye everlasting doors; and the King of glory shall come in.

Who is this King of glory? The LORD strong and mighty, the LORD mighty in battle.

Lift up your heads, O ye gates; even lift them up, ye everlasting doors; and the King of glory shall come in.

Who is this King of glory? the LORD of hosts, he is the King of glory.

## SELECTION 9
### PSALM 22:1-22

MY God, my God, why hast thou forsaken me? why art thou so far from helping me, and from the words of my roaring?

O my God, I cry in the daytime, but thou hearest not; and in the night season, and am not silent.

But thou art holy, O thou that inhabitest the praises of Israel.

Our fathers trusted in thee: they trusted, and thou didst deliver them.

They cried unto thee, and were delivered: they trusted in thee, and were not confounded.

But I am a worm, and no man; a reproach of men, and despised of the people.

All they that see me laugh me to scorn: they shoot out the lip, they shake the head, saying,

He trusted on the LORD that he would deliver him: let him deliver him, seeing he delighted in him.

But thou art he that took me out of the womb: thou didst make me hope when I was upon my mother's breasts.

I was cast upon thee from the womb: thou art my God from my mother's belly.

Be not far from me; for trouble is near; for there is none to help.

Many bulls have compassed me: strong bulls of Bashan have beset me round.

They gaped upon me with their mouths, as a ravening and a roaring lion.

I am poured out like water, and all my bones are out of joint: my heart is like wax; it is melted in mine inmost parts.

My strength is dried up like a potsherd; and my tongue cleaveth to my jaws; and thou hast brought me into the dust of death.

For dogs have compassed me: the assembly of the wicked have inclosed me: they pierced my hands and my feet.

I may count all my bones: they look and stare upon me.

They part my garments among them, and cast lots upon my vesture.

But be not thou far from me, O LORD: O my strength, haste thee to help me.

Deliver my soul from the sword; my darling from the power of the dog.

Save me from the lion's mouth: for thou hast heard me from the horns of the wild oxen.

I will declare thy name unto my brethren: in the midst of the congregation will I praise thee.

## SELECTION 10
### PSALM 25

UNTO thee, O LORD, do I lift up my soul.

O my God, I trust in thee: let me not be ashamed, let not mine enemies triumph over me.

# Psalter Selections

Yea, let none that wait on thee be ashamed: let them be ashamed which transgress without cause.

Show me thy ways, O Lord; teach me thy paths.

Lead me in thy truth, and teach me: for thou art the God of my salvation; on thee do I wait all the day.

Remember, O Lord, thy tender mercies and thy lovingkindnesses; for they have been ever of old.

Remember not the sins of my youth, nor my transgressions: according to thy mercy remember thou me for thy goodness' sake, O Lord.

Good and upright is the Lord: therefore will he teach sinners in the way.

The meek will he guide in judgment: and the meek will he teach his way.

All the paths of the Lord are mercy and truth unto such as keep his covenant and his testimonies.

For thy name's sake, O Lord, pardon mine iniquity; for it is great.

What man is he that feareth the Lord? him shall he teach in the way that he shall choose.

His soul shall dwell in prosperity; and his seed shall inherit the earth.

The secret of the Lord is with them that fear him; and he will show them his covenant.

Mine eyes are ever toward the Lord; for he shall pluck my feet out of the net.

Turn thee unto me, and have mercy upon me; for I am solitary and afflicted.

The troubles of my heart are enlarged: O bring thou me out of my distresses.

Look upon mine affliction and my pain; and forgive all my sins.

Consider mine enemies; for they are many; and they hate me with cruel hatred.

O keep my soul, and deliver me: let me not be ashamed; for I put my trust in thee.

Let integrity and uprightness preserve me; for I wait on thee.

Redeem Israel, O God, out of all his troubles.

## SELECTION 11

Psalm 26:8-12

Lord, I have loved the habitation of thy house, and the place where thine honour dwelleth.

Gather not my soul with sinners, nor my life with bloody men:

In whose hands is mischief, and their right hand is full of bribes.

But as for me, I will walk in mine integrity: redeem me, and be merciful unto me.

My foot standeth in an even place: in the congregations will I bless the Lord.

Psalm 27

The Lord is my light and my salvation; whom shall I fear? the Lord is the strength of my life; of whom shall I be afraid?

When the wicked, even mine enemies and my foes, came upon me to eat up my flesh, they stumbled and fell.

Though an host should encamp against me, my heart shall not fear: though war should rise against me, in this will I be confident.

One thing have I desired of the Lord, that will I seek after; that I may dwell in the house of the Lord all the days of my life, to behold the beauty of the Lord, and to enquire in his temple.

For in the time of trouble he shall hide me in his pavilion: in the secret of his tabernacle shall he hide me; he shall set me up upon a rock.

# Psalter Selections

And now shall mine head be lifted up above mine enemies round about me: therefore will I offer in his tabernacle sacrifices of joy; I will sing, yea, I will sing praises unto the LORD.

Hear, O LORD, when I cry with my voice: have mercy also upon me, and answer me.

When thou saidst, Seek ye my face; my heart said unto thee, Thy face, LORD, will I seek.

Hide not thy face far from me; put not thy servant away in anger: thou hast been my help; leave me not, neither forsake me, O God of my salvation.

When my father and my mother forsake me, then the LORD will take me up.

Teach me thy way, O LORD, and lead me in a plain path, because of mine enemies.

Deliver me not over unto the will of mine enemies: for false witnesses are risen up against me, and such as breathe out cruelty.

I had fainted, unless I had believed to see the goodness of the LORD in the land of the living.

Wait on the LORD: be of good courage, and he shall strengthen thine heart: wait, I say, on the LORD.

### SELECTION 12

#### PSALM 28

UNTO thee will I cry, O LORD my rock; be not silent to me: lest, if thou be silent to me, I become like them that go down into the pit.

Hear the voice of my supplications, when I cry unto thee, when I lift up my hands toward thy holy oracle.

Draw me not away with the wicked, and with the workers of iniquity, which speak peace to their neighbours, but mischief is in their hearts.

Give them according to their deeds, and according to the wickedness of their endeavours: give them after the work of their hands; render to them their desert.

Because they regard not the works of the LORD, nor the operation of his hands, he shall destroy them, and not build them up.

Blessed be the LORD, because he hath heard the voice of my supplications.

The LORD is my strength and my shield; my heart trusted in him, and I am helped: therefore my heart greatly rejoiceth; and with my song will I praise him.

The LORD is their strength, and he is the saving strength of his anointed.

Save thy people, and bless thine inheritance: feed them also, and lift them up for ever.

#### PSALM 29

GIVE unto the LORD, O ye mighty, give unto the LORD glory and strength.

Give unto the LORD the glory due unto his name; worship the LORD in the beauty of holiness.

The voice of the LORD is upon the waters: the God of glory thundereth: the LORD is upon many waters.

The voice of the LORD is powerful; the voice of the LORD is full of majesty.

The voice of the LORD breaketh the cedars; yea, the LORD breaketh the cedars of Lebanon.

He maketh them also to skip like a calf; Lebanon and Sirion like a young wild ox.

The voice of the LORD divideth the flames of fire.

The voice of the LORD shaketh the

# Psalter Selections

wilderness; the LORD shaketh the wilderness of Kadesh.

**The voice of the LORD maketh the hinds to calve, and layeth bare the forests: and in his temple doth every one speak of his glory.**

The LORD sitteth upon the flood; yea, the LORD sitteth King for ever.

**The LORD will give strength unto his people; the LORD will bless his people with peace.**

### SELECTION 13

#### PSALM 30

I WILL extol thee, O LORD; for thou hast lifted me up, and hast not made my foes to rejoice over me.

**O LORD my God, I cried unto thee, and thou hast healed me.**

O LORD, thou hast brought up my soul from the grave: thou hast kept me alive, that I should not go down to the pit.

**Sing unto the LORD, O ye saints of his, and give thanks at the remembrance of his holiness.**

For his anger endureth but a moment; in his favour is life: weeping may endure for a night, but joy cometh in the morning.

**And in my prosperity I said, I shall never be moved.**

LORD, by thy favour thou hast made my mountain to stand strong: thou didst hide thy face, and I was troubled.

**I cried to thee, O LORD; and unto the LORD I made supplication.**

What profit is there in my blood, when I go down to the pit? Shall the dust praise thee? shall it declare thy truth?

**Hear, O LORD, and have mercy upon me: LORD, be thou my helper.**

Thou hast turned for me my mourning into dancing: thou hast put off my sackcloth, and girded me with gladness;

**To the end that my glory may sing praise to thee, and not be silent. O LORD my God, I will give thanks unto thee for ever.**

#### PSALM 31:1-14

IN thee, O LORD, do I put my trust; let me never·be ashamed: deliver me in thy righteousness.

**Bow down thine ear to me; deliver me speedily: be thou my strong rock, for an house of defence to save me.**

For thou art my rock and my fortress; therefore for thy name's sake lead me, and guide me.

**Pull me out of the net that they have hidden for me: for thou art my strength.**

Into thine hand I commit my spirit: thou hast redeemed me, O LORD God of truth.

**I have hated them that regard lying vanities: but I trust in the LORD.**

I will be glad and rejoice in thy mercy: for thou hast considered my trouble; thou hast known my soul in adversities;

**And hast not shut me up into the hand of the enemy: thou hast set my feet in a large room.**

Have mercy upon me, O LORD, for I am in trouble: mine eye is consumed with grief, yea, my soul and my belly.

**For my life is spent with grief, and my years with sighing: my strength faileth because of mine iniquity, and my bones are consumed.**

I was a reproach among all mine enemies, but especially among my neighbours, and a fear to mine acquaintance: they that did see me without fled from me.

# Psalter Selections

I am forgotten as a dead man out of mind: I am like a broken vessel.

For I have heard the slander of many: fear was on every side: while they took counsel together against me, they devised to take away my life.

But I trusted in thee, O Lord: I said, Thou art my God.

### SELECTION 14

#### Psalm 31:15-24

MY times are in thy hand: deliver me from the hand of mine enemies, and from them that persecute me.

Make thy face to shine upon thy servant: save me for thy mercies' sake.

Let me not be ashamed, O Lord; for I have called upon thee: let the wicked be ashamed, and let them be silent in the grave.

Let the lying lips be put to silence; which speak grievous things proudly and contemptuously against the righteous.

Oh how great is thy goodness, which thou hast laid up for them that fear thee; which thou hast wrought for them that trust in thee before the sons of men!

Thou shalt hide them in the secret of thy presence from the pride of man: thou shalt keep them secretly in a pavilion from the strife of tongues.

Blessed be the Lord: for he hath showed me his marvellous kindness in a strong city.

For I said in my haste, I am cut off from before thine eyes: nevertheless thou heardest the voice of my supplications when I cried unto thee.

O love the Lord, all ye his saints: for the Lord preserveth the faithful, and plentifully rewardeth the proud doer.

Be of good courage, and he shall strengthen your heart, all ye that hope in the Lord.

#### Psalm 32

BLESSED is he whose transgression is forgiven, whose sin is covered.

Blessed is the man unto whom the Lord imputeth not iniquity, and in whose spirit there is no guile.

When I kept silence, my bones waxed old through my roaring all the day long.

For day and night thy hand was heavy upon me: my moisture is turned into the drought of summer.

I acknowledged my sin unto thee, and mine iniquity have I not hid. I said, I will confess my transgressions unto the Lord; and thou forgavest the iniquity of my sin.

For this shall every one that is godly pray unto thee in a time when thou mayest be found: surely in the floods of great waters they shall not come nigh unto him.

Thou art my hiding place; thou shalt preserve me from trouble; thou shalt compass me about with songs of deliverance.

I will instruct thee and teach thee in the way which thou shalt go: I will guide thee with mine eye.

Be ye not as the horse, or as the mule, which have no understanding: whose mouth must be held in with bit and bridle, lest they come near unto thee.

Many sorrows shall be to the wicked: but he that trusteth in the Lord, mercy shall compass him about.

Be glad in the Lord, and rejoice, ye righteous: and shout for joy, all ye that are upright in heart.

# Psalter Selections

## SELECTION 15

### Psalm 33

REJOICE in the Lord, O ye righteous: for praise is comely for the upright.

Praise the Lord with harp: sing unto him with the psaltery and an instrument of ten strings.

Sing unto him a new song; play skilfully with a loud noise.

For the word of the Lord is right; and all his works are done in truth.

He loveth righteousness and judgment: the earth is full of the goodness of the Lord.

By the word of the Lord were the heavens made; and all the host of them by the breath of his mouth.

He gathereth the waters of the sea together as an heap: he layeth up the depth in storehouses.

Let all the earth fear the Lord: let all the inhabitants of the world stand in awe of him.

For he spake, and it was done; he commanded, and it stood fast.

The Lord bringeth the counsel of the heathen to nought: he maketh the devices of the people of none effect.

The counsel of the Lord standeth for ever, the thoughts of his heart to all generations.

Blessed is the nation whose God is the Lord; and the people whom he hath chosen for his own inheritance.

The Lord looketh from heaven; he beholdeth all the sons of men.

From the place of his habitation he looketh upon all the inhabitants of the earth.

He fashioneth their hearts alike; he considereth all their works.

There is no king saved by the multitude of an host: a mighty man is not delivered by much strength.

An horse is a vain thing for safety: neither shall he deliver any by his great strength.

Behold, the eye of the Lord is upon them that fear him, upon them that hope in his mercy;

To deliver their soul from death, and to keep them alive in famine.

Our soul waiteth for the Lord: he is our help and our shield.

For our heart shall rejoice in him, because we have trusted in his holy name.

Let thy mercy, O Lord, be upon us, according as we hope in thee.

## SELECTION 16

### Psalm 34

I WILL bless the Lord at all times: his praise shall continually be in my mouth.

My soul shall make her boast in the Lord: the humble shall hear thereof, and be glad.

O magnify the Lord with me, and let us exalt his name together.

I sought the Lord, and he heard me, and delivered me from all my fears.

They looked unto him, and were lightened: and their faces were not ashamed.

This poor man cried, and the Lord heard him, and saved him out of all his troubles.

The angel of the Lord encampeth round about them that fear him, and delivereth them.

O taste and see that the Lord is good: blessed is the man that trusteth in him.

O fear the Lord, ye his saints: for there is no want to them that fear him.

# Psalter Selections

The young lions do lack, and suffer hunger: but they that seek the LORD shall not want any good thing.

Come, ye children, hearken unto me: I will teach you the fear of the LORD.

What man is he that desireth life, and loveth many days, that he may see good?

Keep thy tongue from evil, and thy lips from speaking guile.

Depart from evil, and do good; seek peace, and pursue it.

The eyes of the LORD are upon the righteous, and his ears are open unto their cry.

The face of the LORD is against them that do evil, to cut off the remembrance of them from the earth.

The righteous cry, and the LORD heareth, and delivereth them out of all their troubles.

The LORD is nigh unto them that are of a broken heart; and saveth such as be of a contrite spirit.

Many are the afflictions of the righteous: but the LORD delivereth him out of them all.

He keepeth all his bones: not one of them is broken.

Evil shall slay the wicked: and they that hate the righteous shall be held guilty.

The LORD redeemeth the soul of his servants: and none of them that trust in him shall be held guilty.

## SELECTION 17

### PSALM 36

THE transgression of the wicked saith within my heart, that there is no fear of God before his eyes.

For he flattereth himself in his own eyes, until his iniquity be found to be hateful.

The words of his mouth are iniquity and deceit: he hath left off to be wise, and to do good.

He deviseth mischief upon his bed; he setteth himself in a way that is not good; he abhorreth not evil.

Thy mercy, O LORD, is in the heavens; and thy faithfulness reacheth unto the clouds.

Thy righteousness is like the great mountains; thy judgments are a great deep: O LORD, thou preservest man and beast.

How excellent is thy lovingkindness, O God! therefore the children of men put their trust under the shadow of thy wings.

They shall be abundantly satisfied with the fatness of thy house; and thou shalt make them drink of the river of thy pleasures.

For with thee is the fountain of life: in thy light shall we see light.

O continue thy lovingkindness unto them that know thee; and thy righteousness to the upright in heart.

Let not the foot of pride come against me, and let not the hand of the wicked remove me.

There are the workers of iniquity fallen: they are cast down, and shall not be able to rise.

### PSALM 37:1-9

FRET not thyself because of evildoers, neither be thou envious against the workers of iniquity.

For they shall soon be cut down like the grass, and wither as the green herb.

Trust in the LORD, and do good; so shalt thou dwell in the land, and verily thou shalt be fed.

# Psalter Selections

Delight thyself also in the LORD; and he shall give thee the desires of thine heart.

Commit thy way unto the LORD; trust also in him; and he shall bring it to pass.

And he shall bring forth thy righteousness as the light, and thy judgment as the noonday.

Rest in the LORD, and wait patiently for him: fret not thyself because of him who prospereth in his way, because of the man who bringeth wicked devices to pass.

Cease from anger, and forsake wrath: fret not thyself in any wise to do evil.

For evildoers shall be cut off: but those that wait upon the LORD, they shall inherit the earth.

### SELECTION 18

#### PSALM 37:23-40

THE steps of a good man are ordered by the LORD: and he delighteth in his way.

Though he fall, he shall not be utterly cast down: for the LORD upholdeth him with his hand.

I have been young, and now am old; yet have I not seen the righteous forsaken, nor his seed begging bread.

He is ever merciful, and lendeth; and his seed is blessed.

Depart from evil, and do good; and dwell for evermore.

For the LORD loveth judgment, and forsaketh not his saints; they are preserved for ever: but the seed of the wicked shall be cut off.

The righteous shall inherit the land, and dwell therein for ever.

The mouth of the righteous speaketh wisdom, and his tongue talketh of judgment.

The law of his God is in his heart; none of his steps shall slide.

The wicked watcheth the righteous, and seeketh to slay him.

The LORD will not leave him in his hand, nor condemn him when he is judged.

Wait on the LORD, and keep his way, and he shall exalt thee to inherit the land: when the wicked are cut off, thou shalt see it.

I have seen the wicked in great power, and spreading himself like a green bay tree.

Yet he passed away, and, lo, he was not: yea, I sought him, but he could not be found.

Mark the perfect man, and behold the upright: for the end of that man is peace.

But the transgressors shall be destroyed together: the end of the wicked shall be cut off.

But the salvation of the righteous is of the LORD: he is their strength in the time of trouble.

And the LORD shall help them, and deliver them: he shall deliver them from the wicked, and save them, because they trust in him.

### SELECTION 19

#### PSALM 39

I SAID, I will take heed to my ways, that I sin not with my tongue: I will keep my mouth with a bridle, while the wicked is before me.

I was dumb with silence, I held my peace, even from good; and my sorrow was stirred.

My heart was hot within me, while I was musing the fire burned: then spake I with my tongue,

# Psalter Selections

LORD, make me to know mine end, and the measure of my days, what it is; that I may know how frail I am.

Behold, thou hast made my days as an handbreadth; and mine age is as nothing before thee: verily every man at his best state is altogether vanity.

Surely every man walketh in a vain show: surely they are disquieted in vain: he heapeth up riches, and knoweth not who shall gather them.

And now, Lord, what wait I for? my hope is in thee.

Deliver me from all my transgressions: make me not the reproach of the foolish.

I was dumb, I opened not my mouth; because thou didst it.

Remove thy stroke away from me: I am consumed by the blow of thine hand.

When thou with rebukes dost correct man for iniquity, thou makest his beauty to consume away like a moth: surely every man is vanity.

Hear my prayer, O LORD, and give ear unto my cry; hold not thy peace at my tears: for I am a stranger with thee, and a sojourner, as all my fathers were.

O spare me, that I may recover strength, before I go hence, and be no more.

PSALM 40:1-11

I WAITED patiently for the LORD; and he inclined unto me, and heard my cry.

He brought me up also out of an horrible pit, out of the miry clay, and set my feet upon a rock, and established my goings.

And he hath put a new song in my mouth, even praise unto our God: many shall see it, and fear, and shall trust in the LORD.

Blessed is that man that maketh the LORD his trust, and respecteth not the proud, nor such as turn aside to lies.

Many, O LORD my God, are thy wonderful works which thou hast done, and thy thoughts which are to us-ward: they cannot be reckoned up in order unto thee: if I would declare and speak of them, they are more than can be numbered.

Sacrifice and offering thou didst not desire; mine ears hast thou opened: burnt offering and sin offering hast thou not required.

Then said I, Lo, I come: in the volume of the book it is written of me,

I delight to do thy will, O my God: yea, thy law is within my heart.

I have preached righteousness in the great congregation: lo, I have not refrained my lips, O LORD, thou knowest.

I have not hid thy righteousness within my heart; I have declared thy faithfulness and thy salvation: I have not concealed thy lovingkindness and thy truth from the great congregation.

Withhold not thou thy tender mercies from me, O LORD: let thy lovingkindness and thy truth continually preserve me.

## SELECTION 20

PSALM 40:11-17

WITHHOLD not thou thy tender mercies from me, O LORD: let thy lovingkindness and thy truth continually preserve me.

For innumerable evils have compassed me about: mine iniquities have taken hold upon me, so that I am not able to look up; they are more than the hairs of mine head: therefore my heart faileth me.

# Psalter Selections

Be pleased, O LORD, to deliver me: O LORD, make haste to help me.

Let them be ashamed and confounded together that seek after my soul to destroy it; let them be driven backward and put to shame that wish me evil.

Let them be desolate for a reward of their shame that say unto me, Aha, aha.

Let all those that seek thee rejoice and be glad in thee: let such as love thy salvation say continually, The LORD be magnified.

But I am poor and needy; yet the Lord thinketh upon me; thou art my help and my deliverer; make no tarrying, O my God.

PSALM 41

BLESSED is he that considereth the poor: the LORD will deliver him in time of trouble.

The LORD will preserve him, and keep him alive; and he shall be blessed upon the earth: and thou wilt not deliver him unto the will of his enemies.

The LORD will strengthen him upon the bed of languishing: thou hast changed all his bed in his sickness.

I said, LORD, be merciful unto me: heal my soul; for I have sinned against thee.

Mine enemies speak evil of me, When shall he die, and his name perish?

And if he come to see me, he speaketh vanity: his heart gathereth iniquity to itself; when he goeth abroad, he telleth it.

All that hate me whisper together against me: against me do they devise my hurt.

An evil disease, say they, cleaveth fast unto him: and now that he lieth he shall rise up no more.

Yea, mine own familiar friend, in whom I trusted, which did eat of my bread, hath lifted up his heel against me.

But thou, O LORD, be merciful unto me, and raise me up, that I may requite them.

By this I know that thou favourest me, because mine enemy doth not triumph over me.

And as for me, thou upholdest me in mine integrity, and settest me before thy face for ever.

Blessed be the LORD God of Israel from everlasting, and to everlasting. Amen, and Amen.

SELECTION 21

PSALM 42

AS the hart panteth after the water brooks, so panteth my soul after thee, O God.

My soul thirsteth for God, for the living God: when shall I come and appear before God?

My tears have been my meat day and night, while they continually say unto me, Where is thy God?

When I remember these things, I pour out my soul in me: for I had gone with the multitude, I went with them to the house of God, with the voice of joy and praise, with a multitude that kept holyday.

Why art thou cast down, O my soul? and why art thou disquieted in me? hope thou in God: for I shall yet praise him for the help of his countenance.

O my God, my soul is cast down within me: therefore will I remember thee from the land of Jordan, and of the Hermonites, from the hill Mizar.

Deep calleth unto deep at the noise of thy waterspouts: all thy waves and thy billows are gone over me.

# Psalter Selections

Yet the LORD will command his lovingkindness in the daytime, and in the night his song shall be with me, and my prayer unto the God of my life.

I will say unto God my rock, Why hast thou forgotten me? why go I mourning because of the oppression of the enemy?

**As with a sword in my bones, mine enemies reproach me; while they say daily unto me, Where is thy God?**

Why art thou cast down, O my soul? and why art thou disquieted within me? hope thou in God: for I shall yet praise him, who is the health of my countenance, and my God.

### PSALM 43

JUDGE me, O God, and plead my cause against an ungodly nation: O deliver me from the deceitful and unjust man.

For thou art the God of my strength: why dost thou cast me off? why go I mourning because of the oppression of the enemy?

**O send out thy light and thy truth: let them lead me; let them bring me unto thy holy hill, and to thy tabernacles.**

Then will I go unto the altar of God, unto God my exceeding joy: yea, upon the harp will I praise thee, O God my God.

**Why art thou cast down, O my soul? and why art thou disquieted within me? hope in God: for I shall yet praise him, who is the health of my countenance, and my God.**

### SELECTION 22

### PSALM 44

WE have heard with our ears, O God, our fathers have told us, what work thou didst in their days, in the times of old.

How thou didst drive out the heathen with thy hand, and plantedst them; how thou didst afflict the people, and cast them out.

For they got not the land in possession by their own sword, neither did their own arm save them: but thy right hand, and thine arm, and the light of thy countenance, because thou hadst a favour unto them.

**Thou art my King, O God: command deliverances for Jacob.**

Through thee will we push down our enemies: through thy name will we tread them under that rise up against us.

**For I will not trust in my bow, neither shall my sword save me.**

But thou hast saved us from our enemies, and hast put them to shame that hated us.

**In God we boast all the day long, and praise thy name for ever.**

But thou hast cast off, and put us to shame; and goest not forth with our armies.

**Thou makest us to turn back from the enemy: and they which hate us spoil for themselves.**

Thou hast given us like sheep appointed for meat; and hast scattered us among the heathen.

**Thou sellest thy people for nought, and dost not increase thy wealth by their price.**

Thou makest us a reproach to our neighbours, a scorn and a derision to them that are round about us.

**Thou makest us a byword among the heathen, a shaking of the head among the people.**

My confusion is continually before me, and the shame of my face hath covered me,

# Psalter Selections

For the voice of him that reproacheth and blasphemeth; by reason of the enemy and avenger.

All this is come upon us; yet have we not forgotten thee, neither have we dealt falsely in thy covenant.

Our heart is not turned back, neither have our steps declined from thy way;

Though thou hast sore broken us in the place of dragons, and covered us with the shadow of death.

If we have forgotten the name of our God, or stretched out our hands to a strange god;

Shall not God search this out? for he knoweth the secrets of the heart.

Yea, for thy sake are we killed all the day long; we are counted as sheep for the slaughter.

Awake, why sleepest thou, O Lord? arise, cast us not off for ever.

Wherefore hidest thou thy face, and forgettest our affliction and our oppression?

For our soul is bowed down to the dust: our belly cleaveth unto the earth.

Arise for our help, and redeem us for thy mercies' sake.

## SELECTION 23

### Psalm 45

MY heart is inditing a good matter: I speak of the things which I have made touching the king: my tongue is the pen of a ready writer.

Thou art fairer than the children of men: grace is poured into thy lips: therefore God hath blessed thee for ever.

Gird thy sword upon thy thigh, O most mighty, with thy glory and thy majesty.

And in thy majesty ride prosperously because of truth and meekness and righteousness; and thy right hand shall teach thee terrible things.

Thine arrows are sharp in the heart of the king's enemies; whereby the people fall under thee.

Thy throne, O God, is for ever and ever: the sceptre of thy kingdom is a right sceptre.

Thou lovest righteousness, and hatest wickedness: therefore God, thy God, hath anointed thee with the oil of gladness above thy fellows.

All thy garments smell of myrrh, and aloes, and cassia, out of the ivory palaces, whereby they have made thee glad.

Kings' daughters were among thy honourable women: upon thy right hand did stand the queen in gold of Ophir.

Hearken, O daughter, and consider, and incline thine ear; forget also thine own people, and thy father's house;

So shall the king greatly desire thy beauty: for he is thy Lord; and worship thou him.

And the daughter of Tyre shall be there with a gift; even the rich among the people shall intreat thy favour.

The king's daughter is all glorious within: her clothing is of wrought gold.

She shall be brought unto the king in raiment of needlework: the virgins her companions that follow her shall be brought unto thee.

With gladness and rejoicing shall they be brought: they shall enter into the king's palace.

Instead of thy fathers shall be thy children, whom thou mayest make princes in all the earth.

# Psalter Selections

I will make thy name to be remembered in all generations: therefore shall the people praise thee for ever and ever.

## SELECTION 24

### Psalm 46

GOD is our refuge and strength, a very present help in trouble.

Therefore will not we fear, though the earth be removed, and though the mountains be carried into the midst of the sea;

Though the waters thereof roar and be troubled, though the mountains shake with the swelling thereof.

There is a river, the streams whereof shall make glad the city of God, the holy place of the tabernacles of the most High.

God is in the midst of her; she shall not be moved: God shall help her, and that right early.

The heathen raged, the kingdoms were moved: he uttered his voice, the earth melted.

The Lord of hosts is with us; the God of Jacob is our refuge.

Come, behold the works of the Lord, what desolations he hath made in the earth.

He maketh wars to cease unto the end of the earth; he breaketh the bow, and cutteth the spear in sunder; he burneth the chariot in the fire.

Be still, and know that I am God: I will be exalted among the heathen, I will be exalted in the earth.

The Lord of hosts is with us; the God of Jacob is our refuge.

### Psalm 47

O CLAP your hands, all ye people; shout unto God with the voice of triumph.

For the Lord most high is terrible; he is a great King over all the earth.

He shall subdue the people under us, and the nations under our feet.

He shall choose our inheritance for us, the excellency of Jacob whom he loved.

God is gone up with a shout, the Lord with the sound of a trumpet.

Sing praises to God, sing praises: sing praises unto our King, sing praises.

For God is the King of all the earth: sing ye praises with understanding.

God reigneth over the heathen: God sitteth upon the throne of his holiness.

The princes of the people are gathered together, even the people of the God of Abraham: for the shields of the earth belong unto God: he is greatly exalted.

## SELECTION 25

### Psalm 48

GREAT is the Lord, and greatly to be praised in the city of our God, in the mountain of his holiness.

Beautiful for situation, the joy of the whole earth, is mount Zion, on the sides of the north, the city of the great King.

God is known in her palaces for a refuge.

For, lo, the kings were assembled, they passed by together.

They saw it, and so they marvelled; they were troubled, and hasted away.

Fear took hold upon them there, and pain, as of a woman in travail.

Thou breakest the ships of Tarshish with an east wind.

As we have heard, so have we seen in the city of the Lord of hosts, in the

# Psalter Selections

city of our God: God will establish it for ever.

We have thought of thy loving kindness, O God, in the midst of thy temple.

According to thy name, O God, so is thy praise unto the ends of the earth: thy right hand is full of righteousness.

Let mount Zion rejoice, let the daughters of Judah be glad, because of thy judgments.

Walk about Zion, and go round about her: count the towers thereof.

Mark ye well her bulwarks, consider her palaces; that ye may tell it to the generation following.

For this God is our God for ever and ever: he will be our guide even unto death.

### Psalm 50:1-15

THE mighty God, even the LORD, hath spoken, and called the earth from the rising of the sun unto the going down thereof.

Out of Zion, the perfection of beauty, God hath shined.

Our God shall come, and shall not keep silence: a fire shall devour before him, and it shall be very tempestuous round about him.

He shall call to the heavens from above, and to the earth, that he may judge his people.

Gather my saints together unto me; those that have made a covenant with me by sacrifice.

And the heavens shall declare his righteousness: for God is judge himself.

Hear, O my people, and I will speak; O Israel, and I will testify against thee: I am God, even thy God.

I will not reprove thee for thy sacrifices or thy burnt offerings, to have been continually before me.

I will take no bullock out of thy house, nor he goats out of thy folds.

For every beast of the forest is mine, and the cattle upon a thousand hills.

I know all the fowls of the mountains: and the wild beasts of the field are mine.

If I were hungry, I would not tell thee: for the world is mine, and the fulness thereof.

Will I eat the flesh of bulls, or drink the blood of goats?

Offer unto God thanksgiving; and pay thy vows unto the most High:

And call upon me in the day of trouble: I will deliver thee, and thou shalt glorify me.

## SELECTION 26

### Psalm 51

HAVE mercy upon me, O God, according to thy lovingkindness: according unto the multitude of thy tender mercies blot out my transgressions.

Wash me thoroughly from mine iniquity, and cleanse me from my sin.

For I acknowledge my transgressions: and my sin is ever before me.

Against thee, thee only, have I sinned, and done this evil in thy sight: that thou mightest be justified when thou speakest, and be clear when thou judgest.

Behold, I was shapen in iniquity; and in sin did my mother conceive me.

Behold, thou desirest truth in the inward parts: and in the hidden part thou shalt make me to know wisdom.

Purge me with hyssop, and I shall be clean: wash me, and I shall be whiter than snow.

Make me to hear joy and gladness;

# Psalter Selections

that the bones which thou hast broken may rejoice.

Hide thy face from my sins, and blot out all mine iniquities.

**Create in me a clean heart, O God; and renew a right spirit within me.**

Cast me not away from thy presence; and take not thy holy spirit from me.

**Restore unto me the joy of thy salvation; and uphold me with thy free spirit.**

Then will I teach transgressors thy ways; and sinners shall be converted unto thee.

**Deliver me from bloodguiltiness, O God, thou God of my salvation: and my tongue shall sing aloud of thy righteousness.**

O Lord, open thou my lips; and my mouth shall show forth thy praise.

**For thou desirest not sacrifice; else would I give it: thou delightest not in burnt offering.**

The sacrifices of God are a broken spirit: a broken and a contrite heart, O God, thou wilt not despise.

**Do good in thy good pleasure unto Zion: build thou the walls of Jerusalem.**

Then shalt thou be pleased with the sacrifices of righteousness, with burnt offering and whole burnt offering: then shall they offer bullocks upon thine altar.

## SELECTION 27

### Psalm 52

WHY boastest thou thyself in mischief, O mighty man? the goodness of God endureth continually.

**Thy tongue deviseth mischiefs; like a sharp razor, working deceitfully.**

Thou lovest evil more than good; and lying rather than to speak righteousness.

**Thou lovest all devouring words, O thou deceitful tongue.**

God shall likewise destroy thee for ever, he shall take thee away, and pluck thee out of thy dwelling place, and root thee out of the land of the living.

**The righteous also shall see, and fear, and shall laugh at him:**

Lo, this is the man that made not God his strength; but trusted in the abundance of his riches, and strengthened himself in his wickedness.

**But I am like a green olive tree in the house of God: I trust in the mercy of God for ever and ever.**

I will praise thee for ever, because thou hast done it: and I will wait on thy name; for it is good before thy saints.

### Psalm 53

THE fool hath said in his heart, There is no God. Corrupt are they, and have done abominable iniquity: there is none that doeth good.

God looked down from heaven upon the children of men, to see if there were any that did understand, that did seek God.

Every one of them is gone back: they are altogether become filthy; there is none that doeth good, no, not one.

Have the workers of iniquity no knowledge? who eat up my people as they eat bread: they have not called upon God.

There were they in great fear, where no fear was: for God hath scattered the bones of him that encampeth against thee: thou hast put them to shame, because God hath despised them.

Oh that the salvation of Israel were come out of Zion! When God bringeth back the captivity of his people, Jacob shall rejoice, and Israel shall be glad.

# Psalter Selections

## SELECTION 28

### Psalm 56

BE merciful unto me, O God: for man would swallow me up; he fighting daily oppresseth me.

**Mine enemies would daily swallow me up: for they be many that fight against me, O thou most High.**

What time I am afraid, I will trust in thee.

**In God I will praise his word, in God I have put my trust; I will not fear what flesh can do unto me.**

Every day they wrest my words: all their thoughts are against me for evil.

**They gather themselves together, they hide themselves, they mark my steps, when they wait for my soul.**

Shall they escape by iniquity? in thine anger cast down the people, O God.

**Thou dost count my wanderings: put thou my tears into thy bottle: are they not in thy book?**

When I cry unto thee, then shall mine enemies turn back: this I know; for God is for me.

**In God will I praise his word: in the LORD will I praise his word.**

In God have I put my trust: I will not be afraid what man can do unto me.

**Thy vows are upon me, O God: I will render praises unto thee.**

For thou hast delivered my soul from death: wilt not thou deliver my feet from falling, that I may walk before God in the light of the living?

### Psalm 57

BE merciful unto me, O God, be merciful unto me: for my soul trusteth in thee: yea, in the shadow of thy wings will I make my refuge, until these calamities be overpast.

**I will cry unto God most high; unto God that performeth all things for me.**

**He shall send from heaven, and save me from the reproach of him that would swallow me up. God shall send forth his mercy and his truth.**

My soul is among lions: and I lie even among them that are set on fire, even the sons of men, whose teeth are spears and arrows, and their tongue a sharp sword.

**Be thou exalted, O God, above the heavens; let thy glory be above all the earth.**

They have prepared a net for my steps; my soul is bowed down: they have digged a pit before me, into the midst whereof they are fallen themselves.

**My heart is fixed, O God, my heart is fixed: I will sing and give praise.**

Awake up, my glory; awake, psaltery and harp: I myself will awake early.

**I will praise thee, O Lord, among the people: I will sing unto thee among the nations.**

For thy mercy is great unto the heavens, and thy truth unto the clouds.

**Be thou exalted, O God, above the heavens: let thy glory be above all the earth.**

## SELECTION 29

### Psalm 61

HEAR my cry, O God; attend unto my prayer.

**From the end of the earth will I cry unto thee, when my heart is overwhelmed: lead me to the rock that is higher than I.**

For thou hast been a shelter for me, and a strong tower from the enemy.

**I will abide in thy tabernacle for ever: I will trust in the covert of thy wings.**

# Psalter Selections

For thou, O God, hast heard my vows: thou hast given me the heritage of those that fear thy name.

Thou wilt prolong the king's life: and his years as many generations.

He shall abide before God for ever: O prepare mercy and truth, which may preserve him.

So will I sing praise unto thy name for ever, that I may daily perform my vows.

### Psalm 62

TRULY my soul waiteth upon God: from him cometh my salvation.

He only is my rock and my salvation; he is my defence; I shall not be greatly moved.

How long, all of you, will ye rush upon a man to slay him, as a leaning wall and as a tottering fence?

They only consult to cast him down from his excellency: they delight in lies: they bless with their mouth, but they curse inwardly.

My soul, wait thou only upon God; for my expectation is from him.

He only is my rock and my salvation: he is my defence; I shall not be moved.

In God is my salvation and my glory: the rock of my strength, and my refuge, is in God.

Trust in him at all times; ye people, pour out your heart before him: God is a refuge for us.

Surely men of low degree are vanity, and men of high degree are a lie: to be laid in the balance, they are altogether lighter than vanity.

Trust not in oppression, and become not vain in robbery: if riches increase, set not your heart upon them.

God hath spoken once; twice have I heard this; that power belongeth unto God.

Also unto thee, O Lord, belongeth mercy: for thou renderest to every man according to his work.

## SELECTION 30

### Psalm 63

O GOD, thou art my God; early will I seek thee: my soul thirsteth for thee, my flesh longeth for thee in a dry and thirsty land, where no water is;

To see thy power and thy glory, so as I have seen thee in the sanctuary.

Because thy lovingkindness is better than life, my lips shall praise thee.

Thus will I bless thee while I live: I will lift up my hands in thy name.

My soul shall be satisfied as with marrow and fatness; and my mouth shall praise thee with joyful lips:

When I remember thee upon my bed, and meditate on thee in the night watches.

Because thou hast been my help, therefore in the shadow of thy wings will I rejoice.

My soul followeth hard after thee: thy right hand upholdeth me.

But those that seek my soul, to destroy it, shall go into the lower parts of the earth.

They shall fall by the sword: they shall be a portion for foxes.

But the king shall rejoice in God; every one that sweareth by him shall glory: but the mouth of them that speak lies shall be stopped.

### Psalm 65

PRAISE waiteth for thee, O God, in Sion: and unto thee shall the vow be performed.

# Psalter Selections

O thou that hearest prayer, unto thee shall all flesh come.

Iniquities prevail against me: as for our transgressions, thou shalt purge them away.

Blessed is the man whom thou choosest, and causest to approach unto thee, that he may dwell in thy courts: we shall be satisfied with the goodness of thy house, even of thy holy temple.

By terrible things in righteousness wilt thou answer us, O God of our salvation; who art the confidence of all the ends of the earth, and of them that are afar off upon the sea:

Which by his strength setteth fast the mountains; being girded with power:

Which stilleth the noise of the seas, the noise of their waves, and the tumult of the people.

They also that dwell in the uttermost parts are afraid at thy tokens: thou makest the outgoings of the morning and evening to rejoice.

Thou visitest the earth, and waterest it: thou greatly enrichest it with the river of God, which is full of water: thou preparest them corn, when thou hast so provided for it.

Thou waterest the ridges thereof abundantly: thou settlest the furrows thereof: thou makest it soft with showers: thou blessest the springing thereof.

Thou crownest the year with thy goodness; and thy paths drop fatness.

They drop upon the pastures of the wilderness: and the little hills rejoice on every side.

The pastures are clothed with flocks; the valleys also are covered over with corn; they shout for joy, they also sing.

## SELECTION 31

### Psalm 66

MAKE a joyful noise unto God, all ye lands:

Sing forth the honour of his name: make his praise glorious.

Say unto God, How terrible art thou in thy works! through the greatness of thy power shall thine enemies submit themselves unto thee.

All the earth shall worship thee, and shall sing unto thee; they shall sing to thy name.

Come and see the works of God: he is terrible in his doing toward the children of men.

He turned the sea into dry land: they went through the flood on foot: there did we rejoice in him.

He ruleth by his power for ever; his eyes behold the nations: let not the rebellious exalt themselves.

O bless our God, ye people, and make the voice of his praise to be heard:

Which holdeth our soul in life, and suffereth not our feet to be moved.

For thou, O God, hast proved us: thou hast tried us, as silver is tried.

Thou broughtest us into the net; thou laidst affliction upon our loins.

Thou hast caused men to ride over our heads; we went through fire and through water: but thou broughtest us out into a wealthy place.

I will go into thy house with burnt offerings: I will pay thee my vows, which my lips have uttered, and my mouth hath spoken, when I was in trouble.

I will offer unto thee burnt sacrifices of fatlings, with the incense of rams; I will offer bullocks with goats.

Come and hear, all ye that fear God,

# Psalter Selections

and I will declare what he hath done for my soul.

I cried unto him with my mouth, and he was extolled with my tongue.

If I regard iniquity in my heart, the Lord will not hear me:

But verily God hath heard me; he hath attended to the voice of my prayer.

Blessed be God, which hath not turned away my prayer, nor his mercy from me.

### SELECTION 32
#### Psalm 67

GOD be merciful unto us, and bless us; and cause his face to shine upon us;

That thy way may be known upon earth, thy saving health among all nations.

Let the people praise thee, O God; let all the people praise thee.

O let the nations be glad and sing for joy: for thou shalt judge the people righteously, and govern the nations upon earth.

Let the people praise thee, O God; let all the people praise thee.

Then shall the earth yield her increase; and God, even our own God, shall bless us.

God shall bless us; and all the ends of the earth shall fear him.

#### Psalm 68:1-20

LET God arise, let his enemies be scattered: let them also that hate him flee before him.

As smoke is driven away, so drive them away: as wax melteth before the fire, so let the wicked perish at the presence of God.

But let the righteous be glad; let them rejoice before God: yea, let them exceedingly rejoice.

Sing unto God, sing praises to his name: extol him that rideth upon the heavens by his name JAH, and rejoice before him.

A father of the fatherless, and a judge of the widows, is God in his holy habitation.

God setteth the solitary in families: he bringeth out those which are bound with chains: but the rebellious dwell in a dry land.

O God, when thou wentest forth before thy people, when thou didst march through the wilderness;

The earth shook, the heavens also dropped at the presence of God: even Sinai itself was moved at the presence of God, the God of Israel.

Thou, O God, didst send a plentiful rain, whereby thou didst confirm thine inheritance, when it was weary.

Thy congregation hath dwelt therein: thou, O God, hast prepared of thy goodness for the poor.

The Lord gave the word: great was the company of those that published it.

Kings of armies did flee apace: and she that tarried at home divided the spoil.

Though ye lie among the sheepfolds, yet shall ye be as the wings of a dove covered with silver, and her feathers with yellow gold.

When the Almighty scattered kings in it, it was white as snow in Salmon.

The hill of God is as the hill of Bashan; an high hill as the hill of Bashan.

Why leap ye, ye high hills? this is the hill which God desireth to dwell in; yea, the LORD will dwell in it for ever.

The chariots of God are twenty thousand, even thousands of angels: the Lord is among them, as in Sinai, in the holy place.

# Psalter Selections

Thou hast ascended on high, thou hast led captivity captive: thou hast received gifts for men; yea, for the rebellious also, that the LORD God might dwell among them.

**Blessed be the Lord, who daily loadeth us with benefits, even the God of our salvation.**

He that is our God is the God of salvation; and unto GOD the Lord belong the issues from death.

### SELECTION 33

PSALM 69:1-17

SAVE me, O God; for the waters are come in unto my soul.

**I sink in deep mire, where there is no standing: I am come into deep waters, where the floods overflow me.**

I am weary of my crying: my throat is dried: mine eyes fail while I wait for my God.

**They that hate me without a cause are more than the hairs of mine head: they that would destroy me, being mine enemies wrongfully, are mighty: then I restored that which I took not away.**

O God, thou knowest my foolishness; and my sins are not hid from thee.

**Let not them that wait on thee, O Lord GOD of hosts, be ashamed for my sake: let not those that seek thee be confounded for my sake, O God of Israel.**

Because for thy sake I have borne reproach; shame hath covered my face.

**I am become a stranger unto my brethren, and an alien unto my mother's children.**

For the zeal of thine house hath eaten me up; and the reproaches of them that reproached thee are fallen upon me.

**When I wept, and chastened my soul with fasting, that was to my reproach.**

I made sackcloth also my garment; and I became a proverb to them.

**They that sit in the gate speak against me; and I was the song of the drunkards.**

But as for me, my prayer is unto thee, O LORD, in an acceptable time: O God, in the multitude of thy mercy hear me, in the truth of thy salvation.

**Deliver me out of the mire, and let me not sink: let me be delivered from them that hate me, and out of the deep waters.**

Let not the waterflood overflow me, neither let the deep swallow me up, and let not the pit shut her mouth upon me.

**Hear me, O LORD; for thy lovingkindness is good: turn unto me according to the multitude of thy tender mercies.**

And hide not thy face from thy servant; for I am in trouble: hear me speedily.

### SELECTION 34

PSALM 69:18-36

DRAW nigh unto my soul, and redeem it: deliver me because of mine enemies.

**Thou hast known my reproach, and my shame, and my dishonour: mine adversaries are all before thee.**

Reproach hath broken my heart; and I am full of heaviness: and I looked for some to take pity, but there was none; and for comforters, but I found none.

**They gave me also gall for my food; and in my thirst they gave me vinegar to drink.**

Let their table become a snare before them: and that which should have been for their welfare, let it become a trap.

# Psalter Selections

Let their eyes be darkened, that they see not; and make their loins continually to shake.

Pour out thine indignation upon them, and let thy wrathful anger take hold of them.

**Let their habitation be desolate; and let none dwell in their tents.**

For they persecute him whom thou hast smitten; and they talk to the grief of those whom thou hast wounded.

**Add inquity unto their iniquity: and let them not come into thy righteousness.**

Let them be blotted out of the book of the living, and not be written with the righteous.

**But I am poor and sorrowful: let thy salvation, O God, set me up on high.**

I will praise the name of God with a song, and will magnify him with thanksgiving.

**This also shall please the Lord better than an ox or bullock that hath horns and hoofs.**

The humble shall see this, and be glad: and your heart shall live that seek God.

**For the Lord heareth the poor, and despiseth not his prisoners.**

Let the heaven and earth praise him, the seas, and every thing that moveth therein.

**For God will save Zion, and will build the cities of Judah: that they may dwell there, and have it in possession.**

The seed also of his servants shall inherit it: and they that love his name shall dwell therein.

### Psalm 70

MAKE haste, O God, to deliver me; make haste to help me, O Lord.

Let them be ashamed and confounded that seek after my soul: let them be turned backward, and put to confusion, that desire my hurt.

**Let them be turned back for a reward of their shame that say, Aha, aha.**

Let all those that seek thee rejoice and be glad in thee: and let such as love thy salvation say continually, Let God be magnified.

**But I am poor and needy: make haste unto me, O God: thou art my help and my deliverer; O Lord, make no tarrying.**

### SELECTION 35
#### Psalm 72:1-19

GIVE the king thy judgments, O God, and thy righteousness unto the king's son.

**He shall judge thy people with righteousness, and thy poor with judgment.**

The mountains shall bring peace to the people, and the little hills, by righteousness.

**He shall judge the poor of the people, he shall save the children of the needy, and shall break in pieces the oppressor.**

They shall fear thee as long as the sun and moon endure, throughout all generations.

**He shall come down like rain upon the mown grass: as showers that water the earth.**

In his days shall the righteous flourish; and abundance of peace so long as the moon endureth.

**He shall have dominion also from sea to sea, and from the river unto the ends of the earth.**

They that dwell in the wilderness shall bow before him; and his enemies shall lick the dust.

**The kings of Tarshish and of the**

# Psalter Selections

isles shall bring presents: the kings of Sheba and Seba shall offer gifts.

Yea, all kings shall fall down before him: all nations shall serve him.

For he shall deliver the needy when he crieth; the poor also, and him that hath no helper.

He shall spare the poor and needy, and shall save the souls of the needy.

He shall redeem their soul from deceit and violence: and precious shall their blood be in his sight.

And he shall live, and to him shall be given of the gold of Sheba: prayer also shall be made for him continually; and daily shall he be praised.

There shall be an handful of corn in the earth upon the top of the mountains; the fruit thereof shall shake like Lebanon: and they of the city shall flourish like grass of the earth.

His name shall endure for ever: his name shall be continued as long as the sun: and men shall be blessed in him: all nations shall call him blessed.

Blessed be the LORD God, the God of Israel, who only doeth wondrous things.

And blessed be his glorious name for ever: and let the whole earth be filled with his glory; Amen, and Amen.

## SELECTION 36

### PSALM 73

TRULY God is good to Israel, even to such as are of a clean heart.

But as for me, my feet were almost gone; my steps had well nigh slipped.

For I was envious at the foolish, when I saw the prosperity of the wicked.

For there are no bands in their death: but their strength is firm.

They are not in trouble as other men; neither are they plagued like other men.

Therefore pride compasseth them about as a chain; violence covereth them as a garment.

Their eyes stand out with fatness: they have more than heart could wish.

They are corrupt, and speak wickedly concerning oppression: they speak loftily.

They set their mouth against the heavens, and their tongue walketh through the earth.

Therefore his people return hither: and waters of a full cup are wrung out to them.

And they say, How doth God know? and is there knowledge in the most High?

Behold, these are the ungodly, who prosper in the world; they increase in riches.

Verily I have cleansed my heart in vain, and washed my hands in innocency.

For all the day long have I been plagued, and chastened every morning.

If I say, I will speak thus; behold, I should offend against the generation of thy children.

When I thought to know this, it was too painful for me;

Until I went into the sanctuary of God; then understood I their end.

Surely thou didst set them in slippery places: thou castedst them down into destruction.

How are they brought into desolation, as in a moment! they are utterly consumed with terrors.

As a dream when one awaketh; so, O Lord, when thou awakest, thou shalt despise their image.

Thus my heart was grieved, and I was pricked in my reins.

# Psalter Selections

So foolish was I, and ignorant: I was as a beast before thee.

Nevertheless I am continually with thee: thou hast holden me by my right hand.

Thou shalt guide me with thy counsel, and afterward receive me to glory.

Whom have I in heaven but thee? and there is none upon earth that I desire beside thee.

My flesh and my heart faileth: but God is the strength of my heart, and my portion for ever.

For, lo, they that are far from thee shall perish: thou hast destroyed all them that go a whoring from thee.

But it is good for me to draw near to God: I have put my trust in the Lord GOD, that I may declare all thy works.

### SELECTION 37

#### PSALM 74

O GOD, why hast thou cast us off for ever? why doth thine anger smoke against the sheep of thy pasture?

Remember thy congregation, which thou hast purchased of old; the rod of thine inheritance, which thou hast redeemed; this mount Zion, wherein thou hast dwelt.

Lift up thy feet unto the perpetual desolations; even all that the enemy hath done wickedly in the sanctuary.

Thine enemies roar in the midst of thy congregations; they set up their ensigns for signs.

A man was famous according as he had lifted up axes upon the thick trees.

But now they break down the carved work thereof at once with axes and hammers.

They have cast fire into thy sanctuary, they have defiled by casting down the dwelling place of thy name to the ground.

They said in their hearts, Let us destroy them together: they have burned up all the assemblies of God in the land.

We see not our signs: there is no more any prophet: neither is there among us any that knoweth how long.

O God, how long shall the adversary reproach? shall the enemy blaspheme thy name for ever?

Why withdrawest thou thy hand, even thy right hand? pluck it out of thy bosom.

For God is my King of old, working salvation in the midst of the earth.

Thou didst divide the sea by thy strength: thou brakest the heads of the sea monsters in the waters.

Thou brakest the heads of leviathan in pieces, and gavest him to be meat to the people inhabiting the wilderness.

Thou didst cleave the fountain and the flood: thou driedst up mighty rivers.

The day is thine, the night also is thine: thou hast prepared the light and the sun.

Thou hast set all the borders of the earth: thou hast made summer and winter.

Remember this, that the enemy hath reproached, O LORD, and that the foolish people have blasphemed thy name.

O deliver not the soul of thy turtledove unto the multitude of the wicked: forget not the congregation of thy poor for ever.

Have respect unto the covenant: for the dark places of the earth are full of the habitations of cruelty.

O let not the oppressed return ashamed: let the poor and needy praise thy name.

Arise, O God, plead thine own cause:

# Psalter Selections

remember how the foolish man reproacheth thee daily.

Forget not the voice of thine enemies: the tumult of those that rise up against thee increaseth continually.

## SELECTION 38
### Psalm 77

I CRIED unto God with my voice, even unto God with my voice; and he gave ear unto me.

In the day of my trouble I sought the Lord: my sore ran in the night, and ceased not: my soul refused to be comforted.

I remembered God, and was troubled: I complained, and my spirit was overwhelmed.

Thou holdest mine eyes waking: I am so troubled that I cannot speak.

I have considered the days of old, the years of ancient times.

I call to remembrance my song in the night: I commune with mine own heart: and my spirit made diligent search.

Will the Lord cast off for ever? and will he be favourable no more?

Is his mercy clean gone for ever? doth his promise fail for evermore?

Hath God forgotten to be gracious? hath he in anger shut up his tender mercies?

And I said, This is my infirmity: but I will remember the years of the right hand of the most High.

I will remember the works of the Lord: surely I will remember thy wonders of old.

I will meditate also of all thy work, and talk of thy doings.

Thy way, O God, is in the sanctuary: who is so great a God as our God?

Thou art the God that doest wonders: thou hast declared thy strength among the people.

Thou hast with thine arm redeemed thy people, the sons of Jacob and Joseph.

The waters saw thee, O God, the waters saw thee; they were afraid: the depths also were troubled.

The clouds poured out water: the skies sent out a sound: thine arrows also went abroad.

The voice of thy thunder was in the heaven: the lightnings lightened the world: the earth trembled and shook.

Thy way is in the sea, and thy path in the great waters, and thy footsteps are not known.

Thou leddest thy people like a flock by the hand of Moses and Aaron.

## SELECTION 39
### Psalm 80

GIVE ear, O Shepherd of Israel, thou that leadest Joseph like a flock; thou that dwellest between the cherubim, shine forth.

Before Ephraim and Benjamin and Manasseh stir up thy strength, and come and save us.

Turn us again, O God, and cause thy face to shine; and we shall be saved.

O Lord God of hosts, how long wilt thou be angry against the prayer of thy people?

Thou feedest them with the bread of tears; and givest them tears to drink in great measure.

Thou makest us a strife unto our neighbours: and our enemies laugh among themselves.

Turn us again, O God of hosts, and cause thy face to shine; and we shall be saved.

# Psalter Selections

Thou hast brought a vine out of Egypt: thou hast cast out the heathen, and planted it.

Thou preparedst room before it, and didst cause it to take deep root, and it filled the land.

The hills were covered with the shadow of it, and the boughs thereof were like the goodly cedars.

She sent out her boughs unto the sea, and her branches unto the river.

Why hast thou then broken down her hedges, so that all they which pass by the way do pluck her?

The boar out of the wood doth waste it, and the wild beast of the field doth devour it.

Return, we beseech thee, O God of hosts: look down from heaven, and behold, and visit this vine;

And the vineyard which thy right hand hath planted, and the branch that thou madest strong for thyself.

It is burned with fire, it is cut down: they perish at the rebuke of thy countenance.

Let thy hand be upon the man of thy right hand, upon the son of man whom thou madest strong for thyself.

So will not we go back from thee: quicken us, and we will call upon thy name.

Turn us again, O Lord God of hosts, cause thy face to shine; and we shall be saved.

### SELECTION 40

#### Psalm 84

HOW amiable are thy tabernacles, O Lord of hosts!

My soul longeth, yea, even fainteth for the courts of the Lord: my heart and my flesh crieth out for the living God.

Yea, the sparrow hath found an house, and the swallow a nest for herself, where she may lay her young, even thine altars, O Lord of hosts, my King, and my God.

Blessed are they that dwell in thy house: they will be still praising thee.

Blessed is the man whose strength is in thee; in whose heart are the ways of them.

Who passing through the valley of Baca make it a well; the rain also filleth the pools.

They go from strength to strength, every one of them in Zion appeareth before God.

O Lord God of hosts, hear my prayer: give ear, O God of Jacob.

Behold, O God our shield, and look upon the face of thine anointed.

For a day in thy courts is better than a thousand. I had rather be a doorkeeper in the house of my God, than to dwell in the tents of wickedness.

For the Lord God is a sun and shield: the Lord will give grace and glory: no good thing will he withhold from them that walk uprightly.

O Lord of hosts, blessed is the man that trusteth in thee.

#### Psalm 85

LORD, thou hast been favourable unto thy land: thou hast brought back the captivity of Jacob.

Thou hast forgiven the iniquity of thy people, thou hast covered all their sin.

Thou hast taken away all thy wrath: thou hast turned thyself from the fierceness of thine anger.

Turn us, O God of our salvation, and cause thine anger toward us to cease.

# Psalter Selections

Wilt thou be angry with us for ever? wilt thou draw out thine anger to all generations?

**Wilt thou not revive us again:** that thy people may rejoice in thee?

Show us thy mercy, O Lord, and grant us thy salvation.

**I will hear what God the Lord will speak:** for he will speak peace unto his people, and to his saints: but let them not turn again to folly.

Surely his salvation is nigh them that fear him; that glory may dwell in our land.

**Mercy and truth are met together;** righteousness and peace have kissed each other.

Truth shall spring out of the earth; and righteousness shall look down from heaven.

**Yea, the Lord shall give that which is good;** and our land shall yield her increase.

Righteousness shall go before him; and shall set us in the way of his steps.

### SELECTION 41
#### Psalm 86

BOW down thine ear, O Lord, hear me: for I am poor and needy.

**Preserve my soul; for I am holy:** O thou my God, save thy servant that trusteth in thee.

Be merciful unto me, O Lord: for I cry unto thee daily.

**Rejoice the soul of thy servant:** for unto thee, O Lord, do I lift up my soul.

For thou, Lord, art good, and ready to forgive; and plenteous in mercy unto all them that call upon thee.

**Give ear, O Lord, unto my prayer;** and attend to the voice of my supplications.

In the day of my trouble I will call upon thee: for thou wilt answer me.

**Among the gods there is none like unto thee, O Lord;** neither are there any works like unto thy works.

All nations whom thou hast made shall come and worship before thee, O Lord; and shall glorify thy name.

**For thou art great, and doest wondrous things:** thou art God alone.

Teach me thy way, O Lord; I will walk in thy truth: unite my heart to fear thy name.

**I will praise thee, O Lord my God, with all my heart:** and I will glorify thy name for evermore.

For great is thy mercy toward me: and thou hast delivered my soul from the lowest hell.

**O God, the proud are risen against me,** and the assemblies of violent men have sought after my soul; and have not set thee before them.

But thou, O Lord, art a God full of compassion, and gracious, longsuffering, and plenteous in mercy and truth.

**O turn unto me, and have mercy upon me;** give thy strength unto thy servant, and save the son of thine handmaid.

Show me a token for good; that they which hate me may see it, and be ashamed: because thou, Lord, hast helped me, and comforted me.

#### Psalm 87

HIS foundation is in the holy mountains.

The Lord loveth the gates of Zion more than all the dwellings of Jacob.

**Glorious things are spoken of thee,** O city of God.

I will make mention of Rahab and Babylon to them that know me: behold

# Psalter Selections

Philistia, and Tyre, with Ethiopia; this man was born there.

And of Zion it shall be said, This and that man was born in her: and the highest himself shall establish her.

The LORD shall count, when he writeth up the people, that this man was born there.

As well the singers as the players on instruments shall be there: all my springs are in thee.

### SELECTION 42

#### PSALM 89:1-37

I WILL sing of the mercies of the LORD for ever: with my mouth will I make known thy faithfulness to all generations.

For I have said, Mercy shall be built up for ever: thy faithfulness shalt thou establish in the very heavens.

I have made a covenant with my chosen, I have sworn unto David my servant,

Thy seed will I establish for ever, and build up thy throne to all generations.

And the heavens shall praise thy wonders, O LORD: thy faithfulness also in the congregation of the saints.

For who in the heaven can be compared unto the LORD? who among the sons of the mighty can be likened unto the LORD?

God is greatly to be feared in the assembly of the saints, and to be had in reverence of all them that are about him.

O LORD God of hosts, who is a strong LORD like unto thee? or to thy faithfulness round about thee?

Thou rulest the raging of the sea: when the waves thereof arise, thou stillest them.

Thou hast broken Rahab in pieces, as one that is slain; thou hast scattered thine enemies with thy strong arm.

The heavens are thine, the earth also is thine: as for the world and the fulness thereof, thou hast founded them.

The north and the south thou hast created them: Tabor and Hermon shall rejoice in thy name.

Thou hast a mighty arm: strong is thy hand, and high is thy right hand.

Justice and judgment are the habitation of thy throne: mercy and truth shall go before thy face.

Blessed is the people that know the joyful sound: they shall walk, O LORD, in the light of thy countenance.

In thy name shall they rejoice all the day: and in thy righteousness shall they be exalted.

For thou art the glory of their strength: and in thy favour our horn shall be exalted.

For the LORD is our defence; and the Holy One of Israel is our king.

Then thou spakest in vision to thy holy one, and saidst, I have laid help upon one that is mighty; I have exalted one chosen out of the people.

I have found David my servant; with my holy oil have I anointed him:

With whom my hand shall be established: mine arm also shall strengthen him.

The enemy shall not exact upon him; nor the son of wickedness afflict him.

And I will beat down his foes before his face, and plague them that hate him.

But my faithfulness and my mercy shall be with him: and in my name shall his horn be exalted.

I will set his hand also in the sea, and his right hand in the rivers.

He shall cry unto me, Thou art my

# Psalter Selections

father, my God, and the rock of my salvation.

Also I will make him my firstborn, higher than the kings of the earth.

**My mercy will I keep for him for evermore, and my covenant shall stand fast with him.**

His seed also will I make to endure for ever, and his throne as the days of heaven.

**If his children forsake my law, and walk not in my judgments;**

If they break my statutes, and keep not my commandments;

**Then will I visit their transgression with the rod, and their iniquity with stripes.**

Nevertheless my lovingkindness will I not utterly take from him, nor suffer my faithfulness to fail.

**My covenant will I not break, nor alter the thing that is gone out of my lips.**

Once have I sworn by my holiness that I will not lie unto David.

**His seed shall endure for ever, and his throne as the sun before me.**

It shall be established for ever as the moon, and as a faithful witness in heaven.

### SELECTION 43

#### PSALM 90

LORD, thou hast been our dwelling place in all generations.

**Before the mountains were brought forth, or ever thou hadst formed the earth and the world, even from everlasting to everlasting, thou art God.**

Thou turnest man to destruction; and sayest, Return, ye children of men.

**For a thousand years in thy sight are but as yesterday when it is past, and as a watch in the night.**

Thou carriest them away as with a flood; they are as a sleep: in the morning they are like grass which groweth up.

**In the morning it flourisheth, and groweth up; in the evening it is cut down, and withereth.**

For we are consumed by thine anger, and by thy wrath are we troubled.

**Thou hast set our iniquities before thee, our secret sins in the light of thy countenance.**

For all our days are passed away in thy wrath: we spend our years as a tale that is told.

**The days of our years are threescore years and ten; and if by reason of strength they be fourscore years, yet is their strength labour and sorrow; for it is soon cut off, and we fly away.**

Who knoweth the power of thine anger? even according to thy fear, so is thy wrath.

**So teach us to number our days, that we may apply our hearts unto wisdom.**

Return, O LORD, how long? and let it repent thee concerning thy servants.

**O satisfy us early with thy mercy; that we may rejoice and be glad all our days.**

Make us glad according to the days wherein thou hast afflicted us, and the years wherein we have seen evil.

**Let thy work appear unto thy servants, and thy glory unto their children.**

And let the beauty of the LORD our God be upon us: and establish thou the work of our hands upon us; yea, the work of our hands establish thou it.

### SELECTION 44

#### PSALM 91

HE that dwelleth in the secret place of the most High shall abide under the shadow of the Almighty.

# Psalter Selections

I will say of the LORD, He is my refuge and my fortress: my God; in him will I trust.

Surely he shall deliver thee from the snare of the fowler, and from the noisome pestilence.

He shall cover thee with his feathers, and under his wings shalt thou trust: his truth shall be thy shield and buckler.

Thou shalt not be afraid for the terror by night; nor for the arrow that flieth by day;

Nor for the pestilence that walketh in darkness; nor for the destruction that wasteth at noonday.

A thousand shall fall at thy side, and ten thousand at thy right hand; but it shall not come nigh thee.

Only with thine eyes shalt thou behold and see the reward of the wicked.

Because thou hast made the LORD, which is my refuge, even the most High, thy habitation;

There shall no evil befall thee, neither shall any plague come nigh thy dwelling.

For he shall give his angels charge over thee, to keep thee in all thy ways.

They shall bear thee up in their hands, lest thou dash thy foot against a stone.

Thou shalt tread upon the lion and adder: the young lion and the dragon shalt thou trample under feet.

Because he hath set his love upon me, therefore will I deliver him: I will set him on high, because he hath known my name.

He shall call upon me, and I will answer him: I will be with him in trouble; I will deliver him, and honour him.

With long life will I satisfy him, and show him my salvation.

## SELECTION 45

### PSALM 92

IT is a good thing to give thanks unto the LORD, and to sing praises unto thy name, O most High:

To show forth thy lovingkindness in the morning, and thy faithfulness every night,

Upon an instrument of ten strings, and upon the psaltery; upon the harp with a solemn sound.

For thou, LORD, hast made me glad through thy work: I will triumph in the works of thy hands.

O LORD, how great are thy works! and thy thoughts are very deep.

A brutish man knoweth not; neither doth a fool understand this.

When the wicked spring as the grass, and when all the workers of iniquity do flourish; it is that they shall be destroyed for ever:

But thou, LORD, art most high for evermore.

For, lo, thine enemies, O LORD, for, lo, thine enemies shall perish; all the workers of iniquity shall be scattered.

But my horn shalt thou exalt like the horn of a wild ox: I shall be anointed with fresh oil.

Mine eye also shall see my desire on mine enemies, and mine ears shall hear my desire of the wicked that rise up against me.

The righteous shall flourish like the palm tree: he shall grow like a cedar in Lebanon.

Those that be planted in the house of the LORD shall flourish in the courts of our God.

# Psalter Selections

They shall still bring forth fruit in old age; they shall be fat and flourishing;

To show that the LORD is upright: he is my rock, and there is no unrighteousness in him.

### PSALM 93

THE LORD reigneth, he is clothed with majesty; the LORD is clothed with strength, wherewith he hath girded himself: the world also is established, that it cannot be moved.

Thy throne is established of old: thou art from everlasting.

The floods have lifted up, O LORD, the floods have lifted up their voice; the floods lift up their waves.

The LORD on high is mightier than the noise of many waters, yea, than the mighty waves of the sea.

Thy testimonies are very sure: holiness becometh thine house, O LORD, for ever.

### SELECTION 46

### PSALM 94

O LORD God, to whom vengeance belongeth; O God, to whom vengeance belongeth, show thyself.

Lift up thyself, thou judge of the earth: render a reward to the proud.

LORD, how long shall the wicked, how long shall the wicked triumph?

How long shall they utter and speak hard things? and all the workers of iniquity boast themselves?

They break in pieces thy people, O LORD, and afflict thine heritage.

They slay the widow and the stranger, and murder the fatherless.

Yet they say, The LORD shall not see, neither shall the God of Jacob regard it.

Understand, ye brutish among the people: and ye fools, when will ye be wise?

He that planted the ear, shall he not hear? he that formed the eye, shall he not see?

He that chastiseth the heathen, shall not he correct? he that teacheth man knowledge, shall not he know?

The LORD knoweth the thoughts of man, that they are vanity.

Blessed is the man whom thou chastenest, O LORD, and teachest him out of thy law;

That thou mayest give him rest from the days of adversity, until the pit be digged for the wicked.

For the LORD will not cast off his people, neither will he forsake his inheritance.

But judgment shall return unto righteousness: and all the upright in heart shall follow it.

Who will rise up for me against the evildoers? or who will stand up for me against the workers of iniquity?

Unless the LORD had been my help, my soul had almost dwelt in silence.

When I said, my foot slippeth; thy mercy, O LORD, held me up.

In the multitude of my thoughts within me thy comforts delight my soul.

Shall the throne of iniquity have fellowship with thee, which frameth mischief by a law?

They gather themselves together against the soul of the righteous, and condemn the innocent blood.

But the LORD is my defence; and my God is the rock of my refuge.

And he shall bring upon them their

# Psalter Selections

own iniquity, and shall cut them off in their own wickedness; yea, the LORD our God shall cut them off.

### SELECTION 47

#### PSALM 95

O COME, let us sing unto the LORD: let us make a joyful noise to the rock of our salvation.

Let us come before his presence with thanksgiving, and make a joyful noise unto him with psalms.

For the LORD is a great God, and a great King above all gods.

In his hand are the deep places of the earth: the strength of the hills is his also.

The sea is his, and he made it: and his hands formed the dry land.

O come, let us worship and bow down: let us kneel before the LORD our maker.

For he is our God; and we are the people of his pasture, and the sheep of his hand. To day if ye will hear his voice,

Harden not your heart, as in the provocation, and as in the day of temptation in the wilderness:

When your fathers tempted me, proved me, and saw my work.

Forty years long was I grieved with this generation, and said, It is a people that do err in their heart, and they have not known my ways:

Unto whom I sware in my wrath that they should not enter into my rest.

#### PSALM 96

O SING unto the LORD a new song: sing unto the LORD, all the earth.

Sing unto the LORD, bless his name; show forth his salvation from day to day.

Declare his glory among the heathen, his wonders among all people.

For the LORD is great, and greatly to be praised: he is to be feared above all gods.

For all the gods of the nations are idols: but the LORD made the heavens.

Honour and majesty are before him: strength and beauty are in his sanctuary.

Give unto the LORD, O ye kindreds of the people, give unto the LORD glory and strength.

Give unto the LORD the glory due unto his name: bring an offering, and come into his courts.

O worship the LORD in the beauty of holiness: fear before him, all the earth.

Say among the heathen that the LORD reigneth: the world also shall be established that it shall not be moved: he shall judge the people righteously.

Let the heavens rejoice, and let the earth be glad; let the sea roar, and the fulness thereof.

Let the field be joyful, and all that is therein: then shall all the trees of the wood rejoice before the LORD:

For he cometh, for he cometh to judge the earth: he shall judge the world with righteousness, and the people with his truth.

### SELECTION 48

#### PSALM 97

THE LORD reigneth; let the earth rejoice; let the multitude of isles be glad thereof.

Clouds and darkness are round about him: righteousness and judgment are the habitation of his throne.

A fire goeth before him, and burneth up his enemies round about.

# Psalter Selections

His lightnings enlightened the world: the earth saw, and trembled.

The hills melted like wax at the presence of the LORD, at the presence of the Lord of the whole earth.

The heavens declare his righteousness, and all the people see his glory.

Confounded be all they that serve graven images, that boast themselves of idols: worship him, all ye gods.

Zion heard, and was glad; and the daughters of Judah rejoiced because of thy judgments, O LORD.

For thou, LORD, art high above all the earth: thou art exalted far above all gods.

Ye that love the LORD, hate evil: he preserveth the souls of his saints; he delivereth them out of the hand of the wicked.

Light is sown for the righteous, and gladness for the upright in heart.

Rejoice in the LORD, ye righteous; and give thanks at the remembrance of his holiness.

### PSALM 98

O SING unto the LORD a new song; for he hath done marvellous things: his right hand, and his holy arm, hath gotten him the victory.

The LORD hath made known his salvation: his righteousness hath he openly showed in the sight of the heathen.

He hath remembered his mercy and his truth toward the house of Israel: all the ends of the earth have seen the salvation of our God.

Make a joyful noise unto the LORD, all the earth: make a loud noise, and rejoice, and sing praise.

Sing unto the LORD with the harp; with the harp, and the voice of a psalm.

With trumpets and sound of cornet make a joyful noise before the LORD, the King.

Let the sea roar, and the fulness thereof; the world, and they that dwell therein.

Let the floods clap their hands: let the hills be joyful together before the LORD;

For he cometh to judge the earth: with righteousness shall he judge the world, and the people with equity.

## SELECTION 49

### PSALM 99

THE LORD reigneth; let the people tremble: he sitteth between the cherubim; let the earth be moved.

The LORD is great in Zion; and he is high above all the people.

Let them praise thy great and terrible name; for it is holy.

The king's strength also loveth judgment; thou dost establish equity, thou executest judgment and righteousness in Jacob.

Exalt ye the LORD our God, and worship at his footstool; for he is holy.

Moses and Aaron among his priests, and Samuel among them that call upon his name; they called upon the LORD, and he answered them.

He spake unto them in the cloudy pillar: they kept his testimonies, and the ordinance that he gave them.

Thou answeredst them, O LORD our God: thou wast a God that forgavest them, though thou tookest vengeance of their inventions.

Exalt the LORD our God, and worship at his holy hill; for the LORD our God is holy.

# Psalter Selections

### Psalm 100

MAKE a joyful noise unto the LORD, all ye lands.

Serve the LORD with gladness: come before his presence with singing.

Know ye that the LORD he is God: it is he that hath made us, and not we ourselves; we are his people, and the sheep of his pasture.

Enter into his gates with thanksgiving, and into his courts with praise: be thankful unto him, and bless his name.

For the LORD is good; his mercy is everlasting; and his truth endureth to all generations.

### Psalm 101

I WILL sing of mercy and judgment: unto thee, O LORD, will I sing.

I will behave myself wisely in a perfect way. O when wilt thou come unto me? I will walk within my house with a perfect heart.

I will set no wicked thing before mine eyes: I hate the work of them that turn aside; it shall not cleave to me.

A perverse heart shall depart from me: I will not know a wicked person.

Whoso slandereth his neighbour in secret, him will I cut off; him that hath an high look and a proud heart will not I suffer.

Mine eyes shall be upon the faithful of the land, that they may dwell with me: he that walketh in a perfect way, he shall serve me.

He that worketh deceit shall not dwell within my house: he that telleth lies shall not tarry in my sight.

I will early destroy all the wicked of the land; that I may cut off all wicked doers from the city of the LORD.

## SELECTION 50

### Psalm 103

BLESS the LORD, O my soul: and all that is within me, bless his holy name.

Bless the LORD, O my soul, and forget not all his benefits:

Who forgiveth all thine iniquities; who healeth all thy diseases;

**Who redeemeth thy life from destruction; who crowneth thee with lovingkindness and tender mercies;**

Who satisfieth thy mouth with good things; so that thy youth is renewed like the eagle's.

The LORD executeth righteousness and judgment for all that are oppressed.

He made known his ways unto Moses, his acts unto the children of Israel.

The LORD is merciful and gracious, slow to anger, and plenteous in mercy.

He will not always chide: neither will he keep his anger for ever.

**He hath not dealt with us after our sins; nor rewarded us according to our iniquities.**

For as the heaven is high above the earth, so great is his mercy toward them that fear him.

**As far as the east is from the west, so far hath he removed our transgressions from us.**

Like as a father pitieth his children, so the LORD pitieth them that fear him.

For he knoweth our frame; he remembereth that we are dust.

As for man, his days are as grass: as a flower of the field, so he flourisheth.

For the wind passeth over it, and it is gone; and the place thereof shall know it no more.

But the mercy of the LORD is from everlasting to everlasting upon them that

# Psalter Selections

fear him, and his righteousness unto children's children;

To such as keep his covenant, and to those that remember his commandments to do them.

The LORD hath prepared his throne in the heavens; and his kingdom ruleth over all.

Bless the LORD, ye his angels, that excel in strength, that do his commandments, hearkening unto the voice of his word.

Bless ye the LORD, all ye his hosts; ye ministers of his, that do his pleasure.

Bless the LORD, all his works in all places of his dominion: bless the LORD, O my soul.

### SELECTION 51
#### PSALM 104

BLESS the LORD, O my soul. O LORD my God, thou art very great; thou art clothed with honour and majesty.

Who coverest thyself with light as with a garment: who stretchest out the heavens like a curtain:

Who layeth the beams of his chambers in the waters: who maketh the clouds his chariot: who walketh upon the wings of the wind:

Who maketh his angels spirits; his ministers a flaming fire:

Who laid the foundations of the earth, that it should not be removed for ever.

Thou coveredst it with the deep as with a garment: the waters stood above the mountains.

At thy rebuke they fled; at the voice of thy thunder they hasted away.

They go up by the mountains; they go down by the valleys unto the place which thou hast founded for them.

Thou hast set a bound that they may not pass over; that they turn not again to cover the earth.

He sendeth the springs into the valleys, which run among the hills.

They give drink to every beast of the field: the wild asses quench their thirst.

By them shall the fowls of the heaven have their habitation, which sing among the branches.

He watereth the hills from his chambers: the earth is satisfied with the fruit of thy works.

He causeth the grass to grow for the cattle, and herb for the service of man: that he may bring forth food out of the earth;

And wine that maketh glad the heart of man, and oil to make his face to shine, and bread which strengtheneth man's heart.

The trees of the LORD are full of sap; the cedars of Lebanon, which he hath planted;

Where the birds make their nests: as for the stork, the fir trees are her house.

The high hills are a refuge for the wild goats; and the rocks for the conies.

He appointed the moon for seasons: the sun knoweth his going down.

Thou makest darkness, and it is night: wherein all the beasts of the forest do creep forth.

The young lions roar after their prey, and seek their meat from God.

The sun ariseth, they gather themselves together, and lay them down in their dens.

Man goeth forth unto his work and to his labour until the evening.

O LORD, how manifold are thy works! in wisdom hast thou made them all: the earth is full of thy riches.

# Psalter Selections

So is this great and wide sea, wherein are things creeping innumerable, both small and great beasts.

There go the ships: there is that leviathan, whom thou hast made to play therein.

These wait all upon thee; that thou mayest give them their meat in due season.

That thou givest them they gather: thou openest thine hand, they are filled with good.

Thou hidest thy face, they are troubled: thou takest away their breath, they die, and return to their dust.

**Thou sendest forth thy spirit, they are created: and thou renewest the face of the earth.**

The glory of the LORD shall endure for ever: the LORD shall rejoice in his works.

**He looketh on the earth, and it trembleth: he toucheth the hills, and they smoke.**

I will sing unto the LORD as long as I live: I will sing praise to my God while I have my being.

**My meditation of him shall be sweet: I will be glad in the LORD.**

Let the sinners be consumed out of the earth, and let the wicked be no more. Bless thou the LORD, O my soul. Praise ye the LORD.

### SELECTION 52

PSALM 106:1-23, 47, 48

PRAISE ye the LORD. O give thanks unto the LORD; for he is good: for his mercy endureth for ever.

**Who can utter the mighty acts of the LORD? who can show forth all his praise?**

Blessed are they that keep judgment, and he that doeth righteousness at all times.

**Remember me, O LORD, with the favour that thou bearest unto thy people: O visit me with thy salvation;**

That I may see the good of thy chosen, that I may rejoice in the gladness of thy nation, that I may glory with thine inheritance.

**We have sinned with our fathers, we have committed iniquity, we have done wickedly.**

Our fathers understood not thy wonders in Egypt; they remembered not the multitude of thy mercies; but provoked him at the sea, even at the Red sea.

**Nevertheless he saved them for his name's sake, that he might make his mighty power to be known.**

He rebuked the Red sea also, and it was dried up: so he led them through the depths, as through the wilderness.

**And he saved them from the hand of him that hated them, and redeemed them from the hand of the enemy.**

And the waters covered their enemies: there was not one of them left.

**Then believed they his words; they sang his praise.**

They soon forgat his works; they waited not for his counsel:

**But lusted exceedingly in the wilderness, and tempted God in the desert.**

And he gave them their request; but sent leanness into their soul.

**They envied Moses also in the camp, and Aaron the saint of the LORD.**

The earth opened and swallowed up Dathan, and covered the company of Abiram.

**And a fire was kindled in their company; the flame burned up the wicked.**

# Psalter Selections

They made a calf in Horeb, and worshipped the molten image.

Thus they changed their glory into the similitude of an ox that eateth grass.

They forgat God their saviour, which had done great things in Egypt;

Wondrous works in the land of Ham, and terrible things by the Red sea.

Therefore he said that he would destroy them, had not Moses his chosen stood before him in the breach, to turn away his wrath, lest he should destroy them.

Save us, O LORD our God, and gather us from among the heathen, to give thanks unto thy holy name, and to triumph in thy praise.

Blessed be the LORD God of Israel from everlasting to everlasting: and let all the people say, Amen. Praise ye the LORD.

### SELECTION 53

#### PSALM 107:1-22

O GIVE thanks unto the LORD, for he is good: for his mercy endureth for ever.

Let the redeemed of the LORD say so, whom he hath redeemed from the hand of the enemy;

And gathered them out of the lands, from the east, and from the west, from the north, and from the south.

They wandered in the wilderness in a solitary way; they found no city to dwell in.

Hungry and thirsty, their soul fainted in them.

Then they cried unto the LORD in their trouble, and he delivered them out of their distresses.

And he led them forth by the right way, that they might go to a city of habitation.

Oh that men would praise the LORD for his goodness, and for his wonderful works to the children of men!

For he satisfieth the longing soul, and filleth the hungry soul with goodness.

Such as sit in darkness and in the shadow of death, being bound in affliction and iron;

Because they rebelled against the words of God, and contemned the counsel of the most High:

Therefore he brought down their heart with labour; they fell down, and there was none to help.

Then they cried unto the LORD in their trouble, and he saved them out of their distresses.

He brought them out of darkness and the shadow of death, and brake their bands in sunder.

Oh that men would praise the LORD for his goodness, and for his wonderful works to the children of men!

For he hath broken the gates of brass, and cut the bars of iron in sunder.

Fools because of their transgression, and because of their iniquities, are afflicted.

Their soul abhorreth all manner of meat; and they draw near unto the gates of death.

Then they cry unto the LORD in their trouble, and he saveth them out of their distresses.

He sent his word, and healed them, and delivered them from their destructions.

Oh that men would praise the LORD for his goodness, and for his wonderful works to the children of men!

And let them sacrifice the sacrifices of thanksgiving, and declare his works with rejoicing.

# Psalter Selections

## SELECTION 54

### Psalm 107:23-43

THEY that go down to the sea in ships, that do business in great waters;

These see the works of the Lord, and his wonders in the deep.

For he commandeth, and raiseth the stormy wind, which lifteth up the waves thereof.

They mount up to the heaven, they go down again to the depths: their soul is melted because of trouble.

They reel to and fro, and stagger like a drunken man, and are at their wit's end.

Then they cry unto the Lord in their trouble, and he bringeth them out of their distresses.

He maketh the storm a calm, so that the waves thereof are still.

Then they are glad because they be quiet; so he bringeth them unto their desired haven.

Oh that men would praise the Lord for his goodness, and for his wonderful works to the children of men!

Let them exalt him also in the congregation of the people, and praise him in the assembly of the elders.

He turneth rivers into a wilderness, and the water-springs into dry ground;

A fruitful land into barrenness, for the wickedness of them that dwell therein.

He turneth the wilderness into a standing water, and dry ground into water-springs.

And there he maketh the hungry to dwell, that they may prepare a city for habitation;

And sow the fields, and plant vineyards, which may yield fruits of increase.

He blesseth them also, so that they are multiplied greatly; and suffereth not their cattle to decrease.

Again, they are minished and brought low through oppression, affliction, and sorrow.

He poureth contempt upon princes, and causeth them to wander in the wilderness, where there is no way.

Yet setteth he the poor on high from affliction, and maketh him families like a flock.

The righteous shall see it, and rejoice: and all iniquity shall stop her mouth.

Whoso is wise, and will observe these things, even they shall understand the lovingkindness of the Lord.

## SELECTION 55

### Psalm 110

THE Lord said unto my Lord, Sit thou at my right hand, until I make thine enemies thy footstool.

The Lord shall send the rod of thy strength out of Zion: rule thou in the midst of thine enemies.

Thy people shall be willing in the day of thy power, in the beauties of holiness from the womb of the morning: thou hast the dew of thy youth.

The Lord hath sworn, and will not repent, Thou art a priest for ever after the order of Melchizedek.

The Lord at thy right hand shall strike through kings in the day of his wrath.

He shall judge among the heathen, he shall fill the places with the dead bodies; he shall wound the heads over many countries.

He shall drink of the brook in the way: therefore shall he lift up the head.

# Psalter Selections

### Psalm 111

PRAISE ye the Lord. I will praise the Lord with my whole heart, in the assembly of the upright, and in the congregation.

The works of the Lord are great, sought out of all them that have pleasure therein.

His work is honourable and glorious: and his righteousness endureth for ever.

He hath made his wonderful works to be remembered: the Lord is gracious and full of compassion.

He hath given meat unto them that fear him: he will ever be mindful of his covenant.

He hath showed his people the power of his works, that he may give them the heritage of the heathen.

The works of his hands are verity and judgment; all his commandments are sure.

They stand fast for ever and ever, and are done in truth and uprightness.

He sent redemption unto his people: he hath commanded his covenant for ever: holy and reverend is his name.

The fear of the Lord is the beginning of wisdom: a good understanding have all they that do his commandments: his praise endureth for ever.

### SELECTION 56

### Psalm 112

PRAISE ye the Lord. Blessed is the man that feareth the Lord, that delighteth greatly in his commandments.

His seed shall be mighty upon earth: the generation of the upright shall be blessed.

Wealth and riches shall be in his house: and his righteousness endureth for ever.

Unto the upright there ariseth light in the darkness: he is gracious, and full of compassion, and righteous.

A good man showeth favour, and lendeth: he will guide his affairs with discretion.

Surely he shall not be moved for ever: the righteous shall be in everlasting remembrance.

He shall not be afraid of evil tidings: his heart is fixed, trusting in the Lord.

His heart is established, he shall not be afraid, until he see his desire upon his enemies.

He hath dispersed, he hath given to the poor; his righteousness endureth for ever; his horn shall be exalted with honour.

The wicked shall see it, and be grieved; he shall gnash with his teeth, and melt away: the desire of the wicked shall perish.

### Psalm 113

PRAISE ye the Lord. Praise, O ye servants of the Lord, praise the name of the Lord.

Blessed be the name of the Lord from this time forth and for evermore.

From the rising of the sun unto the going down of the same the Lord's name is to be praised.

The Lord is high above all nations, and his glory above the heavens.

Who is like unto the Lord our God, who dwelleth on high,

Who humbleth himself to behold the things that are in heaven, and in the earth!

He raiseth up the poor out of the dust, and lifteth the needy out of the dunghill;

That he may set him with princes, even with the princes of his people.

He maketh the barren woman to keep house, and to be a joyful mother of children. Praise ye the Lord.

# Psalter Selections

## SELECTION 57

### Psalm 114

WHEN Israel went out of Egypt, the house of Jacob from a people of strange language;

Judah was his sanctuary, and Israel his dominion.

The sea saw it, and fled: Jordan was driven back.

The mountains skipped like rams, and the little hills like lambs.

What ailed thee, O thou sea, that thou fleddest? thou Jordan, that thou wast driven back?

Ye mountains, that ye skipped like rams; and ye little hills, like lambs?

Tremble, thou earth, at the presence of the Lord, at the presence of the God of Jacob;

Which turned the rock into a standing water, the flint into a fountain of waters.

### Psalm 115

NOT unto us, O Lord, not unto us, but unto thy name give glory, for thy mercy, and for thy truth's sake.

Wherefore should the heathen say, Where is now their God?

But our God is in the heavens: he hath done whatsoever he hath pleased.

Their idols are silver and gold, the work of men's hands.

They have mouths, but they speak not: eyes have they, but they see not:

They have ears, but they hear not: noses have they, but they smell not:

They have hands, but they handle not: feet have they, but they walk not: neither speak they through their throat.

They that make them are like unto them; so is every one that trusteth in them.

O Israel, trust thou in the Lord: he is their help and their shield.

O house of Aaron, trust in the Lord: he is their help and their shield.

Ye that fear the Lord, trust in the Lord: he is their help and their shield.

The Lord hath been mindful of us: he will bless us; he will bless the house of Israel; he will bless the house of Aaron.

He will bless them that fear the Lord, both small and great.

The Lord shall increase you more and more, you and your children.

Ye are blessed of the Lord which made heaven and earth.

The heaven, even the heavens, are the Lord's: but the earth hath he given to the children of men.

The dead praise not the Lord, neither any that go down into silence.

But we will bless the Lord from this time forth and for evermore. Praise the Lord.

## SELECTION 58

### Psalm 116

I LOVE the Lord, because he hath heard my voice and my supplications.

Because he hath inclined his ear unto me, therefore will I call upon him as long as I live.

The sorrows of death compassed me, and the pains of hell gat hold upon me: I found trouble and sorrow.

Then called I upon the name of the Lord; O Lord, I beseech thee, deliver my soul.

Gracious is the Lord, and righteous; yea, our God is merciful.

The Lord preserveth the simple: I was brought low, and he helped me.

# Psalter Selections

Return unto thy rest, O my soul; for the LORD hath dealt bountifully with thee.

**For thou hast delivered my soul from death, mine eyes from tears, and my feet from falling.**

I will walk before the LORD in the land of the living.

**I believed, therefore have I spoken: I was greatly afflicted:**

I said in my haste, All men are liars.

**What shall I render unto the LORD for all his benefits toward me?**

I will take the cup of salvation, and call upon the name of the LORD.

**I will pay my vows unto the LORD now in the presence of all his people.**

Precious in the sight of the LORD is the death of his saints.

O LORD, truly I am thy servant; I am thy servant, and the son of thine handmaid: thou hast loosed my bonds.

I will offer to thee the sacrifice of thanksgiving, and will call upon the name of the LORD.

**I will pay my vows unto the LORD now in the presence of all his people,**

In the courts of the LORD's house, in the midst of thee, O Jerusalem. Praise ye the LORD.

### PSALM 117

**O PRAISE the LORD, all ye nations: praise him, all ye people.**

For his merciful kindness is great toward us: and the truth of the LORD endureth for ever. Praise ye the LORD.

### SELECTION 59

### PSALM 118

O GIVE thanks unto the LORD; for he is good: because his mercy endureth for ever.

**Let Israel now say, that his mercy endureth for ever.**

Let the house of Aaron now say, that his mercy endureth for ever.

**Let them now that fear the LORD say, that his mercy endureth for ever.**

I called upon the LORD in distress: the LORD answered me, and set me in a large place.

**The LORD is on my side; I will not fear: what can man do unto me?**

The LORD taketh my part with them that help me: therefore shall I see my desire upon them that hate me.

**It is better to trust in the LORD than to put confidence in man.**

It is better to trust in the LORD than to put confidence in princes.

**All nations compassed me about: but in the name of the LORD will I destroy them.**

They compassed me about; yea, they compassed me about: but in the name of the LORD I will destroy them.

**They compassed me about like bees; they are quenched as the fire of thorns: for in the name of the LORD I will destroy them.**

Thou hast thrust sore at me that I might fall: but the LORD helped me.

**The LORD is my strength and song, and is become my salvation.**

The voice of rejoicing and salvation is in the tabernacles of the righteous: the right hand of the LORD doeth valiantly.

**The right hand of the LORD is exalted: the right hand of the LORD doeth valiantly.**

I shall not die, but live, and declare the works of the LORD.

**The LORD hath chastened me sore: but he hath not given me over unto death.**

# Psalter Selections

Open to me the gates of righteousness: I will go into them, and I will praise the LORD:

**This gate of the LORD, into which the righteous shall enter.**

I will praise thee: for thou hast heard me, and art become my salvation.

**The stone which the builders refused is become the head stone of the corner.**

This is the LORD's doing; it is marvellous in our eyes.

**This is the day which the LORD hath made; we will rejoice and be glad in it.**

Save now, I beseech thee, O LORD: O LORD, I beseech thee, send now prosperity.

**Blessed be he that cometh in the name of the LORD: we have blessed you out of the house of the LORD.**

God is the LORD, which hath showed us light: bind the sacrifice with cords, even unto the horns of the altar.

**Thou art my God, and I will praise thee: thou art my God, I will exalt thee.**

O give thanks unto the LORD; for he is good: for his mercy endureth for ever.

### SELECTION 60

PSALM 119:1-24

BLESSED are the undefiled in the way, who walk in the law of the LORD.

**Blessed are they that keep his testimonies, and that seek him with the whole heart.**

They also do no iniquity: they walk in his ways.

**Thou hast commanded us to keep thy precepts diligently.**

O that my ways were directed to keep thy statutes!

Then shall I not be ashamed, when I have respect unto all thy commandments.

I will praise thee with uprightness of heart, when I shall have learned thy righteous judgments.

**I will keep thy statutes: O forsake me not utterly.**

Wherewithal shall a young man cleanse his way? by taking heed thereto according to thy word.

**With my whole heart have I sought thee: O let me not wander from thy commandments.**

Thy word have I hid in mine heart, that I might not sin against thee.

**Blessed art thou, O LORD: teach me thy statutes.**

With my lips have I declared all the judgments of thy mouth.

**I have rejoiced in the way of thy testimonies, as much as in all riches.**

I will meditate in thy precepts, and have respect unto thy ways.

**I will delight myself in thy statutes: I will not forget thy word.**

Deal bountifully with thy servant, that I may live, and keep thy word.

**Open thou mine eyes, that I may behold wondrous things out of thy law.**

I am a stranger in the earth: hide not thy commandments from me.

**My soul breaketh for the longing that it hath unto thy judgments at all times.**

Thou hast rebuked the proud that are cursed, which do err from thy commandments.

**Remove from me reproach and contempt; for I have kept thy testimonies.**

Princes also did sit and speak against me: but thy servant did meditate in thy statutes.

**Thy testimonies also are my delight and my counsellors.**

# Psalter Selections

## SELECTION 61

### Psalm 119:33-56

TEACH me, O Lord, the way of thy statutes; and I shall keep it unto the end.

**Give me understanding, and I shall keep thy law; yea, I shall observe it with my whole heart.**

Make me to go in the path of thy commandments; for therein do I delight.

**Incline my heart unto thy testimonies, and not to covetousness.**

Turn away mine eyes from beholding vanity; and quicken thou me in thy way.

**Stablish thy word unto thy servant, who is devoted to thy fear.**

Turn away my reproach which I fear: for thy judgments are good.

**Behold, I have longed after thy precepts: quicken me in thy righteousness.**

Let thy mercies come also unto me, O Lord, even thy salvation, according to thy word.

**So shall I have wherewith to answer him that reproacheth me: for I trust in thy word.**

And take not the word of truth utterly out of my mouth; for I have hoped in thy judgments.

**So shall I keep thy law continually for ever and ever.**

And I will walk at liberty: for I seek thy precepts.

**I will speak of thy testimonies also before kings, and will not be ashamed.**

And I will delight myself in thy commandments, which I have loved.

**My hands also will I lift up unto thy commandments, which I have loved; and I will meditate in thy statutes.**

Remember the word unto thy servant, upon which thou hast caused me to hope.

**This is my comfort in my affliction: for thy word hath quickened me.**

The proud have had me greatly in derision: yet have I not declined from thy law.

**I remembered thy judgments of old, O Lord; and have comforted myself.**

Horror hath taken hold upon me because of the wicked that forsake thy law.

**Thy statutes have been my songs in the house of my pilgrimage.**

I have remembered thy name, O Lord, in the night, and have kept thy law.

**This I had, because I kept thy precepts.**

## SELECTION 62

### Psalm 119:89-112

FOR ever, O Lord, thy word is settled in heaven.

**Thy faithfulness is unto all generations: thou hast established the earth, and it abideth.**

They continue this day according to thine ordinances: for all are thy servants.

**Unless thy law had been my delights, I should then have perished in mine affliction.**

I will never forget thy precepts: for with them thou hast quickened me.

**I am thine, save me; for I have sought thy precepts.**

The wicked have waited for me to destroy me: but I will consider thy testimonies.

**I have seen an end of all perfection: but thy commandment is exceeding broad.**

O how love I thy law! it is my meditation all the day.

**Thou through thy commandments**

# Psalter Selections

hast made me wiser than mine enemies: for they are ever with me.

I have more understanding than all my teachers: for thy testimonies are my meditation.

I understand more than the ancients, because I keep thy precepts.

I have refrained my feet from every evil way, that I might keep thy word.

I have not departed from thy judgments: for thou hast taught me.

How sweet are thy words unto my taste! yea, sweeter than honey to my mouth!

Through thy precepts I get understanding: therefore I hate every false way.

Thy word is a lamp unto my feet, and a light unto my path.

I have sworn, and I will perform it, that I will keep thy righteous judgments.

I am afflicted very much: quicken me, O LORD, according unto thy word.

Accept, I beseech thee, the freewill offerings of my mouth, O LORD, and teach me thy judgments.

My soul is continually in my hand: yet do I not forget thy law.

The wicked have laid a snare for me: yet I erred not from thy precepts.

Thy testimonies have I taken as an heritage for ever: for they are the rejoicing of my heart.

I have inclined mine heart to perform thy statutes alway, even unto the end.

## SELECTION 63

### PSALM 121

I WILL lift up mine eyes unto the hills, from whence cometh my help.

My help cometh from the LORD, which made heaven and earth.

He will not suffer thy foot to be moved: he that keepeth thee will not slumber.

Behold, he that keepeth Israel shall neither slumber nor sleep.

The LORD is thy keeper: the LORD is thy shade upon thy right hand.

The sun shall not smite thee by day, nor the moon by night.

The LORD shall preserve thee from all evil: he shall preserve thy soul.

The LORD shall preserve thy going out and thy coming in from this time forth, and even for evermore.

### PSALM 122

I WAS glad when they said unto me, Let us go into the house of the LORD.

Our feet shall stand within thy gates, O Jerusalem.

Jerusalem is builded as a city that is compact together:

Whither the tribes go up, the tribes of the LORD, unto the testimony of Israel, to give thanks unto the name of the LORD.

For there are set thrones of judgment, the thrones of the house of David.

Pray for the peace of Jerusalem: they shall prosper that love thee.

Peace be within thy walls, and prosperity within thy palaces.

For my brethren and companions' sakes, I will now say, Peace be within thee.

Because of the house of the LORD our God I will seek thy good.

### PSALM 123

UNTO thee lift I up mine eyes, O thou that dwellest in the heavens.

Behold, as the eyes of servants look unto the hand of their masters, and as

# Psalter Selections

the eyes of a maiden unto the hand of her mistress; so our eyes wait upon the LORD our God, until that he have mercy upon us.

**Have mercy upon us, O LORD, have mercy upon us: for we are exceedingly filled with contempt.**

Our soul is exceedingly filled with the scorning of those that are at ease, and with the contempt of the proud.

### SELECTION 64

#### PSALM 124

IF it had not been the LORD who was on our side, now may Israel say;

**If it had not been the LORD who was on our side, when men rose up against us:**

Then they had swallowed us up alive, when their wrath was kindled against us:

**Then the waters had overwhelmed us, the stream had gone over our soul:**

Then the proud waters had gone over our soul.

**Blessed be the LORD, who hath not given us as a prey to their teeth.**

Our soul is escaped as a bird out of the snare of the fowlers: the snare is broken, and we are escaped.

**Our help is in the name of the LORD, who made heaven and earth.**

#### PSALM 125

THEY that trust in the LORD shall be as mount Zion, which cannot be removed, but abideth for ever.

**As the mountains are round about Jerusalem, so the LORD is round about his people from henceforth even for ever.**

For the rod of the wicked shall not rest upon the lot of the righteous; lest the righteous put forth their hands unto iniquity.

**Do good, O LORD, unto those that be good, and to them that are upright in their hearts.**

As for such as turn aside unto their crooked ways, the LORD shall lead them forth with the workers of iniquity: but peace shall be upon Israel.

#### PSALM 126

WHEN the LORD turned again the captivity of Zion, we were like them that dream.

Then was our mouth filled with laughter, and our tongue with singing: then said they among the heathen, The LORD hath done great things for them.

**The LORD hath done great things for us; whereof we are glad.**

Turn again our captivity, O LORD, as the streams in the south.

**They that sow in tears shall reap in joy.**

He that goeth forth and weepeth, bearing precious seed, shall doubtless come again with rejoicing, bringing his sheaves with him.

### SELECTION 65

#### PSALM 127

EXCEPT the LORD build the house, they labour in vain that build it: except the LORD keep the city, the watchman waketh but in vain.

**It is vain for you to rise up early, to sit up late, to eat the bread of sorrows: for so he giveth his beloved sleep.**

Lo, children are an heritage of the LORD: and the fruit of the womb is his reward.

**As arrows are in the hand of a mighty man; so are children of the youth.**

# Psalter Selections

Happy is the man that hath his quiver full of them: they shall not be ashamed, but they shall speak with the enemies in the gate.

### Psalm 128

BLESSED is every one that feareth the Lord; that walketh in his ways.

For thou shalt eat the labour of thine hands: happy shalt thou be, and it shall be well with thee.

Thy wife shall be as a fruitful vine by the sides of thine house: thy children like olive plants round about thy table.

Behold, that thus shall the man be blessed that feareth the Lord.

The Lord shall bless thee out of Zion: and thou shalt see the good of Jerusalem all the days of thy life.

Yea, thou shalt see thy children's children, and peace upon Israel.

## SELECTION 66

### Psalm 129

MANY a time have they afflicted me from my youth, may Israel now say:

Many a time have they afflicted me from my youth: yet they have not prevailed against me.

The plowers plowed upon my back: they made long their furrows.

The Lord is righteous: he hath cut asunder the cords of the wicked.

Let them all be confounded and turned back that hate Zion.

Let them be as the grass upon the housetops, which withereth afore it groweth up:

Wherewith the mower filleth not his hand; nor he that bindeth sheaves his bosom.

Neither do they which go by say, The blessing of the Lord be upon you: we bless you in the name of the Lord.

### Psalm 130

OUT of the depths have I cried unto thee, O Lord.

Lord, hear my voice: let thine ears be attentive to the voice of my supplications.

If thou, Lord, shouldest mark iniquities, O Lord, who shall stand?

But there is forgiveness with thee, that thou mayest be feared.

I wait for the Lord, my soul doth wait, and in his word do I hope.

My soul waiteth for the Lord more than they that watch for the morning: I say, more than they that watch for the morning.

Let Israel hope in the Lord: for with the Lord there is mercy, and with him is plenteous redemption.

And he shall redeem Israel from all his iniquities.

## SELECTION 67

### Psalm 132

LORD, remember David, and all his afflictions:

How he sware unto the Lord, and vowed unto the mighty God of Jacob;

Surely I will not come into the tabernacle of my house, nor go up into my bed;

I will not give sleep to mine eyes, or slumber to mine eyelids,

Until I find out a place for the Lord, an habitation for the mighty God of Jacob.

Lo, we heard of it at Ephratah: we found it in the fields of the wood.

We will go into his tabernacles: we will worship at his footstool.

# Psalter Selections

Arise, O LORD, into thy rest; thou, and the ark of thy strength.

Let thy priests be clothed with righteousness; and let thy saints shout for joy.

For thy servant David's sake turn not away the face of thine anointed.

The LORD hath sworn in truth unto David; he will not turn from it; Of the fruit of thy body will I set upon thy throne.

If thy children will keep my covenant and my testimony that I shall teach them, their children shall also sit upon thy throne for evermore.

For the LORD hath chosen Zion; he hath desired it for his habitation.

This is my rest for ever: here will I dwell; for I have desired it.

I will abundantly bless her provision: I will satisfy her poor with bread.

I will also clothe her priests with salvation: and her saints shall shout aloud for joy.

There will I make the horn of David to bud: I have ordained a lamp for mine anointed.

His enemies will I clothe with shame: but upon himself shall his crown flourish.

## PSALM 133

BEHOLD, how good and how pleasant it is for brethren to dwell together in unity!

It is like the precious ointment upon the head, that ran down upon the beard, even Aaron's beard: that went down to the skirts of his garments;

As the dew of Hermon, and as the dew that descended upon the mountains of Zion: for there the LORD commanded the blessing, even life for evermore.

## SELECTION 68

### PSALM 134

BEHOLD, bless ye the LORD, all ye servants of the LORD, which by night stand in the house of the LORD.

Lift up your hands in the sanctuary, and bless the LORD.

The LORD that made heaven and earth bless thee out of Zion.

### PSALM 135

PRAISE ye the LORD. Praise ye the name of the LORD; praise him, O ye servants of the LORD.

Ye that stand in the house of the LORD, in the courts of the house of our God.

Praise the LORD; for the LORD is good: sing praises unto his name; for it is pleasant.

For the LORD hath chosen Jacob unto himself, and Israel for his peculiar treasure.

For I know that the LORD is great, and that our LORD is above all gods.

Whatsoever the LORD pleased, that did he in heaven, and in earth, in the seas, and all deep places.

He causeth the vapours to ascend from the ends of the earth; he maketh lightnings for the rain; he bringeth the wind out of his treasuries.

Who smote the firstborn of Egypt, both of man and beast.

Who sent tokens and wonders into the midst of thee, O Egypt, upon Pharaoh, and upon all his servants.

Who smote great nations, and slew mighty kings;

Sihon king of the Amorites, and Og king of Bashan, and all the kingdoms of Canaan:

And gave their land for an heritage, an heritage unto Israel his people.

# Psalter Selections

Thy name, O Lord, endureth for ever; and thy memorial, O Lord, throughout all generations.

For the Lord will judge his people, and he will repent himself concerning his servants.

**The idols of the heathen are silver and gold, the work of men's hands.**

They have mouths, but they speak not; eyes have they, but they see not;

**They have ears, but they hear not; neither is there any breath in their mouths.**

They that make them are like unto them: so is every one that trusteth in them.

**Bless the Lord, O house of Israel: bless the Lord, O house of Aaron:**

Bless the Lord, O house of Levi: ye that fear the Lord, bless the Lord.

**Blessed be the Lord out of Zion, which dwelleth at Jerusalem. Praise ye the Lord.**

### SELECTION 69

#### Psalm 136

O GIVE thanks unto the Lord; for he is good: for his mercy endureth for ever.

**O give thanks unto the God of gods: for his mercy endureth for ever.**

O give thanks to the Lord of Lords: for his mercy endureth for ever.

**To him who alone doeth great wonders: for his mercy endureth for ever.**

To him that by wisdom made the heavens: for his mercy endureth for ever.

**To him that stretched out the earth above the waters: for his mercy endureth for ever.**

To him that made great lights: for his mercy endureth for ever:

**The sun to rule by day: for his mercy endureth for ever:**

The moon and stars to rule by night: for his mercy endureth for ever.

**To him that smote Egypt in their firstborn: for his mercy endureth for ever:**

And brought out Israel from among them: for his mercy endureth for ever:

**With a strong hand, and with a stretched out arm: for his mercy endureth for ever.**

To him which divided the Red sea into parts: for his mercy endureth for ever:

**And made Israel to pass through the midst of it: for his mercy endureth for ever:**

But overthrew Pharaoh and his host in the Red sea: for his mercy endureth for ever.

**To him which led his people through the wilderness: for his mercy endureth for ever.**

To him which smote great kings: for his mercy endureth for ever:

**And slew famous kings: for his mercy endureth for ever:**

Sihon king of the Amorites: for his mercy endureth for ever:

**And Og the king of Bashan: for his mercy endureth for ever:**

And gave their land for an heritage: for his mercy endureth for ever:

**Even an heritage unto Israel his servant: for his mercy endureth for ever.**

Who remembered us in our low estate: for his mercy endureth forever:

**And hath redeemed us from our enemies: for his mercy endureth for ever.**

Who giveth food to all flesh: for his mercy endureth for ever.

# Psalter Selections

O give thanks unto the God of heaven: for his mercy endureth for ever.

## SELECTION 70
### PSALM 139

O LORD, thou hast searched me, and known me.

Thou knowest my downsitting and mine uprising, thou understandest my thought afar off.

Thou compassest my path and my lying down, and art acquainted with all my ways.

For there is not a word in my tongue, but, lo, O LORD, thou knowest it altogether.

Thou hast beset me behind and before, and laid thine hand upon me.

Such knowledge is too wonderful for me; it is high, I cannot attain unto it.

Whither shall I go from thy spirit? or whither shall I flee from thy presence?

If I ascend up into heaven, thou art there: if I make my bed in hell, behold, thou art there.

If I take the wings of the morning, and dwell in the uttermost parts of the sea;

Even there shall thy hand lead me, and thy right hand shall hold me.

If I say, Surely the darkness shall cover me; even the night shall be light about me.

Yea, the darkness hideth not from thee; but the night shineth as the day: the darkness and the light are both alike to thee.

For thou hast possessed my reins: thou hast covered me in my mother's womb.

I will praise thee; for I am fearfully and wonderfully made: marvellous are thy works; and that my soul knoweth right well.

My substance was not hid from thee, when I was made in secret, and curiously wrought in the lowest parts of the earth.

Thine eyes did see my substance, yet being unperfect; and in thy book all my members were written, which in continuance were fashioned, when as yet there was none of them.

How precious also are thy thoughts unto me, O God! how great is the sum of them!

If I should count them, they are more in number than the sand: when I awake, I am still with thee.

Surely thou wilt slay the wicked, O God: depart from me therefore, ye bloody men.

For they speak against thee wickedly, and thine enemies take thy name in vain.

Do not I hate them, O LORD, that hate thee? and am not I grieved with those that rise up against thee?

I hate them with perfect hatred: I count them mine enemies.

Search me, O God, and know my heart: try me, and know my thoughts:

And see if there be any wicked way in me, and lead me in the way everlasting.

## SELECTION 71
### PSALM 141

LORD, I cry unto thee: make haste unto me; give ear unto my voice, when I cry unto thee.

Let my prayer be set forth before thee as incense; and the lifting up of my hands as the evening sacrifice.

Set a watch, O LORD, before my mouth; keep the door of my lips.

Incline not my heart to any evil thing, to practise wicked works with men that

# Psalter Selections

work iniquity: and let me not eat of their dainties.

Let the righteous smite me; it shall be a kindness: and let him reprove me; it shall be an excellent oil, which shall not break my head: for yet my prayer also shall be in their calamities.

**When their judges are overthrown in stony places, they shall hear my words; for they are sweet.**

Our bones are scattered at the grave's mouth, as when one cutteth and cleaveth wood upon the earth.

**But mine eyes are unto thee, O God the Lord: in thee is my trust; leave not my soul destitute.**

Keep me from the snares which they have laid for me, and the gins of the workers of iniquity.

**Let the wicked fall into their own nets, whilst that I withal escape.**

### Psalm 142

I CRIED unto the Lord with my voice; with my voice unto the Lord did I make my supplication.

**I poured out my complaint before him; I showed before him my trouble.**

When my spirit was overwhelmed within me, then thou knewest my path. In the way wherein I walked have they secretly laid a snare for me.

**I looked on my right hand, and beheld, but there was no man that would know me: refuge failed me; no man cared for my soul.**

I cried unto thee, O Lord: I said, Thou art my refuge and my portion in the land of the living.

**Attend unto my cry; for I am brought very low: deliver me from my persecutors; for they are stronger than I.**

Bring my soul out of prison, that I may praise thy name: the righteous shall compass me about; for thou shalt deal bountifully with me.

## SELECTION 72
### Psalm 144

BLESSED be the Lord my strength, which teacheth my hands to war, and my fingers to fight:

**My goodness, and my fortress; my high tower, and my deliverer; my shield, and he in whom I trust; who subdueth my people under me.**

Lord, what is man, that thou takest knowledge of him! or the son of man, that thou makest account of him!

**Man is like to vanity: his days are as a shadow that passeth away.**

Bow thy heavens, O Lord, and come down: touch the mountains, and they shall smoke.

**Cast forth lightning, and scatter them: shoot out thine arrows, and destroy them.**

Send thine hand from above; rid me, and deliver me out of great waters, from the hand of strangers;

**Whose mouth speaketh vanity, and their right hand is a right hand of falsehood.**

I will sing a new song unto thee, O God: upon a psaltery and an instrument of ten strings will I sing praises unto thee.

**It is he that giveth salvation unto kings: who delivereth David his servant from the hurtful sword.**

Rid me, and deliver me from the hand of strangers, whose mouth speaketh vanity, and their right hand is a right hand of falsehood:

**That our sons may be as plants grown up in their youth; that our daughters may be as corner stones, polished after the similitude of a palace:**

# Psalter Selections

That our garners may be full, affording all manner of store: that our sheep may bring forth thousands and ten thousands in our streets:

**That our oxen may be strong to labour; that there be no breaking in, nor going out; that there be no complaining in our streets.**

Happy is that people, that is in such a case: yea, happy is that people, whose God is the Lord.

### SELECTION 73

#### Psalm 143

HEAR my prayer, O Lord, give ear to my supplications: in thy faithfulness answer me, and in thy righteousness.

**And enter not into judgment with thy servant: for in thy sight shall no man living be justified.**

For the enemy hath persecuted my soul; he hath smitten my life down to the ground; he hath made me to dwell in darkness, as those that have been long dead.

**Therefore is my spirit overwhelmed within me; my heart within me is desolate.**

I remember the days of old; I meditate on all thy works; I muse on the work of thy hands.

**I stretch forth my hands unto thee: my soul thirsteth after thee, as a thirsty land.**

Hear me speedily, O Lord: my spirit faileth: hide not thy face from me, lest I be like unto them that go down into the pit.

**Cause me to hear thy lovingkindness in the morning; for in thee do I trust: cause me to know the way wherein I should walk; for I lift up my soul unto thee.**

Deliver me, O Lord, from mine enemies: I flee unto thee to hide me.

**Teach me to do thy will; for thou art my God: thy spirit is good; lead me into the land of uprightness.**

Quicken me, O Lord, for thy name's sake: for thy righteousness' sake bring my soul out of trouble.

**And of thy mercy cut off mine enemies, and destroy all them that afflict my soul: for I am thy servant.**

#### Psalm 146

PRAISE ye the Lord. Praise the Lord, O my soul.

**While I live will I praise the Lord: I will sing praises unto my God while I have any being.**

Put not your trust in princes, nor in the son of man, in whom there is no help.

**His breath goeth forth, he returneth to his earth; in that very day his thoughts perish.**

Happy is he that hath the God of Jacob for his help, whose hope is in the Lord his God:

**Which made heaven, and earth, the sea, and all that therein is: which keepeth truth for ever:**

Which executeth judgment for the oppressed: which giveth food to the hungry. The Lord looseth the prisoners:

**The Lord openeth the eyes of the blind: the Lord raiseth them that are bowed down: the Lord loveth the righteous:**

The Lord preserveth the strangers; he relieveth the fatherless and widow: but the way of the wicked he turneth upside down.

**The Lord shall reign for ever, even thy God, O Zion, unto all generations. Praise ye the Lord.**

# Psalter Selections

## SELECTION 74

### Psalm 145

I WILL extol thee, my God, O king; and I will bless thy name for ever and ever.

**Every day will I bless thee; and I will praise thy name for ever and ever.**

Great is the Lord, and greatly to be praised; and his greatness is unsearchable.

**One generation shall praise thy works to another, and shall declare thy mighty acts.**

I will speak of the glorious honour of thy majesty, and of thy wondrous works.

**And men shall speak of the might of thy terrible acts: and I will declare thy greatness.**

They shall abundantly utter the memory of thy great goodness, and shall sing of thy righteousness.

**The Lord is gracious, and full of compassion; slow to anger, and of great mercy.**

The Lord is good to all: and his tender mercies are over all his works.

**All thy works shall praise thee, O Lord; and thy saints shall bless thee.**

They shall speak of the glory of thy kingdom, and talk of thy power;

**To make known to the sons of men his mighty acts, and the glorious majesty of his kingdom.**

Thy kingdom is an everlasting kingdom, and thy dominion endureth throughout all generations.

**The Lord upholdeth all that fall, and raiseth up all those that be bowed down.**

The eyes of all wait upon thee; and thou givest them their meat in due season.

**Thou openest thine hand, and satisfiest the desire of every living thing.**

The Lord is righteous in all his ways, and holy in all his works.

**The Lord is nigh unto all them that call upon him, to all that call upon him in truth.**

He will fulfil the desire of them that fear him: he also will hear their cry, and will save them.

**The Lord preserveth all them that love him: but all the wicked will he destroy.**

My mouth shall speak the praise of the Lord: and let all flesh bless his holy name for ever and ever.

## SELECTION 75

### Psalm 147

PRAISE ye the Lord: for it is good to sing praises unto our God; for it is pleasant; and praise is comely.

**The Lord doth build up Jerusalem: he gathereth together the outcasts of Israel.**

He healeth the broken in heart, and bindeth up their wounds.

**He appointeth the number of the stars; he calleth them all by their names.**

Great is our Lord, and of great power: his understanding is infinite.

**The Lord lifteth up the meek: he casteth the wicked down to the ground.**

Sing unto the Lord with thanksgiving; sing praise upon the harp unto our God:

**Who covereth the heaven with clouds, who prepareth rain for the earth, who maketh grass to grow upon the mountains.**

He giveth to the beast his food, and to the young ravens which cry.

**He delighteth not in the strength of the horse: he taketh not pleasure in the legs of a man.**

# Psalter Selections

The LORD taketh pleasure in them that fear him, in those that hope in his mercy.

Praise the LORD, O Jerusalem; praise thy God, O Zion.

For he hath strengthened the bars of thy gates; he hath blessed thy children within thee.

He maketh peace in thy borders, and filleth thee with the finest of the wheat.

He sendeth forth his commandment upon earth: his word runneth very swiftly.

He giveth snow like wool: he scattereth the hoarfrost like ashes.

He casteth forth his ice like morsels: who can stand before his cold?

He sendeth out his word, and melteth them: he causeth his wind to blow, and the waters flow.

He showeth his word unto Jacob, his statutes and his judgments unto Israel.

He hath not dealt so with any nation: and as for his judgments, they have not known them. Praise ye the LORD.

### SELECTION 76

#### PSALM 148

PRAISE ye the LORD. Praise ye the LORD from the heavens: praise him in the heights.

Praise ye him, all his angels: praise ye him, all his hosts.

Praise ye him, sun and moon: praise him, all ye stars of light.

Praise him, ye heavens of heavens, and ye waters that be above the heavens.

Let them praise the name of the LORD: for he commanded, and they were created.

He hath also stablished them for ever and ever: he hath made a decree which shall not pass.

Praise the LORD from the earth, ye dragons, and all deeps:

Fire, and hail; snow, and vapours; stormy wind fulfilling his word:

Mountains, and all hills; fruitful trees, and all cedars:

Beasts, and all cattle; creeping things, and flying fowl:

Kings of the earth, and all people; princes, and all judges of the earth:

Both young men, and maidens; old men, and children:

Let them praise the name of the LORD: for his name alone is excellent; his glory is above the earth and heaven.

He also exalteth the horn of his people, the praise of all his saints; even of the children of Israel, a people near unto him. Praise ye the LORD.

#### PSALM 149

PRAISE ye the LORD. Sing unto the LORD a new song, and his praise in the congregation of saints.

Let Israel rejoice in him that made him: let the children of Zion be joyful in their King.

Let them praise his name in the dance: let them sing praises unto him with the timbrel and harp.

For the LORD taketh pleasure in his people: he will beautify the meek with salvation.

Let the saints be joyful in glory: let them sing aloud upon their beds.

Let the high praises of God be in their mouth, and a two-edged sword in their hand;

To execute vengeance upon the heathen, and punishments upon the people;

To bind their kings with chains, and their nobles with fetters of iron;

To execute upon them the judgment written: this honour have all his saints. Praise ye the LORD.

# Psalter Selections

### Psalm 150

**PRAISE ye the Lord. Praise God in his sanctuary: praise him in the firmament of his power.**

Praise him for his mighty acts: praise him according to his excellent greatness.

**Praise him with the sound of the trumpet: praise him with the psaltery and harp.**

Praise him with the timbrel and dance: praise him with stringed instruments and organs.

**Praise him upon the loud cymbals: praise him upon the high sounding cymbals.**

Let every thing that hath breath praise the Lord. Praise ye the Lord.

The following selections will be found appropriate:

Anniversaries: 24, 25, 40, 43, 57
Birth of Christ: 3, 19, 35, 42
National: 15, 72, 74
Preparatory Services: 14, 26, 39
Resurrection of Christ: 4, 8, 24, 45, 55
Suffering and Death of Christ: 9, 33
Thanksgiving: 30, 38, 47, 49, 50, 53, 59, 69, 76
The Lord's Supper: 4, 8, 50, 58, 59, 63, 67
In Times of Trouble: 10, 19, 22, 37, 38, 39, 44, 71

# FORMS FOR PUBLIC PROFESSION OF FAITH, BAPTISM, THE LORD'S SUPPER, AND SERVICES OF ORDINATION AND INSTALLATION OF CHURCH OFFICERS

## PUBLIC PROFESSION OF FAITH IN THE LORD JESUS CHRIST

*In order to aid those who contemplate making public profession of faith in Christ to understand the implication of this significant act and to perform it intelligently, it is important that the pastor conduct classes in Christian doctrine both for covenant youth and for any others who may manifest an interest in the way of salvation.*

*Before permitting any one to make profession of his faith in the presence of the congregation, the session shall examine him in order to assure itself so far as possible that he possesses the doctrinal knowledge requisite for active faith in the Lord Jesus Christ, relies for salvation on the merits of Christ alone, and is determined by the grace of God to lead a Christian life.*

*On the occasion of public profession of faith in the Lord Jesus Christ, the minister shall ask the candidate these, or equivalent questions:*

1. Do you believe the Bible, consisting of the Old and New Testaments, to be the Word of God, and its doctrine of salvation to be the perfect and only true doctrine of salvation?

2. Do you confess that because of your sinfulness you abhor and humble yourself before God, and that you trust for salvation not in yourself but in the Lord Jesus Christ alone?

3. Do you acknowledge Jesus Christ as your sovereign Lord and do you promise, in reliance on the grace of God, to serve him with all that is in you, to forsake the world, to mortify your sinful nature, and to lead a godly life?

4. Do you agree to submit in the Lord to the government of this church and, in case you should be found delinquent in doctrine or life, to heed its discipline?

## THE SACRAMENT OF BAPTISM

*Before the administration of the sacrament of baptism, the minister shall give instruction, in the following or similar language, concerning the institution and nature of the sacrament.*

Baptism is a sacrament ordained by the Lord Jesus Christ. It is a sign and seal of the inclusion of the person who is baptized in the covenant of grace. Teaching that we and our children are conceived and born in sin, it witnesses and seals unto us the remission of sins and the bestowal of all the gifts of salvation through union with Christ. Baptism with water signifies and seals cleansing from sin by the blood and the Spirit of Christ, together with our death unto sin and our resurrection unto newness of life by virtue of the death and resurrection of Christ. Since these gifts of salvation are the gracious provision of the triune God, who is pleased to claim us as his very own, we are baptized into the name of the Father and of the Son and of the Holy Ghost. And since baptized persons are called upon to assume the obligations of the covenant, baptism summons us to renounce the devil, the world and the flesh and to walk humbly with our God in devotion to his commandments.

### BAPTISM OF AN INFANT

*When an infant is to be baptized, the minister shall proceed to give instruction, in the following or similar language, concerning the ground of infant baptism.*

Although our young children do not yet understand these things, they are nevertheless to be baptized. For the promise of the covenant is made to believers and to their seed, as God declared

# FORMS FOR PUBLIC PROFESSION OF FAITH, BAPTISM, AND SERVICES OF ORDINATION AND INSTALLATION OF CHURCH OFFICERS

unto Abraham: "And I will establish my covenant between me and thee and thy seed after thee throughout their generations for an everlasting covenant, to be a God unto thee and to thy seed after thee." In the new dispensation no less than in the old, the children of the faithful, born within the church, have, by virtue of their birth, interest in the covenant and right to the seal of it and to the outward privileges of the church. For the covenant of grace is the same in substance under both dispensations, and the grace of God for the consolation of believers is even more fully manifested in the new dispensation. Moreover, our Saviour admitted little children into his presence, embracing and blessing them, and saying, "Of such is the kingdom of God." So the children of the covenant are by baptism distinguished from the world and solemnly received into the visible church.

*Before the baptism of an infant, the minister shall require that the parents acknowledge the duty of believers to present their children for holy baptism and that they assume publicly their responsibility for the Christian nurture of their children, proposing the following or similar questions:*

1. Do you acknowledge that, although our children are conceived and born in sin and therefore are subject to condemnation, they are holy in Christ, and as members of his church ought to be baptized?

2. Do you promise to instruct your child in the principles of our holy religion as revealed in the Scriptures of the Old and New Testaments, and as summarized in the Confession of Faith and Catechisms of this church; and do you promise to pray with and for your child, to set an example of piety and godliness before him, and to endeavor by all the means of God's appointment to bring him up in the nurture and admonition of the Lord?

### BAPTISM OF AN ADULT

*When an adult is to be baptized, the minister shall follow the opening statement on the institution and nature of the sacrament of baptism with instruction, in the following or similar language, concerning the distinctive basis of the baptism of adults.*

Although the children of believers are to be baptized as members of the covenant, the baptism of adults must await their own profession of faith in Christ. Having come to years of discretion, they become the heirs of salvation and members of the visible church only by way of personal belief in and acceptance of Christ as Saviour and Lord. So our Lord Jesus Christ commanded his church to make disciples of all nations, baptizing them into the name of the Father and of the Son and of the Holy Ghost.

*Prior to the baptism of an adult, the person to be baptized, having previously made profession of faith before the session, shall be required to confess his faith in the Lord Jesus Christ publicly by answering the questions printed above under* PUBLIC PROFESSION OF FAITH IN THE LORD JESUS CHRIST.

## THE SACRAMENT OF THE LORD'S SUPPER

*Before the administration of the Lord's Supper, the minister shall read the words of the institution of the sacrament from one of the evangelists or from I Corinthians XI. Thereupon he shall give instruction as to its institution and nature.*

The Lord's Supper is an ordinance instituted by our Lord Jesus Christ. Until his coming again it is to be observed for a perpetual remembrance of the sacrifice of himself in his death. The physical elements, representing the broken body and the shed blood of the Saviour, are received by true believers as signs and seals of all the benefits of his sacrifice upon the cross. They signify and seal remission of sins and nourishment and growth in Christ, and are a bond and pledge of communion of believers with him and with each other as members of his mystical body. As signs and seals of the covenant of grace they not only declare that God is faithful and true to fulfill the promises of the covenant but they also summon us to all the duties of the children of God, and call us to renewed consecration in gratitude for his salvation.

# FORMS FOR PUBLIC PROFESSION OF FAITH, BAPTISM, AND SERVICES OF ORDINATION AND INSTALLATION OF CHURCH OFFICERS

*The minister shall then declare who may come to the Lord's table and who are excluded, according to the Word of God.*

It is my solemn duty to warn the uninstructed, the profane, the scandalous, and those who secretly and impenitently live in any sin, not to approach the holy table lest they partake unworthily, not discerning the Lord's body, and so eat and drink condemnation to themselves. Nevertheless, this warning is not designed to keep the humble and contrite from the table of the Lord, as if the supper were for those who might be free from sin. On the contrary, we who are invited to the supper, coming as guilty and polluted sinners and without hope of eternal life apart from the grace of God in Christ, confess our dependence for pardon and cleansing upon the perfect sacrifice of Christ, base our hope of eternal life upon his perfect obedience and righteousness, and humbly resolve to deny ourselves, crucify our sinful natures, and follow Christ as becomes those who bear his name. Let us therefore in accordance with the admonition of the apostle Paul, examine our minds and hearts to determine whether such discernment is ours, to the end that we may partake to the glory of God and to our growth in the grace of Christ.

*After prayer and thanksgiving the minister shall take the bread and, having broken it, give it to the people saying:*

Our Lord Jesus Christ, the same night in which he was betrayed, having taken bread and blessed and broken it, gave it to his disciples—as I, ministering in his name, give this bread unto you—saying: "Take, eat; this is my body, which is given for you; this do in remembrance of me."

*Having given the bread, the minister shall take the cup and give it to the people saying:*

Our Saviour also took the cup and having given thanks—as has been done in his name—he gave it to his disciples, saying: "This cup is the new covenant in my blood, which is shed for many for the remission of sins; drink ye all of it."

*After a prayer of thanksgiving, an offering may be taken for the relief of the poor or for some other sacred purpose.*

*A psalm or hymn should then be sung, and the congregation dismissed with the following or some other benediction:*

"Now the God of peace, who brought again from the dead the great shepherd of the sheep with the blood of an eternal covenant, even our Lord Jesus, make you perfect in every good thing to do his will, working in you that which is well-pleasing in his sight, through Jesus Christ; to whom be the glory for ever and ever. Amen."

## SERVICES OF ORDINATION

### OF RULING ELDERS OR DEACONS

*When* RULING ELDERS *are to be ordained or installed, the minister shall state, in the following or similar language, the warrant and nature of the office:*

The office of ruling elder is based upon the kingship of our Lord Jesus Christ, who provided for his church officers who should rule in his name. Paul and Barnabas "appointed . . . elders in every church"; and Paul commanded that those who "rule well be counted worthy of double honor, especially those who labor in the word and in teaching." In this passage the Scriptures distinguish between elders who labor particularly in the Word and in doctrine — usually called ministers or pastors — and elders who join with the minister in the government and discipline of the church — generally called ruling elders.

It is the duty and privilege of ruling elders, in the name and by the authority of our ascended king, to rule over particular churches, and, as servants of our great shepherd, to care for his flock. Holy Scripture enjoins them: "Take heed unto yourselves, and to all the flock, in which the Holy

# FORMS FOR PUBLIC PROFESSION OF FAITH, BAPTISM, AND SERVICES OF ORDINATION AND INSTALLATION OF CHURCH OFFICERS

Spirit hath made you bishops, to feed the church of God, which he purchased with his own blood." As a consequence, ruling elders must be zealous in maintaining the purity of the ministration of the Word and sacraments. They must conscientiously exercise discipline and uphold the good order and peace of the church. With love and humility they should promote faithfulness on the part of both elders and deacons in the discharge of their duties. Moreover, they should have particular regard to the doctrine and conduct of the minister of the Word, in order that the church may be edified, and may manifest itself as the pillar and ground of the truth.

If they are to fill worthily so sacred an office, ruling elders must adorn sound doctrine by holy living, setting an example of godliness in all their relations with men. Let them walk with exemplary piety and diligently discharge the obligations of their office; and "when the chief shepherd shall be manifested," they "shall receive the crown of glory that fadeth not away."

*When* DEACONS *are to be ordained or installed, the minister shall state, in the following or similar language, the warrant and nature of the office:*

The office of deacon is based upon the solicitude and love of Christ for his own people. So tender is our Lord's interest in their temporal needs that he considers what is done unto one of the least of his brethren as done unto him. For he will say to those who have ministered to his little ones: "I was hungry, and ye gave me meat; I was thirsty, and ye gave me drink; I was a stranger, and ye took me in; naked, and ye clothed me; I was sick, and ye visited me; I was in prison, and ye came unto me."

In the beginning the apostles themselves ministered to the poor, but subsequently, in order that they might be able to devote themselves wholly to prayer and the ministry of the Word, they committed that responsibility to others, having directed the people to choose men of good report, full of the Holy Spirit and of wisdom. Since the days of the apostles the church has recognized the care of the poor as a distinct ministry of the church committed to deacons.

The duties of deacons consist of encouraging members of the church to provide for those who are in want, seeking to prevent poverty, making discreet and cheerful distribution to the needy, praying with the distressed and reminding them of the consolations of Holy Scripture.

If they are to fill so sacred an office, deacons must adorn sound doctrine by holy living, setting an example of godliness in all their relations with men. Let them walk with exemplary piety and diligently discharge the obligations of their office; and "when the chief shepherd shall be manifested," they "shall receive the crown of glory that fadeth not away."

*The minister, having stated the warrant and nature of the office of ruling elder or deacon, together with the character proper to be sustained, and the duties to be fulfilled by the officer elect, shall propose to the candidate, in the presence of the congregation, the following questions:*

1. Do you believe the Scriptures of the Old and New Testaments to be the Word of God, the only infallible rule of faith and practice?
2. Do you sincerely receive and adopt the Confession of Faith and Catechisms of this church, as containing the system of doctrine taught in the Holy Scriptures?
3. Do you approve of the government and discipline of The Orthodox Presbyterian Church?
4. Do you accept the office of ruling elder (or deacon, as the case may be) in this congregation, and promise faithfully to perform all the duties thereof?
5. Do you promise to study the purity, peace and unity of the church?

*The elder, or deacon, elect having answered these questions in the affirmative, the minister shall address to the members of the church the following question:*

Do you, the members of this church, acknowledge and receive this brother as a ruling elder (or deacon), and do you promise to yield to him all that honor, encouragement and obedience in the Lord, to which his office, according to the Word of God, and the constitution of this church entitles him?

*The members of the church having answered this question in the affirmative, by holding up their right hands, the minister shall proceed to set apart the candidate by prayer to the office of ruling elder (or deacon, as the case may be).*

# FORMS FOR PUBLIC PROFESSION OF FAITH, BAPTISM, AND SERVICES OF ORDINATION AND INSTALLATION OF CHURCH OFFICERS

## OF MINISTERS

*When a* MINISTER *is to be ordained or installed, the moderator of the presbytery or another member appointed to preside in his stead shall state, in the following or similar language, the warrant and nature of the office of minister:*

The Word of God clearly teaches that the office of minister was instituted by the Lord Jesus Christ. The apostle Paul declares that our Lord "gave some to be apostles; and some, prophets; and some, evangelists; and some, pastors and teachers; for the perfecting of the saints, unto the work of ministering, unto the building up of the body of Christ."

The duties of the minister of Christ may briefly be set forth under the following heads: the faithful exposition of the Word of God and its application to the needs of the hearers, in order that the unconverted may be reconciled to God and that the saints may be built up in their most holy faith; the offering of prayer to the Lord on behalf of the congregation; the administration of the sacraments of baptism and the Lord's Supper; and the exercise, in conjunction with the ruling elders, of the government and discipline of the church.

The office of the minister is the first in the church for dignity and usefulness. The person who fills this office is designated in Scripture by different names expressive of his various duties. As he has the oversight of the flock of Christ, he is termed bishop. As he feeds them with spiritual food, he is termed pastor. As he serves Christ in his church, he is termed minister. As it is his duty to be grave and prudent, and an example to the flock, and to govern well in the house of God, he is termed presbyter or elder. As he is sent to declare the will of God to sinners, and to beseech them to be reconciled to God through Christ, he is termed ambassador. As he is commanded to warn the house of Israel against the enemies of God and his Word, he is termed watchman. And, as he dispenses the manifold grace of God and the ordinances instituted by Christ, he is termed steward of the mysteries of God.

*The presiding minister, having recited the proceedings of the presbytery preparatory to this transaction and having pointed out the nature and importance of the ordinance, shall propose to the candidate the following questions:*

1. Do you believe the Scriptures of the Old and New Testaments to be the Word of God, the only infallible rule of faith and practice?

2. Do you sincerely receive and adopt the Confession of Faith and Catechisms of this church, as containing the system of doctrine taught in the Holy Scriptures?

3. Do you approve of the government and discipline of The Orthodox Presbyterian Church?

4. Do you promise subjection to your brethren in the Lord?

5. Have you been induced, as far as you know your own heart, to seek the office of the holy ministry from love to God and a sincere desire to promote his glory in the gospel of his Son?

6. Do you promise to be zealous and faithful in maintaining the truths of the gospel, and the purity and peace of the church, whatever persecution or opposition may arise unto you on that account?

7. Do you engage to be faithful and diligent in the exercise of all private and personal duties which become you as a Christian and a minister of the gospel, as well as in all relative duties and the public duties of your office, endeavoring to adorn the profession of the gospel by your conversation, and walking with exemplary piety before the flock over which God shall make you overseer?

8. Are you now willing to take the charge of this congregation, agreeably to your declaration when you accepted their call? And do you promise to discharge the duties of a pastor to them as God shall give you strength?

*When a candidate is to be ordained to the office of* EVANGELIST, *(or* TEACHER*) the following is to be substituted for question No. 8:*

Are you now willing to undertake the work of an evangelist (or teacher) and do you promise to discharge the duties which may be incumbent upon you in this character as God may give you strength?

# FORMS FOR PUBLIC PROFESSION OF FAITH, BAPTISM, AND SERVICES OF ORDINATION AND INSTALLATION OF CHURCH OFFICERS

## SERVICE OF INSTALLATION OF A PASTOR

*The presiding minister shall state to the congregation the design of the meeting and briefly recite the proceedings of the presbytery relative thereto. And then he shall propose to the minister to be installed the following or similar questions:*

1. Are you now willing to take charge of this congregation as its pastor, agreeably to your declaration when you accepted its call?

2. Do you conscientiously believe and declare, as far as you know your own heart, that in taking upon you this charge, you are influenced by a sincere desire to promote the glory of God and the good of his church?

3. Do you solemnly promise that, by the assistance of the grace of God, you will endeavor faithfully to discharge all the duties of a pastor to this congregation, and will be careful to maintain a deportment in all respects becoming a minister of the gospel of Christ, agreeably to your ordination engagements?

*Following the answering of the questions for ordination and installation of a pastor the presiding minister shall propose to the people of the congregation the following questions:*

1. Do you, the people of this congregation, continue to profess your readiness to receive           , whom you have called to be your minister?

2. Do you promise to receive the word of truth from his mouth with meekness and love, and to submit to him in the due exercise of discipline?

3. Do you promise to encourage him in his arduous labor and to assist his endeavors for your instruction and spiritual edification?

4. And do you engage to continue to him, while he is your pastor, that competent worldly maintenance which you have promised, and whatever else you may see needful for the honor of religion and his comfort among you?

# THE WESTMINSTER CONFESSION OF FAITH

The Westminster Confession of Faith is perhaps the most notable expression in creedal form of the truths of the Bible. It was the work of that Assembly of divines which was called together by Parliament and met in London, at Westminster Abbey, during the years 1643-1648. It was this Assembly which also produced the Larger and Shorter Catechisms. The Confession and the Catechisms are used by many churches as their doctrinal standards, subordinate to the Word of God. The text of the Confession as given on the following pages is in the form adopted by the Orthodox Presbyterian Church and except for a few revisions, which are largely concerned with the relation of the civil magistrate to the church, it agrees with the text of the original manuscript of the Confession.

# THE WESTMINSTER CONFESSION OF FAITH

## CHAPTER I
### Of the Holy Scripture

I. Although the light of nature, and the works of creation and providence do so far manifest the goodness, wisdom, and power of God, as to leave men unexcusable; yet are they not sufficient to give that knowledge of God, and of His will, which is necessary unto salvation. Therefore it pleased the Lord, at sundry times, and in divers manners, to reveal Himself, and to declare that His will unto His Church; and afterwards, for the better preserving and propagating of the truth, and for the more sure establishment and comfort of the Church against the corruption of the flesh, and the malice of Satan and of the world, to commit the same wholly unto writing: which maketh the Holy Scripture to be most necessary; those former ways of God's revealing His will unto His people being now ceased.

II. Under the name of Holy Scripture, or the Word of God written, are now contained all the books of the Old and New Testament, which are these:

Of the Old Testament:

| | | |
|---|---|---|
| *Genesis* | *II Chronicles* | *Daniel* |
| *Exodus* | *Ezra* | *Hosea* |
| *Leviticus* | *Nehemiah* | *Joel* |
| *Numbers* | *Esther* | *Amos* |
| *Deuteronomy* | *Job* | *Obadiah* |
| *Joshua* | *Psalms* | *Jonah* |
| *Judges* | *Proverbs* | *Micah* |
| *Ruth* | *Ecclesiastes* | *Nahum* |
| *I Samuel* | *The Song of Songs* | *Habakkuk* |
| *II Samuel* | *Isaiah* | *Zephaniah* |
| *I Kings* | *Jeremiah* | *Haggai* |
| *II Kings* | *Lamentations* | *Zechariah* |
| *I Chronicles* | *Ezekiel* | *Malachi;* |

Of the New Testament:

| | | |
|---|---|---|
| *The Gospels according to Matthew Mark Luke John* | *Galatians* | *The Epistle of James* |
| | *Ephesians* | |
| | *Philippians* | *The first and second Epistles of Peter* |
| | *Colossians* | |
| | *Thessalonians I* | |
| | *Thessalonians II* | *The first, second, and third Epistles of John* |
| *The Acts of the Apostles* | *To Timothy I* | |
| | *To Timothy II* | |
| *Paul's Epistles to the Romans Corinthians I Corinthians II* | *To Titus* | *The Epistle of Jude* |
| | *To Philemon* | |
| | *The Epistle to the Hebrews* | *The Revelation of John* |

All which are given by inspiration of God to be the rule of faith and life.

III. The books commonly called Apocrypha, not being of divine inspiration, are no part of the canon of the Scripture, and therefore are of no authority in the Church of God, nor to be any otherwise approved, or made use of, than other human writings.

IV. The authority of the Holy Scripture, for which it ought to be believed, and obeyed, dependeth not upon the testimony of any man, or Church; but wholly upon God (who is truth itself) the author thereof: and therefore it is to be received, because it is the Word of God.

V. We may be moved and induced by the testimony of the Church to an high and reverent esteem of the Holy Scripture. And the heavenliness of the matter, the efficacy of the doctrine, the majesty of the style, the consent of all the parts, the scope of the whole (which is, to give all glory to God), the full discovery it makes of the only way of man's salvation, the many other incomparable excellencies, and the entire perfection thereof, are arguments

# THE WESTMINSTER CONFESSION OF FAITH

whereby it doth abundantly evidence itself to be the Word of God: yet notwithstanding, our full persuasion and assurance of the infallible truth and divine authority thereof, is from the inward work of the Holy Spirit bearing witness by and with the Word in our hearts.

VI. The whole counsel of God concerning all things necessary for His own glory, man's salvation, faith and life, is either expressly set down in Scripture, or by good and necessary consequence may be deduced from Scripture: unto which nothing at any time is to be added, whether by new revelations of the Spirit, or traditions of men. Nevertheless, we acknowledge the inward illumination of the Spirit of God to be necessary for the saving understanding of such things as are revealed in the Word: and that there are some circumstances concerning the worship of God, and government of the Church, common to human actions and societies, which are to be ordered by the light of nature, and Christian prudence, according to the general rules of the Word, which are always to be observed.

VII. All things in Scripture are not alike plain in themselves, nor alike clear unto all: yet those things which are necessary to be known, believed, and observed for salvation, are so clearly propounded, and opened in some place of Scripture or other, that not only the learned, but the unlearned, in a due use of the ordinary means, may attain unto a sufficient understanding of them.

VIII. The Old Testament in Hebrew (which was the native language of the people of God of old), and the New Testament in Greek (which, at the time of the writing of it, was most generally known to the nations), being immediately inspired by God, and, by His singular care and providence, kept pure in all ages, are therefore authentical; so as, in all controversies of religion, the Church is finally to appeal unto them. But, because these original tongues are not known to all the people of God, who have right unto, and interest in the Scriptures, and are commanded, in the fear of God, to read and search them, therefore they are to be translated into the vulgar language of every nation unto which they come, that, the Word of God dwelling plentifully in all, they may worship Him in an acceptable manner; and, through patience and comfort of the Scriptures, may have hope.

IX. The infallible rule of interpretation of Scripture is the Scripture itself: and therefore, when there is a question about the true and full sense of any Scripture (which is not manifold, but one), it must be searched and known by other places that speak more clearly.

X. The supreme judge by which all controversies of religion are to be determined, and all decrees of councils, opinions of ancient writers, doctrines of men, and private spirits, are to be examined, and in whose sentence we are to rest, can be no other but the Holy Spirit speaking in the Scripture.

## CHAPTER II

### Of God, and of the Holy Trinity

I. There is but one only, living, and true God, who is infinite in being and perfection, a most pure spirit, invisible, without body, parts, or passions; immutable, immense, eternal, incomprehensible, almighty, most wise, most holy, most free, most absolute; working all things according to the counsel of His own immutable and most righteous will, for His own glory; most loving, gracious, merciful, long-suffering, abundant in goodness and truth, forgiving iniquity, transgression, and sin; the rewarder of them that diligently seek Him; and withal, most just, and terrible in His judgments, hating all sin, and who will by no means clear the guilty.

II. God hath all life, glory, goodness, blessedness, in and of Himself; and is alone in and unto Himself all-sufficient, not standing in need of any creatures which He hath made, nor deriving any glory from them, but only manifesting His own glory in, by, unto, and upon them. He is the alone fountain of all being, of whom, through whom, and to whom are all things; and hath most sovereign dominion over them, to do by them, for them, or upon them whatsoever Himself pleaseth. In His sight all things are open and manifest, His knowledge is infinite, infallible, and independent upon the creature, so as nothing is to Him contingent, or uncertain. He is most holy in all His counsels, in all His works, and in all His commands. To Him is due from angels and men, and every other creature, whatsoever worship, service, or obedience He is pleased to require of them.

III. In the unity of the Godhead there be three persons, of one substance, power, and eternity: God the Father, God the Son, and God the Holy Ghost: the Father is of none, neither begotten, nor proceeding; the Son is eternally begotten of the Father; the Holy Ghost eternally proceeding from the Father and the Son.

# THE WESTMINSTER CONFESSION OF FAITH

## CHAPTER III

### Of God's Eternal Decree

I. God, from all eternity, did, by the most wise and holy counsel of His own will, freely, and unchangeably ordain whatsoever comes to pass: yet so, as thereby neither is God the author of sin, nor is violence offered to the will of the creatures; nor is the liberty or contingency of second causes taken away, but rather established.

II. Although God knows whatsoever may or can come to pass upon all supposed conditions, yet hath He not decreed anything because He foresaw it as future, or as that which would come to pass upon such conditions.

III. By the decree of God, for the manifestation of His glory, some men and angels are predestinated unto everlasting life; and others foreordained to everlasting death.

IV. These angels and men, thus predestinated, and foreordained, are particularly and unchangeably designed, and their number so certain and definite, that it cannot be either increased or diminished.

V. Those of mankind that are predestinated unto life, God, before the foundation of the world was laid, according to His eternal and immutable purpose, and the secret counsel and good pleasure of His will, hath chosen, in Christ, unto everlasting glory, out of His mere free grace and love, without any foresight of faith, or good works, or perseverance in either of them, or any other thing in the creature, as conditions, or causes moving Him thereunto; and all to the praise of His glorious grace.

VI. As God hath appointed the elect unto glory, so hath He, by the eternal and most free purpose of His will, foreordained all the means thereunto. Wherefore, they who are elected, being fallen in Adam, are redeemed by Christ, are effectually called unto faith in Christ by His Spirit working in due season, are justified, adopted, sanctified, and kept by His power, through faith, unto salvation. Neither are any other redeemed by Christ, effectually called, justified, adopted, sanctified, and saved, but the elect only.

VII. The rest of mankind God was pleased, according to the unsearchable counsel of His own will, whereby He extendeth or withholdeth mercy, as He pleaseth, for the glory of His sovereign power over His creatures, to pass by; and to ordain them to dishonour and wrath for their sin, to the praise of His glorious justice.

VIII. The doctrine of this high mystery of predestination is to be handled with special prudence and care, that men, attending the will of God revealed in His Word, and yielding obedience thereunto, may, from the certainty of their effectual vocation, be assured of their eternal election. So shall this doctrine afford matter of praise, reverence, and admiration of God; and of humility, diligence, and abundant consolation to all that sincerely obey the Gospel.

## CHAPTER IV

### Of Creation

I. It pleased God the Father, Son, and Holy Ghost, for the manifestation of the glory of His eternal power, wisdom, and goodness, in the beginning, to create, or make of nothing, the world, and all things therein whether visible or invisible, in the space of six days; and all very good.

II. After God had made all other creatures, He created man, male and female, with reasonable and immortal souls, endued with knowledge, righteousness, and true holiness, after His own image; having the law of God written in their hearts, and power to fulfil it: and yet under a possibility of transgressing, being left to the liberty of their own will, which was subject unto change. Beside this law written in their hearts, they received a command, not to eat of the tree of the knowledge of good and evil; which while they kept, they were happy in their communion with God, and had dominion over the creatures.

## CHAPTER V

### Of Providence

I. God the great Creator of all things doth uphold, direct, dispose, and govern all creatures, actions, and things, from the greatest even to the least, by His most wise and holy providence, according to His infallible fore-knowledge, and the free and immutable counsel of His own will, to the praise of the glory of His wisdom, power, justice, goodness, and mercy.

# THE WESTMINSTER CONFESSION OF FAITH

II. Although, in relation to the fore-knowledge and decree of God, the first Cause, all things come to pass immutably, and infallibly; yet, by the same providence, He ordereth them to fall out, according to the nature of second causes, either necessarily, freely, or contingently.

III. God, in His ordinary providence, maketh use of means, yet is free to work without, above, and against them, at His pleasure.

IV. The almighty power, unsearchable wisdom, and infinite goodness of God so far manifest themselves in His providence, that it extendeth itself even to the first fall, and all other sins of angels and men; and that not by a bare permission, but such as hath joined with it a most wise and powerful bounding, and otherwise ordering, and governing of them, in a manifold dispensation, to His own holy ends; yet so, as the sinfulness thereof proceedeth only from the creature, and not from God, who, being most holy and righteous, neither is nor can be the author or approver of sin.

V. The most wise, righteous, and gracious God doth oftentimes leave, for a season, His own children to manifold temptations, and the corruption of their own hearts, to chastise them for their former sins, or to discover unto them the hidden strength of corruption and deceitfulness of their hearts, that they may be humbled; and, to raise them to a more close and constant dependence for their support upon Himself, and to make them more watchful against all future occasions of sin, and for sundry other just and holy ends.

VI. As for those wicked and ungodly men whom God, as a righteous Judge, for former sins, doth blind and harden, from them He not only withholdeth His grace whereby they might have been enlightened in their understandings, and wrought upon in their hearts; but sometimes also withdraweth the gifts which they had, and exposeth them to such objects as their corruption makes occasions of sin; and, withal, gives them over to their own lusts, the temptations of the world, and the power of Satan, whereby it comes to pass that they harden themselves, even under those means which God useth for the softening of others.

VII. As the providence of God doth, in general, reach to all creatures; so, after a most special manner, it taketh care of His Church, and disposeth all things to the good thereof.

## CHAPTER VI

### Of the Fall of Man, of Sin, and of the Punishment thereof

I. Our first parents, being seduced by the subtilty and temptation of Satan, sinned, in eating the forbidden fruit. This their sin, God was pleased, according to His wise and holy counsel, to permit, having purposed to order it to His own glory.

II. By this sin they fell from their original righteousness and communion with God, and so became dead in sin, and wholly defiled in all the parts and faculties of soul and body.

III. They being the root of all mankind, the guilt of this sin was imputed; and the same death in sin, and corrupted nature, conveyed to all their posterity descending from them by ordinary generation.

IV. From this original corruption, whereby we are utterly indisposed, disabled, and made opposite to all good, and wholly inclined to all evil, do proceed all actual transgressions.

V. This corruption of nature, during this life, doth remain in those that are regenerated; and although it be, through Christ, pardoned, and mortified; yet both itself, and all the motions thereof, are truly and properly sin.

VI. Every sin, both original and actual, being a transgression of the righteous law of God, and contrary thereunto, doth, in its own nature, bring guilt upon the sinner, whereby he is bound over to the wrath of God, and curse of the law, and so made subject to death, with all miseries spiritual, temporal, and eternal.

## CHAPTER VII

### Of God's Covenant with Man

I. The distance between God and the creature is so great, that although reasonable creatures do owe obedience unto Him as their Creator, yet they could never have any fruition of Him as their blessedness and reward, but by some voluntary condescension on God's part, which He hath been pleased to express by way of covenant.

# THE WESTMINSTER CONFESSION OF FAITH

II. The first covenant made with man was a covenant of works, wherein life was promised to Adam; and in him to his posterity, upon condition of perfect and personal obedience.

III. Man, by his fall, having made himself uncapable of life by that covenant, the Lord was pleased to make a second, commonly called the covenant of grace; wherein He freely offereth unto sinners life and salvation by Jesus Christ; requiring of them faith in Him, that they may be saved, and promising to give unto all those that are ordained unto eternal life His Holy Spirit, to make them willing, and able to believe.

IV. This covenant of grace is frequently set forth in Scripture by the name of a testament, in reference to the death of Jesus Christ the Testator, and to the everlasting inheritance, with all things belonging to it, therein bequeathed.

V. This covenant was differently administered in the time of the law, and in the time of the gospel: under the law, it was administered by promises, prophecies, sacrifices, circumcision, the paschal lamb, and other types and ordinances delivered to the people of the Jews, all foresignifying Christ to come; which were, for that time, sufficient and efficacious, through the operation of the Spirit, to instruct and build up the elect in faith in the promised Messiah, by whom they had full remission of sins, and eternal salvation; and is called the old Testament.

VI. Under the gospel, when Christ, the substance, was exhibited, the ordinances in which this covenant is dispensed are the preaching of the Word, and the administration of the sacraments of Baptism and the Lord's Supper: which, though fewer in number, and administered with more simplicity, and less outward glory, yet, in them, it is held forth in more fulness, evidence and spiritual efficacy, to all nations, both Jews and Gentiles; and is called the new Testament. There are not therefore two covenants of grace, differing in substance, but one and the same, under various dispensations.

## CHAPTER VIII

### Of Christ the Mediator

I. It pleased God, in His eternal purpose, to choose and ordain the Lord Jesus, His only begotten Son, to be the Mediator between God and man, the Prophet, Priest, and King, the Head and Saviour of His Church, the Heir of all things, and Judge of the world: unto whom He did from all eternity give a people, to be His seed, and to be by Him in time redeemed, called, justified, sanctified, and glorified.

II. The Son of God, the second person in the Trinity, being very and eternal God, of one substance and equal with the Father, did, when the fulness of time was come, take upon Him man's nature, with all the essential properties, and common infirmities thereof, yet without sin; being conceived by the power of the Holy Ghost, in the womb of the virgin Mary, of her substance. So that two whole, perfect, and distinct natures, the Godhead and the manhood, were inseparably joined together in one person, without conversion, composition, or confusion. Which person is very God, and very man, yet one Christ, the only Mediator between God and man.

III. The Lord Jesus, in His human nature thus united to the divine, was sanctified, and anointed with the Holy Spirit, above measure, having in Him all the treasures of wisdom and knowledge; in whom it pleased the Father that all fulness should dwell; to the end that, being holy, harmless, undefiled, and full of grace and truth, He might be thoroughly furnished to execute the office of a mediator, and surety. Which office He took not unto Himself, but was thereunto called by His Father, who put all power and judgment into His hand, and gave Him commandment to execute the same.

IV. This office the Lord Jesus did most willingly undertake; which that He might discharge, He was made under the law, and did perfectly fulfil it; endured most grievous torments immediately in His soul, and most painful sufferings in His body; was crucified, and died, was buried, and remained under the power of death, yet saw no corruption. On the third day He arose from the dead, with the same body in which He suffered, with which also He ascended into heaven, and there sitteth at the right hand of His Father, making intercession, and shall return, to judge men and angels, at the end of the world.

V. The Lord Jesus, by His perfect obedience, and sacrifice of Himself, which He, through the eternal Spirit, once offered up unto God, hath fully satisfied the justice of His Father; and purchased, not only reconciliation, but an everlasting inheritance in the kingdom of heaven, for all those whom the Father hath given unto Him.

# THE WESTMINSTER CONFESSION OF FAITH

VI. Although the work of redemption was not actually wrought by Christ till after His incarnation, yet the virtue, efficacy, and benefits thereof were communicated unto the elect, in all ages successively from the beginning of the world, in and by those promises, types, and sacrifices, wherein He was revealed, and signified to be the seed of the woman which should bruise the serpent's head; and the Lamb slain from the beginning of the world; being yesterday and today the same, and for ever.

VII. Christ, in the work of mediation, acts according to both natures, by each nature doing that which is proper to itself; yet, by reason of the unity of the person, that which is proper to one nature is sometimes in Scripture attributed to the person denominated by the other nature.

VIII. To all those for whom Christ hath purchased redemption, He doth certainly and effectually apply and communicate the same; making intercession for them, and revealing unto them, in and by the Word, the mysteries of salvation; effectually persuading them by His Spirit to believe and obey, and governing their hearts by His Word and Spirit; overcoming all their enemies by His almighty power and wisdom, in such manner, and ways, as are most consonant to His wonderful and unsearchable dispensation.

## CHAPTER IX

### Of Free-Will

I. God hath endued the will of man with that natural liberty, that it is neither forced, nor, by any absolute necessity of nature, determined to good, or evil.

II. Man, in his state of innocency, had freedom, and power to will and to do that which was good and well pleasing to God; but yet, mutably, so that he might fall from it.

III. Man, by his fall into a state of sin, hath wholly lost all ability of will to any spiritual good accompanying salvation: so as, a natural man, being altogether averse from that good, and dead in sin, is not able, by his own strength, to convert himself, or to prepare himself thereunto.

IV. When God converts a sinner, and translates him into the state of grace, He freeth him from his natural bondage under sin; and, by His grace alone, enables him freely to will and to do that which is spiritually good; yet so, as that by reason of his remaining corruption, he doth not perfectly, nor only, will that which is good, but doth also will that which is evil.

V. The will of man is made perfectly and immutably free to good alone, in the state of glory only.

## CHAPTER X

### Of Effectual Calling

I. All those whom God hath predestinated unto life, and those only, He is pleased, in His appointed and accepted time, effectually to call, by His Word and Spirit, out of that state of sin and death, in which they are by nature, to grace and salvation, by Jesus Christ; enlightening their minds spiritually and savingly to understand the things of God, taking away their heart of stone, and giving unto them a heart of flesh; renewing their wills, and, by His almighty power, determining them to that which is good, and effectually drawing them to Jesus Christ: yet so, as they come most freely, being made willing by His grace.

II. This effectual call is of God's free and special grace alone, not from anything at all foreseen in man, who is altogether passive therein, until, being quickened and renewed by the Holy Spirit, he is thereby enabled to answer this call, and to embrace the grace offered and conveyed in it.

III. Elect infants, dying in infancy, are regenerated, and saved by Christ, through the Spirit, who worketh when, and where, and how He pleaseth: so also are all other elect persons who are uncapable of being outwardly called by the ministry of the Word.

IV. Others, not elected, although they may be called by the ministry of the Word, and may have some common operations of the Spirit, yet they never truly come unto Christ, and therefore cannot be saved: much less can men, not professing the Christian religion, be saved in any other way whatsoever, be they never so diligent to frame their lives according to the light of nature, and the laws of that religion they do profess. And, to assert and maintain that they may, is very pernicious, and to be detested.

# THE WESTMINSTER CONFESSION OF FAITH

## CHAPTER XI

### Of Justification

I. Those whom God effectually calleth, He also freely justifieth: not by infusing righteousness into them, but by pardoning their sins, and by accounting and accepting their persons as righteous; not for anything wrought in them, or done by them, but for Christ's sake alone; nor by imputing faith itself, the act of believing, or any other evangelical obedience to them, as their righteousness; but by imputing the obedience and satisfaction of Christ unto them, they receiving and resting on Him and His righteousness, by faith; which faith they have not of themselves, it is the gift of God.

II. Faith, thus receiving and resting on Christ and His righteousness, is the alone instrument of justification: yet is it not alone in the person justified, but is ever accompanied with all other saving graces, and is no dead faith, but worketh by love.

III. Christ, by His obedience and death, did fully discharge the debt of all those that are thus justified, and did make a proper, real, and full satisfaction to His Father's justice in their behalf. Yet, inasmuch as He was given by the Father for them; and His obedience and satisfaction accepted in their stead; and both, freely, not for anything in them; their justification is only of free grace; that both the exact justice and rich grace of God might be glorified in the justification of sinners.

IV. God did, from all eternity, decree to justify all the elect, and Christ did, in the fulness of time, die for their sins, and rise again for their justification: nevertheless, they are not justified, until the Holy Spirit doth, in due time, actually apply Christ unto them.

V. God doth continue to forgive the sins of those that are justified; and, although they can never fall from the state of justification, yet they may, by their sins, fall under God's fatherly displeasure, and not have the light of His countenance restored unto them, until they humble themselves, confess their sins, beg pardon, and renew their faith and repentance.

VI. The justification of believers under the old testament was, in all these respects, one and the same with the justification of believers under the new testament.

## CHAPTER XII

### Of Adoption

I. All those that are justified, God vouchsafeth, in and for His only Son Jesus Christ, to make partakers of the grace of adoption, by which they are taken into the number, and enjoy the liberties and privileges of the children of God, have His name put upon them, receive the spirit of adoption, have access to the throne of grace with boldness, are enabled to cry, Abba, Father, are pitied, protected, provided for, and chastened by Him, as by a Father: yet never cast off, but sealed to the day of redemption; and inherit the promises, as heirs of everlasting salvation.

## CHAPTER XIII

### Of Sanctification

I. They, who are once effectually called, and regenerated, having a new heart, and a new spirit created in them, are further sanctified, really and personally, through the virtue of Christ's death and resurrection, by His Word and Spirit dwelling in them: the dominion of the whole body of sin is destroyed, and the several lusts thereof are more and more weakened and mortified; and they more and more quickened and strengthened in all saving graces, to the practice of true holiness, without which no man shall see the Lord.

II. This sanctification is throughout, in the whole man; yet imperfect in this life, there abiding still some remnants of corruption in every part; whence ariseth a continual and irreconcilable war, the flesh lusting against the Spirit, and the Spirit against the flesh.

III. In which war, although the remaining corruption, for a time, may much prevail; yet, through the continual supply of strength from the sanctifying Spirit of Christ, the regenerate part doth overcome; and so, the saints grow in grace, perfecting holiness in the fear of God.

# THE WESTMINSTER CONFESSION OF FAITH

## CHAPTER XIV

### Of Saving Faith

I. The grace of faith, whereby the elect are enabled to believe to the saving of their souls, is the work of the Spirit of Christ in their hearts, and is ordinarily wrought by the ministry of the Word, by which also, and by the administration of the sacraments, and prayer, it is increased and strengthened.

II. By this faith, a Christian believeth to be true whatsoever is revealed in the Word, for the authority of God Himself speaking therein; and acteth differently upon that which each particular passage thereof containeth; yielding obedience to the commands, trembling at the threatenings, and embracing the promises of God for this life, and that which is to come. But the principal acts of saving faith are accepting, receiving, and resting upon Christ alone for justification, sanctification, and eternal life, by virtue of the covenant of grace.

III. This faith is different in degrees, weak or strong; may be often and many ways assailed, and weakened, but gets the victory: growing up in many to the attainment of a full assurance, through Christ, who is both the author and finisher of our faith.

## CHAPTER XV

### Of Repentance unto Life

I. Repentance unto life is an evangelical grace, the doctrine whereof is to be preached by every minister of the Gospel, as well as that of faith in Christ.

II. By it, a sinner, out of the sight and sense not only of the danger, but also of the filthiness and odiousness of his sins, as contrary to the holy nature, and righteous law of God; and upon the apprehension of His mercy in Christ to such as are penitent, so grieves for, and hates his sins, as to turn from them all unto God, purposing and endeavouring to walk with Him in all the ways of His commandments.

III. Although repentance be not to be rested in, as any satisfaction for sin, or any cause of the pardon thereof, which is the act of God's free grace in Christ; yet it is of such necessity to all sinners, that none may expect pardon without it.

IV. As there is no sin so small, but it deserves damnation; so there is no sin so great, that it can bring damnation upon those who truly repent.

V. Men ought not to content themselves with a general repentance, but it is every man's duty to endeavour to repent of his particular sins, particularly.

VI. As every man is bound to make private confession of his sins to God, praying for the pardon thereof; upon which, and the forsaking of them, he shall find mercy; so, he that scandalizeth his brother, or the Church of Christ, ought to be willing, by a private or public confession, and sorrow for his sin, to declare his repentance to those that are offended, who are thereupon to be reconciled to him, and in love to receive him.

## CHAPTER XVI

### Of Good Works

I. Good works are only such as God hath commanded in His holy Word, and not such as, without the warrant thereof, are devised by men, out of blind zeal, or upon any pretence of good intention.

II. These good works, done in obedience to God's commandments, are the fruits and evidences of a true and lively faith: and by them believers manifest their thankfulness, strengthen their assurance, edify their brethren, adorn the profession of the Gospel, stop the mouths of the adversaries, and glorify God, whose workmanship they are, created in Christ Jesus thereunto, that, having their fruit unto holiness, they may have the end, eternal life.

III. Their ability to do good works is not at all of themselves, but wholly from the Spirit of Christ. And that they may be enabled thereunto, beside the graces they have already received, there is required an actual influence of the same Holy Spirit, to work in them to will, and to do, of His good pleasure: yet are they not hereupon to grow negligent, as if they were not bound

# THE WESTMINSTER CONFESSION OF FAITH

to perform any duty unless upon a special motion of the Spirit; but they ought to be diligent in stirring up the grace of God that is in them.

IV. They who, in their obedience, attain to the greatest height which is possible in this life, are so far from being able to supererogate, and to do more than God requires, as that they fall short of much which in duty they are bound to do.

V. We cannot by our best works merit pardon of sin, or eternal life at the hand of God, by reason of the great disproportion that is between them and the glory to come; and the infinite distance that is between us and God, whom, by them, we can neither profit, nor satisfy for the debt of our former sins, but when we have done all we can, we have done but our duty, and are unprofitable servants: and because, as they are good, they proceed from His Spirit; and as they are wrought by us, they are defiled, and mixed with so much weakness and imperfection, that they cannot endure the severity of God's judgment.

VI. Notwithstanding, the persons of believers being accepted through Christ, their good works also are accepted in Him; not as though they were in this life wholly unblameable and unreprovable in God's sight; but that He, looking upon them in His Son, is pleased to accept and reward that which is sincere, although accompanied with many weaknesses and imperfections.

VII. Works done by unregenerate men, although for the matter of them they may be things which God commands; and of good use both to themselves and others: yet, because they proceed not from an heart purified by faith; nor are done in a right manner, according to the Word; nor to a right end, the glory of God, they are therefore sinful, and cannot please God, or make a man meet to receive grace from God: and yet, their neglect of them is more sinful and displeasing unto God.

## CHAPTER XVII

### Of the Perseverance of the Saints

I. They, whom God hath accepted in His Beloved, effectually called, and sanctified by His Spirit, can neither totally nor finally fall away from the state of grace, but shall certainly persevere therein to the end, and be eternally saved.

II. This perseverance of the saints depends not upon their own free will, but upon the immutability of the decree of election, flowing from the free and unchangeable love of God the Father; upon the efficacy of the merit and intercession of Jesus Christ, the abiding of the Spirit, and of the seed of God within them, and the nature of the covenant of grace: from all which ariseth also the certainty and infallibility thereof.

III. Nevertheless, they may, through the temptations of Satan and of the world, the prevalency of corruption remaining in them, and the neglect of the means of their preservation, fall into grievous sins; and, for a time, continue therein: whereby they incur God's displeasure, and grieve His Holy Spirit, come to be deprived of some measure of their graces and comforts, have their hearts hardened, and their consciences wounded; hurt and scandalize others, and bring temporal judgments upon themselves.

## CHAPTER XVIII

### Of the Assurance of Grace and Salvation

I. Although hypocrites and other unregenerate men may vainly deceive themselves with false hopes and carnal presumptions of being in the favour of God, and estate of salvation (which hope of theirs shall perish): yet such as truly believe in the Lord Jesus, and love Him in sincerity, endeavouring to walk in all good conscience before Him, may, in this life, be certainly assured that they are in the state of grace, and may rejoice in the hope of the glory of God, which hope shall never make them ashamed.

II. This certainty is not a bare conjectural and probable persuasion grounded upon a fallible hope; but an infallible assurance of faith founded upon the divine truth of the promises of salvation, the inward evidence of those graces unto which these promises are made, the testimony of the Spirit of adoption witnessing with our spirits that we are the children of God, which Spirit is the earnest of our inheritance, whereby we are sealed to the day of redemption.

# THE WESTMINSTER CONFESSION OF FAITH

III. This infallible assurance doth not so belong to the essence of faith, but that a true believer may wait long, and conflict with many difficulties before he be partaker of it: yet, being enabled by the Spirit to know the things which are freely given him of God, he may, without extraordinary revelation, in the right use of ordinary means, attain thereunto. And therefore it is the duty of everyone to give all diligence to make his calling and election sure, that thereby his heart may be enlarged in peace and joy in the Holy Ghost, in love and thankfulness to God, and in strength and cheerfulness in the duties of obedience, the proper fruits of this assurance; so far is it from inclining men to looseness.

IV. True believers may have the assurance of their salvation divers ways shaken, diminished, and intermitted; as, by negligence in preserving of it, by falling into some special sin which woundeth the conscience and grieveth the Spirit; by some sudden or vehement temptation, by God's withdrawing the light of His countenance, and suffering even such as fear Him to walk in darkness and to have no light: yet are they never utterly destitute of that seed of God, and life of faith, that love of Christ and the brethren, that sincerity of heart, and conscience of duty, out of which, by the operation of the Spirit, this assurance may, in due time, be revived; and by the which, in the mean time, they are supported from utter despair.

## CHAPTER XIX

*Of the Law of God*

I. God gave to Adam a law, as a covenant of works, by which He bound him and all his posterity to personal, entire, exact, and perpetual obedience, promised life upon the fulfilling, and threatened death upon the breach of it, and endued him with power and ability to keep it.

II. This law, after his fall, continued to be a perfect rule of righteousness; and, as such, was delivered by God upon Mount Sinai, in ten commandments, and written in two tables: the four first commandments containing our duty towards God; and the other six, our duty to man.

III. Beside this law, commonly called moral, God was pleased to give to the people of Israel, as a church under age, ceremonial laws, containing several typical ordinances, partly of worship, prefiguring Christ, His graces, actions, sufferings, and benefits; and partly, holding forth divers instructions of moral duties. All which ceremonial laws are now abrogated, under the new testament.

IV. To them also, as a body politic, He gave sundry judicial laws, which expired together with the State of that people; not obliging any other now, further than the general equity thereof may require.

V. The moral law doth for ever bind all, as well justified persons as others, to the obedience thereof; and that, not only in regard of the matter contained in it, but also in respect of the authority of God the Creator, who gave it. Neither doth Christ, in the Gospel, any way dissolve, but much strengthen this obligation.

VI. Although true believers be not under the law, as a covenant of works, to be thereby justified, or condemned; yet is it of great use to them, as well as to others; in that, as a rule of life informing them of the will of God, and their duty, it directs and binds them to walk accordingly; discovering also the sinful pollutions of their nature, hearts, and lives; so as, examining themselves thereby, they may come to further conviction of, humiliation for, and hatred against sin, together with a clearer sight of the need they have of Christ, and the perfection of His obedience. It is likewise of use to the regenerate, to restrain their corruptions, in that it forbids sin: and the threatenings of it serve to show what even their sins deserve; and what afflictions, in this life, they may expect for them, although freed from the curse thereof threatened in the law. The promises of it, in like manner, show them God's approbation of obedience, and what blessings they may expect upon the performance thereof: although not as due to them by the law as a covenant of works. So as, a man's doing good, and refraining from evil, because the law encourageth to the one, and deterreth from the other, is no evidence of his being under the law; and, not under grace.

VII. Neither are the forementioned uses of the law contrary to the grace of the Gospel, but do sweetly comply with it; the Spirit of Christ subduing and enabling the will of man to do that freely, and cheerfully, which the will of God, revealed in the law, requireth to be done.

# THE WESTMINSTER CONFESSION OF FAITH

## CHAPTER XX

### Of Christian Liberty, and Liberty of Conscience

I. The liberty which Christ hath purchased for believers under the Gospel consists in their freedom from the guilt of sin, the condemning wrath of God, the curse of the moral law; and, in their being delivered from this present evil world, bondage to Satan, and dominion of sin; from the evil of afflictions, the sting of death, the victory of the grave, and everlasting damnation; as also, in their free access to God, and their yielding obedience unto Him, not out of slavish fear, but a child-like love and willing mind. All which were common also to believers under the law. But, under the new testament, the liberty of Christians is further enlarged, in their freedom from the yoke of the ceremonial law, to which the Jewish Church was subjected; and in greater boldness of access to the throne of grace, and in fuller communications of the free Spirit of God, than believers under the law did ordinarily partake of.

II. God alone is Lord of the conscience, and hath left it free from the doctrines and commandments of men, which are, in anything, contrary to His Word; or beside it, if matters of faith, or worship. So that, to believe such doctrines, or to obey such commands, out of conscience, is to betray true liberty of conscience: and the requiring of an implicit faith, and an absolute and blind obedience, is to destroy liberty of conscience, and reason also.

III. They who, upon pretence of Christian liberty, do practice any sin, or cherish any lust, do thereby destroy the end of Christian liberty, which is, that being delivered out of the hands of our enemies, we might serve the Lord without fear, in holiness and righteousness before Him, all the days of our life.

IV. And because the powers which God hath ordained, and the liberty which Christ hath purchased, are not intended by God to destroy, but mutually to uphold and preserve one another, they who, upon pretence of Christian liberty, shall oppose any lawful power, or the lawful exercise of it, whether it be civil or ecclesiastical, resist the ordinance of God. And, for their publishing of such opinions, or maintaining of such practices, as are contrary to the light of nature, or to the known principles of Christianity (whether concerning faith, worship, or conversation), or to the power of godliness; or, such erroneous opinions or practices, as either in their own nature, or in the manner of publishing or maintaining them, are destructive to the external peace and order which Christ hath established in the Church, they may lawfully be called to account, and proceeded against, by the censures of the Church.

## CHAPTER XXI

### Of Religious Worship, and the Sabbath Day

I. The light of nature showeth that there is a God, who hath lordship and sovereignty over all, is good, and doth good unto all, and is therefore to be feared, loved, praised, called upon, trusted in, and served, with all the heart, and with all the soul, and with all the might. But the acceptable way of worshipping the true God is instituted by Himself, and so limited by His own revealed will, that He may not be worshipped according to the imaginations and devices of men, or the suggestions of Satan, under any visible representation, or any other way not prescribed in the Holy Scripture.

II. Religious worship is to be given to God, the Father, Son, and Holy Ghost; and to Him alone; not to angels, saints, or any other creature: and, since the fall, not without a Mediator; nor in the mediation of any other but of Christ alone.

III. Prayer, with thanksgiving, being one special part of religious worship, is by God required of all men: and, that it may be accepted, it is to be made in the name of the Son, by the help of His Spirit, according to His will, with understanding, reverence, humility, fervency, faith, love, and perseverance; and, if vocal, in a known tongue.

IV. Prayer is to be made for things lawful; and for all sorts of men living, or that shall live hereafter: but not for the dead, nor for those of whom it may be known that they have sinned the sin unto death.

V. The reading of the Scriptures with godly fear, the sound preaching and conscionable hearing of the Word, in obedience unto God, with understanding, faith, and reverence, singing of psalms with grace in the heart; as also, the due administration and worthy receiving of the sacraments instituted by Christ, are all parts of the ordinary religious worship of God: beside religious oaths, vows, solemn fastings, and thanksgivings upon special occasions, which are, in their several times and seasons, to be used in an holy and religious manner.

# THE WESTMINSTER CONFESSION OF FAITH

VI. Neither prayer, nor any other part of religious worship, is now, under the Gospel, either tied unto, or made more acceptable by any place in which it is performed, or towards which it is directed: but God is to be worshipped everywhere, in spirit and truth; as, in private families daily, and in secret, each one by himself; so, more solemnly in the public assemblies, which are not carelessly or wilfully to be neglected, or forsaken, when God, by His Word or providence, calleth thereunto.

VII. As it is the law of nature, that, in general, a due proportion of time be set apart for the worship of God; so, in His Word, by a positive, moral, and perpetual commandment binding all men in all ages, He hath particularly appointed one day in seven, for a Sabbath, to be kept holy unto Him: which, from the beginning of the world to the resurrection of Christ, was the last day of the week; and, from the resurrection of Christ, was changed into the first day of the week, which, in Scripture, is called the Lord's Day, and is to be continued to the end of the world, as the Christian Sabbath.

VIII. This Sabbath is then kept holy unto the Lord, when men, after a due preparing of their hearts, and ordering of their common affairs beforehand, do not only observe an holy rest, all the day, from their own works, words, and thoughts about their worldly employments and recreations, but also are taken up, the whole time, in the public and private exercises of His worship, and in the duties of necessity and mercy.

## CHAPTER XXII
### Of Lawful Oaths and Vows

I. A lawful oath is a part of religious worship, wherein, upon just occasion, the person swearing solemnly calleth God to witness what he asserteth, or promiseth, and to judge him according to the truth or falsehood of what he sweareth.

II. The name of God only is that by which men ought to swear, and therein it is to be used with all holy fear and reverence. Therefore, to swear vainly, or rashly, by that glorious and dreadful Name; or, to swear at all by any other thing, is sinful, and to be abhorred. Yet, as in matters of weight and moment, an oath is warranted by the Word of God, under the new testament as well as under the old; so a lawful oath, being imposed by lawful authority, in such matters, ought to be taken.

III. Whosoever taketh an oath ought duly to consider the weightiness of so solemn an act, and therein to avouch nothing but what he is fully persuaded is the truth: neither may any man bind himself by oath to anything but what is good and just, and what he believeth so to be, and what he is able and resolved to perform.

IV. An oath is to be taken in the plain and common sense of the words, without equivocation, or mental reservation. It cannot oblige to sin; but in anything not sinful, being taken, it binds to performance, although to a man's own hurt. Nor is it to be violated, although made to heretics, or infidels.

V. A vow is of the like nature with a promissory oath, and ought to be made with the like religious care, and to be performed with the like faithfulness.

VI. It is not to be made to any creature, but to God alone: and, that it may be accepted, it is to be made voluntarily, out of faith, and conscience of duty, in way of thankfulness for mercy received, or for the obtaining of what we want, whereby we more strictly bind ourselves to necessary duties; or, to other things, so far and so long as they may fitly conduce thereunto.

VII. No man may vow to do anything forbidden in the Word of God, or what would hinder any duty therein commanded, or which is not in his own power, and for the performance whereof he hath no promise of ability from God. In which respects, popish monastical vows of perpetual single life, professed poverty, and regular obedience, are so far from being degrees of higher perfection, that they are superstitious and sinful snares, in which no Christian may entangle himself.

## CHAPTER XXIII
### Of the Civil Magistrate

I. God, the supreme Lord and King of all the world, hath ordained civil magistrates, to be, under Him, over the people, for His own glory, and the public good: and, to this end, hath armed them with the power of the sword, for the defence and encouragement of them that are good, and for the punishment of evil doers.

# THE WESTMINSTER CONFESSION OF FAITH

II. It is lawful for Christians to accept and execute the office of a magistrate, when called thereunto: in the managing whereof, as they ought especially to maintain piety, justice, and peace, according to the wholesome laws of each commonwealth; so, for that end, they may lawfully, now under the new testament, wage war, upon just and necessary occasion.

III. Civil magistrates may not assume to themselves the administration of the Word and sacraments; or the power of the keys of the kingdom of heaven; or, in the least, interfere in matters of faith. Yet, as nursing fathers, it is the duty of civil magistrates to protect the Church of our common Lord, without giving the preference to any denomination of Christians above the rest, in such a manner that all ecclesiastical persons whatever shall enjoy the full, free, and unquestioned liberty of discharging every part of their sacred functions, without violence or danger. And, as Jesus Christ hath appointed a regular government and discipline in His Church, no law of any commonwealth should interfere with, let, or hinder, the due exercise thereof, among the voluntary members of any denomination of Christians, according to their own profession and belief. It is the duty of civil magistrates to protect the person and good name of all their people, in such an effectual manner as that no person be suffered, either upon pretence of religion or of infidelity, to offer any indignity, violence, abuse, or injury to any other person whatsoever: and to take order, that all religious and ecclesiastical assemblies be held without molestation or disturbance.

IV. It is the duty of people to pray for magistrates, to honour their persons, to pay them tribute or other dues, to obey their lawful commands, and to be subject to their authority, for conscience sake. Infidelity, or difference in religion, doth not make void the magistrates' just and legal authority, nor free the people from their due obedience to them: from which ecclesiastical persons are not exempted, much less hath the Pope any power and jurisdiction over them in their dominions, or over any of their people; and, least of all, to deprive them of their dominions, or lives, if he shall judge them to be heretics, or upon any other pretence whatsoever.

## CHAPTER XXIV
### Of Marriage and Divorce

I. Marriage is to be between one man and one woman: neither is it lawful for any man to have more than one wife, nor for any woman to have more than one husband, at the same time.

II. Marriage was ordained for the mutual help of husband and wife, for the increase of mankind with legitimate issue, and of the Church with an holy seed; and for preventing of uncleanness.

III. It is lawful for all sorts of people to marry, who are able with judgment to give their consent. Yet it is the duty of Christians to marry only in the Lord. And therefore such as profess the true reformed religion should not marry with infidels, papists, or other idolaters: neither should such as are godly be unequally yoked, by marrying with such as are notoriously wicked in their life, or maintain damnable heresies.

IV. Marriage ought not to be within the degrees of consanguinity or affinity forbidden by the Word. Nor can such incestuous marriages ever be made lawful by any law of man or consent of parties, so as those persons may live together as man and wife.

V. Adultery or fornication committed after a contract, being detected before marriage, giveth just occasion to the innocent party to dissolve that contract. In the case of adultery after marriage, it is lawful for the innocent party to sue out a divorce: and, after the divorce, to marry another, as if the offending party were dead.

VI. Although the corruption of man be such as is apt to study arguments unduly to put asunder those whom God hath joined together in marriage: yet, nothing but adultery, or such wilful desertion as can no way be remedied by the Church, or civil magistrate, is cause sufficient of dissolving the bond of marriage: wherein, a public and orderly course of proceeding is to be observed; and the persons concerned in it not left to their own wills, and discretion, in their own case.

## CHAPTER XXV
### Of the Church

I. The catholic or universal Church, which is invisible, consists of the whole number of the elect, that have been, are, or shall be gathered into one, under Christ the Head thereof; and is the spouse, the body, the fulness of Him that filleth all in all.

# THE WESTMINSTER CONFESSION OF FAITH

II. The visible Church, which is also catholic or universal under the Gospel (not confined to one nation, as before under the law), consists of all those throughout the world that profess the true religion; and of their children: and is the kingdom of the Lord Jesus Christ, the house and family of God, out of which there is no ordinary possibility of salvation.

III. Unto this catholic visible Church Christ hath given the ministry, oracles, and ordinances of God, for the gathering and perfecting of the saints, in this life, to the end of the world: and doth, by His own presence and Spirit, according to His promise, make them effectual thereunto.

IV. This catholic Church hath been sometimes more, sometimes less visible. And particular Churches, which are members thereof, are more or less pure, according as the doctrine of the Gospel is taught and embraced, ordinances administered, and public worship performed more or less purely in them.

V. The purest Churches under heaven are subject both to mixture and error; and some have so degenerated, as to become no Churches of Christ, but synagogues of Satan. Nevertheless, there shall be always a Church on earth, to worship God according to His will.

VI. There is no other head of the Church but the Lord Jesus Christ. Nor can the Pope of Rome, in any sense, be head thereof.

## CHAPTER XXVI
### Of the Communion of Saints

I. All saints, that are united to Jesus Christ their Head, by His Spirit, and by faith, have fellowship with Him in His graces, sufferings, death, resurrection, and glory: and, being united to one another in love, they have communion in each other's gifts and graces, and are obliged to the performance of such duties, public and private, as do conduce to their mutual good, both in the inward and outward man.

II. Saints by profession are bound to maintain an holy fellowship and communion in the worship of God, and in performing such other spiritual services as tend to their mutual edification; as also in relieving each other in outward things, according to their several abilities and necessities. Which communion, as God offereth opportunity, is to be extended unto all those who, in every place, call upon the name of the Lord Jesus.

III. This communion which the saints have with Christ, doth not make them in any wise partakers of the substance of His Godhead; or to be equal with Christ in any respect: either of which to affirm is impious and blasphemous. Nor doth their communion one with another, as saints, take away, or infringe the title or propriety which each man hath in his goods and possessions.

## CHAPTER XXVII
### Of the Sacraments

I. Sacraments are holy signs and seals of the covenant of grace, immediately instituted by God, to represent Christ, and His benefits; and to confirm our interest in Him: as also, to put a visible difference between those that belong unto the Church, and the rest of the world; and solemnly to engage them to the service of God in Christ, according to His Word.

II. There is, in every sacrament, a spiritual relation, or sacramental union, between the sign and the thing signified: whence it comes to pass, that the names and effects of the one are attributed to the other.

III. The grace which is exhibited in or by the sacraments rightly used, is not conferred by any power in them; neither doth the efficacy of a sacrament depend upon the piety or intention of him that doth administer it: but upon the work of the Spirit, and the word of institution, which contains, together with a precept authorizing the use thereof, a promise of benefit to worthy receivers.

IV. There be only two sacraments ordained by Christ our Lord in the Gospel; that is to say, Baptism, and the Supper of the Lord: neither of which may be dispensed by any, but by a minister of the Word lawfully ordained.

V. The sacraments of the old testament, in regard of the spiritual things thereby signified and exhibited, were, for substance, the same with those of the new.

# THE WESTMINSTER CONFESSION OF FAITH

## CHAPTER XXVIII

### Of Baptism

I. Baptism is a sacrament of the new testament, ordained by Jesus Christ, not only for the solemn admission of the party baptized into the visible Church; but also, to be unto him a sign and seal of the covenant of grace, of his ingrafting into Christ, of regeneration, of remission of sins, and of his giving up unto God, through Jesus Christ, to walk in newness of life. Which sacrament is, by Christ's own appointment, to be continued in His Church until the end of the world.

II. The outward element to be used in this sacrament is water, wherewith the party is to be baptized, in the name of the Father, and of the Son, and of the Holy Ghost, by a minister of the Gospel, lawfully called thereunto.

III. Dipping of the person into the water is not necessary; but Baptism is rightly administered by pouring, or sprinkling water upon the person.

IV. Not only those that do actually profess faith in and obedience unto Christ, but also the infants of one, or both, believing parents, are to be baptized.

V. Although it be a great sin to contemn or neglect this ordinance, yet grace and salvation are not so inseparably annexed unto it, as that no person can be regenerated, or saved, without it; or, that all that are baptized are undoubtedly regenerated.

VI. The efficacy of Baptism is not tied to that moment of time wherein it is administered; yet, not withstanding, by the right use of this ordinance, the grace promised is not only offered, but really exhibited, and conferred, by the Holy Ghost, to such (whether of age or infants) as that grace belongeth unto, according to the counsel of God's own will, in His appointed time.

VII. The sacrament of Baptism is but once to be administered unto any person.

## CHAPTER XXIX

### Of the Lord's Supper

I. Our Lord Jesus, in the night wherein He was betrayed, instituted the sacrament of His body and blood, called the Lord's Supper, to be observed in His Church, unto the end of the world, for the perpetual remembrance of the sacrifice of Himself in His death; the sealing all benefits thereof unto true believers, their spiritual nourishment and growth in Him, their further engagement in and to all duties which they owe unto Him; and, to be a bond and pledge of their communion with Him, and with each other, as members of His mystical body.

II. In this sacrament, Christ is not offered up to His Father; nor any real sacrifice made at all, for remission of sins of the quick or dead; but only a commemoration of that one offering up of Himself, by Himself, upon the cross, once for all: and a spiritual oblation of all possible praise unto God, for the same: so that the popish sacrifice of the mass (as they call it) is most abominably injurious to Christ's one, only sacrifice, the alone propitiation for all the sins of His elect.

III. The Lord Jesus hath, in this ordinance, appointed His ministers to declare His word of institution to the people; to pray, and bless the elements of bread and wine, and thereby to set them apart from a common to an holy use; and to take and break the bread, to take the cup, and (they communicating also themselves) to give both to the communicants; but to none who are not then present in the congregation.

IV. Private masses, or receiving this sacrament by a priest, or any other, alone; as likewise, the denial of the cup to the people, worshipping the elements, the lifting them up, or carrying them about, for adoration, and the reserving them for any pretended religious use; are all contrary to the nature of this sacrament, and to the institution of Christ.

V. The outward elements in this sacrament, duly set apart to the uses ordained by Christ, have such relation to Him crucified, as that, truly, yet sacramentally only, they are sometimes called by the name of the things they represent, to wit, the body and blood of Christ; albeit, in substance and nature, they still remain truly and only bread and wine, as they were before.

VI. That doctrine which maintains a change of the substance of bread and wine, into the substance of Christ's body and blood (commonly called transubstantiation) by consecration of a

# THE WESTMINSTER CONFESSION OF FAITH

priest, or by any other way, is repugnant, not to Scripture alone, but even to common sense, and reason; overthroweth the nature of the sacrament, and hath been, and is, the cause of manifold superstitions; yea, of gross idolatries.

VII. Worthy receivers, outwardly partaking of the visible elements, in this sacrament, do then also, inwardly by faith, really and indeed, yet not carnally and corporally but spiritually, receive, and feed upon, Christ crucified, and all benefits of His death: the body and blood of Christ being then, not corporally or carnally, in, with, or under the bread and wine; yet, as really, but spiritually, present to the faith of believers in that ordinance, as the elements themselves are to their outward senses.

VIII. Although ignorant and wicked men receive the outward elements in this sacrament; yet, they receive not the thing signified thereby; but, by their unworthy coming thereunto, are guilty of the body and blood of the Lord, to their own damnation. Wherefore, all ignorant and ungodly persons, as they are unfit to enjoy communion with Him, so are they unworthy of the Lord's table; and cannot, without great sin against Christ, while they remain such, partake of these holy mysteries, or be admitted thereunto.

## CHAPTER XXX
### Of Church Censures

I. The Lord Jesus, as King and Head of His Church, hath therein appointed a government, in the hand of Church officers, distinct from the civil magistrate.

II. To these officers the keys of the kingdom of heaven are committed; by virtue whereof, they have power, respectively, to retain, and remit sins; to shut that kingdom against the impenitent, both by the Word, and censures; and to open it unto penitent sinners, by the ministry of the Gospel; and by absolution from censures, as occasion shall require.

III. Church censures are necessary, for the reclaiming and gaining of offending brethren, for deterring of others from the like offences, for purging out of that leaven which might infect the whole lump, for vindicating the honour of Christ, and the holy profession of the Gospel, and for preventing the wrath of God, which might justly fall upon the Church, if they should suffer His covenant, and the seals thereof, to be profaned by notorious and obstinate offenders.

IV. For the better attaining of these ends, the officers of the Church are to proceed by admonition; suspension from the sacrament of the Lord's Supper for a season; and by excommunication from the Church; according to the nature of the crime, and demerit of the person.

## CHAPTER XXXI
### Of Synods and Councils

I. For the better government, and further edification of the Church, there ought to be such assemblies as are commonly called synods or councils: and it belongeth to the overseers and other rulers of the particular churches, by virtue of their office, and the power which Christ hath given them for edification and not for destruction, to appoint such assemblies; and to convene together in them, as often as they shall judge it expedient for the good of the Church.

II. It belongeth to synods and councils, ministerially to determine controversies of faith, and cases of conscience; to set down rules and directions for the better ordering of the public worship of God, and government of His Church; to receive complaints in cases of maladministration, and authoritatively to determine the same: which decrees and determinations, if consonant to the Word of God, are to be received with reverence and submission; not only for their agreement with the Word, but also for the power whereby they are made, as being an ordinance of God appointed thereunto in His Word.

III. All synods or councils, since the Apostles' times, whether general or particular, may err; and many have erred. Therefore they are not to be made the rule of faith, or practice; but to be used as a help in both.

IV. Synods and councils are to handle, or conclude nothing, but that which is ecclesiastical: and are not to intermeddle with civil affairs which concern the commonwealth, unless by way of humble petition in cases extraordinary; or, by way of advice, for satisfaction of conscience, if they be thereunto required by the civil magistrate.

# THE WESTMINSTER CONFESSION OF FAITH

## CHAPTER XXXII

*Of the State of Men after Death, and of the Resurrection of the Dead*

I. The bodies of men, after death, return to dust, and see corruption: but their souls, which neither die nor sleep, having an immortal subsistence, immediately return to God who gave them: the souls of the righteous, being then made perfect in holiness, are received into the highest heavens, where they behold the face of God, in light and glory, waiting for the full redemption of their bodies. And the souls of the wicked are cast into hell, where they remain in torments and utter darkness, reserved to the judgment of the great day. Beside these two places, for souls separated from their bodies, the Scripture acknowledgeth none.

II. At the last day, such as are found alive shall not die, but be changed: and all the dead shall be raised up, with the self-same bodies, and none other (although with different qualities), which shall be united again to their souls for ever.

III. The bodies of the unjust shall, by the power of Christ, be raised to dishonour: the bodies of the just, by His Spirit, unto honour; and be made conformable to His own glorious body.

## CHAPTER XXXIII

*Of the Last Judgment*

I. God hath appointed a day, wherein He will judge the world, in righteousness, by Jesus Christ, to whom all power and judgment is given of the Father. In which day, not only the apostate angels shall be judged, but likewise all persons that have lived upon earth shall appear before the tribunal of Christ, to give an account of their thoughts, words, and deeds; and to receive according to what they have done in the body, whether good or evil.

II. The end of God's appointing this day is for the manifestation of the glory of His mercy, in the eternal salvation of the elect; and of His justice, in the damnation of the reprobate, who are wicked and disobedient. For then shall the righteous go into everlasting life, and receive that fulness of joy and refreshing, which shall come from the presence of the Lord; but the wicked who know not God, and obey not the Gospel of Jesus Christ, shall be cast into eternal torments, and be punished with everlasting destruction from the presence of the Lord, and from the glory of His power.

III. As Christ would have us to be certainly persuaded that there shall be a day of judgment, both to deter all men from sin; and for the greater consolation of the godly in their adversity: so will He have that day unknown to men, that they may shake off all carnal security, and be always watchful, because they know not at what hour the Lord will come; and may be ever prepared to say, Come Lord Jesus, come quickly, Amen.

Finis.

---

The text of the Confession of Faith of the Assembly of Divines at Westminster, except for those slight revisions adopted by The Orthodox Presbyterian Church, is that derived from the original manuscript written by Cornelius Burges in 1646, edited by S. W. Carruthers and published by the Presbyterian Church of England in 1946. This text has been used because it is believed to be the most correct text of the Westminster Confession of Faith so far available.

INDEXES

Index of Authors, Translators, Arrangers and Sources

Index of Composers, Arrangers and Sources

Alphabetical Index of Tunes

Metrical Index of Tunes

Index of Scripture References in Hymns

Index of Subjects and Occasions

Index of Hymns

# Index of Authors, Translators, Arrangers, and Sources

A., J. E., 703.
Addison, Joseph (1672-1719), 51, 103.
Alexander, Mrs. C. M., 680.
Alexander, Cecil Frances (1823-1895), 180, 184, 214, 255, 491, 636, 639.
Alexander, James Waddell (1804-1859), 178.
Alford, Henry (1810-1871), 234, 615.
Allen, James (1734-1804), 189.
Altenburg, Johann Michael (1584-1640), 470.
Ambrose of Milan (340-397), 56, 165, 339.
Anatolius, (7th Century), 342, 513.
Anon., xiv, xv, 89, 90, 92, 120, 121, 131, 147, 151, 153, 201, 249, 251, 268, 286, 312, 329, 364, 365, 397, 483, 485, 512, 542, 558, 559, 641, 644, 652, 657.
Aquinas, Thomas (c. 1225-1274), 361.
Argyll, John, Duke of (1845-1914), 82.
Arnold, John: *Compleat Psalmodist,* (1740), 198.
Associate Reformed Presbyterian *Psalter* (1931), 15, 279, 305.

BABCOCK, Maltbie D. (1858-1901), 109.
Bajus, John (1901-    ), 196.
Baker, Sir Henry W. (1821-1877), 141, 266, 412, 622.
Baker, Mary A., 701.
Baker, Theodore (1851-1934), 286.
Bakewell, John (1721-1819), 128.
Barbauld, Anna L. (1743-1825), 112.
Baring-Gould, Sabine (1834-1924), 490, 666.
Baxter, Richard (1615-1691), 17.
Beddome, Benjamin (1717-1795), 262, 298.
Bede, The Venerable (673-735), 212.
Benson, Louis F. (1855-1930), 56.
Bernard of Clairvaux (1091-1153), 178, 549.
Bernard of Cluny (12th century), 604.
Bickersteth, Edward H. (1825-1906), 24, 356, 357, 377, 590.
Birks, Thomas R. (1810-1883), 104.
Black, James M. (b. 1859), 727.
Bliss, Philip P. (1838-1876), 175, 660, 679, 681, 722.
Bode, John E. (1816-1874), 552.
Bonar, Horatius (1808-1889), 73, 185, 219, 221, 310, 396, 403, 411, 430, 441, 495, 496, 503, 532, 573, 609, 688.
Booth, Herbert, 420.
Borthwick, Jane (1813-1897), 504, 572, 579.
Breuckner, H., 584.
Breviary of Châlons-sur-Marne (1736), 485.
Bridges, Matthew (1800-1894), 216.
Brooks, Phillips (1835-1893), 152.
Brown, Jessie H. (1861-1921), 680.
Brownlie, John (1859-1925), 23, 236, 362.
Buckoll, Henry J. (1803-1871), 334.
Buell, Hattie E., 720.
Burns, James D. (1823-1864), 349, 610, 655.
Burton, Henry (b. 1840), 391.
Burton, John (1773-1822), 674.
Busch, Calvin A. (1911-    ), 353.

C., O. B., 329.
Camp, Mabel Johnston (1871-    ), 687.
Campbell, Jane M. (1817-1878), 614.
Campbell, Robert (1814-1868), 365.
Canitz, F. R. L. von (1654-1699), 334.
Cassel, E. Taylor, 695.
Caswall, Edward (1814-1878), 131, 158, 190, 542.
Cawood, John (1775-1852), 317.
Cennick, John (1718-1755), 237, 337, 499.
Chandler, John (1806-1876), 120.
Chapman, J. Wilbur (1859-1918), 432, 689.
Charlesworth, Vernon J. (b. 1839), 719.
Chisholm, Thomas O. (b. 1866), 27.
Chorley, Henry F. (1808-1872), 617.
Christian Reformed *Psalter Hymnal, The* (1927), 33.
*Church Hymns* (1871), 536.
Church of Scotland, *Book of Psalms, The* (1886), 38.
Claudius, Matthias (1740-1815), 614.
Clausnitzer, Tobias (1619-1684), 220.
Clement of Alexandria (c. 150-c. 220), 117.
Clements, John R. (b. 1868), 730.
Clephane, Elizabeth C. (1830-1869), 137, 177.
Codner, Elizabeth (1824-1919), 527.
Coghill, Anna L. (1836-1907), 728.
Collier, Edward A., 511.
Collyer, William B. (1782-1854), 240.
Colquhoun, Frances S. (1809-1877), 479.
Conder, Josiah (1789-1855), 49, 58, 96.
Cook, Joseph S. (1860-1933), 640.
Cooper, Edward (1770-1833), 88.
Cory, Julia Cady (1882-    ), 83.
Cotterill, Thomas (1779-1823), 240, 262, 322, 421, 457.
Cousin Anne R. (1824-1906), 599.
Cowper, William (1731-1800), 21, 188, 258, 309, 520.
Cox, Frances E. (1812-1897), 203, 210, 602.
Crewdson, Jane (1809-1863), 517.
Crosby, Fanny J. (1820-1915), 345, 465, 505, 608, 665, 667, 675, 683, 685, 697, 704, 707, 713, 726.
Cummins, James J. (1795-1867), 472.
Cushing, William O. (1823-1903), 551, 651.

DAVIES, Samuel (1723-1761), 71.
Deck, James G. (1802-1884), 546.
Deck, Mary Anne S. (1813-1902), 662.
Denny, Sir Edward (1796-1889), 232.
Dexter, Henry M. (1821-1890), 117.
Dickson, David (1583-1663), 603.
Dix, William C. (1837-1898), 154, 191, 405.
Doane, George W. (1799-1859), 116, 347, 378.
Dobell, John (1757-1840), 325.
Doddridge, Philip (1702-1751), 98, 162, 282, 322, 350, 401, 480, 498, 561, 589, 612.
Dodge, Mary Mapes, 645.
Döving, Carl (1867-1937), 409.
Downton, Henry (1818-1885), 611.

691

## INDEX OF AUTHORS

Draper, Bourne H. (1775-1843), 380.
Duffield, George, Jr. (1818-1888), 477.
Duncan, Mary Lundie (1814-1840), 642.
Dwight, Timothy (1752-1817), 280.

EDMESTON, James (1791-1867), 340, 591.
Ellerton, John (1826-1893), 183, 199, 316, 327, 338, 404, 617, 625, 628, 631.
Elliott, Charlotte (1789-1871), 140, 431, 471, 529, 575.
Elliott, Emily E. S. (1836-1897), 170.
Elven, Cornelius (1797-1873), 416.
Evans, Jonathan (c. 1748-1809), 187.
Everest, Charles W. (1814-1877), 507.

FABER, Frederick W. (1814-1863), 31, 487.
Fawcett, John (1740-1817), 265, 285, 319.
Featherstone, William R. (1842-1870), 547.
Findlater, Sarah B. (1823-1907), 233, 624.
Fortunatus, Venantius H. C. (c. 530-609), 174, 194, 199.
Foster, Frederick W. (1760-1835), 315.
Francis, Benjamin (c. 1720-1768), 425.
Francis, Samuel Trevor (1834-1925), 453.
Franck, Johann (1618-1677), 550.
Fraser, M., 649.
Freystein, Johann B. (1671-1718), 476.

GATES, Ellen H., 729.
Gates, Mary C. (c. 1850-1905), 379.
Gellert, Christian F. (1715-1769), 203, 596.
Geneva *Psalter* (1545), 135.
Gerhardt, Paul (1607-1676), 119, 150, 178, 246, 506, 560.
Gill, Thomas H. (1819-1906), 287, 436, 576.
Gilmore, Joseph H. (1834-1918), 500.
*Gloria in Excelsis*, 92.
Goode, William (1762-1816), 130.
Grant, Sir Robert (1779-1838), 13.
Gray, James M. (1851-1935), 698, 721.
Gregor, Christian (1723-1801), 504.
Gregory Nazianzen (325-390), 23.
Gregory the Great (c. 540-604), 134.
Grigg, Joseph (1734-1799), 425.
Grodski, Michal (16th century), 196.
Gurney, Dorothy F. (1858-1932), 625.
Gurney, John H. (1802-1862), 621.

HALL, Elvina M. (b. 1818), 690.
Hankey, Katherine (1834-1911), 387, 521.
Harbaugh, Henry (1817-1867), 438, 623.
Hart, Joseph (1712-1768), 254, 393.
Hartsough, Lewis (1828-1919), 406.
Hastings, Thomas (1784-1872), 209, 274, 388, 459, 518.
Havergal, Frances R. (1836-1879), 118, 213, 235, 252, 424, 492, 493, 494, 536, 587.
Haweis, Thomas (1732-1820), 351, 457.
Hawks, Annie S. (1835-1918), 710.
Hayn, Henrietta L. von (1724-1782), 643.
"Haward," in Dobell's *Selections* (1806), 325.
Heber, Reginald (1783-1826), 87, 167, 314, 344, 358, 383, 489.

Hedge, Frederick H. (1805-1890), 81.
Heermann, Johann (1585-1647), 179, 181, 296.
Heinrich of Laufenberg (15th century), 355.
Held, Heinrich (d., c. 1659), 247.
Herbert, George (1593-1632), 555.
Hewitt, Eliza E. (1851-1920), 676, 723.
Hill, Rowland: *Psalms and Hymns* (1783), 559.
Hodder, Edwin (1837-1904), 257.
Hoffman, Elisha A. (1839-1929), 718.
Holland, Henry Scott (1847-1918), 620.
Homer, Charlotte G., 672.
Hopper, Edward (1818-1888), 497.
How, William Walsham (1823-1897), 169, 267, 281, 324, 367, 414, 558, 618.
Hughes, Thomas, 468.
Humphreys, Joseph (b. 1720), 443.
Hunter, William (1811-1877), 144.
Hurn, William (1754-1829), 386.
*Hymnary, The* (1872), 485.
*Hymns Ancient and Modern* (1861), 268.
*Hymns Ancient and Modern* (1875), 278.
*Hymns for the Young* (1832), 644.

IRISH *Psalter* (1898), 229.

JACOBI, John Christian (1670-1750), 246.
John of Damascus (8th century), 197, 200.
Johnston, Julia H., 705.
Joseph the hymnographer (9th century), 284.

"K" in Rippon's *Selection* (1787), 80.
Keble, John (1792-1866), 60, 346, 354.
Kelly, John (d. 1890), 506.
Kelly, Thomas (1769-1854), 192, 215, 217, 225, 228, 275, 382.
Ken, Thomas (1637-1711), xvi, 331, 341.
Kennedy, Benjamin H. (1804-1889), 558.
Kethe, William (16th century), 1.
Key, Francis Scott (1779-1843), 69.
King, John (1789-1858), 646.
Kirkland, Patrick Miller (b. 1857), 208.
Knollis, Francis M. (1815-1863), 598.
Kuiper, Henry J. (1886-    ), 634.

LAMBERTS, Lambertus J. (1881-1949), 348.
Landstad, Magnus B. (1802-1880), 409.
Lang, J. D., 596.
Lathbury, Mary A. (1841-1913), 256, 343.
Laurenti, Laurentius (1660-1722), 233.
Leeson, Jane E. (1807-1882), 354, 654.
Lillenas, Haldor (1885-    ), 702.
Lloyd, William F. (1791-1853), 577.
Logan, John, 498.
Longstaff, William D. (1822-1894), 706.
Löwenstern, Matthäus A. von (1594-1648), 473.
Lowry, Robert (1826-1899), 206, 677, 710.
Loy, Matthias (1828-1915), 449.
Luke, Jemima T. (1813-1906), 650.
Luther, Martin (1483-1546), 81, 91, 155, 165, 166, 207, 461.
Lynch, Thomas T. (1818-1871), 261, 519.
Lyte, Henry F. (1793-1847), 70, 114, 335, 593.

692

# INDEX OF AUTHORS

McCheyne, Robert Murray (1813-1843), 600.
Macduff, John Ross (1818-1895), 238.
Mackay, William P. (1839-1885), 634.
McKeever, Harriet Burn (1807-1887), 661.
Madan, Martin (1726-1790), 128, 237.
Magdeburg, Joachim (c. 1525?), 558.
Mair, William (1830-1920), 194.
Mant, Richard (1776-1848), 2, 42.
March, Daniel (1816-1909), 691.
Marriott, John (1780-1825), 376.
Martin, Civilla D. (1868-1948), 696, 725.
Martin, W. C., 711, 717.
Mason, John (1645-1694), 592.
Massie, Richard (1800-1887), 207.
Matheson, George (1842-1906), 594.
Matson, William T. (1833-1906), 456.
Mattes, John C., 153.
Medley, Samuel (1738-1799), 126, 138.
Mentzer, Johann (1658-1734), 11.
Mercer, William (1811-1873), 344.
Midlane, Albert (1825-1909), 297.
Miller, John (d. 1810), 315.
Milman, Henry H. (1791-1868), 172.
Milton, John (1608-1674), 30, 294.
Mohr, Joseph (1792-1848), 161.
Monsell, John S. B. (1811-1875), 464, 484.
Montgomery, James (1771-1854), 14, 164, 224, 253, 283, 299, 300, 313, 360, 364, 384, 475, 556, 566, 568, 663.
Moore, Thomas (1779-1852), 518.
Moravian Collection, (1724), 18.
Morison, John (1749-1798), 123, 163, 359, 516.
Morris, Eliza F. (1821-1874), 466.
Morris, George P. (1802-1864), 455.
Mote, Edward (1797-1874), 582.
Münster *Gesangbuch,* (1677), 129.
Mure, Sir William, 77.
Murray, Robert (1832-1909), 368.

Neale, John Mason (1818-1866), 122, 147, 159, 173, 197, 200, 202, 268, 284, 339, 342, 389, 483, 513, 604.
Neander, Joachim (1650-1680), 50, 132.
Nelson, Augustus, 174.
Nelson, Horatio, 3rd Earl (1823-1913), 329.
Neumark, Georg (1631-1681), 567.
Neumeister, Erdmann (1671-1756), 394.
*New Christian Hymnal, The* (1929), 79.
Newton, John (1725-1807), 79, 127, 142, 241, 269, 318, 320, 402, 423, 530, 531, 544, 613.
Nicolai, Philipp (1556-1608), 231, 434.
Noel, Caroline M. (1817-1877), 124.

Oakeley, Frederick (1802-1880), 151.
Oakey, Emily Sullivan (1829-1883), 647.
Olearius, Johannes (1611-1684), 148.
Oliver, Richard J., 673.
Olivers, Thomas (1725-1799), 32.
Osler, Edward (1798-1863), 16.
Owen, Frances M. (1843-1883), 486.
Owens, Pricilla J. (1829-1899), 370.

P., F. B. (16th or 17th century), 603.
Palmer, Horatio R. (1834-1907), 658.
Palmer, Ray (1808-1887), 93, 134, 249, 410, 454, 545, 549.
*Parish Hymn Book, The* (1863), 483.
Parker, William H. (1845-1929), 638.
Perronet, Edward (1726-1792), 218.
Phelps, S. Dryden (1816-1895), 538.
Pierson, Arthur T. (1837-1911), 714.
Phillimore, Greville (1821-1884), 328.
Pigott, Jean Sophia, 139.
Plumptre, Edward H. (1821-1891), 502.
Pollard, Adelaide A. (1862-1934), 574.
Pollock, Thomas Benson (1836-1896), 244, 278, 418.
Pott, Francis (1832-1909), 8, 201.
Prentiss, Elizabeth Payson (1818-1878), 548.
Prid, William (fl. 1585), 603.
Prudentius, Aurelius Clemens (348-413), 122.
*Psalms and Hymns,* Rowland Hill, (1783), 559.
Pusey, Philip (1799-1855), 473.

Raffles, Thomas (1788-1863), 407, 553.
Rankin, Jeremiah E. (1828-1904), 632.
Rawley, Francis H. (b. 1854), 709.
Rawson, George (1807-1889), 43, 248.
Reformed Presbyterian *Book of Psalms* (1940), 74, 84, 230.
Reynolds, William M., 165.
Rhodes, Sarah Betts (1829-1904), 637.
Rinkart, Martin (1586-1649), 86.
Rippon, John (1751-1836), 218.
Rippon's *Selection* (1787), 80, 218.
Roberts, Daniel C. (1841-1907), 616.
Robertson, William (1820-1864), 352.
Robinson, Robert (1735-1790), 5, 400.
Rodigast, Samuel (1649-1708), 94.
Root, George F. (1820-1895), 693.
Rossetti, Christina G. (1830-1894), 115.
Rous, Francis (1579-1658), 77.
Russell, Arthur T. (1806-1874), 193.
Rutherford, Samuel (1600-1661), 599.
Ryland, John (1753-1825), 543.

*Sabbath Hymn Book* (1858), 155.
Sacer, Gottfried W. (1635-1699), 210.
Sammis, James H. (d. 1919), 700.
Sankey, Ira D. (1840-1908), 719.
Schaefer, William J. (1891-   ), 132.
Schaeffer, Charles W. (1813-1896), 247.
Scheidt, Christian L. (1709-1761), 399, 584.
Schenk, Heinrich T. (1656-1727), 602.
Schlegel, Katharina von (b. 1697), 579.
Schmolck, Benjamin (1672-1737), 304, 333, 572.
Schütz, Johann J. (1640-1690), 4.
Schwedler, Johann C. (1672-1730), 435.
Scott, Sir Walter (1771-1832), 242.
Scottish *Paraphrases* (1751), 98, 442, 601.
Scottish *Paraphrases* (1781), 28, 272, 277, 359, 422, 498, 516, 606.

693

# INDEX OF AUTHORS

Scottish *Psalter, The* (1650), 7, 19, 77, 97, 239.
Scriven, Joseph (1819-1886), 533.
Sears, Edmund H. (1810-1876), 157.
Sellers, E. O., 671.
Shepherd, Anne H. (1809-1857), 648.
Shepherd, Fred S., 670.
Sherwin, William F. (1826-1888), 686.
Shirley, Walter (1725-1786), 189.
Shrubsole, William (1759-1829), 372.
Shurtleff, Ernest W. (1862-1917), 488.
Sleeper, W. T. (c. 1840-1920), 715.
Small, James G. (1817-1888), 433.
Smith, Samuel F. (1808-1895), 388.
Smith, Walter Chalmers (1824-1908), 35.
Spaeth, Harriet R. (1845-1925), 153.
Spafford, Horatio G. (1828-1888), 580.
Spitta, Carl J. P. (1801-1859), 624.
Stead, Louisa M. R., 699.
Steele, Anne (1716-1778), 259, 562.
Stennett, Samuel (c. 1727-1795), 143.
Sternhold, Thomas (d. 1549), 524.
Stevenson, Isabel (1843-1890), 630.
Stites, Edgar Page, 682.
Stocker, John, 245.
Stockton, John H. (1813-1877), 724.
Stone, Samuel J. (1839-1900), 270, 467.
Stowell, Hugh (1799-1865), 528.
Strasbourg *Psalter* (1545), 135.
Straub, Maria (1838-1898), 635.
Swain, Joseph (1761-1796), 390.

TAPPAN, William B. (1794-1849), 182.
Tate, Nahum, (1652-1715), 156.
Tate and Brady's *New Version* (1696, 1698), 64, 276, 303, 522, 554.
Tate and Brady's *Supplement* (c. 1700), 90.
Taylor, Thomas R. (1807-1835), 605.
*Te Deum*, 90.
Tersteegen, Gerhard (1697-1769), 308, 315.
Theodulph of Orleans (c. 760-821), 173.
Thomas, Alexcenah, 684.
Thomas of Celano (13th century), 242.
Thompson, Alexander R. (1822-1895), 361.
Thompson, J. O., 668.
Thompson, Will L. (1847-1909), 664, 694.
Thring, Godfrey (1823-1903), 319, 366, 452.
Toplady, Augustus M. (1740-1778), 95, 99, 128, 246, 398, 421, 440, 562, 595.
Traditional: English, 160.
Traditional: Italian, 190.
Tuttiett, Lawrence (1825-1897), 243.
Twells, Henry (1823-1900), 336.

UNITED Presbyterian *Bible Songs Hymnal* (1927), 78, 105.
United Presbyterian *Book of Psalms* (1871), 29, 36, 307.
United Presbyterian *Psalter, The* (1912), 6, 9, 10, 12, 25, 34, 36, 37, 39, 41, 44, 45, 46, 47, 53, 54, 55, 57, 59, 61, 63, 65, 66, 68, 75, 76, 85, 100, 101, 107, 108, 110, 111, 125, 227, 260, 264, 288, 289, 290, 291, 295, 301, 306, 369, 381, 385, 408, 415, 417, 445, 446, 448, 450, 451, 462, 463, 469, 474, 508, 509, 510, 514, 515, 523, 526, 535, 539, 540, 541, 557, 563, 564, 565, 569, 570, 571, 578, 581, 583, 585, 619, 626, 656, 678.

WALFORD, William W., 534.
Walmsley, Robert (1831-1905), 669.
Wardlaw, Ralph (1779-1853), 375, 437.
Ware, Henry, Jr. (1794-1843). 627.
Waring, Anna L. (1820-1910), 444.
Warner, Anna B. (1820-1915), 633.
Warner, Susan (1819-1885), 653.
Watts, Isaac (1674-1748), 3, 20, 22, 26, 28, 52, 62, 67, 72, 102, 106, 113, 149, 171, 176, 186, 195, 222, 250, 263, 271, 273, 277, 292, 293, 302, 326, 332, 374, 413, 422, 429, 442, 447, 478, 481, 537, 588, 597, 601, 606.
Webb, Benjamin (1820-1885), 121, 212.
Weissel, Georg (1590-1635), 146.
Wesley, Charles (1707-1788), 112, 133, 136, 145, 168, 198, 205, 223, 226, 237, 323, 330, 392, 426, 427, 458, 460, 482, 586.
Wesley, John (1703-1791), 62, 308, 439, 525, 560.
Weston, Rebecca J., 659.
Whatley, Richard (1787-1863), 344.
Whitcomb, George W., 692.
White, Henry K. (1785-1806), 479.
Whitfield, Frederick (1829-1904), 419.
Whiting, William (1825-1878), 629.
Whitmore, Lady Lucy E. G. (1792-1840), 311.
Whittle, Daniel W. (1840-1901), 708, 712, 716.
Wigner, John M. (1844-1911), 395.
Williams, Isaac (1802-1865), 485.
Williams, Peter (1722-1796), 501.
Williams, William (1717-1791), 373, 501.
Winkworth, Catherine (1829-1878), 50, 86, 91, 94, 146, 148, 150, 166, 181, 220, 231, 296, 304, 312, 333, 355, 470, 476, 550, 567.
Wolcott, Samuel (1813-1886), 371.
Wolfe, Aaron R. (1821-1902), 363.
Woodward, G. R., 435.
Wordsworth, Christopher (1807-1885), 204, 211, 321, 607.
Wotherspoon, Arthur W. (b. 1853), 194.
Wreford, John R. (1800-1881), 428.

*Yattendon Hymnal,* (1899), 179.

ZINZENDORF, Count Nikolaus Ludwig von (1700-1760), 439, 504, 525.

# Index of Composers

## ARRANGERS, AND SOURCES OF THE TUNES

AHLE, Johann R. (1625-1673), 112, 220, 485
Albert, Heinrich (1604-1651), 142
Allen, Alfred R. (1876-1918), 513
Allen, Chester G., 683
Anon., xiv, 36, 80, 151, 159, 207, 359 (509), 640
Arne, Thomas A. (1710-1778), 116 (326, 398)
Arnold, Samuel (1740-1802), 276
*As hymnodus sacer,* Leipzig, (1625), 296
Atkinson, Frederick C. (1841-1897), 310

B., R. E., 659
Bach, Johann Sebastian (1685-1750), 100 (312), 104, 178, 434, 623
Baker, Frederick G. (1840-1872), 162 (303)
Baker, Henry (1835-1910), 507 (549I, 622)
Baker, Sir Henry W. (1821-1877), 389
Balle, C., 591
Bambridge, William S. (1842-1923), 211
Barnard, Charlotte A. (1830-1869), 642
Barnby, Sir Joseph (1838-1896), 128, 131, 281, 287, 311, 350 (516),355, 418, 473, 517, 523 (565), 625, 666
Barnes, Edward Shippen (1887- ), 109
Barthélémon, François, H. (1741-1808), 77 II, 331, 566
Basswood, W. K., 645
Batchellor, Daniel, 659
Beethoven, Ludwig van (1770-1827), xiv, 52, 417
Bilhorn, Peter P. (b. 1861), 709
Black, James M. (b. 1859), 727
Blanton, Leonard Cooper (1920- ), 108
Bliss, Philip P. (1838-1876), 175, 580, 647, 660, 679, 714, 722
*Book of Psalmody,* John Chetham (1718), 481
*Booke of Musicke,* William Damon (1591), 22
Bortniansky, Dimitri (1752-1825), 76, 410, 494, 535, 582
Bourgeois, Louis (c. 1510-1561), xvi, 1, 148, 246, 348, 511, 512, 514
Boyd, William (1847-1928), 496
Bradbury, William B. (1816-1868), 25, 55, 84, 182, 431, 500, 534, 549 II, 633, 644, 650, 652, 674
Braun, Johann G. (17th century), 117 (249, 371)
*Bristol Tune Book* (1876), 241, 345 (390, 472)
Brown, Arthur H. (1830-1926), 297, 313 (611), 342
*Brüder Choral-Buch* (1784), 643

Bruinsma, Henry A. (1916- ) 148, 511
Bullinger, Ethelbert W. (1837-1913), 389, 424, 570
Bunnett, Edward (1834-1923), 261
Burnap, Uzziah C. (1834-1900), 226 (290), 333, 564
Busch, Calvin A. (1911- ), 353

CALDBECK, George T. (1852-1912?), 590
Calkin, J. Baptiste (1827-1905), 96 (628), 202 (378, 478)
Calcott, William H. (1807-1882), 532
Cammin, J., 435
Camp, Harvey, 48
Camp, Mabel Johnston (1871- ), 687
*Cantica Laudis,* Boston (1850), 363 (367)
Cassel, Flora H. (b. 1852), 695
Chadwick, George W. (1854-1931), 397 I
Chetham, John, 481
Chope, Richard R. (1830-1928), 266
*Choral Buch,* J. D. Müller (1754), 546
"Christ ist erstanden" (c. 1100), 207
*Christian Lyre* (1831), 138
Clark, Jeremiah (c. 1670-1707), 113 (215, 294, 524), 416
Clark, Thomas (1775-1859), 98, 601
Clelland, Wilfred G. (1911- ), 130, 230
Clemm, J. B. O., 668
Cobb, Gerald F. (1838-1904), 361
Coles, George (1792-1858), 264
*Collection, The* (1625), 83, 286
*Congregational Church Music* (1853), 307 (618)
Converse, Charles Crozat (1832-1918), 533
Cottman, Arthur (1842-1879), 66 (214, 468), 360 (423)
Crawford, Edward Patrick (1846-1912), 470
Croft, William (1678-1727), 26 I (621), 57 (95, 440), 301
Crofton, Lord Edward (1834-1912), 624
Crosbie, Howard A. (1844-1918), 124
Cruger, Johann (1598-1662), 86, 181, 362 (596)
Cummings, William H. (1831-1915), 168
Cutler, Henry S. (1824-1902), 384 (489)

D., W., 159
Daman, William (c.1580), 22, 412
Danks, Hart P. (d. 1903), 730
Darmstadt *Gesangbuch* (1698), 127 (602)
Darwall, John (1731-1789), 17 (302, 441)

695

# INDEX OF COMPOSERS

Day's *Psalter* (1562), 557
Doane, William H. (1832-1916?), 295, 465, 521, 548, 608, 667, 704, 707, 713
Drese, Adam (1620-1701), 504
Drewett, Edwin (1850-1924), 180 (366, 379)
Dyer, Samuel (1785-1835), 64 (253)
Dykes, John B. (1823-1876), 29, 87, 141, 172, 185, 199, 221, 234, 242, 243, (629), 259 (323, 455), 283, 314, 364 (542), 459, 483, 492, 575, 607

*Easy Hymn Tunes* (1851), 426
Ebeling, Johann G. (1620-1676), 150 (506)
Edson, Louis (18th century), 223 (392)
Edwards, Robert (1797-1862), 369 (393)
Elliott, James W. (1833-1915), 58
Ellor, James, 218
Elvey, Sir George J. (1816-1893), 216 (239), 365 (615)
Emmelar, 688
Evans, David (1874-1948), 208, 306
Ewing, Alexander (1830-1895), 604
Excell, Edwin O. (1851-1921), 402, 653

FILITZ, Friedrich (1804-1876), 190
Fink, Gottfried W. (1783-1846), 257, 606
Fischer, William G. (1835-1912), 387
Flemming, Friedrich Ferdinand (1778-1813), 179
Freylinghausen, Johann A. (1670-1739), 146, 654

GABRIEL, Charles H. (1856-1932), 85 (407), 672, 725
Gardiner, William (1770-1853), 262 (322, 439), 265 (543)
Gastorius, Severus (b. ca. 1650), 94
Gauntlett, Henry J. (1805-1876), 110, 203, 479, 560, 639
Gawler W., *Hymns and Psalms* (1789), 519
*Geistliche Kirchengesang,* Cologne (1623), 3 (212)
*Geistliche Lieder,* Leipzig (1539), 92 (461), 166
*Geistliche Lieder,* Wittenberg (1535), 240
*Geistliche Lieder,* Wittenberg (1543), 91 (449)
*Geistliche Volkslieder,* Paderborn (1850), 192
*Geistliches Gesangbüchlein,* Wittenberg (1524), 165
Geneva *Psalter* (1543), 72
Geneva *Psalter* (1551), 135
Giardini, Felice de (1716-1796), 89
Gilbert, Walter Bond (1829-1910), 107, 300
Gilchrist, W. W., 24
Gläser, Carl G. (1784-1829), 133 (429)
Goodrich, Charles G. (b. 1869), 289
Gordon, Adoniram J. (1836-1895), 547
Goss, Sir John (1800-1880), 63 (70, 122), 158, 222, 226 (290), 493
Gottschalk, Louis M. (1829-1869), 245 (318, 559)

Gould, John E. (1822-1875), 497, 525
Gounod, Charles F. (1818-1893), 247, 330
Gower, John H. (1855-1922), 184 (569, 597), 244 (278), 252, 486, 536
Grape, John T. (b. 1833), 690
Greatorex, Henry W. (1811-1858), xv, 436
Greene, Maurice (1696-1755), 97
Gruber, Franz (1787-1863), 161

HANDEL, George Frederick (1685-1759), 120 (586), 149, 156 (480)
Harding, James P. (1850-1911), 167
Harrison, Ralph (1748-1810), 20 (309), 116 (326, 398)
Hartsough, Lewis (1828-1919), 406
Hassler, Hans Leo (1564-1612), 178
Hastings, Thomas (1784-1872), 106 (143, 258), 209, 275 (382), 421, 528
Hatton, John ( ?-1793), 3 (15, 54)
Havergal, Frances R. (1836-1879), 213, 452
Havergal, William H. (1793-1870), 77 III, 469, 546
Haydn, Franz Josef (1732-1809), 12 (103), 199, 269, 334
Haydn, J. Michael (1737-1806), 13 (136)
*Heilige Seelenlust,* Breslau (1657), 88 (336, 352)
Helmore, Thomas (1811-1890), 147
Hemy, Henri F. (1818-1888), 487
Herbert, John B. (1852-1927), 26 II, 515
Herman, Nikolaus (c. 1480-1561), 123, 339
Hiles, Henry (1826-1904), 553
Hintze, Jakob (17th century), 623
Hodges, John S. B. (1830-1915), 358
Holbrook, Joseph P. (1822-1888), 427 III, 430, 451, 572
Holden, Oliver (1765-1844), 218
Holmes, Henry J. E. (1852-1938), 71 (540)
Hopkins, Edward J. (1818-1901), 316 (510), 328, 397
Horsley, William (1774-1858), 191
Hughes, John (1873-1932), 501
Hullah, John (1812-1884), 520
*Hundert Arien,* Dresden (1694), 476
Husband, Edward (1843-1908), 414
Husband, John J. (1760-1825), 634
*Hymns and Psalms* (1789), 519
*Hymns and Sacred Poems,* Dublin (1749), 19 (277, 446)

IRVINE, Jessie Seymour (1836-1887), 77 III

JACKSON, Robert (1842-1914), 23, 438 (598)
Jeater, William (b. 1858), 115
Jones, Griffith Hugh (1849-1919), 75
Jones, William (1726-1800), 236, 442
Jordan, C. Warwick, 508
Jowett Joseph (1784-1856), 337
Jude, William H. (1851-1922), 491 (626)

*Katholisches Gesangbuch,* Vienna (c. 1774), 346

696

# INDEX OF COMPOSERS

Kingsley, George (1811-1884), 576
Kirkpatrick, William J. (1838-1921), 105, 370, 675, 699, 723
Knapp, William (1698-1768), 612
Knecht, Justin H. (1752-1817), 399, 414
Kocher, Conrad (1786-1872), 154
König, Johann B. (1691-1758), 11
*Koraalboek,* Dutch, 148, 511
*Koralbok,* Swedish (1697), 174
Koschat, Thomas (1845-1914), 663
Kroeger, Ernest R. (1862-1934), 68

LA FEILÉE's *Méthode du Plain Chant* (1808), 219
Lane, Spencer (1843-1903), 475
Langran, James (1835-1909), 467
Leavitt, Joshua, *Christian Lyre* (1831), 138
Leighton, William (c. 1614), 273
LeJeune, George F. (1842-1904), 460 I
Lillenas, Haldor (1885- ), 702
Lindeman, Ludwig M. (1812-1887), 550
Linekar, Thomas Joseph (b. 1858), 45
Lloyd, John Ambrose (1815-1874), 59, 169, 344, 351
Lloyd, William (1786-1852), 118 (193), 385, 419
Löhr, George Augustus (1821-1897), 282
Lorenz, Edmund S. (b. 1854), 711
Lowe, Albert (d. 1886), 5, 9
Lowry, Robert (1826-1899), 206, 391 (538), 505, 677, 710
Luther, Martin (1483-1546), 81, 240
Lwoff, Alexis (1799-1870), 617
*Lyra Davidica* (1708), 198

MCGRANAHAN, James (1840-1907), 40, 450, 670, 681, 703, 712, 716
MacMillan, Sir Ernest (1893- ), 640
Maker, Frederick C. (1844-1927), 177, 395 (573)
Malan, H. A. César (1787-1864), 437 (531), 443
Mann, Arthur H. (1850-1929), 541 (552)
Marsh, Charles H. (1899- ), 689, 692
Marsh, Simeon B. (1798-1875), 427 II
Martin, George Wm. (1828-1881), 125 (403, 581, 609)
Martin, W. Stillman (1862-1935), 696
Mason, Lowell (1792-1872), 14 (375), 21, 53 (69), 65 (274), 74 (227, 263), 114, 126, 133 (188, 429), 149, 163, 176 (578), 186 (413, 225), 230, 285 I, 285 II (561), 292, 320, 321, 325 (386), 363 (367), 383, 388, 422 (447, 522, 537, 627), 448, 454, 562, 563, 728
Mather, William, 38
Matthews, Henry E. (b. 1820), 648
Matthews, T. Richard (1826-1910), 170
Meineke, Charles, xv
Meiningen *Gesangbuch* (1693), 267 (404)
*Melodienbuch von Rautenburg,* 435

Mendelssohn-Bartholdy, Felix (1809-1847), 92 (461), 168, 356, 532
Merrill, William P. (1867-1954), 482
Messiter, Arthur H. (1831-1916), 502
Miller, Edward (1731-1807), 44 (359, 509)
Monk, William H. (1823-1889), 217 (373), 235, 335, 471, 579, 595
Moody, May Whittle (b. 1870), 708
Moore's *Psalm Singer's Pocket Companion* (1756), 272
Mountain, James (1843-1933), 139, 587
Mozart, Wolfgang Amadeus (1756-1791), 126, 484, 691
Mueller, Wenzel, 39
Müller, Hermann von (b. 1859), 637
Müller, J. D.: *Choral Buch* (1754), 546.
Murray, James R. (1841-1905), 529, 641
*Musikalisches Handbuch,* Hamburg (1690), 56 (324, 619)

NÄGELI, Hans G. (1768?-1836), 285 II, 561, 562
Neander, Joachim (1650-1680), 132 (315), 238, 304
Nettleton, Asahel (1783-1844), 400
*Neu Catechismus-Gesangbüchlein,* Hamburg (1598), 210
Neumark, Georg, 567, 584
Neumeister, Erdmann (1671-1756), 394
*New Christian Hymnal, The* (1929), 381
Nicolai, Philipp (1556-1608), 231, 434

OGDEN, William A. (1841-1897), 684
Oliver, Henry K. (1800-1885), 34 (171, 250)
Oliver, Richard J., 673
Owen, William (1814-1893), 187, 420, 462

PAGE, Arthur (b. 1846), 229
Palestrina, Giovanni P. da (1526-1594), 201
Palmer, G. H., 435
Palmer, Horatio R. (1834-1907), 658, 701
*Parish Choir, The* (1850), 329
Parry, Charles Hubert Hastings (1848-1918), 288
Parry, Joseph (1841-1903), 99, 427
Peace, Albert L. (1844-1912), 82, 228, 498, 594
*Pensum Sacrum,* Görlitz (1648), 100 (312)
Phillips, Philip (1834-1895), 729
Pleyel, Ignaz J. (1757-1831), 134 (251), 499
Praetorius, Michael (1571-1621), 153
*Praxis Pietatis Melica* (1668), 50
Price, John (b. 1857), 431 II
Prichard, Rowland Hugh (1811-1887), 145 (432)
Pritchard, T. C. L. (1885- ), 77 III
Prout, Ebenezer (1835-1909), 630
*Psalmodia Evangelica* (1789), 61 (298, 372)
*Psalmodia Sacra,* Gotha (1715), 2
Purday, Charles H. (1799-1885), 463, 592

## INDEX OF COMPOSERS

READ, Daniel (1757-1836), 445
Redhead, Richard (1820-1901), 357 (415, 421, 600)
Redner, Lewis H. (1831-1908), 152
Reinagle, Alexander R. (1799-1877), 51 (544)
Reissiger, Carl G. (1798-1859), 46
Rimbault, Edward F. (1816-1876), 599
Roberts, John (Ieuan Gwyllt) (1822-1877), 43 (194, 527)
Roberts, Robert (b. 1863), 408
Root, George Frederick (1820-1895), 651, 657, 693
Roskamp, Esther J. 353, 394
Rouen church melody, 179
Runyan, William M., 27
Ryley, Geoffrey C. E. (1866-1947), 556

*Sacred Melodies* (1815), 439
*St. Albans Tune Book* (1865), 577
*St. Albans Tune Book* (1875), 308 (456)
Sankey, Ira D. (1840-1908), 78, 137, 551, 682, 719
Schein, Johann Herman (1586-1630), 474
*Schlesischen Volkslieder,* Leipzig (1842), 129
Schneider, Friedrich J. C. (1786-1853), 325 (386)
Scholefield, Clement C. (1839-1904), 248, 338
Schubert, Franz (1797-1828), 24
Schulthes, William (1816-1879), 428 (495)
Schulz, Johann A. P. (1747-1800), 614
Schumann, Robert (1810-1856), 93 (155)
Schumann's *Gesangbuch* (1539), 41, 409
Scottish *Psalter* (1615), 7 (28, 90, 293), 317
Sea, M. A., 649
Sellers, E. O., 671
Sheppard, Franklin L. (1852-1930), 109
Sherwin, William F. (1826-1888), 256, 343, 686
Showalter, A. J., 718
Shrubsole, William (1760-1806), 218, 381
Silcher, Friedrich (1789-1860), 661
Simpson, Robert (1790-1832), 77 II
Smart, Sir George (1776-1867), 77 IV
Smart, Henry (1813-1879), 60 (164, 268), 197 (233, 488), 593 (610)
Smith, H. Percy (1825-1898), 101
Smith, Isaac (c. 1725-c. 1800), 102 (299, 401)
Smith, Robert A. (1780-1829), 195 (457)
Southgate, Thomas B. (1814-1868), 73 (425, 589)
Spohr, Louis (1784-1859), 554
Sprague, P. J., 656
Spratt, Ann B. (b. 1829), 411
Stainer, Sir John (1840-1901), 189, 280 I
Stanley, Samuel (1767-1822), 280 II, 332

Stebbins, George C. (1846-1945), 340, 574, 697, 706, 715, 726
Steggall, Charles (1826-1905), 444
Stevenson, Sir John A. (1762-1833), 410
Stockton, John H. (1813-1877), 144, 724
Stralsund *Gesangbuch* (1665), 50
Strattner, Georg C. (1650-1705), 654
Straub, S. W. (1842-1899), 635
*Students' Hymnal, A,* University of Wales (1923), 555
Sullivan, Sir Arthur S. (1842-1900), 8, 125 (403, 581, 609), 140 (503) 200 (284), 377, 433 (558), 490 (678), 600, 605, 609, 655, 678
Sumner, John B. (19th century), 720
Supplement to *The New Version* (1708), 26 I (621)
Sweetser, Joseph E. (1825-1873), 291, 327
Sweney, John R. (1837-1899), 665, 676, 685
Swets, Seymour (1900- ), 726
Swift, J. Frederick (1847-1931), 638

TALLIS, Thomas (c. 1510-1585), 341
Tans'ur, William (1706-1783), 260, 585
Teschner, Melchior (1584-1635), 119 (173)
Thomas, Rhys, 427 II, 528
Thompson, Will L. (1847-1909), 664, 694
Tomer, William G. (1833-1896), 632
Tours, Berthold (1838-1897), 646
Towner, Daniel B. (1850-1919), 680, 698, 700, 705, 717, 721
Traditional: American, 402
: Danish, 636
: Dutch, 83 (286)
: English, 160, 426, 458
: Finnish, 306
: German, 64 (253), 153, 159, 321, 493
: Irish, 271
: Jewish, 32 (631)
: Polish, 196
: Scottish, 292
: Sicilian, 319
: Silesian, 129
: Welsh, 35 (79, 279), 118 (193), 385, 419), 305 (405), 345, 376, 539, 620
Tschirsch, Wilhelm (1818-1892), 661
Turton, Thomas (1780-1864), 31
Tye, Christopher (c. 1500- c. 1573), 22
Tyler, James S. (1842-1917), 662

URHAN, Chrétien (1790-1845), 599

## INDEX OF COMPOSERS

VALERIUS, Adrianus: The Collection (1625), 83, (286)
Van Andel, Henry J. (1882-), 465
Vander Werp, H., 47
Venua, Frederick M. A. (1788-1872), 6 (18, 64, 374)
Vincent, Charles J. (1852-1934), 590
Viner, William L. (1790-1867), 354
Vries, B. de: *Koraalboek*, 148, 511
Vulpius, Melchior (c. 1560-1615), 4, 568

WADE'S (J. F.) *Cantus Diversi* (1751), 36, 237
Walch, James (1837-1901), 10, 232, 545
Walton, James G. (1821-1905), 487
Ward, Samuel A. (1847-1903), 37 (603)
Warren, George William (1828-1902), 616
Watson, Adam (1845-1912), 669
Webb, George J. (1803-1887), 111 (477)
Webbe, Samuel (1740-1816), 121, 518, 613
Weber, Carl Maria von (1786-1826), 347 (583), 572

Wesley, Samuel S. (1810-1876), 49, 224 (270, 349), 254, 466
Whelpton, George (1847-1930), xiv
Wilkes, John B. (1785-1869), 30
Willan, Healey (1880-    ), 179
Willcox, John H. (1827-1875), 16
Williams, Aaron (1731-1776), 588
Williams, Robert (c. 1781-1821), 205
Williams, Thomas John (1869-1944), 42 (204, 453)
Willis, Richard S. (1819-1900), 157
Wilson, Hugh (1764-1824), 195 (457)
Wilson's *Selection of Psalm Tunes* (1825), 571
Wittenberg *Gesangbuch* (1524), 33 (255)
Woodman, Jonathan C. (1813-1894), 530
Wooldridge, Harry E. (1845-1917), 273
Württemberg *Gesangbuch* (1784), 526

ZEUNER, Heinrich C. (1795-1857), 67 (380)
Zundel, John (1815-1882), 368 (460 II), 396

# ALPHABETICAL INDEX OF TUNES

A Shelter in the Time of Storm .......719
Abergele .......351
Aberystwyth .......427 I
Abschied .......39
Adeste Fideles 36, 80, 151
Ajalon (Redhead No. 76) 357, 415, 421, 600
Alcester .......49
Aletta .......674
Alford .......234
Alice .......408
All Saints New ..384, 489
All Saints Old ....127, 602
All the Way .......505
All Things Bright and Beautiful .......636
All Things Come .......xiv
Allein Gott in der Höh' .......92, 461
Alleluia (Lowe) ......5, 9
Alma .......518
Almsgiving .......575
Alsace .......52
Amazing Grace .......402
Angel Voices .......8
Angel's Story .......541, 552
Angelus .......88, 336, 352
Antioch .......149
Anywhere .......680
Ardudwy .......43, 194
Arfon .......183
Ariel .......126
Arlington ....116, 326, 398
Armageddon .......493
Arnold .......276
Artavia .......397 II
Arthur's Seat ......226, 290
Aurelia .......224, 270, 349
Aus Gnaden soll ich selig werden .......399
Aus meines Herzens Grunde .......210
Austrian Hymn .......269
Autumn .......566
Avondale .......85, 407
Aylesbury .......48
Azmon .......133, 188, 429

Baca .......549 II
Ballerma .......77 II
Beatitudo ....259, 323, 455
Beecher .......368, 460 II
Belmont .......265, 543
Beloit .......46
Benevento .......613
Bentley .......520
Bera .......525
Bethlehem .......606
Bevan .......222
Beverley .......235
Bishop .......451
Bishopgarth .......377
Blaenhafren .......539
Boylston .......285
Bradford .......120, 586
Braun 117, 249, 371, 376
Bread of Life .......256
Breslau .......296
Bring Them In .......684
Brocklesbury .......642
Brookfield ....73, 425, 589
Bryn Calfaria ....187, 420
Brynteg .......59
Bullinger ....389, 424, 570

Caddo .......55
Caersalem .......369, 393
Cairnbrook .......630

Calling Today .......697
Camberwell .......254
Cambria .......345
Canonbury .......93, 155
Caritas .......547
Carol .......157
Children's Praises .......648
Christ Arose .......206
Christ lag in Todesbanden .......207
Christmas .......156, 480
Church Triumphant .. 58
City Bright .......662
Clemm .......668
Clifton .......508
Cloisters .......473
Columbia .......108
Colwyn Bay .......45
Communion .......356
Compassion .......465
Constance .......433, 558
Coronation .......218 I
Coronae .......217, 373
Creation .......12, 103
Crediton .......98, 601
Crimond .......77 III
Crofton .......624
Cross of Jesus .......189
Crucifer .......593, 610
Cwm Rhondda .......501

Dalehurst .......360, 423
Daniel .......660
Darwall's 148th 17, 302, 441
Dedication .......649
Denbigh .......376
Dennis .......285, 561
Devotion .......536
Diadem .......218 III
Diademata .......216, 239
Disciple .......593, 691
Dismissal .......354
Dix .......154
Dominus Regit Me ....141
Downs ......422, 447, 522, 537, 627
Draw Me Nearer .......713
Duane Street .......264
Duke Street .......3, 15, 54
Dundee .......7, 28, 90, 293
Dunfermline .......317
Dunstan .......523, 565

Eagley .......232
Easter Hymn .......198
Ebenezer ...... 42, 204, 453
Eden .......469
Edom .......228
Eifionydd .......169
Ein' feste Burg .......81
Eisenach .......474
Ellacombe .......526
Ellers .......316, 510
Ellon .......657
Elmhurst ....180, 366, 379
Emmanuel .......591
Erhalt uns, Herr ..91, 449
Ernstein .......638
Es ist ein' Ros' entsprungen .......153
Eternity .......466
Eucharistic Hymn .......358
Eudora .......529
Evan .......77 I
Evangel .......521
Evening Praise .......343
Evening Prayer .......340
Eventide (Monk) .......335
Every Day .......703

Every Morning .......328
Ewing .......604
Faben .......16
Faithful .......104
Faithfulness .......27
Federal Street 34, 171, 250
Ferguson .......576
Flemming .......179
For You and For Me 694
Fountain .......188
Frances .......40

Gairney Bridge .......68
Galilee .......491, 626
Germany ....262, 322, 439
Give Me Thy Heart ....723
Gladness .......647
Glasgow .......272
Gloria Patri (Greatorex) .......xv
Gloria Patri (Meineke) .......xv
God Will Take Care of You .......696
Godesberg .......142
Gorton .......417
Gott ein Vater .......661
Gower's Litany ..244, 278
Grace .......705
Grace Church ....134, 251
Green Hill .......498
Greenwood .......327
Gwyneth .......431 II

Haddam .......448
Hamburg .......186, 413
Hanford .......140, 503
Hanover (Croft) .......301
Harwell .......225
Hastings .......209
Haydn .......334
He Is Coming Again..687
He Leadeth Me .......500
He Lifted Me.......672
He Was Wounded for Our Transgressions 673
Hendon .......437, 531
Hermas .......213, 452
Hermon .......21
Herr Jesu Christ 100, 312
Herzliebster Jesu .......181
He's My Friend .......664
Hiding in Thee .......551
Hinchman .......333
His Eye Is on the Sparrow .......725
Hollingside .......459
Holy Desire .......574
Holy Guide .......564
Holy Rood .......297
Holy Trinity .......517
Holywood .......237
Home of the Soul .......729
Horsley .......191
Hosanna .......314
Houghton .......110
Howard .......571
Hursley .......346
Hyfrydol .......145, 432

I Do Believe .......458
I Know Whom I Have Believed .......712
I Love to Tell the Story .......387
I Will Sing the Wondrous Story .......709
In Dulci Jubilo .......159

Innocents .......329
Intercession New .......532
Invitation .......395, 573
Invitation (Root) .......693
Irby .......639
Irene .......248
Irish .......19, 277, 446
Is It the Crowning Day .......692
Iste Confessor .......179
It Is Well .......580

Jehovah Nissi .......470
Jerusalem .......592
Jesus Bids Us Shine ..653
Jesus, I Come .......715
Jesus Loves Me .......633
Jesus, meine Zuversicht .......362, 596
Jesus nimmt die Sünder an .......394
Jesus Paid It All .......690
Jesus Saves .......370
Jewels .......651
Jewett .......572
Joanna .......35, 79, 279

Kedron .......411
Kinsman .......450
Kirby Bedon .......261
Kirkland .......208
Kirkpatrick .......105
Kremser .......83, 286

Laban .......14, 375
Lafayette .......26
Lambeth .......428, 495
Lancashire ..197, 233, 488
Langran .......467
Lasst uns erfreuen ..3, 212
Lauda Sion Salvatorem .......361
Laudate Dominum .......288
Laudes Domini .......131
Leaning on the Everlasting Arms ....718
Lebanon .......396
Leighton .......273
Lenox .......223, 392
Leominster 125, 403, 581, 609
Leoni .......32, 631
Liebster Jesu .......220
Light of the World ....679
Like a River .......587
Lindeman .......550
Lisbon .......445
Lischer .......325, 386
Llanfair .......205
Llangloffan .......305, 405
Llangristiolus .......99
Llef .......75
Lobe den Herren .......50
Lobet den Herrn, ihr.. 4
Lobt Gott, ihr Christen .......123
Longstaff .......706
Longwood .......311
Lord Have Mercy .......731
Lord of Might .......229
Love Divine (Le Jeune) .......460 I
Loving-Kindness .......138
Luther's Hymn .......240
Lux Beata .......82
Lux Prima .......247, 330
Lyons .......13, 136

Macht hoch die Tür ..146
Magnus .......515
Man of Sorrows .......175

700

# ALPHABETICAL INDEX OF TUNES

Manoah .................... 436
Margaret ................... 170
Marion ...................... 502
Marlow ..................... 481
Martha ..................... 130
Martyn .................. 427 II
Martyrdom ....... 195, 457
Maryton .................... 101
Materna ............... 37, 603
Meditation 184, 569, 597
Mein Leben ............... 568
Meirionydd ....... 118, 193, 385, 419
Melcombe ................. 121
Melita .................. 243, 629
Mendebras ................ 321
Mendelssohn ............. 168
Mendon ............... 64, 253
Mercy ........... 245, 318, 559
Meribah .................... 563
Merrial ...................... 666
Migdol ...................... 114
Miles Lane ...... 218 II, 381
Mirfield ........ 66, 214, 468
Miriam ..................... 430
Missionary Chant, 67, 380
Missionary Hymn ...... 383
Moment by Moment .. 708
Monkland ................... 30
Monsell ..................... 464
More About Jesus ...... 676
More Love to Thee .... 548
Morecambe ............... 310
Morning Hymn .......... 331
Morning Star ............. 167
Morwellham .............. 444
Mount Zion ............... 600
Mozart ...................... 484
Mueller ..................... 641
Munich ............... 267, 404
My Anchor Holds ...... 717
My Redeemer ............ 681

Nain .......................... 388
Naomi ....................... 562
National Hymn .......... 616
Neander .............. 238, 304
Near the Cross ........... 704
Need .......................... 710
Nettleton ................... 400
Neumark ............ 567, 584
Newell ........................ 84
Nicaea ........................ 87
No Night There ......... 730
Nor Silver Nor Gold 721
Nothing but the Blood .................... 677
Nun danket ................. 86
Nun komm ................ 165
Nuremberg ........ 112, 485
Nyland ...................... 306

O dass ich tausend .... 11
O heilige Dreifaltigkeit ........ 339
O mein Jesu, ich muss sterben ......... 192
O Quanta Qualia .... 219
Old Hundredth ..xvi, 1, 348
Old 124th .................. 514
Olive's Brow ............. 182
Olivet ........................ 454
Olmutz .............. 176, 578
One Day! ................... 689
Only a Sinner ............ 698
Only Trust Him ........ 724
Onslow ..................... 659
Ortonville ..106, 143, 258
Ostend ...................... 230

Palestrina ................. 201
Park Street 6, 18, 62, 374
Pass Me Not .............. 707

Passion Chorale ........ 178
Pater Omnium ..... 71, 540
Pax Tecum ................. 590
Peace ..................... 397 I
Peace! Be Still! .......... 701
Penitence ........... 308, 456
Penitence (Lane) ...... 475
Pentecost .................. 496
Perfect Love .............. 625
Pilot .......................... 497
Pleading ................... 511
Pleyel's Hymn ........... 499
Poland ...................... 663
Posen ........................ 654
Praise Him ................ 683
Praise My Soul 63, 70, 122
Praise the Lord ......... 667
Providence ................ 635
Prysgol ..................... 462
Psalm 42 (Coblentz) 246

Quebec ....... 507, 549 I, 622

Redhead No. 76 (Ajalon) ........... 357, 415, 421, 600
Refuge ................... 427 III
Regent Square 60, 164, 268
Rehoboth ................... 47
Reliance .................... 486
Rendez à Dieu .......... 512
Rest ............................ 25
Resting ..................... 139
Retreat ..................... 528
Rheidol ..................... 527
Rhiw .......................... 555
Rhuddlan ................. 620
Richards ................... 688
Ripley .................. 53, 69
Ripon ....................... 519
Rockingham Old ......... 44, 359, 509
Rose Hill ................... 291
Rosefield ................... 443
Rossetti ..................... 115
Russian Hymn .......... 617
Rutherford ................ 599

Sabbath ..................... 320
Safe in the Arms of Jesus .............. 608
St. Agnes ......... 364, 542
St. Alban .................. 199
St. Albinus ............... 203
St. Anatolius (Brown) ............. 342
St. Andrew ............... 585
St. Andrew of Crete ..483
St. Anne ............. 26, 621
St. Asaph .................. 211
St. Austell ......... 313, 611
St. Austin ..241, 390, 472
St. Bees .................... 492
St. Botolf .................. 252
St. Catherine ............ 487
St. Cephas ................ 124
St. Christopher ........ 177
St. Chrysostom ..355, 418
St. Clement .............. 338
St. Columba .............. 271
St. Cross ................... 242
St. Cyprian .............. 266
St. Drostane ............. 172
St. Edith ................... 414
St. Edmund .............. 605
St. Etheldreda ............ 31
St. Ethelwald ............ 595
St. Flavian ................ 557
St. Frances ................ 282
St. George ................. 560
St. George's Windsor .......... 365, 615
St. Gertrude ..... 490, 678
St. Godric ................. 283
St. Helena ................ 513

St. Hilda ................... 128
St. John .............. 307, 618
St. Kevin .......... 200, 284
St. Leonard ............... 553
St. Louis ................... 152
St. Luke .................... 416
St. Magnus 113, 215, 294, 524
St. Margaret ............. 594
St. Martin's .............. 260
St. Matthew ..57, 95, 440
St. Michael ................. 72
St. Nicholas ............... 97
St. Oswald .................. 29
St. Peter ............. 51, 544
St. Petersburg ..76, 535, 582
St. Saviour ...... 162, 303
St. Stephen ........ 236, 442
St. Theodulph ....119, 173
St. Thomas ............... 588
Salzburg ................... 623
Samuel ..................... 655
Sanctuary ................. 607
Sandon ..................... 463
Sarratt ...................... 556
Sarum ....................... 281
Saved by Grace ........ 726
Savoy Chapel ..... 96, 628
Sawley ...................... 545
Schönster Herr Jesu ...129
Schubert .................... 24
Schumann ........ 363, 367
Second Parish .......... 353
See Amid the Winter's Snow ........ 158
Seelenbräutigam ...... 504
Seraph ...................... 257
Seymour ........... 347, 583
Sheffield .................... 38
Shepherd .................. 644
Shirland .................... 280
Shortle ...................... 289
Showers of Blessing ..716
Sicilian Mariners ...... 319
Silver Street 102, 299, 401
Soho ................... 350, 516
Soldau ................. 33, 255
Soldiers of Christ ...... 482
Something for Jesus ............ 391, 538
Sommerlied .............. 637
Sound the Battle Cry 686
Southwell .................. 412
Spohr ........................ 554
Stabat Mater ............. 185
State Street .............. 530
Stella ........................ 426
Stephanos ................ 389
Stille Nacht .............. 161
Stobel ....................... 546
Straf mich nicht ....... 476
Stuttgart ...................... 2
Sweet Hour .............. 534
Sweet Story .............. 650
Sympathy ................. 144

Tallis' Evening Hymn 341
Tell Me the Story of Jesus ............. 685
Tempus Adest Floridum ............. 640
Terra Beata .............. 109
Teshiniens ................ 196
Thanet ...................... 337
Thanksgiving (Basswood) ........ 645
Thanksgiving (Gilbert) .... 107, 300
The Child of a King 720
The Cleft of the Rock 675
The Golden Chain ...... 287
The King's Business ..695

The Lord's Prayer (Vater unser) ..41, 409
The Name of Jesus ....711
The New Song .......... 714
The Ninety and Nine 137
The Sweetest Name ....652
Thine the Glory ........ 634
Thirsting .................. 148
Thy God Reigneth .....670
Thy Word Have I Hid in My Heart ........671
Tidings (Tunbridge).. 10
'Tis So Sweet to Trust in Jesus ........ 699
Toplady .................... 421
Toulon ...................... 135
Tours ........................ 646
Trentham .......... 438, 598
Trinity ....................... 89
Truro ........... 61, 298, 372
Trust and Obey ......... 700
Trusting Jesus ........... 682

Unde et Memores ........ 579
Under His Wings ....... 78
University College ..... 479
Upp, min Tunga ...... 174
Uxbridge ....... 74, 227, 263

Veni .......................... 280
Veni Emmanuel ....... 147
Vesper Hymn ........... 410
Victory through Grace ................... 665
Vigil ......................... 577
Vigilate .................... 471
Vision ....................... 295
Vom Himmel hoch ....166
Vox Dilecti ............... 221

Wachet auf ............... 231
Waltham ..... 202, 378, 478
Ward ........................ 292
Wareham .................. 612
Warrington ...... 20, 309
Warum sollt' ich mich denn grämen ..150, 506
Warwick ................... 332
Was Gott tut ............. 94
Waverton .................. 23
Webb ................ 111, 477
Weil ich Jesus Schäflein bin ....... 643
Welcome Voice ........ 406
Wells ........................ 494
Wem in Leidenstagen 190
Wesley ............... 65, 274
What a Friend .......... 533
Whelpton .................. xiv
When the Roll Is Called ................. 727
Wie schön leuchtet der Morgenstern .........434
Wiltshire ............. 77 IV
Winchester New .......... 56, 324, 619
Windsor .............. 22, 381
Wir pflügen ............. 614
Wollt ihr wissen, was mein Preis ........... 435
Wonderful Grace of Jesus .............. 702
Wonderful Love ....... 669
Woodworth .............. 431
Words of Life ........... 722
Work Song ............... 728
Wunderbarer König .......... 132, 315
Wynnstay ................ 344

Ye Children, Come ....656
Yield Not .................. 658

Zerah ........................ 163
Zion ............. 275, 369, 382

# METRICAL INDEX OF TUNES

## S. M.

|  |  |
|---|---|
| Aylesbury | 48 |
| Boylston | 285 I |
| Camberwell | 254 |
| Clifton | 508, 561 |
| Dennis | 285 II |
| Ferguson | 576 |
| Gorton | 417 |
| Greenwood | 327 |
| Holy Rood | 297 |
| Laban | 14, 375 |
| Lisbon | 445 |
| Olmutz | 176, 578 |
| Rhiw | 555 |
| St. Ethelwald | 595 |
| St. George | 560 |
| St. Michael | 72 |
| St. Thomas | 588 |
| Schumann | 363, 367 |
| Shirland | 260 II |
| Silver Street | 102, 299, 401 |
| Soldiers of Christ | 482 |
| Southwell | 412 |
| State Street | 530 |
| Trentham | 438, 598 |
| Veni | 280 I |
| Vigil | 577 |

### S. M. with refrain

| Marion | 502 |
| Welcome Voice | 406 |

### S. M. D.

| Diademata | 216, 239 |
| Lebanon | 396 |
| Leominster | 125, 403, 581, 609 |
| Terra Beata | 109 |

## C. M.

| Abergele | 351 |
| Amazing Grace | 402 |
| Arlington | 116, 326, 398 |
| Arnold | 276 |
| Avondale | 85, 407 |
| Azmon | 133, 188, 429 |
| Ballerma | 77 II |
| Beatitudo | 259, 323, 455 |
| Belmont | 265, 543 |
| Bradford | 120, 586 |
| Caddo | 55 |
| Crediton | 98, 601 |
| Crimond | 77 III |
| Dalehurst | 360, 423 |
| Downs | 422, 447, 522, 537, 627 |
| Dundee | 7, 28, 90, 293 |
| Dunfermline | 327 |
| Eagley | 232 |
| Eden | 469 |
| Evan | 77 I |
| Glasgow | 272 |
| Green Hill | 498 |
| Hermon | 21 |
| Holy Trinity | 517 |
| Horsley | 191 |
| Howard | 571 |
| I Do Believe | 458 |
| Irish | 19, 277, 446 |
| Lafayette | 26 |
| Lambeth | 428, 695 |
| Manoah | 436 |
| Marlow | 481 |
| Martyrdom | 195, 457 |
| Meditation | 184, 569, 597 |
| Mirfield | 66, 214, 468 |
| Naomi | 562 |
| St. Agnes | 364, 542 |
| St. Andrew | 585 |
| St. Anne | 26, 621 |
| St. Columba | 271 |
| St. Etheldreda | 31 |
| St. Flavian | 557 |
| St. Frances | 282 |
| St. Magnus | 113, 215, 294, 524 |
| St. Martin's | 260 |
| St. Nicholas | 97 |
| St. Peter | 51, 544 |
| St. Saviour | 162, 303 |
| St. Stephen | 236, 442 |
| Sawley | 545 |
| Sheffield | 38 |
| Soho | 350, 516 |
| Spohr | 554 |
| Warwick | 332 |
| Wiltshire | 77 IV |
| Windsor | 22, 381 |

### C. M. with repeat

| Antioch | 149 |
| Christmas | 156, 480 |
| Lobt Gott, ihr Christen | 123 |
| Miles Lane | 218 II, 381 |
| Newell | 84 |
| Ortonville | 106, 143, 258 |
| Zerah | 163 |

### C. M. with refrain

| Children's Praises | 648 |
| Coronation | 218 I |
| Diadem | 218 III |
| Every Day | 703 |
| God Will Take Care of You | 696 |
| I Know Whom I Have Believed | 712 |
| Kinsman | 450 |
| Only Trust Him | 724 |
| Providence | 635 |
| Ye Children, Come | 656 |

### C. M. D.

| All Saints New | 384, 489 |
| Bethlehem | 606 |
| Carol | 157 |
| Ellacombe | 526 |
| Jerusalem | 592 |
| Materna | 37, 603 |
| Ostend | 230 |
| Ripon | 519 |
| St. Leonard | 553 |
| St. Matthew | 57, 95, 440 |
| Seraph | 257 |
| Vox Dilecti | 221 |

## L. M.

| Abschied | 39 |
| Alsace | 52 |
| Angelus | 88, 336, 352 |
| Beloit | 46 |
| Bera | 525 |
| Bishop | 451 |
| Breslau | 296 |
| Brookfield | 73, 425, 589 |
| Brynteg | 59 |
| Canonbury | 93, 155 |
| Church Triumphant | 58 |
| Duke Street | 3, 15, 54 |
| Eisenach | 474 |
| Emmanuel | 591 |
| Erhalt uns, Herr | 91, 449 |
| Federal Street | 34, 171, 250 |
| Germany | 262, 322, 439 |
| Grace Church | 134, 251 |
| Hamburg | 186, 413 |
| Herr Jesu Christ | 100, 312 |
| Hursley | 346 |
| Leighton | 273 |
| Llef | 75 |
| Maryton | 101 |
| Melcombe | 121 |
| Mendon | 64, 253 |
| Migdol | 114 |
| Missionary Chant | 67, 380 |
| Morning Hymn | 331 |
| Mozart | 484 |
| O heilige Dreifaltigkeit | 339 |
| Old Hundredth | xvi, 1, 348 |
| Olive's Brow | 182 |
| Onslow | 659 |
| Penitence | 308, 456 |
| Pentecost | 496 |
| Quebec | 507, 549 I, 622 |
| Rest | 25 |
| Retreat | 528 |
| Rockingham Old | 44, 359, 509 |
| Rose Hill | 291 |
| St. Cross | 242 |
| St. Drostane | 172 |
| St. Luke | 416 |
| Sarratt | 556 |
| Soldau | 33, 255 |
| Tallis' Evening Hymn | 341 |
| Truro | 61, 298, 372 |
| Uxbridge | 74, 227, 263 |
| Vom Himmel hoch | 166 |
| Waltham | 202, 378, 478 |
| Ward | 292 |
| Wareham | 612 |
| Warrington | 20, 309 |
| Winchester New | 56, 324, 619 |

### L. M. with repeat

| Baca | 549 II |
| Park Street | 6, 18, 62, 374 |

### L. M. with refrain

| A Shelter in the Time of Storm | 719 |
| Bring Them In | 684 |
| Hosanna | 314 |
| Loving-Kindness | 138 |
| More About Jesus | 676 |
| Saved by Grace | 726 |
| Vision | 295 |

### L. M. D.

| Creation | 12, 103 |
| Duane Street | 264 |
| He Leadeth Me | 500 |
| Sweet Hour | 534 |
| Upp, Min Tunga | 174 |

## 5. 5. 5. 5. 6. 5. 6. 5.

| Laudate Dominum | 288 |

## 5. 5. 6. 5

| Whelpton | xiv |

## 5. 5. 6. 5. 6. 4. 6. 4.

| Jesus Bids Us Shine | 653 |

## 5. 5. 8. 8. 5. 5.

| Seelenbräutigam | 504 |

## 5. 6. 6. 4.

| Sommerlied | 637 |

## 5. 6. 8. 5. 5. 8.

| Schönster Herr Jesu | 129 |

## 6. 4. 6. 4.

| Nain | 388 |

### 6. 4. 6. 4. with refrain

| Need | 710 |

## 6. 4. 6. 4. 6. 6. 4.

| Kedron | 411 |

## 6. 4. 6. 4. D.

| Bread of Life | 256 |
| St. Helena | 513 |

## 6. 4. 6. 4. 6. 6. 4. 4.

| More Love to Thee | 548 |

## 6. 4. 6. 4. 6. 6. 6. 4.

| Cambria | 345 |
| St. Edmund | 605 |
| Something for Jesus | 391, 538 |

### 6. 4. 6. 7. 7. with refrain

| Is It the Crowning Day | 692 |

## 6. 5. 6. 5.

| Ernstein | 638 |
| Gott ein Vater | 661 |
| Merrial | 666 |
| Wem in Leidenstagen | 190 |

## 6. 5. 6. 5. D.

| Hermas | 452 |
| Kirkland | 208 |
| Penitence (Lane) | 475 |
| St. Andrew of Crete | 483 |
| St. Cephas | 124 |

### 6. 5. 6. 5. D. with refrain

| Hermas | 213 |
| Like a River | 587 |
| St. Alban | 199 |
| St. Gertrude | 490, 678 |

702

# METRICAL INDEX OF TUNES

**6. 5. 6. 5. 6. 5. D.**
Armageddon ...............493

**6. 5. 7. 5.**
Dedication ..................649

**6. 5. 7. 5.**
with refrain
Thine the Glory ..........634

**6. 6. 4. 6. 6. 6. 4.**
Braun .........117, 249, 371
Denbigh ........................376
Kirby Bedon ................261
Olivet ............................454
Stobel ............................546
Trinity ............................ 89

**6. 6. 5. 5. 6.**
City Bright ..................662

**6. 6. 5. 6. 6. 5.**
**3. 4. 8. 6.**
Lindeman ....................550

**6. 6. 6. 6.**
Holy Guide ..................564
St. Cyprian ..................266
Second Parish .............353

**6. 6. 6. 6.**
with refrain
Jesus Paid It All ........690

**6. 6. 6. D.**
Devotion ......................536
Laudes Domini ...........131

**6. 6. 6. 6. D.**
Invitation .............395, 573
Jewett ............................572

**6. 6. 6. 6. 8. 8.**
Arthur's Seat .......226, 290
Bevan ............................222
Columbia ....................108
Darwall's
 148th .........17, 302, 441
Haddam ........................448
Lenox ..................223, 392
St. Godric ....................283
St. John ..............307, 618
Samuel ..........................655
Waverton .................... 23

**6. 6. 6. 6. 8. 8.**
with repeat
Lischer ...............325, 386

**6. 6. 7. 7. 7. 8. 5. 5.**
In Dulci Jubilo ..........159

**6. 6. 8. 4. D.**
Leoni ..................32, 631

**6. 6. 8. 6. 6. 8.**
**3. 3. 6. 6.**
Wunderbaren
 König ..............132, 315

**6. 6. 9. 6. 6. 9.**
with refrain
Trust and Obey ..........700

**6. 7. 6. 7. 6. 6. 6. 6.**
Nun danket ................. 86

**7. 4. 7. 4. 7. 7. 7. 4. 4.**
Thy God Reigneth ....670

**7. 5. 7. 5. D.**
The New Song ...........714

**7. 5. 7. 5. 7. 5.**
**7. 5. 8. 8.**
Intercession New ........532

**7. 5. 7. 6.**
with refrain
Daniel ..........................660

**7. 6. 7. 5. D.**
Work Song ..................728

**7. 6. 7. 6.**
Mein Leben ..................568

**7. 6. 7. 6.**
with refrain
All Things Bright
 and Beautiful ..........636
Near the Cross ...........704
No Night There .........730

**7. 6. 7. 6. 3. 3. 6. 6.**
Straf mich nicht ..........476

**7. 6. 7. 6. 6. 7. 6.**
Aus meines Herzens
 Grunde ....................210

**7. 6. 7. 6. 6. 7. 6.**
Es ist ein' Ros'
 entsprungen ................153

**7. 6. 7. 6. 7. 6. 7. 5.**
Rutherford ...................599

**7. 6. 7. 6. D.**
Angel's Story ......541, 552
Aurelia ......224, 270, 349
Bentley ..........................520
Ellon .............................657
Ewing ...........................604
Faithful ........................104
Lancashire ..197, 233, 488
Llangloffan .........305, 405
Meirionydd 118, 193, 385,
 419
Mendebras ....................321
Miriam .........................430
Missionary Hymn .......383
Monsell .........................464
Munich ................267, 404
Nyland ..........................306
Passion Chorale ..........178
Prysgol .........................462
St. Edith ......................414
St. Kevin ...........200, 284
St. Theodulph ....119, 173

Savoy Chapel .........96, 628
Schubert ....................... 24
Tempus Adest
 Floridum ..................640
Tours ............................646
Webb ...................111, 477

**7. 6. 7. 6. D.**
with refrain
Evangel ........................521
I Love to Tell the
 Story .......................387
Safe in the Arms
 of Jesus ...................608
Wir pflügen ................614

**7. 6. 7. 6. 7. 6. 7. 7.**
His Eye Is on the
 Sparrow ...................725

**7. 6. 7. 6. 7. 7. 7. 6.**
Jesus Saves ..................370

**7. 6. 7. 6. 8. 8.**
St. Anatolius
 (Brown) ...................342

**7. 6. 7. 6. 7. 6. 9. 3.**
with refrain
Wonderful Grace of
 Jesus .........................702

**7. 6. 8. 6. D.**
Alford ..........................234

**7. 6. 8. 6. 8. 6. 8. 6.**
St. Christopher ..........177

**7. 7. 6. D.**
Pleading ......................511

**7. 7. 7. 3.**
Vigilate ........................471

**7. 7. 7. 5.**
Eternity .......................466
Irene .............................248

**7. 7. 7. 6.**
Gower's Litany ..244, 278

**7. 7. 7. 7.**
Alcester ........................ 49
Aletta ............................674
Innocents .....................329
Mercy ..........245, 318, 559
Monkland .................... 30
Nun komm, der
 Heiden Heiland ......165
Nuremberg ........112, 485
Pleyel's Hymn ............499
Posen ............................654
St. Austell ..........313, 611
St. Bees .........................492
Seymour ............347, 583
University College ....479

**7. 7. 7. 7.**
with repeat
Hendon ...............437, 531

**7. 7. 7. 7.**
with refrain
Jesus Loves Me ..........633
See Amid the
 Winter's Snow ........158
Trusting Jesus .............682

**7. 7. 7. 7.**
with alleluias
Easter Hymn ..............198
Llanfair ........................205

**7. 7. 7. 7. 4.**
with refrain
Evening Praise ............343

**7. 7. 7. 7. 4. 7.**
Wollt ihr wissen, was
 mein Preis .................435

**7. 7. 7. 7. 7.**
**5. 7. 7. 7. 7.**
Compassion .................465

**7. 7. 7. 7. 7. 7.**
Ajalon (Redhead No. 76)
 357, 415, 421 II, 600
Arfon ...........................183
Dix ...............................154
Every Morning ...........328
Lux Prima ..................330
Mount Zion ................600
Pilot .............................497
Reliance .......................486
Rosefield ......................443
Toplady ..................421 I
Wells ............................494

**7. 7. 7. 7. 7. 7.**
with refrain
My Anchor Holds ......717
Thanksgiving
 (Basswood) .............645

**7. 7. 7. 7. 7. 7.**
with repeat
Sabbath ........................320

**7. 7. 7. 7. D.**
Aberystwyth ...........427 I
Benevento ....................613
Hollingside .................459
Martyn ...................427 II
Refuge ....................427 III
Rehoboth ..................... 47
St. George's,
 Windsor ........365, 615
Salzburg .......................623
Thanksgiving ....107, 300

**7. 7. 7. 7. D.**
with refrain
Mendelssohn ..............168

**7. 7. 7. 8.**
Man of Sorrows ..........175

**7. 7. 8. 7. 7.**
Weil ich Jesu
 Schäflein bin ..........643

**7. 8. 7. 8.**
with alleluias
St. Albinus ..................203

703

# METRICAL INDEX OF TUNES

### 7. 8. 7. 8.
with refrain
Nothing but the
Blood ..........................677

### 7. 8. 7. 8. 7. 7.
Jesus nimmt die
Sünder an ..............394
Jesus, meine
Zuversicht ......362, 596
Hinchman ..................333

### 7. 8. 7. 8. 8. 8.
Liebster Jesu ..............220

### 8. 3. 3. 6.
Thanet ......................337

### 8. 3. 3. 6. 8. 3. 3. 6.
Warum sollt' ich mich
denn grämen....150, 506

### 8. 4. 7. 8. 4. 7.
Haydn ......................334

### 8. 4. 8. 4. 8. 8. 4.
Wynnstay ..................344

### 8. 5. 8. 3.
Bullinger 389 II, 424, 570
Cairnbrook ..................630
Stephanos ..................389 I

### 8. 5. 8. 5.
with refrain
Pass Me Not ..............707

### 8. 5. 8. 5. 8. 4. 3.
Angel Voices .............. 8

### 8. 6. 8. 5.
with refrain
Jewels ......................651

### 8. 6. 8. 6. 6. 6.
with refrain
Words of Life ..........722

### 8. 6. 8. 6. 6. 8. 6.
Fountain ..................188

### 8. 6. 8. 6. 7. 6. 8. 6.
St. Louis ..................152

### 8. 6. 8. 6. 8. 6.
Morwellham ..........444

### 8. 6. 8. 6. 8. 6.
with refrain
God Rest You Merry 160

### 8. 6. 8. 6. 8. 8.
Hastings ..................209

### 8. 6. 8. 6. 8. 8. 4. 4. 3.
He's My Friend ..........664

### 8. 7. 8. 5. D.
with refrain
Resting ..................139

### 8. 7. 8. 7.
Alice ......................408
Brocklesbury ..........642
Cross of Jesus ..........189
Dominus Regit Me ....141
Evening Prayer ........340
Galilee ............491, 626
Martha ..................130
St. Oswald .............. 29
Stuttgart .................. 2

### 8. 7. 8. 7.
with refrain
Clemm ....................668
I Will Sing the
Wondrous Story ......709
My Redeemer ..........681
Showers of Blessing ..716
Sympathy ..................144
Thy Word Have I Hid
in My Heart ..........671
'Tis So Sweet to Trust
in Jesus ..................699

### 8. 7. 8. 7.
with alleluias
Alleluia (Lowe) ........5, 9

### 8. 7. 8. 7. 3. 3. 7.
Rheidol ..................527

### 8. 7. 8. 7. 4. 4. 4. 7.
Caersalem ..........369, 393

### 8. 7. 8. 7. 4. 4. 4. 7. 7.
Bryn Calfaria ....187, 420

### 8. 7. 8. 7. 4. 4. 7.
with repeat
Shepherd ..................644

### 8. 7. 8. 7. 4. 7.
Coronae ............217, 373
St. Austin ..241, 390, 472

### 8. 7. 8. 7. 4. 7.
with repeat
Zion ............275, 369, 382

### 8. 7. 8. 7. 6. 6. 6. 7.
Ein' feste Burg .......... 81

### 8. 7. 8. 7. 7. 7.
All Saints Old ....127, 602
Edom ......................228
Godesberg ..............142
Lux Prima ..............247
Neander ..................304

### 8. 7. 8. 7. 7. 7.
with alleluias
Harwell ..................225

### 8. 7. 8. 7. 7. 7. 8. 8.
Psalm 42 (Coblentz) 246
Thirsting ..............148

### 8. 7. 8. 7. 7. 8. 7. 4.
Christ lag in
Todesbanden ..........207

### 8. 7. 8. 7. 8. 7.
Ardudwy ............43, 194
Dismissal ..................354
Neander ..................238
Praise, My Soul 63, 70, 122
Regent Square ....60, 164, 268
Holywood ..................237
Rhuddlan ..................620
Sicilian Mariners ........319

### 8. 7. 8. 7. 8. 7.
with repeat
Cwm Rhondda ..........501

### 8. 7. 8. 7. 4. 4. 8. 8.
Was Gott tut .......... 94

### 8. 7. 8. 7. D.
All the Way ..........505
Austrian Hymn ..........269
Autumn ..................566
Beecher ........368, 460 II
Bishopgarth ..............377
Blaenhafren ..............540
Constance ........433, 558
Crucifer ............593, 610
Disciple ............593, 691
Ebenezer ....42, 204, 453
Eifionydd ..................169
Faben ...................... 16
Hyfrydol ..........145, 432
Love Divine (Le
Jeune) ..................460 I
Nettleton ..................400
O mein Jesu, ich
muss sterben ..........192
Richards ..................688
Ripley ..................53, 69
St. Asaph ..................211
St. Hilda ..................128
Sanctuary ..................607
The Sweetest Name ....652
Vesper Hymn ..........410
What a Friend ..........533

### 8. 7. 8. 7. 8. 8.
Irby ......................639

### 8. 7. 8. 7. D.
with refrain
Kirkpatrick ..............105
Tell Me the Story
of Jesus ..................685

### 8. 7. 8. 7. 8. 8. 7.
Allein Gott in der
Höh' ............92, 461
Lobet den Herrn, ihr 4
Lord of Might ..........229
Luther's Hymn ..........240
The Golden Chain ......287

### 8. 7. 8. 7. 8. 7. 7. 7.
Beverley ..................235

### 8. 8. 4. 4. 8. 8.
with alleluias
Lasst uns erfreuen 3, 212

### 8. 8. 6.
St. Botolf ..................252

### 8. 8. 6. D.
Colwyn Bay .............. 45
Frances .................. 40
Jehovah Nissi ..........470
Meribah ..................563

### 8. 8. 6. D.
with repeat
Shortle ..................289

### 8. 8. 6. 8. 8. 6. 6.
Ariel ......................126

### 8. 8. 7. 8. 8. 7.
Lauda Sion
Salvatorem ..........361
Stabat Mater ..........185

### 8. 8. 7. 8. 8. 7.
4. 4. 4. 4. 8.
Wie schön leuchtet der
Morgenstern ..........434

### 8. 8. 8.
with alleluias
Palestrina ..................201

### 8. 8. 8. 4.
Almsgiving ..............575
Eudora ..................529
Hanford ..........140, 503

### 8. 8. 8. 6.
Elmhurst ....180, 366, 379
Gwyneth ............431 II
Woodworth ..........431 I

### 8. 8. 8. 6.
with refrain
He Lifted Me ..........672

### 8. 8. 8. 6. 8. 6.
Dunstan ..........523, 565

### 8. 8. 8. 7.
with refrain
The Name of Jesus ....711

### 8. 8. 8. 8. 6.
St. Margaret ..........594

### 8. 8. 8. 8.
with refrain
Veni Emmanuel ......147

### 8. 8. 8. 8. 8. 8.
Gairney Bridge .......... 68
Melita ............243, 629
Pater Omnium ......71, 540
St. Catherine ..........487
St. Chrysostom ...355, 418
St. Petersburg ....76, 535, 582
Stella ......................426
The Lord's Prayer
(Vater unser) ....41, 409

# METRICAL INDEX OF TUNES

**8. 8. 8. 8. 8. 6. 6.**
Macht hoch die Tür ...... 146

**8. 8. 8. 8. D.**
Llangristiolus ............... 99

**8. 8. 9. 7. 8. 6. 10. 7.**
with refrain
Peace! Be Still! ........... 701

**8. 8. 10. 10.**
Teshiniens .................. 196

**8. 9. 8. 8. 9. 8. 6. 6. 4. 8. 8.**
Wachet auf ................. 231

**8. 10. 10. 4.**
Rossetti ..................... 115

**9. 7. 9. 7. 8. 7. 8. 7.**
with refrain
Victory through Grace ... 665

**9. 8. 8. 9.**
with refrain
God Be with You ......... 632

**9. 8. 9. 6. 9. 9. 9. 6.**
Jesus, I Come .............. 715

**9. 8. 9. 8.**
Eucharistic Hymn ........ 358
St. Clement ................. 338

**9. 8. 9. 8. 8. 8.**
Aus Gnaden soll ich selig werden ............ 399
Neumark ............... 567, 584
O dass ich tausend ...... 11

**9. 8. 9. 8. D.**
Rendez à Dieu ............. 512

**9. 9. 9. 6.**
with refrain
Invitation .................... 693

**9. 9. 9. 9.**
Holy Desire ................. 574

**9. 9. 9. 9.**
with refrain
Grace ......................... 705

**9. 9. 9. 11.**
with refrain
He is Coming Again ..... 687

**10. 4. 10. 4. 10. 10.**
Lux Beata .................... 82
Sandon ...................... 463

**10. 7. 10. 7.**
with refrain
Draw Me Nearer ......... 713

**10. 8. 10. 7.**
with refrain
Calling Today ............. 697

**10. 8. 10. 7. 8. 10.**
Wonderful Love .......... 669

**10. 8. 10. 9.**
with refrain
Sound the Battle Cry ... 686

**10. 9. 10. 9.**
with refrain
Leaning on the Everlasting Arms .... 718

**10. 10.**
Pax Tecum .................. 590

**10. 10. 9. 9.**
with alleluias
Only a Sinner ............. 698

**10, 10. 10. 4. 4.**
Sarum ........................ 281

**10. 10. 10. 6.**
Artavia ................... 397 II
Peace ..................... 397 I

**10. 10. 10. 10.**
Communion ................ 356
Ellers ................... 316, 510
Eventide (Monk) ...... 335
Langran ..................... 467
Longwood ................. 311
Morecambe ................ 310
National Hymn .......... 616
O Quanta Qualia ........ 219
Toulon ....................... 135

**10. 10. 10. 10.**
with refrain
Give Me Thy Heart .. 723
Gladness .................... 647
Moment by Moment .. 708

**10. 10. 10. 10. 10.**
Old 124th .................. 514

**10. 10. 10. 10. 10.**
Unde et Memores ....... 579

**10. 10. 11. 11.**
Hanover (Croft) ......... 301
Houghton .................. 111
Lyons ................... 13, 136

**10. 11. 11. 11.**
with refrain
The Child of a King ... 720

**11. 7. 11. 7.**
with refrain
For You and for Me ... 694

**11. 8. 11. 8.**
with refrain
The Cleft of the Rock . 675
Light of the World .... 679

**11. 8. 11. 9.**
with refrain
It Is Well ................... 580

**11. 8. 12. 9.**
Sweet Story ............... 650

**11. 10.**
with refrain
Christ Arose .............. 206

**11. 10. 11. 9.**
Russian Hymn ........... 617

**11. 10. 11. 10.**
Alma .......................... 518
Crofton ...................... 624
Morning Star ............. 167
Perfect Love .............. 625
Wesley ................. 65, 274

**11. 10. 11. 10.**
with refrain
Faithfulness ............... 27
He Was Wounded for Our Transgressions 673
One Day! .................. 689
Tidings (Tunbridge) . 10
Under His Wings ..... 78

**11. 11. 11. 5.**
Cloisters .................... 473
Flemming .............. 179 II
Herzliebster Jesu ....... 181
Iste Confessor ........ 179 I

**11. 11. 11. 11.**
Caritas ...................... 547
Joanna ............. 35, 79, 279
Longstaff .................. 706
Mueller ..................... 641

**11. 11. 11. 11.**
with repeat
Adeste Fideles ............ 80
Poland ...................... 663

**11. 11. 11. 11.**
with refrain
Anywhere .................. 680
Hiding in Thee .......... 551
Magnus ..................... 515
Praise the Lord .......... 667

**11. 11. 11. 12.**
with refrain
Yield Not ................... 658

**11. 12. 12. 10.**
Nicaea ........................ 87

**12. 10. 12. 10. 11. 10.**
with refrain
Praise Him ................. 683

**12. 11. 12. 11.**
Kremser ............... 83, 286

**12. 11. 12. 11.**
with repeat
Adeste Fideles ............ 36

**12. 11. 12. 11.**
with refrain
Nor Silver Nor Gold .. 721

**12. 12. 12. 8.**
with refrain
The King's Business .. 695

**14. 14. 4. 7. 8.**
Lobe den Herren ........ 50

**15. 11. 15. 11.**
with refrain
When the Roll Is Called ...................... 727

**Irregular**
Adeste Fideles ........... 151
All Things Come ....... xiv
Gloria Patri ................ xv
Home of the Soul ...... 729
Lord Have Mercy ..... xiv
Margaret .................... 170
The Ninety and Nine 137
Stille Nacht ............... 161

# Index of Scripture References in Hymns

*Note: The Scripture texts listed below include a number of references which do not appear at the heads of the hymns indicated, but which are appropriate to the subjects dealt with in the hymns. Thus, at least some of the texts cited are alternates to those printed with the hymns.*

### Genesis
| | |
|---|---|
| 1:2 | 255 |
| 1:3 | 376 |
| 1:3-5 | 327 |
| 1:31 | 636 |
| 3:15 | 174 |
| 8:22 | 27 |
| 18:19 | 627 |
| 18:25 | 84 |
| 28:15 | 498 |
| 28:17 | 308 |
| 50:20 | 21 |

### Exodus
| | |
|---|---|
| 4:12 | 631 |
| 13:21 | 269, 501 |
| 15:1 | 200 |
| 19:5 | 700 |
| 20:11 | 106 |
| 25:22 | 528 |
| 32:26 | 493 |

### Numbers
| | |
|---|---|
| 6:24 | 319 |

### Deuteronomy
| | |
|---|---|
| 4:22 | 597 |
| 8:3 | 257 |
| 32:3 | 4 |
| 33:27 | 718 |

### Joshua
| | |
|---|---|
| 24:15 | 624 |

### I Samuel
| | |
|---|---|
| 3:9 | 655 |
| 3:18 | 562 |
| 7:12 | 400 |
| 15:22 | 657 |

### II Samuel
| | |
|---|---|
| 22:2 | 472 |
| 22:3 | 558 |

### I Kings
| | |
|---|---|
| 8:30 | 532 |

### I Chronicles
| | |
|---|---|
| 16:29 | xv |
| 16:31 | 149 |
| 16:35 | 92 |
| 29:13 | 86 |
| 29:14 | xiv, 8, 367 |

### II Chronicles
| | |
|---|---|
| 6:27 | 466 |
| 6:40 | 268 |

### Ezra
| | |
|---|---|
| 8:22 | 612 |

### Nehemiah
| | |
|---|---|
| 1:7 | 418 |
| 9:5 | 14 |
| 9:6 | 636 |
| 9:17 | 412 |

### Job
| | |
|---|---|
| 11:7 | 93 |
| 19:25 | 586 |

### Psalms
| | |
|---|---|
| 1 | 446 |
| 2 | 227 |
| 3 | 469 |
| 4:8 | 341, 342 |
| 5 | 47 |
| 5:1 | 47 |
| 5:3 | 332 |
| 6 | 511 |
| 8:1-6, 9 | 107 |
| 9:1, 2 | 44 |
| 9:7-11 | 44 |
| 10 | 508 |
| 11:1-5, 7 | 48 |
| 12 | 45 |
| 13 | 541 |
| 13:3-4 | 342 |
| 14:2-7 | 474 |
| 15 | 445 |
| 16:1-2, 5-8, 11 | 581 |
| 18:1-2, 6, 9-10, 30 | 524 |
| 18:28 | 21 |
| 19 | 263 |
| 19:1 | 103 |
| 19:1-6, 14 | 104 |
| 19:7 | 266 |
| 19:7-11 | 450 |
| 19:7-14 | 448 |
| 19:8 | 449 |
| 20:1 | 486 |
| 22:23ff | 6 |
| 22:27-30 | 295 |
| 23 | 77, 141, 663 |
| 23:6 | 51 |
| 24 | 66 |
| 24:3, 4 | 502 |
| 24:7 | 146 |
| 25:1-7, 10 | 583 |
| 25:7 | 457 |
| 25:11 | 464 |
| 26:8 | 280, 313 |
| 27 | 568 |
| 27:4 | 304 |
| 27:5 | 79 |
| 29:1-5, 9-11 | 36 |
| 29:11 | 316 |
| 30 | 526 |
| 31:2 | 351 |
| 31:3 | 459 |
| 31:15 | 577 |
| 31:19-24 | 563 |
| 32 | 462 |
| 32:7 | 553 |
| 32:8 | 286 |
| 33:1 | 40 |
| 33:1-12 | 40 |
| 34:1 | 131, 495 |
| 34:1-4, 7-9 | 522 |
| 34:11-15 | 656 |
| 36:5 | 52, 55 |
| 36:5-9 | 52 |
| 36:5-10 | 55 |
| 36:7 | 138, 349 |
| 36:9 | 333 |
| 37:3-7 | 569 |
| 37:4 | 543 |
| 37:5 | 560 |
| 38 | 408 |
| 40:1-5 | 523 |
| 40:2 | 672 |
| 40:9-11, 16-17 | 565 |
| 41:4 | 409 |
| 42 | 554 |
| 42:8 | 344, 347 |
| 43 | 539 |
| 44:20-26 | 515 |
| 45:1-10 | 125 |
| 45:2 | 129 |
| 46 | 37, 292 |
| 46:1 | 81 |
| 46:7 | 616 |
| 46:8-9 | 617 |
| 46:9 | 622 |
| 47 | 61 |
| 47:5 | 210 |
| 47:6 | 634 |
| 48:9-14 | 307 |
| 48:14 | 501 |
| 50:1-6 | 239 |
| 51 | 413 |
| 51:1-15 | 415 |
| 51:7 | 406 |
| 55:22 | 559, 567 |
| 56:3-4, 11-13 | 564 |
| 57:1 | 595 |
| 57:8, 9 | 331, 334 |
| 60:4 | 378 |
| 62 | 571 |
| 62:2 | 719 |
| 63:1-8 | 556 |
| 63:3 | 138 |
| 65:6-13 | 111 |
| 65:11 | 112 |
| 65:1-4, 6-9, 11-13 | 114 |
| 65:1-5 | 306 |
| 66:1-7 | 381 |
| 66:8-9 | 50 |
| 66:16 | 387 |
| 67 | 385 |
| 68:18 | 211 |
| 68:19 | 610 |
| 68:32-35 | 67 |
| 69:16-17, 29-30, 32-36 | 510 |
| 72 | 230, 374 |
| 72:4 | 620 |
| 72:7 | 224 |
| 72:8 | 374 |
| 72:8-14, 17-19 | 678 |
| 72:15 | 703 |
| 72:17 | 224 |
| 72:18-19 | 7 |
| 73:23-28 | 557 |
| 73:23-24 | 500, 506 |
| 73:24 | 611 |
| 73:25 | 115, 503, 556, 707 |
| 76 | 63 |
| 77:13 | 41 |
| 77:13-20 | 41 |
| 78 | 301 |
| 78:1-7 | 293 |
| 79:8-13 | 417 |
| 79:9 | 473 |
| 80:1-3, 8-9, 16-19 | 279 |
| 82:8 | 294, 375 |
| 83 | 57 |
| 84 | 302, 303, 305 |
| 84:4 | 302 |
| 86:1 | 710 |
| 86:1-11 | 75 |
| 86:11 | 456 |
| 87 | 369 |
| 87:3 | 269 |
| 89:1-4, 28-29, 52 | 101 |
| 89:5, 13-18 | 38 |
| 89:9 | 629 |
| 89:13 | 618 |
| 89:14-18 | 619 |
| 90 | 26 |
| 90:1 | 24, 287 |
| 90:12 | 613 |
| 91 | 78, 566 |
| 91:1-6, 11-12, 14 | 74 |
| 91:4 | 78 |
| 91:5 | 340 |
| 92:1-9, 12-15 | 535 |
| 93 | 60, 64 |
| 94:1-5, 8-13, 17-22 | 46 |
| 94:22 | 551 |
| 95 | 102 |
| 95:1-6 | 19 |
| 95:2 | 312 |
| 96:2-3 | 370 |
| 96:13 | 294 |
| 97 | 59 |
| 98 | 15 |
| 98:4 | 149 |
| 99 | 43 |
| 100 | 1, 62 |
| 102:11 | 609 |
| 102:17-28 | 25 |
| 102:24-27 | 22 |
| 103:1-4 | 72, 97 |
| 103:2 | 50, 337 |
| 103:7 | 72 |
| 103:8 | 519 |
| 103:10-22 | 70 |
| 103:13-18 | 85, 97 |
| 103:20, 22 | 8 |
| 104 | 110 |
| 104:1-2, 3, 5 | 13 |
| 105:39-41 | 269 |
| 107:1-9 | 84 |
| 107:15 | 4 |
| 110 | 229 |
| 113 | 49 |
| 113:3 | 329, 338 |
| 113:5-6 | 31 |
| 114 | 39 |
| 115:1-3, 9-14, 18 | 68 |
| 116:12 | 536 |
| 116:12-19 | 537 |
| 117 | 3, 29 |
| 117:2 | 259 |
| 118:1-9, 17-25 | 512 |
| 118:24 | 321, 323, 326 |
| 118:26 | 130 |
| 119:1 | 447 |
| 119:9-16 | 264 |
| 119:11 | 671 |
| 119:17-24 | 260 |
| 119:18 | 257 |
| 119:24 | 259 |
| 119:33-40 | 451 |
| 119:89-96 | 54 |
| 119:94 | 713 |
| 119:97 | 450 |
| 119:105 | 265 |
| 119:130 | 267 |
| 119:144 | 259 |
| 119:176 | 410 |
| 121 | 82 |
| 121:3 | 340 |
| 122 | 276 |
| 123 | 540 |
| 124 | 514 |
| 125 | 585 |

# INDEX OF SCRIPTURE REFERENCES IN HYMNS

| Reference | Page |
|---|---|
| 125:2 | 275 |
| 126 | 290 |
| 126:3 | 11 |
| 126:6 | 299 |
| 127 | 291 |
| 127:1 | 628 |
| 127:3 | 353 |
| 128 | 626 |
| 130 | 461, 463, 570 |
| 130:1, 4 | 412 |
| 131 | 578 |
| 132 | 100 |
| 132:8 | 100 |
| 133 | 283 |
| 134 | 348 |
| 135:1-7 | 12 |
| 136 | 20, 30 |
| 138 | 76 |
| 138:6 | 661 |
| 139:1-12 | 33 |
| 139:12 | 346, 525 |
| 139:14 | 34 |
| 139:14-24 | 34 |
| 139:23 | 455 |
| 142 | 509 |
| 144:12-15 | 289 |
| 145 | 2 |
| 145:10 | 13, 16 |
| 145:15 | 614 |
| 146 | 53 |
| 147:7-8, 15-18 | 113 |
| 148 | 108 |
| 148:1-6 | 16 |
| 148:1, 7 | 17 |
| 148:1-13 | 105 |
| 149 | 288 |
| 149:2 | 588 |
| 150 | 9 |
| 150:6 | xvi, 5, 17 |

## Proverbs

| 3:6 | 567 |
| 3:24 | 666 |
| 18:24 | 142 |
| 23:26 | 723 |

## Ecclesiastes

| 12:6 | 726 |

## Song of Solomon

| 1:3 | 544 |
| 2:8 | 261 |
| 4:16 | 273 |

## Isaiah

| 1:18 | 465, 690 |
| 2:2 | 272 |
| 6:3 | 42, 90, 343 |
| 6:8 | 691 |
| 9:2 | 123, 373 |
| 9:6 | 163 |
| 11:1 | 153 |
| 11:9 | 236 |
| 25:4 | 427 |
| 26:1 | 277 |
| 26:3 | 590 |
| 28:16 | 268 |
| 32:2 | 177, 427, 719 |
| 35:1-2, 10 | 274 |
| 35:10 | 234, 499 |
| 40:1 | 148 |
| 40:1-5 | 148 |
| 40:11 | 117, 354, 643 |
| 40:28 | 28 |
| 41:10 | 80 |
| 42:3 | 468 |
| 42:16 | 21 |

| 43:1-7 | 80 |
| 43:2 | 497 |
| 44:24 | 134 |
| 45:2 | 384 |
| 47:4 | 83 |
| 48:17 | 488 |
| 48:18 | 587 |
| 51:9 | 372 |
| 51:16 | 675 |
| 52:7 | 379, 670 |
| 53:1-8 | 673 |
| 53:3 | 175 |
| 53:4 | 179, 192, 193, 430 |
| 53:5 | 178, 195, 436 |
| 53:6 | 396 |
| 53:9-10 | 181 |
| 55:6 | 345 |
| 55:7 | 465 |
| 57:15 | 31, 309 |
| 58:13 | 321 |
| 59:19 | 686 |
| 59:20 | 147 |
| 60:1, 3 | 274 |
| 60:2 | 386 |
| 61:1 | 133, 162, 715 |
| 61:1, 2 | 392 |
| 61:1-3 | 224 |
| 61:10 | 439, 589 |
| 63:1 | 228 |
| 63:7 | 138 |
| 66:12 | 587 |
| 66:20 | 298 |
| 66:23 | 320 |

## Jeremiah

| 31:3 | 594 |
| 31:33 | xiv |
| 33:16 | 32 |

## Lamentations

| 3:22, 23 | 27, 328 |
| 5:19 | 22 |

## Ezekiel

| 34:26 | 527, 716 |
| 36:27 | 255 |

## Daniel

| 6:13, 16 | 660 |

## Hosea

| 10:12 | 345 |
| 14:1 | 516 |

## Joel

| 2:28 | 253 |

## Micah

| 5:2 | 152 |
| 7:18 | 71, 311 |

## Habakkuk

| 2:20 | 315 |
| 3:2 | 297 |
| 3:17-18 | 520 |

## Haggai

| 2:7 | 145 |
| 2:8 | xiv |

## Zechariah

| 13:1 | 188, 458, 591 |

## Malachi

| 3:6 | 27 |
| 3:17 | 651 |
| 4:2 | 233, 330, 520 |

## Matthew

| 1:21 | 144, 652 |
| 2:2 | 167 |
| 2:10 | 154 |
| 2:10-11 | 154 |
| 2:11 | 164 |
| 3:12 | 615 |
| 4:4 | 364 |
| 4:19, 20 | 491 |
| 5:14 | 443 |
| 5:16 | 653 |
| 6:10 | 575 |
| 7:7 | 531 |
| 8:20 | 170 |
| 9:13 | 393 |
| 9:36 | 140 |
| 9:38 | 668 |
| 10:7 | 380 |
| 10:29 | 725 |
| 11:19 | 432 |
| 11:28 | 155, 221, 389, 391, 395, 405, 467, 697 |
| 11:28, 29 | 390 |
| 11:30 | 561 |
| 12:8 | 322 |
| 13:23 | 317 |
| 13:39 | 615 |
| 13:46 | 592 |
| 14:27 | 513 |
| 16:18 | 490 |
| 16:24 | 507 |
| 18:11 | 684 |
| 18:20 | 309 |
| 21:5 | 172 |
| 21:9 | 314, 646 |
| 22:37, 39 | 659 |
| 25:6 | 119, 231, 233 |
| 25:40 | 282, 366 |
| 26:30 | 363 |
| 26:39 | 572 |
| 26:41 | 471, 476 |
| 27:45-51 | 134 |
| 27:50 | 196 |
| 27:50-52 | 196 |
| 28:2 | 206 |
| 28:6 | 209 |
| 28:7 | 198 |
| 28:9 | 197 |
| 28:19, 20 | 382 |
| 28:20 | 680, 708 |

## Mark

| 1:32, 34 | 336 |
| 2:17 | 406 |
| 2:27, 28 | 325 |
| 4:28-29 | 615 |
| 4:37-41 | 701 |
| 4:39 | 497 |
| 8:38 | 425 |
| 9:24 | 428 |
| 10:4 | 650 |
| 10:14 | 352 |
| 10:16 | 350, 608 |
| 10:26, 27 | 398 |

| 10:29-30 | 377, 593 |
| 11:7, 8 | 172 |
| 15:34 | 183 |

## Luke

| 1:50 | 621 |
| 1:78 | 120 |
| 1:78, 79 | 330 |
| 2:1-14 | 149, 156, 157, 159, 160, 166, 168, 640, 641 |
| 2:12 | 639 |
| 2:15 | 151 |
| 2:16 | 161 |
| 2:25 | 145 |
| 2:51 | 639 |
| 4:18, 19 | 133, 162 |
| 9:26 | 425 |
| 10:2 | 691 |
| 12:6, 7 | 635 |
| 12:24 | 614 |
| 12:32 | 470 |
| 14:13 | 391 |
| 14:16-24 | 271 |
| 14:33 | 491 |
| 15:2 | 394 |
| 15:7 | 137 |
| 15:18 | 311 |
| 15:21 | 356 |
| 18:13 | 407, 416 |
| 18:16 | 650 |
| 21:27 | 687 |
| 22:19 | 360 |
| 22:31, 32 | 475 |
| 22:39 | 182 |
| 22:44 | 464 |
| 23:42 | 23 |
| 24:26 | 201 |
| 24:27 | 685 |
| 24:29 | 335 |
| 24:32 | 208 |
| 24:36 | 261 |
| 24:47 | 371 |

## John

| 1:4 | 56 |
| 1:10 | 169 |
| 1:14 | 122, 150, 165 |
| 1:29 | 150, 191, 431 |
| 3:14-15 | 422 |
| 4:14 | 221 |
| 4:35 | 668 |
| 6:34 | 256 |
| 6:35 | 549 |
| 6:37 | 405, 406, 431 |
| 6:51 | 310 |
| 6:55 | 358 |
| 6:58 | 361 |
| 6:68 | 220, 419, 722 |
| 7:37 | 221, 440 |
| 8:12 | 221, 504, 679 |
| 9:4 | 496, 728 |
| 9:5 | 296, 713 |
| 9:25 | 679 |
| 10:3 | 694 |
| 10:4 | 505 |
| 10:14 | 644 |
| 10:27 | 296, 713 |
| 11:10 | 642 |
| 12:13 | 173 |
| 12:26 | 552 |
| 13:1 | 453 |
| 14:2 | 128, 214 |
| 14:6 | 116 |
| 14:14 | 533 |
| 14:16-17 | 247 |
| 14:21 | 460 |
| 14:26 | 252, 258 |
| 14:27 | xiv, 316 |
| 15:11 | 549 |
| 15:13 | 433 |

# INDEX OF SCRIPTURE REFERENCES IN HYMNS

| | | |
|---|---|---|
| 15:14 ............142, 664 | 6:20 ...........................649 | **Colossians** |
| 15:15 ......................432 | 9:24-25 ....................480 | |
| 15:16 ........................96 | 10:1-4 .......................364 | 1:9-10 ........................630 |
| 15:26 ......................254 | 10:4 ..........................421 | 1:20 ............................185 |
| 16:13 ......................252 | 10:31 ........................555 | 2:15 ............................202 |
| 17:11 ........................91 | 11:23-26 ..................359 | 3:1 ..............................214 |
| 17:17 ......................468 | 11:26 ........................357 | 3:23 ............................555 |
| 19:28 ......................180 | 12:7-11 ....................252 | |
| 19:30 ......................187 | 13:4 ..........................669 | **I Thessalonians** |
| 20:19 ......................208 | 15:20 ..............199, 204 | |
| 21:17 ......................548 | 15:24-26 ..................300 | 3:15 ............................278 |
| | 15:52 ........................241 | 4:16, 17 ..............240, 727 |
| **Acts** | 15:55-57 ........203, 205, | 4:17 ............................235 |
| | 335, 596 | 5:9-10 ........................708 |
| 1:11 ........................212 | 16:13 ........................477 | |
| 2:17 ........................253 | | **II Thessalonians** |
| 2:24 ........................207 | **II Corinthians** | |
| 2:36 ........................215 | | 3:1 ..............................382 |
| 2:39 ..........351, 353, 648 | 3:18 ..........................460 | 3:3 ..............................658 |
| 3:1 ..........................534 | 4:6 ....................296, 339 | |
| 3:8 ..........................133 | 5:14, 15 ...................536 | **I Timothy** |
| 4:21 ........................667 | 5:20 ..........................695 | |
| 4:24 ........................109 | 5:21 ..........................436 | 1:12 ............................479 |
| 5:31 ........................213 | 6:4, 8 ........................503 | 1:15 ............................702 |
| 7:59-60 ...................489 | 8:9 ....................155, 170 | 1:17 ..............................35 |
| 9:1-7 .......................404 | 9:7 ............................368 | 6:12 ....................479, 484 |
| 10:9 ........................529 | 13:14 ..........................89 | 6:15-16 .......................35 |
| 14:17 ......................614 | | |
| 16:9 ........................383 | **Galatians** | **II Timothy** |
| 20:7 ................324, 327 | | |
| 20:24 ......................262 | 1:3-4 .........................715 | 1:12 ........424, 429, 712 |
| 20:32 ......................632 | 1:4 ............................135 | 2:3 ..............................477 |
| 20:36-38 .................632 | 2:20 ............633, 647, 699 | 3:5 ..............................481 |
| 27:23 ......................494 | 3:28 ..........................285 | 3:16 ............................674 |
| | 3:29 ..........................355 | 4:2 ..............................631 |
| **Romans** | 6:9 ............................496 | |
| | 6:14 ..................186, 704 | **Titus** |
| 1:16 ........................429 | | |
| 3:24 ........................439 | **Ephesians** | 2:13 ............................238 |
| 4:7 ..........................189 | | 2:13-14 ......................681 |
| 5:5 ..........................249 | 1:4 ..............................95 | 3:5 ....................403, 441 |
| 5:8 ..........................184 | 1:6 ............69, 402, 698 | 3:7 ..............................584 |
| 5:18 ........................440 | 1:7 ............................467 | |
| 5:20 ........................705 | 1:12-13 ....................682 | **Hebrews** |
| 6:13 ........................573 | 1:20 ..........................226 | |
| 6:19 ................492, 706 | 2:4-7 .........................401 | 1:3 ..........56, 128, 226 |
| 8:12 ........................600 | 2:8-9 .........................399 | 1:6 ..............................225 |
| 8:14 ........................638 | 2:8-10 .........................95 | 2:9 ..........143, 211, 217 |
| 8:15 ........................245 | 2:20 ..........................270 | 2:14 ............................174 |
| 8:16-17 ...................720 | 2:22 ..........................251 | 2:18 ....................658, 680 |
| 8:19, 22 ..................232 | 3:16 ..........................244 | 3:7-8 ..........................693 |
| 8:22 ........................468 | 3:17-19 ...............73, 121 | 4:7 ..............................388 |
| 8:26 ........................248 | 3:17-21 ....................250 | 4:9 ..............................323 |
| 8:28 ..........................21 | 3:19 ..................453, 542 | 4:14, 16 ....................423 |
| 8:31 ........................470 | 4:4-6 .........................270 | 4:15 ............................517 |
| 8:35 ........................427 | 5:20 ..........................645 | 4:16 ..............88, 518, 530 |
| 8:37 ........................479 | 5:25 ..........................625 | 6:17, 18 ................32, 80 |
| 8:38, 39 ............99, 203, | 6:10-11 ....................482 | 6:19 ............................717 |
| 433, 596 | 6:11 ..........................483 | 7:25 ..........128, 223, 724 |
| 9:5 ..........................132 | 6:13 ..........................478 | 9:11, 12 ....................222 |
| 9:20 ..........................93 | 6:13-18 ....................477 | 9:24 ............................213 |
| 9:21 ........................574 | 6:14 ..........................468 | 9:28 ............................689 |
| 10:13 ......................707 | 6:17 ..........................486 | 10:19-22 ...................313 |
| 11:33 ........................93 | | 10:22 ..........................580 |
| 12:1 ............362, 492, 538 | **Philippians** | 11 ................................281 |
| 12:5 ........................270 | | 11:6 ..............................32 |
| 13:1 ........................623 | 1:6 ..............................99 | 11:13 ..........................605 |
| 13:11 ......................452 | 1:21 ..................209, 437 | 11:36-37 ....................607 |
| 14:8 ........................438 | 2:5-8 ..................158, 169 | 12:1 ............................480 |
| 14:17 ......................246 | 2:9 ............217, 546, 652 | 12:1, 2 ........................454 |
| | 2:9, 10 ........218, 611, 711 | 12:2 ..................139, 194 |
| **I Corinthians** | 2:11 ............................235 | 12:24 ..........................190 |
| | 2:10-11 ......................124 | 13:12-13 ....................184 |
| 1:18 ........................521 | 2:15-16 ......................267 | 13:20-21 ............98, 318 |
| 2:2 ..........................435 | 3:14 ............................452 | |
| 2:9 ..........................231 | 4:4 ..............................226 | **James** |
| 3:9 ..........................631 | 4:6 ..............................533 | |
| 3:11 ................270, 582 | 4:7 ..............................426 | 1:1 ..............................576 |
| 5:7 ..........................365 | 4:11 ............................444 | 5:7 ..............................579 |
| 5:8 ..........................207 | 4:19 ..............................79 | |
| 6:19 ........................255 | | |
| 6:19-20 ............368, 493 | | |

| | |
|---|---|
| **I Peter** | |
| 1:7-8 ..........................118 | |
| 1:8 ..............................545 | |
| 1:18, 19 ............190, 721 | |
| 1:23 ............................468 | |
| 2:2 ..............................676 | |
| 2:7 ....................544, 550 | |
| 2:9 ..................................4 | |
| 2:21-22 ......................171 | |
| 2:24 ............................436 | |
| 4:7 ..............................471 | |
| 4:10 ............................367 | |
| 5:4 ....................485, 692 | |
| 5:7 ............637, 688, 696 | |
| 5:8-9 ..........................483 | |

**II Peter**

| |
|---|
| 1:19 ............................232 |
| 2:9 ..............................475 |
| 3:10 ............................242 |
| 3:18 ............................136 |

**I John**

| |
|---|
| 1:5 ................................23 |
| 1:7 ..............................677 |
| 1:9 ....................411, 430 |
| 2:1 ..............................223 |
| 2:6 ..............................171 |
| 3:1, 2 ........442, 443, 699 |
| 3:24 ............................335 |
| 4:16 ............................460 |
| 4:19 ............96, 362, 397, |
| 547, 654 |

**Jude**

| |
|---|
| 3 ..................................487 |

**The Revelation**

| |
|---|
| 1:5-6 ..................127, 714 |
| 1:7 ....................235, 237 |
| 1:8 ..............................122 |
| 1:18 ..................203, 226 |
| 2:10 ..................284, 489 |
| 3:14, 20 ......................414 |
| 3:21 ............................215 |
| 4:5-11 ..........................87 |
| 4:8 ................................88 |
| 5:9 ..............................683 |
| 5:11, 12 ..........5, 126, 234 |
| 5:12 ............128, 136, 219 |
| 5:13 ..............................18 |
| 6:2 ....................217, 665 |
| 6:14-17 ......................242 |
| 7:13-17 ......................606 |
| 11:15 ..........................300 |
| 12:11 ..........................489 |
| 14:3 ............................714 |
| 14:13 ..........................281 |
| 15:3 ..................106, 709 |
| 19:6 ....................58, 300 |
| 19:12 ..........................216 |
| 19:16 ..........................218 |
| 21:1-4 ........................601 |
| 21:2 ............................662 |
| 21:4 ............................598 |
| 21:10 ..................603, 729 |
| 21:16 ..........................730 |
| 21:18 ..........................604 |
| 21:27 ..................467, 662 |
| 22:4 ..................599, 726 |
| 22:5 ............................730 |
| 22:12 ..........................243 |
| 22:16 ..................167, 434 |
| 22:20 ..........................236 |

# INDEX OF SUBJECTS AND OCCASIONS

**Abiding in Christ.** See also *Christ: Abiding with believers*
Arise, my soul, arise..........223
Beneath the cross of Jesus..177
Blessed Lord, in thee
 is refuge......................420
Dying with Jesus................708
Fill thou my life, O Lord....495
I heard the voice of Jesus....221
I've found a Friend..........433
Jesus, I live to thee..............438
Jesus, Lover of my soul......427
Jesus, merciful and mild....459
No, not despairingly..........411
O little town of Bethlehem 152
Shepherd of souls, refresh..364
Sun of my soul....................346
Thou art my hiding-place 553

**Adoption** ..............442-443

**Adoration.** See also *Christ: Praise of; God: Glory of; Holy Spirit: Glory of*
As with gladness men
 of old..............................154
Immortal, invisible, God.... 35
Jesus, I am resting, resting..139
O that I had a
 thousand voices ............ 11
Praise to the Lord,
 the Almighty .................. 50

**Advent.** See *Christ*

**Adversaries.** See also *Satan*
Faith of our fathers............487
Fear not, O little flock........470
From heaven the Lord........474
How long wilt thou
 forget me .......................541
In thy wrath and hot
 displeasure ....................408
Jesus, lead thou on..............504
Jesus, Lord of life
 and glory ........................472
Judge me, God of
 my salvation ..................539
Now Israel may say............514
O God, no longer hold
 thy peace ........................ 57
O Jehovah, hear my words.. 47
O Lord, how are my
 foes increased................469
To God my earnest voice
 I raise ............................509

**Affliction.** See *Tribulation and Suffering*

**Angels**
A little child the
 Saviour came ..................352
All hail the power..............218
Angels, from the realms
 of glory..........................164
Angel voices, ever singing.. 8
God himself is with us......315
God, that madest earth........344
Hark! ten thousand harps..225
Hark! the herald angels......168
Hark! the voice of love......187
Holy, Holy, Holy................ 87
It came upon the midnight..157
Mighty God, while
 angels bless thee............. 5
My God, how wonderful
 thou art .......................... 31
Now unto Jehovah,
 ye sons .......................... 36
O come, all ye faithful........151
O could I speak the
 matchless worth ............126
O God, we praise thee........ 90
Praise, my soul, the King.. 70
Praise the Lord: ye heavens 16
Praise ye, praise ye
 the Lord .........................108
Round the Lord in glory.... 42
Saviour, breathe an
 evening blessing............340
While shepherds watched..156
Ye holy angels bright.......... 17

**Anniversaries**
Fear not, O little flock........470
God, my King, thy might.... 2
God of our fathers..............616
"Great is thy faithfulness" 27
How firm a foundation...... 80
If we have forgotten
 the Name of our God......515
Let children hear the
 mighty deeds .................293
Lord, thou hast been our
 dwelling-place ...............287
My people, give ear............301
Rejoice, ye people.............. 61
When all thy mercies,
 O my God...................... 5b
Within thy temple, Lord....307

**Anxiety.** See also *Tribulation and Suffering*
As pants the hart................554
Commit thou all thy griefs 560

**Apostasy.** See *Church: Militant, Triumph of*

**Ascension, The.** See *Christ*

**Aspiration.** See *Longing for Christ and God*

**Assurance** ..............580-586
All the way my Saviour
 leads me ........................505
Approach, my soul............423
Be not dismayed................696
Blessed Lord, in thee
 is refuge........................420
By grace I'm saved............399
Call Jehovah thy Salvation 566
Fountain of grace, rich......591
From depths of woe I raise 461
From out the depths I cry ..463
I am trusting thee..............424
I know not why God's
 wondrous grace..............712
I lay my sins on Jesus........430
I'm not ashamed to
 own my Lord................429
Jesus lives, and so shall I....596
Jesus, Lover of my soul......427
Jesus, thy blood................439
My Father is rich..............720
O Lord of hosts,
 how lovely .....................305
O Love that will not
 let me go........................594
Peace, perfect peace..........590
Rock of ages, cleft for me..421
This night, O Lord,
 we bless thee..................349
Thou art my hiding-place..553
Though troubles assail us.... 79
Unto the hills around.......... 82
With grateful heart............ 76

**Atonement.** See *Christ: Atoning Work of, Death of, Suffering of*

**Backsliding**
Come, let us to the Lord....516
Come to the Saviour now....395
Father, again in
 Jesus' Name...................311
God of pity, God of grace ..466
Hark! 'tis the Shepherd's
 voice ..............................684
I was a wandering sheep....396
If we have forgotten the
 Name of our God...........515
O Christ, our true . . .
 Light ..............................296

**Baptism** ..................350-355
See also the references beneath Hymn No. 355

709

# INDEX OF SUBJECTS AND OCCASIONS

**Beauty of Christ or God**
Fairest Lord Jesus.............129
I've found the pearl............592
Majestic sweetness.............143
My God how wonderful.... 31

**Believers.** See *Church: Communion of Saints, Covenant People; Faith in Christ*

**Benevolence.** See *Stewardship*

**Bible.** See *Holy Scriptures*

**Birth of Christ.** See *Christ*

**Blessed Hope.** See also *Christ; Second Coming and Judgment of*
Amazing grace....................402
Blest be the tie...................285
How calm and beautiful the morn.........................209
How vast the benefits divine .............................. 95
I know that my Redeemer lives ..................................586
I need thee, precious Jesus 419
Jesus lives, and so shall I 596
Jesus lives! thy terrors.........203
Jesus, thy Name I love......546
Light of the lonely pilgrim's heart..................232
Lo, God to heaven ascendeth .........................210
Man of Sorrows..................175
O quickly come, dread Judge ..............................243
One Day! ............................689
Spirit, strength of all the weak .........................244
The church's one Foundation ......................270
Trembling soul, beset by fears ................................670
When peace, like a river....580
When the trumpet of the Lord shall sound............727

**Blood.** See *Christ*

**Bondage.** See *Deliverance*

**Bread of Life**
As the sun doth daily rise 329
Bread of the world in mercy ..............................358
Break thou the bread of life ..................................256
Christ Jesus lay in death's strong bands...................207
Come, for the feast is spread ............................391
Every morning mercies new ................................328

Jesus, thou Joy of loving hearts ..............................549
Revive thy work, O Lord....297
Zion, to thy Saviour singing ............................361

**Brevity of Life.** See *Life*

**Brotherly Love.** See *Church: Communion of Saints; Friendship: Christian*

**Burdens.** See also *Forgiveness of Sins; Tribulation and Suffering*
A wonderful Saviour .........675
Beneath the cross of Jesus 177
Cast thy burden on the Lord ..................................559
Come to the Saviour now....395
How gentle God's commands ........................561
What a Friend we have......533

**Calling** ....................404-406
How sweet and awful is the place....................271
In loving-kindness Jesus....672
I've found a Friend............433
Jesus calls us.......................491
Jesus is tenderly calling......697
O Christ, our true . . . Light ..............................296
Praise waits for thee in Zion ..............................306
Revive thy work, O Lord....297
Softly and tenderly.............694
"Though your sins be as scarlet" ...........................465
Today the Saviour calls......388
What though I cannot break my chain..................398

**Chastisement**
Give thanks unto the Lord 512
God the All-terrible: King 617
Great King of nations, hear ..............................621
In thy wrath and hot displeasure ......................408
No longer, Lord, despise me ..................................511
O Lord, thou Judge of all  46

**Cheerfulness.** See also *Peace and Joy*
Father, I know that all my life..............................444
When all thy mercies.......... 51

**Children.** See *Baptism; Children's Hymns; Family Worship; Marriage and the Home*

**Children's Hymns** ..633-662
Anywhere with Jesus..........680
Come, let us sing of a . . . love ..............................669
Come to the Saviour..........693
Fairest Lord Jesus...............129
Golden harps are sounding 213
Holy Bible, book divine....674
I love to tell the story..........387
Low in the grave he lay......206
O little town of Bethlehem 152
Onward, Christian soldiers 490
Safe in the arms of Jesus....608
See, amid the winter's snow ..............................158
Silent night! Holy night....161
The great Physician............144
There is a green hill...........184
We have heard the joyful sound ............................370
When we walk with the Lord ..............................700

**Christ, The Lord Jesus** .................115-243

*Abiding with Believers*
Christ hath a garden..........273
Glorious things . . . are spoken ............................269
Jesus, these eyes have never seen ......................545
Jesus, where'er thy people meet....................309
Jesus, with thy church abide ..............................278
Lord Jesus Christ, be present ............................312
Love Divine.......................460
My faith looks up to thee....454

*Adoration of.* See *Praise of*

*Advent of, First* ..........145-149
See also *Birth of; Incarnation of*
Christ, whose glory fills the skies............................330
Hail to the Lord's Anointed .........................224
Hosanna to the living Lord 314
The people that in darkness ..........................123

*Advent of, Second.* See *Second Coming and Judgment of*

*Advocate.* See *Priestly Intercession of*

*Ascension* .................210-214

*Atoning work of* ........174-176
See also *Death of, Suffering of*
A wonderful Saviour..........675
Alas! and did my Saviour bleed ..............................195

710

# INDEX OF SUBJECTS AND OCCASIONS

**Christ** *(Continued)*
All my heart this night......150
Arise, my soul, arise..........223
Blow ye the trumpet, blow 392
By the cross of Jesus..........185
For ever here my rest..........458
Fountain of . . . grace........440
I hear the Saviour say........690
I will sing of my Redeemer 681
I will sing the . . . story......709
Jesus Christ is risen............198
Jesus, thy blood and
  righteousness ................439
Marvelous grace of . . .
  Lord ..................705
My Jesus, I love thee..........547
O Lord, how shall I
  meet thee......................119
Rock of Ages......................421
The Head that once was
  crowned ........................215
Thy life was given for me 536
Thy works, not mine,
  O Christ ........................441
Weary of earth, and laden 467
What can wash away
  my sin............................677
Who hath believed . . .
  the message....................673

**Birth of** ..................150-168
See also *Advent of; Incarnation*

Away in a manger..............641
Gentle Mary laid her
  Child ............................640
Of the Father's love
  begotten ......................122
Once in royal David's city 639
Thou dost reign on high....170

**Blood of.** See also *Death of; Suffering of*

Arise, my soul, arise..........223
Bread of the world in
  mercy ..........................358
Come, ye sinners................393
For ever here my rest
  shall be..........................458
Glory be to Jesus................190
I hear thy welcome voice....406
Jesus, Master, whose I am 494
Jesus, my great High
  Priest ..........................222
Jesus, thy blood and
  righteousness ................439
Just as I am......................431
Let us love, and sing..........127
Marvelous grace of our
  loving Lord....................705
No, not despairingly..........411
Nor silver nor gold............721
O for a thousand tongues....133
What can wash away
  my sin............................677

**Bridegroom.** See also *Church: Bride of Christ*

Go, labor on: . . . be spent 496
How lovely shines the
  Morning Star..................434
Rejoice, all ye believers......233

**Childhood of**

Once in royal David's city 639

**Comforter**

Come, ye disconsolate........518
Comfort, comfort ye my
  people ..........................148
Jesus, Lover of my soul......427
Jesus, what a Friend
  for sinners....................432
The great Physician now
  is near..........................144

**Compassion of.** See also *Love and Grace of*

At even, when the sun
  was set..........................336
"Come unto me, ye weary" 405
His are the thousand
  sparkling rills................180
Our children, Lord............351
Safe in the arms of Jesus....608

**Conquerer.** See also *Kingly Office of; Resurrection of*

All my heart . . . rejoices....150
Conquering now and still
  to conquer....................665
I belong to Jesus................649
My heart doth overflow......125
O Christ, our hope............120
Ride on! ride on in
  majesty ........................172
Saviour of the nations........165
See, the Conqueror mounts 211
The people that in
  darkness sat..................123
Who is this so weak..........169

**Creator.** See also *Work of Creation*

At the Name of Jesus..........124
Crown him with many
  crowns ........................216
Mighty God, while angels
  bless thee...................... 5
O Christ, our hope, our......120
O Christ, our King,
  Creator ........................134
"Welcome, happy
  morning" ......................199
Wondrous King,
  all-glorious ..................132

**Cross of.** See also *Death of*

Beneath the cross of Jesus 177
Jesus, keep me near the
  cross ............................704

Marvelous grace of our
  loving Lord....................705
O Christ, our King,
  Creator ........................134
Sweet the moments............189

**Crucifixion of.** See *Death of; Cross of*

**Death of** ..................184-196
See also *Atoning Work of; Cross of; Sacrifice of; Suffering of*

**Deity of** ..................122-125
A little child the Saviour 352
Alas! and did my Saviour
  bleed ............................195
Crown his head with
  endless blessing ............130
God rest you merry,
  gentlemen ....................160
Hail, thou once despised
  Jesus ............................128
Hark, the herald angels
  sing ..............................168
Jesus, thy Name I love........546
Majestic sweetness sits
  enthroned ....................143
Mighty God, while angels
  bless thee...................... 5
My Saviour's praises I
  will sing ......................703
O come, all ye faithful......151
O love, how deep, how
  broad ..........................121
O Saviour, precious
  Saviour ........................118
O thou, the Eternal Son
  of God ..........................191
See, amid the winter's
  snow ............................158
Silent night! Holy night....161
"Welcome, happy
  morning" ......................199
When, his salvation
  bringing ......................646
When I survey the
  wondrous cross ..............186
Who is this so weak..........169
Wondrous King,
  all-glorious ..................132
Ye servants of God, your
  Master proclaim............136

**Deliverer.** See *God*

**Epiphany of**

As with gladness men
  of old............................154

**Exaltation of** ..........215-219
Alleluia! . . . Hearts to
  heaven ........................204
Alleluia . . . the strife is
  o'er ..............................201
At the Name of Jesus........124

711

# INDEX OF SUBJECTS AND OCCASIONS

**Christ** *(Continued)*

How lovely shines the Morning Star...................434
Lo, God to heaven ascendeth ........................210
Once in royal David's city 639
Rejoice, the Lord is King 226
Saviour, blessed Saviour....452
See, the Conqueror mounts 211
There is no name so sweet 652
Thou art coming, O my Saviour ..........................235
Who is this so weak and helpless .........................169
Ye servants of God............136

**Example of**

Go, labor on: be spent........496
His are the thousand . . . rills ..................................180
My dear Redeemer and my Lord..........................171
O God of mercy, God of might ................................366
Once in royal David's city 639
Saviour, teach me, day by day.................................654
Take time to be holy..........706
Teach me, O Lord, thy holy way..............................456
The Son of God goes forth 489
There is no sorrow, Lord....517
Through good report, . . . Lord ..................................503

**Foundation of the Church.**
See *Christ: Head of the Church*

**Friend.** See also *Christ: Compassion of, Love and Grace of; God: Compassion of, Love and Grace of*

Dying with Jesus.................708
Fairest Lord Jesus...............129
Here from the world we turn ................................345
How lovely shines the Morning Star....................434
I've found a Friend.............433
Jesus is all the world to me 664
Jesus, priceless treasure......550
Jesus, what a Friend..........432
O Jesus, I have promised....552
O Lord, I would delight in thee................................543
Praise to the Lord, the Almighty ........................... 50
'Tis so sweet to trust in Jesus ................................699
What a Friend we have in Jesus...........................533

**Guide.** See also *Example of; Pilgrimage and Guidance*

I am Jesus' little lamb........643

I am trusting thee, Lord Jesus ................................424
Jesus, high in glory............661
Jesus, merciful and mild....459
Lord Jesus Christ, our Lord most dear..................355
My faith looks up to thee 454
My times are in thy hand....577
Saviour, like a Shepherd lead us..............................644
The whole world was lost 679

**Head of the Church**

Alleluia . . . the strife is o'er ..................................201
Behold! the mountain of the Lord............................272
Christ is made the sure Foundation ......................268
"Christ the Lord is risen" 205
Give thanks unto the Lord 512
Glorious things . . . are spoken ..............................269
Shout for . . . Jesus reigns 298
The church's one Foundation ......................270

**Hiding-Place.** See *Christ: Refuge*

**Humanity of**

At even, when the sun was set..............................336
Behold, a Branch is growing ..........................153
One there is, above all others ..............................142
Once in royal David's city 639
There is no sorrow, Lord....517
"Welcome, happy morning" ..........................199

**Humiliation of.** See also *Life, Ministry and Obedience of*

All praise to thee, Eternal Lord ................................155
At the Name of Jesus........124
Behold, a Branch is growing ..........................153
Come, let us sing of a wonderful love.....................669
From heaven high I come 166
Man of Sorrows..................175
One there is, above all others ..............................142

**Incarnation of.** See *Incarnation*

**Intercession of.** See *Priestly Intercession of*

**Judge.** See *Second Coming and Judgment of*

**Kingdom of.** See also *Christ: Son of David*

Come, thou long-expected Jesus ..............................145

Hark! the song of jubilee 300
Jesus lives, and so shall I....596
Joy to the world..................149
Lord Jesus Christ, our Lord ................................355
My song for ever shall record ............................101
Saviour of the nations, come ..............................165

**Kingly Office of** .........224-230
See also *Christ: Lord*

All glory, laud and honor 173
Alleluia . . . the strife is o'er ..................................201
Angels, from the realms....164
At the Name of Jesus........124
Blessing and honor and glory and power..............219
Christ is coming! let creation ..........................238
Conquering now and still to conquer .....................665
Crown him with many crowns ............................216
Crown his head with endless blessing................130
Day of judgment................241
Golden harps are sounding 213
I am a stranger here...........695
I greet thee who my sure Redeemer art..........135
Jesus shall reign..................374
Lift up your heads, ye mighty gates......................146
Lo! He comes, with clouds 237
Look, ye saints....................217
My heart doth overflow......125
O Christ, our King, Creator .............................134
O could I speak the matchless worth..............126
O Jesus, we adore thee.........193
O quickly come, dread Judge ...............................243
O Saviour, precious Saviour ..........................118
The King shall come...........236
The people that in darkness sat.......................123
Thou art coming, O my Saviour ..........................235
When, his salvation bringing ..........................646
Wondrous King, all-glorious .....................132
Ye servants of God............136

**Lamb of God.** See also *Death of; Suffering of; Lord's Supper*

All glory be to thee, Most High....................... 92
All my heart this night......150

712

# INDEX OF SUBJECTS AND OCCASIONS

**Christ** *(Continued)*
Blessing and honor and glory and power..............219
Blow ye the trumpet, blow 392
Christ Jesus lay in death's strong bands....................207
How bright these spirits....606
I lay my sins on Jesus........430
Jesus Christ, our Lord most holy........................196
Jesus, Master, whose I am 494
Jesus, priceless treasure......550
Just as I am........................431
Man of Sorrows..................175
My faith looks up to thee 454
None other Lamb................115
Not all the blood of beasts 176
We praise thee, O God......634

**Life, The**
I greet thee, who my sure Redeemer art...................135
I need thee, precious Jesus 419
Jesus is all the world to me 664
Jesus, my Saviour, look on me..............................140
None other Lamb................115

**Life, Ministry and Obedience of**
..........................................169-173
At even, when the sun was set..............................336
Fierce was the wild billow 513
Hark, the glad sound..........162
Master, the tempest is raging ..............................701
O love, how deep, how broad ..............................121
One Day!..............................689
Shepherd of tender youth....117
Sing, my tongue, how glorious battle..................194
Tell me the story of Jesus 685
Thou art the Way................116
Thy life was given for me 536
When, his salvation bringing ..........................646

**Light, The**
Christ, whose glory fills the skies..............................330
Come, ye faithful................200
I heard the voice of Jesus 221
Jesus, and shall it ever be 425
Jesus, my Saviour, look......140
Jesus, thou Joy of loving hearts ..............................549
Light of light, enlighten me ..................................333
O Christ, our true and only Light..........................296
O come, all ye faithful........151
O Love that wilt not let me go..............................594

O Splendor of God's glory 56
The Spirit breathes upon the Word..........................258
The whole world was lost 679

**Loneliness of**
O thou, the Eternal Son of God..............................191
Throned upon the awful tree ..................................183
'Tis midnight; and on Olive's brow..................182

**Lord.** See also *Kingly Office of*
All hail the power..............218
Christ shall have dominion 678
"Christ the Lord is risen" 205
I belong to Jesus................649
Jesus, Lord of life and glory ..............................472
Jesus, thy Name I love........546
Light of the lonely pilgrim's heart................232
Lord, keep us steadfast...... 91

**Love and Grace of** ....137-144
See also *Compassion of*

A little child the Saviour came ..................................352
Alas! and did my Saviour bleed ..............................195
All my heart this night........150
All praise to thee, Eternal 155
Come to the Saviour now 395
Come, ye sinners, poor........393
Hark! ten thousand harps 225
I am so glad that our Father in heaven..............647
I greet thee, who my sure Redeemer art...................135
I sought the Lord................397
I will sing of my Redeemer 681
In loving-kindness Jesus came ..................................672
I've found a Friend............433
Jesus is tenderly calling......697
Jesus, Lover of my soul......427
Jesus loves me......................633
Jesus, merciful and mild....459
"Jesus sinners doth receive" ..............................394
Jesus, tender Shepherd, hear ..................................642
Jesus, the very thought......542
Let thy blood in mercy poured ..............................362
Lift up your heads, ye mighty gates......................146
Love Divine..........................460
O Christ, our hope..............120
O could I speak the matchless worth..................126
O Jesus, thou art standing 414
O Lord, how shall I meet 119

O love, how deep, how broad ..............................121
O Love that wilt not let me go..............................594
O sacred Head, now wounded ..........................178
O the deep, deep love of Jesus ..............................453
Saviour, like a Shepherd....644
Tell me the old, old story 521
The Lord's our Rock..........719
Yes, for me, for me he careth ..............................688
Yield not to temptation......658
Zion, to thy Saviour singing ..............................361

**Man of Sorrows**
Behold, a Branch is growing ..............................153
Look, ye saints....................217
Man of Sorrows..................175
My sins, my sins, my Saviour ..............................464
Stricken, smitten..................192
'Tis midnight; and on Olive's brow..................182
Who is this so weak..........169

**Master**
I belong to Jesus................649
Jesus, Master, whose I am 494
Master, the tempest is raging ..............................701
O Jesus, I have promised....552
Onward, Christian soldiers 490
Ye servants of God............136

**Mediator, Only, and Redeemer**
..........................................115-121
See also *Atoning Work of*
All glory, laud, and honor 173
I greet thee, who my sure Redeemer art...................135
Nor silver nor gold............721
Praise, Lord, for thee in Zion ..................................114

**Mercy of.** See also *Life, Ministry and Obedience*
Crown his head with endless blessings ..........................130
O thou from whom all goodness flows................457

**Messiah**
Of the Father's love begotten ..............................122
Stricken, smitten..................192
The people that in darkness sat ..................................123
To us a Child of hope is born ..................................163
While shepherds watched 15

713

# INDEX OF SUBJECTS AND OCCASIONS

**Christ** *(Continued)*

**Miracles of.** See also *Miracles*
Fierce was the wild billow 513
Master, the tempest is raging .................................701

**Name of**

All hail the power...............218
How sweet the Name of Jesus ......................................544
Jesus, the very thought......542
Jesus, thy Name I love.........546
None other Lamb ..................115
O for a thousand tongues....133
O Jesus, we adore thee..........193
O Saviour, precious Saviour ...............................118
The great Physician now is near..................................144
The Head that once was crowned with thorns........215
The Name of Jesus................711
The people that in darkness sat ......................................123
There is no name so sweet 652
Thou hidden source of calm repose......................426
To us a Child of hope is born ..................................163
Ye servants of God...............136

**Nativity of.** See *Birth of*

**Passion of.** See *Death of, Suffering of*

**Passover, Our**

At the Lamb's high feast....365
Zion, to thy Saviour singing .............................361

**Patience of**

O Jesus, thou art standing 414

**Praise of** .................126-136
See also *Praise*

A hymn of glory let us sing ....................................212
All glory, laud, and honor 173
All praise to thee, Eternal Lord ..................................155
Blessing and honor and glory ..................................219
Brightest and best...............167
Crown him with many crowns ..............................216
Glory be to Jesus...................190
Hosanna to the living Lord 314
I've found the pearl.............592
Jesus Christ is risen today 198
Jesus shall reign....................374
Jesus, what a Friend.............432
Mighty God, while angels bless thee............................5

My heart doth overflow......125
O come, all ye faithful.........151
O Saviour, precious Saviour ...............................118
Of the Father's love begotten ...........................122
Praise him! Praise him......683
Praise the Saviour................174
Shepherd of tender youth 117
The great Physician.............144
This is the day the Lord hath made............................326

**Presence of.** See also *Abiding in Christ; Christ Abiding with Believers*

Anywhere with Jesus............680
Come, dearest Lord, descend ...............................250
I need thee every hour.........710

**Priestly Intercession of**
..........................................222-223

Christ Jesus lay in death's strong bands......................207
Golden harps are sounding 213
Hail, thou once despised Jesus ..................................128
I know that my Redeemer lives ..................................586
In the hour of trial.............475
Lord, in the morning thou shalt hear my voice.........332
O the deep, deep love of Jesus ..................................453
Saviour, thy dying love......538
Unto my Lord Jehovah said ....................................229

**Prophetic Office of** ....220-221

**Refuge.** See also *Christ: Rock; God: Refuge*

O wonderful Saviour...........675
Beneath the cross of Jesus 177
Jesus, Lover of my soul......427
Jesus, priceless treasure......550
Jesus, thy Name I love........546
Jesus, what a Friend for sinners ..............................432
Lord Jesus Christ, our Lord most dear.................355
None other Lamb..................115
O safe to the Rock................551
Safe in the arms of Jesus....608
The law of God is good......449
Thou art my hiding-place 553
Thou hidden source of calm ..................................426
Thy works, not mine, O Christ ..................................441
Today the Saviour calls......388
What a Friend we have......426

**Rejected**

Stricken, smitten and afflicted .............................192
Who hath believed................673
Who is this so weak.............169

**Resurrection** .............197-209

Father of peace..................... 98
Jesus lives, and so shall I....596
Praise the Saviour................174

**Rock.** See also *Christ: Refuge*

By the cross of Jesus...........185
Cast thy burden on the Lord ..................................559
For all the saints..................281
Glorious things of thee are spoken.........................269
How sweet the Name of Jesus ..................................544
Jesus, my Saviour, look on me ....................................140
My hope is built...................582
Rock of Ages.........................421
Stricken, smitten..................192
The Lord's our Rock...........719

**Sacrifice of.** See also *Death of*

At the Lamb's high feast....365
Jesus, my great High Priest ..................................222

**Saviour.** See also *Atoning Work of, Suffering of*

Around the throne of God 648
As when the Hebrew prophet ..............................422
I am trusting thee, Lord Jesus ..................................424
I greet thee, who my sure Redeemer art....................135
I've found a Friend.............433
Jesus, and shall it ever be 425
Jesus, the very thought......542
Majestic sweetness sits enthroned .........................143
To God be the glory............667
We have heard the joyful sound ..................................370

**Second Coming and Judgment of** ..................................231-243
See also *Blessed Hope; Christ: Judge*

A hymn of glory let us sing ....................................212
At the Name of Jesus..........124
"For my sake . . . go"...........377
Hark! ten thousand harps 225
Hark! the song of jubilee 300
Jesus may come today.........692
Lift up your heads, pilgrims aweary ..............................687
Lo! what a glorious sight....601

# INDEX OF SUBJECTS AND OCCASIONS

**Christ** *(Continued)*
O Lord, how shall I meet thee ............................119
One Day! ............................689
The Lord will come ............294
Thou dost reign on high....170
When he cometh ................651

**Shepherd.** See also *God: Shepherd*
Ah, holy Jesus, how hast thou offended ....................179
Gracious Saviour . . . Shepherd ............................354
Hark! 'tis the Shepherd's voice I hear .......................684
How bright these glorious spirits shine .....................606
I am Jesus' little lamb .........643
I was a wandering sheep....396
I will sing the story .............709
"Jesus sinners doth receive" ............................394
Jesus, tender Shepherd .........642
O dearest Jesus, what law 181
Saviour, like a Shepherd....644
See Israel's gentle Shepherd ............................350
Shepherd of souls, refresh 364
Shepherd of tender youth 117
There were ninety and nine ................................137
Why should cross . . . grieve me ............................506
Zion, to thy Saviour singing ............................361

**Son of David.** See also *Christ: Kingdom of*
All glory, laud and honor 173
All hail the power ................218
Behold, a Branch is growing ............................153
Hail to the Lord's Anointed ............................224
How lovely shines the Morning Star ...................434
Stricken, smitten ...................192
This is the day the Lord....326
While shepherds watched 156

**Son of God.** See *Deity of*

**Substitute.** See also *Atoning Work of, Death of, Suffering of; Imputation*
Ah, holy Jesus, how hast thou offended ....................179
As when the Hebrew prophet ............................422
I lay my sins on Jesus .........430
O love, how deep, how broad ................................121
O love of God, how strong 73
O mystery of love divine....436

**Suffering of** ..............177-183
According to thy . . . word 360
Hail, thou once despised....128
There is a green hill .............184

**Sympathy of.** See *Compassion of, Love and Grace of*

**Teacher.** See also *Christ: Master*
Father of mercies ..................259
Saviour, teach me, day by day ................................654

**Temptation of**
My dear Redeemer ...............171

**"Triumphal Entry" of**
All glory, laud and honor 173
Hosanna to the living Lord 314
Ride on! Ride on ..................172
When, his salvation bringing ............................646

**Way, Truth and Life, The**
By the cross of Jesus ...........185
Fight the good fight .............484
Lo, God to heaven ascendeth ............................210
Thou art the Way .................116

**Word, The**
At the Name of Jesus ...........124
Break thou the bread of life ................................256
Come, thou Almighty King ................................ 89
Father of heaven, whose love ................................ 88
O come, all ye faithful .......151
O Splendor of God's glory 56
O Word of God Incarnate 267

**Words of.**
See also *Voice of Jesus*
Sing them over again to me ................................722

**Christian Education.**
See also *Schools and Colleges*
How shall the young direct 264
O people blest, whose sons 289
Shepherd of tender youth 117

**Christian Life** ............396-609
See *Table of Contents* for subjects

**Christian Race.** See *Race*

**Christian Service** ....491-496
Angel voices, ever singing 8
Father, I know that all my life ............................444
Fountain of good ..................282
Hark! the voice of Jesus....691

Hark! 'tis the Shepherd's voice I hear .......................684
I love to tell the story .........387
Jesus bids us shine ...............653
O God of mercy, God of might ................................366
O Jesus, I have promised....552
Saviour, thy dying love .......538
"Take up thy cross" .............507
Teach me, my God and King ................................555
Teach me, O Lord thy . . . way ................................456
Work, for the night is coming ............................728

**Christian Warfare** 477-490
See also *Conflict with Sin*
A mighty Fortress is our God ................................ 81
Conquering now and still to conquer ............................665
For all the saints who from their labors rest ...................281
God is my strong Salvation 568
Let our choir new anthems raise ................................284
Lift up your heads, ye gates ................................384
Lord, keep us steadfast ......... 91
Sound the battle cry .............686

**Christians**

**Blessedness of**
Behold th' amazing gift ......442
Blessed are the sons of God ................................443
Blest are the undefiled .........447
Blest the man that fears Jehovah ............................626
Come, ye souls by sin afflicted ............................390
How blest is he whose trespass ............................462
Jesus shall reign ..................374
My Father is rich ..................720
That man is blest who, fearing God ...................446

**Communion of.** See *Church: Communion of Saints*

**Example of**
O God of mercy, God of might ............................366
Through all the changing scenes of life ...................522
Thy loving-kindness, Lord 510

**Triumph of**
Am I a soldier of the cross 481
Blessed Lord, in thee is refuge ............................420
Blow ye the trumpet, blow 392
Children of the heavenly King ............................499

715

# INDEX OF SUBJECTS AND OCCASIONS

**Christians** *(Continued)*
Christian, dost thou see them .................................483
Conquering now...................665
For all the saints..................281
Hark! the sound of holy voices ...............................607
Jerusalem the golden............604
Let our choir new anthems 284
Lo! he comes, with clouds 237
O Jehovah, hear my words 47
Out of my bondage.............715
Praise the Lord: ye heavens ............................... 16
See, the Conqueror mounts 211
Soldiers of Christ, arise......482
Ten thousand times ten thousand ..........................234
We gather together to ask the Lord's blessing...........286
Who are these like stars......602

**Church, The**............268-395
See *Table of Contents* for subjects
See also *Israel; Jerusalem*

**Afflicted**
Lord of our life....................473
O God, no longer hold thy peace ................................ 57
The church's one Foundation ........................270

**Attachment to.** See *Love for*

**Beauty and Glory of**
God is our refuge................. 37
Within thy temple, Lord....307

**Bride of Christ**
My heart doth overflow......125
Wake, awake, for night is flying ................................231

**Children of.** See also *Baptism*
Let children hear the mighty deeds..................293
Shepherd of tender youth....117

**Christ's** ....................268-280

**Christ's Presence in**
Glorious things . . . are spoken ............................269
How sweet and awful is the place...........................271
Jesus, with thy church abide ................................278

**Communion of Saints** ..281-285
A parting hymn we sing....363
Children of the heavenly King .................................499
Christ is made the sure Foundation ......................268

Come, let us join with one accord ...............................323
"For my sake . . . go"..........377
Hark! the sound of holy voices ...............................607
I love thy Kingdom, Lord 280
Soldiers who to Christ belong .............................485
Sweet hour of prayer...........534
Ten thousand times ten thousand ..........................234
The church's one Foundation ........................270
Who are these like stars....602

**Cornerstone of.** See also *Christ: Head of the Church*
Christ is made the sure Foundation ......................268
The church's one Foundation ........................270

**Covenant People** .....286-293
All people that on earth.... 1
Almighty God, thy lofty throne ..............................619
Blessed are the sons of God .................................443
Blest the man that fears Jehovah .........................626
Children of the heavenly King .................................499
Exalt the Lord..................... 12
Glorious things . . . are spoken ............................269
God is our refuge................. 37
Kingdoms and thrones......... 67
My people, give ear, attend 301
Now Israel may say............514
O come, O come, Emmanuel ......................147
Our children, Lord.............351
Stand up, and bless the Lord ................................. 14
The God of Abraham praise ............................. 32
The tender love a father has .................................. 85
Ye righteous . . . rejoice.... 40
Zion, founded on the mountains .......................369
Zion stands by hills surrounded ......................275

**Dedication of**
Arise, O Lord, our God....100
Behold! the mountain of the Lord..........................272
God is our refuge................. 37
Within thy temple, Lord....307

**General Assembly**
Behold! the mountain of the Lord..........................272
Shine thou upon us, Lord 631

**Growth of**
Behold! the mountain of the Lord..........................272
How sweet and awful is the place...........................271
O'er the gloomy hills..........373

**In the Old Dispensation**
Exalt the Lord, his praise 12
O 'twas a joyful sound........276

**Israel of God**
All hail the power...............218
Come, ye faithful................200
Comfort, comfort ye my people ..............................148

**Kingdom of God** ........294-301
Arise, O God, and shine....386
I love thy Kingdom, Lord 280
O God, to us show mercy 385
Ye servants of God.............136

**Lord's House** .............302-310
See also *Lord's Day*
All people that on earth.... 1
All ye that fear Jehovah's Name ................................ 6
Behold! the mountain of the Lord..........................272
Blessed Jesus, at thy word 220
Christ is made the sure Foundation ......................268
Hallelujah! . . . In his temple ............................... 9
O Jehovah, hear my words 47
What shall I render to my God..............................537

**Love for**
I love thy Kingdom, Lord 280
Lord of the worlds above....302
O God of hosts, the mighty .............................303
O Lord of hosts, how lovely ..............................305
O 'twas a joyful sound........276
To thy temple I repair.......313

**Militant.** See also *Christian Warfare*
Lord of our life, and God 473

**Officers of.** See *Ministry*

**Permanence of**
The day thou gavest, Lord 338

**Security of**
Behold! the mountain of the Lord..........................272
Christ hath a garden...........273
Glorious things . . . are spoken ............................269

# INDEX OF SUBJECTS AND OCCASIONS

**Church, The** *(Continued)*
God is the refuge of his saints ...292
How glorious Zion's courts ...277
I love thy Kingdom, Lord 280
Jesus, with thy church abide ...278
Zion stands by hills surrounded ...275

**Triumph of.** See also *Gospel: Triumph of*
Arise, O Lord, our God, arise ...100
Come, let us join with one accord...323
Onward, Christian soldiers 490
Rejoice, ye people... 61
Stand up . . . for Jesus...477
The church's one Foundation ...270
The day thou gavest, Lord 338
We gather together to ask 286

**Unity of.** See also *Unity of Believers*
Arm of the Lord, awake....372
O Christ, our . . . only Light ...296
The church's one Foundation ...270
To thee, our God, we fly....618

**Universality of**
Arm of the Lord, awake....372
Behold! the mountain of the Lord...272
The church's one Foundation ...270
The day thou gavest, Lord 338

**Work of**
Jesus, with thy church abide ...278
O Word of God Incarnate 267

**Close of Worship**..316-319
See also *Lord's Day; Church: Lord's House*
A parting hymn we sing....363
Now blessed be the Lord.... 7

**Colleges.**
See *Schools and Colleges*

**Comfort.**
See also *Consolation; Holy Spirit: Comforter*
Be still, my soul...579
Come, ye souls afflicted...390
He leadeth me...500
In the hour of trial...475
My God and Father, day by day...575

O thou from whom all goodness flows...457
Why should cross . . . grieve me...506

**Comforter.** See *Holy Spirit*

**Coming of Christ.** See *Christ: Advent of*

**Coming to Christ.** See also *Evangelistic; Faith; Repentance*
As with gladness men of old ...154
"Come unto me, ye weary" 405
Come, ye souls afflicted...390
I lay my sins on Jesus...430
Just as I am...431
Out of my bondage...715

**Common Duties and Things**
Can a little child like me thank the Father...645
Father, I know that all my life...444
Father, we thank thee...659
Fill thou my life...495
O happy home...624
Take my life, and let it be consecrated...492
Teach me, my God and King ...555
The wise may bring . . . learning ...657

**Communion.**
See *Lord's Supper; Post Communion*

**Communion of Saints.**
See *Church*

**Communion with Christ and God** ...550-553
See also *Union with Christ*
Christ in his Word draws near ...261
Here, O my Lord, I see thee ...310
How sweet and awful is the place ...271
How sweet the Name of Jesus ...544
I am thine, O Lord...713
I lay my sins on Jesus...430
I need thee every hour...710
In sweet communion, Lord 557
Jesus is all the world to me 664
Jesus, Lover of my soul...427
Jesus, these eyes have never seen ...545
O Jesus, thou art standing 414
O Lord, I would delight....543

Softly now the light of day 347
Sweet the moments...189
Take time to be holy...706

**Compassion.** See *Christ: Compassion of, Love and Grace of; God: Compassion of, Love and Grace of*

**Confession of Christ.**
See *Faith in Christ*

**Confession of Sin.**
See also *Repentance*
Ah, holy Jesus, how hast thou offended...179
From depths of woe I raise 461
From out the depths I cry 463
Great King of nations, hear ...621
How blest is he whose trespass ...462
I was a wandering sheep....396
Not all the blood of beasts 176
Weary of earth, and laden 467

**Confidence.**
See also *Assurance; Trust; Trust in God*
A mighty Fortress... 81
Hallelujah, praise Jehovah 53
How long wilt thou forget 541
Jesus, I am resting...139
My soul in silence waits...571
O Jehovah, hear my words 47
O Lord most high, with all my heart... 44
Saviour, breathe an evening blessing...340
The Lord's my Shepherd... 77
Under the care of my God 78
Ye holy angels bright... 17

**Conflict with Sin** ....468-476
See also *Christian Warfare*
Art thou weary...389
Jesus, my Saviour, look on me...140
Out of my bondage...715
Standing by a purpose true 660
Sweet hour of prayer...534
Who is on the Lord's side 493
Who trusts in God...558
Yield not to temptation...658

**Consecration.**
See also *Gratitude; Stewardship; Submission*
Father, I know that all my life...444
Hark! the voice of Jesus....691
I am thine, O Lord...713
I've found a Friend...433
Jesus, I live to thee...438

717

# INDEX OF SUBJECTS AND OCCASIONS

**Consecration** *(Continued)*
Jesus, I my cross have taken .................593
Jesus, keep me near the cross .................704
Jesus, Master, whose I am 494
Jesus, merciful and mild....459
Let thy blood in mercy poured .................362
Majestic sweetness.............143
More love to thee, O Christ .................548
My Jesus, I love thee...........547
O Love that wilt not let me go.................594
O that I had a thousand voices ................. 11
Saviour, blessed Saviour....452
Take my life, and let it be consecrated.................492
Teach me, O Lord, thy . . . way .................456
The God of Abraham praise ................. 32
We have not known thee....418
What shall I render to my God .................537
When I survey the wondrous cross .................186

**Consolation** .............516-518
See also *Comfort*
Abide with me.................335
All the way my Saviour leads .................505
Art thou weary .................389
Be not dismayed whate'er 696
How calm and beautiful....209
Lord, thy Word abideth....266
O sacred Head, now wounded .................178
Why should I feel discouraged .................725

**Constancy.**
See also *Perseverance*
God, my King, thy might 2
Lord, thou has been our dwelling-place .................287
Through all the changing scenes of life.................522

**Contentment.**
See also *Consolation; Peace and Joy; Submission*·

Come, thou Fount.................400
Father, I know that all my life.................444
Fill thou my life.................495
I'm but a stranger here.........605

My Father is rich.................720
Not haughty is my heart....578

**Conversion.**
See *Faith in Christ; Repentance*

**Cornerstone, Laying of.**
See *Church: Dedication of, Cornerstone of*

**Courage**

Conquering now and still to conquer.................665
Lead on, O King eternal....488
Oft in danger, oft in woe....479
Spirit, strength of all the weak.................244
Stand up, stand up for Jesus .................477
Standing by a purpose true 660

**Covenant of Grace** ..97-101
See also *Church: Covenant People*

All glory be to thee, Most High ................. 92
All praise to God who reigns ................. 4
All ye that fear Jehovah's Name ................. 6
Before Jehovah's awful throne ................. 62
By grace I'm saved.................399
How vast the benefits divine ................. 95
To thee, O Comforter Divine .................252

**Covenant People.** See *Church*

**Creation.** See *Work of Creation*

**Cross.** See *Christ*

**Crown of Life.**
See also *Rewards*

Jesus lives, and so shall I....596
Let our choir new anthems 284
Stand up, my soul.................478
Stand up, stand up for Jesus .................477
"Take up thy cross".................507

**Death.** See also *Funerals*
Anticipated

Abide with me.................335
Work, for the night is coming .................728

Of Children

Around the throne of God 648
I am Jesus' little lamb.........643
Jesus loves me.................633
There is a city bright.........662
When he cometh.................651

**Conquered.** See also *Christ: Resurrection of*

At the Lamb's high feast....365
Guide me, O thou great Jehovah .................501
Hark! the voice of love......187
Jesus lives, and so shall I....596
Jesus, my Saviour, look on me.................140
O Christ, our hope.................120
O come, O come Emmanuel .................147
O quickly come, dread Judge .................243
Praise the Saviour, now.......174
See, the Conqueror mounts 211
There is no night in heaven .................598
What, ye ask me, is my prize .................435

**Trusting God in**

Christ, of all my hopes the ground.................437
He leadeth me.................500
In the hour of trial.................475
My faith looks up to thee....454
O thou from whom all goodness .................457
Rock of Ages.................421
Thou art my hiding-place....553

**Decrees of God**..........93-94
See also *Election; God: Sovereignty of*

Father, I know that all my life.................444
Hallelujah, praise Jehovah 105
Like a river glorious..........587

**Dedication.** See *Church*

**Delay, Danger of**

Come to the Saviour..........693
Come, ye sinners, poor.........393
Comfort, comfort ye my people .................148
Great God, what do I see.....240
Jesus is tenderly calling......697
O Lord, thou Judge of all 46
O wherefore do the nations .................227
Softly and tenderly.................694
That day of wrath.................242
Today the Saviour calls......388

**Deliverance** .............512-515
See also *Christ: Deliverer; God: Deliverer*

Call Jehovah thy Salvation 566
Come, ye faithful.................200
I lay my sins on Jesus.........430
I need thee, precious Jesus 419

718

# INDEX OF SUBJECTS AND OCCASIONS

**Deliverance** *(Continued)*
Jesus, Lord of life and glory .................................472
Master, the tempest is raging ...............................701
Out of my bondage...........715
With grateful heart............. 76

**Depravity.**
See *Confession of Sin; Conflict with Sin; Man: Depravity of*

**Devil.** See *Satan*

**Dignity of Man.** See *Man*

**Discipleship.**
See also *Christian Service*
He leadeth me: O blessed 500
Jesus, merciful and mild....459
Lead on, O King eternal....488
O thou to whose ... sight 525
The Son of God goes forth 489
Through good report, ... Lord .........................................503

**Doubt**
Lord, I believe; thy power I own........................................428
Lord, my weak thought in vain................................... 93
O Lord, thou Judge of all 46

**Doxologies**
All praise to thee, my God 341
Awake, my soul..................331
Now blessed be the Lord.... 7
Praise God, from whom all blessings flow.............xiii

**Education, Christian.**
See *Christian Education*

**Effectual Calling.** See *Calling*

**Election** .........................95-96
See also *God: Decrees of, Sovereignty of*
All praise to God who reigns ...................................... 4
How lovely shines the Morning Star..................434
How sweet and awful ........271
I sought the Lord.................397
Jesus, where'er thy people 309
Shout, for ... Jesus reigns 298
Stand up, and bless the Lord .......................................... 14

**Enemies.** See *Adversaries*

**Eternal Life.** See *Heaven; Life Everlasting*

**Evangelistic.** See also *Coming to Christ; Free Offer of the Gospel; Missions*
I am trusting thee, Lord......424
I need thee every hour........710
I was a wandering sheep....396
Marvelous grace of our loving Lord......................705
Not what my hands have done ..................................403
O happy day..........................589
Pass me not, O ... Saviour 707
Rock of Ages.........................421
Tell me the old, old story....521
There were ninety and nine ....................................137
"Though your sins be as scarlet" ...........................465

**Evening.** See *Lord's Day*

**Example of Christ.**
See *Christ*

**Example of Christians.**
See *Christians*

**Faith.** See also *Assurance; Confidence; Trust*

Confession of
I'm not ashamed to own my Lord..........................429
O happy day..........................589
What shall I render to my God............................537
When thy soldiers take their swords...................486

In Christ ..........................419-432
As when the Hebrew prophet ..............................422
Beneath the cross of Jesus 177
By grace I am an heir........584
Christ, of all my hopes........437
For ever here my rest shall 458
I belong to Jesus..................649
I hear thy welcome voice....406
I heard the voice of Jesus....221
I know not why God's wondrous grace..............712
Marvelous grace of our loving Lord......................705
My faith looks up to thee....454
None other Lamb..................115
Not what my hands have done ..................................403
O safe to the Rock...............551
O thou from whom all goodness flows.................457
Simply trusting every day....682
Soldiers who to Christ belong ...............................485
'Tis so sweet to trust..........699

We sing the glorious conquest ..........................404

**Justification by.** See also *Justification*
From depths of woe I raise 461
I am trusting thee, Lord....424
Lord, like the publican I stand ..................................407
Rock of Ages.........................421
The law of God is good....449

Living by
Behold the Throne of grace ...................................530
Faith of our fathers............487
Father, I know that all my life................................444
I know not why God's wondrous grace..............712
In the hour of trial.............475
Jesus, these eyes have never seen..........................545
My faith looks up to thee 454
O thou from whom all goodness flows.................457
Though troubles assail us 79

Prayer for
Lord, I believe; thy power 428

**Faithfulness.** See also *God: Faithfulness of*
Awake, my soul, and with the sun...............................331
Faith of our fathers............487
Go, labor on: spend............496

**False Gods**
Arm of the Lord, awake......372
From Greenland's ... mountains .........................383
Jehovah reigns; let the earth ................................. 59
Not unto us, O Lord of heaven ................................ 68
Sing to the Lord, sing......... 65

**Family.** See *Church: Covenant People; Christian Education; Family Worship; Marriage and the Home*

**Family Worship.**
See also *Children's Hymns*
A mighty Fortress............... 81
Blest the man that fears Jehovah .............................626
Break thou the bread of life ......................................256
God, that madest earth......344
Gracious Saviour, gentle....354
Happy the home when God is there......................627

719

# INDEX OF SUBJECTS AND OCCASIONS

**Family Worship** *(Continued)*

Holy Bible, book divine....674
Lift up your heads, ye mighty gates......................146
My God, is any hour so sweet ...............................529
Now thank we all our God 86
O happy home.....................624
O people blest.....................289
Shepherd of tender youth....117
The King of Love my Shepherd is.......................141
The Lord's my Shepherd.... 77
Unless the Lord the house shall build........................291
When I survey the wondrous cross...............186

**Farewell Service**............632

Blest be the tie.....................285

**Father.** See *God*

**Fasting**

Christian, dost thou see them ...............................483

**Fear, Cast out**

A debtor to mercy alone...... 99
A mighty Fortress................ 81
Commit thou all thy griefs 560
Fear not, O little flock........470
Fierce was the wild billow 513
Give thanks unto the Lord 512
Good Christian men, rejoice ..............................159
Guide me, O thou . . . Jehovah ............................501
How firm a foundation...... 80
How sweet the Name of Jesus ................................544
Saviour, breathe an evening blessing...............340
Stand up, my soul...............478
The day is past and over....342
There is a land of . . . delight ..............................597
Under the care of my God 78
What a fellowship, what a joy divine......................718
What time I am afraid........564
Who trusts in God..............558

**Fear of God**

All ye that fear Jehovah's Name ................................. 6
Amazing grace, how sweet 402
God is known among his people ............................. 63
Lo! God is here: let us adore ............................308

My God, how wonderful thou art............................... 31
O wherefore do the nations 227
Through all the changing scenes of life....................522
Ye children, come, give ear ...............................656
Ye righteous . . . rejoice.... 40

**Following Christ.**
See *Discipleship*

**Foreordination**

All glory be to thee............. 92
All that I am I owe to thee ............................... 34

**Forgiveness of Sins**
...............................461-467

A few more years shall roll 609
As when the Hebrew prophet ............................422
Come, ev'ry soul by sin oppressed .........................724
Come, ye sinners, poor.......393
Comfort, comfort ye my people ............................148
Father of heaven, whose love ................................ 88
For ever here my rest..........458
God, be merciful to me.......415
God the Lord is king.......... 43
Great God of wonders......... 71
I am so glad that our Father in heaven...............647
I am trusting thee, Lord....424
I lay my sins on Jesus.........430
I was a wandering sheep....396
Jesus, thy blood...................439
Just as I am.........................431
Marvelous grace of our loving Lord......................705
No, not despairingly...........411
Not what my hands have done ..............................403
O thou from whom all goodness .........................457
O thou that hear'st sinners 413
Remember not, O God, the sins..........................417
Rock of Ages.......................421
When peace, like a river....580
When the weary, seeking rest ...............................532

**Forsaking the World**

Here from the world we turn ...............................345
Jesus, I my cross have taken ..............................593
My Jesus, I love thee..........547

**Free Offer of the Gospel** .....................387-395
See also *Evangelistic; Invitation: Missions*
See also the references beneath Hymn No. 395

**Friendship, Christian**

Blest be the tie....................285
How beautiful the sight....283
O God of mercy, God of might ..............................366

**Friendship, Divine.**
See *Christ: Friend*

**Funerals.** See also *Death*

Be still, my soul..................579
Come, ye disconsolate........518
Come, ye thankful people 615
For all the saints who from their labors rest......281
I'm but a stranger here......605
Jesus, I live to thee.............438
My Jesus, as thou wilt........572
O God, the Rock of Ages.... 24
O sacred Head, now wounded ..........................178
Our God, our Help in ages 26
Safe in the arms of Jesus....608
Ten thousand times ten thousand .........................234
The Lord's my Shepherd.... 77
The sands of time are sinking ..............................599

**Future Life.**
See *Life Everlasting*

**Future Punishment.**
See *Christ: Second Coming and Judgment of; Wicked: Punishment of*

**Giving.**
See *Stewardship; Offerings*

**God**

**Abiding Presence of.** See also *Omnipresence*

Abide with me.....................335
God himself is with us........315
He leadeth me.....................500
Lo! God is here...................308
Lo! what a glorious sight 601
Lord of the worlds above....302
O God of hosts, the mighty ............................303
To thee, O Lord, I fly.........581
When Israel out of Egypt went ............................... 39

**All-seeing.** See also *Omnipresence of, Omniscience of*

From heaven the Lord with searching eye..................474

720

# INDEX OF SUBJECTS AND OCCASIONS

**God** *(Continued)*

My trust is in the Lord......... 48
O thou to whose
 all-searching sight..........525

**Being of** ..........................31-32

Bow down thine ear, O
 Lord ................................. 75
Immortal, invisible, God.... 35
Mighty God, while angels
 bless thee......................... 5

**Communion with.** See *Communion with Christ and God*

**Compassion of**

"Great is thy faithfulness" 27
How gentle God's
 commands ......................561
In the land of fadeless day 730
O come, my soul, bless
 thou ................................. 10
O thou my soul, bless God 97
The Lord has heard and
 answered prayer............... 25

**Creator.** See *Work of Creation*

**Decrees of.** See *Decrees of God*

**Defender.** See also *God: Refuge; Protection*

Call Jehovah thy Salvation 566
Like Zion's steadfast
 mount ..............................585
O God, my Strength.............524
O Lord, how are my foes
 increased .........................469
O worship the King............. 13
Our God, our Help in
 ages past......................... 26
Praise to the Lord................. 50
When thy soldiers take
 their swords....................486
Who trusts in God, a
 strong .............................558
Why dost thou stand afar 508

**Deliverer; Christ, Deliverer**
See also *Deliverance*

Fear not, O little flock........470
God is my strong Salvation 568
Guide me, O thou . . .
 Jehovah ..........................501
Jesus, Lover of my soul......427
No longer, Lord, despise
 me ..................................511
O come, O come,
 Emmanuel ....................147
O God, most holy are thy
 ways ............................... 41
O Lord, by thee delivered 526
O Lord, how are my foes
 increased .......................469
Remember not, O God,
 the sins..........................417

To God my earnest voice....509
What a Friend we have......533
When Israel out of Egypt
 went ................................ 39

**Divine Perfections of** .......1-86

**Dwelling-Place.** See also *Christ: Refuge; God: Refuge*

Lord thou has been our
 dwelling-place .................287
O God, the Rock of Ages.... 24

**Eternity of** ........................24-26

Great God, how infinite
 art thou........................... 22
Hast thou not known........... 28
High in the heavens............ 52
My God, how wonderful
 thou ................................ 31
O God, we praise thee......... 90
With glory clad, with
 strength arrayed.............. 64

**Faithfulness of** ................74-86

All praise to God who
 reigns ............................. 4
All ye that fear Jehovah's
 Name ............................. 6
As the sun doth daily rise 329
Be not dismayed whate'er 696
Cast thy burden on the
 Lord ...............................559
Come, thou Fount..............400
Every morning mercies
 new ................................328
For ever settled in the
 heavens .......................... 54
God of our fathers.............616
God the Lord is king..........43
"Great is thy faithfulness" 27
Great King of nations,
 hear ...............................621
Hast thou not known........... 28
Let us, with a gladsome
 mind ............................... 30
My Saviour's praises I
 will sing........................703
My song for ever shall
 record ...........................101
O Lord, be thou my helper 45
O Lord, by thec delivered 526
Praise, my soul, the King.... 70
Praise the Lord: ye
 heavens ........................ 16
The King of Love my
 Shepherd .....................141
The Lord is my Shepherd....663
The praises of thy wonders 38
Thy Word is a lamp to
 my feet..........................671
Zion stands by hills
 surrounded ...................275

**Fatherhood of**

God the Lord is King......... 43
O come, my soul bless thou 10
O God, we praise thee........ 90
O thou my soul, bless God 97
Praise, my soul, the King.... 70
The tender love a father
 has ................................ 85

**Fortress.** See also *Christ: Refuge; God: Refuge; Refuge*

A mighty Fortress............. 81

**Glory of** ...........................1-86
See also *Adoration*

Before thy people I confess 565
Hallelujah, praise Jehovah 105
Praise ye, praise ye the
 Lord ..............................108
The heavens declare thy
 glory .............................104
The heavens declare thy
 glory, Lord....................263
The spacious firmament......103
To God be the glory..........667

**Goodness of** ..................49-53

All people that on earth...... 1
All ye that fear Jehovah's
 Name ............................ 6
Come, thou Fount............400
God, my King, thy might.... 2
I sing the almighty power 106
Lord, I lift my soul to thee 583
O praise the Lord, for he is
 good .............................. 84

**Grace of.** See *Love and Grace of; Grace*

**Greatness of**

Bow down thine ear, O
 Lord ............................... 75
O worship the King............ 13
The heavens declare thy
 glory .............................104
The spacious firmament......103

**Guardian**

Like a river glorious..........587
O God, thou art my God
 alone .............................556
Unless the Lord the house
 shall build.....................291

**Guide.** See also *Pilgrimage and Guidance*

All that I am I owe to thee 34
Dear Lord and Master
 mine .............................576
Fight the good fight............484
Give to our God . . . praise 20
If thou but suffer God to
 guide ............................567
Lead on, O King eternal....488

721

## INDEX OF SUBJECTS AND OCCASIONS

**God** *(Continued)*

Lord, thou hast searched me ................................. 33
O praise the Lord, for he is good............................ 84
The King of Love my Shepherd is...................141
The Lord's my Shepherd.... 77
Thy way, not mine, O Lord 573
We gather together............286
We praise thee, O God, our Redeemer, Creator.... 83

**Holiness of** .................42-43

Day is dying in the west....343
Holy, Holy, Holy................. 87
Lord, in the morning..........332
O God, most holy are thy ways ................................... 41
O God, we praise thee; and confess........................ 90

**Immutability of** ...........27-30

All people that on earth...... 1
All ye that fear Jehovah's Name ................................... 6
Before Jehovah's awful throne ................................ 62
Cast thy burden on the Lord ................................559
Great God, how infinite.... 22
"Great is thy faithfulness" 27
My God, how wonderful thou .................................. 31
O come, my soul, bless thou .................................. 10
The Lord has heard and answered prayer.............. 25
The tender love a father has .................................... 85
With glory clad, with strength arrayed............... 64
Zion stands by hills surrounded .....................275

**Incomprehensibility of.** See also *Mystery of God's Ways*

Angel voices, ever singing 8
Hast thou not known.......... 28
If thou but suffer God to guide thee........................567
My God, how wonderful thou art............................ 31
O Light that knew no dawn ................................ 23
O Love of God, how strong ............................... 73
Ye righteous . . . rejoice.... 40

**Indwelling.** See *Holy Spirit*

**Infinity** ..........................21-23

O love of God, how strong 73

**Jehovah**

Arm of the Lord, awake....372
Call Jehovah thy Salvation 566
Guide me, O thou great Jehovah ..........................501
The God of Abraham praise ................................ 32

**Judge.** See also *Christ: Second Coming and Judgment of*

Come, let us sing unto the Lord........................... 15
Judge Eternal, throned........620
Judge me, God of my salvation ........................539
O Lord most high, with all my heart........................... 44
O Lord, thou Judge of all 46
Sing to the Lord, sing......... 65

**Justice of** ........................44-48

Almighty God, thy . . . throne ..............................619
High in the heavens.......... 52
Stricken, smitten, and afflicted .........................192
The Lord is King!................ 58
The Lord will come and not be slow......................294
The praises of thy wonders 38
Thy mercy and thy truth.... 55
Whate'er my God ordains is right............................... 94

**Keeper of Israel.** See *God: Refuge*

**King.** See also *Majesty of, Sovereignty of*

God the Lord is King......... 43
Hallelujah, praise Jehovah 53
Lead on, O King eternal....488
My Father is rich.................720
Praise, my soul, the King.... 70
The earth, with all that dwell therein.................. 66
The ends of all the earth....295

**Kingdom of.** See *Church: Kingdom of God*

**Love and Grace of** ........69-73
See also *Christ: Compassion of, Love and Grace of; Covenant of Grace; Holy Spirit: Efficacious Grace of*

As when the Hebrew prophet ............................422
Be not dismayed whate'er 696
Come, let us sing of a wonderful love..................669
Ere I sleep, for every favor 337
God sees the little sparrow 635
God the Lord is king......... 43
God, who made the earth....637

If thou but suffer God to guide thee........................567
Jehovah reigns; let earth.... 59
My God, how wonderful thou .................................. 31
Now thank we all our God 86
O bless the Lord, my soul 72
O come, my soul, bless thou .................................. 10
O God, thou art my God alone ...............................556
O thou my soul, bless God 97
Praise to God, immortal....112
The Lord is my Shepherd....663
The tender love a father has .................................... 85
The Lord's my Shepherd.... 77
Thy loving-kindness, Lord 510
Thy might sets fast the mountains .......................111
We plough the fields..........614
We sing the glorious conquest ..........................404
With grateful heart my thanks I bring................. 76
Zion stands by hills surrounded .....................275

**Majesty of.** See also *God: King*

Hallelujah! Raise, O raise 49
My God, how wonderful thou art............................ 31
My soul, bless the Lord......110
Now unto Jehovah, ye sons 36
O worship the King............ 13
Praise the Lord: ye heavens 16

**Mercies of**

Come, thou Fount...............400
Give to our God immortal 20
"Great is thy faithfulness" 27
I waited for the Lord..........523
Let us with a gladsome mind ................................ 30
Lord, I lift my soul............583
My song for ever shall record ..............................101
O bless the Lord, my soul 72
When all thy mercies, O my God............................ 51

**Mercy of.** See also *Love and Grace of, Compassion of*

All ye that fear Jehovah's Name ................................... 6
Before thee, O God, who knowest all......................409
Bow down thine ear............ 75
From depths of woe I raise 461
From out the depths I cry....463
From the depths my prayer 570
God, be merciful to me......415
Hallelujah, praise Jehovah 53

722

# INDEX OF SUBJECTS AND OCCASIONS

**God** *(Continued)*

In thy wrath and hot displeasure ............408
Lord, like the publican........407
O God, to us show mercy....385
O thou my soul, bless God 97
Out of the deep I call........412
Praise Jehovah, all ye nations ................ 29
Praise to the Lord, the Almighty, the King........ 50
Remember not, O God, the sins of long ago............417
The Lord is rich and merciful ............519
Thy mercy and thy truth.... 55
With broken heart and contrite sigh............416
With grateful heart my thanks I bring............ 76

**Name of.** See also *Christ: Name of*

Blest are the undefiled........447
Hallelujah! Raise, O raise 49
Lord, our Lord, thy ... Name ............107
Now unto Jehovah, ye sons 36
O come, my soul, bless thou ................ 10
Stand up, and bless the Lord ................ 14
The God of Abraham praise ................ 32
The Lord has heard and answered prayer............ 25
Thee we adore, eternal Lord ................ 18

**Nearness of**

Angel voices, ever singing 8
From heaven the Lord........474
Throned upon the awful tree ............183

**Omnipotence of**

Before Jehovah's ... throne 62
Come, my soul, thou must be............334
God is our refuge and our 37
The Lord is King! lift up 58
What though I cannot break ............398
With songs and honors sounding loud............113

**Omnipresence of**

Come, my soul, thou must be............334
I sing the almighty power 106
Lord, thou hast searched me ................ 33
The man who once has found ................ 74

**Omniscience of**

Lord, thou hast searched me 33
Softly now the light of day ............347
The Lord is King! lift up 58
To God my earnest voice....509

**Our Strength**

Fear not, O little flock........470
O God, my Strength..........524

**Pity of.** See also *Compassion of; Christ: Compassion of*

God of pity, God of grace 466
God the All-terrible! King 617
Lo! what a glorious sight....601
No longer, Lord, despise me ............511
O thou my soul, bless God 97

**Power of** ............36-41

Arm of the Lord, awake....372
Call Jehovah thy Salvation 566
God, the Lord, a King........ 60
Hast thou not known, hast thou not heard............ 28
I sing the almighty power 106
Jehovah reigns; let earth 59
The God of Abraham praise ................ 32
The spacious firmament......103
When in his might the Lord ............290

**Praise of.** See also *Praise*

All people that on earth.... 1
All praise to God who reigns ................ 4
Angel voices, ever singing.. 8
Awake, my soul............331
Come, thou Fount............400
Exalt the Lord, his praise.... 12
From all that dwell below 3
God, my king, thy might.... 2
God, the Lord, a King........ 60
Hallelujah! In his temple God ................ 9
Hallelujah, praise Jehovah, from the heavens............105
Hallelujah, praise Jehovah, O my soul............ 53
Hallelujah, Raise, O raise 49
How good it is to thank the Lord............535
Mighty God, while angels bless thee............ 5
My soul, bless the Lord......110
Now blessed be the Lord.... 7
O come, let us sing to the.... 19
O God, we praise thee; and 57
O God most high, with all 44
O praise ye the Lord, and sing ............288
Praise God, from whom all xiii

Praise Jehovah, all ye........ 29
Praise, my soul, the King 70
Praise the Lord: ye heavens ............ 16
Praise to the Lord, the Almighty ............ 50
Praise ye, praise ye the Lord ............108
Rejoice, ye people, homage give............ 61
Round the Lord in glory seated ............ 42
Sing to the Lord, sing........ 65
The Lord is King! lift up 58
Thee we adore, eternal Lord ............ 18
Through all the changing scenes of life............522
To God be the glory............667
We praise thee, O God! for the days of our youth......634
Within thy temple, Lord....307
Ye holy angels bright........ 17
Ye righteous, . . . rejoice.... 40

**Presence of.** See *Omnipresence of*

**Providence of.** See also *Fatherhood of, Love and Grace of, Trust in; Harvest and Thanksgiving; Works of Providence*

All praise to God who reigns ................ 4
My people, give ear............301

**Refuge.** See also *Christ: Refuge; Refuge*

God is our refuge and our strength............ 37
God is the refuge of his saints............292
How great the goodness kept ............563
In sweet communion, Lord ............557
Jehovah's perfect law restores the soul............448
My soul in silence waits....571
O God, my Strength and Fortitude ............524
O God, the Rock of Ages 24
O Lord most high, with all my............ 44
O Lord, thou Judge of all 46
Our God, our Help in ages past............ 26
Praise, Lord, for thee in Zion waits............114
The man who once has found abode............ 74
Thy mercy and thy truth.... 55
To thee, O Lord, I fly........581
Under the care of my God 78
Unto the hills around........ 82
Who trusts in God, a strong abode ............558

723

# INDEX OF SUBJECTS AND OCCASIONS

**God** *(Continued)*

**Searcher of Hearts.** See also *Omniscience of; Heart: Searched*
Have thine own way, Lord 574
If we have forgotten the Name of our God..........515
Searcher of hearts..............455

**Shepherd.** See also *Christ: Shepherd*
All people that on earth...... 1
O God, most holy are thy ways .................................. 41
O thou who the Shepherd of Israel art....................279
The King of Love my Shepherd is....................141
The Lord is my Shepherd....663
The Lord's my Shepherd.... 77

**Sovereignty of** ................57-68
See also *God: King, Omnipotence of*
All glory be to thee, Most High...................... 92
All lands, to God in joyful sounds ..............................381
All that I am I owe to thee 34
Almighty God, thy lofty throne.............................619
Christ, by heavenly hosts....623
Come, let us sing unto the Lord........................ 15
Come, sound his praise abroad ..............................102
Commit thou all thy griefs 560
Exalt the Lord, his praise 12
Father, whate'er of earthly 562
God moves in a mysterious way .................................. 21
God of our fathers, whose almighty hand.................616
Hast thou not known.......... 28
How vast the benefits divine ................................ 95
Lord, my weak thought in vain............................... 93
Now unto Jehovah, ye sons............................ 36
O God, we praise thee; and confess...................... 90
O Trinity, most blessed Light ...............................339
The God of Abraham praise ............................. 32
This is my Father's world 109
'Tis not that I did choose 96
Trembling soul, beset by fears .................................670
Whate'er my God ordains 94
When Israel out of Egypt went .................................. 39
Ye righteous, . . . rejoice.... 40

**Truth of** .........................54-56
A mighty Fortress.............. 81
All people that on earth.... 1
Before Jehovah's . . . throne 62

**Unchangeableness of.** See *Immutability of*

**Will of**
My God and Father, day by day................................575
Searcher of hearts.................455
Whate'er my God ordains 94

**Wisdom of** ......................33-35
See also *Omniscience of*

**Word of.** See *Word of God*

**Works of**
All praise to God, who reigns .............................. 4
Bow down thine ear, O Lord ................................ 75
God, my King, thy might.... 2
Let children hear the mighty deeds...................293
My people, give ear, attend ..............................301
Now blessed be the Lord.... 7
O God, most holy are thy ways............................ 41
O Lord most high, with all my heart........................ 44
O praise the Lord, for he is good............................ 84
The praises of thy wonders 38

**Wrath of**
God is known among his people .............................. 63
Jehovah reigns; let the earth be glad.................... 59
My trust is in the Lord........ 48
No longer, Lord, despise me ...............................511
O God, no longer hold thy peace.......................... 57
O Jehovah, hear my words 47
O thou who the Shepherd of Israel art....................279
O wherefore do the nations ..............................227
Unto my Lord Jehovah said ...............................229
Who is this that comes from Edom.......................228

**God's Works of Providence.**
See *Works of Providence*

**Good Works.**
See also *Obedience*
Fill thou my life, O Lord....495
The law of God is good......449
There is a green hill............184

**Gospel.**
See also *Word of God; Free Offer of the Gospel*

**Excellency of**
Father of mercies.................259
God, in the gospel of his Son..............................262
I love to tell the story..........387
Sing them over again to me ...............................722
Tell me the old, old story 521

**Rejection of.** See *Delay: Danger of*

**Spread of.** See *Missions*

**Triumph of.** See also *Church: Triumph of*
All lands, to God in joyful 381
Arm of the Lord, awake......372
Christ shall have dominion 678
Comfort, . . . ye my people 148
Faith of our fathers............487
Fling out the banner..........378
From all that dwell below.. 3
Hail to the brightness.........274
Hark! the song of jubilee....300
It came upon the midnight 157
Jesus shall reign...................374
Jesus, with thy church abide ...............................278
Lift up your heads, ye gates of brass...................384
Light of the lonely pilgrim's heart ...............................232
O praise ye the Lord, and sing a new song...............288
O Spirit of the living God 253
O'er the gloomy hills...........373
Shout, for . . . Jesus reigns 298
Sound the battle cry............686
The ends of all the earth....295
Zion founded on the mountains .......................369

**Grace.**
See also *God: Love and Grace of; Christ: Love and Grace of; Holy Spirit: Efficacious Grace of; Salvation by Grace*

**Converting**
"Come unto me, ye weary" 405
Lord, with glowing heart.... 69
Shout, for the blessed Jesus reigns.....................298

**Covenant of.** See *Covenant of Grace*

**Efficacious.** See *Holy Spirit*

**Fulness of**
By grace I am an heir..........584
By grace I'm saved, grace....399
Fountain of grace, rich......591

724

# INDEX OF SUBJECTS AND OCCASIONS

**Grace** *(Continued)*

Fountain of never-ceasing grace .................................440
God, in the gospel...............262
Great God of wonders......... 71
How great the goodness kept ...................................563
I hear thy welcome voice....406
I know not why God's wondrous grace...............712
Jesus, Lover of my soul......427
Lord, with glowing heart.... 69
My sins, my sins, my Saviour .............................464
Naught have I gotten.........698
With grateful heart my thanks I bring.................. 76

**Magnified**

From depths of woe I raise 461
Marvelous grace of our loving Lord......................705
Wonderful grace of Jesus..702

**Refreshing** ..................519-527

As pants the hart for cooling streams................554
Awake, my soul, in joyful 138
By grace I'm saved................399
Christ hath a garden............273
Every morning mercies new ...................................328
Glorious things of thee are spoken........................269
God be merciful to me........415
How firm a foundation...... 80
Jesus, Lover of my soul......427
O thou who the Shepherd 279
"There shall be showers" 716
Thy mercy and thy truth.... 55
When all thy mercies, O my God........................ 51
When in his might the Lord ...................................290

**Regenerating.** See also *Holy Spirit: Regenerator*

Naught have I gotten.........698

**Sanctifying**

Christ, of all my hopes........437
I need thee, precious Jesus 419

**Saving.** See *Salvation by Grace*

**Sovereign.**

Come, dearest Lord, descend .............................250
I sought the Lord................397
Not what my hands have done ...................................403
We sing the glorious conquest ...........................404

**Gratitude.**
See also *Thankfulness*

Alas! and did my Saviour bleed ...............................195
All people that on earth.... 1
Brightest and best of the sons of the morning........167
Come, thou Fount...............400
Jesus, and shall it ever be....425
Remember not, O God, the sins of long ago.................417
Searcher of hearts, . . . erase ...............................455
When this passing world....600

**Growth in Grace.**
See *Sanctification*

**Guidance.**
See also *Christ: Guide; God: Guide; Holy Spirit: Guide; Pilgrimage and Guidance*

Commit thou all thy griefs 560
How precious is the book 265
How shall the young direct 264
Lord, thy Word abideth......266
Teach me, O Lord, thy . . . way ...................................456

**Happiness.** See also *Joy; Peace and Joy*

Hallelujah! . . . In his temple ............................... 9

**Hardening.** See *Christ: Rejected; Delay: Danger of*

**Harvest and Thanksgiving** .........614-615
See also the references beneath Hymn No. 615

**Harvest and Thanksgiving, Spiritual**

Alleluia! . . . hearts to heaven ...............................204
Come, ye thankful people 615
Far and near the fields........668
Hark! the voice of Jesus....691

**Healing.** See also *Sickness*

Have thine own way, Lord 574
The Lord is rich..................519

**Heart**

**Contrite**

Before thee, God, who knoweth ...........................409
God, be merciful to me......415
In thy wrath and hot displeasure ..........................408
Lord, like the publican......407

O thou that hear'st when sinners cry......................413
With broken heart..............416

**Pure**

O thou that hear'st..............413
Rejoice, ye pure in heart....502

**Searched**

Jehovah's perfect law restores the soul...............448
O thou to whose . . . sight 525

**Surrendered**

"Give me thy heart"..........723
O Jesus, thou art standing 414
Take me, O my Father........410

**Heaven.** See also *Resurrection and the Life Everlasting*

**Anticipated**

Children of the heavenly King ...............................499
Come, we that love the Lord ...................................588
I will sing you a song........729
I'm but a stranger here......605
In the land of fadeless day 730
Jerusalem the golden........604
Lo, God to heaven ascendeth ..........................210
Lo! what a glorious sight....601
Lord of the Sabbath, hear us..............................322
Majestic sweetness..............143
My Jesus I love thee............547
O God, the Rock of Ages..... 24
O Mother dear, Jerusalem 603
Safe in the arms of Jesus....608
Saviour, blessed Saviour....452
The God of Abraham praise ................................ 32
The golden gates are lifted 214
The sands of time are sinking ...............................599
There is a land of pure delight ...............................597
There is no night in heaven ...............................598
Till he come! O let the words linger....................357
Weary of earth, and laden 467
Your harps, ye . . . saints....595

**Christ in.** See *Christ: Exaltation of*

**Home**

I am a stranger here............695
Jesus may come today........692
Soldiers who to Christ belong .............................485

**Kingdom of.** See *Christ: Kingdom of; Church: Kingdom of God*

725

## INDEX OF SUBJECTS AND OCCASIONS

**Heaven** *(Continued)*

*Redeemed in*

Around the throne of God 648
Come to the Saviour............693
Hark! the sound of . . .
 voices .................................607
How bright these . . .
 spirits ..................................606
Lo, God to heaven
 ascendeth .........................210
O could I speak the . . .
 worth ..................................126
Rejoice, all ye believers......233
The golden gates are lifted 214
There is a city bright..........662
When he cometh..................651
Who are these like stars......602
The Head that once was
 crowned with thorns......215
Thou art coming, O my
 Saviour ............................235

*Reunion in*

Be still, my soul....................579
Blest be the tie......................285
For all the saints who . . .
 rest ....................................281
How beautiful the sight....283
I will sing you a song........729
Ten thousand times ten
 thousand ..........................234

*Worship in*

Golden harps are sounding 213
Hark! ten thousand harps 225
My God, how wonderful
 thou art............................. 31
O that I had a thousand
 voices ................................ 11
O worship the King.......... 13
Praise God, from whom all xiii
Praise the Lord: ye heavens 16
Round the Lord in glory.... 42
Saviour, blessed Saviour....452
See, the Conqueror mounts 211
With harps and with viols 714

**Hell.** See also *Christ: Second Coming and Judgment of; Wicked: Punishment of; God: Wrath of*

Alleluia! . . . The strife
 is o'er..................................201
Jesus, my great high priest 222
Onward, Christian soldiers 490
Stand up, my soul................478
"Welcome, happy
 morning" ..........................199

**Holiness, Christian.**
See also *Sanctification*

Lord, who shall come to
 thee ....................................445

Take time to be holy............706
That man is blest who,
 fearing God......................446

**Holiness of God.** See *God*

**Holy Scriptures**......256-267
See also *Law of God*

Holy Bible, book divine....674
How firm a foundation....... 80
I am so glad that our
 Father in heaven..............647
Jesus loves me......................633
Thy Word is a lamp............671
We praise thee, O God......634

*Illumination of*

More about Jesus..................676
Thy Word is like a garden 257

*Infallibility of*

By grace I am an heir..........584
By grace I'm saved..............399

*Sufficiency of*

God, in the gospel of his
 Son ....................................262
Most perfect is the law........450

**Holy Spirit**..............244-255

Holy Spirit, hear us..............638
Hosanna to the living Lord 314

*Anointing of*

Come, O Creator Spirit......251
Hark, the glad sound!........162
Shine thou upon us, Lord 631

*Baptism of*

O Spirit of the living God 253

*Comforter*

All glory be to thee,
 Most High........................ 92
Come, Holy Spirit, come....254
Come, O come, thou . . .
 Spirit ..................................247
Come, O Creator Spirit......251
Come to our poor nature's
 night ..................................248
Come, thou Almighty King 89
Here from the world we
 turn ....................................345
Holy Ghost, dispel . . .
 sadness ..............................246
Lord, keep us steadfast....... 91
Spirit of God, that moved
 of old..................................255
To thee, O Comforter
 Divine ................................252

*Descent of*

This day at thy creating
 word ..................................324
Welcome, delightful morn 325

*Dove*

Gracious Spirit, Dove
 Divine ................................245
Spirit of God, that moved
 of old..................................255
Thou, whose almighty
 word ..................................376
Welcome, delightful morn 325

*Efficacious Grace of*

Amazing grace — how
 sweet ..................................402
Come, for the feast is
 spread ................................391
I sought the Lord..................397
Revive thy work, O Lord....297
To Thee, O Comforter
 Divine ................................252
What though I cannot
 break ..................................398
We sing the glorious
 conquest ............................404

*Grieving the*

Spirit of God, that moved
 of old..................................255
Today the Saviour calls......388

*Guide*

Come, O Creator Spirit
 blest ....................................251
Come to our poor nature's
 night ..................................248
Gracious Spirit, Dove
 Divine ................................245
Lord, in the morning..........332

*Illuminator*

As the sun doth daily rise 329
Blessed Jesus, at thy word 220
Break thou the bread of
 life ......................................256
Come, Holy Spirit, come....254
Gracious Spirit, Dove
 Divine ................................245
Here from the world we
 turn ....................................345
Holy Ghost, dispel . . .
 sadness ..............................246
O Splendor of God's glory 56
Simply trusting every day 682
The Spirit breathes upon
 the Word..........................258
Thou, whose almighty
 word ..................................376

*Indwelling*

Come, dearest Lord,
 descend ..............................250

726

# INDEX OF SUBJECTS AND OCCASIONS

**Holy Spirit** *(Continued)*
Come, Holy Ghost, in love 249
Come, Holy Spirit, come....254
Come, O come, thou . . .
  Spirit .................................247
Holy Ghost, dispel . . .
  sadness .............................246
Spirit of God, that moved
  of old...................................255
Spirit, strength of all the
  weak ...................................244

*Intercessor*
Come to our poor
  nature's night...................248

*Invocation of*
Come, dearest Lord,
  descend .............................250
Come, Holy Ghost, in love 249
Come, Holy Spirit, come....254
Come, O come thou . . .
  Spirit .................................247
Come, O Creator Spirit
  blest ...................................251
Come to our poor
  nature's night...................248
To thee, O Comforter
  Divine ...............................252

*Praise of.* See also *Praise*
Come, O Creator Spirit
  blest ...................................251
To thee, O Comforter
  Divine ...............................252

*Prayers to*
Come, O come thou . . .
  Spirit .................................247
Come to our poor
  nature's night...................248
Gracious Spirit, Dove
  Divine ...............................245
Holy Ghost, dispel . . .
  sadness .............................246
Holy Spirit, hear us............638
O Spirit of the living God 253
Spirit of God, that moved
  of old...................................255
Spirit, strength of all the
  weak ...................................244

*Regenerator*
Come, Holy Spirit, come....254
Come, O come thou . . .
  Spirit .................................247
Come to our poor
  nature's night...................248
Father of heaven, whose
  love ...................................... 88
Holy Ghost, dispel . . .
  sadness .............................246
O Lord our God, arise........375

O Spirit of the living God 253
To thee, O Comforter
  Divine ...............................252

*Teacher*
Come, Holy Spirit, come....254
Come, my soul, thou must
  be waking.........................334
Come, O come, thou . . .
  Spirit .................................247
Come to our poor nature's
  night .................................248
More about Jesus.................676
Spirit, strength of all the
  weak ...................................244
To thee, O Comforter
  Divine ...............................252

*Witness of*
Come, O Creator Spirit
  blest ...................................251
Lord, I hear of showers......527

**Holy Trinity**.................87-92
Alleluia! . . . Hearts to heaven
  and voices raise...............204
Angel voices, ever singing 8
Christ is made the sure
  foundation .......................268
Eternal Father, strong to
  save ...................................629
Hark! the sound of holy
  voices ...............................607
Lord Jesus Christ, be
  present now......................312
Now thank we all our God 86
O day of rest and gladness 321
O Lord our God, arise........375
O Trinity, most blessed
  Light .................................339
Praise God, from whom all xiii
Searcher of hearts...............455
This day at thy creating
  word .................................324
Thou, whose almighty
  word .................................376
To thee, O Comforter
  Divine ...............................252
We praise thee, O God......634

**Home.**
See *Marriage and the Home*

**Home Missions.** See *Missions*

**Hope** ........................539-541
Come, let us to the Lord....516
From out the depths I cry 463
From the depths my prayer 570
"Great is thy faithfulness" 27
Judge Eternal, throned.......620
My hope is built...................582
O thou, the Eternal Son......191

**House of God.**
See *Church: Lord's House*

**Humility.**
See also *Christ: Humiliation of*
Dear Lord and Master
  mine .................................576
Have thine own way, Lord 574
O Light that knew no dawn 23

**Hymns for Informal
Occasions** ...............663-730

**Illumination.**
See *Holy Spirit: Illuminator*

**Imitation of Christ.**
See also *Christ: Example;
Discipleship*
A parting hymn we sing....363
I lay my sins on Jesus.........430
See, amid the winter's
  snow .................................158

**Immanuel.**
See *Christ: Advent of, Birth of*

**Immortality.**
See *Life Everlasting; Resurrection
and the Life Everlasting*

**Imprecatory Psalms**
O God, no longer hold
  thy peace........................... 57
O Jehovah, hear my words 47
O Lord, thou Judge of all 46

**Imputation, of
Righteousness**
A debtor to mercy alone....... 99
By the cross of Jesus
  standing ...........................185
Fountain of . . . grace.........440
Here, O my Lord, I see
  thee ...................................310
Jesus, thy blood and
  righteousness ...................439
My hope is built...................582
O mystery of love divine....436
Praise the Saviour, now......174
There is a green hill............184
Thy works, not mine, O
  Christ ...............................441
Weary of earth, and laden 467
When this passing world....600
Who hath believed after
  hearing .............................673

**Imputation, of Sin**
Ah, holy Jesus, how hast
  thou offended..................179
Alas! and did my Saviour
  bleed .................................195

# INDEX OF SUBJECTS AND OCCASIONS

**Imputation** *(Continued)*
I lay my sins on Jesus........430
Majestic sweetness..............143
Not all the blood of beasts 176
O dearest Jesus, what law 181
O Jesus, we adore thee......193
O mystery of love divine....436
O sacred Head, now
   wounded ..........................178
O thou, the Eternal Son
   of God..............................191
Stricken, smitten..................192
Sweet the moments..............189
Who hath believed after
   hearing the message........673

**Incarnation.** See also *Christ: Advent of, Birth of*
Ah, holy Jesus, how hast
   thou offended....................179
Fountain of . . . grace........440
O Lord, how shall I meet
   thee ..................................119
O love, how deep, how
   broad ................................121
O Word of God Incarnate 267

**Informal Occasions.** See *Hymns for Informal Occasions*

**Inspiration of Scriptures.** See *Holy Scriptures*

**Installations.** See *Ministry: Ordinations*

**Intercession of Christ.** See *Christ: Priestly Intercession of*

**Intercession of Christians.** See *Prayer; Supplications*

**Intercession of the Holy Spirit.** See *Holy Spirit*

**Invitation.** See also *Free Offer of the Gospel*
Come, every soul by sin
   oppressed ........................724
"Come unto me, ye weary" 405
Jesus is tenderly calling
   thee home........................697
Marvelous grace of our
   loving Lord......................705
The Lord is rich and
   merciful ..........................519
Trembling soul, beset by
   fears ................................670
Ye children, come, give
   ear ....................................656

**Invocation.**
See also *Holy Spirit*
Come, thou Almighty King 89

Father of heaven..................88
Lord of the Sabbath,
   hear us..............................322

**Israel.** See also *Church: In the Old Dispensation; Covenant People; Kingdom of God*

*In Canaan*
My people, give ear............301

*In the Desert*
My people, give ear............301
O thou who the Shepherd
   of Israel art......................279
There is a land of pure
   delight ............................597
When Israel out of Egypt
   went ..................................39

*In Exile*
Your harps, ye saints..........595

*Restoration of*
Arm of the Lord, awake......372
From heaven the Lord with
   searching eye..................474
When in his might the
   Lord ................................290

*Salvation of*
Come, ye faithful................200

**Jehovah.** See *God*

**Jerusalem.** See also *Church*
Comfort, comfort ye..........148
Jerusalem the golden..........604
O Mother dear, Jerusalem 603
Rejoice, ye pure in heart....502

**Jesus.** See *Christ: Name of*

**Joy.** See also *Peace and Joy*
All people that on earth......1
Angel voices, ever singing 8
Before Jehovah's . . .
   throne ..............................62
Dear Lord and Master
   mine..................................576
Happy the home when God
   is there............................627
How blest is he whose
   trespass ..........................462
Jesus, I am resting, resting 139
Jesus, the very thought........542
Jesus, thou Joy of loving
   hearts ..............................549
Joy to the world..................149
O could I speak the . . .
   worth ..............................126
O for a thousand tongues....133
Rejoice, the Lord is King....226
Rejoice, ye people, homage 61

The Head that once was
   crowned with thorns......215
Thou art coming, O my
   Saviour ............................235

**Judgment.**
See also *Christ: Second Coming and Judgment of; God: Judge*
God that madest earth........344
Hosanna to the living Lord 314
Jesus, Lord of life..............472
O God, thy judgments give
   the King..........................230

**Justification** ..........439-441
See also *Faith: in Christ, Justification by; Forgiveness of Sins*
Before thee, God, who
   knowest all......................409
Blessed are the sons of
   God ..................................443

**King.** See *Christ: Kingly Office of; God: King*

**Kingdom.**
See *Church: Kingdom of God; Christ: Kingdom of*

**Knowledge**
God is known among his
   people ..............................63
I know not why God's . . .
   grace ................................712
When this passing world 600

**Labor**
God, that madest earth........344
My soul, bless the Lord......110
Work, for the night is
   coming ............................728

**Lamb of God.** See *Christ*

**Law of God**............448-451
See also *Holy Scriptures*
Blest are the undefiled ......447
For ever settled in the
   heavens .......................... 54
Fountain of . . . grace........440
God the Lord is King......... 43
Let us love, and sing..........127
That man is blest who,
   fearing God....................446
Thy servant, blessed by thee,
   shall live........................260

**Life**
*Brevity of.* See also *Death; Harvest and Thanksgiving*
A few more years shall roll 609
Day is dying in the west....343
Hallelujah, praise Jehovah 53

728

## INDEX OF SUBJECTS AND OCCASIONS

**Life** *(Continued)*
I'm but a stranger here......605
Jesus, I my cross have taken ..................593
O come, my soul, bless thou ..................10
O God, the Rock of Ages....24
Our God, our Help in ages past ..................26
Saviour, breathe an evening blessing ..................340
Softly now the light of day 347
Some day the silver cord....726
The Lord has heard and answered prayer..............25
The sands of time are sinking ..................599
The tender love a father has ..................85
Work, for the night is coming ..................728

Christ, The. See *Christ*

Everlasting. See also *Heaven; Resurrection and the Life Everlasting*
Be still, my soul..............579
Ten thousand times ten thousand ..................234
The Lord's my Shepherd....77

Sacredness of
Father, I know that all my life..................444
Fill thou my life, O Lord 495

**Light.** See also *Christ; Holy Scriptures: Illumination of; Holy Spirit: Illuminator*
God, the Lord, a King........60
High in the heavens, Eternal God..................52
Jesus bids us shine..............653
O Light that knew no dawn 23
This is the day of light........327
Thy mercy and thy truth....55

Longing for Christ and God
As pants the hart..............554
Bow down thine ear, O Lord ..................75
Come, Holy Ghost, in love 249
Gracious Spirit, Dove Divine ..................245
Here, O my Lord, I see thee ..................310
His are the thousand sparkling rills ..................180
I am thine, O Lord..............713
I need thee every hour........710
I need thee, precious Jesus 419
In sweet communion, Lord 557

Jesus, high in glory..............661
Jesus, keep me near the cross ..................704
Jesus, merciful and mild....459
Jesus, priceless treasure......550
Jesus, thou Joy of ... hearts ..................549
Light of the lonely pilgrim's heart..................232
Love Divine..................460
More love to thee..................548
My faith looks up to thee 454
None other Lamb..................115
O Lord of hosts, how lovely ..................305
O thou that hear'st when sinners cry..................413
O thou to whose ... sight 525
Open now thy gates of beauty ..................304
Safely through another week ..................320
Saviour, like a Shepherd lead us..................644
Some day the silver cord....726
Take me, O my Father........410
Tell me the old, old story 521
Tell me the story of Jesus 685
Thou dost reign on high....170
We have not known thee....418
Why should cross ... grieve me..................506

Lord, Christ as. See *Christ*

Lord's Day ..............320-349
See also *Close of Worship; Opening of Worship*

Evening ..................335-349

Jesus, Lord, Redeemer........208
Now the day is over..........666

Morning ..................328-334

Holy, Holy, Holy..................87
O Splendor of God's glory 56
When morning gilds the skies ..................131

Lord's House. See *Church*

Lord's Supper ........356-365
See also the references beneath Hymn No. 365

Love
Abiding in Christ's or God's
How lovely shines the Morning Star ..................434
For Christ or God......542-549; 554-557
All the way my Saviour leads ..................505

By the cross of Jesus..........185
Christ, of all my hopes......437
I love to tell the story........387
I was a wandering sheep....396
Jesus calls us..................491
Lord, with glowing heart 69
Majestic sweetness..............143
O God, my Strength..........524
O Jesus, I have promised....552
One there is, above all........142
Saviour, teach me, day by day ..................654
Saviour, thy dying love......538
The Name of Jesus..............711
The wise may bring their learning ..................657
There is a green hill..........184
There is no name so sweet 652
'Tis not that I did choose....96
Why should cross ... grieve me..................506

Of Brethren. See *Friendship: Christian*

Of Christ or God. See *God: Compassion of, Love and Grace of; Christ: Love and Grace of*

For the Church. See *Church*

Prayer for
More love to thee..............548

**Man**

Depravity of. See also *Original Sin*
Blessed Jesus, at thy word 220
God, be merciful to me......415
What though I cannot break my chain..................398

Dignity of
How good it is to thank....535
Lord, our Lord, thy ... Name ..................107
Not unto us, O Lord of heaven ..................68

Marriage and the Home ..................624-628
See also *Baptism; Children's Hymns; Family Worship*
Unless the Lord the house shall build..................291

Martyrs
All hail the power..............218
Faith of our fathers..............487
Fear not, O little flock........470
Hark! the sound of ... voices ..................607
How bright these ... shine 666
Let our choir new anthems 284
O God, we praise thee........90

729

# INDEX OF SUBJECTS AND OCCASIONS

**Martyrs** *(Continued)*
The Son of God goes forth 489
Thee we adore, eternal Lord .................................. 18

**Mary, the Virgin.**
See also *Christ: Birth of*
Jesus Christ, our Lord most holy ........................ 196

**Means of Grace.**
See *Baptism; Lord's Supper; Prayer; Word of God*

**Mediator, Christ as.**
See *Christ: Atoning Work of, Blood of, Priestly Intercession of*

**Meekness.** See *Humility*

**Mercy of God.**
See *God: Love and Grace of; Christ: Compassion of, Love and Grace of*

**Mercy-seat**
Approach my soul ............... 423
Come, ye disconsolate ........ 518
From every stormy wind .... 528
Jesus, where'er thy people 309
My God, how wonderful thou art ............................. 31
Out of the deep I call ........ 412
To thy temple I repair ........ 313

**Millennium**
See *Church: Kingdom, of God; Christ: Kingly Office of*

**Ministry**
Far and near the fields ........ 668
Hark! the voice of Jesus .... 691
I love to tell the story ........ 387
Shine thou upon us, Lord 631

Of Christ. See *Christ: Life, Ministry and Obedience of*

Ordinations ........................ 631
Comfort, . . . ye my people 148
Exalt the Lord, his praise .... 12
"For my sake and the gospel's, go" .................... 377
Fountain of good ................ 282
Go, labor on; spend ............ 496
Lead on, O King eternal .... 488
O God of Bethel ................. 498
O Spirit of the living God 253
Send thou, . . . to every place .............................. 379
Speed thy servants, Saviour 382
Take my life, and let it be consecrated ............... 492
Through good report . . . Lord ................................. 503

When I survey the wondrous cross ................ 186
When thy soldiers take ...... 486
Who is on the Lord's side 493
Ye Christian heralds .......... 380

**Miracles.** See also *Christ*
Jesus Christ, our Lord ........ 196
My people, give ear ............ 301
O Christ, our King, Creator Lord .................... 134
O God, most holy are thy ways .......................... 41
When Israel out of Egypt went ................................. 39

**Missions** .................. 369-386
See also *Free Offer of the Gospel*
Anywhere with Jesus .......... 680
Before Jehovah's . . . throne ............................. 62
Blow ye the trumpet, blow 392
Christ shall have dominion ........................... 678
Come, let us sing unto the Lord ........................... 15
Far and near the fields ........ 668
From all that dwell below the skies ............................. 3
Hail to the brightness ........ 274
Hark! the voice of Jesus .... 691
Jesus shall reign ................. 374
Kingdoms and thrones to God ................................... 67
O God of truth ................... 468
O Spirit of the living God 253
Shout, for . . . Jesus reigns 298
Sing to the Lord, sing ........ 65
The ends of all the earth .... 295
The heavens declare thy glory, Lord ...................... 263
Speed thy servants, Saviour 382

**Missions, Success of.**
See also *Gospel: Triumph of*
Behold! the mountain of the Lord .......................... 272

**Missionaries.** See *Ministry; Missions*

**Morning.** See *Lord's Day*

**Mortality.** See *Life: Brevity of*

**Music**
Angel voices, ever singing 8
Come, let us sing to the Lord our God ................. 15
Golden harps are sounding 213
Hallelujah! . . . In his temple .................................. 9

O could I speak the . . . worth .............................. 126
O praise ye the Lord .......... 288
With harps and with viols 714

**Mystery of God's Ways.**
See also *God: Incomprehensibility of*
God is our refuge and ........ 37
God is the refuge of his saints ............................. 292
God moves in a mysterious way ................................. 21
I know not why God's . . . grace ............................. 712
Lord, my weak thought ...... 93
Thy way, not mine, O Lord ................................. 573

**Mystical Union.**
See *Union with Christ*

**Name.** See *Christ; God*

**National** .................. 616-623
Lift up your heads, ye mighty gates ...................... 146
Onward, Christian soldiers ........................... 490
The ends of all the earth .... 295
The Son of God goes forth 489
Ye righteous . . . rejoice .... 40

**Nativity.** See *Christ: Advent of, Birth of*

**Nature, God in.**
See also *Work of Creation; Works of Providence*
Each little flower that opens ................................ 636
Fairest Lord Jesus .............. 129
Give to our God . . . praise 20
God, the Lord, a King ........ 60
"Great is thy faithfulness" 27
O love of God, how strong 73
O worship the King ............ 13
Praise the Lord: ye heavens ............................. 16
We plough the fields .......... 614
When Israel out of Egypt went ................................ 39
With glory clad, with strength arrayed ............... 64

**Nearness to Christ or God.**
See also *God: Nearness of*
Why should cross . . . grieve me ......................... 506

**Need for Christ or God.**
Come, ye sinners, poor ...... 393
Here, O my Lord, I see thee ................................. 310

# INDEX OF SUBJECTS AND OCCASIONS

**Need for Christ** *(Continued)*
I heard the voice of Jesus....221
I need thee every hour.........710
I need thee, precious Jesus 419
Jesus, and shall it ever be 425
Jesus, Lover of my soul......427
Just as I am..........................431
Lord, I believe; thy power 428
O Lord, I would delight....543
O thou from whom all goodness flows..................457
Sun of my soul.....................346
What, ye ask me, is my prize ................................435

**New Year.** See *Opening and Closing of the Year*

**Oaths.** See *Vows*

**Obedience** ...............444-447
Come, ye souls . . . afflicted .............................390
Dear Lord and Master mine ..................................576
God, in the gospel...............262
God is known among his people ................................63
Hushed was the evening hymn ..................................655
Jesus bids us shine................653
Jesus calls us.........................491
My dear Redeemer and my Lord............................171
Saviour, teach me, day by day .....................................654
"Take up thy cross"............507
Teach me, O Lord, thy . . . way ....................................456
Teach me, O Lord, thy way of truth.....................451
The wise may bring their learning ............................657
When we walk with the Lord ..................................700
Who is on the Lord's side 493
Ye children, come, give ear ......................................656
Yield not to temptation......658

**Obedience of Christ.**
See *Christ: Life, Ministry and Obedience of*

**Offer of Salvation.** See *Free Offer of the Gospel*

**Offerings.** See also *Stewardship*
Brightest and best of the sons of the morning........167
The wise may bring their learning ............................657

**Old Dispensation.**
See *Church in the*

**Opening and Closing of the Year**...................610-613
See also *God: Immutability of; Life, Brevity of; Pilgrimage and Guidance; Protection*

A few more years shall roll 609
My Jesus, as thou wilt........572
My times are in thy hand 577
O God, our Help in ages.... 26
Praise, Lord, for thee in Zion waits........................114
Sometimes a light surprises ..........................520

**Opening of Worship** ...................311-315
See also *Church: Lord's House; Lord's Day: Processionals*

Come, sound his praise......102
Come, thou Almighty King 89
Come, thou Fount...............400
Father of heaven, whose love ................................... 88
O come, let us sing............. 19
O that I had a thousand voices ............................... 11
Stand up, and bless the Lord ................................. 14

**Ordinations.** See *Ministry*

**Original Sin.** See also *Man: Depravity of*
From heaven the Lord with searching eye...................474
O Christ, our King, Creator, Lord....................134
O for a thousand tongues 133
The whole world was lost 679

**Pain.** See also *Tribulation and Suffering*
O God, my Strength and Fortitude .........................524
Thou art my hiding-place 553

**Pardon.** See *Forgiveness of Sins*

**Parents.**
See *Marriage and the Home*

**Passover.** See also *Christ*
The day of resurrection......197

**Pastor.** See *Ministry*

**Patience of Christians**
Christian, seek not . . . repose ..............................471

Father, I know that all my life ..................................444
For ever trusting in the Lord ..................................569
God of pity, God of grace 466
He leadeth me.....................500
If thou but suffer God to guide thee.......................567
Jesus, lead thou on...............504
My soul in silence waits....571
The Son of God goes forth 489
To thee, O Lord, I lift mine eyes ................................540
What'er my God ordains.... 94

**Patriotism.** See *National*

**Pattern.** See *Christ: Example of*

**Peace**
Blest are the undefiled........447
By the cross of Jesus...........185
Fierce was the wild billow 513
God is my strong Salvation .........................568
It came upon the midnight 157
Lord of our life, and God 473
My God, is any hour so sweet ...............................529
O God, thy judgments give 230
Saviour, again . . . we raise ................................316
This is the day of light......327
When peace, like a river....580
While shepherds watched 156

Civil
God the All-terrible! King 617
O God of love, O King......622
To thee, our God, we fly....618

Ecclesiastical
How beautiful the sight....283
Lord of our life, and God 473
O 'twas a joyful sound........276

**Peace and Joy**...........587-592
See also *Cheerfulness; Contentment; Peace*

All the way my Saviour leads me.........................505
Children of the . . . King....499
Christ in his Word draws near ..................................261
Comfort, . . . ye my people 148
Jesus may come today.........692
Jesus, priceless treasure......550
Light of light, enlighten me ...................................333
O people blest, whose sons 289
Rejoice, ye pure in heart....502
Sometimes a light surprises ..........................520

731

# INDEX OF SUBJECTS AND OCCASIONS

**Peace and Joy** *(Continued)*
The day of resurrection.......197
Thou art my hiding-place 553
Thou hidden source of calm repose........................426

**Penitence.** See *Repentance*

**Pentecost.** See *Holy Spirit*

**Persecution.** See *Martyrs*

**Perseverance** ...........593-596
See also *Constancy; Preservation of Christians*

Am I a soldier of the cross 481
Christian, dost thou see them ................................483
Christian seek not . . . repose ................................471
Lord, keep us steadfast...... 91
Oft in danger, oft in woe 479
Rejoice, ye pure in heart....502

**Pilgrimage and Guidance** ..................497-505
See also *Christ: Guide; God: Guide*

Anywhere with Jesus...........680
Art thou weary.....................389
Awake, my soul....................480
Come, my soul, thy suit......531
Come, thou Fount................400
Father, whate'er of . . . bliss ..................................562
Jesus, I my cross have taken ................................593
Lord, I lift my soul to thee 583
O God, thou art my God....556
Saviour, blessed Saviour....452
The God of Abraham praise ................................ 32
Thy servant, blessed by thee ..................................260
What a fellowship, what a joy divine........................718
Your harps, ye . . . saints....595

**Pity.**
See *Christ: Compassion of; God: Compassion of, Pity of*

**Poor.**
See also *Offerings; Poverty*

Father of mercies, in thy Word ................................259
Fountain of good.................282
Hallelujah, praise Jehovah 53
Hallelujah! Raise, O raise 49
Hark, the glad sound...........162
My Jesus, as thou wilt.........572
O bless the Lord, my soul 72
O God, thy judgments give 230
Why dost thou stand afar 508

**Poverty**
My Father is rich..................720
Sometimes a light surprises 520
When the weary, seeking rest ..................................532

**Post Communion**
Christ Jesus lay in death's strong bands....................207
Christ, of all my hopes........437
Father of peace, and God.... 98
God is our refuge................. 37
God is the refuge of his saints ..............................292
Jesus, the very thought of thee ..................................542
Let thy blood in mercy poured ............................362
Love Divine.........................460
O mystery of love divine....436
Praise the Saviour, now......174
The King of Love my Shepherd is.......................141
The Lord's my Shepherd.... 77
With grateful heart............. 76

**Praise.** See also *Christ; God; Holy Spirit*

Before thy people I confess 565
Blessed Jesus, at thy word 220
Fill thou my life..................495
Lord, with glowing heart.... 69
We praise thee, O God, our ..................................... 83

**Prayer** .........................528-534
See also *Supplications; Christ: Priestly Intercession of*

Bow down thine ear, O Lord ................................. 75
Christian, seek not yet repose ............................471
Jesus, high in glory.............661
Jesus, where'er thy people 309
Lord of the Sabbath............322
This night, O Lord, we bless ................................349

**Answered**
No longer, Lord, despise me ..................................511
O Lord, how are my foes increased .........................469
The Lord has heard and answered .......................... 25

**Encouragement in**
Approach, my soul, the mercy-seat ........................423
Behold the Throne of grace ..............................530
Come, my soul, thy suit....531
From every stormy wind....528
What a Friend we have......533

**Examples of.** See *Supplications*

**Power of**
There is no sorrow, Lord, too light........................517

**Times of**
My God, is any hour so sweet ..............................529
Sweet hour of prayer..........534
This is the day of light........327

**Prayers.** See *Supplications*

**Preaching**
"For my sake and the gospel's, go".......................377

**Preparatory Service.** See also *Christ: Atoning Work of, Death of, Suffering of; Repentance*

Bow down thine ear, O Lord ................................. 75
Come, ye disconsolate........518
From depths of woe I raise 461
From out the depths I cry 463
I lay my sins on Jesus........430
Lord, thou hast searched me ................................... 33
My sins, my sins, my Saviour ............................464
None other Lamb................115
O Christ, our hope.............120
O love, how deep, how broad ..............................121
O love of God, how strong 73
Searcher of hearts...............455

**Presence of Christ.** See *Christ*

**Preservation of Christians.**
See also *Perseverance; Protection; Church: Security of*

A debtor to mercy alone.... 99
Come, thou Fount...............400
I am trusting thee, Lord....424
I will sing the . . . story......709
I'm not ashamed to own my Lord............................429
I've found a Friend.............433
Jesus lives! thy terrors now ................................203
Jesus, Lover of my soul......427
Jesus, my great High Priest ..............................222
Lord of our life, and God 473
Lord, thou hast been our dwelling-place ................287
Master, the tempest is raging ..............................701
O God, the Rock of Ages.... 24
O praise the Lord................ 84
Our God, our Help in ages past.......................... 26

# INDEX OF SUBJECTS AND OCCASIONS

**Preservation of Christians**
*(Continued)*
The day is past and over....342
The Lord is my Shepherd....663
The Lord's our Rock..........719
The man who once has
  found abode.................. 74
Though the angry surges
  roll ............................717
Though troubles assail us  79
Under the care of my God  78
Who trusts in God............558
Why should I feel
  discouraged ..................725

**Pride.**  See also *Humility*
O Lord, thou Judge of all  46

**Processionals.** See also *Lord's Day; Opening of Worship*
Before Jehovah's . . .
  throne ........................ 62
Christ is made the sure
  foundation ...................268
Crown him with many
  crowns ........................216
Crown his head with
  endless blessing.............130
Give to our God . . . praise  20
God, the Lord, a King........ 60
O bless the Lord, my soul  72
O come, O come,
  Emmanuel ...................147
Praise, my soul, the King.... 70
Praise to the Lord, the
  Almighty ..................... 50
Rejoice, ye pure in heart....502
The Lord is King! lift up  58

**Profession.** See *Faith in Christ*

**Promises**
Come, ye disconsolate........518
Day of judgment..............241
How firm a foundation...... 80
I heard the voice of Jesus....221
Jesus, merciful and mild....459
My song for ever shall
  record ........................101
O God, thy judgments give 230
O Jesus, I have promised....552
O Lord, be thou my Helper  45
Soldiers who to Christ
  belong ........................485

**Prophecy Fulfilled**
Behold a Branch is
  growing ......................153
Of the Father's love
  begotten .....................122

**Prophets**
Thee we adore, eternal
  Lord .......................... 18

**Prosperity**
Blest the man that fears
  Jehovah ......................626
O people best, whose sons 289

**Protection.**  See also *Preservation; Refuge*
Father, again in Jesus'
  Name .........................311
God of our fathers............616
How sweet the name of
  Jesus .........................544
Kingdoms and thrones to
  God belong.................. 67
Lord, keep us steadfast...... 91
Now the day is over.........666
O Lord, be thou my helper  45
Saviour, breathe an evening
  blessing .....................340
This night, O Lord, we
  bless .........................349
Through all the changing
  scenes ........................522
Thy mercy and thy truth.... 55
Unless the Lord the house
  shall build..................291
Unto the hills around........ 82

**Providence.**
See *Works of Providence*

**Punishment.**
See *Christ: Second Coming and Judgment of; Hell; Wicked*

**Purity**
God, the Lord, a King...... 60
The earth, with all that
  dwell therein................ 66

**Race, The Christian**
Awake, my soul...............480
Fight the good fight..........484

**Recessionals.**  See *Close of Worship; Processionals*

**Reconciliation.**  See also *Forgiveness of Sins*
Arise, my soul, arise.........223
Hark, the herald angels
  sing ..........................168

**Redemption.**  See also *Christ: Atoning Work of*
Nor silver nor gold...........721
There is a fountain...........188

**Reformation Day**
A mighty Fortress............ 81
Before Jehovah's . . .
  throne ........................ 62

Christian, dost thou see......483
Fear not, O little flock........470
How firm a foundation...... 80
If we have forgotten the
  Name of our God...........515
Lord, keep us steadfast...... 91
Our God, our Help in
  ages past..................... 26
Praise the Lord: ye heavens 16
The church's one
  Foundation ..................270
When Israel out of Egypt
  went .......................... 39

**Refuge.**  See also *Christ; God*
Approach my soul, the
  mercy-seat ..................423
Blessed Lord, in thee is
  refuge ........................420
How firm a foundation...... 80

**Regeneration.**
See also *Holy Spirit; Regenerator*
Christ for the world we
  sing ..........................371
Here from the world we
  turn ..........................345
I hear the Saviour say.......690
Shout, for the blessed
  Jesus reigns.................298

**Rejoicing in God.**
See also *Joy; Peace and Joy*
Before thy people I confess 565
Come, let us sing to the
  Lord our God............... 15
I waited for the Lord........523

**Renunciation.**  See *Forsaking the World*

**Repentance** ............407-418
Come, let us to the Lord....516
Father, again in Jesus'
  Name we meet...............311
I am a stranger here.........695
If we have forgotten the
  Name of our God...........515
Not worthy, Lord.............356
There were ninety and
  nine ..........................137

**Resignation.**
See *Patience of Christians*

**Rest**
Come, let us join with one
  accord .......................313
Come, ye souls . . .
  afflicted .....................390
Conquering now..............665
For ever here my rest
  shall be......................458

733

# INDEX OF SUBJECTS AND OCCASIONS

**Rest** *(Continued)*
I heard the voice of Jesus....221
Jesus, I am resting...............139
Jesus, my Saviour, look on me ......140
Now the day is over............666
O day of rest and gladness 321
Some day the silver cord....726
The Lord is rich and merciful .....519
This day at thy creating word ......324
This is the day of light........327
What, ye ask me, is my prize ......435

**Resurrection and the Life Everlasting** ....597-609
*See also Resurrection of Believers*
A wonderful Saviour..........675
Around the throne of God 648
Day of judgment..................241
For all the saints who . . . rest ......281
I will sing you a song........729
In the land of fadeless day 730
Jesus lives, and so shall I....596
Let our choir new anthems 284
Lo, God to heaven ascendeth ......210
Some day the silver cord....726
The God of Abraham praise ...... 32
The golden gates are lifted 214
There is a city bright..........662

**Resurrection of Believers**
Am I a soldier of the cross 481
Christ the Lord is risen......205
Great God, what do I see 240
How calm and beautiful....209
Jesus lives! thy terrors now ......203
Lift up, . . . your voices......202
Lo! He comes, with clouds 237
That day of wrath..................242
"Welcome, happy morning" ......199
When the trumpet of the Lord shall sound..........727
With harps and with viols 714
Thou art coming, O my Saviour ......235

**Resurrection of Christ.**
*See Christ*

**Resurrection of All Men**
Day of judgment..................241
Great God, what do I see....240
Lo! He comes, with clouds 237
That day of wrath..................242

**Reverence**
God himself is with us........315
My God, how wonderful thou art.......... 31

**Revival.** *See also Evangelistic*
Revive thy work, O Lord....297
"There shall be showers"....716
When . . . the Lord arose....290

**Rewards.**
*See also Crown of Life*
Awake, my soul, stretch every nerve..........480
Jesus may come today........692
Let us love, and sing.........127
Look, ye saints, the sight....217
Most perfect is the law....450
My soul in silence waits....571
O God of hosts, the mighty ......303
Soldiers who to Christ belong ......485
The Son of God goes forth to war......489

**Riches.** *See also Prosperity*
The wise may bring their learning ......657
Unless the Lord the house shall build......291

**Rock.** *See Christ; God: Refuge*

**Rulers.** *See also National*
To thee, our God, we fly....618

**Sabbath.** *See also Lord's Day*
A few more years shall roll 609

**Sacraments.**
*See Baptism; Lord's Supper*

**Sacrifice.** *See also Christ: Atoning Work of, Death of, Sacrifice of, Suffering of*
Jesus, I my cross have taken ......593
Light of light, enlighten me ......333

**Saints in Heaven.**
*See also Heaven*
Holy, Holy, Holy.............. 87

**Salvation by Grace** 396-403
*See also Christ: Saviour; Evangelistic; Grace*
A debtor to mercy alone...... 99
All glory be to thee.......... 92

All praise to God who reigns ...... 4
Awake, my soul, in joyful lays ......138
Blow ye the trumpet, blow 392
By grace I am an heir........584
Come, ye sinners, poor........393
From depths of woe I raise 461
How sweet is the place......271
How vast the benefits......... 95
I hear the Saviour say........690
I know that my Redeemer lives ......586
I will sing the . . . story....709
"Jesus sinners doth receive" ......394
Just as I am......................431
Lord, with glowing heart.... 69
Naught have I gotten..........698
Some day the silver cord....726
The law of God is good......449
With broken heart and contrite sigh..........416
Wonderful grace of Jesus 702

**Sanctification** ........452-460
*See also Conflict with Sin; Gratitude; Holiness of Christians; Obedience; Submission; Trust in God; Tribulation and Suffering*
Christ, of all my hopes......437
Father of peace, and God.... 98
Holy Bible, book divine....674
I am thine, O Lord............713
I will sing of my Redeemer ......681
Jehovah's perfect law........448
Lord of the worlds above....302
More about Jesus..............676
O Light that knew no dawn 23
O thou that hearest............414
Revive thy work..................297
There is a city bright..........662
We have not known thee....418

**Satan**
A mighty Fortress.............. 81
Christian, dost thou see them ......483
Christian, seek not yet repose ......471
God rest you merry, gentlemen ......160
Jesus, priceless treasure......550
Let our choir new anthems 284
Lift up, . . . your voices now ......202
Onward, Christian soldiers ......490
Rise, my soul, to watch......476
Though troubles assail us 79

734

# INDEX OF SUBJECTS AND OCCASIONS

**Satan** *(Continued)*
"Welcome, happy morning" ...........................199
When peace, like a river....580

**Schools and Colleges.**
See also *Christian Education*
Lead on, O King eternal....488
Onward, Christian soldiers ............................490
Stand up, . . . for Jesus......477
Take my life, and let it be consecrated ......................492
When I survey the . . . cross ..................................186
When thy soldiers take . . . their swords .....................486
Who is on the Lord's side 493

**Scripture.** See *Holy Scriptures*

**Searcher of Hearts**
All that I am I owe to thee 34
Before thee, God who knowest all........................409
Come, my soul, thou must be waking.........................334

**Seasons.** See also *Harvest and Thanksgiving; Opening and Closing of the Year*
With songs and honors sounding ..........................113

**Second Coming.** See *Christ*

**Security.** See *Preservation*

**Seeking**

*Christ or God Seeking Man*
Come, let us sing of a wonderful love.................669
There were ninety and nine ...................................37
Trembling soul, beset........670

*Man Seeking Christ or God*
Here from the world we turn ..................................345
I think when I read that sweet story of old.............650
The earth, with all that dwell ..................................66

**Self-Denial**
Jesus, I my cross have taken ................................593
"Take up thy cross"..........507

**Self-Examination.** See also *Preparatory Service*
All that I am I owe to thee 34
God, be merciful to me......415

Jehovah's perfect law.........448
We have not known thee....418

**Servants of Christ or God.**
See also *Obedience*
Dear Lord and Master mine .................................576
Exalt the Lord, . . . proclaim ............................12
O Light that knew no dawn 23

**Service for Christ and God.**
See *Christian Service; Discipleship*

**Service to man.** See *Christian Service*

**Shepherd.** See *Christ; God*

**Sickness.** See also *Healing*
His are the thousand . . . rills ..................................180
In the hour of trial............475
Jesus, Lord of life and glory ................................472

**Sin**
Confession of.
See *Confession of Sin*
Conflict with. See *Conflict with Sin; Christian Warfare*

Conviction of
Alas! and did my Saviour bleed ................................195
My sins, my sins, my Saviour ..............................464
The law of God is good......449

Forgiveness of. See *Forgiveness of Sins*

Imputation of. See *Imputation*

Original. See *Original Sin*

Repentance for. See *Repentance*

**Social Justice.** See also *God; Justice of*
Hallelujah, praise Jehovah ............................53
Hallelujah! Raise, O raise 49
Judge Eternal......................620
O God, thy judgment give 230

**Soldiers of Christ.** See also *Christian Warfare; Conflict with Sin*
Jesus, with thy church abide ..................................278
Rejoice, ye people, homage 61

**Sonship.** See *Adoption*

**Sorrow.** See *Tribulation and Suffering*

**Sorrow for Sin.**
See *Repentance*

**Sowing and Reaping**
Almighty God, thy Word is cast................................317
Open now thy gates............304
Sow in the morn thy seed 299
When . . . the Lord arose 290

**Stars**
Day is dying in the west....343
Lord, our Lord, thy . . . Name ...............................107
The heavens declare thy glory ..................................104
The spacious firmament......103

**Steadfastness.** See *Perseverance*

**Stewardship** ...........366-368
Saviour, thy dying love......538
Thy life was given for me 536

**Submission** ............572-579
Father, what'er of earthly bliss ...................................562
If thou but suffer God........567
More love to thee................548
Searcher of hearts..............455
Take me, O my Father........410
Whate'er my God ordains 94
When peace, like a river....580
Your harps, ye . . . saints....595

**Suffering of Christ.**
See *Christ*

**Suffering of Christians.** See *Tribulation and Suffering*

**Supplications.** See also *Prayer; Love: Prayers for*

*General*
As the sun doth daily rise 329
Come, thou Almighty King 89
God of pity, God of grace 466
Jesus, my Saviour, look on me...............................140
Light of light, enlighten me ...................................333

*For Blessings*
Lord, I lift my soul to thee 583
Lord, I hear of showers......527
Sun of my soul....................346
"There shall be showers"....716
To thee, our God we fly......618

735

# INDEX OF SUBJECTS AND OCCASIONS

**Supplications** *(Continued)*

**For the Church**
Jesus, with thy church abide ..................278

**For Deliverance**
Judge me, God of my salvation ..................539
Lord of our life..............473
O thou from whom all goodness ..................457
Why dost thou stand afar 508

**For God's Presence**
Open now thy gates............304
Pass me not, O . . . Saviour 707

**For Guidance**
Jesus, lead thou on..............504
Jesus, Saviour, pilot me......497
O God of Bethel................498

**For Light**
Thou, whose almighty word ..................376

**For Mercy**
Great King of nations, hear ..................621
If we have forgotten the Name of our God....515
Jesus, Lord of life and glory ..................472
O Light that knew no dawn 23

**For Missions**
Far and near the fields........668

**For Peace**
O God of love, O King of peace..............622

**For Protection**
God, that madest earth......344
Jesus, Lover of my soul......427
O Jehovah, hear my words 47
Saviour, breathe a . . . blessing ..................340
The day is past and over....342
To God my . . . voice I raise ..................509

**For Revival**
Revive thy work, O Lord....297

**For Sanctification**
Fill thou my life, O Lord 495
Gracious Saviour, gentle Shepherd ..................354
Jesus, Master, whose I am..494
Jesus, merciful and mild....459
Judge Eternal ..................620
Love Divine ..................460

More love to thee..................548
O Splendor of God's glory 56
O thou to whose . . . sight..525
Teach me, O Lord, thy holy way ..................456
Teach me, O Lord, thy way of truth ..................451

**For Temporal Blessings**
At even when the sun was set ..................336

**For Triumph of the Gospel**
Light of the lonely pilgrim's heart ..................232

**Sympathy of Christ.**
See *Christ: Compassion of; Love and Grace of*

**Sympathy of Christians.**
See also *Love*
Blest be the tie that binds our hearts ..................285

**Teacher.** See *Christ*

**Temperance.** See also *Conflict with Sin*
O people blest, whose sons 289
Soldiers of Christ, arise......482
The earth, with all that dwell therein ..................66
Why dost thou stand afar..508

**Temptation of Christians.**
See also *Conflict with Sin*
O Jesus, I have promised....552
Teach me, O Lord, thy . . . way..................456

**Thankfulness** ........535-538
See also *Gratitude; Harvest and Thanksgiving*
Can a little child like me thank the Father ..................645
Father, we thank thee........659
O bless the Lord, my soul..72
When all thy mercies, O my God..................51

**Throne of Grace.**
See *Mercy-seat*

**Total Depravity.** See *Man: Depravity of*

**Travellers.**
Eternal Father, strong to save..................629
Fierce was the wild billow 513
Holy Father, in thy mercy 630
Peace, perfect peace............590
Your harps, ye . . . saints 595

**Trials.** See also *Temptation of Christians; Tribulation and Suffering*
If thou but suffer God........567
In the hour of trial..........475
O safe to the Rock............551
Thou art my hiding-place 553
What a Friend we have......533
Zion stands by hills surrounded ..................275

**Tribulation and Suffering** ............506-511
Am I a soldier of the cross 481
Art thou weary ..................389
At even, when the sun was set ..................336
Be still, my soul: the Lord is on thy side..................579
Christian, dost thou see them ..................483
God is the refuge of his saints..................292
My Jesus, as thou wilt........572
O thou from whom all goodness flows ..................457
Though the angry surges roll ..................717
Though troubles assail us..79
Whate'er my God ordains..94

**Prayer in**
Our God, our Help in ages past ..................26
Sometimes a light surprises 520

**Trinity.** See *Holy Trinity*

**"Triumphal Entry."**
See *Christ*

**Trouble.** See *God: Refuge; Tribulation and Suffering*

**Trust in God**..........558-571
All the way my Saviour leads..................505
As pants the hart..............554
Be not dismayed whate'er..696
Be still, my soul: the Lord 579
Father, whate'er of . . . bliss ..................562
Fight the good fight..........484
From depths of woe I raise 461
From out the depths I cry 463
Give thanks unto the Lord 512
God is our refuge . . . strength ..................37
God is the refuge of his saints ..................292
God moves in a mysterious way ..................21
God, who made the earth 637

# INDEX OF SUBJECTS AND OCCASIONS

**Trust in God** *(Continued)*

How firm a foundation...... 80
In thy wrath and hot
 displeasure ......................408
Like a river glorious...........587
Lord, my weak thought....... 93
My hope is built....................582
My Jesus, as thou wilt.........572
My times are in thy hand....577
My trust is in the Lord...... 48
O Lord, how are my foes
 increased .........................469
Simply trusting every day..682
Sometimes a light
 surprises ..........................520
The man who once has
 found abode .................... 74
This night, O Lord,
 we bless thee...................349
'Tis so sweet to trust...........699
To thee, O Lord, I fly.........581
Trembling soul, beset
 by fears............................670
What a fellowship .............718
Whate'er my God ordains.. 94
When we walk with
 the Lord ........................700
Why should cross . . .
 grieve me .......................506
Why should I feel
 discouraged ...................725

**Trust.** See also *Faith*

Anywhere with Jesus..........680
God that madest earth........344

**Truth.** See also *Christ: The Way, the Truth and the Life; God: Truth of*

Break thou the bread
 of life................................256
O Lord our God, arise........375
O God of truth....................468

**Unchangeableness** See *God: Immutability of*

**Union with Christ** 433-438

Blessed are the sons
 of God ............................443
Dying with Jesus.................708
Jesus, Master, whose I am 494
O love of God, how strong 73
The church's one
 Foundation ....................270
The Head that once was
 crowned with thorns..... 215
Yes, for me, for me he
 careth .............................688

**Unity of Believers.** See also *Church: Communion of Saints, Unity of*

Blessed are the sons
 of God ............................443

Happy the home when
 God is there.....................627
How beautiful the sight
 of brethren who agree....283
I greet thee, who my sure
 Redeemer art ..................135
O quickly come, dread
 Judge ..............................243

**Vanity of Riches.** See *Riches*

**Victory.** See *Christ: Resurrection of; Christian Warfare; Church: Triumph of; Death Conquered; Soldiers of Christ*

**Virgin Birth.**
See *Christ: Birth of*

**Virgin Mary.**
See *Mary, the Virgin*

**Voice of Jesus**

I am thine, O Lord.............713
I hear thy welcome voice....406
I heard the voice of Jesus..221
Softly and tenderly..............694
Today the Saviour calls......388
Weary of earth,
 and laden ........................467

**Vows**

All ye that fear
 Jehovah's Name ............. 6
God is known among
 his people......................... 63
O God of Bethel.................498
O happy day........................589
What shall I render
 to my God.......................537

**Waiting upon God**

Blessed Lord, in thee
 is refuge .........................420
For ever trusting in
 the Lord..........................569
From out the depths I cry 463
Hallelujah, praise Jehovah 53
Hast thou not known......... 28
To thee, O Lord, I lift.......540

**Walking with God.** See also *Nearness to Christ or God; God: Nearness of*

Fill thou my life, O Lord 495

**Wandering from God.**
See *Backsliding*

**War.** See *Christian Warfare; Conflict with Sin*

**Warning.**
See *Delay; Danger of*

**Watchfulness**

Christian seek not
 . . . repose......................471
Day of judgment................241
Great God, what do I see 240
Rejoice, all ye believers......233
Rise, my soul, to watch......476
"Wake, awake, for night" 231

**Water of Life**

Glorious things . . .
 are spoken ....................269
Guide me, O thou . . .
 Jehovah .........................501
I heard the voice of Jesus 221
Thy mercy and thy truth.... 55

**Way.** See *Christ*

**Wealth.** See *Riches*

**Wedding Hymns.**
See *Marriage and the Home*

**Wicked, Punishment of.**
See also *Christ: Second Coming and Judgment of*

How good it is to thank....535
O Jehovah, hear my words 47
Thy mercy and thy truth.... 55
When this passing world 600
Who is this that comes
 from Edom ....................228

**Will of God.** See *God*

**Witnessing**

Before thy people I confess 565
Go, labor on: spend............496
I love to tell the story........387
I'm not ashamed to own
 my Lord .........................429
Jesus bids us shine..............653
O for a thousand tongues 133
Sing to the Lord, sing........ 65
Standing by a purpose true 660
There is a fountain.......... 188
Through all the changing
 scenes of life..................522

**Word of God.**
See also *Christ; Holy Scriptures*

A mighty Fortress............. 81
Almighty God, thy Word
 is cast like seed..............317
Blessed Jesus, at thy word 220
For ever settled in the
 heavens ......................... 54
O God of truth....................468
Shine thou upon us, Lord 631
The mighty God, the Lord 239

737

# INDEX OF SUBJECTS AND OCCASIONS

**Word of God** *(Continued)*
Through good report . . . Lord .................503
With grateful heart my thanks I bring............ 76

**Work, Christian.**
See *Christian Service; Missions; Obedience*

**Work of Creation** 102-109
See also *Nature: God in*

All people that on earth.... 1
Angel voices, ever singing.. 8
Before Jehovah's . . . throne 62
God, that madest earth......344
God, who made the earth 637
Not unto us, O Lord of heaven .................. 68
O come, let us sing............ 19
Sing to the Lord, sing........ 65

**Works of God.** See *God*

**Works of Providence** .......110-114
See also *Nature, God in*

God sees the little sparrow 635
High in the heavens, Eternal ......................... 52
How gentle God's commands ...................... 561
How good it is to thank....535
Now thank we all our God 86
The heavens declare thy glory .......................104

The heavens declare thy glory, Lord...............263
The man who once has found .................. 74
Though trouble assail us.... 79

**Worship.**
See also *Church: Lord's House; Lord's Day; Close of Worship; Opening of Worship*

Angels, from the realms of glory...........................164
O worship the King............ 13
Sing to the Lord, sing........ 65
Thee we adore, eternal Lord 18

**Wrath of God.**
See *God; Christ: Second Coming and Judgment of*

**Year, Opening and Closing of.** See *Opening and Closing of the Year*

**Yoke of Christ**
Art thou weary....................389
Dear Lord and Master mine .................576

**Youth.** See also *Children*
How shall the young direct 264
My Jesus, I love thee........547
O people blest, whose sons 289

**Zeal.** See also *Consecration; Courage*

Awake my soul, stretch every nerve ................... 480
Christ for the world we sing ...........................371
Go, labor on: spend............496
We sing the glorious conquest .........................404

**Zion.** See also *Church: Lord's House; Israel; Jerusalem*

Arise, O Lord, our God, arise .................100
Arm of the Lord, awake......372
Come, we that love the Lord .................588
Glorious things . . . are spoken .......................269
God the Lord is King......... 43
Hail to the brightness........274
How glorious Zion's courts ..................277
Like Zion's steadfast mount .................585
O 'twas a joyful sound........276
Praise, Lord, for thee in Zion waits .......................114
The mighty God, the Lord 239
Zion, founded on the mountains .......................369
Zion stands . . . surrounded .....................275
Zion to thy Saviour singing ..........................361

738

# INDEX OF HYMNS

| Hymn | | Hymn | |
|---|---|---|---|
| A debtor to mercy alone | 99 | Awake, my soul, stretch every nerve | 480 |
| A few more years shall roll | 609 | Away in a manger | 641 |
| A hymn of glory let us sing | 212 | | |
| A little child the Saviour came | 352 | Be not dismayed whate'er betide | 696 |
| A mighty Fortress is our God | 81 | Be still, my soul: the Lord is on thy side | 579 |
| A parting hymn we sing | 363 | Before Jehovah's awful throne | 62 |
| A Shelter in the Time of Storm | 719 | Before thee, God, who knowest all | 409 |
| A wonderful Saviour is Jesus my Lord | 675 | Before thy people I confess | 565 |
| Abide with me: fast falls the eventide | 335 | Behold, a Branch is growing | 153 |
| According to thy gracious word | 360 | Behold th' amazing gift of love | 442 |
| Ah, holy Jesus, how hast thou offended | 179 | Behold! the mountain of the Lord | 272 |
| Alas! and did my Saviour bleed | 195 | Behold the Throne of grace | 530 |
| All glory be to thee, Most High | 92 | Beneath the cross of Jesus | 177 |
| All glory, laud, and honor to thee | 173 | Blessed are the sons of God | 443 |
| All hail the power of Jesus' Name | 218 | Blessed Jesus, at thy word | 220 |
| All lands, to God in joyful sounds | 381 | Blessed Lord, in thee is refuge | 420 |
| All my heart this night rejoices | 150 | Blessing and honor and glory and power | 219 |
| All people that on earth do dwell | 1 | Blest are the undefiled in heart | 447 |
| All praise to God, who reigns above | 4 | Blest be the tie that binds our hearts | 285 |
| All praise to thee, Eternal Lord | 155 | Blest the man that fears Jehovah | 626 |
| All praise to thee, my God, this night | 341 | Blow ye the trumpet, blow | 392 |
| All that I am I owe to thee | 34 | Bow down thine ear, O Lord, and hear | 75 |
| All the way my Saviour leads me | 505 | Bread of the world in mercy broken | 358 |
| All Things Bright and Beautiful | 636 | Break thou the bread of life | 256 |
| All things come of Thee, O Lord | xiv | Brightest and best of the sons | |
| All ye that fear Jehovah's Name | 6 | of the morning | 167 |
| Alleluia! . . . hearts to heaven | 204 | Bring Them In | 684 |
| Alleluia . . . the strife is o'er | 201 | By grace I am an heir of heaven | 584 |
| Almighty God, thy lofty throne | 619 | By grace I'm saved | 399 |
| Almighty God, thy Word is cast like seed | 317 | By the cross of Jesus standing | 185 |
| Am I a soldier of the cross | 481 | | |
| Amazing grace—how sweet the sound | 402 | Call Jehovah thy Salvation | 566 |
| Angel voices, ever singing | 8 | Can a little child like me thank the Father | 645 |
| Angels, from the realms of glory | 164 | Cast thy burden on the Lord | 559 |
| Anywhere with Jesus I can safely go | 680 | Children of the heavenly King | 499 |
| Approach, my soul, the mercy-seat | 423 | Christ, by heavenly hosts adored | 623 |
| Arise, my soul, arise | 223 | Christ for the world we sing | 371 |
| Arise, O God, and shine | 386 | Christ hath a garden walled around | 273 |
| Arise, O Lord, our God, arise | 100 | Christ in his Word draws near | 261 |
| Arm of the Lord, awake, awake | 372 | Christ is coming! let creation | 238 |
| Around the throne of God in heaven | 648 | Christ is made the sure Foundation | 268 |
| Art thou weary, art thou languid | 389 | Christ Jesus lay in death's strong bands | 207 |
| As pants the hart for cooling streams | 554 | Christ, of all my hopes the ground | 437 |
| As the sun doth daily rise | 329 | Christ shall have dominion | 678 |
| As when the Hebrew prophet raised | 422 | "Christ the Lord is risen today" | 205 |
| As with gladness men of old | 154 | Christ, whose glory fills the skies | 330 |
| At even, when the sun was set | 336 | Christian, dost thou see them | 483 |
| At the Lamb's high feast we sing | 365 | Christian, seek not yet repose | 471 |
| At the Name of Jesus every knee shall bow | 124 | Come, dearest Lord, descend and dwell | 250 |
| At thy feet, our God and Father | 610 | Come, every soul by sin oppressed | 724 |
| Awake, my soul, and with the sun | 331 | Come, for the feast is spread | 391 |
| Awake, my soul, in joyful lays | 138 | Come, Holy Ghost, in love | 249 |

## INDEX OF HYMNS

| Hymn | | Hymn |
|---|---|---|
| Come, Holy Spirit, come.................................. 254 | Father, we thank thee for the night............ | 659 |
| Come, let us join with one accord................ 323 | Father, whate'er of earthly bliss.................... | 562 |
| Come, let us sing of a wonderful love........ 669 | Fear not, O little flock, the foe..................... | 470 |
| Come, let us sing unto the Lord................... 15 | Fierce was the wild billow............................... | 513 |
| Come, let us to the Lord our God................ 516 | Fight the good fight with all thy might........ | 484 |
| Come, my soul, thou must be waking.......... 334 | Fill thou my life, O Lord my God................. | 495 |
| Come, my soul, thy suit prepare................... 531 | Fling out the banner! let it float................. | 378 |
| Come, O come, thou quick'ning Spirit........ 247 | For all the saints who from their labors rest | 281 |
| Come, O Creator Spirit blest......................... 251 | For ever here my rest shall be....................... | 458 |
| Come, sound his praise abroad..................... 102 | For ever settled in the heavens..................... | 54 |
| Come, thou Almighty King............................ 89 | For ever trusting in the Lord......................... | 569 |
| Come, thou Fount of every blessing............ 400 | "For my sake and the gospel's, go"............... | 377 |
| Come, thou long-expected Jesus................... 145 | For thy mercy and thy grace.......................... | 611 |
| Come to our poor nature's night.................. 248 | Fountain of good, to own thy love............... | 282 |
| Come to the Saviour, make no delay............ 693 | Fountain of grace, rich, full and free............ | 591 |
| Come to the Saviour now............................... 395 | Fountain of never-ceasing grace................... | 440 |
| "Come unto me, ye weary"............................. 405 | From all that dwell below the skies............. | 3 |
| Come, we that love the Lord......................... 588 | From depths of woe I raise to thee.............. | 461 |
| Come, ye disconsolate..................................... 518 | From every stormy wind that blows............. | 528 |
| Come, ye faithful, raise the strain................ 200 | From Greenland's icy mountains................... | 383 |
| Come, ye sinners, poor and wretched.......... 393 | From heaven high I come to you.................. | 166 |
| Come, ye souls by sin afflicted..................... 390 | From heaven the Lord with searching eye.... | 474 |
| Come, ye thankful people, come................... 615 | From out the depths I cry, O Lord............... | 463 |
| Comfort, comfort ye my people.................... 148 | From the depths my prayer ascendeth......... | 570 |
| Commit thou all thy griefs and ways.......... 560 | | |
| Conquering now and still to conquer.......... 665 | Gentle Mary laid her child............................. | 640 |
| Crown him with many crowns....................... 216 | "Give me thy heart," says the Father above | 723 |
| Crown his head with endless blessing......... 130 | Give thanks unto the Lord, Jehovah............ | 512 |
| | Give to our God immortal praise................. | 20 |
| Dare to be a Daniel......................................... 660 | Gloria Patri ....................................................... | xv |
| Day is dying in the west................................ 343 | Glorious things of thee are spoken ............. | 269 |
| Day of judgment! day of wonders................ 241 | Glory be to Jesus.............................................. | 190 |
| Dear Lord and Master mine........................... 576 | Glory be to the Father .................................. | xv |
| Dear Lord, today, our child........................... 353 | Go, labor on: spend, and be spent............... | 496 |
| Doxology ............................................................ xvi | God, be merciful to me................................... | 415 |
| Draw nigh, draw nigh, Emmanuel *see* | God be with you till we meet again............ | 632 |
|   O come, O come, Emmanuel................... 147 | God himself is with us.................................... | 315 |
| Dying with Jesus, by death reckoned mine 708 | God, in the gospel of his Son........................ | 262 |
| | God is known among his people.................. | 63 |
| Each little flower that opens........................ 636 | God is my strong Salvation............................ | 568 |
| Ere I sleep, for every favor........................... 337 | God is our refuge and our strength............. | 37 |
| Eternal Father, strong to save...................... 629 | God is the refuge of his saints..................... | 292 |
| Every Day Will I Bless Thee......................... 703 | God moves in a mysterious way................... | 21 |
| Every morning mercies new.......................... 328 | God, my king, thy might confessing............ | 2 |
| Exalt the Lord, his praise proclaim............. 12 | God of our fathers, whose almighty hand.... | 616 |
| | God of pity, God of grace.............................. | 466 |
| Fairest Lord Jesus, Ruler of all nature......... 129 | God rest you merry, gentlemen.................... | 160 |
| Faith of our fathers! living still.................... 487 | God sees the little sparrow fall..................... | 635 |
| Far and near the fields are teeming............ 668 | God, that madest earth and heaven............. | 344 |
| Father, again in Jesus' Name we meet......... 311 | God the All-terrible! King, who ordainest | 617 |
| Father, I know that all my life..................... 444 | God, the Lord, a King remaineth................. | 60 |
| Father of heaven, whose love profound....... 88 | God the Lord is King...................................... | 43 |
| Father of mercies, in thy Word.................... 259 | God, who made the earth.............................. | 637 |
| Father of peace, and God of love................ 98 | God Will Take Care of You........................... | 696 |
| | Golden harps are sounding............................ | 213 |

740

# INDEX OF HYMNS

| Hymn | | Hymn | |
|---|---|---|---|
| Good Christian men, rejoice | 159 | How gentle God's commands | 561 |
| Grace! 'tis a charming sound | 401 | How glorious Zion's courts appear | 277 |
| Gracious Saviour, gentle Shepherd | 354 | How good it is to thank the Lord | 535 |
| Gracious Spirit, Dove Divine | 245 | How great the goodness kept in store | 563 |
| Great God, how infinite art thou | 22 | How long wilt thou forget me | 541 |
| Great God of wonders! all thy ways | 71 | How lovely shines the Morning Star | 434 |
| Great God, we sing that mighty hand | 612 | How precious is the book divine | 265 |
| Great God, what do I see and hear | 240 | How shall the young direct their way | 264 |
| "Great is thy faithfulness" | 27 | How sweet and awful is the place | 271 |
| Great King of nations, hear our prayer | 621 | How sweet the Name of Jesus sounds | 544 |
| Guide me, O thou great Jehovah | 501 | How vast the benefits divine | 95 |
| | | Hushed was the evening hymn | 655 |
| Hail, thou once despised Jesus | 128 | | |
| Hail to the brightness of Zion's glad morning | 274 | I am a stranger here | 695 |
| | | I am Jesus' little lamb | 643 |
| Hail to the Lord's Anointed | 224 | I am so glad that our Father in heaven | 647 |
| Hallelujah! ... In his temple | 9 | I am thine, O Lord, I have heard thy voice | 713 |
| Hallelujah, praise Jehovah | 105 | I am trusting thee, Lord Jesus | 424 |
| Hallelujah, praise Jehovah, O my soul | 53 | I belong to Jesus | 649 |
| Hallelujah! Raise, O raise | 49 | I greet thee, who my sure Redeemer art | 135 |
| Happy the home when God is there | 627 | I hear the Saviour say | 690 |
| Hark! ten thousand harps and voices | 225 | I hear thy welcome voice | 406 |
| Hark, the glad sound! the Saviour comes | 162 | I heard the voice of Jesus say | 221 |
| Hark! the herald angels sing | 168 | I know not why God's wondrous grace | 712 |
| Hark! the song of jubilee | 300 | I know that my Redeemer lives | 586 |
| Hark! the sound of holy voices | 607 | I Know Whom I Have Believed | 712 |
| Hark! the voice of Jesus crying | 691 | I lay my sins on Jesus | 430 |
| Hark! the voice of love and mercy | 187 | I love thy Kingdom, Lord | 280 |
| Hark! 'tis the Shepherd's voice I hear | 684 | I love to tell the story | 387 |
| Hast thou not known, hast thou not heard | 28 | I need thee every hour | 710 |
| Have thine own way, Lord | 574 | I need thee, precious Jesus | 419 |
| He Is Coming Again | 687 | I sing the almighty power of God | 106 |
| He leadeth me: O blessed thought | 500 | I sought the Lord, and afterward I knew | 397 |
| He Lifted Me | 672 | I think when I read that sweet story of old | 650 |
| He Was Wounded For Our Transgressions | 673 | I waited for the Lord most high | 523 |
| Hear our prayer, O Lord | xiv | I was a wandering sheep | 396 |
| Here from the world we turn | 345 | I will sing of my Redeemer | 681 |
| Here, O my Lord, I see thee face to face | 310 | I will sing the wondrous story | 709 |
| High in the heavens, Eternal God | 52 | I will sing you a song of that beautiful land | 729 |
| His are the thousand sparkling rills | 180 | If thou but suffer God to guide thee | 567 |
| His Eye Is on the Sparrow | 725 | If we have forgotten the Name of our God | 515 |
| Holy Bible, book divine | 674 | I'm but a stranger here, heaven is my home | 605 |
| Holy Father, in thy mercy, hear | 630 | I'm not ashamed to own my Lord | 429 |
| Holy Ghost, dispel our sadness | 246 | Immortal, invisible, God only wise | 35 |
| Holy, Holy, Holy, Lord God Almighty | 87 | In loving-kindness Jesus came | 672 |
| Holy Spirit, hear us | 638 | In sweet communion, Lord, with thee | 557 |
| Home of the Soul | 729 | In the hour of trial, Jesus, plead for me | 475 |
| Hosanna to the living Lord | 314 | In the land of fadeless day | 730 |
| How beautiful the sight of brethren who agree | 283 | In thy wrath and hot displeasure | 408 |
| | | Is It the Crowning Day | 692 |
| How blest is he whose trespass | 462 | It came upon the midnight clear | 157 |
| How bright these glorious spirits shine | 606 | I've found a Friend, O such a Friend | 433 |
| How calm and beautiful the morn | 209 | I've found the pearl of greatest price | 592 |
| How firm a foundation, ye saints of the Lord | 80 | Jehovah reigns; let earth be glad | 59 |
| | | Jehovah's perfect law restores the soul | 448 |

741

## INDEX OF HYMNS

| Hymn | | | Hymn |
|---|---|---|---|
| Jerusalem the golden | 604 | Lift up your heads, pilgrims aweary | 687 |
| Jesus, and shall it ever be | 425 | Lift up your heads, ye gates of brass | 384 |
| Jesus bids us shine | 653 | Lift up your heads, ye mighty gates | 146 |
| Jesus calls us: o'er the tumult | 491 | Light of light, enlighten me | 333 |
| Jesus Christ is risen today | 198 | Light of the lonely pilgrim's heart | 232 |
| Jesus Christ, our Lord most holy | 196 | Like a river glorious | 587 |
| Jesus, high in glory | 661 | Like Zion's steadfast mount are they | 585 |
| Jesus, I am resting, resting | 139 | Lo! God is here: let us adore | 308 |
| Jesus, I Come | 715 | Lo, God to heaven ascendeth | 210 |
| Jesus, I live to thee | 438 | Lo! he comes, with clouds descending | 237 |
| Jesus, I my cross have taken | 593 | Lo! what a glorious sight appears | 601 |
| Jesus is all the world to me | 664 | Look, ye saints, the sight is glorious | 217 |
| Jesus is tenderly calling thee home | 697 | Lord, dismiss us with thy blessing | 319 |
| Jesus, keep me near the cross | 704 | Lord, have mercy upon us | xiv |
| Jesus, lead thou on | 504 | Lord, I believe; thy power I own | 428 |
| Jesus lives, and so shall I | 596 | Lord, I hear of showers of blessing | 527 |
| Jesus lives! thy terrors now can no longer | 203 | Lord, I lift my soul to thee | 583 |
| Jesus, Lord of life and glory | 472 | Lord, in the morning thou shalt hear | 332 |
| Jesus, Lord, Redeemer | 208 | Lord Jesus Christ, be present now | 312 |
| Jesus, Lover of my soul | 427 | Lord Jesus Christ, our Lord most dear | 355 |
| Jesus loves me, this I know | 633 | Lord, keep us steadfast in thy Word | 91 |
| Jesus, Master, whose I am | 494 | Lord, like the publican I stand | 407 |
| Jesus may come today | 692 | Lord, my weak thought in vain would climb | 93 |
| Jesus, merciful and mild | 459 | Lord of our life, and God of our salvation | 473 |
| Jesus, my great High Priest | 222 | Lord of the Sabbath, hear us pray | 322 |
| Jesus, my Saviour, look on me | 140 | Lord of the worlds above | 302 |
| Jesus Paid It All | 690 | Lord, our Lord, thy glorious Name | 107 |
| Jesus, priceless treasure | 550 | Lord, thou hast been our dwelling-place | 287 |
| Jesus, Saviour, pilot me | 497 | Lord, thou hast searched me, and dost know | 33 |
| Jesus shall reign where'er the sun | 374 | Lord, thou lov'st the cheerful giver | 368 |
| "Jesus sinners doth receive" | 394 | Lord, thy Word abideth | 266 |
| Jesus, tender Shepherd, hear me | 642 | Lord, who shall come to thee | 445 |
| Jesus, the very thought of thee | 542 | Lord, with glowing heart I'd praise thee | 69 |
| Jesus, these eyes have never seen | 545 | Love Divine, all loves excelling | 460 |
| Jesus, thou Joy of loving hearts | 549 | Low in the grave he lay | 206 |
| Jesus, thy blood and righteousness | 439 | | |
| Jesus, thy Name I love | 546 | Majestic sweetness sits enthroned | 143 |
| Jesus! what a Friend for sinners | 432 | Man of Sorrows! | 175 |
| Jesus, where'er thy people meet | 309 | Marvelous grace of our loving Lord | 705 |
| Jesus, with thy church abide | 278 | Master, the tempest is raging | 701 |
| Joy to the world! the Lord is come | 149 | Mighty God, while angels bless thee | 5 |
| Judge Eternal, throned in splendor | 620 | Moment by Moment | 708 |
| Judge me, God of my salvation | 539 | More about Jesus would I know | 676 |
| Just as I am, without one plea | 431 | More love to thee, O Christ | 548 |
| | | Most perfect is the law of God | 450 |
| Kingdoms and thrones to God belong | 67 | My Anchor Holds | 717 |
| | | My dear Redeemer and my Lord | 171 |
| Lead on, O King eternal | 488 | My faith looks up to thee | 454 |
| Leaning on the Everlasting Arms | 718 | My Father is rich in houses and lands | 720 |
| Let children hear the mighty deeds | 293 | My God and Father, day by day | 575 |
| Let our choir new anthems raise | 284 | My God, how wonderful thou art | 31 |
| Let thy blood in mercy poured | 362 | My God, is any hour so sweet | 529 |
| Let us love, and sing, and wonder | 127 | My heart doth overflow | 125 |
| Let us, with a gladsome mind | 30 | My hope is built | 582 |
| Lift up, lift up your voices now | 202 | | |

742

# INDEX OF HYMNS

| | Hymn | | Hymn |
|---|---|---|---|
| My Jesus, as thou wilt | 572 | O God, thou art my God alone | 556 |
| My Jesus, I love thee | 547 | O God, thy judgments give the King | 230 |
| My people, give ear, attend to my word | 301 | O God, to us show mercy | 385 |
| My Saviour's praises I will sing | 703 | O God, we praise thee; and confess | 90 |
| My sins, my sins, my Saviour | 464 | O happy day, that fixed my choice | 589 |
| My song for ever shall record | 101 | O happy home, where thou art loved | 624 |
| My soul, bless the Lord | 110 | O happy land, whose sons in youth *see* | |
| My soul in silence waits for God | 571 | O people blest, whose sons in youth | 289 |
| My times are in thy hand | 577 | O Jehovah, hear my words | 47 |
| My trust is in the Lord | 48 | O Jesus, I have promised | 552 |
| | | O Jesus, thou art standing | 414 |
| Naught have I gotten but what I received | 698 | O Jesus, we adore thee | 193 |
| No longer, Lord, despise me | 511 | O Light that knew no dawn | 23 |
| No Night There | 730 | O little town of Bethlehem | 152 |
| No, not despairingly come I to thee | 411 | O Lord, be thou my helper true | 45 |
| None other Lamb, none other Name | 115 | O Lord, by thee delivered | 526 |
| Nor silver nor gold hath obtained | | O Lord, how are my foes increased | 469 |
| my redemption | 721 | O Lord, how shall I meet thee | 119 |
| Not all the blood of beasts | 176 | O Lord, I would delight in thee | 543 |
| Not haughty is my heart | 578 | O Lord most high, with all my heart | 44 |
| Not unto us, O Lord of heaven | 68 | O Lord of Hosts, how lovely the place | 305 |
| Not what my hands have done | 403 | O Lord our God, arise | 375 |
| Not worthy, Lord! to gather up the crumbs | 356 | O Lord, thou Judge of all the earth | 46 |
| Nothing But the Blood | 677 | O love, how deep, how broad, how high | 121 |
| Now blessed be the Lord our God | 7 | O love of God, how strong and true | 73 |
| Now Israel may say, and that in truth | 514 | O Love that wilt not let me go | 594 |
| Now may he who from the dead | 318 | O Mother dear, Jerusalem | 603 |
| Now thank we all our God | 86 | O mystery of love divine | 436 |
| Now the day is over | 666 | O people blest, whose sons in youth | 289 |
| Now unto Jehovah, ye sons of the mighty | 36 | O perfect Love | 625 |
| | | O praise the Lord, for he is good | 84 |
| O bless our God with one accord | 348 | O praise ye the Lord and sing a new song | 288 |
| O bless the Lord, my soul | 72 | O quickly come, dread Judge of all | 243 |
| O Christ, our hope, our heart's desire | 120 | O sacred Head, now wounded | 178 |
| O Christ, our King, Creator, Lord | 134 | O safe to the Rock that is higher than I | 551 |
| O Christ, our true and only Light | 296 | O Saviour, precious Saviour | 118 |
| O come, all ye faithful | 151 | O Spirit of the living God | 253 |
| O come, let us sing to the Lord | 19 | O Splendor of God's glory bright | 56 |
| O come, my soul, bless thou the Lord | 10 | O that I had a thousand voices | 11 |
| O come, O come, Emmanuel | 147 | O the deep, deep love of Jesus | 453 |
| O could I speak the matchless worth | 126 | O thou from whom all goodness flows | 457 |
| O day of rest and gladness | 321 | O thou my soul, bless God the Lord | 97 |
| O dearest Jesus, | | O thou that hear'st when sinners cry | 413 |
| what law hast thou broken | 181 | O thou the Eternal Son of God | 191 |
| O Father all creating | 628 | O thou to whose all-searching sight | 525 |
| O for a thousand tongues to sing | 133 | O thou who the Shepherd of Israel art | 279 |
| O God, most holy are thy ways | 41 | O Trinity, most blessed Light | 339 |
| O God, my Strength and Fortitude | 524 | O 'twas a joyful sound to hear | 276 |
| O God, no longer hold thy peace | 57 | O wherefore do the nations rage | 227 |
| O God of Bethel, by whose hand | 498 | O Word of God Incarnate | 267 |
| O God of hosts, the mighty Lord | 303 | O worship the King all glorious above | 13 |
| O God of love, O King of peace | 622 | O'er the gloomy hills of darkness | 373 |
| O God of mercy, God of might | 366 | Of the Father's love begotten | 122 |
| O God of truth, whose living Word | 468 | Oft in danger, oft in woe | 479 |
| O God, the Rock of Ages | 24 | Once in royal David's city | 639 |

743

# INDEX OF HYMNS

| | Hymn | | Hymn |
|---|---|---|---|
| One day when heaven was filled with his praises | 689 | Shout, for the blessed Jesus reigns | 298 |
| One there is, above all others | 142 | Silent night! Holy night | 161 |
| Only a Sinner | 698 | Simply trusting every day | 682 |
| Only Trust Him | 724 | Sing, my tongue, how glorious battle | 194 |
| Onward, Christian soldiers | 490 | Sing them over again to me | 722 |
| Open now thy gates of beauty | 304 | Sing to the Lord, sing his praise | 65 |
| Our children, Lord, in faith and prayer | 351 | Softly and tenderly Jesus is calling | 694 |
| Our God, our Help in ages past | 26 | Softly now the light of day | 347 |
| Out of my bondage, sorrow and night | 715 | Soldiers of Christ, arise | 482 |
| Out of the deep I call to thee | 412 | Soldiers who to Christ belong | 485 |
| | | Some day the silver cord will break | 726 |
| Pass me not, O gentle Saviour | 707 | Sometimes a light surprises | 520 |
| Peace, perfect peace | 590 | Sound the battle cry | 686 |
| Praise God from whom all blessings flow | xvi | Sow in the morn thy seed | 299 |
| Praise him! Praise him | 683 | Speed thy servants, Saviour, speed them | 382 |
| Praise Jehovah, all ye nations | 29 | Spirit of God, that moved of old | 255 |
| Praise, Lord, for thee in Zion waits | 114 | Spirit, strength of all the weak | 244 |
| Praise, my soul, the King of heaven | 70 | Stand up, and bless the Lord | 14 |
| Praise the Lord: ye heavens adore him | 16 | Stand up, my soul; shake off thy fears | 478 |
| Praise the Saviour, now and ever | 174 | Stand up, stand up for Jesus | 477 |
| Praise to God, immortal praise | 112 | Standing by a purpose true | 660 |
| Praise to the Lord, the Almighty | 50 | Stricken, smitten, and afflicted | 192 |
| Praise waits for thee in Zion | 306 | Sun of my soul, thou Saviour dear | 346 |
| Praise ye, praise ye the Lord | 108 | Supreme in wisdom as in power *see* Hast thou not known, hast thou not heard | 28 |
| Rejoice, all ye believers | 233 | Sweet hour of prayer | 534 |
| Rejoice, the Lord is King | 226 | Sweet the moments, rich in blessing | 189 |
| Rejoice, ye people, homage give | 61 | | |
| Rejoice, ye pure in heart | 502 | Take me, O my Father, take me | 410 |
| Remember not, O God, the sins of long ago | 417 | Take my life, and let it be consecrated | 492 |
| Revive thy work, O Lord | 297 | Take time to be holy | 706 |
| Ride on! ride on in majesty | 172 | "Take up thy cross," the Saviour said | 507 |
| Rise, my soul, to watch and pray | 476 | Teach me, my God and King | 555 |
| Rock of Ages, cleft for me | 421 | Teach me, O Lord, thy holy way | 456 |
| Round the Lord in glory seated | 42 | Teach me, O Lord, thy way of truth | 451 |
| | | Tell me the old, old story | 521 |
| Safe in the arms of Jesus | 608 | Tell me the story of Jesus | 685 |
| Safely through another week | 320 | Ten thousand times ten thousand | 234 |
| Saved by Grace | 726 | That day of wrath, that dreadful day | 242 |
| Saviour, again to thy dear Name we raise | 316 | That man is blest who, fearing God | 446 |
| Saviour, blessed Saviour, listen while we sing | 452 | The Child of a King | 720 |
| Saviour, breathe an evening blessing | 340 | The Church's one Foundation | 270 |
| Saviour, like a Shepherd lead us | 644 | The day is past and over | 342 |
| Saviour of the nations, come | 165 | The day of resurrection | 197 |
| Saviour, teach me, day by day | 654 | The day thou gavest, Lord, is ended | 338 |
| Saviour, thy dying love | 538 | The earth, with all that dwell therein | 66 |
| Searcher of hearts, from mine erase | 455 | The ends of all the earth shall hear | 295 |
| See, amid the winter's snow | 158 | The God of Abraham praise | 32 |
| See Israel's gentle Shepherd stand | 350 | The golden gates are lifted up | 214 |
| See, the Conqueror mounts in triumph | 211 | The great Physician now is near | 144 |
| Send thou, O Lord, to every place | 379 | The Head that once was crowned with thorns | 215 |
| Shepherd of souls, refresh and bless | 364 | The heavens declare thy glory | 104 |
| Shepherd of tender youth | 117 | The heavens declare thy glory, Lord | 263 |
| Shine thou upon us, Lord | 631 | The King of Love my Shepherd is | 141 |

# INDEX OF HYMNS

| | Hymn | | Hymn |
|---|---|---|---|
| The King shall come when morning dawns | 236 | Thy loving-kindness, Lord is good and free | 510 |
| The law of God is good and wise | 449 | Thy mercy and thy truth, O Lord | 55 |
| The Light of the World Is Jesus | 679 | Thy might sets fast the mountains | 111 |
| The Lord has heard and answered prayer | 25 | Thy servant, blessed by thee, shall live | 260 |
| The Lord is King! lift up thy voice | 58 | Thy way, not mine, O Lord | 573 |
| The Lord is my Shepherd, no want shall I know | 663 | Thy Word Have I Hid in My Heart | 671 |
| The Lord is rich and merciful | 519 | Thy Word is a lamp to my feet | 671 |
| The Lord will come and not be slow | 294 | Thy Word is like a garden, Lord | 257 |
| The Lord's my Shepherd, I'll not want | 77 | Thy works, not mine, O Christ | 441 |
| The Lord's our Rock, in him we hide | 719 | Till he come! O let the words linger | 357 |
| The man who once has found abode | 74 | 'Tis midnight; and on Olive's brow | 182 |
| The mighty God, the Lord, hath spoken | 239 | 'Tis not that I did choose thee | 96 |
| The Name of Jesus is so sweet | 711 | 'Tis so sweet to trust in Jesus | 699 |
| The people that in darkness sat | 123 | To God be the glory | 667 |
| The praises of thy wonders, Lord | 38 | To God my earnest voice I raise | 509 |
| The sands of time are sinking | 599 | To thee, O Comforter Divine | 252 |
| The Son of God goes forth to war | 489 | To thee, O Lord, I fly | 581 |
| The spacious firmament on high | 103 | To thee, O Lord, I lift mine eyes | 540 |
| The Spirit breathes upon the Word | 258 | To thee, our God, we fly for mercy | 618 |
| The tender love a father has | 85 | To thy temple I repair | 313 |
| The whole world was lost in the darkness of sin | 679 | To us a Child of hope is born | 163 |
| The wise may bring their learning | 657 | Today the Saviour calls | 388 |
| Thee we adore, eternal Lord | 18 | Trembling soul, beset by fears | 670 |
| There is a city bright | 662 | Trust and Obey | 700 |
| There is a fountain filled with blood | 188 | Trusting Jesus | 682 |
| There is a green hill far away | 184 | 'Twas on that night when doomed to know | 359 |
| There is a land of pure delight | 597 | | |
| There is no name so sweet on earth | 652 | Under the care of my God, the Almighty | 78 |
| There is no night in heaven | 598 | Unless the Lord the house shall build | 291 |
| There is no sorrow, Lord, too light | 517 | Unto my Lord Jehovah said | 229 |
| "There shall be showers of blessing" | 716 | Unto the hills around do I lift up | 82 |
| There were ninety and nine | 137 | | |
| This day at thy creating word | 324 | "Wake, awake, for night is flying" | 231 |
| This is my Father's world | 109 | We gather together to ask the Lord's blessing | 286 |
| This is the day of light | 327 | We give thee but thine own | 367 |
| This is the day the Lord hath made | 326 | We have heard the joyful sound | 370 |
| This night, O Lord, we bless thee | 349 | We have not known thee as we ought | 418 |
| Thou art coming, O my Saviour | 235 | We plough the fields, and scatter | 614 |
| Thou art my hiding-place, O Lord | 553 | We praise thee, O God! for the days of our youth | 634 |
| Thou art the Way: to thee alone | 116 | We praise thee, O God, our Redeemer, Creator | 83 |
| Thou didst leave thy throne *see* Thou dost reign on high | 170 | We sing the glorious conquest | 404 |
| Thou dost reign on high | 170 | Weary of earth, and laden with my sin | 467 |
| Thou hidden source of calm repose | 426 | Welcome, delightful morn | 325 |
| Thou, whose almighty word | 376 | "Welcome, happy morning" | 199 |
| Though the angry surges roll | 717 | What a fellowship, what a joy divine | 718 |
| Though troubles assail us | 79 | What a Friend we have in Jesus | 533 |
| "Though your sins be as scarlet" | 465 | What can wash away my sin | 677 |
| Throned upon the awful tree | 183 | What shall I render to my God | 537 |
| Through all the changing scenes of life | 522 | What though I cannot break my chain | 398 |
| Through good report and evil, Lord | 503 | What time I am afraid | 564 |
| Thy God Reigneth | 670 | What, ye ask me, is my prize | 435 |
| Thy life was given for me | 536 | Whate'er my God ordains is right | 94 |
| | | When all thy mercies, O my God | 51 |

745

# INDEX OF HYMNS

| Hymn | | Hymn | |
|---|---|---|---|
| When he cometh, when he cometh | 651 | With broken heart and contrite sigh | 416 |
| When, his salvation bringing | 646 | With glory clad, with strength arrayed | 64 |
| When I survey the wondrous cross | 186 | With grateful heart my thanks I bring | 76 |
| When in his might the Lord arose | 290 | With harps and with viols | 714 |
| When Israel out of Egypt went | 39 | With songs and honors sounding loud | 113 |
| When morning gilds the skies | 131 | Within thy temple, Lord | 307 |
| When peace, like a river | 580 | Wonderful grace of Jesus | 702 |
| When the Roll Is Called Up Yonder | 727 | Wonderful Love | 669 |
| When the trumpet of the Lord shall sound | 727 | Wonderful Words of Life | 722 |
| When the weary, seeking rest | 532 | Wondrous King, all-glorious | 132 |
| When this passing world is done | 600 | Work, for the night is coming | 728 |
| When thy soldiers take their swords | 486 | | |
| When we walk with the Lord | 700 | Ye children, come, give ear to me | 656 |
| While shepherds watched their flocks | 156 | Ye Christian heralds, go proclaim | 380 |
| While with ceaseless course the sun | 613 | Ye holy angels bright | 17 |
| Who are these like stars appearing | 602 | Ye righteous, in the Lord rejoice | 40 |
| Who hath believed | 673 | Ye servants of God, your Master proclaim | 136 |
| Who is on the Lord's side | 493 | Yes, for me, for me he careth | 688 |
| Who is this so weak and helpless | 169 | Yield not to temptation | 658 |
| Who is this that comes from Edom | 228 | Your harps, ye trembling saints | 595 |
| Who trusts in God, a strong abode | 558 | | |
| Why dost thou stand afar | 508 | Zion, founded on the mountains | 369 |
| Why should cross and trial grieve me | 506 | Zion stands by hills surrounded | 275 |
| Why should I feel discouraged | 725 | Zion, to thy Saviour singing | 361 |